
Demco 291-B5

CALIF. STAR
OIL WORKS CO.
1875 - 1901

PACIFIC COAST
OIL CO.
1879 - 1906

MISSION
TRANSFER CO.
1882 - 86/87

STANDARD OIL CO.
(CALIF.)
1906 - 26

S.O. CO.
(IOWA) ●
1885 - 1906

STD. OIL (OHIO)
PACIFIC DIV.
1878 - 85

SCOFIELD
& TEVIS
1880 - 83

FORMATIVE YEARS IN THE FAR WEST

FORMATIVE YEARS
IN THE FAR WEST

A History of Standard Oil Company of California
and Predecessors Through 1919

32326

By

Gerald T. White

APPLETON-CENTURY-CROFTS
Division of Meredith Publishing Company
New York

PRINTED IN THE UNITED STATES OF AMERICA

For Rita

PREFACE

Business history as a field of formal study first came into being at Harvard University about thirty-five years ago at a time when the literature on business fell predominantly into two categories: the syrup-sweet stories that business firms have occasionally put out about themselves, in which a blemish or hint of error rarely showed, and the product of the muckraker. Of the two, the muckraker's product had by far the wider audience. It gave the reader a sense of reality for, unlike the literature put out by the companies, it was frequently documented—often to the records of some court or government hearing where a business firm had appeared either guilty or suspect of dereliction. The muckraker's error, it seems to me, is that he made the part stand for the whole. Or, to change the figure, his picture was out of focus because he lacked access to the records of business. His perspective, a friend has remarked, was similar to that of a writer on marriage who did his research mainly in the records of divorce courts.

Today, while some muckraker writing and its treacly opposite is still being done, there is also a more substantial literature. This consists of solidly researched histories written from a fullness of records and with the author free to reveal his findings. These more impressive volumes have become possible because an increasing number of companies have offered to open their records for study. They know that business has a much more creditable record than many of its critics have been willing to admit, and they have come to realize that they have more to gain from an attempt at unvarnished truth than from a highly glossed and tailored story. The growth of this new literature has been gratifying to scholars who have long recognized business as one of the principal institutions shaping our society and yet hard to evaluate because so much of the relevant records have been unavailable.

This first volume of a history of the Standard Oil Company of California we hope is a worthy addition to the numerous scholarly business histories that have been published in recent years. It grew out of a decision made by the company late in 1953 to finance the writing of a history that would speak to the needs of students of enterprise and at the same time appeal to the interested general reader. The company offered assurance of free access to its records and support in finding relevant materials elsewhere; it also promised complete freedom in writing the manuscript. These commitments the company has scrupulously observed.

This book carries the history of Standard of California and its predecessors down to 1919. That year has been chosen as an appropriate terminal date not only because of the advent of the K. R. Kingsbury administration, running from 1919 to 1937, but also because of significant departures from past practice that began to occur about the end of World War I. These departures helped give the company thereafter a far larger geographic scope and a different character—owing to the rise of men with scientific training to positions of power and to the recognition of the values of systematic research—than it had in its earlier years, when so-called "practical" men were in control.

Within this volume, the main divisions occur around 1900 (Chapter IX) and 1911 (Chapter XV). For more than a quarter century prior to 1900, this history is a study of origins, as companies like California Star and Pacific Coast Oil—Standard of California's western predecessors—were attempting to build a California-based industry, and Rockefeller's Standard Oil Company was active in the West solely as a marketer. Between 1900 and 1911, as the California industry boomed, the Standard Oil Company expanded its western activities to create a large and integrated business responsible to its international headquarters at 26 Broadway, New York City. Thereafter, the independent Standard Oil Company (California), freed by the Supreme Court's antitrust decree, pushed rapidly forward until by 1919 it had surpassed in total assets all other onetime Standard units except the former parent, the Standard Oil Company (New Jersey).

The research for this volume has been arduous and challenging. This is true partly because so little writing has been done about oil in California in the nineteenth century and also because the San Francisco earthquake and fire of 1906 proved so destructive to records. Consequently, we have had to range widely: to the archives of the Standard Oil Company (Ohio) in Cleveland and of the Standard Oil Company (New Jersey) in New York; to the National Archives and the Library of Congress in Washington; to the oil history collections of E. L. DeGolyer and of the Technical History Project of the American Petroleum Institute in Dallas; and up and down the state of California.

At times, we have been able to observe the company and its predecessors through the eyes of competitors, an unusual and valuable experience for a business historian. For example, in piecing out company records for the period prior to 1906, we have benefited especially from three major collections, hitherto used lightly or not at all. One of these, the papers of Thomas R. Bard, partly located with the Bard Family at Somis, California, and partly in the Huntington Library, give the views of a founder of the Union Oil Company and of an active figure in California oil from 1865 to 1900. A second collection, that of a co-founder of Union, Lyman Stewart, has as its principal theme the oil interests of the Stewart family in California over more than thirty years after Lyman Stewart came West in 1883. Housed in the library of the Bible Institute of Los Angeles, this collection consists of more than 20,000 letters. The third of these discoveries, located in the National Archives, consists of several hundred interviews made by investigators of the federal Bureau of Corporations, plus a draft report on the California oil industry that was intended to be a fourth volume in the Bureau's study of the Standard Oil Company early in this century, but was never published.

After 1906 the company's records gradually become greater in volume and more varied in type, making the problem of selection more critical. Our principal criterion has been the unifying one of determining whether the records contributed to an understanding of the company's management. As for the earlier years, we have sought to avoid writing of the company in an insular way and have tried always to relate its history to developments elsewhere in the industry, especially in the West.

Like other major company and industry histories, this book is the result of a team effort. I am especially indebted to Joseph W. Smith, who is chiefly responsible for Chapters IX through XIII and for Chapter XVIII, and to Albert E. Haase, who shared in the early research and writing and who skilfully edited drafts of many of the chapters. The book has also benefited from the research contributions at various times of Mrs. Elizabeth B. Currier, Mrs. Max Stern, and Professor John S. Ewing of the Graduate School of Business at Stanford University. Mrs. Gladys B. Hunt has been invaluable, supplying order to our files, typing notes and manuscript, and assisting in research.

R. G. Follis, Chairman of the Board, and T. S. Petersen, President, have given the history their firm and understanding support throughout the period of its preparation. Walter J. Held has been our helpful liaison; we have profited, too, from the friendly interest of members of the company's History Committee, particularly Glen M. Foster, its chairman, and S. Z. Natcher, manager of the Public Relations Department.

For their generous assistance in supplying materials and, at times, for other help, I am deeply grateful to the following: the late E. L. DeGolyer, Dallas, Texas; Richard Bard, Somis, California; Professor J. O. Henry and Arnold D. Ehlert, Librarian, of the Bible Institute of Los Angeles; Meyer Fishbein, Industrial Records Division, National Archives; Earle L. Scofield, El Segundo, California; John B. Tompkins, Head of Public Services, Bancroft Library; Miss Haydée Noya, Department of Manuscripts, Huntington Library; G. M. Buckingham, executive secretary, ESSO Educational Foundation, New York City; R. D. Packard, vice-president (retired), Standard Oil Company (Ohio); Mrs. H. C. Zeis, Steubenville, Ohio; Harold Ostly, County Clerk, Los Angeles; Allan R. Ottley, California Section Librarian, California State Library; James T. Abajian, Librarian, California Historical Society; Ralph Arnold, Santa Barbara; Robert Wakefield, Oakland; Miss Alice Greathouse, Richmond; Morris Barnard, Ventura; E. E. Manhard, Secretary, Pacific Gas & Electric Company; Miss Irene Simpson, Curator, Wells Fargo History Room; Mrs. Alys Freeze, Western History Department, Denver Public Library; and Mrs. Amy Rose, Librarian, Pillsbury, Madison & Sutro, San Francisco. The history also owes much to numerous Standard veterans whom we interviewed and who supplied us with a great deal of helpful data. Too numerous to list here, their names are to be found frequently in the notes for the later chapters, especially Chapter XV. The Standard Oil library, headed by Mrs. Margaret Rocq and later by Mrs. Elizabeth Roth, uniformly made our path smoother; they supplied answers to a host of queries.

For reading the manuscript in draft form and for making many helpful suggestions, I am deeply indebted to Professor Henrietta M. Larson of the Graduate School of Business Administration, Harvard University. I am also grateful to William H. Hutchinson of Chico, California, for his valuable comments on the first eight chapters.

This list of acknowledgments cannot end without my noting two other most valuable sources of support: the administration of San Francisco State College, which allowed me two years of leave during the course of writing the manuscript, and my wife, Rita, who has helped me in countless ways.

GERALD T. WHITE

San Francisco, California
October, 1961

CONTENTS

ILLUSTRATIONS

TABLES

I

THE BEGINNINGS OF A
CALIFORNIA OIL INDUSTRY

Standard Oil is a household word to most Americans, though not all of them realize that the name today is shared by a number of independent companies which are sturdy competitors. Among the largest, with assets of more than $3,000,000,000 in 1961, is the Standard Oil Company of California. Like all others bearing the Standard name, it is an offshoot of the old Trust, built up by John D. Rockefeller and his associates over more than forty years before the Supreme Court's famed antitrust decision in 1911 forced the dissolution of their organization into some thirty companies.

The Standard name first came to the Far West in 1878 when the original Standard Oil Company, incorporated in Ohio, set up a marketing agency at San Francisco, which soon became the regional headquarters for a number of Standard's agencies. But for more than two decades the Rockefeller organization took no part in other phases of the western oil industry—producing, transporting, and refining. Not until 1900 was an entry made, just as California was rocketing to prominence as an oil state. At that time the Standard Oil Company (New Jersey) bought the Pacific Coast Oil Company and within a few years poured many millions of dollars into it. In 1906 all of Standard's Far Western operations were consolidated into Pacific Coast Oil, which was redesignated as the Standard Oil Company (California). This name endured until the current slightly modified one was acquired in 1926 through a merger and reincorporation in Delaware.

The Standard Oil Company of California thus differs from most Standard companies in having a dual heritage. In addition to its ancestral link to Rockefeller, the company has another line of inheritance. Through the Pacific Coast Oil Company and its predecessors, this line runs far back into the history of California, a state that in cumulative oil production ranks second only to Texas.

The early years of the great Rockefeller combination have been studied intensively, notably by Allan Nevins, Ralph and Muriel Hidy, Harold Williamson and Arnold Daum, and, more controversially nearly sixty years ago, by Ida Tarbell.[1] By contrast, the beginnings of the California oil industry are little known, in spite of their significance to

1

the West and to western oil companies. If the oil hunters had failed to
find oil, or if western refiners had been totally unsuccessful in turning
out products of value, Standard of California, for example, would be
a much different and less important company today; indeed, there might
be no such company at all.

It seems appropriate, therefore, to begin the history of Standard of
California with a sketch of the mid-nineteenth century efforts to found
an oil industry in California—a story that has long languished in the
shadows because of the contemporary importance of a more glamorous
mineral, gold.

2

The pale beginnings of a California oil industry go back to the
1850's. These abortive early efforts had a background in events outside
as well as within California. The success in England late in the 1840's
of James Young, a Scotch chemist, in deriving a lubricant, called coal
oil, by the slow, low-temperature distillation of coal, was soon known
in the United States, as was also the triumph of a Canadian physician
and geologist, Abraham Gesner, in turning out an illuminating oil by
distilling asphaltum pitch from the island of Trinidad and Albert
"bitumen" from New Brunswick. Gesner settled on the name "kerosene" for his oil. Within a decade followers of Gesner and Young, like
Samuel Downer of Boston, were refining illuminating oil in the East
to compete with high-priced whale oil and a less costly illuminant,
camphene, which was a mixture of alcohol and turpentine.[2]

In California, meanwhile, geologists were busy charting the resources
of the state. Bitumen, according to John Trask, a licentiate of Yale and
the first State Geologist, was among its most abundant minerals,
especially in Southern California. Trask found that bituminous (asphalt)
springs or seepages abounded along the coast.[3] His findings were cor-
roborated by members of government surveys looking for railroad and
wagon routes within California. Colonel James Williamson, the leader
of an expedition in 1852, claimed to have noted on the Ojai Rancho,
a few miles northeast of Ventura and some fifty miles northwest of
Los Angeles, "A rich vein of mineral Bitumen, resembling the famous
coal of Nova Scotia (called Albert), burning as well and of a superior
quality."[4] The next year, William P. Blake, a young graduate of Yale
and the geologist with a successor party, reported briefly on the "bituminous effusions" he had found along the coast for some 300 miles south
of San Francisco. So did Thomas Antisell, a physician and chemist who
served as geologist with a third expedition in 1855. In a more extended

account he singled out for special comment thirteen areas, of which a number later became prominent oil fields. One territory Antisell mentioned lay in the Santa Susana mountains of northwestern Los Angeles County—where in Pico Canyon was to be the state's first commercial field and the stronghold of the Pacific Coast Oil Company.[5]

These investigators of California's resources recognized that bitumen was potentially a valuable mineral. An obvious use was as a construction material for flooring and roofing. Paving the streets of the towns was another. A still more valuable outlet, Trask believed, was for manufacturing illuminating gas. If supplies were adequate and costs of collection and transportation reasonable, he forecast a "much greater . . . revenue" from marketing bitumen for distillation into gas than from Southern California's current economic mainstay, the cattle trade. In 1853, at the time Trask wrote, the San Francisco Gas Company was laying pipe to make the California metropolis the first city in the West illumined by gas.[6] Surely other western communities (like Sacramento the next year) would be turning to what had become by the fifties "the largest and fastest growing branch of the illuminating industry in America."[7] Trask's optimism was fully shared by William Blake: "The value of this material for making pavements, cements, and in the manufacture of gas and oils, cannot be lightly estimated, and it should be regarded as one of the valuable mineral productions of the state."[8]

California soon put to the test these prophecies of the geologists. The prediction that bitumen would be used for pavements, roofs, and cements was readily fulfilled. Indians had long used it as a construction material; the rapid growth of towns in the West merely expanded the market and brought a new outlet as pavement. By 1855 asphalt was paving the streets of San Francisco.[9] In spite of the predictions of Trask and Blake, however, there is little evidence that the earliest western gas companies experimented with bitumen; like most of the gas companies of the East, they continued to use coal.[10]

Early in the next decade, two forward-looking San Francisco lamp oil and camphene merchants, using eastern methods, tried to refine a good lamp oil from California bitumen. A leading wholesale druggist and camphene manufacturer named Charles Morrill built a half-dozen retorts to distill oil from coastal deposits at Carpenteria, a few miles below Santa Barbara. Morrill may or may not have turned out the "several thousand gallons" of illuminating oil with which he was afterwards credited, but it is obvious that he had no enduring commercial success.[11]

One of Morrill's competitors, a whale oil and camphene merchant named George S. Gilbert, also took up the attempt to develop an oil industry in California. Using a 400-gallon retort, Gilbert in the spring of 1860 began working with liquid asphaltum, or "brea," gathered from the bottom of an old shaft that had been dug for coal near what later became Westlake Park in Los Angeles. The next year he transferred his attention to the deposits on the Ojai Rancho some fifty miles to the northwest. Gilbert's "refinery," which was located near the west end of the rancho, was destroyed by fire just as it began to operate. He soon rebuilt it and nearby sank a well or shaft-and-well to a depth of about 62 feet in a futile attempt to add to his seepage oil. A few months later his refinery burned again. Thereafter Gilbert was content to carry on as a storekeeper in nearby Ventura. He claimed to have manufactured over 16,000 gallons of illuminating and lubricating oils of good quality, but his claims did not always escape challenge from those who knew him best. One harsh judgment was that "he would rather tell a lie than the truth under any circumstances."[12] Nevertheless, Gilbert influenced the course of oil development far more than Morrill, for he was always ready to tell of his experiences to any who would listen and who chose to be convinced.

3

These ventures, though disappointing, proved merely a prelude to other and frequently larger efforts. The Civil War provided one incentive. Western oil dealers soon found their normal trade relations with the East disrupted by the conflict. Their turpentine for manufacturing camphene, for example, came principally from the Carolinas, which by 1862 were cut off behind the Northern blockade. New sources in California, induced by a bounty offered by the legislature, were not sufficient to meet western needs. Kerosine imports from the North, too, were less predictable and more costly because of war conditions.[13]

But there was another reason—and in the long run a far more important one—why Californians struggled so energetically to supply their own oil products. The success of Colonel E. L. Drake in drilling the first commercial oil well near Titusville, Pennsylvania, in August, 1859, soon sent a wave of excitement across the continent. As oil well followed oil well in the industry's cradle area in northwestern Pennsylvania, more and more kerosine refiners were turning from coal or other bituminous substances to liquid petroleum for their raw material.[14] Numerous oil seepages in California offered the hope that a great new source of mineral wealth might also be found in the West.

Before the year 1861 was out, events in California gave clear evidence of the impact of the Drake well. During the summer and fall Californians made what has been hailed as their first attempt to duplicate Drake's success, drilling "on the principle of artesian wells" an 80-foot hole that proved dry on the Davis Ranch in Humboldt County some 200 miles north of San Francisco and a few miles south of Eureka.[15] San Franciscans also read with interest that autumn of an "oil spring" that had been discovered at Moody Gulch a few miles west of San Jose and about 45 miles south of the Golden Gate.[16] And in the San Joaquin Valley there were the first stirrings of activity with respect to seepages in the flat, alkali lands which within a few years became the western part of Kern County.[17]

Of greater moment than any of these happenings were the goings-on across the bay from San Francisco in Contra Costa County, where beginning in June, 1861, a group of San Franciscans banded together to develop the Cañada de la Brea (Tar Canyon), about six miles east of what is today Standard of California's Richmond refinery. The two principal figures in this endeavor were Edward Conway, chief clerk in the office of Edward Fitzgerald Beale, the U.S. Surveyor-General for California, and Captain James H. White. White, a man who would play many roles in the 1860's, including land agent, mineralogist, producer, engineer, refiner, and chemist, served as superintendent for the enterprise, which was incorporated in November, 1863, as E. Conway & Company with an authorized capital of $60,000. By that time more than $10,000 had been spent putting down an 87-foot well and erecting a simple refinery, but the undertaking proved unsuccessful and was abandoned the next year.[18]

Conway and his associates were not giving up, however. Instead, they had turned to oil lands in Southern California, where Captain White had scouted intermittently since 1861. Influenced by George S. Gilbert, they acquired nearly 100,000 acres, mainly east of Ventura, under options or deeds of purchase. Potentially, the most valuable of this acreage was the northern half of the lands of the ex-Mission San Buenaventura, lying a mile or two from the Ojai on the southern slope of Sulphur Mountain.

E. Conway & Company clearly had in mind making these lands the basis for a promotional venture. Early in 1864 White wrote a glowing report on the oil prospects of the properties, especially the ex-Mission, which he pronounced "almost fabulous." He described six separate locations of petroleum springs or clusters of springs; in fact, it was his opinion that the whole area underlying Sulphur Mountain was "one mass of petroleum." The oil, he claimed, was "unsurpassed" as a lubricant and "equal to any" as an illuminant, and the high yield— 38 per cent illuminating oil and 48 per cent lubricating oil from one sample—offered the promise of marketing not only in the West but also among countries bordering the Pacific, including China and Japan. White suggested that concrete reservoirs be constructed to receive the oil and that iron pipe be laid to carry it to the coast.[19]

His report had been written little more than a month when an opportunity arose suddenly to support it with an opinion of much greater worth. In April, 1864, Benjamin Silliman, Jr., head of the chemistry department at Yale and a distinguished mining consultant, arrived on the West Coast to investigate various mining properties. For years, Silliman had reported on coal, iron, gold, silver, and other mineral lands. Presumably for eastern clients, the Yale professor began his western tour with an inspection of a number of properties in California and Nevada, including the mines of the Comstock. His presence in California excited the interest of Conway and White, for Silliman had an unmatched reputation as an authority on petroleum. His famed report, *Rock Oil, or Petroleum from Venango, Pennsylvania, with Special Reference to its Use for Illumination and Other Purposes,* had given the promoters of the Drake well the faith and financial support to carry on to a successful conclusion. Late in June, Silliman agreed to examine the lands of E. Conway & Company for $2,500 and expenses.[20]

The Yale scientist spent four or five days looking over the Conway lands in Santa Barbara and Los Angeles counties before making his report. During this time he talked with Gilbert and absorbed some of the optimism of that glib promoter. For a day he had Captain White as his companion, whose report he may have read. Echoing White, Silliman wrote of the Sulphur Mountain area, "The entire range, from east to west, is one great fountain of mineral or naphtha, oozing through the outcrops in oil wells, which, losing the more volatile portions by evaporation, give origin to extensive deposits of asphaltum, or mineral pitch, through which, at intervals, the oil still struggles." The Conway lands reaching into the range, he stated, offered "a remarkable and almost unrivaled source of . . . mineral oil, favorably situated for cheap extraction . . . likely to be limited . . . only by the number of artesian wells" put down. At their option, the owners could either sell "the crude material" or manufacture "the refined article." According to one newspaper account, Silliman believed "oil could be obtained within two hundred feet" under the surface asphalt deposits.[21]

4

The end of July found Silliman in Arizona with an expedition which Tom Scott, vice president of the Pennsylvania Railroad, had sent out to investigate mineral resources adjacent to a proposed route for a Pacific railroad. Levi Parsons, a San Francisco ex-judge and promoter, and John Wyeth, a Philadelphia chemist, were Scott's chief lieutenants; George Noble, a Scott nephew, who had picked up some of Silliman's enthusiasm for oil while in Southern California, was another member of the party. The upshot was that Noble persuaded the Scott leaders to turn their attention to oil. It was an enthusiasm they found Tom Scott fully shared, for with Andrew Carnegie he had made many thousands of dollars from an investment in the Columbia Oil Company, one of the most successful of the early Pennsylvania ventures. In the summer of 1864, moreover, a wild boom was commanding the attention of the East; from $3 to $4 a barrel at the beginning of the year, oil had climbed to almost $14 in July. With eastern prices like these, there could hardly have been a more attractive moment for launching a speculation.[22]

Parsons and Wyeth first sought the Ojai Rancho, where Gilbert had made his principal efforts and which Silliman ranked above all other California oil properties. While working for Conway, he had written a ringing endorsement of the Ojai to a speculative-minded brother-in-law, John Barker Church: "The oil is struggling to the surface at every available point, and is running down the rivers for miles and miles. . . . As a ranch, it is a splendid estate, but its value is its almost fabulous wealth in the best of oil." Church and a partner were already negotiating for the Ojai when the Scott leaders turned up. The two groups merged, with the understanding that the Church faction would have a one-third interest and that Silliman would receive $1,500 for a "professional report on the property."[23]

The purchase of the Ojai early in September was followed almost at once by an agreement giving Scott a 10 per cent interest in the lands of E. Conway & Company.[24] Practically all of the Conway lands were close to the Ojai. But for Parsons and Wyeth this was only the beginning. Within the next six months they took over properties containing nearly 275,000 acres, comprised chiefly of seven great ranchos in Southern California. About 6,700 acres, however, lay far to the north near the Davis Ranch in Humboldt County.[25] One territory they did not get was Pico Canyon in northwestern Los Angeles County, despite vigorous efforts by Parsons to encompass the canyon by "correcting" the boundaries of a neighboring rancho.[26] Pico Canyon maintained its status as public land, which permitted the attempts at oil development there to be made under a system of mining claims that followed the practice of gold miners on the public domain.[27]

Development of the most likely of the Scott properties in Southern California was entrusted to three companies that were set up in the spring of 1865. The California Petroleum Company, for which a prospectus was issued as early as December, 1864, received the 18,000-acre Ojai for its territory. Almost simultaneously a prospectus was also issued for the Philadelphia & California Petroleum Company, which took over for development a majestic spread of 187,000 acres, comprising the Simi, San Francisco, and Las Posas ranchos, some miles east and south of the Ojai. The third of these enterprises, the Pacific Coast Petroleum Company, had the responsibility of developing the Scott lands further north in southern San Luis Obispo County, but it never got beyond the planning stage.[28]

The promotional character of all three companies was evident from the start. The lofty capitals authorized for each—$10,000,000 apiece for the first two companies, and $5,000,000 for the third—was one obvious indication. So was the unrestrained language used in soliciting stock subscriptions, which in the case of each company leaned heavily on the reputation of Professor Silliman and included a report by him on its property. The prospectus for the California Petroleum Company, for example, quoted Silliman's enthusiastic private letter to his brother-in-law as an indication of the Ojai's vast oil resources and left little unsaid concerning the disposition of the product, either as crude or refined oil. It pointed to markets for refined products along the Pacific Coast, from British Columbia to Chile, to Australia, Europe, and even the East Coast of the United States. The prospectus also stressed the possibility of marketing crude oil as fuel—for steamships as well as for steam power on land—and for the manufacture of illuminating gas in the West.[29]

Silliman was best qualified to serve as an "expert" with respect to the Ojai, on which he had prepared a report in September, 1864, in accordance with the agreement between Church and Parsons. The Yale scientist listed the half-dozen principal "natural outcrops of rock oil" and prophesied that both the vast surface deposits of asphalt and the petroleum beneath could be distilled to provide valuable products. "The whole development is amazing, and it is plain to the least instructed person that the amount of oil capable of being produced here is almost without limit." He accepted as "probable" an estimate offered by Gilbert that distilling the crude would yield about 50 per cent illuminating oil and a balance comprised almost wholly of light and heavy machine oils. "The experience of Titusville is well known," he concluded. "Suffice it to say, that having made the first researches on the products of Oil Creek, long before any wells were bored there, I am of the opinion that the promise of a remarkable development [here] is far better than it was in the Pennsylvania or Ohio regions—since so famous."[30]

Silliman's first-hand knowledge of the lands owned by the Philadelphia & California Petroleum Company was slight. Its Las Posas and Simi ranchos he had viewed only from a stage on the way to Los Angeles, and its San Francisco Rancho he had never seen. Nevertheless, in February, 1865, following his return to the East, he agreed to prepare a report on these properties. He included in his report the results of an analysis of oil, presumably from the springs in Pico Canyon which Parsons was striving to bring within the limits of the San Francisco Rancho. The analysis showed between 40 and 50 per cent illuminating oil, a yield Silliman believed "could be raised to 60 per cent." Even more rashly, from notes supplied to him, Silliman wrote an at least equally enthusiastic evaluation of the lands of the Pacific Coast Petroleum Company, which he had never seen.[31]

These highly optimistic and rather irresponsible reports quickly embroiled him in controversy. More cautious scientists, like Josiah D. Whitney, the head of the California State Geological Survey, and William H. Brewer, Whitney's former assistant, were shocked and disgusted. In their eyes, Silliman had lent his name to a "swindle."[32] Brewer, who had become a professor at Yale, wrote unequivocally in March, 1865, in response to queries from the editor of the *Springfield Republican:* "I am not aware that petroleum in the sense in which that term is used in Pennsylvania is found in California. I think that at the present state of our knowledge, good illuminating oils *can not* be profitably made in California from the asphaltum or its kindred substances. . . . I do not advise friends to invest, or not to invest, in mineral stocks; but my opinion . . . can be seen from the data I have given you."[33] Some California publications also wrote scathingly of Silliman and his findings, but in general the western journals had kind words to say concerning the boost he had given the state's oil.[34]

Meanwhile, Scott and his associates had begun the commitment of funds to turn their California Petroleum and Philadelphia & California companies into going concerns. Early in 1865 a cargo of drilling and refining equipment for California Petroleum—drilling tools, three boilers and engines, casing, and a retort for refining—was making the long voyage around Cape Horn.[35] Manpower, partially drawn from Army ranks, was also dispatched westward. Dr. Jonathan Letterman, onetime medical director of the Army of the Potomac, arrived in mid-February at Camulos in the Santa Clara Valley above Ventura to superintend the work of the Philadelphia & California Petroleum Company; William H. Stone, the superintendent of the California Petroleum Company, came to the Ojai later in the spring. Stone found already on the scene a young and capable subordinate, Thomas R. Bard, who had preceded him by a few months and who would have a long and distinguished career as landowner, oilman, and political figure in California. Another subordinate, a young chemist named Stephen F. Peckham, followed Stone out as refiner for the company. Peckham, who had been a Brown University undergraduate, had attempted petroleum refining briefly in his native Providence in 1861 and, after Civil War service, was on the threshold of a career that would bring him considerable renown as a chemist and a petroleum specialist. California Petroleum used Peckham's skills solely for carrying on experiments, for the company never discovered refinable oil in commercial quantities. But the experience would quicken and deepen the interest in oil held by the young scientist.[36]

The two Scott companies endured a parallel experience of failure. On the Ojai and neighboring Cañada Larga, California Petroleum worried down seven wells, the deepest only 600 feet, by the spring of 1867. Drillers were plagued, so Bard wrote, by "bad luck with tar, gravel, boulders, and broken tools and a thousand other ills. . . ." Years later he commented, "Our locations were *wild* and were made without the slightest reference to the local geology and with the idea that oil would be struck here in enormous quantities no matter where we bored."[37] The drillers were little prepared to deal with problems posed by formations that were crushed, broken, and sharply tilted, compared with the easily pierced strata that underlay the surface of the Pennsylvania oil region. Ojai #6, begun late in 1866, was as close to success as they got. After spurting over the derrick at the end of May, 1867, the well caved and then settled down to a flow of about five barrels daily of 18° gravity oil.[38] The Philadelphia & California Petroleum Company did not accomplish even this much. Its three wells put down near Camulos were failures in every respect. The company did set up a small refinery operated with oil obtained from seepages and later from tunnels bored into the hills, but the kerosine was so poor as to be virtually unsalable.[39]

Far to the north in Humboldt County Scott's nephew, George Noble,

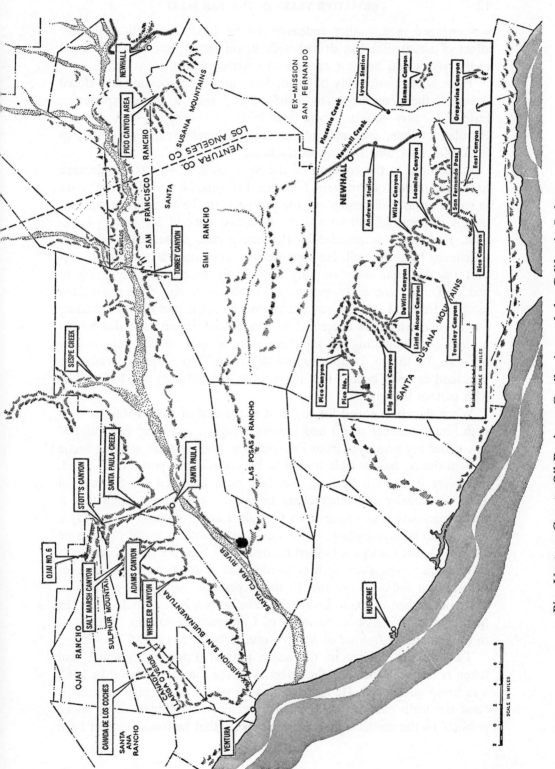

Pico-Ventura County Oil Region—Cradle Area of the California Industry

was engaged in a smaller endeavor during 1865. His well, a shallow effort of about 300 feet drilled with steam power, showed a little oil at the year's end but not enough to encourage further work.[40]

Their hopes thoroughly blighted, Scott and his associates had closed down all their enterprises by 1868. It had been a costly experience; instead of easy returns, there had been only outgo. For California Petroleum alone, estimates of the total expenditures ran as high as $200,000, excluding the cost of the land.[41]

A footnote to the collapse of the Scott companies was the damage to the reputation of Professor Silliman. For this, his foolhardy behavior in so enthusiastically endorsing the prospects of the Scott properties was largely responsible, but so was the detective work of Stephen F. Peckham. Peckham was amazed by the heavy, viscous material he found unrelieved by lighter oil. He soon became convinced that Silliman's report on the Ojai was "stupidly or wilfully false from beginning to end."[42] During the early months of 1866 the young refiner collected samples from oil springs and tunnels on the Ojai and the surrounding countryside which he subjected to distillation. In no case did he get a yield of illuminating oil anywhere near as high as that reported by Silliman for the oil sample supposedly from Pico Springs. Gradually, Peckham came to believe that the sample sent Silliman had been salted with eastern kerosine.[43]

When Peckham sailed for the East at the end of July, 1866, he took with him a number of oil and asphalt samples, including one "dipped . . . under my own eye" from Pico Springs. Shortly after arriving home in Providence, he was able to add to his collection a portion of the oil, ostensibly from Pico Springs, that had been analyzed for Silliman in 1865. Its density and other characteristics convinced Peckham that it was a concoction of crude from Cañada Larga, adjacent to the Ojai, mixed with an equal amount of a well-known eastern brand of kerosine (Devoe's) that George S. Gilbert carried in his Ventura store. Peckham's own sample from Pico Springs yielded, on distillation, 13.5 per cent kerosine—a far cry from the 40 to 50 per cent reported by Silliman. The young chemist made known his conclusions in an article, "On the Supposed Falsification of Samples of California Petroleum," published in the *American Journal of Science and Arts* for May, 1867.[44]

Two months earlier in the same journal Professor Silliman had taken note of the fact that the integrity of the sample analyzed in 1865 was being questioned. He asserted that he would investigate vigorously, "and the truth cannot long remain concealed."[45] Silliman never spoke publicly of the matter again. It seems likely that he found he had been victimized by John Barker Church and kept silent rather than "involve his sister in a scandal." So Peckham reasoned years later.[46]

Silliman suffered for his silence. Angry investors in the Scott enterprises brought his name into suits filed in both Philadelphia and New York. He was charged with having been "bribed" to write favorable reports on the properties of the companies. In the academic realm, too, he was subjected to attack. William H. Brewer reported from Yale that there was "a very strong sentiment . . . in favor of getting rid of" Silliman, and Josiah D. Whitney termed his continued employment "a disgrace." Bowing to pressure, Silliman did resign as professor of chemistry in Yale College in 1869 and the Sheffield Scientific School in 1870, though he continued to serve on the faculty of the medical school. His reputation, made especially lustrous by his report on oil in Pennsylvania, had been badly tarnished by his too careless investigations concerning the same mineral in California.[47]

5

The Scott enterprises were the outstanding manifestations of the California boom of the middle 1860's, but there was many another entry in the race for an oil bonanza. According to one estimate, seventy-five "associations" with authorized capitals aggregating roughly $50,-000,000 were "actively engaged in exploring for oil in California." Some thirty-three were located in Humboldt County, about a dozen in Colusa County in the Sacramento Valley, and the balance were scattered all the way to Los Angeles on both sides of the Coast Range.[48]

Most of these companies never got beyond the paper stage. Speculative enterprises, they seemed willing to wait until somebody else struck oil. A few enterprisers limited themselves to dipping from oil springs, as in the Pico region of northwestern Los Angeles County or in western Kern County at the southern end of the San Joaquin Valley. Near Buena Vista Lake in Kern County, the Buena Vista Petroleum Company began to refine a little oil taken from shallow pits dug in the summer of 1864 adjacent to a seepage. During the next three years some 4,000 gallons of refined oil were reported to have been manufactured, but the cost of freighting the oil to market and, presumably, its low quality made the venture unprofitable.[49]

Elsewhere there were more pretentious efforts to find oil. A few miles west of San Jose at Moody Gulch in Santa Clara County, Dr. Vincent Gelcich, a colorful thirty-four-year-old promoter, began a long career chasing oil rainbows by leasing a seepage in July, 1863, which lumbermen had discovered two years before. After coming West as an Army surgeon, Gelcich had married a niece of Pio Pico, the last governor of California under the Mexican flag. Gelcich used his lease to organize the Santa Clara Petroleum Company, which began drilling with a steam rig early in 1865. The next year its well, down 470 feet, was yielding a little oil but far from enough for a paying proposition. Two neighboring wells offered even less encouragement to their owners.[50]

Southwestern Humboldt County, where nearly forty wells were drilled in 1865 and 1866, was clearly the greatest center of oil excitement. Much of the territory there was public land, in contrast to the great ranchos of Southern California; also, the Union Mattole Company, a San Francisco concern, brought in a well yielding small quantities of a light, greenish oil, suggestive of Pennsylvania's, sufficiently early in the boom to set off a rash of competing efforts. In June, 1865, Union Mattole shipped around 100 gallons. It sent out larger quantities, running up to fifteen barrels (of 42 gallons each) at intervals over the next two years, supplying virtually all the crude oil that was shipped from Humboldt County.[51]

Union Mattole found a buyer in Stanford Brothers, located in San Francisco at 123 California Street, which years later would become the first address of the Standard Oil Company in the West. Stanford Brothers was the largest of the western oil firms. In 1856 three of the brothers, Asa Phillips, Charles, and Josiah, had given up storekeeping in Sacramento and the Mother Lode country to take over the Pacific Oil and Camphene Works from William Bailey, a former partner of George S. Gilbert. Distilling camphene and importing illuminants and lubricants from the East, they soon expanded the firm into an international enterprise. Charles, at New York, handled most of the purchasing, a task he had performed during their days as general merchandisers and wholesalers; A. P. stayed on in San Francisco, and Josiah opened a branch in Lima, Peru. Leland Stanford, who had bought the Sacramento store when his brothers switched to oil, was their Sacramento outlet. Two younger brothers, DeWitt Clinton and Thomas W. Stanford, also foresook storekeeping to set up branches of the oil firm in Sydney and Melbourne, Australia. Henry Bates, who may have been a relative, was the manager for New Zealand.[52]

The Humboldt strike aroused the interest of the Stanfords, for it suggested the possibility of gradually freeing themselves from dependence on the East for their oils. Shortly, they were advertising:[53]

> Having refined the first petroleum from the Union Mattole Company's well and purchased the same of them, thereby fully testing our works,

we are now prepared to refine at the lowest rates, any quantity of oil that may be offered, and satisfaction guaranteed.

The highest market price for crude oil.

Parties having oil to refine please make application at our office.

The brothers also began buying up shares of the Union Mattole Company. But they did not stake their oil fortunes solely on Humboldt County. In the summer of 1865 they moved to give the ex-Mission San Buenaventura its first test by acquiring 2,560 acres of the lands of E. Conway & Company on the south flank of Sulphur Mountain.[54]

Another San Francisco oil house, Hayward & Coleman, followed closely after Stanford Brothers in purchasing a neighboring part of the ex-Mission. This firm had as its senior partner, Alvinza Hayward, the possessor of one of the West's great mining fortunes. Like Stanford Brothers, Hayward & Coleman hoped to use California crude to help meet its needs for illuminants and lubricants.[55]

The two firms hit upon a new technique for developing their leases, which was soon imitated by others, especially the Scott companies. Instead of drilling, they drove tunnels slanting slightly upward as much as 400 feet into the sharply tilted strata of the mountain. Tunneling was a costly job, running as high as $8 a foot. It was also dangerous, for gas collecting in the tunnels could explode unless adequate ventilation was provided by blowers or by a vertical air shaft. But during the sixties far more light oil drained from these tunnels than was procured in any other way. From five tunnels in Wheeler Canyon, the Hayward firm gathered 2,570 barrels of crude ranging in gravity from 27° to 30° or higher during the first year of operation (to October, 1866). Beginning slightly earlier, Stanford Brothers had collected to the same date about 1,200 barrels from seven tunnels located a mile or two away in Saltmarsh Canyon.[56]

Hayward & Coleman and Stanford Brothers brought their crude to San Francisco for distillation into lamp and lubricating oils. As a guide for refining, Stanford Brothers used the second edition of Abraham Gesner's *A Practical Treatise on Coal, Petroleum and Other Distilled Oils*. The lighter fractions were boiled off in stills, condensed, treated with sulfuric acid and caustic soda, and then were allowed to bleach in shallow tanks for several days. The Stanford firm achieved a yield of about 25 per cent illuminating oil, though much of this output was of an uncommonly heavy 35° gravity in order to avoid a federal sales tax of 20¢ a gallon on lighter oils. Heavier fractions, amounting, roughly, to another 25 per cent, were offered to the trade as lubricants.

Both firms occasionally used crude oil or the residuum from distillation as fuel for heating their stills.[57]

Stanford Brothers pushed their refined products energetically. "Comet" illuminating oil was advertised as "superior to any Eastern oil," with a money-back guarantee. They spoke about as proudly of their "Machine Oil," which was claimed "to excel all other oils, and . . . at lower rates." The facts, however, were otherwise. As Peckham had noted, California kerosine burned with "a dull and smoky flame" from excessive carbon. The lubricating oils Peckham considered "very inferior," containing no paraffin and flowing almost like water. California crude oil also provided a much smaller proportion of refined products than did the crude of Pennsylvania. The yield of illuminating and lubricating oils at the Stanford refinery was slightly less than 50 per cent, compared with about 90 per cent for eastern refiners, of which more than half was highly valued kerosine.[58]

California's refined products in the 1860's clearly were marginal, being readily marketable only so long as the better products imported from the East were in short supply. That opportunity passed rapidly following the Civil War, for crude production in Pennsylvania jumped more than 70 per cent between 1864 and 1866. With more crude going through eastern refineries, a larger volume of products was available for export. Receipts at San Francisco, the center of the western oil trade, climbed from 55,321 cases (containing two tins of five gallons each) in 1865 to 132,252 cases in 1867. Kerosine prices that ran as high as $1.70 or more a gallon in the former year, by 1867 had fallen to 54¢ or less. The sharp decline in prices, combined with the low yield from California crude, the low quality of the refined oils, and the relatively high refining costs in the West (for sulfuric acid, caustic soda, barrels, cases, etc.) brought virtually to a halt this first major attempt to derive valuable products from the state's petroleum.[59]

Hayward & Coleman was the first to give up the battle. After turning out some 40,000 gallons of kerosine, it suspended refining in June, 1867. Stanford Brothers, which had manufactured 100,000 gallons, continued as a kerosine refiner for a few more months before concentrating solely on lube oils. The two firms were once again almost totally dependent on the East for their marketing needs.[60]

As the outlook for western refined products darkened, for a brief period the prospect of using petroleum as fuel captured the attention of Californians. A series of dramatic experiments during the summer of 1867 in Boston harbor, where Colonel Henry R. Foote had installed his patented oil burner on the naval gunboat *Palos,* aroused nation-

Benjamin Silliman, Jr.

Stephen F. Peckham

Thomas R. Bard

George S. Gilbert

wide interest. On its first cruise the *Palos* achieved a maximum speed of fifteen nautical miles per hour—four miles faster than its record while using coal. Less than four barrels of oil were consumed during the twenty-five-mile trip, compared with an estimate of six to eight tons of coal. Instead of eight men to shovel coal, an engine-room crew of two sufficed to handle the valves; to highlight the absence of ashes and dust, the floor of the room had been carpeted. The engine got up steam much more rapidly with oil than with coal, and at the end of the voyage the fires were extinguished almost instantly. Foote's efforts caused him to be hailed as a second Fulton.[61]

The *Palos* experiments came at a time when the western press was noting the need for "a more condensed fuel" to facilitate the direct steamer service over the Great Circle route between San Francisco and the Orient recently inaugurated by the Pacific Mail Steamship Company. One of its ships, the *Colorado,* meeting bad weather, had arrived from the Orient early in 1867 with little more than a day's coal on board. The vessel could have carried more coal, of course, reducing the cargo space, or it could have departed from the most direct route to take on coal at Honolulu, extending the voyage by several days. If petroleum could be used, however, it offered a more desirable option, for sufficient petroleum would require only about two-thirds of the storage space needed for coal. And if petroleum could power marine engines, obviously it could also power engines on land. "The consumption of [petroleum] in the furnaces of land and marine engine boilers," said the *Mining & Scientific Press,* "has become one of the most important, if not indeed *the* most important mechanical and commercial question of the day."[62]

While Foote was catching the nation's eye, James H. White, Conway's old associate and the refining consultant to Stanford Brothers, was winning a good deal of regional acclaim for his experiments using petroleum to generate steam power for stationary engines. White's process, apparently, was very similar to that of Colonel Foote. Petroleum was heated in an iron retort, into which water gas from super-heated steam was injected to burn with the vaporized oil in order to bring about more perfect combustion.[63]

San Franciscans were offered a chance to compare the two processes when two of Foote's agents arrived from the East early in 1868 and began demonstrating his burner "propelling the machinery of [a] brass foundry and machine shop" on Mission Street, an exhibition that attracted "crowds of curious and interested visitors." Three months later, in April, a bay steamer, the *Amelia,* made a seven-mile trial run with the eastern burner. Not to be outdone, White soon had his burners firing the boilers of the Aetna Iron Works, a leading San Francisco foundry. He also fitted up one of San Francisco's steam fire engines with a burner. Crude oil for these experiments came from the Sulphur Mountain properties of Stanford Brothers and Hayward & Coleman.[64]

By the end of 1868, interest in petroleum as fuel had died down, both in the East and the West. The experiments, even on the *Palos,* were less than a complete success. The Chief of the Navy Bureau of Steam Engineering noted, for example, the danger of explosion, the evaporation loss in storage, and the pervasive and intolerable odor of petroleum in poorly ventilated quarters. But the crucial factor was economic, both at sea and on land. In 1867, according to the Navy report, an equivalent amount of power could be generated from coal for about one-eighth of the cost of petroleum.[65]

The disparity was less in California, where there were no high-grade coal deposits. Most coal was imported and relatively costly. Nevertheless, cost figures offered for White's burner following a three-month trial at the Aetna foundry during the summer of 1868 slightly favored coal. The price of petroleum may have been made arbitrarily low to accomplish even this result, for petroleum was figured at about $3.15 a barrel compared to the $5.00 Hayward & Coleman had claimed the year before as the cost of producing and delivering oil to San Francisco.[66] A further deterrent to the use of petroleum was the small and uncertain supply, almost wholly from the Sulphur Mountain area, and the disinclination of oilmen to pour further funds into the search following the collapse of the boom of the mid-1860's.

The failure of fuel oil to catch on coincided roughly with the withdrawal of the last of the pioneer western refiners. The three-month trial at the Aetna Iron Works was barely over before White left the field. In September, 1868, he sold to George Pettit a small lubricating oil refinery that he had operated at San Francisco since 1865 with animal and vegetable oils and crude from Sulphur Mountain.[67] By the end of 1868 Stanford Brothers was also on the way out. Josiah Stanford, who had taken over the San Francisco house and refinery, sold them in November, 1869, to his brother-in-law, John W. Allyne, and a partner, William H. White.[68]

In Southern California a small refinery with which Charles Stott, a veteran San Francisco oil merchant and camphene distiller, had been experimenting at the eastern end of the ex-Mission, lay idle for the " 'won't pay' reason." So a census enumerator reported in 1870. Stott had come to Santa Paula Canyon in 1867, driven a tunnel, and refined the crude by a new process that he had patented. It made use of jets of steam to distill crude oil that had been heated to a temperature below the boiling point, and continued the steam treatment in a rectifier, thus accomplishing a more perfect fractionation, and getting a clearer, sweeter-smelling kerosine, so Stott claimed, than by the common practice of distilling at high temperatures and treating the distillate with acid. But, financially at least, his process proved no more successful than that used by his larger western rivals.[69]

In the producing end of the business, the situation was much like that in refining. The census enumerator found little going on, even in the Sulphur Mountain district. California Petroleum and the Philadelphia & California Petroleum companies, like Stott, were no longer operating. The Hayward tunnels, representing an investment of about $25,000, were yielding about 1,000 gallons daily, "most of which flows away and is lost." The "very limited quantity" saved was used principally at Ventura for burning brick and as a lubricant. Saltmarsh Canyon, the Stanford property, on which about $35,000 had been spent, showed a little greater activity. Virtually all of its production, amounting to about 200 gallons daily, found a market, especially with Allyne & White in San Francisco.[70]

Through Allyne & White, the former refinery of Stanford Brothers had continued to operate. Their most important customer was the recently completed Central Pacific Railroad, which took both refined and crude oil for lubricating purposes. California crude replaced lard oil in the journal boxes of freight and passenger cars, and Allyne & White's specialty, "Golden State Lubricating Oil," was used as a higher quality lubricant. This arrangement also served the interest of Leland Stanford, president of the railroad, in assuring a market for the crude from Saltmarsh Canyon, which had passed into his hands in 1866. Allyne & White had at least one other railroad, the Utah Central, as a customer, but the greater general demand in the West was by far for animal and vegetable oils, or for petroleum lubes from the East.[71]

In 1870, except for the less important firm of George Pettit, Allyne & White were about the sole spark of life in an almost defunct industry.[72]

6

The principal weakness of the California oil industry during the 1860's stemmed from the too easy assumption that the numerous surface indications of oil gave promise of about as ready and profitable development as had occurred in Pennsylvania. This self-deception fed on the outrageous claims of some promoters and the slipshod investigations of Benjamin Silliman, Jr.; the result was disillusionment and despair.

Oil hunters soon learned that finding oil in California was much more difficult than in Pennsylvania. The geology of California, marked by frequently tilted and folded strata, was decidedly unlike that of the older Oil Region. "A more difficult formation through which to bore can scarcely be imagined," wrote Peckham of two of the wells of the California Petroleum Company.[73] The still simple techniques and relatively light tools that had worked in the East proved hardly adequate in California. California Petroleum found, for example, that drilling with steam power and using cable tools weighing 500 to 600 pounds was scarcely more effective than the more common and primitive springpole method by which, using a resilient pole to suspend the tools, a forked stick as a fulcrum, and stirrups, wells were stamped or "kicked down" by manpower.[74] The lack of success at drilling in 1865 was undoubtedly one reason, coupled with the pitch of the strata, that caused Stanford Brothers and Hayward & Coleman, and finally the Scott companies, to turn to tunneling. A greater understanding of the subsurface formations, greater skill at drilling, and improved drilling equipment were among the obvious prerequisites for a larger success in finding oil in California.

The chemical characteristics of California crude also posed an unpleasant riddle. As in producing, the methods used in the East did not bring equally good results on the Pacific Coast. They did not deal effectively with a crude that, compared with Pennsylvania oil, contained more carbon and almost no paraffin. Despite valiant efforts of men like Charles Stott and James H. White, western refiners made little headway in solving the riddle during the 1860's. The products they turned out were readily marketable only when the supply of eastern oils was limited and high-priced.

Nevertheless, the years of the boom had proven the presence of oil. There was the prospect of much more if the earth's secrets could be unlocked. And at the same time that men of enterprise were seeking new methods for manufacturing high-quality kerosine and lubricants, they were also encouraged by other possible outlets for crude oil as a substitute for costly, imported coal—notably for fuel and in the manufacture of illuminating gas. In the West petroleum for fuel, even though it failed adoption in the sixties, was a much more live option than in the East, where coal was plentiful and cheap.

Undoubtedly, the most searching survey of the California industry made during the sixties was by its most serious student, S. F. Peckham. After his year with the California Petroleum Company, he prepared a long report for the state geologist, Josiah D. Whitney. Peckham supplied a wealth of data on the industry as it was in mid-1866, to which he added the results of his research on the oil and asphalt samples he had carried East. The young scientist took a position between the "falsehood and exaggeration" of Silliman, which he had so bitterly condemned, and the pessimism of Whitney. Peckham denied that expectations for the California industry "will admit of comparison with those . . . in Pennsylvania," but he felt certain that solutions for the problems of producing and refining eventually would be found.[75]

Indeed, he hoped that his laboratory research would contribute to that end. During the fall of 1866 Peckham hit upon the idea of "cracking" California crude under a pressure of about 30 pounds per square inch in order to increase the yield of illuminating oil. After drawing off the kerosine distillate (43° gravity), he redistilled the heavier distillate under the same pressure and got a second, though much smaller, amount of 43° oil. His greatest success was with the Pico sample; distilling under pressure, he derived almost 62 per cent illuminating oil, compared with 13.5 per cent by conventional methods. This was one of the earliest attempts on record at pressure cracking, so meaningful in the twentieth century in increasing the output of light products, especially gasoline. Peckham believed that his experiment had a secondary value in increasing the ratio of illuminating to lubricating oil to better than 3 to 1, which conformed more closely to the proportionate market demand for the two products. The outcome of his research caused W. H. Brewer to write Whitney, "It seems to me . . . of a considerable importance economically."[76] But the young scientist had no remedy for those characteristics of California petroleum—the excessive carbon responsible for imperfect combustion and the absence of paraffin—that made it, in his judgment, an essentially different substance from the petroleum of Pennsylvania.[77]

Peckham's conclusions concerning the future of California petroleum were generally optimistic: "Whatever disappointments and failure may have attended attempts to develop these resources upon a scale and by methods wholly applicable to another region . . . no candid and properly informed person can for a moment doubt that a reasonable degree of success will attend attempts to develop [them], when a wild fever of speculation shall have been succeeded by a desire to obtain from a new and untried substance such products as by patience and experiment . . . may be found. . . ." One outcome, he felt sure, would be the

II

THE REVIVAL AT PICO

The California industry that emerged in the 1870's presented a sharp contrast to the scene of the middle sixties. Gone were the eastern speculators with their grandiose schemes. Missing, too, was any figure of Tom Scott's stature. The halting recovery in Southern California during the new decade was based on western capital, and the frame within which exploration and development occurred was that of western needs and hopes. Where the East continued to make its contribution was in an advancing technology, brought to California by oil veterans from Pennsylvania. These men had much more experience than the few who had come in the earlier decade, but like their predecessors they soon learned that California oil offered no easy road to fortune.

Gradually, drillers made a little headway in finding oil; unfortunately, refiners were unable to show similar progress in their difficult art. The problem of land titles, too, began to plague the California industry. During the Tom Scott era, the chief efforts at development, as in the East, had been on private lands; in the 1870's, the principal oil region, the Pico, was on the public domain. How the oilmen acquired a clear title to public lands was a legal question that intermittently would bring turmoil to the western industry for more than half a century. There were so many chances for conflicting claims, and also frequent uncertainty concerning government policy with respect to the oil lands.

Leadership early in the revival was supplied chiefly by local capitalists in Los Angeles, a town of about 8,000, and in the much smaller town of Ventura. Such communities had few men with the resources necessary to nurse along an industry of this type. Bankers, professional men, real estate dealers, shopkeepers, farmers—they nearly all failed, ending their gamble short of funds and luck. But with their aid the industry did recover sufficiently to become once again a likely speculation for San Francisco capital. Within a few years dominance in California oil had shifted to San Francisco, a city of about 200,000, where the California Star Oil Works Company, the principal venture of the era, had its headquarters.

2

The first seeds of a revival were sown early in the 1870's as a result of a gas war in San Francisco. The Metropolitan Gas Works, making its bid with a petroleum process, was vying with another new concern, the City Gas Company, and the old San Francisco Gas Company for the illuminating gas business of the city. As a matter of fact, Metropolitan was a re-entry in the contest, for it had been briefly a marginal competitor of San Francisco Gas a few years before. Organized in 1863, Metropolitan took its name from a prominent company in New York City that had pioneered in manufacturing gas from petroleum and then was forced to drop the process when crude oil prices soared in 1864. The western Metropolitan listed as a principal incorporator Charles Hosmer, who had helped finance George S. Gilbert in his experiments with "liquid brea" at Los Angeles. It did not get under way until 1867, however, and then only on a small scale and for a single year.[1]

Metropolitan's rejuvenation occurred in 1871 under new leadership. Its supporters were a number of well-known businessmen, including the hardware merchants, Joseph Stow and W. W. Montague; a crockery and glassware importer, R. A. Swain; and A. P. Brayton and Ira P. Rankin of the Pacific Iron Works. Most of them were also directors of the Pacific Pneumatic Gas Company, a San Francisco concern organized in 1869 to install "gas-makers" in homes and public buildings under the Rand-Loveless patent, to which it held the West Coast rights. The gas machines used "gasolene" imported from the East to carburet air for illuminating gas. They were sold especially for country residences or for homes and buildings in communities too small to have a gasworks. Through Metropolitan, the Pacific Pneumatic promoters hoped to break into the urban trade as well.[2]

It was April, 1872, a full year after the take-over, before their company was ready to operate. In the meantime, Metropolitan built a sizable plant containing a still, retort, condensing chamber, exhauster, and other equipment at Tenth and Channel Streets. Two storage tanks with a joint capacity of 100,000 gallons and a 400,000 cubic feet gas-holder were also erected, and mains were laid into the business district. Metropolitan extolled the virtues of its product: "Superior to coal gas in light and purity and moves through meters less swiftly."! Petroleum was distilled at a low temperature and the vapors passed into a red-hot retort for conversion into fixed or permanent gas. The vapors were channelled next into the condensing chamber, where the portion not converted into permanent gas liquefied and was withdrawn for redistillation. The permanent gas was then drawn off by the exhauster for storage and sale to consumers.[3]

For its raw material Metropolitan looked principally to Ventura County, split off from Santa Barbara County by an act of 1872. There was grand talk of a demand for 1,000 barrels a day, to the delight of the oilmen. They began collecting oil that had been running to waste. Thomas R. Bard considered drilling a test well, and Charles Stott resumed his search in Santa Paula Canyon. But the gas company actually never took more than about 500 barrels a month, paying $4.50 and $5.00 a barrel for oil delivered at San Francisco.[4]

As the small size of these purchases indicate, Metropolitan failed to fulfill the hopes of its owners. The company had trouble with its gas-making process under the Gale-Rand patent, culminating in April, 1873, when an explosion in the retort room blew off the roof and badly burned seven workmen. And it was too lightly financed to withstand a deadly rate war. Metropolitan, with a nominal capital of $1,000,000, was competing against two powerful coal-gas rivals. The San Francisco Gas Company had grown between 1854 and 1870 almost without challenge; the City Gas Company, incorporated in 1870, drew its strength from such prominent western financiers as Alvinza Hayward, Lloyd Tevis, James Ben Ali Haggin, and Henry E. Robinson, who had made large fortunes from mines and real estate. When the leaders of Metropolitan first planned their venture, coal gas was selling at $5.75 per thousand cubic feet; they believed they could make a profit at $3.50. By the spring of 1873, however, price cutting had forced the rate to $1.60, a ruinous rate for all three competitors. In April the two larger concerns merged to form the San Francisco Gas Light Company and then bought out Metropolitan, ending for the time the use of petroleum for gas in San Francisco. Ventura oilmen were left with a trade running from 100 to 150 barrels a month to gas companies that had sprung up in a half-dozen small towns ranging from Santa Barbara to Red Bluff.[5]

The impact of Metropolitan on the state's oil industry, however, had reached beyond Ventura to the mountain canyons of the Santa Susanas, of which Pico was the best known. In February, 1872, two months before Metropolitan began to operate, Dr. Vincent Gelcich arrived at the Russ House in San Francisco, beating the drums for the oil of the Pico region. Disappointed in the boom of the middle 1860's, in which he was most active at Moody Gulch, Gelcich was ready for a new effort. He brought with him "several gallons of oil" that had been "dipped . . . from springs," and as a part of his fanfare let it be known that "an experimental shipment of 100 barrels" was on its way to San Francisco. His words were received with an enthusiasm not accorded oil talk in years. The *Mining & Scientific Press* warmly endorsed the development of the Santa Susana oil "deposits." It foresaw a good lamp oil and a residuum valuable for gas and fuel. The *Press* commented, too, on the medicinal and disinfectant qualities of petroleum which Gelcich, as a doctor and coroner of Los Angeles, had also seen fit to mention.[6]

One outcome of the Gelcich visit was the organizing of the Leaming Petroleum Company, with an authorized capital of $1,000,000, to develop a 160-acre claim in Leaming Canyon, about five miles southeast of Pico Canyon. Gelcich received a half-interest in the company in return for deeding the claim to a group of five incorporators that included A. W. Von Schmidt, a former president, and Joseph Stow, the current president, of the Metropolitan Gas Works. Little, if any, work was actually done on the claim, but the press did not forget.[7] The *Commercial Herald* commented in September:[8]

> We shall not affect to disguise our astonishment at the apparent apathy of capitalists, or our surprise that they should give preference to enterprises of a far less permanent or generally beneficial character. We import Eastern petroleum to the value of over two million dollars' worth every year, while we have [an] abundance of our own, close at hand. It reminds us of the time when we imported our houses from Maine, while we resided on the confines of immense redwood forests and fine lumber regions; or paying $50 per barrel for Eastern flour, while living in a country capable of raising grain enough to feed millions of people.

Apathy continued to reign in San Francisco, where Metropolitan was having its troubles. Gelcich was to do better, however, in his home community of Los Angeles. In doing so, he would bring a prominence to the territory in and near Pico Canyon which that region had not yet achieved.

To understand this important happening, we must look at the earlier history of the Pico—a history that brought together some of the most famous Californians of the era, both Mexican and Yankee.

3

Up to this time the Pico region, consisting of a series of steep and rugged canyons cutting into the northern slope of the Santa Susana mountains, had been bright with promise but of little account otherwise. The canyons, unnamed and unimportant until the middle 1860's, spread from Pico, Moore, and DeWitt at the most northwesterly point down through Lyon, Towsley, Wiley, Leaming, Rice, and East to the southeast, all within a little more than five miles. Within the canyons shallow oil-bearing sandstones lay exposed, giving rise to numerous and prolific seepages. Just below East Canyon the Santa Susanas joined the San Gabriel Mountains to the east, barring easy access to the San Fernando Valley except by a toll road, painstakingly cleft through rock, that General Edward Fitzgerald Beale, owner of the franchise, had rebuilt between 1862 and 1864.[9] Even as late as World War I, this road provided the sole means by which vehicles from the San Joaquin Valley could enter Southern California: "a sheer cut eighty feet deep through conglomerate rock with grades of twenty-nine per cent, so narrow that only one vehicle could pass through at a time and so steep-sided that now and then a boulder dropped from the wall upon some unfortunate traveller."[10] North of this forbidding entry lay a narrow and irregularly shaped valley along the upper Santa Clara River.

The territory above Beale's cut at San Fernando Pass first made news in 1842 when the original California gold discovery took place in Placerita Canyon, lying in the San Gabriel Mountains some five or six miles opposite the mouth of Pico Canyon. Prospectors flocked to the region. Undoubtedly, they observed the evidences of oil, but it was gold they were seeking. Except as a curiosity, the oil seepages were avoided. Gradually, the placers petered out after yielding a few hundred thousand dollars, and by the fifties the valley was being used chiefly for grazing.[11]

As the oil excitement swelled late in 1864, Californians began to look more closely at the seepages of the Santa Susanas. Before the year was out General Beale was on the scene with a Dr. Alsop from Massachusetts to view one promising location. Beale, who had won a touch of national fame as a hero in the Mexican War, was one of the state's greatest land barons, with holdings of more than 200,000 acres, principally in the southern San Joaquin Valley. Edward Conway, his subordinate when Beale was U.S. Surveyor-General for California, may first have drawn his attention to oil, for in the summer of 1864 Beale put up the money for Silliman's report on the Southern California properties of the Conway company and advanced the company an additional $7,000. These transactions could readily have helped arouse his interest in oil prospects north of his toll road and on the route to his San Joaquin Valley ranchos.

Another eminent Californian, Don Andres Pico, brother of the last Mexican governor, Pio Pico, and commander of the Mexican forces in the Mexican War, lived a few miles away from the Santa Susana canyons in the former Mission San Fernando. He had reason to be even more interested in the oil outlook than Beale, with whom he had been on friendly terms ever since the two men had distinguished themselves on opposite sides in the battle of San Pasquale. Don Andres had been one of the largest landholders and cattlemen in Southern California, but extravagant living and a succession of disastrous seasons for his cattle ranges had laid him low. Most of his lands he had lost. Finally in 1862, all his cattle and horses, except for a few strays, were gathered up and sold at auction to satisfy his creditors. All that he retained was 2,000 acres around the Mission and a small herd of cattle, kept by his son, Romulo, and the vaqueros, Jesus Hernandez and Ramon Perea. For the desperate don, oil seemed to offer a badly needed opportunity to repair his fortune. Lesser figures, some of whom, like Pico, gave their names to canyons in the Santa Susanas, were also anxious to take a chance on oil.[12]

A common problem for all those eagerly eying the seepages was the status of the canyons as public lands, the property of the United States government. The most available instrument for gaining rights in the canyons, in the judgment of most oil hunters, was a California statute, the Possessory Act of 1852, which was designed to preserve order on the public domain by protecting the earliest occupant from attack by other parties. Under the Possessory Act, citizens were eligible to a single claim of 160 acres, "clearly bounded," provided at least $200 was spent improving the property. All it could accomplish was to maintain an individual in possession. The act, too, was obviously designed to offer protection for agriculture and grazing, and not for mineral rights.[13]

Despite these deficiencies, during the first months of 1865 nearly one hundred claims were taken up in the Santa Susanas under the Possessory Act.[14] The Picos were in the game early. On January 24, the twenty-three-year-old Romulo filed for a "Naptha Spring in Petroleum ravine," some three miles from the mouth of Pico Canyon. The Picos had learned of the spring from Hernandez and Perea, who, according to one colorful account, stumbled upon it while on a hunting trip. Romulo's hurried action in filing for what soon became known as Pico Springs, without any recompense to the vaqueros, aroused their resentment. Two other claims were also spoken for by the Picos: through Don Andres, to a seepage in DeWitt Canyon, and through a son-in-law, H. C. Wiley, to a spring in Wiley Canyon which was surpassed in the region by Pico Springs alone.[15]

Because homesteading offered, at best, an uncertain route to a title for oil lands, prospectors, taking a page from the Mother Lode, gradually shifted the basis for their claims to mining law. Their precedent was the healthy habit of self-government which gold miners had exhibited on public lands all over the West. Every gold diggings had its fixed rules and by-laws enacted by the miners for governing their claims. The by-laws of hardly two of the mining districts agreed in every particular, but the title they gave was sufficient for all practical purposes. They had long enjoyed the protection of the state courts. Congress had given tacit acceptance by refusing to pass laws governing mining titles, and an act of 1864 organizing the federal courts for Nevada explicitly recognized miner's rights as established under the various "camp" laws.[16]

Oil hunters in Humboldt County had set up a petroleum mining district as early as November, 1864. Gradually, the practice spread to other petroleum centers on the public domain. In March, 1865, a county-wide Los Angeles Asphaltum and Petroleum Mining District was organized; almost four months later, on June 24, the oilmen of the canyons of the Santa Susanas withdrew to form the San Fernando Petroleum Mining District. This pattern for oil development seemed in line with federal policy, for Californians learned at the end of May that henceforth "petroleum tracts" would be withheld from agricultural entry and treated strictly as mineral lands.[17]

The codes of the Los Angeles and San Fernando districts were essentially the same. Upon a "Petroleum, Naptha or Asphaltum bearing lead," or deposit, each claim was limited to "one thousand feet square" (approximately 23 acres), with a single exception: The discoverer of a lead was entitled to a double claim. The code also permitted holding a lead "severally or jointly" by a group of locators, so that labor requirements and the costs of development could be shared. Such a grouping of claims was a familiar arrangement in California. To hold a claim, the locator had to do a day's work each month until his labor amounted to the "value of One Hundred Dollars." Upon proof of this, the claim would be forfeited only if actually abandoned.

Enforcement of these rules was entrusted to a Mining Recorder, annually elected by the miners themselves. It was his duty to investigate and approve or disapprove each claim. It was his responsibility, too, to keep records relating to the filing and transfer of claims. Fees and "travelling expenses" provided his compensation. Christopher Leaming, who earlier had taken a claim under the Possessory Act to a seepage in Leaming Canyon, was chosen Mining Recorder in the first election of the San Fernando district.

As insurance, many, if not most, of those who had homesteaded under the Possessory Act also put their claims on the books of the mining districts. The claim to Pico Springs was recorded with the Los Angeles district on March 22, though the names of the six locators (including the "discoverer") necessary to hold the 160 acres have been lost along with the records of the district. Romulo and Andres Pico were undoubtedly listed, and perhaps H. C. Wiley; the names of Hernandez and Perea, apparently, were also recorded.[18]

But Hernandez still felt aggrieved and angry. So General Beale reported to Romulo in May, after stopping at the house of Hernandez, accompanied by his sheep-ranching partner, Colonel Robert S. Baker. Beale found that Hernandez had put his case to a lawyer and was planning to file for Pico Springs "as the owner and occupant in actual possession" under the Possessory Act of 1852, with the intention of selling his rights "to anyone who would buy," except the Picos. Therefore, wrote Beale, he and Baker decided to make the purchase, "as much to *save you* as to benefit ourselves, and if they have the title you and Don Andres shall have half of what we bought." Hernandez and Perea filed for the Springs on May 22 at Los Angeles and immediately disposed of their rights for $300 to Colonel Baker, a "forty-niner" who had come from Rhode Island at the age of twenty-four and who had become one of the largest and wealthiest landholders in Southern California.[19]

Eleven weeks later, on August 8, a relocation of the claims to Pico Springs was placed on the books of the San Fernando Petroleum Mining District because, according to the document, the original locators (including Romulo and Don Andres) had "failed to comply with the . . . laws" of the district. General Beale, Colonel Baker, Pio Pico, Juan and Francisco Forster, and Sanford Lyon were the new locators. The interest of Beale and Baker, who divided the extra claim of the discoverer, balanced the Pico interest, apparently in fulfillment of the compromise that Beale had suggested to Romulo. Pio and the Forsters (Juan, the brother-in-law, and Francisco, a nephew of Don Andres) may have been merely dummy entrymen for Don Andres and his son but, more likely, they had taken over the rights of their relatives. The sixth locator, Sanford Lyon, was a small sheep-rancher living at Lyons Station, eight or nine miles from the Springs; it was to him that the others looked for the work to make the Springs pay out.[20]

Two claims by different parties under the Possessory Act, and two locations by different locators under mining law, to say nothing of possible changes in federal rulings and federal law—this was the sort of situation that could arise with respect to public oil lands, leading to litigation and slowing oil development.

Actually, the Pico region was probably more important during the boom of the sixties for claims filed in preparation for development than for work performed. By the end of 1865 nearly 200 individual claims covering an area, if combined, of roughly seven square miles had been entered on the books of the San Fernando district; almost 100 more were recorded during the first six months of 1866. The number of persons involved, however, was much smaller. For some, like Sanford Lyon,

Beale, Baker, and Christopher Leaming, filing claims seemed almost
a pastime. They were interested, most of them, in establishing a position
for the future rather than in investing scarce dollars, especially while
the San Fernando was handicapped in access to the San Francisco
market. Shipments from the Pico region required a relatively costly,
cumbersome haul of about sixty miles over mountains and plains to
the port of San Pedro, compared with an easier wagon trip of from
ten to thirty miles for oil that found an outlet through Ventura.[21]

When S. F. Peckham visited the San Fernando district in June, 1866,
he noted that some work had been done in six of the nine canyons—
Pico, Moore, DeWitt, Towsley, Wiley, and Rice. In all, the young
chemist counted seven springpole wells from 45 to 177 feet in depth
and seven tunnels, ranging from less than 30 to 180 feet. The adjoining
canyons of Wiley and Towsley, where the same operator had sunk two
wells and driven five tunnels, supplied the most impressive center of
activity. Cumulative production from Wiley Canyon over a ten-month
span, however, had been only 280 barrels, and the reported yield of
better than three barrels a day from the Towsley well was of heavy oil.
At Pico Springs, which Peckham considered "the most valuable . . .
natural outflow yet discovered" because of its high gravity (28°), Sanford Lyon was dipping about a half-barrel a day from a basin that had
been dug to trap the oil. "The labor that has been expended [in the
district]," Peckham concluded, "amounts to little more than prospective
[sic] operations."[22]

A little of this modest production may have made its way to San
Francisco, but more went to the single-still refinery of A. A. Polhemus
that was operating by May, 1866, in Los Angeles. It was a short-lived
affair with a history reminiscent of the Ojai refining venture of George
S. Gilbert in 1861. Twice Polhemus was burned out, and by the end
of the year he had given up.[23]

So had nearly all the San Fernando oil hunters, as the boom came
to an end. During more than five years between Peckham's visit and
January, 1872, just twenty-seven claims for five locations were registered
with Christopher Leaming, of which the last was entered in October,
1867.[24]

Curiously, the Pico "in-law," Vincent Gelcich, for a first time was
listed as a claimant in the San Fernando with the final three of this group
of five locations. After visiting with his wife, Petra, at the home of
her uncle, Don Andres, in February, 1866, he had warmly endorsed
the prospects of the region in a Los Angeles County newspaper.[25] In
1872 he was ready and waiting to snap up the promotional opportunity

that the Metropolitan Gas Works appeared to offer. And as Metropolitan faded from the scene, Gelcich marshalled his resources for a try in his home community.

4

The tactic Gelcich hit upon to advance his oil fortunes was a more vigorous effort along the same lines he had used in San Francisco the year before—to paint a bright picture in the Los Angeles press of the opportunities in the San Fernando. On April 12, 1873, just as the Metropolitan Gas Works was reaching its end, the *Los Angeles Star* carried the story of a wire to Gelcich from James Renaud, drilling on the Rice claim: "We have struck big oil." Renaud talked fancifully of a flow of eight barrels a day. Shortly, Gelcich visited the claim in Rice Canyon. Upon his return, he spread the word that he had bought out his partners and was sending an additional crew of six men to speed the work.[26]

It must have been obvious to Gelcich—and to other promotionally minded oilmen—that establishing a refinery in Los Angeles would greatly aid their cause. At the end of May he touched off a campaign for a refining company with a letter to the *Los Angeles Star*. The editor lent his support, drawing figures pretty much out of his hat to prove that the net profits from such a venture would run above 70 per cent.[27]

This appeal led to a series of organizational meetings and the incorporation of the Los Angeles Petroleum Refining Company on July 30, 1873, with an authorized capital of $300,000 that was divided into 3,000 shares. The original eighteen stockholders, who signed for 420 shares, comprised many of the leaders of the Los Angeles community, including H. C. Austin, editor of the *Los Angeles Express;* F. P. F. Temple, a pioneer banker; Beale & Baker; M. W. Childs, a hardware merchant; Pio Pico; Vincent Gelcich; and B. L. Peel, secretary of the Board of Trade. Temple took over the office of president, and Peel was the secretary-treasurer.[28]

Another part of the preliminaries was planning for an adequate supply of crude. Three of the founders, Vincent Gelcich, M. W. Childs, and H. C. Austin, agreed to furnish oil from their claims for five cents a gallon. Colonel R. S. Baker did even better. For the first six months, the Colonel told his colleagues, the refinery could have oil from Pico Springs for free.[29]

Like Gelcich, Colonel Baker had never given up on the prospects of the San Fernando. When in 1872 a U.S. Deputy Surveyor restored the township encompassing Pico Springs to agricultural entry, Baker viewed the event as an opportunity. In November, 1872, he paid $750 to the University of California for scrip to 120 acres under the Morrill Act, which had made large grants of rights to public lands as an endowment for an agricultural and engineering college in each state. The Colonel used his scrip for a location that included the Springs and overlapped the claim to a homestead of Hernandez and Perea, which he had purchased, and the mining location of August 8, 1865, in which he was recorded as owning three-fourteenths. He did not follow through to perfect a title of ownership at this time, but he had set up another way to reach for the Springs. More than most, Baker had reason to be interested in the refinery as an outlet for San Fernando crude.[30]

At the close of 1873, ground was broken for the refinery at Lyons Station (also known as Petroliopolis), a stage stop two or three miles north of the San Fernando Pass. It took Captain William B. Smith, the superintendent, until late April, 1874, to finish the job at a cost of about $3,000. The establishment was a modest one, equipped with a single fifteen-barrel still that had been fabricated in San Francisco. Wooden flumes were installed for running the crude from storage tanks, and a pipeline supplied water from a nearby spring.[31]

On April 26 the refinery was "fired up." Optimistic news stories soon began to appear puffing its kerosine as "clearer, purer and [of] better illuminating properties" than eastern oil. But the mood of optimism passed quickly. By July the papers were saying merely that the home product was "superior" and "non-explosive." Soon they were saying nothing at all. Obviously, Captain Smith had had no more success, and perhaps even less, than some of his predecessors in dealing with the troublesome characteristics of California crude.[32]

This outcome might have been more disheartening, except for the fact that the attention of Gelcich and his associates had been diverted to another and sensational refining process, the property of a "Spanish-American gentleman" named Rudolfo Carreras. Carreras appeared upon the scene just about the time the Lyons Station refinery was ready to operate. He proved a wonderful salesman. One evening in April Carreras demonstrated his process to the Los Angeles Petroleum Refining Company directors, who had assembled in Dr. Gelcich's rooms for the occasion. He unveiled a tin basin, fitted with filters impregnated with mysterious chemicals, into which he slowly poured two gallons of San Fernando crude. In less than one minute, as the directors watched, a clear "refined oil" began running from a faucet at its bottom. The yield was above 96 per cent, compared with an estimated 30 per cent by conventional refining. The *Los Angeles Express* hailed the bizarre demonstration as "an almost miraculous triumph of science and genius."[33]

Two months later, with more elaborate equipment, Carreras repeated his experiment, getting a yield of above 40 per cent from black, tarry crude which Captain Smith had rejected at Lyons Station. Vials of the oil were distributed among his audience of some fifty leading citizens. Lamps were filled and lit; each burned with "a brilliant, steady, and cheerful flame." The only problem appeared to be whether sufficient oil could be produced in the San Fernando to make full use of the process. If this hurdle could be surmounted, said an enthralled reporter, "then the commerce of illuminating and lubricating oils will hereafter date from Los Angeles instead of Pennsylvania."[34]

Not all Southern Californians were equally gullible. One who was not taken in was Thomas R. Bard, who asked for a demonstration when he was approached to enlist the financial aid of Tom Scott. To an associate, Bard wrote, "Carreras has a very romantic story to tell how he came into the possession of his secret & says that the discoverer is dead & that he alone knows his secret, which is very *Spanish* and fishy. He claims to do entirely too much, like the miller who promised to give 105 lbs meal for each 100 lbs of wheat." But Carreras was wary of satisfying so critical an observer. By the spring of 1875 faith in his process was on the wane.[35]

For all his flimflam, Carreras did give his hosts an incentive to step up their search for oil. Deep within Towsley Canyon on the Temple claim (of which F. P. F. Temple, the banker-president of the Los Angeles Petroleum Refining Company, and Carreras were among the locators) the first drilling with steam power in the history of the San Fernando began in July, 1874. With a 50-foot derrick and a portable steam rig, the well was put down 470 feet by early 1875, producing a little oil but plagued by caving. It was the most ambitious effort the district had yet seen.[36]

The superintendent of the well was William H. Spangler, a veteran of Tionesta Creek, Oleopolis, Pithole, Tidioute, Triumph Hill, and Babylon in the Pennsylvania Oil Regions.[37] He was a precursor of other experienced oilmen soon to appear, quickening the pace of oil development and broadening the base of its financial support. They ushered in a period of transition in which control of the San Fernando would pass from Los Angeles to San Francisco.

5

Two former Pennsylvanians, Denton Cyrus Scott and Robert C. Mc-Pherson, were of especial importance in this invasion, for along with their oil skills they combined promotional talents of a high order. Glib, buoyant, expansive, they were the kind who could see millions in everything. During 1875 their activities helped stimulate the filing of 161 claims for 35 separate locations, reflecting the rising hopes for the San Fernando. And the tide continued; the next year 199 claims for 61 locations were recorded.[38]

D. C. Scott arrived in Los Angeles late in March, 1875. He was a tall, rather handsome fellow of thirty, who had come to San Francisco a few months earlier after nine years in the Pennsylvania fields, where at various times he had played the roles of roustabout, driller, and well-owner. His success in the eastern Oil Regions, obviously, had not been great, and he was eager for a chance in a new area. Within a few weeks Scott was joined by a younger partner, John G. Baker, who was another migrant from Pennsylvania.[39]

Scott and Baker decided as an opening venture to try for a lease of the shut-down refinery at Lyons Station and to refine oil from the seepages and tunnels of the San Fernando. Getting a lease to the refinery proved no problem; the Los Angeles Petroleum Refining Company was deep in debt, and many of its stockholders, including Gelcich, were delinquent in paying a stock assessment. Scott also talked in April to Colonel Robert S. Baker, who gave him verbal permission to collect oil from Pico Springs and to drill there in return for one-eighth of the oil. The Colonel represented himself, so Scott said later, as merely one of the owners, but "as he had advanced the most of the money to work the claim . . . he controlled the others."[40]

With these deals behind them, Scott and Baker were ready to begin business, which they called the Star Oil Works. Shortly, they were advertising for crude at $2 a barrel, and some of their kerosine was shipped to Los Angeles for trial. As refiner, the partners gained the services of William Schumacher, who claimed "more than sixteen years experience" in the East, including Cleveland. F. P. F. Temple was sufficiently impressed that at the end of May he let Scott borrow $600.[41]

During the summer their brisk confidence snared a financial angel. According to the later testimony of Scott, Nathaniel J. Clarke agreed "to furnish . . . money to carry on the business" in return for a one-third interest in their refining operations and a one-fifth interest in any producing wells. Clarke was a part-owner of the Los Angeles Boring Company, organized in March, 1875, for which Scott had earlier agreed to serve as manager.[42]

With money at hand, Scott and Baker took up plans for drilling at Pico Springs. To manage the drilling, they turned to C. A. (Alex)

Mentry, a recent arrival in Los Angeles whom Scott had known in Pennsylvania. Mentry was a sturdy and resourceful driller, only twenty-six years of age, who had more than 100 wells in the East to his credit. In mid-August he began rigging up a three-pole derrick and improvising tools. His chisel and stem he made from an old railroad axle, and his rig consisted of a springpole. In little more than three weeks Mentry kicked down a well, Pico #1, to a depth of 120 feet. He got a production of ten to twelve barrels a day, which was the best showing yet made by any well in California. In time, through Pacific Coast Oil, this well passed to Standard of California, the oldest upon its roster and the first in the West to which the term "commercial" can accurately be applied. By the end of 1875 Mentry completed two shallower wells, both of which yielded some oil.[43]

In spite of Mentry's success, the fortunes of the Star Oil Works took a downward turn. For one thing, Nathaniel Clarke, after advancing $1,505, ceased his support late in October, 1875, when Los Angeles was caught up in a panic following the failure of the Bank of California in San Francisco in August and the first closing of Temple & Workman (F. P. F. Temple's bank) in September. For another, at Lyons Station William Schumacher was meeting the customary fate of all refiners who had worked with California crude, a fact that not even complimentary news stories could disguise. During October, Schumacher left the employ of the Star Oil Works.[44]

On both counts, Scott and Baker received some badly needed relief from the activities of Robert C. McPherson. A born salesman, McPherson had left Pennsylvania in 1873 after more than a decade in the oil fields and had come to California as an agent for Farrar & Trefts of Buffalo, New York, who were well-known manufacturers of steam engines and boilers. When he visited the Star Oil Works in the San Fernando in June, 1875, he may have been seeking to sell one of his engines, but it is obvious that he came away impressed by the prospects of the region.[45]

Returning to San Francisco, McPherson drummed up support for an oil venture and traveled East in the autumn to purchase up-to-date drilling equipment to develop some 200 acres in mining claims he had acquired in and around Pico Canyon. These claims he deeded to the San Francisco Petroleum Company, which he organized in mid-December in association with Robert C. Page, a prominent stockbroker, and several other San Francisco capitalists. San Francisco Petroleum had a nominal capital of $10,000,000, a figure no California oil company had dared use since the days of Tom Scott. McPherson's rig, consisting of two sets of boring tools weighing about 2,000 pounds each, fishing tools to lift the boring tools in case of accident, and a 15-horsepower Farrar & Trefts engine, was by far the finest Californians had yet seen. He put it to work early in 1876 on the heights a scant half mile east of Pico Springs.[46]

While in Pennsylvania, McPherson had also taken on the responsibility of recruiting a refiner for Lyons Station, for the repeated failures at refining appeared to be the greatest single threat to effective oil development. A long-established but small Titusville refiner named John A. Scott was the man he approached. McPherson told him, so Scott said later, that "they had found some green oil in California and had been unable to refine it, . . . that he would like to have me come out and try, and that a large amount of money could be made if I succeeded." Scott agreed to make the trip. His fare was paid by Reuben Denton, another San Franciscan whom McPherson had interested in oil.[47]

The upshot was that the Star Oil Works got a new refiner and, in Reuben Denton, a new financial backer. J. A. Scott took charge at Lyons Station in mid-January, 1876, where one of his first tasks was rerunning some forty barrels of kerosine that Los Angeles merchants had returned as "not marketable." The refiner was heartened by the results of his special, secret process, which made no use of sulfuric acid. It turned out better oil than any yet made in California. D. C. Scott and John Baker were delighted. At the end of February, they took an option to buy the refinery for $1,500.[48]

Reuben Denton, too, had reason to be pleased at the refiner's progress, but not at the slipshod way Scott and Baker were doing business. In little more than three months they had drawn on him for about $8,000 to clear up back bills and to support their current operations. Beyond this rapid drain, Denton was also disturbed by the tenuous hold of the partners on Pico Springs. In February, 1876, Sanford Lyon, a co-holder with Colonel R. S. Baker and others in the relocation of August, 1865, brought in a 170-foot well close to the Star Oil wells which (according to Lyon) started off at about sixteen barrels a day. The Colonel's verbal permission, which was so readily revocable, seemed a dubious base indeed on which to build a business.[49]

To protect his investment, Denton in mid-March took over the Star Oil Works from Scott and Baker for what was owed him and commenced to put its affairs in better shape. Within a month he secured a lease to an area 1,000 feet square that centered on Pico Springs but excluded the well of Sanford Lyon. The lease gave Denton the right to four wells at a royalty of one-eighth of the production. It required a depth for one of at least 500 feet unless a "full flowing well" was found earlier. The duration of the lease was fixed at three years, after which the wells would pass to the lessors. It was understood, too, that the lease was subject to cancellation if Denton failed to operate the wells "properly, and in a workmanlike manner" for ninety days. Colonel Baker, who signed for himself and General Beale, handled the negotiations for the lessors; Sanford Lyon and Christopher Leaming (who had acquired a share in Lyon's interest) were the other signers, in addition to Denton. The interest of the Pico family was not represented.[50]

In some of its terms the lease was harsh, especially the limitation to three years, but it was an obvious improvement over the previous loose arrangement. Encouraged, Denton followed through on Scott's option of February, buying the refinery at Lyons Station on April 19, a week after the lease was signed. Earlier he had linked J. A. Scott more firmly to the Star Oil Works by giving him a one-fifth interest in the business.[51]

While these negotiations were being completed, Denton traveled to San Francisco to find financial allies. He sought out R. C. Page, the stockbroker who had been McPherson's strong supporter. Page agreed to pay $6,000 for a half-interest and soon rounded up a notable group of associates: Andrew Jackson Bryant, the newly elected mayor of San Francisco and a prominent figure in insurance circles; Mark L. McDonald, one of the West's chief speculators in mines and minerals; and Charles Jones, who was also a mining capitalist. On April 18 Denton signed over a half-interest in his Pico lease to A. J. Bryant. It was an indication of the progress at San Fernando that Denton was able to bring men of this caliber to his side.[52]

Early in May, 1876, these five men launched the Star Oil Works Company with an authorized capital of $1,000,000 as successor to the Star Oil Works, and then, on June 16, reincorporated as the California Star Oil Works Company. The reincorporation apparently was triggered by a threatened suit of Nathaniel Clarke against Reuben Denton as successor to Scott and Baker to recover the money Clarke had advanced the Star Oil Works. The incorporators of the Star Oil Works Company had no desire to see the name of their enterprise drawn into the suit. In every particular except name the two charters of incorporation were identical, envisioning a business that would engage in all phases of the oil industry. A. J. Bryant was elected president, and his brother-in-law, Joseph S. Taylor, a safe and lock merchant, took over the office of secretary.[53]

A first manifestation of the new leadership was an expansion into Ventura County, where for two or three years a small oil revival had been going on led by W. G. Adams, a rancher, and Frank Thayer, a former gold miner and druggist. Later they were joined by a "business partner," a Ventura storekeeper named E. A. Edwards. In 1875 Adams & Thayer had gained a lease to the oil lands at the eastern end of the ex-Mission. From collecting oil at the abandoned properties of Stanford Brothers, Alvinza Hayward, and Charles Stott, they progressed to springpole drilling in Adams Canyon, a mile or two away from the Stanford tunnels, where early in 1876 they brought in a well that produced a little oil. They began two more. Buying this oil and erecting a plant to refine it at Ventura, adjacent to cheap water transportation, seemed an attractive gamble to the leaders of the Star Oil Works Company.[54]

Page and Denton made a beginning in mid-May, 1876, when they contracted with Adams & Thayer to pay $2.75 a barrel for 5,000 barrels a month. At the time this production was thoroughly unrealistic, but it bespoke the hopes of both sides. A site for a refinery on the Ventura waterfront was also speedily acquired. For $275 Star Oil purchased the thirty-barrel still that Tom Scott's Philadelphia & California Petroleum Company had used a decade earlier, but other equipment did not come so cheaply. It is barely possible that the cost of the plant may have approached the $6,000 reported in the press when it began to operate in September under the general supervision of J. A. Scott from Lyons Station.[55]

There was progress, too, in the San Fernando, where R. C. Page had also been busy. Early in June a twenty-barrel still was installed at Lyons Station. The next month Mentry started preparations for drilling Pico #4 with an antiquated steam rig that had once belonged to a Tom Scott company. When Mentry completed the well on September 26 at a depth of 370 feet, it produced twenty-five barrels a day, helping to test the enlarged capacity of the refinery. This amazing well, the longest-lived in the history of the West, in 1961 was still yielding almost a barrel daily of 37° gravity oil.[56]

Speeding the delivery of oil to the refinery was another matter that received the company's attention. By mid-June Mentry had run a line of pipe about a mile and a half down the rugged, upper end of Pico Canyon. At the terminus of the line, teamsters loaded barrels, filled from a 250-barrel tank, for conveyance in their heavy, great-wheeled wagons over rough terrain for the remaining seven and a half miles to Lyons Station. Originally, the company had planned to extend its pipeline, the first in California, all the way, but it had become clear that the days of the refinery at Lyons Station were numbered. During the summer of 1876 the Southern Pacific Railroad was laying the last lengths of track north of the San Fernando tunnel, completing its line between Los Angeles and San Francisco and, incidentally, opening the Pico region to rail transportation. The Southern Pacific bypassed Lyons Station by about a mile. Until California Star (CSOW) determined upon a new site along the railroad, there was little reason to finish the pipeline.[57]

Yet another significant step, following incorporation, was the decision to market J. A. Scott's Lustre kerosine in San Francisco. An initial shipment of fifty barrels was made in mid-June, and a promise of much larger deliveries must have taken into account the predicted production of the new Ventura refinery. The oil arrived at a propitious moment, just before eastern kerosine started a steep price climb. Devoe's Brilliant, the leading eastern brand at San Francisco, jumped from 25¢ a gallon in June, 1876, to 37¢ at the end of August, and to 44¢ in December. These higher prices coincided with a decline in eastern crude oil inventories during the year of more than 30 per cent to about two and a half million barrels. The prospect of a larger quantity of California kerosine and of better quality in times like these quickened interest in the California Star Oil Works Company.[58]

Two keen observers of the changing oil scene, both in the nation and within California, were the veteran San Francisco oil merchant, Frederick B. Taylor, and his junior partner, Demetrius G. Scofield. For two or three months during the summer of 1876 they studied the outlook before deciding to enter the California industry. They became deeply interested in California Star and the San Fernando district. Likely oil lands in Ventura County, both on private ranchos and the public domain, also attracted them. Later on, in the fall of 1877, to a lesser extent they became active in the Moody Gulch territory about 250 miles north of Pico along the Coast Range, a matter that will be noted in greater detail in the following chapter.

The significance of the entry of Taylor and Scofield was that they were oil professionals. For them oil was not a marginal speculation, as it was for Page or Bryant or Mark McDonald. Zealously, the two partners strove to retrace the steps of Stanford Brothers a decade earlier, to build an integrated industry that could supply California and perhaps other areas bordering the Pacific. Their efforts measurably advanced the cause of oil in California.

6

Taylor and Scofield deserve a larger mention, for after September, 1876, they quickly became the principal figures in the California industry.

The early years of Frederick Bayard Taylor, like those of a number of other pioneer oilmen, are somewhat obscure. Born in New York in 1836, he came to San Francisco in 1852 with his father, William H. Taylor, who was briefly a partner with the brothers Alexander and Charles Stott in an oil and camphene business. Following the break-up of the partnership, W. H. Taylor sold lamps and then, by 1854, was distilling camphene on Lombard Street in North Beach with his eighteen-year-old son. Shortly, the father appears to have returned to New York, leaving the operation of the distillery to his son. By the end of the decade, at least, F. B. Taylor had expanded the business to include coal oil and animal oils, imported from the East, with W. H. Taylor apparently serving as his New York agent. After the Civil War, F. B. Taylor also returned to New York. For a year or two his firm was not listed among the San Francisco oil houses, but by 1869 Taylor was again in the West. In the kerosine trade, he was a vigorous competitor of the merchant, Alvinza Hayward (formerly, Hayward & Coleman), who held the agency for the brands of the Devoe Manufacturing Company of New York. Taylor had some strong connections, too, with eastern firms. He was the West Coast agent for Samuel Downer's of Boston, for the Manhattan Oil Company, and, at the beginning of the seventies, for the Gaslight brand of Bostwick & Tilford.[59]

It was through his tie to Downer's that Taylor first met Demetrius G. Scofield, who years later would become the first president of the independent Standard Oil Company (California). Like Taylor, Scofield was a New Yorker, born in New York City in February, 1843. At twenty-one, he went to the Oil Regions of Pennsylvania, where in his own words he "owned interests in wells and operated and managed the same." In this way he gained an early knowledge of producing with which he was to be identified through most of his life. After four or five years, Scofield returned to New York City as a minor oil broker associated with the Downer Kerosene Oil Company, for whom he made a trip to San Francisco in 1870. He stayed on as Taylor's bookkeeper. Within a year or two Scofield was back in New York serving as Taylor's agent and then, in 1874, journeyed to Japan to explore that great, undeveloped market for kerosene. Scofield bore the impressive title of "Bearer of Dispatches to Their Excellencies, the Governors of Kanagawa" (the province of the open port of Yokohama), an honor bestowed on him by Charles Wolcott Brooks, the consul for Japan in California. Nothing came of the trip, but it offers impressive evidence of the larger dreams of Taylor and his young partner.[60]

For a while, Scofield was also drawn into speculation in securities of western mining companies, a pursuit which threatened to end his oil ties. In the spring of 1875 he paid $5,000 for a seat on the Pacific Stock Exchange and within a few months was using almost all of his time for his new career as stockbroker and speculator. At first his speculations in Comstock securities paid out handsomely, earning him a reputation as "perhaps the heaviest operator on the . . . Exchange." Early in August, 1876, however, he was forced to suspend with liabilities of around $208,000, of which $26,000 represented a loan from F. B. Taylor. Chastened, Scofield settled his debts for about forty cents on the dollar. Thereafter, he turned his back on the stock market and devoted himself wholeheartedly to the oil interests of the Taylor firm.[61]

Taylor and Scofield first traveled in pursuit of oil property to Southern California, where on July 5 they visited Pico Canyon, with R. C. McPherson and Sanford Lyon as their guides. McPherson told Mentry that Taylor was proposing to purchase an interest, and the Pico super-intendent permitted the visitor to gauge the flow of Pico #2 with a "five gallon can . . . , timing the length . . . it took to fill . . . by his watch." Mentry next made the well "spurt" by agitating it with a sand pump. "A column of oil," so Lyon recalled later, "rushed up twenty feet above the ground." It made a good rehearsal, but for the San Franciscans Pico was merely a part of their reconnaissance. They journeyed on, along with McPherson, into Ventura County. In Ice Spring Canyon, near Santa Paula Creek, Taylor joined McPherson and two others in locating an eighty-acre claim. Later events strongly suggest that they probably also stopped at the Ojai Rancho and at the Ventura refinery of California Star.[62]

For Taylor, September was the month of decision, with California Star a principal target. In mid-month the press carried the news that the first shipment of products from the Ventura refinery (managed by D. C. Scott) had been made to F. B. Taylor & Company. Before September was over, the oil merchant had purchased a 30 per cent interest in California Star and, with Scofield, had joined the board of directors. Together, they supplanted R. C. Page and Reuben Denton, who had withdrawn from the company, as the chief decision-makers. Shortly, Taylor took the title of General Manager. Scofield functioned as his adviser and field man. The evidence seems clear that the other stock-holders were pleased to have such a capable pair take over the man-agement of CSOW.[63]

Taylor and Scofield did not stop with their stock interest. They apparently believed that the non-renewable, three-year, four-well Pico lease which Denton had secured provided a much too limited future for the company. At least, this seems one reasonable explanation for Taylor's purchase of the rights to Pico Springs of Juan and Francisco Forster and Sanford Lyon and Christopher Leaming under the relocation of August 8, 1865. On September 28, Taylor paid $6,000 to Romulo Pico for the rights of the two Forsters, which Romulo had bought a few months earlier. A month later, on October 28, Sanford Lyon and Christopher Leaming accepted $2,000 for their one-seventh, which made Taylor's holdings under the relocation equal to the three-sevenths of General Beale and Colonel Baker. Perhaps because he considered it unnecessary, the San Francisco oilman did not acquire the remaining one-seventh held by Pio Pico. If Taylor could make his rights good versus Beale and Baker, he had greatly strengthened the position of California Star at Pico Springs.[64]

Elsewhere around Pico Canyon, Taylor acquired at least 300 acres in undeveloped claims during the fall of 1876, for what undoubtedly was a modest outlay.[65]

In Ventura County, securing oil rights to the recurrently alluring Ojai Rancho became the chief goal of Taylor and Scofield. During the summer of 1876 the Ventura storekeeper, E. A. Edwards, was hawking a lease to the Ojai that he had persuaded Albert Gerberding, brother-in-law of the agent for the rancho, Thomas R. Bard, to approve as Bard's attorney-in-fact while Bard was honeymooning in Europe.

The terms were not onerous: a twenty-five-year lease of the whole rancho, in return for an expenditure of $1,000 the first year and continued development thereafter, plus a one-fifth royalty of any oil produced. Edwards assigned the lease to Taylor, Scofield, and R. C. McPherson around the end of September, only to receive an angry blast from Bard a couple of weeks later. Bard charged that the lease was "unauthorized" and "void," but he was willing to entertain on offer for the purchase of oil rights to the most likely tracts on the rancho.[66]

The result was that Scofield paid Bard $1,000 for a sixty-day option to F. B. Taylor & Company on 5,860 acres, comprising about one-third of the Ojai, at a price of $25,000. Evidently, Taylor and Scofield considered the transaction warranted sharing the risk, for purchasing the oil rights was merely a first cost beyond which lay much larger expenditures for development. They may have hoped to draw on the other stockholders of CSOW, but if so, they were quickly disappointed. The California Star stockholders agreed to an assessment of $1 per share ($10,000), bringing the paid-in capital to $25,000 in order to buy modern drilling equipment and to move and enlarge the refinery, but that was about as far as they would go. To find allies, Taylor and Scofield looked to the East.[67]

Scofield departed for Pennsylvania in mid-December carrying a list of articles and machinery that Mentry had prepared for him. He placed the order with Gibbs & Sterrett of Titusville, a well-known supplier of oil well and refining equipment, for which F. B. Taylor & Company became the West Coast agent.[68]

Raising capital for the Ojai, the other part of his mission, Scofield found much more troublesome. The names of the men he approached are in some measure a matter of conjecture. One likely candidate was Foster W. Mitchell, an oil millionaire of Franklin, Pennsylvania, whose producing firm Scofield had once served as secretary. Another was Cyrus D. Angell, who had made a fortune applying some simple geological observations in his search for oil. Still others were officials of the Standard Oil Company, especially John D. Archbold, and probably some of the men Scofield had known through the Downer Kerosene Oil Company. Evidently, the traveler from California was more successful in arousing interest than in gaining assurances of support. Early in January, he wired Bard from New York asking for a sixty-day extension of his option, which Bard granted. Scofield knocked on doors at Cleveland, including perhaps the office of John D. Rockefeller, on his way West. In March, 1877, he wrote Bard from San Francisco that he had wired the interested parties "to come out as soon as possible." But no one came that year.[69]

F. B. Taylor & Company failed to secure any of the Ojai. However, in September, 1877, through D. C. Scott it did gain a lease from Bard to forty acres in Coche Canyon on the neighboring Rancho Cañada Larga. Earlier, in October, 1876, Scott had taken leases of an unknown size on the Rancho Santa Ana, adjoining the Ojai to the west, and on the Rancho El Rincon, further west along the Santa Barbara County coast, which he assigned to F. B. Taylor in August, 1877. All three leases were for ten years and required a one-eighth royalty of the oil produced. They lay almost due west from Pico, within a fifty-mile expanse that by 1877 was frequently referred to as the Southern California "oil belt."[70]

Government lands, especially in the bald and rugged canyons of Ventura County, were another lure for F. B. Taylor & Company. Santa Paula Canyon, at the eastern end of Sulphur Mountain, was one center where the Taylor forces located a number of claims. Another and even greater center were the small canyons along Sespe Creek, about a dozen miles east of the Ojai. Though difficult of access, they abounded in oil seepages. Prospectors had penetrated this region early in 1876 and during the summer had set up the Sespe Petroleum Mining District to regularize their claims. One group, led by M. S. Patrick and Dr. John S. Griffin, organized the Los Angeles Oil Company in September, with a nominal capital of $1,000,000, to develop several attractive locations. Taylor and Scofield followed not far behind, using a former Pennsylvanian, W. H. Ramsey, as their agent. Ramsey proved an efficient operator, getting "dummy" locators to lend their names for the recording of claims that were later deeded to F. B. Taylor & Company. Principally by this device, he laid hold of 110 claims amounting to about 2,500 acres by the spring of 1877. To some angry Venturans, this looked like a monopolistic grab.[71]

The roundup of lands was merely a first step; the payoff, obviously, lay in finding oil and refining it successfully. And the time was ripe, a fact which the many enthusiastic news stories in the California press during 1877 make impressively clear. At the beginning of the year, with eastern crude oil inventories at a very low figure and kerosine prices high, the *San Francisco Post* wrote, "Never before was there such a favorable time for opening the oil territory of this state." The vision of the press, too, extended beyond California to the export market. At more exalted moments, some papers entertained the hope that California was destined to "divide the oil trade of the world," with Japan, China, Australia, and India seeming the most important and likely targets.[72]

Such optimism, we can be sure, was not foreign to the thinking of Taylor and Scofield. Their program, as it unfolded in 1877, involved the effort to increase production at Pico by deeper drilling; the construction of a larger, up-to-date refinery accessible to rail transportation to handle the Pico crude; exploratory drilling on their Ventura lands, in an attempt to provide a large and dependable supply of light oil for the refinery at the port of Ventura; and, toward the close of the year, a revolutionary change in rail transportation as one of a series of moves designed to bring about economies and to improve the marketability of CSOW's refined products. They also continued to hope that some of the contacts Scofield had made in the East, including Standard Oil, would yet come to their aid and speed and expand their activities.

7

A prelude to deeper drilling at Pico was a levy on California Star's stockholders of fifty cents a share ($5,000) in mid-April, just before Mentry began deepening Pico #1, for the cost of the new equipment had more than used up the funds raised earlier. It was an assessment that the stockholders found easy to pay because of the sudden and dramatic success achieved with the new rig from Titusville. Within three days it had punched down #1 an additional 55 feet to a depth of 175 feet, striking an oil sand that caused the oil to spurt high on the derrick and to more than triple its production to thirty barrels daily. A wave of excitement swept through Southern California. Mentry continued his drilling to a depth of 370 feet without, however, increasing the well's output.[73]

The success at #1 made building a new refinery to supersede the inadequate plant at Lyons Station even more urgent. At the end of April a five-acre site was selected on the San Francisco Rancho at Andrews Station, nearly a mile northwest of Lyons Station, on the outskirts of what is today the town of Newhall. Andrews Station, a stage stop on the route down the Santa Clara Valley to Ventura, was attractive chiefly for its location adjacent to the Southern Pacific Railroad and for a bountiful water supply from springs for refining operations.[74]

Construction, carefully supervised by J. A. Scott, began in May and took about three months. Storage tanks of 20 to 100 barrels capacity were scattered about a hillside, from which crude oil was charged by gravity into the stills below. Two of the stills, 15 and 20 barrels in size, had seen service at Lyons Station. A new still, of the so-called cheesebox type, was a 120-barrel affair. All three were set on brick foundations and were direct fired. The heavy residual oil from earlier refining runs was used as fuel, with steam being injected into the oil to atomize it and to intensify the heat. Petroleum gases from the hot stills passed into a condenser, 5 x 5 x 125 feet, consisting of 1,400 feet of two-inch and three-inch iron pipe submerged in the water, from which the illuminating oils traveled to a lead-lined agitator, where they were treated with chemicals and agitated with air to improve their burning quality. A unique final step was a special treatment made much of by J. A. Scott, a secret he never divulged.[75]

At Andrews Station, California Star turned out a somewhat longer list of products, including small quantities of benzine and a 300° F. fire test safety illuminating oil for use on ships and railroads and in factories and mines. The company continued to manufacture a light lubricating oil (24° gravity) for machinery and a heavy lubricant (19° gravity) for sawmills, quartz mills, and railroad journal boxes. But kerosine in two grades, Lustre and Prime White, were the chief breadwinners. Kerosine refining was still a difficult task, for the oil had to be "run and re-run several times" in order to turn out a salable product. According to Scofield's later testimony, the "actual output" of kerosine at Andrews Station "never averaged over 750 gallons per day." At maximum, the

Lyons-Andrews Station and Ventura refineries in 1877 could not have turned out more than 200,000 gallons, which was about 10 per cent of a California consumption estimated that year at 2,000,000 gallons. Probably the amount manufactured was a good deal less.[76]

Completing the new refinery came none too soon, for Mentry's well-deepening campaign, which had been stalled for some weeks by a water shortage, was resumed late in August. Meanwhile he had laid a one-and-a-half-mile pipeline from a neighboring canyon in order to provide an adequate water supply for the steam drilling machinery. Well #3, put down to 170 feet from its earlier springpole depth of 65 feet, gave only about five barrels daily. The result at #2 was more encouraging. Early in October, at 240 feet, it pumped about thirty barrels daily, a production that was maintained at 300 feet. And the response from #4 was awesome. Early in November, it spurted to the top of the 65-foot derrick, then flowed at about seventy barrels daily before being finished off at 560 feet. This was an embarrassing amount, for it increased the total Pico production to considerably more than the capacity of the refinery. Mentry pumped the other wells but little, while awaiting for #4's "copious stream" to subside. He also arranged for two more 500-barrel tanks, bringing the total tankage at Pico to 3,000 barrels, supplemented by about 300 barrels at the refinery.[77]

A by-product of Mentry's triumph was a quickened interest elsewhere in the Pico, though not to an extent involving much cash. Most men chose merely to continue an old game, buying claims or locating new ones. By 1877 the San Fernando district was pretty well plastered with claims, but locators could still find some open areas. A total of 131 claimants registered for 46 locations during 1877, and 144 claimants for 49 locations followed the same procedure the next year. Vincent Gelcich, once more aflame with hope, reorganized the Leaming Petroleum Company during 1877 without, however, being able to find funds for drilling. And R. C. McPherson, who, like Gelcich, had a remarkable skill in press relations, attempted unsuccessfully to hire Mentry away from California Star for a bonus of $500 and a wage increase of a dollar a day. As the only other "active borer" in the district, McPherson had known only humiliation for his San Francisco Petroleum Company. In two wells his tools had stuck fast: in the first at 633 feet, and in the second at nearly 1,000 feet, the deepest well yet drilled in Southern California. It was a record that gave him little consolation.[78]

8

In Ventura County preliminary work got under way on the Santa Ana Rancho at the western end of Sulphur Mountain during the spring of 1877, even before Taylor and Scofield had settled upon a corporate vehicle to carry on the enterprise. The imposing name chosen for their new concern, the Standard Oil Company of California, was an apparent reflection of their continuing desire for an alliance with the great eastern organization. Incorporated on July 26, 1877, with an authorized capital of $2,500,000 divided into 50,000 shares, it was empowered to engage in any activity associated with the oil industry. D. C. Scott, who had been Taylor's energetic lessor and who was to become the company's manager, was given a one-eighth interest. The remaining shares were split equally between F. B. Taylor, D. G. Scofield, A. J. Bryant, and Mark L. McDonald. The hope of the Rockefeller organization's eventual involvement may have persuaded Bryant and McDonald to join up, but there was also a more immediate factor. If the Standard Oil Company of California made a sizable light oil strike, CSOW's Ventura refinery would be able to develop more fully its substantial advantage in freight rates over Andrews Station in serving the San Francisco market. Taylor took over as president of the new company, and Scofield became its secretary.[79]

Drilling began in earnest in August on the Santa Ana Rancho after a rig arrived from Titusville. The well, called the Lady Emma (after Scofield's wife), went down almost without incident, accompanied by many an optimistic forecast. In December, at 810 feet, work was suspended, however, for no oil had been discovered. Scott had similar bad luck with his Los Coches well on the Cañada Larga. In January, 1878, after more than three months, the well was down 820 feet and filled with water. This record gave California Star no reason to follow through on a contingent order with Gibbs & Sterrett for a 150-barrel still for its Ventura refinery.[80]

The outcome of Scott's efforts was an unpleasant surprise for Taylor and Scofield, who had been carrying the Standard Oil Company of California on a credit basis. In January, 1878, two Ventura suppliers sued the company for a total in excess of $1,000; presumably, too, the two rigs at the wells were unpaid for. To take care of these bills and to get the company on a sound financial footing, the directors levied an assessment of forty cents a share ($20,000), payable at the end of January.[81]

No further activity followed on the part of the Standard Oil Company of California. For this, the reason seems plain: California crude was becoming almost a drug on the market, as kerosine prices fell steadily around the end of 1877. In Ventura County, the producers, Adams, Thayer & Edwards, were skirting the margins of bankruptcy; only the

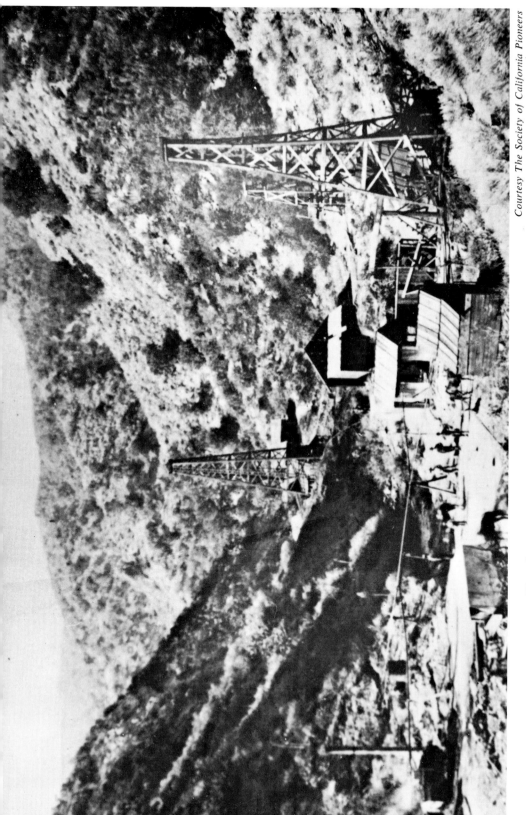

Pico Canyon, probably June, 1877. Pico #4 in the foreground

Edward F. Beale

Robert S. Baker

Andres Pico

Vincent Gelcich

Los Angeles Oil Company, high in Sespe Canyon, kept vigorously at work. And California Star was having great difficulty in disposing of its refined products at satisfactory prices.[82]

9

Marketing, all along, had proven a troublesome activity for the Taylor forces. The low quality of California Star oils had been part of the problem, which no bombast of John A. Scott or the company could hide. The truth of the matter was that, like Stanford Brothers in the 1860's, Scott had found California crude something of a riddle. He discovered that eastern processes were inadequate, and he could not come up with the necessary modifications to turn out a good kerosine. Smoky and smelly, the California product found a market most readily, as in the earlier decade, when eastern oils were relatively scarce and high-priced. Customers were apt to be people of low income like the Chinese, who accounted for almost 10 per cent of the population of San Francisco and of the state in 1880 and who could not afford to be too particular.[83]

The generous praise frequently bestowed on a home product by western newspapers was matched at other times by a brutal frankness concerning its deficiencies. California kerosine was usually described simply as "Earth Oil," and occasionally as of a dangerously low fire test. "Some 300 barrels Earth Oil from Los Angeles county have recently been received here, part sold for lubricating purposes and the balance as a substitute for Eastern Refined Kerosene," wrote the *Commercial Herald* in September, 1876. "Extreme caution is needful on the part of the consumer." A few months later an enterprising reporter for the *San Francisco Post* found that a slack-filled tin of Scott's premium-grade Lustre burned at 136° F. instead of 150° F., as advertised, and that samples of lower-grade oil would ignite at temperatures below 100° F. Retailers were reported at times to have imposed on the public by surreptitiously blending California oil with eastern, or by marketing the western product from barrels and cases bearing the names of well-known eastern brands.[84]

Prices at which F. B. Taylor wholesaled California kerosine obviously had to be lower than for imported oil. Early in 1877, for example, the quotation for Lustre was 40¢ a gallon, 10¢ less than for two eastern premium brands, Downer's and Elaine. California Star's Prime White was offered at 35¢, compared with 44¢ for Devoe's Brilliant, the most popular of the 110° F. fire test oils. The disparities in price increased somewhat during the first half of 1877. Evidently, a longer acquaintance with the western oils did little to win them popular favor. Moreover, prices for all kerosines began to fall off rapidly, as crude oil production picked up in Pennsylvania and the early wells of the great Bradford field began to come in.[85]

California Star could hope for a breakthrough in refining to improve its competitive position, but another and, it proved, more feasible objective was to reduce freight costs from Andrews Station to San Francisco. In the days of the Lyons Station refinery, oil had to be carted to the railroad and shipped to San Francisco at a charge of $3 a barrel. For the return of the barrel, an additional $1 was levied. The over-all cost for freight ran above 10¢ a gallon, which was considerably more than on oil imported from the East. It was also well above the approximately 3¢ a gallon for water transportation from the Ventura refinery—reason enough for Taylor and Scofield to be deeply interested in finding light oil in Ventura County.[86]

The California Star executives found an answer to high railroad rates through conversations with Isaac E. Blake, a Denver marketer who had come to California in the spring of 1877 to check on the production at Pico. In Colorado two or three years earlier Blake had worked a revolution in the transportation of oil products by substituting bulk shipments in tank cars for more costly shipments in barrels and cases. A tank car of his design carried 3,200 gallons in two 40-barrel tanks, located one at each end of what seemed otherwise a conventional freight car. Dry freight could be loaded into the area between the tanks, so that the railroad need not charge for the return of an empty car. After the Andrews Station refinery was opened, Blake let California Star have the use of a tank car or two. The Southern Pacific gave a rate of $75 a car to San Francisco, reducing the cost to approximately 2.3¢ per gallon, which was less than for water freight from Ventura.[87]

Isaac E. Blake would join Scofield as one of the leading western oilmen of the nineteenth century. A clergyman's son born in Boden, Canada, in 1845, he had spent most of his early years in Massachusetts. He was a big man, better than six feet tall and weighing about 200 pounds, in contrast to the short and rather slight figure of Scofield. In most other ways, however, the two men were much alike. They were about the same age; they had had somewhat similar careers; and they were both highly sanguine in temperament. Each had served an apprenticeship in producing before turning to marketing. Blake first went to the Pennsylvania oil regions in 1865, a year after Scofield. As a driller and well-owner, he put together a considerable fortune, only to lose it all and $40,000 besides in 1872 because of his zeal for oil speculations. Within a couple of years thereafter, Blake shifted to marketing in Colorado, where early in 1875 he joined a brother-in-law and some local men in organizing the Continental Oil Company of Colorado. A few months later, in November, he was the principal incorporator of a second and larger concern, the Continental Oil & Transportation Company, which was incorporated in Iowa with an authorized capital of $500,000 comprised of 5,000 shares. Blake signed for 2,440 of the 4,000 shares issued at the time of incorporation. In 1877 he came to California bearing the title of General Manager of the Continental Oil & Transportation Company west of the Missouri River.[88]

Blake's warm estimate of the oil holdings of F. B. Taylor & Company and California Star's urgent need for tank cars led to the establishment of a joint enterprise on November 27, 1877, called the Continental Oil & Transportation Company of California. The California concern was capitalized at $250,000, divided into 2,500 shares, of which 1,240 were assigned to the Iowa corporation, the Continental Oil & Transportation Company. George S. Guernsy, a Council Bluffs physician and a director of the Iowa corporation, and I. E. Blake were each listed for 5 shares. The remaining 1,250 went to F. B. Taylor & Company: F. B. Taylor, 623 shares, D. G. Scofield, 622 shares, and George F. Bragg, 5 shares. Guernsy was elected president of the California company; Blake became its general superintendent, and Scofield its secretary. By the end of the year several more cars of the Continental Oil & Transportation Company (CO&T) had arrived at the Andrews Station refinery.[89]

But supplying tank cars had become only one of the functions of CO&T; it had also taken on the role of distributor for California Star. Plans were made for CO&T to build and operate a large plant in San Francisco and to set up outlets elsewhere in the state, to which the products of CSOW and oils brought overland from the East would be transported in bulk and then cased or barreled and sold. At San Francisco, the plans called for a can-manufacturing establishment. The new plants at San Francisco and Los Angeles were ready in the spring of 1878. Within a few months, at least two others followed. Shortly, the old attempt to market Lustre as a 150° premium oil was abandoned; instead, it was downgraded to 110° and the same oil offered the public under the new brands, Aladdin and Eureka. CO&T also encouraged dealers to have oil put up under brands of their own choosing. And for the first time attention was given to marketing in the Pacific area outside the United States.[90]

California Star's leaders had reason to bestir themselves, for the competition of eastern oils was becoming steadily more intense. During 1877 a jump of more than 40 per cent in eastern crude production helped erase all traces of a short kerosine supply that had been present the year before. In the West, kerosine inventories virtually doubled (to 2,190,000 gallons). Prices, in consequence, fell away; in December, Devoe's Brilliant sold at San Francisco for 26.5¢ a gallon, approximately the same as at the end of 1875. Soon the prices of Devoe's and other leading eastern brands would drop further.[91]

Refining and marketing would seem to have offered California Star problems enough, but in 1878 the outlook for the company was made still more uncertain by a threat from another quarter. Early in the year, through court action, Colonel Robert S. Baker began an attempt to drive California Star from the Pico and to take away its wells.

10

This storm, which had been brewing for some time, centered on the question of ownership of the Pico claim. Its origins lay in the conflicting locations of 1865 under homestead and mining law that offered so fruitful a field for controversy. Since July, 1876, California Star had sent Beale and Baker no statement of the Pico production nor of the one-eighth royalty specified in the lease. The company, obviously, had learned of the relocation of August, 1865, and of the rights of the Forsters and Sanford Lyon (later purchased by Taylor) and of Pio Pico. For nearly a year Beale and Baker took no action; then, following Mentry's achievement in increasing the yield of Pico #1, they appeared at the offices of CSOW in San Francisco early in June, 1877, to demand an accounting. More than that, they demanded the statement "in the form of an acknowledgment that the premises were held by [California Star] for Beale and Baker alone," an acknowledgment the company refused to give.[92]

Beale and Baker based their contention of total ownership on their purchase of the homestead rights of the vaqueros, Hernandez and Perea, in May, 1865. Any interest of Sanford Lyon, they asserted, came solely from them for his work in developing the claim. They maintained that the relocation of August, 1865, was fraudulent, and that the rights under the relocation were merely a "pretended interest." Nonetheless, in May, 1877, Baker had considered it prudent to acquire the remaining interest under the relocation from Pio Pico, the seventy-six-year-old former governor, through a deed of trust.[93]

California Star's leaders also showed considerable insecurity by responding to Beale and Baker with two separate attempts at compromise. The first, made while the Southern Californians were still in San Francisco, was drafted by D. G. Scofield. After listing a greatly exaggerated statement of the landholdings of F. B. Taylor & Company (48,221 acres), Scofield wrote, "Could also probably secure control . . . of the Cal. Star Oil Works Co. should you go in with us. Our idea would be for you to go in with us jointly on the above land. . . ." The second, made by A. J. Bryant and Mark McDonald, suggested that both sides should deed their controversial rights to the company, in return for which the Southern California pair would receive one-half of the stock of CSOW and the privilege of naming three of the five directors. Beale and Baker chose to gamble on winning the whole of the Pico claim, however, in preference to accepting either offer.[94]

From thoughts of compromise, Taylor and Scofield soon swung to the offensive. Learning that Baker was attempting to get a title to Pico Springs with University of California scrip, Taylor reasoned that there must be "some defect in the original location." Consequently, on July 23, 1877, he had James Feore, CSOW's agent at Andrews Station, quietly post a notice on the property, announcing still another relocation of the Springs as the Pioneer Petroleum Claim. The notice bore the names of Feore and six San Franciscans, including George Loomis and George F. Bragg, who were well-known merchants; C. R. Greathouse, a prominent attorney; and James McDonald, a banker and brother of Mark McDonald. When the relocation was presented to Christopher Leaming, however, he refused to enter it on his books. To Beale and Baker this whole affair probably seemed an irrelevance, for they were much more afraid of the relocation of 1865. From Washington, where he was working hard to achieve a patent with University scrip, Beale wrote Baker early in January of 1878, "My own fear is that we have lost the case, but it is worth a struggle and I will do all I can to retrieve it."[95]

The Southern Californians were given more room for maneuver when heavy rains of unprecedented duration disrupted operations at the Pico shortly after the beginning of the new year. Mentry hired extra teams to haul crude to the refinery, but to little avail. Mire and mud and swollen creek waters made the road to Andrews Station at times "absolutely impassible." The torrential waters also temporarily washed out rail service to San Francisco. Tanks at the wells and the refinery were filled to capacity. Despite further attempts by Mentry to cut back production, on four occasions during February and March he was forced to dump crude from storage in order to accommodate new oil. This turmoil was a windfall for Beale and Baker, for it permitted them to go into court charging that California Star had violated the lease by failing to operate their property in a "workmanlike manner." They alleged that the company had allowed much oil to be wasted and had cut back production to about a quarter of the capacity of the wells. They asked the court to declare the lease forfeit and to require California Star to pay the royalty owed them, plus $150,000 in damages. Beale and Baker also requested that a receiver be appointed at once to operate the property until a decision was handed down.[96]

Their suit, begun on March 22, 1878, in Los Angeles, came two days after California Star, in a forestalling move, had begun legal action at San Francisco seeking a settlement of the vexatious question of owner-ship of the Pico claim. The company admitted to no other motives than a desire to know to whom it owed royalty oil and to be free from harassment. These two suits were the opening salvos of a legal battle that raged in courtrooms in San Francisco and Los Angeles and in the offices of the U.S. Land Commissioner at Los Angeles and of the Com-missioner of the General Land Office in Washington. "A Transcontinental Lawsuit," said the *Los Angeles Herald* in an appropriate headline.[97]

California Star, led by Taylor and Scofield, anxiously sought a new basis for compromise in order to get on with its main concern, the oil business. At least, this seems the most plausible explanation for an assessment of $2.50 a share ($25,000) voted by the company's directors in mid-May. Five of the seven stockholders at the time held 9,985 of the 10,000 shares: F. B. Taylor, 2,995; H. E. Robinson, 2,990; A. J. Bryant, 2,000; J. A. Scott, 1,000; and James McDonald, 1,000 shares. Except for Scott, they were all moneyed men, with property, in Sco-field's words, "exceeding in value one million dollars." Henry E. Robin-son, a mining capitalist, was reputed to be worth more than a million alone. Nevertheless, the assessment failed, apparently because Beale and Baker refused to deal—$50,000 for the two acres on which the wells stood, according to what may have been a slightly inaccurate news-paper story.[98]

A companion assessment of ten cents a share ($5,000) was voted by the directors of the Standard Oil Company of California on May 22. This capital would have put the Ventura County company back in business, and success by the company in finding oil would have dimin-ished the dependence of California Star on the troublesome Pico. The failure of the CSOW levy, however, spelled failure for the Standard assessment as well. Taylor and Scofield were willing to pay, but Bryant and Mark McDonald refused, and D. C. Scott perhaps could not.[99]

Litigation without conclusion continued to be the fate of California

Star. Both sides energetically collected depositions for the most important case, which was heard in Los Angeles during the summer of 1878. Forty-five men supplied evidence. Twenty-five testified to earlier oil experience in Pennsylvania, offering an interesting indication of the skilled manpower that had been drawn to Southern California within a few years. Most of the witnesses supported California Star; of those with experience in Pennsylvania, seventeen lined up behind the company, compared to eight for Beale and Baker.[100]

R. C. McPherson, the superintendent of the San Francisco Petroleum Company, was the chief witness for the plaintiffs. Three months earlier, Baker had attempted to put him in as receiver at Pico, and McPherson had good reason to believe that he and his men would operate the wells if CSOW was dispossessed. The San Francisco superintendent vigorously supported testimony offered earlier that attacked Mentry for gross negligence. He stressed most heavily the charge that Mentry had caused a loss of oil by failing to pump the wells continuously, allowing water, accumulating in the oil, to force it into other outlets away from the wells. McPherson also claimed that California Star had been dilatory in providing sufficient tankage. As a result, when production outran storage early in 1878, oil had been wasted.[101]

California Star's numerous witnesses offered a firm and lengthy rebuttal. Foremost in his own defense was Alex Mentry. The Pico superintendent affirmed staunchly that he had always pumped the wells sufficiently to protect them from water damage. But to pump them steadily, he argued, would have been poor management, for additional costly tankage would have been required to store oil so manifestly in excess of refining needs. Moreover, the longer the oil was stored, the greater would be the "evaporation of the volatile portions." After thirty days, according to Mentry's estimate, the loss in volume from evaporation would be "fully 25 per cent," and after six months, the oil would be "unfit for refining." In Mentry's judgment, nature clearly provided the best storage. The Pico superintendent also maintained that the disruption of rail traffic by washouts had been wholly responsible for his failure to get tankage in time to handle the heavy increase in production caused by Pico #4, and that the total loss of crude run off in excess of capacity amounted to less than ninety barrels. Other witnesses gave Mentry steadfast support. Probably most notable was the widely renowned Cyrus D. Angell, who had come to California from Pennsylvania early in 1878. Angell asserted that the Pico wells had been "worked and operated intelligently, carefully and properly," and endorsed Mentry as a man of "first class reputation."[102]

Still other witnesses, especially D. G. Scofield and I. E. Blake, addressed much of their testimony to the marketing situation in California. Both men stated that, apart from California Star, the total demand for crude oil in the state did not exceed fifty barrels monthly. Scofield also pointed to the keen competition being met by the company in the kerosine trade. California Star had been forced to close its Ventura refinery, and at Andrews Station it was offering kerosine for as little as $4.00 to $4.20 a barrel (10¢ a gallon).[103]

11

The outlook for California Star, however viewed, was not a happy one. With Pico production more than adequate for so uncertain a market, there was little incentive to continue deeper drilling, the one option open to the company under its lease. Indeed, 1878 was a year of curtailed activity at Pico. John A. Scott, whose capabilities as a refiner had been more and more under fire, was one of the men let go. During the fall of 1878 the shift of the village of Newhall four miles south to a site bordering Andrews Station furnished about the only excitement in the Pico region.[104]

Marketing, especially, gave the company much to ponder. The setting up of a "branch office" of the Standard Oil Company (Ohio) at San Francisco in June was particularly disturbing, for the eastern giant had made arrangements with the railroads to deliver oil to California at extremely low rates. "The Standard . . . is determined, if possible, to crush out the developments of oil on this coast," commented the *Ventura Signal,* which had picked up the news early. By August, Devoe's Brilliant (which had passed to Standard) was being offered at 19¢ a gallon in lots of 1,000 cases. "At this low price there can be no profit in the production of the Star Earth Oils from the southern part of California," was the probably correct surmise of the *Commercial Herald.*[105]

More and more, California Star was forced to turn to what it hoped was a less competitive and discriminating foreign market. During the four months ending in July, 1878, the company sent above 2,000 cases (20,000 gallons) of kerosine to the Hawaiian Islands, and made other shipments to Japan, the Samoan Islands, and Mexico. The move was a wise one, for some export oil shipped by eastern refiners was of extremely low quality. In fact, some 3,000 cases, apparently of eastern origin, were returned from Honolulu early in 1879. "This . . . the authorities there condemned as unsafe to use," said the *Commercial Herald,* "and . . . send back . . . to blow up our people, who are less careful of human life than even those of the Hawaiian Kingdom." But any advantage possessed by California Star was limited and could readily be removed by improvement in the quality of the eastern oils.[106]

During these dark months Taylor and Scofield looked increasingly to the East for relief and to the oilmen with whom Scofield had talked early in 1877. They were especially buoyed in February, 1878, by the arrival of Cyrus D. Angell, who was undoubtedly the most prominent producer yet to visit California. A former merchant, he had begun his oil career in 1867 in Pennsylvania. Within a few years he gained fame for a theory that oil would be found extending between and beyond known oil fields in "belts" of identical or closely similar geologic formations to those underlying the fields. His theory proved a phenomenal success in the eastern oil regions, where he became the sole or part owner of several hundred wells and at one time claimed a production of more than 14,000 barrels monthly.[107]

Angell came to California, spurred by the belief that a large and relatively untapped oil belt stretched west from the Pico to the Pacific. Before leaving Pennsylvania, he had also discussed his plans with John D. Archbold and had come away convinced that the Standard Oil Company was willing to consider sharing in a California venture. From February on, at times with a colleague, Angell spent "very often . . . days and nights continuously" at the Pico wells "for the purpose of determining the value of the property and the character and peculiarities of oil lands on the Pacific Coast." Further to the west, his chief interest was the Sulphur Mountain region on the ex-Mission Rancho.[108]

It was not long before Angell developed an abounding enthusiasm for the opportunity before him. Taylor and Scofield were eager for an alliance, and the owners of the ex-Mission were willing to negotiate a sale of oil rights. But despite correspondence with Archbold, he learned "nothing decisive" concerning participation by the Standard Oil Company. Finally, in an attempt to bring the matter to a head, at the end of March he addressed a letter to John D. Rockefeller. The opportunity in California, he wrote Rockefeller, compared favorably to those offered by the great Bradford and Butler County fields in Pennsylvania before their development. For "an investment not exceeding a quarter million dollars," he dangled before Standard's president an undivided half-interest in all properties of F. B. Taylor & Company, including refining and transportation facilities, and in the lands on which he was seeking an option. Like others both earlier and later, Angell also stressed the proximity of California oil to the "Islands of the Pacific and the densely populated regions of Asia," a trade he thought it would soon surely monopolize. "The parties in interest here realize the importance of association & co-opperative [sic] action with you and warmly desire it, and only ask an investigation on your part feeling entire confidence in the results."[109]

But the letter from Angell evoked no favorable response. A month earlier Rockefeller and other Standard leaders had suffered a suit for several million dollars for breach of contract in a producing operation carried on jointly with outsiders in Pennsylvania; apparently as a result, Standard decided to cease its producing efforts, which were never large, and to limit itself solely to purchasing crude oil. Even if this decision had not been made, it would have been a great departure for Rockefeller to have endorsed a venture so remote from the older Oil Regions.[110]

Angell continued to maintain close ties with F. B. Taylor & Company. He also kept on with his negotiations for oil rights on the ex-Mission, for which he ultimately offered $100,000. In the fall of 1878 Angell was gone from California for several weeks seeking to round up support in the East, but to no avail.[111]

Meanwhile the news of his action in soliciting Standard had leaked to the California press. In October a story got out that the "Standard Oil Company of Pennsylvania" had purchased the ex-Mission oil belt. Six weeks later another false rumor appeared in a Los Angeles paper, announcing that Standard, "through its agent, who has been here about a year," had bought McPherson's San Francisco Petroleum Company and paid $75,000 for the "Beale and Baker claim."[112]

The faltering western industry and California Star were to find rescue, however, not in the East but in San Francisco. During 1879 new leaders brought a new company into being. In doing so, they cleared the way for renewed effort by settling the dispute over ownership of that most valuable of all California oil properties, the Pico claim.

III

NEW LEADERS
AND A NEW COMPANY

In California oil history, the last years of the 1870's mark a
time of transition, witnessing the end of F. B. Taylor's
dominance and the emergence of new leaders. Two prominent San
Francisco capitalists, Charles N. Felton and Lloyd Tevis, entered the
industry despite its bleak outlook. They saw an opportunity to take over
at little cost to themselves, and they shared the hopes of the earlier
operators that oil could supply the basis for a large and profitable
business. They were willing to gamble time, effort, and money to make
it so.

Their main instrument was the Pacific Coast Oil Company, which
Felton organized in 1879. The result of no abrupt decision, it came into
being nearly two years after Felton had made his initial investment in
oil lands. As the company got under way, Felton was joined in a loose
alliance by Lloyd Tevis, one of the greatest western capitalists of the
nineteenth century. Within a few years, these two men built around
Pacific Coast Oil an integrated oil enterprise of a magnitude not yet
known in California.

It is desirable at this point to become acquainted with Charles Felton
and the circumstances that aroused his interest in oil. A leading petroleum
broker of the period, George Upshur, has gone so far as to call him "the
father of the California oil industry."[1] This statement can readily be
disputed, for there are other possible claimants like Edward Conway,
Thomas R. Bard, Vincent Gelcich, and D. G. Scofield. None of them,
however, matched Felton's combination of management and resources
during the industry's formative years.

2

Felton was a sturdily built man of medium height, and somewhat
austere. With his moustache and imperial and his well-tailored clothes,
he looked like some dapper citizen of the Second Empire. Contempo-
raries viewed him as a shrewd and energetic millionaire. Coming to
California from New York in 1849 at the age of twenty-one, Felton rose
to prominence during the Gold Rush and its aftermath. Like so many
others, he had spent three or four years at mining before he learned

that there were easier and quicker ways to wealth. Thereafter, he gained considerable financial success in the gold country, first as a merchant at Downieville and Marysville and later as a Nevada City banker before moving to San Francisco in 1863. Felton had also found time to serve in various years as under-sheriff and tax collector in Yuba County and later as a state assemblyman. This joining together of private and public careers, capped by two terms in Congress and two years in the United States Senate, was to be a distinguishing feature of his whole life.[2]

The former Nevada City banker soon became a conspicuous figure in San Francisco financial circles. Like many another western capitalist, he speculated in gold and silver mines and their securities. As a broker and speculator, he attracted the attention of the flamboyant William C. Ralston, a founder of the Bank of California and the city's outstanding financier. In 1868 Ralston headed a group of business leaders, including Lloyd Tevis, who drafted Felton for the office of Assistant Treasurer of the United States and Treasurer of the Mint at San Francisco. These posts he held until April, 1873, when he resigned to attend to his personal affairs.[3]

Events at Moody Gulch in 1877 appear to have drawn Felton's attention to oil. Located about sixteen miles southwest of San Jose and within thirty miles of his country home at Menlo Park, the Gulch had made news during the oil boom of the 1860's when Vincent Gelcich organized the Santa Clara Petroleum Company, it may be recalled, in an unsuccessful attempt to exploit a seepage there. The revival of the mid-seventies made Moody Gulch seem worth another try. In March, 1877, a group of local promoters joined Alonzo Dillabaugh, a Pennsylvanian who claimed twelve years of oil experience, in leasing 200 acres that embraced the earlier well site and organized a new Santa Clara Petroleum Company.[4]

Articles of incorporation had hardly been filed before the San Jose newspapers were puffing up the enterprise. The *Mercury* reported that the company had a well which "it is thought . . . will flow 1,000 gallons per day." The *Argus* gave a glowing account of "a magnificent petroleum well" and threw in a rumor of a copper mine for good measure. Results were actually nothing of the sort. As late as mid-June the well was down only 60 feet, and a claim of the company to a daily production of five barrels was undoubtedly a gross exaggeration.[5]

The San Jose newspapers were following with even greater interest the doings of Colonel Zaccur P. Boyer, a promoter from Pennsylvania who had recently come to San Jose with the West Coast rights to the Lowe patent for manufacturing illuminating gas. This process had been developed a few years before by T. S. C. Lowe, a talented inventor who had won a good deal of fame as chief of the aeronautic section of the army during the Civil War. It made use of petroleum to carburet water gas, producing a brighter flame than gas manufactured by the older coal-gas method. Steam was jetted through glowing coal on the floor of a vertical retort at the same time that petroleum was sprayed upon the coal from above. The vaporized mixture passed from the retort into a superheater, where it was fixed into permanent gas by contact with white-hot bricks. Three gallons of crude oil (21 pounds) and 50 pounds of coal were required to make 1,000 cubic feet of gas. The Lowe process had been successfully introduced into several eastern cities before Boyer came West. San Jose, with a population of about 12,000, must have seemed an attractive target to the Colonel, for the high price and low quality of the coal gas provided by the San Jose Gas Company were arousing much dissatisfaction. The possibility of finding oil nearby probably also appealed to him.[6]

San Jose was Boyer's second stop on what he hoped would be a triumphal western tour. Earlier he had visited Virginia City, Nevada, a mining center of nearly 30,000, where he had persuaded local capitalists to join him in planning a Lowe gas plant to challenge the local coal-gas company. At San Jose he was likewise successful in rounding up financial support and late in May gained a twenty-five-year franchise for his Garden City Gas Company. Charles B. Hensley, the president of the company, was a business acquaintance of Lloyd Tevis; another prominent investor, Charles Hadsell had been a co-owner with Felton of the Alameda Water Company. Boyer drew up plans for a gasworks capable of producing 25,000 cubic feet daily, which he located "immediately north of the roundhouse of the South Pacific [Coast] Railroad," a narrow gauge road that was being built west from San Jose toward Moody Gulch and Santa Cruz.[7]

When construction of the gasworks got under way in August, Boyer turned to the financially feeble Santa Clara Petroleum Company as a likely supplier of the oil he would need. He bought into the company, took over its management, and agreed to advance funds for its operations. To give Moody Gulch a serious test, he hired William E. Youle, a driller from Pennsylvania who had worked for R. C. McPherson in Pico Canyon. But Boyer did not intend to let his oil fortunes rest on so small a base. Between August and the end of the year he took seven leases in the Moody territory, three in partnership with Charles Hadsell. In December he launched two new concerns, the United States Oil Company and the San Jose Petroleum Company, of which Hadsell became the president.[8]

Boyer had looked forward to sharing in still more land. The flurry of activity at Moody Gulch had brought R. C. McPherson, D. G. Scofield, and F. B. Taylor to the scene. Late in August, McPherson began to take up leases and led Boyer to believe that they would be partners. On the other hand, Scofield and Taylor understood that they would share with McPherson to the extent of two-thirds. When McPherson recorded six leases in his own name in mid-September, an infuriated Boyer, according to one dramatic account, hunted him down and took some of the leases at pistol point as a half-interest. Taylor and Scofield were more temperate; they sued McPherson.[9]

It was these controversial leases that McPherson sold to Charles N. Felton for $500 on September 29, 1877. They represented Felton's first investment in oil lands since 1865, when he had engaged in a couple of small and ineffectual speculations.[10]

The role of Felton in acquiring the six leases, whether as peacemaker or in self-interest, is difficult to make out, for he was acquainted with all the parties to the controversy. Through Charles Hadsell, Felton had a line to Boyer; indeed, so far as we know, Felton raised no objection when in March, 1878, the United States Oil Company prepared to drill on one of the leases he had bought from McPherson. And Felton must also have been acquainted with Taylor and Scofield. He may have known them as speculators in mining stocks, but he could also have known them through his relatives. At Moody Gulch, Taylor and Scofield did not limit themselves solely to McPherson's efforts; they took a few leases on their own and, as in Southern California, located many mining claims on government land. One of the names they used for a locator was George Loomis, a brother-in-law of Felton and the owner of a large dry-goods store on Kearney Street opposite the Plaza in San Francisco, who had figured a few months earlier in the attempted relocation of the claim at Pico Springs. Another was Leander D. Fisk, a clerk under Felton at the United States Mint and bookkeeper for George Ives, who was also a Felton relative and a prominent San Francisco stockbroker.[11]

Whatever may have been Felton's interest, he made no move to develop the leases or to acquire additional land for more than a year. Nor did F. B. Taylor & Company or McPherson undertake development work around Moody Gulch. The drilling that went on was done solely by Boyer and his associates, as they struggled to get their Garden City Gas Company into operation and to supply it with oil.

In both endeavors they had a difficult time. Delays in receiving materials from the East slowed completion of the Garden City system. Garden City, moreover, suffered harassment from its entrenched rival.

Early in 1878 the San Jose Gas Company got an injunction, charging that the new company was laying pipe too close to its mains. San Jose also cut in half its gas rate of $5 per thousand cubic feet. At Moody Gulch, meanwhile, the well of the Santa Clara Petroleum Company had been put down to 900 feet by March, 1878, without discovering oil in commercial quantities. The lesser efforts of the United States Oil Company had no better outcome.[12]

Garden City began service early in June, 1878, bringing a taste of triumph to its founders, even though the oil it used probably came from Ventura County. A San Jose newspaper wrote rapturously of the "clear bright light . . . , the very finest quality of gas ever made on this coast. . . ." Excitement over the new process carried to the neighboring city of San Francisco, where a population of nearly 225,000 was restless and dissatisfied with its gas monopoly. Toward the end of June, Mayor A. J. Bryant, the Board of Supervisors, and other officials from San Francisco paid the Garden City plant a formal visit, which Boyer made into a gala occasion. At a banquet following the tour Supervisor F. A. Gibbs remarked that "it was humiliating to come from metropolitan San Francisco, lit with its miserable excuse for gas . . . , to agricultural San Jose and find it with one of the finest lights one ever saw" at two-thirds the cost. Gibbs urged Boyer to come to San Francisco to seek a franchise, to which Boyer replied that all he asked was a fair chance.[13]

Garden City's triumph was short-lived. In July a municipal contract for street-lighting went to the San Jose Gas Company at $1.50 per thousand cubic feet, a full dollar less than the bid of Garden City. A brief rate war soon had the new company on the ropes, for it was deep in debt. Boyer was hard put for funds. One of his principal associates, Charles Hensley, was on the road to bankruptcy and the other, Charles Hadsell, was unwilling to invest more capital. During August two suits for a total of nearly $3,000 were filed against the Garden City company.[14]

To protect his own solvency and perhaps Garden City, on August 22 Boyer sued the Santa Clara Petroleum Company and the United States Oil Company for $15,584. He charged that Santa Clara owed him $7,667 for advances and $3,600 for a year's salary; the amount owed by the United States Oil Company he placed at $4,317.[15]

Within two months Boyer's suits had been dismissed and a settlement reached. Colonel Boyer, Charles Hadsell, Charles Felton, and F. B. Taylor were the participants. On October 3 these four men agreed to assign their interests in twenty-one leases in the Moody Gulch territory to the Santa Clara company, to which the lands of the San Jose Petroleum

Company were added later in the month. By that time Charles Felton had become president and the largest stockholder in the Santa Clara company.[16] A companion outcome of the negotiations, apparently, was a take-over by Felton of the Garden City Gas Company. About four months later on February 1, 1879, Felton sold Garden City to the San Jose Gas Company for a one-third stock interest in the older company, which linked the Garden City plant into its system.[17]

We can only speculate what prompted Felton to acquire the Boyer enterprises in the fall of 1878 and to draw F. B. Taylor & Company and perhaps Charles Hadsell into an alliance within the Santa Clara Petroleum Company. Clearly, the possibility of developing an oil supply for gas companies using the Lowe process figured prominently in his plans. His taking command of the Santa Clara company meant additional financial strength for that faltering concern. But Felton's vision reached beyond Moody Gulch. He had in view nothing less than control of the California oil industry.[18]

3

At the Gulch, where McPherson became his superintendent, Felton built up his holdings to more than 2,000 acres through additional leases by April of 1879, but his greater efforts were made in Southern California. His program there was admirably timed, for the boom in the San Fernando was over. Oil items were no longer crowding the news columns. Many of those holding mining claims had lost heart. More than that, money was extremely tight. The California historian, John S. Hittell, has written of 1877 as the onset of a depression which "continued to grow worse for 4 years," during which the state's banking resources declined by more than $30,000,000. Some veterans, like Gelcich, were having difficulty finding money to cover taxes on their claims. For lack of funds, the San Francisco Petroleum Company had been stalled for over a year, and the California Star, impoverished and locked in controversy, was on something of a caretaker basis. It was a time when a man with ready cash could go a long way.[19]

In January, 1879, Felton made his first important purchase in the San Fernando when he paid $1,000 for the ninety-two-acre Wiley claim, probably the most promising property in the district after Pico Springs. At about the same time he bought an interest in eleven claims for $8,250 from the ubiquitous Dr. Gelcich. Negotiations with another of the pioneers, the Los Angeles hardware merchant, Marcus W. Childs, took longer, for Felton's attorney was dissatisfied with the search of the records made by a Los Angeles firm of title examiners. Not until after a second search did Felton acquire Childs' rights in twelve claims on January 27, 1880. On the same day he also bought the interest of Christopher Leaming in twenty-one claims. In addition to his outright possession of the Wiley, these purchases let him share in the ownership of a number of other important claims: the San Fernando, just east of Pico Springs; the Moore and DeWitt, a little further to the southeast; and the Gelcich claim in Rice Canyon which had led to the formation of the Los Angeles Petroleum Refining Company in 1873.[20]

The efforts to take over California Star and the San Francisco Petroleum Company have left a far fainter trace upon the record, but there is little doubt that Felton had negotiations under way at least by the beginning of 1879. The San Francisco company, which was the first of these companies to come under his control, gave Felton a stronger position on the San Fernando claim, for the San Fernando was the site of its wells. Negotiations for California Star were more intricate, more important, and longer drawn out. Felton's hopes show through, however, in his incorporation of the Pacific Coast Oil Company (PCO) on February 19, 1879.[21]

The organization of Pacific Coast Oil to develop his growing oil interests was a logical step. Chartered with an authorized capital of $1,000,000, it was empowered to enter all phases of the industry, from producing to marketing. It was also specifically authorized to hold stock in other oil companies, like California Star and the San Francisco Petroleum Company. Indeed, the name of George M. Hedges, bookkeeper for F. B. Taylor & Company, as one of the five incorporators strongly suggests that plans to take over California Star were already well advanced. The other incorporators, in addition to Felton, were his brother-in-law, George Loomis; Leander D. Fisk, his former clerk; and E. H. Forester, secretary for what was probably a Felton mining company. Felton subscribed to all 10,000 shares of stock except those necessary to qualify the other four men as directors.[22]

The intent behind PCO seems clear enough, but the company remained merely a paper concern for several months, a state of affairs for which the long-standing controversy between F. B. Taylor, California Star, and General Beale and Colonel Baker over ownership of the Pico claim was probably responsible. No legal decision had been handed down; no compromise had been reached. Until ownership of the Pico wells was cleared up, neither Felton nor anyone else could be sure of the value of California Star. A settlement of the dispute, however, was not far off.

4

During the early months of 1879 Beale and Baker were engaged in a final drive to get the Pico wholly for themselves. While their suit of 1878 against Taylor and California Star remained dormant, the Southern California pair were seeking a patent by two separate routes. In Washington, the General was persevering in the attempt to use University land scrip; in Los Angeles, the Colonel was preparing an application under the Placer Mining Act of May, 1872. This he submitted to the local Land Office at the end of March.[23]

Baker's application retraced carefully their claim to a patent. He based their case on the deed the vaqueros, Hernandez and Perea, had given him on May 22, 1865, a transaction which he stated had been recorded on the books of the Los Angeles Asphaltum and Petroleum Mining District. The assertion was easy to make, for the records of this predecessor of the San Fernando Petroleum Mining District had been lost. Since the San Fernando district recognized as valid the claims recorded earlier in the Los Angeles district, so ran his argument, no relocation was necessary. The only obligation required by the new district was the regular performance of work necessary to hold the claim, which Baker said he and Beale had faithfully met. Their rights, according to the Colonel, ran clear and true from the deed of 1865.

Affidavits from William P. Reynolds, the recorder of the Los Angeles district in 1865, and Christopher Leaming, the San Fernando recorder, supported his contentions. In addition to confirming the loss of the records, Reynolds stated "that the applicants . . . and their grantors . . . were in the actual, notorious, continuous and adverse possession of . . . Pico Oil Springs Mining Claim and that their said possession was maintained and perfected in compliance with the rules and regulations of said District. . . ." Reynolds made no reference to the filing of any other claim to the Pico, such as the location of March 22, 1865, mentioned in the relocation of August, 1865, in the San Fernando records, nor did Leaming refer to the rival claims.[24]

Reynolds also stated that the rules and regulations of the Los Angeles district had disappeared. This was not true, however, for a copy recorded in March, 1865, exists today in the county recorder's office in Los Angeles. These "mining laws," which dealt solely with the location of claims 1,000 feet square, the perfection of titles, and their transfer to other parties, at the very least make doubtful that the homestead of Hernandez and Perea was ever written on the books of the Los Angeles district. Locators who were limited to individual mining claims of twenty-three acres would hardly have looked with favor on the recording of a claim to a 160-acre homestead that was so valuable for its oil. Or if the practice was tolerated in one instance, surely other locators would have followed it. The fact that no homesteads appear on the records of the San Fernando district, which began in June, 1865, casts further doubt on this contention of the Colonel.[25]

But Baker's application never got far enough to be disputed. It was rejected by the Los Angeles Land Office at the moment of submission because the claim was "embraced in a University Location of the State of Cal. and for further reason that a contest involving said tract between the Star Oil Works Co. [actually F. B. Taylor] and the State of Cala. [sic] is now pending before the Hon. Commissioner General Land Office." Taylor, who since 1877 had been trying to upset Baker's use of University land scrip, at least temporarily had blocked his attempt under the Placer Act as well.[26]

Taylor was also on the alert to protect his interests (and those of California Star) when the Beale and Baker lease to Denton expired on April 12, 1879. The order he obtained from a San Francisco court, appointing a receiver to operate the property until the dispute over ownership was settled, was another unpleasant surprise to the Colonel. Toward the end of April Baker came to San Francisco to attempt to get the court order vacated and, if possible, to effect a general settlement. A week or two later he was joined by his partner, General Beale.[27]

The Southern Californians found that a new adversary, Lloyd Tevis, was helping handle the controversy for California Star. His skill at negotiation was proverbial. This big man of "strong and wiry frame, erect figure, quick . . . step and dignified demeanor" could be gracious, charming, stern or defiant. His hand in settlements, like those between the City Gas Company and the San Francisco Gas Company, and the Sutro tunnel dispute among the mining companies of the Comstock, caused one writer to assert, "Hardly a controversy has arisen about a great interest in the State of California or in the city of San Francisco, in which Mr. Tevis has not figured as a counsellor, negotiator, or arbitrator." The oil industry scarcely qualified as "a great interest," but settling this dispute at least would help it grow. For Beale and Baker, Tevis was a dangerous antagonist.[28]

The negotiations were still without a firm conclusion when Tevis left for the East about the middle of May. Undoubtedly to hasten matters, on the day following California Star filed a new suit against Baker and offered him a compromise settlement. Baker became angry and refused to sign, but he softened in the month before Tevis returned. A series of moves in the Pico country had probably made a compromise seem more desirable both to him and to Beale.[29]

During May and June the news clearly indicated that California Star had come within Felton's orbit. At the beginning of May the *Los Angeles Herald* reported that seven carloads of two-inch pipe had arrived at Newhall to build a seven-mile line connecting California Star's Pico wells with the refinery. Charles Felton was identified as the owner of the pipe. Alex Mentry, the superintendent at Pico, laid the line. From Newhall, Sanford Lyon kept the Colonel informed of still other developments. Early in June, Mentry was preparing to put up rigs on the Wiley claim and on a claim neighboring the Pico and to redrill McPherson's well on the San Fernando. These properties were known to be in Felton's control. Mentry was also drilling for water on the grounds of the refinery, to which oil was flowing through Felton's line. The oil flowed at the direction of the receiver, for Baker had been unable to get the court order vacated. Beale and Baker were no longer opposing middle-sized capitalists like Taylor but capitalists of Nob Hill stature.[30]

On June 28, 1879, the Southern Californians surrendered. The agreement they accepted probably had been altered little, if at all, from that offered in May. The other signers were A. J. Bryant, still the president of California Star, F. B. Taylor, and A. E. Davis, a San Francisco realtor well known to Felton and Tevis. Davis had acquired an interest in Taylor's property in the Pico territory and must also have become a California Star stockholder. He was president of the South Pacific Coast Railroad (which served Moody Gulch) and of the Pacific Coast Petroleum Company, a small company for which Youle was drilling on Pescadero Creek about thirty miles south of San Francisco. Tevis signed the document as guarantor that California Star, Taylor, and Davis would meet their obligations.[31]

The chief provision of the settlement bound all parties to convey to California Star their rights to the Pico claim and the property on it, paving the way for the claim to be patented on September 14, 1880, under the application Baker had submitted the year before.[32] In return for assigning their rights, Beale and Baker were offered a three-sevenths interest (4,286 shares) in California Star. This fraction, incidentally, was their proportionate share in the claim under the relocation of August 8, 1865.[33]

Other terms of the settlement were of less importance. As a payment for any royalty due under the Denton lease, Beale and Baker accepted $2,500. They were given a veto over future assessments on California Star's stock, for an assessment could be levied only with the approval of all parties to the settlement. Baker, moreover, was to become one of the company's five directors. Another provision was of more dubious value. The parties agreed that California Star would develop no other "oil territory" so long as its Pico property produced sufficient oil to meet "market demand." Probably for this reason, at the beginning of July Mentry ceased preparations for drilling outside the Pico claim.[34] There were other means, however, by which the majority interest in California Star could carry on outside development when it so desired. Foremost was the Pacific Coast Oil Company.

The ending of the dispute permitted California Star to operate free from controversy, but there was an even more important auxiliary outcome. During the negotiations with Beale and Baker, or shortly thereafter—we cannot be sure—Tevis decided to join Felton in taking over the interests of F. B. Taylor & Company. This event was of great significance because of the resources that Tevis could command. He was no run-of-the-mill millionaire. Like Felton, he had arrived in California in 1849 and, like Felton also, he had found his path to fortune elsewhere than in the mines. In 1850, at Sacramento, he formed a general financial partnership with his brother-in-law, James Ben Ali Haggin, which three years later they removed to San Francisco. Here, over the years, the genial Tevis took part in many a big deal. He was an organizer of the California State Telegraph Company (which he sold to Western Union at a large profit); a promoter and, for one year, president of the fledgling Southern Pacific Railroad; an organizer of the City Gas Company and a large stockholder in its successor, the San Francisco Gas Light Company; and an investor in numerous mining enterprises, including the Homestake in South Dakota and the Ontario in Utah with George Hearst. Undoubtedly, Tevis was best known for his conquest of the Wells Fargo Express Company. Organizing the Pacific Union Express Company with Charles Crocker and others in 1868, he threatened the older company with devastating competition by getting an exclusive contract for carrying express on the Central Pacific Railroad and then bought a controlling interest in Wells Fargo as its stock plummeted. In 1872 he became the Wells Fargo president.

By 1879, at the age of fifty-five, Tevis held a position in western financial circles rivaling that of the Big Four of the Central Pacific or any of the kings of the Comstock. Two years later a contemporary wrote of his partnership with Haggin: "There is scarcely a work or project of magnitude on the Pacific Coast, from the western slope of the Rocky Mountains to the ocean shore, from the Mexican boundary line to the British Dominion, in which they are not largely or materially interested. . . ."[35] With Tevis joining Felton, the chances of the California oil industry becoming a "project of magnitude" were greatly enhanced.

5

Following the settlement of June, 1879, and the decision of Tevis to enter the industry, the dismantling of F. B. Taylor & Company was gradually pushed to a conclusion.

One action taken by Felton was highly unusual in corporate history. In spite of the fact that the articles of the Pacific Coast Oil Company filed in February, 1879, were "complete and proper in all respects," a second set of articles was filed at Sacramento on September 10, 1879. The differences between the two sets are minor. The one significant new power specifically authorized the company to lease oil refineries and warehouses. It may have been added because the settlement of June, 1879, permitted majority control, rather than liquidation, of California Star with its refineries at Andrews Station and Ventura. The list of incorporators and subscribers for shares show two other differences: In the September articles, Felton subscribed to director's shares only; and second, the name of James Lawler was substituted for that of E. H. Forester among the incorporators. Lawler was a young lawyer in the firm of Charles Greathouse and Gordon Blanding. Greathouse was a cousin and Blanding the son-in-law of Lloyd Tevis. Conceivably, these latter two changes were made to accommodate a Tevis interest.[36]

It is at this time that PCO became a functioning organization, and it is from September 10, 1879, that the company later reckoned its birth. A day after filing the new articles, Felton deeded PCO all his rights in "land, oil or petroleum claims, oil wells, tanks, oil machinery and mining and drilling fixtures . . . within the San Fernando Petroleum Mining District," and "all that line of pipe . . . running from the lower or receiving tank of the Pico Oil Wells to the refinery near Andrews Station. . . ." On the same day, as a quitclaim, F. B. Taylor deeded PCO his interest in land and in oil-producing equipment within the District. Although there are no documents to prove it, it seems likely that about this time PCO also acquired the Standard Oil Company of California and Taylor's minority holding in the Santa Clara Petroleum Company.[37]

Three months later, on December 15, 1879, the 100,000 shares of the PCO stock were issued, divided equally between Felton and Taylor interests. Felton relinquished five shares each to George Loomis and L. D. Fisk; F. B. Taylor, who received his 50,000 shares as trustee, transferred five shares to D. G. Scofield. These five men comprised the original board of directors. Felton was elected president of the PCO; Loomis, vice president; Fisk, secretary; and Scofield, auditor.[38]

It seems reasonably certain that the trustee shares were issued with the understanding that they would be liquidated, and that Lloyd Tevis held an option on them. On January 3, 1880, Taylor endorsed approximately one-third of the shares (16,661 ⅔) to Tevis, who turned them over to Scofield. This transaction may have been related to one of the day before when Scofield and Tevis's son, Harry, bought the firm of F. B. Taylor & Company, which they renamed Scofield & Tevis. Another third of the shares was transferred to I. E. Blake, Trustee, on April 9, 1880. This may also have been tied to the business dealings of Tevis. Early in January of 1880 he and Blake were reported to have purchased the interest of F. B. Taylor in the Continental Oil & Transportation Company of California, and Tevis later increased his ownership. It seems possible that he paid Blake, CO&T's president, with PCO stock. The last third of the shares was sold to Tevis in March, 1881. He used five to qualify his son, Harry, as a PCO director, replacing F. B. Taylor, and let the balance go to L. D. Fisk, Trustee.[39]

As the Taylor holdings were liquidated, Felton and Tevis emerged as the dominant figures in the California industry, although their relative participation cannot be told exactly. Even the PCO stock certificate book is inadequate for this purpose because the certificates issued in the names of trustees leave obscure the actual owners. There can be little question, however, that the news stories of 1880 repetitively linking Felton and Tevis as the "leading men" in the PCO and allied companies reflected the situation accurately. Two later statements are also worth noting. In January, 1882, the *Commercial Herald* reported that PCO was "under the control of Charles N. Felton and the firm of Scofield & Tevis, they being the principal stockholders. . . ." And early in 1885 Blake told a close friend, Milton Stewart of Titusville, that "all the different Oil Co's, no matter by what name known, were under one and the same ownership—himself [Blake] and Felton representing one half and Tevis and Scofield the other half. . . ." Stewart went on to say, "Felton and Tevis are evidently the moneyed men, the one taking Blake and the other Scofield under his wing. . . ." The record fails to substantiate an equality of ownership, even in PCO, but it does indicate a community of interest.[40]

Lloyd Tevis was the less prominent of the two leaders in day-to-day affairs, for among his wide-ranging interests oil was never more than a sideshow. His power, however, pervaded all aspects of the industry. Through Scofield and Harry Tevis, he was able to play a strong hand in PCO, affecting its decisions in regard to producing and refining. And in marketing he was the principal force. Scofield & Tevis, the former Taylor house, depended mainly on him for its capital. Tevis also gradually became the largest stockholder in both the Continental Oil & Transportation Company of California and the earlier CO&T that Blake had incorporated in 1875 in Iowa to market in the Rocky Mountain territory.[41]

There is evidence, too, that Felton was influential in the CO&T of California. He became a stockholder in the California company and had strong ties to Blake. When Blake left for the East early in 1884, it was Felton's brother-in-law, George Loomis, who took over the management as vice president. But Felton was mainly active in the producing and refining end of the business. He was a director and, for at least a year, president of California Star, and both president and director in the Santa Clara, San Francisco, and Standard Oil companies. Except for CO&T of California, all of these companies were wholly or partially owned by Pacific Coast Oil, which was Felton's chief center of power.[42]

6

Shortly after the reincorporation of PCO in September, 1879, President Felton traveled in the East for nearly two months laying plans for the new company. Oil need not have been the sole reason for his trip, but it must have supplied the principal motive. Visiting eastern cities with Lowe gas plants undoubtedly comprised a part of his journey, and Baltimore, a city of 330,000 people, was a likely stop. In the Maryland metropolis a Consumers Mutual Gas Light Company, established in 1876, was producing nearly thirty times as much carburetted water gas as the Garden City plant in San Jose and was competing successfully with two older coal gas rivals. Felton had been home less than a month when he joined William Sharon of the famed Comstock family, Sharon's son-in-law, Frank G. Newlands, Charles Holmes, and others in organizing a corporation with a name closely paralleling that of the Baltimore gas company. Their Consumers Mutual Gas Works was incorporated early in December, 1879, with a nominal capital of $10,000,000 to operate with the Lowe process in San Francisco.[43]

Almost simultaneously in Oakland, California's second city, with a population of 34,000, Felton learned of the interest of the Oakland Gas Light Company in switching from coal to water gas. The company made its decision in April, 1880, and Scofield & Tevis offered to furnish the necessary oil for $2 a barrel.[44]

But gas-making, though important, was not the only oil market Felton was contemplating. Like his predecessors, he was well aware of the opportunity in the West for products refined from California crude, especially kerosine, if they could match eastern imports in quality. And beyond the West lay Mexico, the Pacific islands, and the Orient. It seems almost certain that Felton visited the Oil Regions of Pennsylvania while on his eastern trip to recruit skilled refiners.[45]

There is little evidence that Felton believed finding oil would be a major problem, for events at Moody Gulch in the fall of 1879 contributed to a sense of security and even to jubilance.

7

At Moody Gulch during the summer of 1879 McPherson had been joined by a pair of experienced Pennsylvania drillers, the brothers William and Daniel Dull, whom I. E. Blake had persuaded to come to California. They proceeded to put down a well about 100 feet distant from Boyer's earlier effort. For weeks their drilling went on virtually unnoticed until suddenly, early in October, a flowing well came in, producing all sorts of excited comment as well as oil. The *San Jose Herald* reported that "a perfect stream of the oleaginous fluid burst forth from the mouth, rising to a hight [sic] of 75 to 80 feet, and deluging the ground for rods around." The *San Jose Mercury,* in an equally buoyant account, gave full credit to "Charlie Felton, a man of indomitable pluck and a solid substratum of coin," and to the "sound judgment and true grit" of R. C. McPherson. It estimated the daily production at sixty barrels "of the finest green oil, of from 46 to 47 standard gravity," and announced that in little more than a week some 300 barrels of crude had been shipped from Alma, a railroad station a little more than a mile away. Shortly, the *Herald* informed its readers that "oil sharps" believed McPherson had "only struck the rim of a pool or lake of oil." In November, A. L. McPherson, the young brother of the superintendent, laid a two-inch pipeline to a 250-barrel tank at the Alma station. The South Pacific Coast Railroad, delighted at the prospect of an oil traffic, built a 400-foot siding.[46]

By December, the reports were no longer quite so rapturous. One observer scaled down the production to a mere eight to fourteen barrels a day. Nonetheless, the well had been enough to generate a heady optimism. Beginning late in October, Superintendent McPherson gathered in another 765 acres with six leases. By the end of October the Dull brothers were preparing to put down two more wells, one at the Gulch and the second about three miles to the southeast on land that McPherson had leased earlier in the year.[47]

The Moody strike was taken as bringing in a field on the threshold of the principal western market. But there was also another ground for excitement. The crude more closely resembled Pennsylvania crude than any yet found in California. Like the best Appalachian oil, it was green in color, light in gravity, and had a paraffin base. Presumably, the refining methods that had hitherto been unsuccessful in the West would work with this oil.[48]

At first the Moody crude was shipped to the California Star refinery at Andrews Station, which soon was almost doubled in size by the addition of a 150-barrel still and a second agitator. This was merely a makeshift arrangement, however. To use a refinery more than 400 miles away for any sizable production would hardly be economic. The purchase by Lloyd Tevis early in November of forty acres bordering the railroad about a mile east of the Gulch appears to have been made as a site for a refinery, for PCO later took it over from Tevis at cost. After returning from the East, Felton paid $1,600 for another possible location along the tracks of the Southern Pacific on the outskirts of San Jose. He relinquished this 160-acre tract about a year later, for in the meantime the refiners who had followed him to California had settled on still another site as more desirable.[49]

8

The refiners who joined the Pacific Coast Oil Company at the beginning of 1880 were two well-known veterans from the Oil Regions, Charles F. Thumm and George R. Miller. Thumm, in fact, had entered refining at Pittsburgh, with a plant manufacturing illuminating oil from coal, at least a year or more before Colonel Drake brought in his famous well in August, 1859. Switching to crude oil during the Civil War, he later moved to Oil City, where he proved a vigorous and imaginative refiner. With an associate, Thumm in 1870 initiated a series of patents anticipating the effective development of continuous distillation that would supersede the "batch" or single-still method after 1900. Miller was less prominent. A refiner since 1868, he had worked for several Pennsylvania companies, including the Octave Oil Works in Titusville, where he had been the assistant superintendent.[50]

Thumm and Miller visited several possible sites for a refinery, including the properties purchased by Tevis and Felton, before they finally decided on an eight-acre tract on the southwestern tip of the island of Alameda immediately across the bay from San Francisco. PCO paid $30,000 for this high-priced land in February, 1880. Alameda Point seemed preferable to a location nearer the Gulch because it was on a spur of the Central Pacific Railroad, connecting with Newhall, in addition to being the eastern terminus of the narrow gauge South Pacific Coast Railroad. It could easily receive crude from Southern California if the Moody field should prove disappointing. The site was also accessible for ships and possessed an adequate supply of fresh water for refining.[51]

The two refiners designed an impressive, up-to-date plant that was intended to process about 500 barrels of crude daily. For turning out naphthas and kerosine, they put up a small continuous still, a 900-barrel crude still, a condensing box, two 400-barrel steam stills, a large agitator, and two bleachers. Six tar stills, each of 38-barrels capacity, a smaller condensing box, two small agitators, and eight settling tanks were installed to manufacture the lube oils. Except for the horizontal continuous still, all others were of the common "cheese-box" type. For safety from fire, Thumm built storage tanks along the northern edge of the tract away from the stills, and put the pipelines underground. The other principal structures were a pump and boiler house; a tank house containing water tanks and a laboratory; a receiving house, through which the oils flowed from the condensers; and a warehouse, occupied in part by case and can machinery capable of turning out 1,000 cases a day. At the northeast corner of the refinery a small building was set up, where Thumm and Miller had their offices along with Irving T. Ballard, the business manager.[52] Costing $160,117, including the land, the refinery was accurately proclaimed "the largest and most complete west of Cleveland, Ohio," the home of the Standard Oil Company.[53]

While construction was going on, PCO introduced the public to the mysteries of refining. One reporter wrote:[54]

> When ready for refining the petroleum is conducted by [a] system of pipes . . . into a continuous still, through which it passes, the gases being extracted during the process. By an ingenious contrivance the gas can be saved and either sold for illuminating purposes or utilized in the refinery as fuel. The dirt and other foreign matter is also extracted in this still. . . . [The oil] is next taken to a still of some 45,000 [actually, 36,601] gallons capacity, and having under it eight furnaces. Here [it] is subjected to forty-eight hours' continuous cooking at a temperature of about 900 degrees. When in the form of vapor, it passes through a number of pipes into a condensing box 225 feet in length. The pipes are surrounded by water, and by the time the oil has passed through them it has resumed its liquid shape. The entire length of pipe in the condensing box is slightly in excess of two miles. From the

condenser the oil proceeds to the receiving house almost immediately adjoining, where the oil, now called distillate, separates itself according to its respective gravities, and by gravitation flows into six tanks, the gasoline and benzine finding their respective receptacles, and the heavier grades doing the same. The gasoline and benzine are finished by undergoing a purifying process in a 12,000 [actually 16,800] gallon [steam] still, where they are not only purified but separated into their different grades as gasoline, 74 gasoline [naphtha], 63 benzine, etc. The heavier illuminating or kerosene oils are pumped into an agitator, where by means of currents of air they are thoroughly purified and mixed with sulphuric and other acids and sodas possessing neutralizing and purifying qualities. From here it goes to the bleachers, two large 40,000 gallon tanks, where the 'water white' color is given and the fire test applied. If the oil is not equal to the required standard, it is brought up to it before being finally put up for shipment. In the bleachers the oil is also separated into the respective grades of 110, 120, and 150 fire test kerosene and 300 fire test headlight and lighthouse oil. From the final process the oil comes out finished, and is conducted to a number of 125,000 gallon tanks, where it awaits shipment in bulk or is conducted to the warehouse to be barreled and canned for the retail trade.

The lubricating oils are manufactured by a similar process, from the residue remaining in the large still in which the oil is first evaporated into the condensing-box and which was not distilled at the light heat required for the illuminating oils. The residue is pumped into six small stills, where it is subjected to an additional heat of 1,100 degrees, which vaporizes it when it passes through a similar though smaller condensing box, and thence through the various separating, agitating and bleaching processes until it, too, comes out divided into its respective grades of light and heavy lubricating oils ready for shipment. The refinery, when completed, will have a storage capacity of over 1,000,000 gallons, and will be able to manufacture 20,000 gallons per day.

This description leaves little to be added, though the separation of the various fractions of the oil was hardly so mechanical. While condensation was going on, a still man for the lighter oils and a still man for lubes would be in the receiving house at what were called "look boxes" (cast-iron boxes with a plate-glass front), directing each grade of oil into its special tank, as the oil grew heavier. The cycle for the manufacture of lubes, like that for the lighter products, was expected to last about forty-eight hours. At the end of the run, the residue in the tar stills would be a solid coke, to be cleaned out and used for fuel.[55]

As the refinery neared completion in June of 1880, PCO made a proud announcement: "On or about July 15, we shall be prepared to supply this market and will offer to the wholesale trade exclusively the best quality of Refined Petroleum Oils." PCO advertised a 175° fire test headlight oil, and 150° and 110° illuminating oils, all strictly water white in color; a 300° fire test mineral illuminating oil; lubricating oil in three grades, light (29° gravity), medium (24°), and heavy (19°); refined paraffine wax; and all grades of naphtha from "our new refinery, . . . one of the completest ever erected. . . ." The news was well received. "[It] looks as if our oil trade henceforth would be as much a local

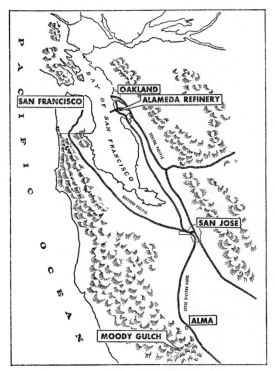

Moody Gulch and the Alameda Refinery

business as sugar refining," the *San Francisco Merchant* commented hopefully. Importers were reported sending few orders to the East while they awaited developments at Alameda.[56]

The PCO announcement soon began to appear like a hollow boast, however, as weeks passed without anything on the market. The truth was that the production at Moody Gulch, supplemented by Pico crude diverted from Andrews Station, gave too small a supply to permit the refinery to open on schedule. Consequently, when it started up, probably in mid-August, there was no fanfare. The first news item, in fact, was not an announcement of the initial run of crude but a cry from oyster-men that their beds off Alameda Point were being damaged by refinery waste. It was an ironic beginning for "the largest refinery west of Cleveland."[57]

Price quotations first appeared in trade papers in mid-September, along with a claim that PCO had "orders ahead for nearly eight weeks production." For "lots of 1,000 cases" of its best kerosine (150° illuminating oil), a price of 25¢ a gallon was quoted. Two weeks later "low test" 110° kerosine was added to the price list at 19¢. The PCO kerosine was competing in a market that by 1879 had passed almost wholly into the control of Standard Oil. The western company's low test oil more closely approached Standard's comparable brands in price than did its higher quality product. Devoe's Brilliant and Pratt's Radiant, the 110° brands of Standard, never sold for more than a cent above the PCO price during the last months of 1880, but the gap between Pearl and Pratt's Astral, Standard's 150° oils, and their PCO competitor ranged from 1.5¢ to 5.5¢ These better oils commanded the bulk of the trade. PCO's 150° oil, obviously, was little match in quality for the eastern brands.[58]

At the end of the year, in its annual review, the *Commercial Herald* gloomily observed that the "new refinery . . . had been unable to run to any extent owing to the small quantity of crude oil produced in the State. The fact that California oil is so far inferior in quality to the eastern importation, leads many dealers to believe that the production in this state will never be a success." Five months later the *Merchant* noted, "The supply of California refined oil is not very large, but . . . ample for legitimate demand."[59]

Improving the marketability of the kerosine was the primary responsibility of the refiners. One tack Thumm tried was to devise a more effective lamp burner, on which he received a patent in August, 1881. "Even in the use of heavy petroleum oils produced on the Pacific slope of the United States the smoke is all consumed," Thumm stated in his application. But his invention, which consisted of a reflector plate within the cone of the lamp to induce more perfect combustion, was at best only partially successful. And a solution to the problem of turning out a good 150° oil continued to elude him. Perhaps this was the reason why Thumm returned to the East late in 1881, leaving Miller in charge at Alameda.[60]

The responsibility for increasing crude oil production lay elsewhere. This shortage, which was crippling to the refinery, proved fatal to the plan Felton and his associates were nurturing to use the Lowe process for manufacturing gas in San Francisco. Their Consumers Mutual Gas Works never got beyond the paper stage. Scofield and his superintendents, McPherson and Mentry, had enough to do trying to find sufficient crude to keep the refinery going.

9

At Moody, McPherson had had mixed results. Only four of the eight wells put down in 1880 found oil. The two on which work had begun late in 1879 had been abandoned, and a third, on the Moody lease, was another dry hole. Not until September, nearly a year after the heartening strike of October, 1879, did McPherson bring in a second producer, Moody #4, which flowed initially at the rate of 100 barrels a day. Although three smaller wells came in before 1880 was over, the drillers had learned that their chances for oil were slim outside the heart of the Gulch. Moreover, hopes over the Moody were dimmed because the wells fell off rapidly in production. To the spring of 1884, when the wells were all but shut down, Moody Gulch had yielded about 24,000 barrels, which was only a seven to ten weeks' supply for the refinery when running at capacity. The Moody, with its limited territory and thin oil sands, was obviously no major field.[61]

The only other Northern California production came from a few shallow wells on Tunitas Creek in the Half Moon Bay area about twenty miles down the coast from San Francisco. PCO took their oil, which was probably overestimated at five barrels a day. It was of little consequence in meeting the need of the Alameda works.[62]

Only in Southern California, it seemed, was there the prospect of sufficient crude. Getting the oil was no easy task, however. For the PCO executives, their Pico territory offered a number of troublesome problems: the lack of an adequate water supply, of skilled manpower and equipment, and the insecurity of many mining titles. These had to be solved before the company could put on an intensive drilling campaign.

Mentry was marshalling his slender resources as best he could, though rarely was he able to keep more than one rig working. In November, 1879, he began to drill again on the Pico claim, and by October, 1880, had brought in two fine wells near the famous CSOW (Pico) #4. Along with the strikes at Moody Gulch, they were mainly responsible for pushing California's production from an average of little more than 100 barrels daily in 1880 to nearly 275 barrels in 1881.[63]

Elsewhere in the San Fernando District the Pico superintendent was less fortunate. In 1880 he drilled a shallow dry hole on the Wiley claim. On the property of the San Francisco Petroleum Company he put down a 1,500 foot well that cost more than $13,000 before it was completed in June, 1881, but it gave little oil. Nearby, Mentry started a third well in March, 1881, experiencing a series of heartbreaking setbacks, caving walls, lost tools, parted casing, and renewed caving, before at last, after eighteen months, he brought in a good producer at 1,300 feet in September of 1882.[64]

Meanwhile, through this span of more than two years, Scofield and his backers were trying to remove the bottlenecks to a larger effort. Foremost was getting an adequate supply of water for the engines at Pico, a problem that had been troubling Mentry intermittently since 1876, when steam power had superseded the springpole. Felton's pipeline, built in 1879, had as its main purpose to bring water to the canyon from an artesian well at Newhall. The line also carried crude to the refinery, but that was a secondary function.[65] As the new Pico wells came in, it became increasingly impractical to use the same line for both water and oil. PCO might have laid a second pipeline from Newhall, but this seemed a dubious solution, for the refinery also used water from the well in its operations.

As a better source, Scofield chose the Santa Clara River, about four miles northwest of Pico Canyon on the San Francisco Rancho. In September of 1881 the company began building a pump station and a two-inch pipeline which, because of the precipitous terrain, followed a roundabout course of nearly nine miles to the wells. PCO installed two engines at the pump station to assure a flow of water if one broke down. Toward the end of the line, it erected a 1,300-barrel tank on the rim of Pico Canyon, from which water could be distributed to the whole area. In 1883, because of heavy drilling, the company paralleled its earlier line with a four-inch pipeline, bringing its total investment in the station and lines to nearly $40,000.[66]

The legality of mining titles was another important matter tormenting PCO. By the summer of 1880 company executives had discovered that carelessness in handling the affairs of the San Fernando Petroleum Mining District threatened their hold on many claims. PCO could drill on CSOW's Pico patent and be sure of its legal position, but nearly everywhere else in some measure uncertainty reigned.

In July, 1880, the law firm of Greathouse & Blanding began to uncover flaws, which it put forth in an opinion covering the rights of the company under the deeds to Felton from M. W. Childs and Christopher Leaming.[67] The opinion, given after an exhaustive search of each of thirty-one claims in the records of the District, Los Angeles County,

Newhall Refinery in the early 1880's

Charles N. Felton

Lloyd Tevis

Alameda Refinery about 1881

and the United States Land Office, was devastating. The lawyers reported that they could verify the boundaries of only a few. They had found the detailed map that Leaming had prepared in 1867 when he surveyed the District and plotted the claims. Thereafter Leaming had outlined each new claim on his map, but the lawyers believed that rarely, if at all, did he go over the ground and stake it out "so that honest inquirers may find the location on the ground by marks," as required by federal law and by the rules of the District. Consequently, the claims were often defined in terms of the boundaries of adjoining claims. If one was located imperfectly, such was likely to be the fate of its neighbors. The attorneys reported of the Rice claim:

> Both the notice of location and the records . . . are lost. We obtained a description . . . from the records of Los Angeles County, but it commenced at a certain oak tree which was not located with reference to any section corner or line, or natural or artificial monument. We endeavored to locate . . . [it] so that it would agree with the surrounding claims. . . . As it is mainly guesswork, the map we present cannot be relied upon to show the exact location of the Rice claim and those depending upon it.

Greathouse & Blanding found other complications. The valuable San Fernando claim, for example, contained 229.57 acres, but federal mining law fixed a maximum of 160 acres. The Pitt Hole claim overlapped the boundary of the San Francisco Rancho; Pico #2 overlapped the Simi Rancho. On several the $100 minimum of work required by the District had not been met, and others were invalid because of failure to do a day's work a month.

The attorneys recommended that "all the claims should be relocated, complying . . . with . . . the laws of Congress respecting mining locations . . . and . . . the subdivisions of the Government survey."[68] By the end of 1880, Albert G. Ruxton, the U.S. Deputy Mineral Surveyor at Los Angeles, had carefully gone over and relocated twenty-four of PCO's claims, placing posts at points along the boundaries and noting the natural landmarks, trees, and brush. To assure the hold of the PCO on the San Fernando, he split it into three claims. The company made sixteen additional locations between January, 1881, and April, 1882.[69] These actions did not clear up every title, but they had made the company's position considerably more secure.

During this period of uncertainty, it is hardly surprising that Felton

sought to acquire oil lands in neighboring Ventura County as a pre-
cautionary measure, if nothing more. In 1880 he took a lease on the oil
belt of the ex-Mission from its San Francisco owners, Rudolph Steinbach and Horace W. Carpentier. The territory was almost quiescent,
commanding only the feeble efforts of W. G. Adams, harassed by
creditors, and D. C. Scott, whose resources, as always, were slender.
Felton bought out both of these veterans and took a quitclaim from
Scott to California Star's Ventura refinery, which Scott had been operating. Beyond giving Scott limited support to drill in Santa Paula
Canyon, Felton did little else. The production from the ex-Mission in
1881 was rarely more than twenty barrels a day; it was heavier than
the Pico crude, and therefore less attractive for refining. Discouraged
by Felton's limited endeavor, the ex-Mission owners ordered him off
and leased their property at the end of 1881 to a San Francisco oil
merchant, A. C. Dietz.[70]

Some miles east of the ex-Mission lay the rugged Sespe territory,
where the Los Angeles Oil Company had made a promising oil strike
early in 1879. In the summer of 1881 PCO contracted for the production
of the Los Angeles well, estimated at from thirty to forty barrels daily,
and planned to receive it by extending its pipeline down the valley
from the Santa Clara pump station. This source of supply soon ceased
however, when the well was wrecked in the course of a fight among the
owners of the company.[71]

Felton and Scofield made a greater effort at Sespe by reviving the
Standard Oil Company of California. Mainly in 1881, the company
acquired forty-three claims totaling 6,400 acres in the Little Sespe
Petroleum Mining District. Some, like the Scofield and Ocean View,
the company probably located, but others, like 2 Widows #2, Bashe
Bullzouk, Midnight Glare, and Black Death, sound less like names
supplied by the company's agents. Perhaps $10,000 was spent in this
campaign. For several years the Standard Oil Company added gradually
to its claims in the Sespe as a reserve territory, but the PCO leaders
continued to make the San Fernando District their principal area of development.[72]

10

Early in 1882 PCO was at last ready for a major drilling effort. While
taking steps to find a water supply and to protect its mining titles, it
had also been assembling manpower and equipment. In mid-May the
Los Angeles Herald reported that Scofield and his company were
planning to spend "some $300,000 in developing the Pico oil district"

and were "now sinking some fifteen new wells." A recent well, CSOW #7, had "struck a stream of oil." "And we are heartily glad," the paper added, "because the whole enterprising band who have developed this local interest are whole-souled and thorough-paced gentlemen, who took big chances and poured out their money like water before a phenomenal success rewarded their efforts."[73]

As a reflection of current events, the news story was a gross exaggeration, but taken as a forecast, it was not wide of the mark. Two wells were being drilled at the time it was published. Two months later, this number had increased to four, and in another six months five strings of tools were working. In all, PCO started sixteen wells during 1882 and 1883. Except for one well at Wiley Springs, the others were all on the Pico patent or the adjoining San Fernando claim.[74]

The total cost of this search for oil we can only conjecture. There is some information in official records and reports suggesting that the *Herald*'s figure of $300,000 was not far wrong. One contemporary source, a report of the U.S. Deputy Mineral Surveyor in December, 1885, permits an estimate of about $255,000 if the Santa Clara water system is included. Another source is a statement of the Assistant State Mineralogist following a visit to Pico in 1887. He cited $10 a foot as the "general average cost" of drilling in the 1880's, but added, "if you are favorably situated or lucky," the cost might be only $5 to $6. At $10, these wells would have required an investment of $241,000. At $7.50 a foot, which is more nearly the cost indicated in the surviving well records, the investment would be $180,000. The cost of water and oil lines, tanks, roads, and houses, would raise this figure to about $256,000.[75]

To head so great an effort, Felton and Scofield turned once again to Pennsylvania. They were not dissatisfied with Mentry, but they felt it wise to seek a man of broad experience in the great fields of the East. M. Robert Craig, whom they hired to be the Pico manager, came from the famed Bradford field in Pennsylvania, where he had served as a superintendent for the Forest Oil Company. He was considered "a competent . . . and skillful oil man."[76] The sharp increase in activity following his arrival in the summer of 1882 suggests that some drilling crews were also recruited to help him.

Like others before him, Craig soon learned that his eastern experience had not completely prepared him for conditions in the Pico. He had not drilled before in brush-covered steep ravines, which at times made it hard to find a level place six yards square on which to erect the 72-foot derricks. Subsurface formations also proved more difficult than those in the East. Instead of lying nearly horizontal, the Pico formations were crushed, broken, and sharply tilted. The softness of the rock made caving an ever-present hazard; the pitch of the strata made it hard to drill a straight hole. His crews were troubled by the problem of getting casing down to strengthen the well walls before caving occurred, and by "stuck" drilling tools in caved or crooked holes. Sometimes weeks passed while "fishing" went on for the great 60-foot, 2,000-pound tools. Consequently, Craig found that, in general, it took longer to put down a well in California than in the East. Three wells drilled in 1882 and 1883 took six months or less, but five others ranging in depth from 1,275 to 1,778 feet required from ten to twenty months.

In spite of such difficulties, Craig could feel highly pleased with the outcome. Of the fourteen wells completed by June, 1884, just three were dry. The best, San Francisco #4, drilled by W. E. Youle, who had returned to the scene of McPherson's old wells, gave an initial production in June, 1883, of 225 barrels a day, which was a record for California. Almost a year later it was yielding about 75 barrels daily. The wells, moreover, furnished a light, refinable oil, ranging in gravity from 40° to 42°.[77]

Because of the new production, the Alameda refinery and the older works at Newhall (Andrews Station) had all the crude they could handle, though as usual in this period the exact production is difficult to determine. In the spring of 1884 Felton reported the yield at Pico as 560 barrels daily, either just before or just after an 80-barrel well came in; in December, Lyman Stewart guessed 650 barrels. W. E. Youle estimated California's oil output that year at 187,209 barrels; the United States Geological Survey accepted 262,000, which is probably high.[78] Even by the most conservative estimates, as shown in Table 1, five years of effort were paying out.

Table 1: Crude Oil Production in California 1879-1884

Year	Barrels	Average Barrels Per Day
1879	13,543	37
1880	41,981	115
1881	99,860	274
1882	128,635	352
1883	142,857	391
1884	187,209	512

Source: See Appendix, Table I

A footnote to this great campaign was an attempt by PCO to find oil west of California Star's Pico patent on the neighboring Simi Rancho, which the agents of Tom Scott had swept up in 1865. Less than two hundred yards separated the boundaries of the two properties. In mid-November, 1882, Scofield concluded lengthy negotiations with the Simi owners for a lease of the eastern end, providing for a royalty of one-eighth of the production and the drilling of at least one well a year. The Simi venture was brief and disappointing. Beginning in October, 1883, drillers spent ten months getting down a dry hole to 1,300 feet. The company started no more wells and in March, 1885, surrendered the lease.[79]

The Simi affair is especially noteworthy because two months after drilling began, in December, 1883, PCO sublet its well to Lyman Stewart and Wallace L. Hardison, two oilmen who had moved West that year from Pennsylvania.[80] This was part of a significant change in producing policy, of which we shall have much more to say later on.

11

A companion event to the Simi lease in the fall of 1882 was the purchase of oil rights to the ex-Mission by the Felton and Tevis group. This speculation was of a different order, for which I. E. Blake was largely responsible. It was the prospect for fuel oil, and not refinable oil, that he had argued in persuading his associates to return to the ex-Mission.[81] With a keen promoter's eye, the CO&T president had recognized that for years Californians had been looking tentatively toward oil as a substitute for coal and that this interest was very much alive. Gas companies were already offering an attractive market. In 1881 a Central Gas Company using the Lowe process had brought renewed competition into the San Francisco gas trade. It had grown from a plant erected earlier that year to serve the Palace Hotel, with A. D. Sharon, the manager of the Palace, as an incorporator. The total sale of crude oil to California gas companies in 1881 was estimated at one million gallons.[82]

Some encouraging developments had also occurred suggesting potentially even larger outlets for fuel oil. After several years of experiment, the Ventura oil veteran, E. A. Edwards, took out a patent early in 1882 on an improved oil burner. From his burner, steam to vaporize the oil and air to aid combustion issued along with the oil in a concentric flow and gave a steady flame, Edwards claimed, in contrast to other models, in which the steam, oil and air, mixing within the burner, frequently supplied too little oil because of the steam pressure, causing the flame to go out. A Los Angeles foundry was employing his burner as early as May, 1881, and a number of other firms later tried it. Edwards himself had close ties to Blake, for since August, 1881, he had been superintendent of the Southwestern Division of the Continental Oil & Transportation Company of California.[83]

Other experiments were going on in the shops of the Central Pacific Railroad at Sacramento, where for several months in 1879 A. J. Stevens, the general master mechanic, had run tests using fuel oil to power a stationary engine. In 1882 these tests were resumed after Stevens had seen some Russian designs for oil-burning locomotives. Blake, who was well acquainted in railroad circles, must have known of Stevens' work. Apparently, Blake also discussed his plans with railroad officials.[84]

His negotiations with Steinbach and Carpentier, the ex-Mission owners, came at an opportune time, for A. C. Dietz, the lessee of their oil rights, was floundering along, little to their satisfaction. This burly, bearded oil merchant, whose firm was founded in 1851, about the same time as that of F. B. Taylor, was attempting to travel the same road that Taylor had tried earlier: to extend his business backward to include refining and producing. In October, 1880, he had set up a "lubricating works" at Berkeley to refine Ventura crude and then in 1882, using W. G. Adams as superintendent, had entered into producing as successor to Felton on the ex-Mission lease. He had also made a deal with D. C. Scott to develop production in Stott Canyon on the northeast corner of the lease. But, strapped for funds, Dietz was accomplishing little more than had Felton the year before.[85]

Blake's negotiations soon matured into a conditional agreement, signed on October 24, 1882, that fixed a price of $100,000 for the oil rights and for surface rights for roads, pipelines, and tanks. This amount was payable in progressively larger installments over four years after July 1, 1883, the date that the lease to Dietz expired. As an evidence of good faith, Blake promised to spend $50,000 developing the property during the first year.[86]

He lost no time incorporating the new enterprise. Using four CO&T employees, including his nephew, Frank E. Davis, on October 26 Blake set up the Mission Transfer Company, which was empowered to own oil lands and "in any and every way to deal" in oil and oil products. Significantly, its articles did not include the power to drill for oil. Mission Transfer was authorized a capital of $250,000, divided into 2,500 shares. Blake subscribed to 249 in his own name and held 1,226 more as trustee, which undoubtedly became the interest of Felton and Tevis. The only other large holdings were 500 shares issued under trusteeship to Charles N. Shaw, who was the son-in-law of A. N. Towne, the general manager of the Central Pacific, and 100 shares taken by Irving T. Ballard, the manager of the Alameda refinery. Blake's brother-in-law, Charles S. Barrett of Titusville, took 50 shares. Frank E. Davis was named president of the company, and Shaw became secretary.[87]

The future of Mission Transfer was still somewhat uncertain, however. Under the terms of his lease, Dietz could buy the oil rights by matching within thirty days the price Steinbach and Carpentier had agreed to accept from any other party. But Dietz could not raise $100,000. Instead, late in November he bought the surface rights to 401 acres at the eastern end of the ex-Mission, subject to the limitation that the owners of the oil rights would have access to the land for oil producing and transportation. His purchase lay directly athwart the only route from the town of Santa Paula to Adams, Saltmarsh, and Stott canyons, which were among the chief oil territories on the ex-Mission.[88]

By the beginning of 1883, Blake and Davis were hard at work preparing to put their company in business. While Blake was in the East looking for oilmen to develop the ex-Mission, Davis was conferring with Dietz, D. C. Scott, and W. G. Adams, who were already on the property. In January he discussed terms for leases with each of them, but he took no action beyond providing Scott with a drilling outfit to speed the work in Stott Canyon.

Davis also asked Dietz to permit Mission Transfer to lay pipe, install pumping equipment and erect a storage tank on his 401 acres before his lease expired, to which Dietz agreed cordially enough. Taking him at his word, Davis ordered material and equipment. Beginning in May, Mission Transfer constructed its Santa Paula pump station on the Dietz property and ran a two-inch pipeline about a half-mile northwest to Stott Canyon; at its Ventura terminal, it erected a 3,000-barrel tank. Toward the end of May, the *Ventura Signal* carried the news of just how large Blake's plans really were: Mission Transfer would lay a pipeline all the way from the Pico wells to Ventura and build a steamer to carry oil to San Francisco.[89]

The company had committed about $55,000, including the cost of materials, when in June Dietz had a change of heart. He ordered the company's men off his property. Later, in San Francisco, he bluntly notified "Charley Felton and Mr. Loomis" to stay off and collected firearms and ammunition to back up his words. In July, Mission Transfer took Dietz to court. The ensuing litigation brought the company almost to a standstill until it won the case in June of 1884.[90]

12

By that time the great surge by the California oil allies had ended. Carrying out Blake's plans for Mission Transfer could still require a substantial investment, but Mission Transfer was, after all, merely a side venture. The heart of the alliance was Pico, from which the crude went chiefly to the Alameda refinery, after which the products were marketed through outlets of the Continental Oil & Transportation Company of

Table 2: Estimated Oil Investments of the Felton and Tevis
Alliance—ca. July 1, 1884*

Initial lands acquisitions, Pico and Santa Clara, 1877-80	$ 25,000
Cost of the oil interests of Taylor and associates and of the San Francisco and Santa Clara Petroleum companies, 1878-79 . .	75,000
Moody Gulch, 10 wells (@ $5 per foot) 1879-80	50,000
Newhall (Andrews Station) Refinery additions and pipeline, 1879-83	20,000
Alameda Refinery	160,000
Pico (6 wells, CSOW, PCO and SF Petroleum, 1879-81) Pico (16 wells, CSOW, PCO and SF Petroleum, 1882–84) } @ $7.50 per ft.	221,000
Pico: Other expenditures (roads, gathering lines, tanks, etc.) . .	35,000
Santa Clara River pump station and line	40,000
Standard Oil Company of California (Sespe), 1881-82	10,000
Mission Transfer Company	55,000
Stations and tank cars of the CO&T companies	150,000
Total	$841,000

*No attempt has been made to establish the investment in working capital. For PCO it probably amounted to from 5 to 10 per cent of the fixed assets; for the CO&T companies, it may have equaled the fixed assets.
Source: See note 91.

California. The amount invested in these endeavors by 1884 can only be surmised in the absence of financial records, but Table 2, based on fragmentary evidence, is probably a fairly close estimate.

This large investment had been made principally through assessments on stock (except California Star) and by plowing back all "profits" as late as the beginning of 1884. For the Pico producing companies, at least, profits was a loosely used term, for their accounting made no allowance for depreciation or depletion and did not even write off the cost of dry holes.[92] By 1884, the Californians had built up a sizable industry which was in balance in its major phases, from producing to marketing. But they continued to be troubled by the low quality of kerosine turned out at their refineries. And in marketing they were facing a situation even more urgent. Their marketer, the Continental Oil & Transportation Company of California, for more than two years had been engaged in an all-out battle with the Pacific Department of the Standard Oil Company (Ohio). Until that conflict was resolved, Felton and Tevis believed it was time to call a halt.

IV

THE STRUGGLE FOR
THE WESTERN MARKET, 1879-1885

By 1879 the Standard Oil Company (Ohio) had become the dominant factor in the western market. This was, of course, no regional phenomenon, for in the later seventies John D. Rockefeller and his companies were invading the field of distribution throughout the nation. Previously, the Rockefeller companies had not been marketers but had distributed their oils through many different wholesalers. This system had revealed grave defects. A wholesaling firm naturally operated in its own interest, which did not always square perfectly with the interest of its Rockefeller supplier. For example, a firm occasionally marketed inferior oils under a Rockefeller brand to increase its profits. In other instances, for lack of capital, or vigor, or imagination, the wholesaler was not doing as large a volume of business as was possible. Many times a firm divided its attention among various products, of which oil was only one. More efficient sales outlets were needed to handle a greater flow of products if Standard was to reap the maximum advantage from its refineries. Mainly for these reasons, the Rockefeller leaders began to turn from their earlier almost exclusive preoccupation with refining and transportation to enter marketing as well. In the words of Colonel W. P. Thompson, one of Rockefeller's keenest advisers, they were planning "the foundation of a most magnificent commercial system."[1]

The origins of this movement dated back several years. As early as 1873, Rockefeller had bought a half-interest in Chess, Carley & Company, an important dealer with headquarters in Louisville, which distributed oil products throughout most of the southeastern United States. Over the next four years the drive for marketing outlets gained greater momentum, and by 1879 Rockefeller companies held a strong position in almost every major market from New England to California. This had been accomplished mainly by buying up or into the larger established distributors, but in some instances Rockefeller had formed new organizations, such as the Consolidated Tank Line Company for the states north and west of Missouri.[2] In the Rocky Mountains and on the West Coast, Rockefeller followed still another course, for, as we have noted, the original Standard company, the Standard Oil Company (Ohio), became the marketer.

2

Before Ohio Standard came to California in 1878, the Far West was already largely supplied by refineries of the Standard combination. Between 1872 and 1874 Rockefeller had brought under his control three important New York refiners who sold a part of their oil on the Pacific Coast: J. A. Bostwick & Company, the Devoe Manufacturing Company, and Charles Pratt & Company. Devoe, which had the prominent mining millionaire, Alvinza Hayward, as its San Francisco agent until 1876, was the largest western seller. Its Brilliant, a kerosine of 110° fire test, and its better grade Nonpareil were household words. The Daylight and Gaslight brands of Bostwick & Tilford (predecessor to J. A. Bostwick & Company) were widely used at the beginning of the seventies, as were the Radiant and Astral kerosines of Charles Pratt & Company throughout the decade. These refiners sent the great bulk of their oil to California by clipper around Cape Horn, although both Bostwick & Tilford and Devoe made a few rail shipments as early as 1870 and 1871. Bostwick & Tilford bought oil carrying their trademark in Cleveland for these early shipments; Devoe sent its oil direct from New York. Thereafter for most of the decade the overland route was rarely used because rail rates from the East were considerably higher than water rates around the Horn.[3] Probably the high rail rates also kept Ohio Standard from marketing in California prior to 1878.

Of the three New York refiners, J. A. Bostwick & Company (Bostwick & Tilford) is the most important for our story because of the role the Tilfords subsequently played in Standard's western trade. The route by which they entered the oil business and later the Standard combination is not entirely clear. It seems certain, however, that Jabez A. Bostwick was the man who brought them into the business, and that the Tilford father, John B. Tilford, a Lexington, Kentucky, banker, supplied part, if not all, of the capital for their joint oil venture. According to a colorful Tilford family account, Bostwick was a pious young Bible peddler when he met the Lexington banker shortly after the Civil War. Tilford liked the personable and aggressive young man but not his line of work. He told Bostwick that he was "much too smart" to be selling Bibles. In the course of their conversation Bostwick talked of an opportunity to peddle kerosine in New York City, with the result that the banker financed a partnership for Bostwick and John B. Tilford, Jr., the eldest of his five sons. According to a more likely version, Bostwick had been a bookkeeper in the Tilford bank before becoming a cotton broker in Cincinnati and later moved to New York toward the close of the Civil War. The New York house, known as Bostwick &

Tilford, soon changed its business to become an oil brokerage firm.[4]

The firm prospered in its new line. It also entered refining, acquiring a controlling interest in the Long Island Oil Company, which it made a vigorous competitor of the larger New York refiners, Devoe and Charles Pratt. Late in 1871, however, J. A. Bostwick and John B. Tilford, Jr., came to a parting of the ways. Each partner set up a new firm, J. A. Bostwick & Company and J. B. Tilford, Jr. & Company. Within a year each of the firms had become a part of the Rockefeller organization.[5]

In the West, the centralization of Standard's marketing operations proceeded slowly. Even after the New York refiners had been bought up, their western business continued to be carried on through separate outlets. Not until July, 1877, were their brands vested in a sole agent, George M. Blake, Alvinza Hayward's longtime salesman and secretary. "A combination has recently been formed in New York," said the *Commercial Herald* in explanation, but for some time the Rockefeller role was only dimly recognized.[6]

The next spring the Rockefeller leaders decided to take the business from Blake and to operate it as a branch house of Ohio Standard. Two of the Tilford sons, Wesley Hunt and Edward A. Tilford, were sent to San Francisco to set up the new arrangement. For each of the brothers, it was probably their first important assignment. Wesley, the older of the pair, was an earnest, hard-driving young man of twenty-eight who had been in oil marketing for almost a decade. After two years at Columbia College, he had joined Bostwick & Tilford and later had served as a junior partner in his brother's firm. For Wesley, this western assignment was a stepping stone in a brilliant career, marked by his appointment as treasurer of the Standard Oil Trust at thirty-seven, and followed by service as treasurer, vice president and director of the Standard Oil Company (New Jersey). E. A. Tilford, formerly a clerk in J. B. Tilford & Company, would also become prominent in Standard's marketing organization. The brothers took over from Blake late in June, after which Wesley returned to the East, leaving E. A. Tilford behind as head of the three-man, second-story office at 123 California Street. This modest establishment, so much in keeping with Standard Oil practice, the younger brother made a sort of regional command post during the fourteen years he served as Rockefeller's western leader.[7]

E. A. Tilford heralded Standard's arrival in San Francisco by advertisements in both the daily and commercial press to make the company and its products better known. "The largest Manufacturers of

Illuminating Oils in the World," he proclaimed, "CONSEQUENTLY THE CHEAPEST SELLERS." To the brands of kerosine sold by Blake, Tilford added Standard's own 150° fire test Pearl Oil ("Made by ourselves and never known to cause an accident"), and extended his line to include gasoline, benzine, a 300° fire test mineral seal oil, and a paraffin lubricating oil. He played upon the company's reputation for quality, cautioning the public to "Beware of Inferior Oils put up in Second-hand cans," and asked that he be notified of any such underhanded effort.[8]

Undoubtedly the chief change under the new arrangement was substituting rail for water transportation. Standard had found that the railroads were willing to grant favorable rates, for they were anxious to gain a hold on the growing oil traffic. The West, in consequence, could be served, cheaply and quickly, from Cleveland. The *Commercial Herald* commented in January of 1879:[9]

> The Standard Company we are informed have made special contracts with the railroads which places them in a position to supply this coast with Oil quicker and in better condition than shipments by sea. It frequently happens that a cargo by sea comes in a degraded condition, cases stained and oil leaking badly, necessitating one's hauling and repairing at a considerable expense. . . . On the other [hand] shipments by rail come . . . in good order and with regularity.

Near the end of 1879 the same paper sized up the situation more perceptively:[10]

> The Standard Oil Company seems to have the control of the markets of the Pacific Slope . . . bringing now all their oils by rail instead of by sea as heretofore. They have by reason of this arrangement freight facilities and advantages not possessed by other shippers, and consequently they feed the trade upon terms that defy all competition from other importing houses.

With a grip of that kind, Standard had little reason to expand its western organization. Until 1882 it held forth solely in San Francisco. It had no traveling salesmen, depending upon prices and quality to bring in the trade. Merchants appeared in person or mailed in their orders. Standard supplied San Francisco dealers from a small warehouse which the company had built near the railroad at Third and Townsend streets; orders from outside the city it handled mainly by dropping off cars from Cleveland at the waypoint nearest to the purchaser.[11]

Tilford usually sold the Standard oils under their proper brand names, but he made an exception for one large customer, Yates & Company, which marketed Standard's kerosine as its own "Starlight Oil, the Safest & Purest Oil in the World." For several years Charles Yates had been an energetic distributor around San Francisco Bay and in the Sacramento and San Joaquin valleys. In San Francisco as early as 1882 he was delivering oil in bulk by tank wagon, the first to do so in the West and among the first anywhere. Yates had placed upon his wagon a simple square tank of galvanized iron holding 360 gallons, with a hole on top for filling the tank and a single valve at the end to supply customers.[12]

Standard's operations under this simple pattern, according to the *Commercial Herald*, enabled it to handle about nine-tenths of the western oil traffic in 1880. It could only continue to do so, however, in the absence of strong competition. By 1880 a challenger was already at hand, the Continental Oil & Transportation Company of California, which was being revitalized by Tevis and Felton.[13]

3

The entry of Tevis and Felton marked a new day for the Continental Oil & Transportation Company. Its chief purpose remained the same: to sell both eastern and California oils in the western market. But the means to that end had become more powerful and varied as the result of new financing. Backed by his wealthy principals, the CO&T president, Isaac E. Blake, quickly carried the battle to Standard. He did this by building a large, efficient sales organization and by offering good oil at low prices.

At the beginning of 1880 CO&T had four stations, San Francisco, Los Angeles, Sacramento, and San Jose. Blake used them as a nucleus for a rapid expansion. Within six months he was advertising additional CO&T outlets at Oakland, Stockton, Marysville, and San Diego in California; Elko and Reno in Nevada; and Portland, Oregon. During the next year Tucson, Arizona, was added. Most of these stations could hardly have been large, but they gave CO&T a direct contact with customers in various western communities not possible for its eastern competitor. The CO&T Company of California was operated in close alliance with an Iowa corporation, the Continental Oil & Transportation Company, the Rocky Mountain marketer that Blake had founded in 1875 and of which he was also the president.[14]

Blake brought experienced oilmen into his California organization and supplied his major stations with staffs, large for the day, to seek out the trade. For example, in 1882 at San Francisco he had at least three salesmen, a bookkeeper, and a teamster. Irvine Graham, of the affiliated oil house of Scofield & Tevis, also worked alongside CO&T's sales organization. These men divided their time between a warehouse at Fifth and Berry streets and an office and sales room which early in 1881 the company had made the neighbor of Standard at 123 California Street. Blake had his office there, as did the secretary, Harry Tevis.[15]

The two other major stations of the company were at Sacramento and Los Angeles. Blake made Sacramento his center for distributing eastern oils to California's interior valleys in order to avoid the higher freight costs from San Francisco. The Los Angeles station, where E. A. Edwards was in charge, served the southern end of the state and Arizona.[16]

Blake challenged his eastern rival all along the line. He ferreted out weak spots. Standard was most vulnerable in lube oils, a field in which western refiners had been having fair success. As manager of the lube business, in 1883 he recruited Charles J. Woodbury, who had been a leading lube specialist for Standard at Cleveland before leaving in 1881. Within little more than a year Woodbury added several western railroads and numerous sawmills and ironworks to CO&T's growing list of customers.[17]

The principal battleground, however, was in the kerosine trade. While Blake could hope for the day when the Pacific Coast Oil Company would turn out a large volume of high quality kerosine at Alameda, his immediate concern was finding a sufficient supply among the independent eastern refiners. By 1882 Blake had opened an office in Cleveland. It was an opportune move, for the independents were looking for additional outlets. Their output, which had been as low as 10 per cent of the national total in 1878, was climbing to a new high of almost 25 per cent early in 1883. One source Blake tapped was Scofield, Shurmer & Teagle, a tenacious Cleveland foe of Rockefeller.[18]

Blake's plan was to offer oils of a quality equivalent to Standard's at lower prices. This he hoped to do, not by importing eastern oil in cases, each of two five-gallon tins, which was Standard's usual practice, but by bringing the oil in bulk and distributing it mainly in barrels. Savings in packing and transportation he intended to pass on to the customer. The patented combination cars, first used by Blake in 1875 to supply oil to Denver, were a central part of his scheme. These cars, it will be recalled, contained a galvanized oil tank at each end, with space between in which the railroads could haul dry freight and the oil company thus escape a charge for the return run when the tanks were empty. When Standard first began to occasionally ship bulk oil in the conventional boiler-type cars, it paid $110 for the return of each empty car.[19]

Blake's search for economies in transportation did not end with the combination car. He struck hard and effectively for rebates. The fact that Lloyd Tevis was a close associate of Leland Stanford and Charles Crocker and was president of Wells Fargo, a leading customer of the western railroads, undoubtedly helped Blake. He also had the respect and confidence of railroad executives. J. C. Stubbs, the general freight agent of the Central Pacific, was more than friendly. Early in 1881, on one occasion, he wrote glowingly of Blake to a colleague on another line: "I have always found him trustworthy and can certify that he is worthy of credence even when 'talking for rates.' And that is more than you can say of most men."[20]

There is some reason to believe that Standard at first underrated Blake's ability to get what he wanted from the railroads. According to one story, a Standard official, perhaps E. A. Tilford, bragged to Blake, "We know of methods of which you know nothing about in getting rebates on large shipments." Later a government investigation showed that the CO&T companies had gained about $80,000 in rebates over a period in which Standard got about $10,000. The revelation caused the official to volunteer, in admiration, that "Blake had the most genius in the manipulation of railroads of any man on the continent."[21] This was high praise indeed from a Rockefeller subordinate.

CO&T of California advertised its 150° premium kerosine, Continental Safety Oil, as "GUARANTEED equal to Best Cased Oil in the Market." The company told the trade that to prevent any "discoloration or deterioration of the oil," the tanks in its combination cars were "thoroughly cleansed and painted before each trip." Its customers could, if they chose, purchase the oil in five-gallon cans, filled and cased at the larger stations, but in keeping with the drive to cut costs, the company featured barrel delivery at three cents a gallon less. This was a substantial saving, from 10 to 20 per cent under the usual price for cased goods.

By 1881 the company was advertising a patented portable barrel, "the acme of perfection" for handling and storage. Each barrel, it pointed out, could serve as tankage for the dealer. It was actually two barrels in one—an inner of tinned steel plate encased in an iron-bound blue wooden barrel, with the space between filled with a protective substance. Another special feature was a bung at both the top and the bottom, permitting the barrel to be emptied from either end. CO&T paid the charge for the return of barrels from any station on the

Central Pacific Railroad or an affiliated line. The company also advertised a "jacket can," a five-gallon tin sheathed in a wooden jacket that swung forward on rockers, permitting the consumer to pour oil without lifting the can.

There were other aspects to the service offered by CO&T. In communities where it had stations, it delivered free. In San Francisco, and probably at other stations, it used tank wagons for bulk deliveries. CO&T also published a handy pocket guide of freight rates from each station to the neighboring towns, which allowed the customer to know in advance the total cost of his order.[22]

While developing its system of merchandising, CO&T began to get a larger volume of refined oils from Alameda. Alameda's 150° high-test kerosine continued to be inferior, but the PCO refiners were doing better with their 110° oil, which in Thumm's patented lamp, according to one report, gave as good a light as eastern oil. The *Journal of Commerce* in a survey of 1881 commented on the "astounding increase in receipts of California coal oil" and stated that PCO's low test kerosine was driving the lower grade eastern oil out of the market. Some was exported, chiefly to Mexico, Central America, and the Hawaiian Islands, and there was again talk of a possibly large Asiatic trade. The press noted, too, that a good deal of distillate and crude oil was being sold to gas companies.[23]

The main San Francisco business papers, the *Commercial Herald* and the *Journal of Commerce*, regularly published figures on the oil trade. These statistics seem at times hardly reliable, but in spite of their shortcomings, they show the improved position of California kerosine. According to the *Commercial Herald*, 3,517,550 gallons of crude (84 per cent of California's production) came to Alameda in 1881. If all of this oil was refined, the Alameda works would have turned out about 900,000 gallons of high- and low-test kerosine. A lower estimate, given to the U.S. Bureau of the Census in March, 1882, placed the California kerosine output at around 400,000 gallons annually. The shipments of eastern kerosine into the state in 1881 were reported by the *Journal of Commerce* as approximately 1,200,000 gallons, which seems far too low and impossible to reconcile with a figure of 4,500,000 gallons given by the census informant as the total consumption of eastern kerosine on the Pacific Coast.[24] Even the census figures, however, indicate that California kerosine was making headway in its home market.

The CO&T line of kerosines, lube oils, benzine, distillate, and crude oil was only partially competitive with Standard.[25] Low-test California kerosine offered competition only to the degree that it drew customers from Standard's high-test products, for low-test kerosine was no longer being sold by the eastern company. Standard sold no distillate and crude oil in the West at all. But the profits CO&T derived from their sale helped strengthen its competition in the kerosine trade.

At the beginning of 1882 CO&T was offering the West three different grades. Its premium Continental Safety Oil, imported from the East, sold for 31¢ a gallon in cases and for 28¢ in barrels, which was 1.5¢ less in cases and 4.5¢ less in barrels than for Standard's competing brands. In addition, CO&T sold two California kerosines. One was a new 130° kerosine, marketed in cases at 23¢ and in barrels at 20¢. The other, a 110° oil called "Standard," was sold at 20¢ and 17¢.[26] The extent of the sale of the California products depended upon their quality and the price gap between low- and high-test oils. The greater the gap, the greater was the opportunity for the California oils.

In two years CO&T had come a long way. In that short interval it may, in fact, have wrested leadership from Standard in the western oil trade, running to $1,000,000 or more a year.

4

CO&T's challenge brought W. H. Tilford out from New York in 1881. The eastern executive came to San Francisco to observe and counsel with his younger brother before returning to Standard's headquarters to seek clearance for a more forceful marketing program. The program was twofold: to set up a number of well-located western stations and to intensify price competition, both by paralleling CO&T in emphasizing bulk distribution and by making price reductions on cased goods. Consequently, the years 1882-1884 were keenly competitive, and the western payroll, growing to about twenty-five employees at the end of 1884, showed the result.[27]

In 1882 the San Francisco office was expanded, adding Charles Watson and a second warehouseman to the bookkeeper and warehouseman who had hitherto been E. A. Tilford's sole subordinates. Watson, who had formerly worked for Standard as a clerk at Weehawken, New Jersey, was beginning a career in the West that would extend over the next thirty-seven years. He was hired as "Chief Clerk" to Tilford, but he soon took on the construction and supervision of new stations as his principal responsibility.

The investment at San Francisco when Watson arrived—$3,640, of which $1,000 was for the warehouse—was not much. Nor was the office, located above a wholesale meat firm, as he described it:[28]

We had just one room, a good sized room. . . . It was all partitioned off into four compartments. The door opened into the alley, or reception room, or hallway, and then the bookkeeper's desk made one part of it and I had one room.

No salesmen. We didn't have any. Merchants would come in and leave their orders.

"Drumming the town" was among Watson's earliest duties. Every afternoon he went out on the street to call on the big merchants, like Hills Brothers, Tillman & Bendel, and Tibbetts & Company.

Shortly after Watson came, the company began to build up its San Francisco station, leasing land at Fifth and Berry streets adjacent to the plant of CO&T and erecting a warehouse costing about $13,000 that was suitable for bulk storage as well as for cased goods. Standard also financed four new tank wagons for Yates & Company to make that firm a more effective competitor of CO&T and Scofield & Tevis. In March of 1883 the little fleet of five—three of 360 gallons capacity and two of 500 gallons—paraded up Market Street, all in line. The parade gave notice of Standard's determination to develop a large bulk oil business at San Francisco.

At about the same time the company started construction of stations elsewhere. The program consisted in part of small plants at Sacramento and Stockton, from which it could market directly in the Sacramento and San Joaquin valleys, territory which had previously been served by Yates & Company. Standard also planned a small storage depot across San Francisco Bay at Oakland. These plants were ready late in 1882. The Sacramento and Stockton stations, each costing about $4,000, were plain one-and-a-half story brick structures, about 20 x 60 feet in size located alongside the railroad. They contained a circular tank 14 feet in diameter and 14 feet high, in addition to storage for cased goods and a small office. An agent and a teamster comprised the staff at each station. George C. Flanders, a former Yates' employee, was the Stockton agent, and W. G. Stubbs the agent at Sacramento. As general sales representatives, they handled the office chores, unloaded cased goods, and pumped out the tank cars by hand; the teamsters toured the stores and business houses twice a day, delivering barrels of oil in the forenoons and cases in the afternoons.

Construction of other stations started the next year. In September, 1883, a "two-wagon" station, costing about $7,500, was opened at Los Angeles. The next month the $8,000 station at Salt Lake, with subordinate storage at Ogden, began business. A third, costing $12,000, went up at Portland in the spring of 1884. Flanders moved to Portland as agent, and John McLean replaced Flanders at Stockton. Because of their long years of service, these two men rank along with Tilford and Watson as pioneers in Standard's marketing story.[29]

In general, the entry of Standard into these communities went along smoothly, but in two of the cities Standard suffered from rough tactics by competitors. Neither Continental Oil & Transportation nor Whittier, Fuller & Company, a paint and oil firm with a smaller string of stations, was pleased to see their eastern rival move outward from San Francisco. When they could, they made use of local governments and laws to torment Standard.

Watson had his first troublesome experience while building the warehouse at Oakland in 1882. Standard's neighbors charged that the new plant was a fire hazard, erected without specific authorization from the city council. Watson was arrested. He believed that CO&T and Whittier, Fuller had joined hands to influence Standard's new neighbors to make the charge. It was soon dismissed, however, and Watson met with no further embarrassment.

A more serious incident occurred the next year in Salt Lake City, where E. A. Tilford had anticipated no trouble. Tilford had thoughtfully leased land for the station from the mayor and felt protected by a city ordinance permitting an oil business at the site he had chosen. But in June, 1883, after Standard had spent several thousand dollars building an adobe warehouse, the city council repealed the ordinance. Watson was certain that CO&T (Iowa), which had a station in Salt Lake, was behind the repeal. When he opened the station in October, Watson was hauled into court. Not until Tilford found competent legal counsel was the company freed from harassment.[30]

The other part of the program of W. H. Tilford was price competition. Between January and the late summer of 1882, Standard's cased oil dropped from 32.5¢ to 24¢ a gallon, causing the *Journal of Commerce* to comment that coal oil "is now at bed rock here." This price, or lower, endured until the spring of 1884. In addition, in the spring of 1883 Standard began to sell a 150° bulk oil for as little as 16¢ a gallon and also re-entered the 110° field.[31]

But CO&T usually matched or kept ahead of Standard in this price warfare. It advertised "discounts to the trade" for both case and barrel goods and ordinarily kept its published prices for Continental Safety Oil a half cent or more a gallon under the competing Standard brands. For nine or ten months following May, 1883, the company widened the gap between its case and barrel prices from three to eight or nine cents. For most of the year its premium Safety Oil was selling in barrels for 14¢—an unheard of figure. CO&T also made reductions and widened the margin in price between cases and barrels for its lower quality oils. These bargain prices undoubtedly helped push the volume of coal oil sales to a new high in 1883, but not profits. "There has been little money made the past year, [the] majority of sales being near the cost of transportation," said the *Commercial Herald* in its year-end summary.[32]

Standard's price cutting probably would have been more effective if the company had been able to maintain its reputation for quality. During the summer of 1883, however, its products fell off alarmingly in public favor. "There has been much complaint of the poor quality, even among the highest priced and fancy brands," the *Commercial Herald* observed. The Cleveland refinery was being taxed to the limit to meet the soaring demands of its market, which included the Mississippi Valley and the Rockies as well as the Far West. Rockefeller himself took note of the situation. In November he wrote a Cleveland executive, "I am not so desirous for a large yield of Water White as to take any risk whatever as to the quality. . . . We must go very carefully and regain our lost reputation [in the West] for quality." This concern for Standard's good name continued for some time; almost a year later an entry in the "Works Diary" at Cleveland read: "W. H. Tilford says go ahead with W. W. [Water White] 110 to California as soon as we can furnish something we know to be all right."[33]

The long struggle had done no good for either side. The westerners had more to fear the longer it went on, for Standard could much more readily endure low profits or even losses. Perhaps the sale in December, 1883, of the paint and oil business of Scofield & Tevis to Whittier, Fuller & Company, the third important western oil marketer, was one result of the conflict. F. B. Taylor's old house had set up branches at Sacramento, Los Angeles, and Portland under the new ownership, but in the oil trade it was something of an anomaly, for it overlapped with the Continental Oil & Transportation Company. Following the sale to Whittier, Fuller, the rest of the business of Scofield & Tevis as a commission house was liquidated.[34]

Early in 1884 the first steps were taken to bring the long price war to a close. Blake may have made the initial move, for he was in New York at least by April and remained there for most of the year. A limited understanding appears to have been reached with Standard in the spring, which provided for the price of bulk oil to conform more closely to that for cased goods and for a smaller increase in cased oil prices.[35]

While Blake was in New York, John D. Rockefeller was in the West, sizing up the need for a settlement. Late in April Rockefeller traveled to California by private railroad car accompanied by his wife, four children, and other relatives and friends on what was clearly a vacation trip. The holiday had as a main purpose touring the newly opened southern route to California. But the two-week stopover in San Francisco, beginning on May 4, certainly involved more than a sight-seeing excursion.[36] Rockefeller undoubtedly talked with E. A. Tilford, and it is possible that Tevis and Felton and members of Whittier, Fuller & Company took part in some of the discussions.

Late in the summer Tevis joined Blake in New York for a series of meetings with Standard, at which Whittier, Fuller also was represented. The negotiators for the three firms reached an agreement on November 1, 1884. Its terms are not known, but subsequent events make almost certain that it related to mergers of the marketing operations of CO&T (Iowa) and Standard in the Rocky Mountain territory and of all three marketing companies along the Pacific Coast. The two-way merger went forward rapidly. On December 26, 1884, a new concern, the Continental Oil Company, was incorporated in Iowa with a capital of $300,000 to operate the combined properties. The CO&T negotiators (principally Tevis) received three-eighths of the stock; I. E. Blake, with headquarters in Denver, became president of the new company. Shortly, Blake was writing to West Coast friends: "The Standard interests and our interests are thoroughly harmonized, and the distributing interests on the Pacific Coast are moving in close harmony with the Standard."[37]

The merger on the Pacific Coast came off less smoothly, however, apparently because Whittier, Fuller proved balky. When a second Iowa corporation, called the Standard Oil Company, was formed on June 10, 1885, the oil business of Whittier, Fuller was not included. Instead, the Standard Oil Company (Iowa) was the outcome of the union of CO&T of California with Ohio Standard's Far Western stations.

Iowa Standard was the larger of the two new companies. Capitalized at $600,000, it was empowered to deal "in petroleum and its products, oils and naval stores, lead and paints." John D. Archbold, who later succeeded Rockefeller as head of the Standard organization, Wesley H. Tilford, and Standard's famed legal counsel, S. C. T. Dodd, were its incorporators. Lloyd Tevis, Archbold, W. H. Tilford, E. A. Tilford, and George H. Vilas became the first directors. Although the Tevis faction was given a 40 per cent stock interest, the company officers were all Standard men: E. A. Tilford, president; W. H. Tilford, vice president; and the Trust's chief auditor, George Vilas, secretary and treasurer.[38] Standard, through the Tilfords, was obviously going to call the tune.

5

It seems probable that the Rockefeller interests treated the CO&T owners generously in these mergers. Such was the usual Rockefeller policy in removing troublesome competitors, and there is no reason to believe an exception occurred here. Surviving accounting records, however, permit no estimate of the relative contributions of the two sides to the Continental Oil Company and only a very general estimate of their contributions to the Standard Oil Company (Iowa). In the latter case, Ohio Standard gave up five stations and a storage depot, valued at $45,242; CO&T's generally smaller and more numerous stations were accepted at about the same figure. The other and more important plant item was tank cars. CO&T supplied ninety-eight patented combination cars, accepted at $90,650, and Standard contributed forty-seven cylinder cars, for $33,200. The combination cars may have been deliberately overvalued to make the merger more attractive to CO&T, for the accounting records at the end of 1885 show a write-off of $120 per car. But, in view of the $95 Standard paid that year on every cylinder car returned empty to the East, it is also obvious that Standard could place a high value on the patented model. Within sixteen months the Iowa company sold all of its cylinder cars while retaining those of the combination type. The balance of the stock, amounting to almost $400,000, was issued against merchandise, accounts receivable, and cash. The records indicate that Standard contributed a larger share of these items than CO&T.[39] A final, and potentially valuable, benefit to Tevis and Felton was that Standard agreed to take over from CO&T as the principal marketer for the refined oils of the Pacific Coast Oil Company.

Tevis and Felton were probably quite willing to accept minority ownership in 1885. Almost two years of price warfare had shown them the danger of prolonged conflict with Rockefeller.[40] Moreover, the future of the California oil industry no longer appeared so bright. The problem of producing a quality kerosine continued to vex the Alameda refiners, and their low-test product had a favorable market only when eastern kerosines were relatively high in price. In the summer of 1884 eastern crude (yielding, proportionately, about three times as much kerosine as California crude) reached a low of 51¢ a barrel, the lowest figure in many years.[41]

The two financiers may also have been influenced by the fact that by 1884 drillers who were seeking to extend the margins of the Pico fields east and west were finding little or no oil. If no other significant field were discovered, the California industry inevitably would continue to be small. Tevis and Felton had lost their earlier eagerness for the search.[42]

So closely related were CO&T and PCO in the public mind that the West needed a word of explanation concerning the new arrangement. Both Felton and Scofield, in separate interviews, took pains to point out that PCO was no party to the merger.[43] They emphasized that the PCO relationship to CO&T had been merely that of a producing and refining company to its marketer. Scofield also gave his view of the reasons behind the merger:

> The former company [Continental Oil and Transportation] and the Pacific department of the Standard have each been distributors of petroleum oils in the Pacific States and Territories, the trade having been about equally divided between them; each company keeping up separate offices, warehouses and agencies in all the prominent cities and distributing points on the Pacific Coast. For a considerable time these two companies have been working in complete harmony, by which all friction has been avoided, the arrangement proving so satisfactory that a closer relation, and one in which the cost of distribution could be greatly economized, was deemed desirable. Negotiations to this end resulted in the formation of a new company called the Standard Oil Company (of Iowa), who purchased all the plant, merchandise and business of both the Continental Oil & Transportation Company and the Pacific department of the Standard Oil Company (of Cleveland), each of the latter companies receiving in payment therefor their proportions of stock in the new company. Thus you will see that neither party has retired from the field, but simply consolidated their large interests, which will greatly economize the cost of distribution, necessitating but one establishment in each place, where formerly there were two, and each set of stockholders being fairly represented in the new company.

The Scofield statement seems accurate, so far as it goes, but there also is little doubt that the formation of Iowa Standard marked an end to great endeavor by Tevis and Felton. Almost simultaneously, in July, 1885, George Loomis entered the PCO office to prepare to take over the presidency from his brother-in-law, Charles Felton. Since at least the start of the year Scofield had been the PCO vice president. Felton, who in 1884 had been elected to Congress, left for Washington in November, 1885. He served for two terms and then, after a two-year lapse, went to the United States Senate between 1891 and 1893 to fill out the term of George Hearst.[44] Felton continued to keep his hand in PCO's affairs, especially when not in Washington, but he did not resume the office of president so long as Loomis lived.

As for Standard, the merger all but assured its dominance in western marketing. A few months before the merger, for $10,000 E. A. Tilford bought out C. A. Low, a San Francisco commission merchant who had been an oil importer for almost two decades.[45] Standard's sole sizable remaining competitor was Whittier, Fuller & Company. But the struggle with that company, reminiscent in many ways of the contest with CO&T, belongs to a later period.

V

FELTON AND TEVIS
TURN CONSERVATIVE

The middle 1880's proved almost as much a turning point in producing as in marketing for the western allies. With an ample supply of crude for refining and with the market so uncertain, there was little incentive to continue the costly gamble of seeking more production through drilling new wells. Instead, after 1883 the leaders of the Pacific Coast Oil Company limited producing activity almost wholly to reviving failing wells through deeper drilling, a program that proved remarkably successful.[1] Their Pico production fell off less than one-sixth from the record of 1884 during the next three years. This large flow of oil, provided by so limited an additional investment, helped pave the way for the payment of substantial dividends by the Pico companies after the spring of 1884. For Felton and Tevis the middle eighties were a time of profit-taking and consolidation, a story that can be pieced together only from meager records.

But there was another, and more enduring, outcome. As the Californians slackened their efforts, leadership in the search for oil passed into new hands. The shift resulted from Blake's success in finding Pennsylvanians to develop the lands of his Mission Transfer Company, which Felton and Tevis helped to finance. Wallace Hardison and Lyman Stewart, the men whom Blake induced to come West in 1883, also took leases from PCO and the Standard Oil Company of California, an arrangement which permitted Felton and Tevis to continue the search for oil without risk to their capital. Because the lease terms required that a lessor sell crude solely to the leasing company, the arrangement also allowed them to control the production of crude in California for a few years longer. The larger significance of these events, however, is that Hardison and Stewart, who were experienced oilmen, gradually superseded the San Francisco capitalists as the principal force in the California industry. These were years of retreat on the part of Felton and Tevis and of the emergence of new leaders.

2

When Blake traveled to Pennsylvania late in 1882 looking for oilmen to take leases from Mission Transfer, he turned to two Titusville oper-

ators, Lyman and Milton Stewart. They shared his sanguine temperament. He had known them since the days immediately following the
Civil War when he was a member of the first drilling crew ever hired
by Lyman Stewart. This was about a year before a fabulous strike in
1867 on the Tallman farm in northern Venango County, a success which
produced oil worth $1,750,000 for the Stewarts and their partners.
Later, before leaving for Colorado in 1874, Blake had been a partner
with Milton, the elder and more conservative brother, who nonetheless
was an inveterate speculator and wildcatter, one of the best known in
the Oil Regions.[2]

Lyman was particularly vulnerable to the persuasive words of his
former driller, whom the Stewarts called "Smoothy." Blake's message had
a special meaning for him because of the financial disaster he had suffered
following the Tallman strike. While Milton had stayed with oil and added
to his fortune, Lyman by 1872 had lost his through an unwise investment in a Pennsylvania competitor of the McCormick Reaper Works.
Thereafter he stayed close to oil, operating a family firm, Lyman Stewart
& Company, for which Milton supplied most of the capital.[3]

During these lean years Lyman was also a partner in Hardison,
Stewart & Company. Wallace L. Hardison, his partner, was a younger
brother of Harvey Hardison, one of the Stewart drillers, and was Lyman's
junior by about ten years. The two men were different in many ways.
Wallace was a robust, hearty, six-footer, while Lyman was slight and
fastidious. Wallace, though religious, lacked the extremes of Stewart's
piety, which included never working, or even traveling, on a Sunday.
Wallace loved the hurly-burly of the oil fields; his partner preferred a
white collar role. But they shared an enthusiasm for oil. While operating
in the great Bradford field, the two men spent many a night talking
into the early hours of the next morning about oil and the problems of
drilling. They made at least one contribution to drilling technology, a
device to keep water from entering the wells which helped launch a
company in which Lyman held a stock interest.[4]

Neither their invention nor their oil ventures brought the partners
the success they desired. While Lyman stayed on in the Oil Regions, by
the end of the 1870's Hardison was raising cattle on a Kansas ranch,
of which Lyman was a joint owner. Hardison was also president of a
small bank in Salina, Kansas, and of another in Eldred, Pennsylvania.
The resources of the partners were still sufficiently modest, however, that
in a dark moment in 1885 Lyman could allude to himself and Hardison
as "poor ex-producers of the Bradford field."[5]

In April, 1883, Lyman Stewart came to California to investigate the opportunity that Blake had urged in Titusville. Blake had told the Stewarts that the ex-Mission was entirely in his control and that he "did not have to consult anybody" in arranging terms for leases. The forty-two-year-old Lyman was taken at once to the ex-Mission, but his tour did not stop there. Blake accompanied him to the Pico, where Lyman saw the wells of California Star, PCO, and the San Francisco Petroleum companies, and to the Sespe district, where the Standard Oil Company of California held forth. Blake pointed out to his friend that Felton and Tevis had hundreds of acres of valuable land awaiting development which they were willing to lease on favorable terms. Late in April, Lyman wrote his brother the terms offered for drilling at Pico, as he understood them: "We get all the oil until all our expenses are paid and 25% of the cost of our machinery, tubing, etc. The Co. will lay water line and oil line for fuel to our locations free of charge, but will charge the cost of pumping the water and $1.50 per bbl. for the oil."[6]

Lyman was so pleased that he wired Wallace Hardison and John Irwin, a cousin and a driller for Lyman Stewart & Company, to join him. Within two weeks they were in California, where they were soon sharing Lyman's enthusiasm at what seemed a three-way play: the Pico, where so much success was already evident, the ex-Mission, and the lands of the Standard Oil Company of California, where oil had been discovered in lesser quantity.[7]

While Lyman stayed on in the West, Hardison returned to Pennsylvania to raise capital, recruit manpower, and assemble equipment. By July he had taken care of these matters and, with his brother, Harvey, was heading West with more than thirty men under six-month contracts. Hardison had gathered the funds for this venture from the Stewart and Hardison families and from friends. Lyman Stewart & Company furnished 24 per cent. Milton was also an important participant in his own right. Two Titusville friends of the Stewarts, J. A. Neill and J. D. Downing, shared in the 51 per cent majority interest of the Stewart faction, and another Titusville oil figure, C. P. Collins, joined with the Hardisons.[8]

Meantime, Lyman Stewart had arranged for three leases. Hardison, Stewart & Company received drilling rights from Mission Transfer in Saltmarsh Canyon, the center of the producing activities of the Stanford Brothers in the middle 1860's; from Standard of California, Smith Farm in Santa Paula Canyon at the western edge of the Sespe District; and from PCO, scattered parcels in the Pico running from the San Fernando claim about three miles southeast toward Wiley Canyon. The leases were drafted in May by Blake, Stewart, and Gordon Blanding, PCO's attorney. As a basic condition, Stewart agreed that Hardison, Stewart & Company would drill no other California lands without the consent of their lessors and that the oil produced would be sold exclusively to the companies controlled by Felton and Tevis. Stewart committed his firm to an expenditure of more than $100,000 and to a speedy drilling schedule. Since the lands were regarded as virtually proven oil territory, he agreed to share profits equally with the lessors on the production of each well after drilling expenses and 25 per cent of the cost of equipment had been recovered. The expense of dry holes was not shared but was to be exclusively the risk of the partners. On the other hand, Stewart understood that lumber, water, and fuel oil for their drilling operations would be made available at low cost.[9]

Mission Transfer made one other arrangement, apart from Hardison, Stewart & Company. Adams Canyon, from which Saltmarsh Canyon forked to the northwest, Blake pledged to W. W. Dull, the driller at Moody Gulch, whom Stewart later came to believe was merely a front for Blake.[10] Adams was an attractive territory where the Ventura partnership of Adams, Thayer & Edwards had drilled several wells in the middle 1870's. Whatever disappointment Stewart may have felt at losing Adams Canyon soon lost its edge, however, for the dispute between A. C. Dietz and Mission Transfer kept everyone from the ex-Mission until the court handed down its decision in June of 1884.

It was unfortunate for future good relations between the PCO group and the Pennsylvanians that the leases drafted in May were not executed because Felton was in the East on business. When he returned, he viewed some of the terms unfavorably, especially in the Pico lease, which he considered too generous. Revised drafts were drawn in August, 1883, and sent to Lyman Stewart in Titusville, where he had gone to wind up his eastern affairs. Instead of signing the revisions, Lyman returned them for further negotiation. Consequently, the drilling operations got under way with the leases unsigned and no complete understanding between the parties.[11]

3

During the balance of 1883, however, the fact that the leases were unsigned and that disagreement had arisen over the terms little disturbed Hardison and Stewart. The partners were confident that the differences could be ironed out. Their minds were taken up much more with the outlook for finding oil and with operational matters. The Pennsylvanians were far more interested in PCO's San Francisco #4 [PCO #13], for example—which came in late in June with a production of 225 barrels a day—than they were in the details of legal documents. While Hardison was in the East making arrangements for men and machinery, John Irwin was busy with preparations for drilling.

The warm hopes of the Pennsylvanians were aroused by their initial drilling sites: on the San Fernando claim about a quarter mile east of San Francisco #4; on the Moore claim in DeWitt Canyon, about a mile southeast of the first site; and a location on Smith Farm in Santa Paula Canyon in the Sespe Petroleum Mining District of Ventura County. Lyman appointed Irwin superintendent at Smith Farm, where drilling began on the last day of July. Harvey Hardison had charge of operations on the San Fernando and Moore claims.[12]

In the beginning, their relations with PCO could hardly have been more harmonious. These were honeymoon months. PCO seemed especially anxious to help, offering drilling items at bargain prices. In October, Wallace Hardison wrote warmly of PCO's superintendent, "Craig will do anything for us." And Hardison felt as secure with PCO's San Francisco leaders. In December, he commented at length on a talk with Felton and on another with Scofield and Lloyd Tevis, whom he obviously found more congenial. "They will do anything for us," he wrote. "We're solid with Tevis (confidential)." It was at this time that the partners took over the well PCO had started on the Simi Rancho in an attempt to extend westward its oil lands in Pico Canyon.[13]

The good feeling gradually dissolved, however, in the face of multiple disappointments. Hope for a fortune was one thing; achieving it, the partners found, was quite another. The Hardison, Stewart drillers met the same problems their PCO colleagues had wrestled with earlier. The formations, which were faulted and tilted, were unlike anything they had known in Pennsylvania. Crooked holes, caving walls, and lost tools caused delays and mounting expenses. The drillers had also encountered a new problem, the presence of water, which hitherto had not troubled Craig and his drilling crews. At Smith Farm, Irwin brought in a well that flowed sulfur water. On the last day of 1883, he gave up, having lost his tools because of caving.[14] The partners did not drill again on this lease from the Standard Oil Company of California.

Their success on the San Fernando and Moore claims, where by the end of the year five wells were being put down, was hardly greater. Hardison tried to cement off the water at one of their San Fernando wells—the first cementing job, Youle wrote, he had ever seen. But to no avail. Late in January, 1884, the partners were running only three strings of tools, including the one on the Simi. They suffered another blow when an unprecedented rainfall, estimated at over 20 inches, interrupted work for almost a month. Repairs had to be made and boilers and rigs dug out of the mud before drilling could be resumed.[15]

Stewart let most of the crews go at the end of their contracts in February, reducing the payroll by about two-thirds. Meanwhile, through assessments on the partners, he tried to keep the firm from bankruptcy. In April, he told a friend: "We are very much disappointed at the result of our operations here. We are not producing any oil. We are located only 400 feet distance . . . from a well [San Francisco #4] which has produced $50,000 worth of oil since we came here. We are below the bottom of it (this good well) without oil. Our humiliating song is 'up like a rocket, down like a stick.' " Two months later he remarked wryly, ". . . we have not yet succeeded in completing any wells in this country, and while we have marketed no oil as yet we have had lots of *experience.*" By that time Hardison, Stewart & Company had invested approximately $130,000, which included $50,000 in drilling equipment largely idle. In July, Hardison left to try to raise funds in Kansas and the East, staying away for more than six months.[16]

Their only new hope during the early months of 1884 came from the financial straits of D. C. Scott, who in January had received a ten-year lease from Thomas R. Bard to oil lands on the Ojai Rancho. Covering 2,400 acres, the lease included the site of old #6, the one promising well Bard had drilled for the California Petroleum Company during the boom of the sixties. Scott lacked the capital to handle his lease. In desperation, he sought out I. E. Blake, who suggested that a quarter-interest be given to W. W. Dull and a half-interest to Hardison, Stewart & Company. This arrangement was informally agreed to, with the understanding that Scott would pay no assessment on his quarter until the other parties had invested $4,500.[17]

Irwin and Dull began putting down a well near old #6 toward the end of February, 1884, and started a second in March. Heavy oil was struck at a shallow depth in both wells. Stewart estimated that a number of such wells could be brought in, each producing about ten barrels a day. He was less certain whether such heavy oil could be pumped through a pipeline.[18]

But Hardison, Stewart & Company urgently needed a far better opportunity. In mid-April, Stewart informed his brother he had written Felton that "we cannot longer continue [at Pico] unless they . . . give us a *dead sure* location. . . ." Finally, toward the end of May, to keep the partners in the field, Felton offered a desirable site. It was not at the edge of the Pico, like their earlier attempts, but high on a ridge between two of California Star's best producers, and about 200 yards distant from each. True, the site was not easy to get to; it required the construction of a bridge 105 feet long and 45 feet high. But it revived Lyman's sagging spirits. "I shall be much disappointed," he wrote Milton, "if we do not have a flowing well within sixty days."[19]

Stewart might have tempered his optimism by recalling another statement he had written earlier, "We are always on the eve of important developments which are never made, at least not in accordance with our expectations." Such was the story of the well they called the "Star." They were cursed with a crooked hole and lost tools until, finally, just before the arrival of an order from Lyman to shut down, the first oil flowed on November 26, 1884.[20]

4

The long series of failures and misfortunes soured relations between the Pennsylvanians and the Californians. Harmony gave way to bitterness. The situation was not helped by a long absence of Blake from California, for he was the one man Hardison and Stewart trusted. At the end of 1884 their friend was in Denver tending to the affairs of the Continental Oil Company. Hardison and Stewart became suspicious, resentful, convinced they were not receiving a fair deal from the other PCO leaders. And there were considerable grounds for their feelings.

The lack of a firm agreement with PCO over their Pico drilling sites was one part of the trouble. Milton first succumbed to suspicion. "Did you ever succeed in getting your papers from the P.C.O. Co. in proper shape?" he inquired of Lyman in March of 1884. "The last time you referred to the matter you couldn't understand why you didn't receive them. And if you have received them, do you find them satisfactory?" Recalling a visit of Felton to Titusville, he warned in June: "I would advise you to have an eye open and *wide open,* for that man Felton. When I saw him here a year ago, I set him down as [a] sharper of the first water and you will surely so find him out if you're not cautious. Are you quite certain your leases or contracts are all right? . . . I would take *nothing for granted.* . . ."[21]

As the months passed without a settlement, the language turned to acid. "Scoundrels," Lyman Stewart called the PCO leaders. W. L. Hardison described them as a "set of unprincipled fellows." "The facts are," he wrote Lyman, "we have got completely fooled, first in the character of the territory, second, by the character of the parties we are dealing with. . . ."[22]

The situation on the ex-Mission, where the hopes of the partners were buoyed briefly and then dashed, also contributed to the ill-feeling.

Courtesy Continental Oil Company

W. H. Tilford   I. E. Blake

Stock Certificate, H. L. Tevis, Trustee, Standard Oil Company (Iowa)

$100,000.00

CAN BE SAVED to the

PACIFIC COAST

IN ONE YEAR by all families
purchasing their

Illuminating Oils
IN BULK.

The Continental Oil and Transportation Co.
OF CALIFORNIA

Have introduced their TANK CARS for the transportation of Oils in
bulk from the refineries at the East, also the PATENT PORTABLE
BARREL (with reversible faucet) in which to ship bulk Oil to the
Dealers; and the 5 Gallon

"LITTLE WILL" CAN

(which the cut on the left represents)

IN WHICH CONSUMERS CAN
PURCHASE

CONTINENTAL
SAFETY OIL

of their Grocer or Oil Dealer at 3 cents per
gallon less than the cased price for the same
grade Oil, and as over Four Million Gallons of
Oil are consumed annually on this Coast, the
above amount of money can be saved, if

Continental Safety Oil in **BULK** is used.   It is Water White, High
Fire Test, Free from Odor, and gives universal satisfaction.

It is sold in every City, Town and Village on the Coast.

Ask your Grocer or Oil Dealer for it, and take no other.

Courtesy California Historical Society, San Francisco

Advertisement in 1882

Courtesy Union Oil Company

Lyman Stewart

Courtesy Union Oil Company

Wallace Hardison

Courtesy Huntington Library, San Marino, California

George Loomis

Courtesy Mrs. Henriette Lehman

Gordon Blanding

The *Santa Cruz*—the first carrier of bulk oil on the Pacific Coast

The *Piedmont*—an early oil-burning ferry boat on San Francisco Bay

In June, 1884, with a favorable decision in *Mission Transfer* v. *Dietz,* Blake's company started up again with a rush. Mission Transfer commenced laying a two-inch line connecting the Ojai with Santa Paula, for which Hardison, Stewart supplied part of the pipe, and completed a much longer link from Santa Paula to Ventura, reported as twenty-six miles in all. The company also planned to build tanks for installation on vessels of the Pacific Coast Steamship Company to transport oil in bulk to San Francisco, but this scheme was deferred, apparently for lack of funds.[23]

Meanwhile, in August Blake had closed out Dull's interest in Adams Canyon (which Dull had made no attempt to develop) and had offered it to Hardison and Stewart. He guaranteed them $1 a barrel for production from the Ojai and ex-Mission and promised that the ex-Mission lease would be revised in their favor when he came to California. These promises encouraged Stewart in September to put down in Adams Canyon a couple of shallow wells, which proved dry. More heartening was the $1,000 Mission Transfer paid the partners for Ojai oil, their first return from the sale of crude after more than a year of effort.[24]

When Blake came to Santa Paula in October, he appeared to be as good as his word. Stewart wrote Hardison that Blake had "consented to very reasonable and fair terms" for an enlarged lease embracing Adams, Saltmarsh, and Wheeler canyons. Stewart reported: "They guarantee $1.00 per bbl. up to 200 bbls. per day, and ½ of the excess obtained over and above $2.00 by them. We are to keep one well drilling until the production reaches 100 barrels. No specification as to depth. All payments for oil to be made at M. T. Co's office in Santa Paula on the 10th of each month." This last provision with its prospect of a steady income was especially pleasing to the partners.[25]

Unfortunately, Blake had promised more than he could deliver. In spite of his assurances, Blake was not the ultimate power in Mission Transfer. His company was deep in debt to Felton and Tevis, who had advanced $35,000 for the pipeline and other improvements. They were unwilling to guarantee a minimum price. Nor would they accept the provision for monthly payments without modification. Felton claimed that the partners owed PCO a large sum for lumber, fuel, water, and other supplies used at Pico, and that this debt should be offset from the funds that Mission Transfer owed Hardison, Stewart for oil and pipe. Stewart also heard a disquieting rumor that the PCO leaders had no desire to tie up so much of the ex-Mission with a single party.[26] This was hardly the outcome he had expected.

The anger of the partners mounted still higher toward the close of

1884 when PCO employees began relocating mining claims at Pico on property that Blake had represented as belonging to PCO at the time of the negotiations with Stewart in 1883. During September and October six claims were filed that blanketed the old San Fernando and Moore claims. These were deeded to the Occidental Asphalt Company, a concern existing only on paper which Felton and Tevis had incorporated in Nevada in June of 1883. It is not clear why the relocations were necessary, nor why Occidental, and not PCO, took over the claims. All that can be said is that Felton and Tevis must have feared flaws in the earlier locations, and that they believed having Occidental handle the relocations would better serve their purpose. But to Hardison, Stewart the relocations looked like one more evidence of bad faith.[27]

5

These months of crisis impelled the Pennsylvanians to consider lands outside the control of Felton and Tevis. Their contracts forbade developing such lands without the approval of the San Francisco capitalists, but the longer matters continued unsettled, the more certain Hardison and Stewart became of the desirability of looking for new territory. For one thing, they hoped a threat of this kind would help force a settlement. In November, 1884, Stewart wrote Mission Transfer, obviously for the eyes of Felton and Scofield:[28]

> We perhaps need not remind you that we have now been here nearly a year and a half with our men and plant, that we adhered strictly to the spirit of our arrangement in reference to taking no interest without your consent in any territory which you do not control, that we with our men and plant are practically idle, that it must be evident that it is not good business for us to continue in this state of inactivity, and that unless a lease is made under which we can go ahead and work in a business way we will be under the necessity of asking to be released from the obligation to confine our operations to territory controlled by you.

Two weeks later he wrote John Irwin from Newhall, "I came up today to meet Mr. Scofield but have not met him yet. If we can't accomplish anything with him, will turn our attention for the present to prospecting."[29]

Stewart was less than frank in describing his devotion to the commitment, for as early as May, 1884, both he and Irwin had been scouting for oil lands in Ventura and Los Angeles counties. Lyman hesitated to prospect very far from Los Angeles because he was "watched so closely." Consequently, most of the prospecting was done by John Irwin. By the early months of 1885, Irwin had collected oil samples from many seepages, including Torrey, Sespe, and Coche canyons, the Simi Rancho, and Carpenteria.[30]

The best bet for Hardison, Stewart, however, lay in another direction. Their participation in the Ojai lease with Scott and Dull had given them a drilling opportunity on lands not owned by the western companies, but, more important, it gave them access to Bard, who still had high hopes of producing oil on his properties. More than that, Bard had the friendship of other important Southern California landholders and capitalists. He had first learned of Hardison and Stewart when they took over PCO's Simi well in December, 1883. Their work on the Ojai soon convinced him that they were competent oilmen. By the end of October, 1884, they had invested more than $8,500 in drilling four shallow wells. Dull had put in less than $2,000, and Scott's investment was nil.[31]

Gradually, Bard drew closer to the Pennsylvanians. The delay of Mission Transfer in settling for Ojai oil affected him as well as Hardison and Stewart, for the company was also taking his royalty of one-eighth of the production under the lease. The delay, moreover, gave Hardison and Stewart no incentive to drill more wells and add to the royalty, which early in 1885 was little more than a barrel a day. Finally, after discussions with his attorney and co-holder of the Ojai, Charles Fernald, Bard demanded an accounting from Mission Transfer in March, 1885. He also threatened to rescind the lease to D. C. Scott.[32]

Bard was thinking of leasing the Ojai to Hardison, Stewart & Company, a plan Fernald thoroughly approved. More tentatively, the two men were also considering setting up a company with the Pennsylvanians to work their combined properties and to lease new territories. But they did not follow through at this time. Bard delayed canceling the Scott lease because wells had been drilled on one tract under its terms and he feared a legal fight. He decided to wait until he had a clearer case.[33]

6

By early 1885, however, the PCO leaders appeared ready to come to terms with Hardison, Stewart. The end of the marketing struggle with Standard, which provided a calmer atmosphere in which to consider matters of lesser consequence, may have had some effect. So may the wave of relocations in the Pico late in 1884 and early in 1885, which supplied PCO with a greater sense of security. Another favorable development was a series of successful experiments using fuel oil in the shops of the Central Pacific Railroad, making the ex-Mission seem a brighter prospect. In February of 1885, too, the railroad began to convert its ferries on San Francisco Bay from coal to oil.[34]

There was also an immediate decision to be made over the disposition of the oil from Hardison, Stewart's "Star" well, on the site of the "dead sure" location Stewart had requested in the spring of 1884. In three months since the end of November, 1884, it had flowed about 2,000 barrels, and Stewart hoped to increase its production by pumping. Another well of the partners, on the old San Fernando claim, completed in the fall of 1884, was yielding about ten barrels a day. In mid-February at Newhall, Felton and Scofield negotiated an agreement that gave Hardison and Stewart $1.50 a barrel.[35] PCO required that its income from products from each barrel of crude cover 20¢ for pipeage to Newhall, 66¢ for transportation to Alameda, 51¢ for refining costs, and supply some refining profit above the amount paid Hardison, Stewart. At the time of the agreement PCO's refinery earnings were either 26¢ or 17¢ a barrel, depending on whether or not Alameda manufactured high-test kerosine, which gave the larger figure. Table 3, showing the higher profit, offers an interesting picture of the yield and market value of PCO's refined products (except lubes) at this time.

Table 3: Products, Yields, and Earnings from a Barrel of Crude at the Alameda Refinery—March, 1885[36]

Products	Yields Per Cent	Gallons	Price per Gallon	Total Income
Gasoline (86°)	3	1.26	$ .19	$ .2394
Naphtha (63°, 74°)	12	5.04	.09	.4536
Kerosine, Water White	12	5.04	.15	.7560
Kerosine, Standard White	15	6.30	.10	.6300
Gas oil	13	5.46	.07	.3822
Fuel oil	40	16.80	.04	.6720
Waste	5	2.10	0	0
Total	100	42.00		$3.13

Transportation and refining costs $1.37
Payment to Hardison, Stewart & Co. 1.50
Refining profit .... .26
$3.13

The negotiators were less successful in drawing up terms to govern future drilling at Pico. Felton and Scofield offered a smaller acreage for development than in 1883, which Hardison and Stewart accepted reluctantly. The partners sought to shift part of the costs of future dry holes to PCO, which Felton and Scofield refused to accept. The greatest stumbling block, however, was the extent of the partners' indebtedness to PCO for timber, fuel, and water used in their past drilling activities. Hardison and Stewart finally settled for leases that covered only their two wells.[37]

Toward the end of May the two sides met in San Francisco for a series of bargaining sessions concerned chiefly with the ex-Mission. Blake and Tevis were present for Mission Transfer, in addition to Felton and Scofield. The negotiations were hard fought. Even after an agreement was reached on June 10, 1885, Hardison confessed to his partner, "I am not feeling very good. I guess Tevis *scared me* when he pulled [on] his coat."[38]

The outcome, nevertheless, supplied a workable arrangement for developing the ex-Mission and marked a turning point in the relations between the two sides. Under the new agreement, the partners received exclusive rights to the ex-Mission, including Adams, Wheeler, and Saltmarsh canyons, for a term of 47 years. They were to begin drilling immediately and to continue until a production of 6,000 barrels a month had been reached. At that point they were to suspend drilling until it became necessary to maintain the 6,000 barrel rate, or until Mission Transfer raised the ceiling. This figure, which was less than one-half of the Pico production, suggests how much heavy oil the San Franciscans believed the western market could take. Mission Transfer, for its part, guaranteed a flat price of $1 a barrel at the well on all oil heavier than 35°. For lighter oil, if discovered, it agreed to a formula similar to the one used to determine the price for the partners' Pico crude. The company also replaced the cumbersome profit-sharing provision of 1883 for each producing well with a flat royalty of one-eighth of the production.[39]

Mission Transfer made one other important concession. Unlike the Pico leases, which continued to require PCO's approval for oil operations by Hardison, Stewart & Company in Los Angeles County, the ex-Mission lease contained no parallel limitation for Ventura County. The ex-Mission lease supplied an opportunity, though a small one, for independence for the partners.[40] Hardison, Stewart could seek oil wherever they chose, but presumably the production, as from the Ojai, would go to swell the business of Mission Transfer. The company could easily build extensions to its pipeline to take the oil, and no other purchaser would be so readily available.

7

These settlements with Hardison, Stewart & Company, so meaningful to the partners and to the future course of the California industry, had far less significance for their San Francisco signers. The value to Felton and Tevis lay in postponing and limiting the commitment of their capital for future drilling to supply crude for their refineries and markets. At the moment, this was no great issue. Deepening just five of the Pico wells a few hundred feet late in 1884 and in 1885 had proved sufficient to maintain production at a level fully equal to the needs of the refineries. Indeed, with the addition of the production of the two Hardison, Stewart wells, the Pico yield in 1885 was probably a little higher than in the preceding year.[41]

To handle this production, PCO expanded its Alameda plant. The principal need was for more storage. Between 1884 and 1887 the number of tanks grew from fourteen of undetermined capacity to forty capable of holding 75,000 barrels of crude oil and refined products. PCO also added a 200-barrel steam still to improve the quality of its gasoline and a 100-barrel lubricating oil still to do the same for its lubes—two products for which the market outlook was especially promising.[42]

The emphasis on better products seems also to have brought about a downgrading of the older Newhall refinery, with its capacity of around 100 barrels daily. After April, 1885, Newhall no longer manufactured kerosine and other refined products for Southern California. Instead, it distilled the lighter fractions for finishing at Alameda and sold as much of the residuum for fuel oil as the Southern California market would take.[43]

Transporting oil from Newhall to Alameda provided PCO with a more critical problem when CO&T ceased to perform this service following its merger with Standard's western stations in July, 1885. Patent rights to the CO&T combination tank cars were a part of the merger, causing Felton to believe that any cars purchased by PCO would need be of the boiler type. Evidently, the Southern Pacific intended to charge PCO a higher rate than under the former arrangement, for as a counter-move Felton revived a plan, talked of as early as May, 1883, to substitute pipeline transportation from Pico to Ventura and waterborne bulk shipments to Alameda for rail transportation from Newhall. Early in July, he ordered Mission Transfer, as agent for PCO, to build a thirty-mile two-inch pipeline connecting Pico Springs with its line at Santa Paula. Mission Transfer completed the line in less than three months, but weather and other hazards intervened before it was tested. Floods ripped it apart at two places, and it was cut by a rancher, C. A. Storke, who claimed that it interfered with his plowing. A court battle dragged on for more than eighteen months before Storke was permanently restrained from harming the line.[44]

The pipeline, nevertheless, had brought the Southern Pacific to terms. Faced with the loss of its oil traffic, the railroad reduced its rate between Newhall and Alameda from 66¢ to 50¢ a barrel in October, 1885. PCO, in accepting this concession, purchased 55 cars of from 120 to 140 barrels capacity by the end of the year at a total cost of $33,400. The pipeline, as a result, saw almost no service, but it was a potent inducement for the railroad to keep its rate low. The line, costing probably around $45,000, paid for itself in savings on rail freight in less than three years.[45]

The PCO executives continued to look for opportunities to reduce the costs of transportation. A gradual increase in the flow of oil from the ex-Mission caused them to follow through with their plans for bulk shipments from Ventura. Hitherto, Ventura oil had always been sent to San Francisco in iron drums and barrels. Early in 1886 Mission Transfer arranged for the Pacific Coast Steamship Company to place a 760-barrel tank in the hull of the *Santa Cruz,* a steamer of 361 tons. In September another Pacific Coast Steamship vessel, the 260-ton *Alexander Duncan,* was similarly outfitted. These vessels provided opportunities for shipments from Ventura to San Francisco every six days at 46¢ a barrel, which was less than the rail rate from Newhall. The difference was not enough, however, to cause PCO to reverse its earlier decision to send the Pico crude by rail.[46]

While these changes were being made, PCO was also considering the requirements for further drilling at Pico. A desirable move, if not a necessity, was to seek a new source of water. The water problem had been considered settled forever when an elaborate pump station was erected on the Santa Clara River in 1881 and a larger line was laid from the station two years later. Unfortunately, the supply from the Santa Clara River was not the answer, either in quantity or quality. In the fall of the year that river frequently was little more than a creek of brackish water. Late in 1885 PCO turned in its search to 187 acres, owned by Alex Mentry, that contained a bountiful spring about two miles east of Newhall in Placerita Canyon. One of Felton's last acts before leaving in November, 1885, to take his seat in Congress was to visit the property and approve this purchase for $6,000. Shortly, PCO shifted its pump station to the new site.[47]

The company did not start a well at the Pico, however, until November of 1886. Another look at Moody Gulch, where Dull and McPherson were cleaning out old wells and considering drilling again, may have been one reason.[48] The delay may also have been due to a crisis stemming from developments on the ex-Mission, where Hardison and Stewart were beginning to get a production that threatened the stability of the agreement of June, 1885.

8

The year and more following the settlements of 1885 was a far more exciting time for Hardison, Stewart & Company than for the PCO group. Moves for new oil lands and allies made in the dark months of 1884 began to pay off. Hardison and Stewart exploded all over the landscape.

One area to which Stewart was powerfully drawn was the Brea Rancho, lying five or six miles west of Los Angeles. Its acquisition posed a dilemma, for PCO was not likely to permit the partners to develop oil lands in Los Angeles County apart from the Pico. But Stewart was not to be stopped. He formed a partnership, McFarland, Stewart & Company, with Daniel McFarland, a prominent Los Angeles landowner. Early in 1886, over the protest of PCO, he leased the rancho and by summer was drilling a well.[49] The new firm gave him a means to circumvent PCO and to bid for oil lands elsewhere in the county.

Stewart was also carefully watching events in the Puente Hills southeast of Los Angeles, where the owner of a part of the old Puente Rancho, William Rowland, had joined with William Lacy, a Los Angeles hardware merchant and banker, and employed W. E. Youle as their driller. Near the end of 1885 they brought in a well with a daily production of about ten barrels, roughly equivalent in gravity to the oil from the ex-Mission. This discovery, forecasting another California field, brought Stewart to the scene. He offered to build a pipeline to carry the oil to Los Angeles and to drill the rest of the property. But Rowland and Lacy chose to go it alone and to lay their own pipeline to Puente Station. Stewart had to be content with a few neighboring leases.[50] Scofield did better in negotiating with the Puente partners. They agreed to sell their oil to PCO at $1 a barrel, but this arrangement apparently lasted no more than a year.[51]

In Ventura County, the Pennsylvanians made greater headway because of their tie to Bard. Hardison urged him to sell or lease the Ojai or to join them in its development. Bard was unwilling to sell the oil rights at the price offered, but he revoked his lease to D. C. Scott and in May issued Hardison, Stewart a new lease, to which he added Coche Canyon the next month.[52] Moreover, Bard had decided to support

Hardison and Stewart in their search for land elsewhere. Even before signing over the Ojai, he acted as their agent in acquiring one-third of the oil rights to the Chaffee ranch in Torrey Canyon, a territory they had long coveted.[53]

It was a drive for the Sespe by Hardison and Stewart that finally brought Bard into a direct alliance. The public lands there, as we already know, were dotted with mining claims. Some of the claims had lapsed, thus opening the way for new locations. For example, the Standard Oil Company of California had relinquished its hold on the territory. In July, 1886, Hardison and Stewart filed for twenty-four claims. They also induced Dan McFarland to negotiate with some of the pioneer claim holders and with the Los Angeles Oil Company, which had patented about 1,000 acres. Within a few weeks, the partners talked Bard into joining them and McFarland in organizing a company to develop this new territory. On September 21, 1886, they incorporated the Sespe Oil Company, with McFarland and Bard each subscribing to one-fifth of the stock and Hardison, Stewart & Company taking the remainder.[54]

By that time, however, the Sespe company was preparing to take on a larger role as the owner of a half-interest in the Mission Transfer Company. To understand the background of this important happening, it is necessary to examine the relations between Hardison, Stewart and the PCO group following the settlement of 1885.

9

For more than a year the two sides had gotten along amicably. The new cordiality was a pleasing contrast to everyone after the long months of bickering. Every month the Felton and Tevis companies paid without fail for the oil purchased from the partners. In September of 1885, as the products of the Alameda refinery found a more lucrative market, PCO delighted Hardison and Stewart by increasing the price for Pico crude from $1.50 to $1.71. Felton and Scofield also ordered new storage tanks to handle the production from the ex-Mission.[55]

The ex-Mission lease had become the key relationship between the San Franciscans and Hardison, Stewart. At first, the success of the partners was modest. During the nine months following June, 1885, two of the five wells drilled were dry, and the best of the other three gave an initial production of 30 barrels a day.[56] In the spring of 1886 the ceiling of 6,000 barrels a month written into the lease seemed far away.

And Mission Transfer could justifiably urge the partners on. By the fall of 1885, the Central Pacific Railroad had adapted three of its ferries on San Francisco Bay to use fuel oil in place of coal. The saving on the largest ferry, the *Piedmont,* was reported as slightly above 10 per cent. With the Central Pacific paying $1.70 a barrel for about 140 barrels daily, its account ran to a tidy sum. The railroad was taking at least three-fourths of the fuel oil residuum at Alameda. Some other steamers on the Bay and some Sacramento river boats were also being converted from coal to oil, as were a number of industrial establishments and utilities, especially in Southern California. George Loomis, PCO's president, was impressed, too, by a letter from the master mechanic of the Central Pacific Railroad, who predicted that fuel costs on locomotives might be cut as much as one-third by using oil.[57]

Gradually, the market outlook for PCO products became less favorable, however. Scofield claimed in February, 1886, that the Standard Oil Company (Iowa) was behind more than $70,000 in taking kerosine under the CO&T contract it had assumed at the time of the merger. The amount of kerosine involved was more than half a million gallons, or about four or five months production at Alameda. Scofield stated, sadly, that Standard was "so particular." Two months later PCO resorted to an auction house, S. L. Jones & Company, to sell 5,000 cases (50,000 gallons). More and more, PCO was forced to seek lower-grade foreign markets for its oil. In 1886, according to one trade paper, fully two-thirds of the oil exports from San Francisco were supplied by PCO, principally to Mexico and the Hawaiian Islands. Because of the steep decline in its income, PCO reduced its payment per barrel in June, 1886, for the Pico crude of Hardison, Stewart to $1.31.[58]

The price for fuel oil fell more slowly. At $1.55 a barrel in June, it was only fifteen cents less than at the beginning of the year, but even so small a reduction was disturbing. With the price of the ex-Mission crude fixed at $1.00 and steamer transportation at 46¢, Mission Transfer was receiving only 9¢ for pipeage instead of the 20¢ it had hoped for. Hardison, Stewart believed that the company was still making money; Mission Transfer claimed that it was "running behind."[59]

This was the state of affairs prevailing at the time some sizable strikes were made on the ex-Mission in the spring and early summer of 1886. A well came in early in May with a production of 75 barrels a day. Seven weeks later, another, called "Wild Bill" in honor of W. L. Hardison, doubled that record. A jubilant Hardison foresaw a production of from 10,000 to 12,000 barrels monthly by August.[60] But there was a dark side to their success, for it brought them hard against the ceiling of 6,000 barrels a month laid down in the ex-Mission lease.

George Loomis, who was also the Mission Transfer spokesman, failed to share the enthusiasm of Hardison and Stewart. How could Mission Transfer raise the ceiling and maintain the price at $1 a barrel when the fuel trade already seemed so precarious? Moreover, Adams Canyon was not the only source of new oil. Early in June, Rowland and Lacy reported a well at Puente with a blast of publicity. According to the press, a column of oil rose over the top of the derrick "with a tremendous roar," ushering in a producer good for 200 barrels daily. The Puente strike was not the equal of either of the Adams wells, for it settled down shortly to about 25 barrels. But it did feed the fears of Loomis. He insisted on maintaining the provision forbidding the drilling of new wells after production exceeded 6,000 barrels monthly and offered only 50¢ a barrel for oil produced in excess of that limit, though Hardison and Stewart understood that these matters would be reopened when Blake and Felton could come to the Coast.[61]

The partners accepted passively neither the drilling limitation nor the low price. If they could not bargain effectively with Mission Transfer, they planned to turn to the development of other lands not under the control of that company. And they were considering extending their activities to include transportation, refining, and marketing. Stewart wrote Hardison, "It is very evident that we must take steps soon toward taking care of ourselves. Pipelines, tankage, and refining seem now to be a necessity for the near future. We know there is a margin in handling this oil and taking hold of the other departments of the business is a safe proposition."[62]

When Blake came to Newhall in September of 1886, Hardison injected this note of defiance, pointedly telling his friend that he and Stewart had the allies and territory necessary to enter independently into all phases of the oil business. His threat undoubtedly influenced the negotiations, for the two men soon turned from talk of modifying the ex-Mission lease to a consideration of having the Hardison, Stewart faction buy a half-interest in Mission Transfer. Blake favored the move, provided Hardison and Stewart would agree to use the company to transport and market all of their Ventura production. The two optimists foresaw a large increase in the output of crude, which Blake believed would bring $1.25 a barrel in San Francisco. Fifteen cents a barrel seemed a reasonable rate for water transportation from Ventura County. The remaining $1.10 Blake suggested could be divided by giving the producing interest 85¢, reserving 25¢ for "piping and selling and profit."[63]

After the conference, Blake traveled north to put the proposed alliance in Mission Transfer before Felton, Tevis, and their associates, leaving Hardison to talk with Stewart, Bard, and McFarland. Hardison rosily figured that perhaps $72,000 would be required for an enlarged pipeline and additional tanks to handle a production that he prophesied would run "at least 1000 bbls. . . . daily." He believed that Mission Transfer could more than recoup this investment in a year. Bard and McFarland may well have discounted such warm hopes, but they viewed the purchase favorably and were willing for the Sespe Oil Company to handle the deal.[64]

Blake found his associates willing to sell. The prospective arrangement offered the stockholders of Mission Transfer a chance to realize something on their investment and at the same time linked them with the vigorous Southern Californians. Pessimism may also have influenced their decision. Since September the Central Pacific had bought no fuel oil. Its ferries had gone back to coal in order to use the deposits the railroad had opened in Washington Territory.[65] To replace a fuel oil customer of the size of the Central Pacific was no easy task.

Early in October Bard and Hardison went to San Francisco to begin the negotiations. On the sixth, Hardison wrote Stewart: " 'We met the enemy,' and I will let you judge whether they are ours or we theirs. Call it what you will, I believe that the arrangement if carried out will be a good one." For $75,000 ($60 a share), they had gained a half-interest. Beyond the ex-Mission oil rights, the significant assets of Mission Transfer included about forty miles of two-inch pipeline, two pump stations, 10,625 barrels of tankage, and the company's oil inventory. Bard sealed the bargain by making a payment of $5,000. The balance was payable in equal installments at the end of the second, third, and fourth years, which, Hardison believed, could "be made out of the property if pushed vigorously." At the time of the purchase, the parties agreed that the day-to-day management of the company would be in the hands of the Southern Californians.[66]

This sharing of ownership paved the way for a modified lease. Signed on January 7, 1887, it retained the provision requiring Mission Transfer to take the first 6,000 barrels of the monthly production but eliminated the guarantee of $1 a barrel. In its place the negotiators substituted a complicated schedule under which the return to Hardison, Stewart & Company and the pipeage and water transportation rates would vary according to the price of fuel oil in San Francisco. The higher the selling price, the greater were the allowances for pipeage and transportation as well as the return to the producers. It took a price of $1.60 a barrel for fuel oil to bring the partners $1.00. The new lease also raised the ceiling to 30,000 barrels a month and reserved to the company the right to purchase all, or any part, of the production above 6,000 barrels. The same formula was used to figure the price of this oil, except for the transportation rate, which was fixed at the figure charged by the steamship company.

The modified lease contained other important new terms. For five years Mission Transfer was to receive a commission on each barrel of oil sold, ranging from 5¢ on sales of 200 barrels a day to 2¢ on sales of 1,000 barrels or more. Thereafter, the commission was to be eliminated. Mission Transfer agreed to build as much as 100,000 barrels of tankage to store any oil from the ex-Mission it did not purchase and to charge Hardison, Stewart no more than 1.25¢ a barrel monthly for storage. The lease also indicated that Mission Transfer was planning to build a vessel to provide its own transportation.[67]

Hardison viewed the new balance of power as a sound basis for future harmony. He wrote Stewart: "Now let us . . . have peace and as cordial feeling as possible. . . . Felton will pull with us in the future if I am not greatly mistaken."[68]

10

The fact was, however, that by the time of the purchase the San Franciscans and the Southern Californians were hardly a compatible team. Hardison, who was directing Ventura operations, was eager, active, ready to take the bit in his teeth and go. Filled with optimism, he saw a vastly enlarged and profitable business on the immediate horizon. By contrast, the PCO group in Mission Transfer, led by Loomis, was conservative in outlook and was especially concerned lest production outrun demand. "There is a curious difference in the tone of Mr. Loomis' letter and your enthusiastic way of looking at the prospect for selling oil," Bard wrote Hardison early in 1887, "and there is just about the same difference between the two schools, represented by you and Mr. Loomis, in their ways of doing business." Hardison's own judgment of Loomis was harsh. "Loomis has not got any business in him," he once wrote Lyman Stewart. And Loomis probably viewed Hardison with equal skepticism.[69]

Even before the Mission Transfer stock could be delivered, Hardison was at work planning for the new day. Within forty-eight hours of the purchase, he was asking Loomis to check on the cost of land for a San Francisco terminal near many of the city's large industrial establishments. A few days later, through Hardison, Stewart & Company, he ordered seven miles of two-inch pipe and gave a conditional order for

November delivery of twenty miles of four-inch pipe from the San Francisco firm of Coit & Folsom. He intended to offer this pipe to the Mission Transfer and Sespe Oil companies to handle future increases in production. Hardison was planning additional tankage for Santa Paula and was looking forward to building a refinery at Hueneme, the coastal town Bard had founded fifteen years earlier. Bard grumbled a little at all this rush, as did Milton Stewart in the East. "It strikes me," Bard wrote, "that we are acting a little like some of the Mining Companys [sic] in earlier times that built their expensive mills even before they had uncovered any ore." But he acquiesced.[70]

Hardison and Stewart also proceeded to put their own house in order. On December 28, 1886, they incorporated their partnership as the Hardison & Stewart Oil Company, with an authorized capital of $1,000,-000. The incorporation supplied a more formal and enduring organization for their increasingly valuable properties. Among the incorporators were Thomas R. Bard, Dan McFarland, and Walter S. Chaffee, whose participation suggested the new sources of support for the former partners. Fully 80 per cent of the ownership remained the same, however, as in the partnership.[71]

The Mission Transfer stock was barely in the hands of its new owners before the company felt their impact. On January 13, 1887, the directors voted the first of four assessments, totaling $42 a share in the course of the next seven months, which was spent primarily for pipe, pump stations, tankage, laying new line, and the final two payments for the ex-Mission oil rights.[72] In order to get approval for some of these assessments, the Southern Californians had to batter down the opposition of the San Franciscans.

The initial set-to occurred in February following the completion of the first Sespe well. This was a good well, producing briefly about 100 barrels daily of brownish oil before settling down to about 40 barrels a day. The southerners viewed it as proving an important new field. They asked Mission Transfer to lay a pipeline connecting the well with the main line at Santa Paula, but Loomis demurred. The southerners were not blocked; they were hardly delayed. They got Blake's nephew, Frank Davis, who was the president of Mission Transfer and swing member between the factions on its seven-member board, to start the line and promised their support at the next board meeting.[73]

Further clashes developed over investments for transporting fuel oil to Los Angeles and San Francisco. Hardison desired to purchase tank cars to take advantage of a favorable rate between Santa Paula and Los Angeles that Stewart had negotiated with the Southern Pacific. Loomis was apparently willing for Mission Transfer to lease cars from the Standard Oil Company (Iowa) but not to invest in new cars. Instead of yielding, Hardison ordered fifteen 130-barrel cars for the account of the Sespe Oil Company. When the PCO group refused to approve building a tank ship for Mission Transfer, Hardison, backed by the Sespe company, placed an order in May with the Fulton Iron Works of San Francisco for a $40,000 steam tanker of 3,600 barrels capacity.[74]

A controversy also arose over marketing because Hardison chose Coit & Folsom as Mission Transfer's San Francisco agents. He may have been influenced by Coit & Folsom's grant of easy credit on his purchases of pipe and other supplies, but the San Francisco merchants were also aggressive marketers. During the spring of 1886 they asserted that they would have no difficulty in selling at least 1,000 barrels of fuel oil daily. By August they had signed contracts with eleven Bay Area merchants and firms, including the Fulton and Risdon ironworks and the San Jose Gas Company, at prices ranging from $1.05 to $1.62 a barrel. The trade had not met their expectations, however, largely because of the new price of coal and the hostility of the insurance companies, who viewed fuel oil as a fire hazard. The arrangement with Coit & Folsom found little favor with Loomis and his associates, for they wished to control the marketing of Ventura crude, which competed with fuel oil from Alameda.[75]

By mid-August there were still other sources of contention. Hardison and Stewart desired to put Mission Transfer into refining. They were negotiating with a former employee of the Berkeley Lubricating Works of A. C. Dietz to draw up plans for a refinery at Santa Paula. The Southern California oilmen also hoped to move the company headquarters to Santa Paula from San Francisco.[76]

These and other differences flared at a series of meetings held by the directors of Mission Transfer late in August of 1887. Frank Davis sided with the southerners, who defeated the San Franciscans on all major issues. They voted to take over from the Sespe Oil Company the tank cars and the tank steamer under construction. They agreed to pool the crude from the Sespe and the ex-Mission, taking the oil of the Sespe company on the same basis as that from the ex-Mission above 6,000 barrels a month, and to retain Coit & Folsom as the San Francisco selling agents. The directors authorized W. L. Hardison to seek a permit from the San Francisco city government for Mission Transfer to store fuel oil. They also voted to remove the head office of the company to Santa Paula. "We have our friends? on the run again," Hardison wrote Stewart, "and I need not say that I take *pleasure* in *seeing them*."[77]

The meetings of the Mission Transfer board were hardly at an end before Loomis approached Hardison with an offer to sell the remaining half of the company for $133,386, representing one-half of the net assets. The action of Loomis was undoubtedly prompted by the board meetings, which clearly indicated that the San Franciscans had lost control. They had no desire to support the plunging expansion of the southern oilmen and to permit their capital in Mission Transfer to fashion a rival to the Pacific Coast Oil Company. They held too dark a view of the future and of Hardison for that. Mission Transfer, under Hardison's brash leadership, had lost $3,200 since October, 1886. And PCO was continuing to have trouble in marketing its refined oils. On several occasions in 1887 it had been forced to resort to an auction house.[78] Eastern crude prices, too, were running along at little more than sixty cents a barrel through much of the year, and because of the swelling production of the Ohio fields there was no reason to expect a speedy upturn.[79] There was little or nothing in the oil outlook to encourage the conservative PCO leaders to embark on new and larger ventures.

Hardison reacted to Loomis' offer as another opportunity, for in his eyes Mission Transfer's prospects were even brighter than at the time of the purchase in 1886. Two wells, the first good producers in Adams Canyon in almost a year, were completed in August, 1887. Their combined yield of nearly 200 barrels daily almost doubled the production from the ex-Mission. The Sespe, which had not been producing in 1886, was also yielding around 200 barrels a day. Hardison believed that purchasing the last half of the company would free the southerners from the obstructionism of their northern colleagues and enable them to make the most of the new marketing opportunities. Even as the offer was made, the ferries on San Francisco Bay were again being changed to fuel oil.[80]

At first, Hardison thought the purchase would be an easy matter, for he hoped to persuade Tevis and Blake to keep their sizable interests. The balance he planned to offer to the Sespe Oil Company and to officials of the Southern Pacific Railroad. This scheme would require little additional investment on the part of Hardison and Stewart, who were already near the limit of their resources. Neither Tevis nor Blake wished to retain his stock, however. And the Southern Pacific officials to whom Hardison talked told him that they were "not ready to say that they [would] take any. . . ."[81]

His other recourse was to enlist further the support of Bard and McFarland. At the time, this was not unreasonable. Southern California was experiencing a phenomenal boom, the result in great part of the arrival of the Santa Fe as a competitor of the Southern Pacific two years earlier. The rate war between the rivals caused a reduction in passenger fares from the Midwest from about $125 before the coming of the Santa Fe to a ridiculous temporary low of $1 early in 1887. Visitors poured into Southern California. Many stayed. The population of several of the southern counties jumped a quarter or more. Between 1885 and 1887 Los Angeles County is estimated to have grown from 72,500 to 100,000, and Ventura County from 8,000 to 13,000. Bard had the satisfaction of watching his property values rise, and McFarland also shared in the optimism generated by the boom. It was Hardison's hope that they could be persuaded to take up more of the Mission Transfer stock.[82]

He found them skeptical, however, for their year of experience with Mission Transfer had hardly confirmed his earlier enthusiastic forecast. They were already committed to a joint expenditure of $30,000, and as yet they had seen no profits. McFarland wrote: "Our supposition . . . was that the Mission Transfer Co's business would be developed in a year or two to show sufficient business to justify the price at which we bought. Contrary to this, the past year's business has shown . . . that as managed, it is impossible for the Company to pay, and that it is only a question as to how much it shall lose if the business continues as it is now."[83] The most they would do was to permit the Sespe Oil Company to increase its holdings to two-thirds of the Mission Transfer stock. To close the deal, Hardison and Stewart had to accept personal liability for the rest.[84]

The negotiations, concluded on October 6, 1887, which was the anniversary of the earlier purchase, bound Hardison, Stewart and their allies to a schedule of payments extending over thirty months that rose sharply from $3,000 a month in the first year to $5,000 a month in the next eighteen months before declining again during the last three months. In addition, they were faced with $70,000 still due on the earlier purchase. These payments were to prove a severe test.[85]

Bard, McFarland, and Milton Stewart may have viewed the new investment somewhat skeptically, but Hardison and Lyman Stewart did not. They felt, as had Felton and Tevis before them, that they were at the beginning of a new era in California oil history. They were not even deeply disturbed by the financial hurdles ahead, for they believed they could develop both production and markets at a pace sufficient to take care of their obligations from profits. They went on perfecting their plans for more wells, for the Santa Paula refinery, for a tank ship and more tank cars, for storage in San Francisco, for marketing outlets in Southern California as well as in the north, and for fighting government regulations limiting opportunities for fuel oil. They no longer considered PCO as a dangerous competitor. "There is little to fear from the PCO Co.," Lyman wrote his brother.[86]

11

The sale of Mission Transfer was another evidence of the conservative turn the PCO leaders had taken. Since 1884 caution had supplanted their earlier optimistic outlook. Felton and Tevis had found California oil no bonanza, and they were determined to go slow. Between July, 1884, and the end of 1887, their commitment of additional capital in the Pico companies was limited to about $155,000, as they looked eagerly for profits.[87]

Their careful management at Pico met with considerable success. A minimal amount of drilling that included only one new well (PCO #8) did a remarkable job of maintaining production, for from 1884 through 1887 California Star, PCO, and San Francisco Petroleum produced almost 700,000 barrels. The market price at the well is at least indicated by the payments made Hardison, Stewart & Company, which varied from $1.50 in February, 1885, to $1.71 in September and to $1.31 after June, 1886. PCO's operating costs in producing oil apparently were around 41¢ a barrel. Even the lowest price to Hardison, Stewart, less operating costs (but not including depreciation and depletion, which PCO never computed), would have furnished the Felton and Tevis companies an income from their Pico crude of about $620,000 for the four years. PCO also earned a refining profit on its own production and the oil it purchased. If it was able to maintain the 26¢ per barrel noted in its contract with Hardison, Stewart, its refining profit for these years would have been around $190,000, a figure that is undoubtedly too large.[88]

These profits, whatever may have been their exact amount, obviously offered an opportunity for dividends. California Star, which was responsible for about half of the Pico production, declared a first quarterly dividend ($13,125) in March, 1884. Within four years it had paid out $210,000, of which PCO received four-sevenths.[89] No record of the PCO dividends has survived, but they must have been considerably larger than those of California Star, for PCO's earning power was spread over its own production, the volume of oil passing through the refineries, and its majority ownership in the California Star and San Francisco Petroleum companies.

The dividends, after so long a time of waiting, must have been heartening to the PCO stockholders and have reaffirmed their faith in the Pico. By the end of 1887 the Pico production was falling rapidly, however, and a heavy investment in drilling new wells could not be postponed much longer. The PCO leaders were willing to approve these expenditures, as we shall see, but not to engage in ventures elsewhere that seemed more risky.

For them, the period surrounding the sale of Mission Transfer was a time of consolidation. They completed their withdrawal from Ventura County by deactivating the Standard Oil Company of California. They also deactivated their Santa Clara Petroleum Company in an apparent trade that saw R. C. McPherson, the longtime superintendent at Moody Gulch, take over the property there in exchange for his minority interest in the San Francisco Petroleum Company. The San Francisco company with its three Pico wells was folded into the PCO in May, 1888.[90]

When these moves were over, two companies alone remained, PCO and California Star. Instead of envisioning an oil empire, the PCO executives after 1887 concentrated on the oil-rich Pico and the most valuable of western markets, the San Francisco Bay area, adjacent to their Alameda refinery.

The dreams of empire they left to others.

VI

PCO'S YEARS OF DECLINE

After 1887 the history of PCO has a different significance than in its earlier years. Although still an important company, it was no longer virtually the California industry. New companies sprang up which vied with PCO for leadership. Within a decade important new oil fields were opened, which overshadowed the Pico. These companies and fields require a brief mention, for they supply much of the setting for the PCO story toward the close of the nineteenth century.

PCO's greatest rival was the Union Oil Company.[1] Chartered on October 17, 1890, with an authorized capital of $5,000,000, Union was the ultimate corporate creation of Hardison, Stewart, and Bard. It brought under a single control their three producing concerns, the Hardison & Stewart, Sespe, and Torrey Canyon oil companies, and their transporter, refiner, and marketer, the Mission Transfer Company.

During the 1890's Union exhibited much of the dynamism that earlier had characterized PCO. The San Francisco company watched its southern rival wildcat to the limit of its resources and ultimately take over as California's leading producer. In refining, the work of the southerners was less impressive. Their first refinery, built at Santa Paula in 1888, had a still capacity of 200 barrels—no larger than California Star's old works at Newhall. The crude it processed was considerably heavier than PCO's and more difficult to refine. Santa Paula handled only about one-fourth of Union's production. In 1896, shortly before the Santa Paula refinery was destroyed by fire, Union opened a larger refinery at Oleum on San Francisco Bay about one-third the size of PCO's Alameda works. But its refining showed little improvement. PCO retained whatever leadership a California company might be said to have had in this difficult operation.

Union's marketing achievement was far more substantial. Its growing production of heavy crude, which was unsuited for refining, put the company under great pressure to develop new outlets for fuel oil. The Union executives sought consumers throughout the state. Their labors quickened the development of the fuel trade, which they had helped pioneer before 1890. PCO was a beneficiary, to some extent, of these promotional efforts in its own sales of fuel oil.

A second concern, the Puente Oil Company, was also rising to prominence. This company took its name from the field in the Puente Hills that William Rowland and William Lacy had been developing since the middle eighties. In January, 1892, they incorporated their enterprise with an authorized capital of $2,000,000. By the spring of 1896, Puente had a small refinery, located at Chino, with a still capacity of 500 barrels.[2] The Puente company affected PCO only indirectly, for it stayed in the south. It was a keen competitor of Union, however, especially in the Los Angeles fuel trade. This competition undoubtedly heightened Union's aggressiveness in PCO's home territory.

PCO had little to fear from its rivals, so long as there was no great and sudden leap in production and general economic conditions continued to be favorable. As late as 1892 the state's production was just 385,000 barrels; the Pico share amounted to nearly one-third. A limited amount of oil, of itself, permitted only limited competition. And PCO was fortunate in its home market, for San Francisco with its environs contained roughly 40 per cent of the state's population. PCO could usually sell with ease more oil than Pico produced. The period around 1890 was obviously a time of considerable prosperity for the San Francisco company, but the absence of records precludes a more specific statement.

Conditions changed after 1893, when a major depression and large new sources of oil, especially the Los Angeles City field, created a new and dangerous situation. The company was forced to seek ways of reducing costs and prices in order to withstand the flood of oil. For a while PCO sought economies in transportation, but this tactic became less and less effective, as new fields like Coalinga and Kern River opened up. By 1899, the company was in danger of being pushed aside. In that year the Pico field supplied 6 per cent of the state's production, amounting to 2,642,000 barrels; the next year the Pico share was less than 4 per cent.[3]

Prior to the end of the century, PCO presumably always had access to the necessary capital to reassert its dominance. But the dividends beginning in the middle eighties were not enough to overcome the earlier disillusionment of the PCO leaders. In 1892, for example, R. P. Schwerin, a Southern Pacific official, inquired of Felton whether oil might not some day replace coal as the railroad's fuel. Years later Schwerin recalled how quickly Felton had put an end to that conversation: "The wells are too small. You can't get fuel enough. . . ."[4]

Indeed, in 1892, Felton was starting to reduce his PCO interest, which had grown increasingly large. By that time, except for 16,666⅔ shares listed for D. G. Scofield, all other shares bore his name, either as owner, president and trustee, or trustee, or were qualifying shares for his representatives on the board, George Loomis, George Ives, and C. N. Felton, Jr. In 1883 Felton had purchased 1,510 of the shares earlier held by PCO's secretary, L. D. Fisk, as trustee, and had received 14,166⅔ of the remainder as president and trustee. Later, in two transactions in 1885 and 1889, he had added 17,666⅔ trustee shares that had been issued to I. E. Blake, principally as trustee. Felton's divestment began in February, 1892, when he sold 25,000 shares to Lloyd Tevis.

Within two years Lloyd Tevis had taken over as PCO's principal stockholder. By February, 1894, members of the Tevis family owned 49,115 shares (including those formerly held by D. G. Scofield), compared with 31,239 shares for C. N. Felton and his son. The Blake interest, which had been split in trusteeship between Felton and Tevis and had grown to 19,646 shares, was released late in 1894 to satisfy Blake's creditors.[5]

These shifts in ownership marked no change in policy, however. After E. A. Starke, later PCO's chemist, made a prospecting trip over the western half of Kern County about 1897, he urged Tevis to buy a large acreage in what would become within fifteen years the famed oil fields of McKittrick, Midway, and Sunset. Tevis refused, saying "I don't believe there is oil there, and I don't want any more jackrabbit land."[6] Like Felton, Tevis no longer hoped for an oil empire but rather for a snug and profitable operation.

Following the death of George Loomis in April, 1894, Felton at sixty-six again became the PCO president. Over the next two years he fought a vigorous and fairly successful defensive battle against cheap oil from Los Angeles. When Felton resigned in February, 1896, the top office passed to Gordon Blanding, long PCO's counsel and the son-in-law of Lloyd Tevis.[7] Blanding showed the same concern for careful management that had characterized his predecessors.

In the later 1880's the greatest stimulus to the western oil industry came from the market for gas and fuel oil. For this, the relatively high price of coal was largely responsible. The rapid pace of industrial growth during a decade in which California's population increased by half put an extra burden on the state's supply of imported coal. Old and new industrial plants were in sharp competition for fuel. In 1888, according to the U. S. Geological Survey, coal in California sold at an average price of $4 a ton, its peak for the decade. The better grades of coal, favored by the gas companies, cost considerably more.[8]

The high price of coal encouraged the substitution of oil. Gas companies switched from the manufacture of coal gas to carburetted water gas under the Lowe process. San Francisco's Pacific Gas Improvement Company, which had bought the Central Gas [Light] Company, was using about seventy-five barrels of gas oil daily at the end of 1887. The larger San Francisco Gas Light Company was changing over, and the Los Angeles Gas Company had just completed a similar modification of its plant. Lyman Stewart wrote in January, 1888, that the market for gas oil in San Francisco and Los Angeles was estimated at 220 barrels a day. And George Loomis was looking forward hopefully to a demand nearly three times as large "in six months."[9]

Gas oil became a main item in PCO's trade. It was the last distillate to vaporize from the crude oil, after the lighter fractions, the naphthas (including gasoline) and kerosine, had been taken off. The residuum PCO sold as fuel oil or distilled for lubes at higher temperatures in tar stills. Because gas oil was so eagerly sought, the company increased its output by blending much of its kerosine distillate with fuel oil during these years.[10] PCO guarded no part of its business more jealously than its trade with the gas companies.

Its fuel oil, too, was finding a ready market. Late in 1887 the company was again supplying the ferry steamers on San Francisco Bay. PCO supplemented its stock with occasional purchases of crude from Mission Transfer which it also sold for fuel.[11]

The most vigorous company in the fuel trade, however, was not PCO but Mission Transfer and its San Francisco agents, Coit & Folsom (later Griffith Coit & Company). W. L. Hardison worked up and down the Coast with the zeal of an evangelist marketing the swelling production from the ex-Mission and the Sespe country. Together with Coit, he made many converts in the San Francisco area. Among them during 1887 and 1888 were the Pacific Glass Company, California Wire Works, San Francisco Candle Company, Pacific Rolling Mills, Oakland Electric Light and Motor Company, and the Spring Valley Water Company. These firms reported savings in fuel costs of as much as 50 per cent.[12]

Fuel oil, in fact, was very much on the public mind. The economies resulting from its use was one principal reason, but another was the hostile attitude of the insurance men who considered the new fuel a dangerous fire hazard. Eventually, fuel oil won the day, but for a time its use became a matter of sharp debate.

Two San Francisco fires in 1887 helped arouse the hostility of the insurance community. In March a spectacular fire burned the warehouses of three coal oil merchants, including Yates & Company, on the site of the Continental Oil & Transportation Company's old plant at

Fifth and Berry streets. The second and far larger fire occurred seven months later when the Fulton Iron Works was destroyed with a loss estimated at $250,000. Its destruction was immediately attributed to fuel oil. Even though the "tanks of oil were found intact after the fire," the Pacific Insurance Union urged an ordinance upon San Francisco's Board of Supervisors designed to curb the use of oil as fuel. For the moment, the ordinance was blocked.[13]

A new and more dangerous controversy flared following the destruction of a Southern Pacific ferry, the *Julia,* by an explosion and fire near Vallejo on the morning of February 27, 1888. Twenty-eight lives were lost. A coroner's jury concluded that fuel oil had played a contributory role in the disaster and recommended that its use be forbidden on all steamers carrying passengers. A report of Captain H. S. Lubbock, the Supervising Inspector for Steam Vessels in California, was even more damning. After extended hearings, he found that the "prime cause of the destruction . . . was the explosion of petroleum gas within the furnaces. . . ." On his recommendation, the Secretary of the Treasury, who was responsible for navigation in coastal waters, banned the use of fuel oil on all vessels, both passenger and freight.[14]

Oilmen were in the thick of this debate. They scoffed at the fears of their opponents. While the Lubbock hearings were going on, a PCO spokesman told a reporter, "The volatile naphthas and dangerous elements are all extracted in the preparation of the fuel oil. . . . We think that there is not as much danger . . . as there is in coal containing sulphur, which, at a much lower temperature, is subject to spontaneous combustion." He charged that the antagonism to oil stemmed from the "coal trade" and from ignorance and pointed out that fuel oil had "been used for many years in Russian locomotives and other boilers" almost without incident.[15] PCO had cause to worry if it lost the ferry boats of the Southern Pacific as customers.

W. L. Hardison, Lyman Stewart, and Thomas R. Bard were even more deeply embattled. During much of the month-long hearings before Inspector Lubbock, Bard's attorney, Charles Fernald, was in San Francisco. He employed Captain I. E. Thayer, a prominent marine insurance representative of English and French companies, and John C. Quinn, an experienced engineer, to present the case for oil. Mission Transfer, which footed most of the bills, paid out about $3,700, which was nearly one-eighth of its operating expense for that year.[16]

To the Southern Californians and their San Francisco agents, Griffith Coit & Company, the Lubbock investigation appeared "vital . . . not only for fuel petroleum on water but on shore." After almost a year their pioneer tank vessel, the 352-ton *W. L. Hardison,* was still unfinished due to the fire at the Fulton Iron Works and the engineering problems posed in fitting the seven iron tanks into its hull. They intended for the vessel to burn oil and hoped to encourage other ship-owners to follow their lead. A ban on the use of oil by steamers, they feared, would lead also to new curbs to its use by industry.[17]

They did not even have to await the end of the investigation for this unhappy outcome. Early in May, 1888, the San Francisco Supervisors enacted a harsher ordinance governing fuel oil than the one they had refused to pass a few months before. This they did over the strong protests of a number of Mission Transfer's customers who complained that the measure would result in higher fuel costs and perhaps eliminate the use of oil altogether. After its passage, the president of the Pacific Glass Company bluntly asserted, "The manufacturers of this coast cannot compete against the Eastern companies . . . unless an unjust and unwise law is repealed, and . . . they may use oil as fuel."[18]

It is ironic that the Southern Californians were hurt, not so much by the government regulations they had fought, as by a sudden decline in production from their properties. By the end of the year the congressman from Bard's district, William Vandever, had secured an amendment to federal law permitting the use of fuel oil for experimental purposes on vessels that did not carry passengers.[19] In San Francisco the municipal ordinance that raised the burning test for fuel oil from 80° to 90° Fahrenheit proved less onerous than Hardison had feared. But the production of the Hardison, Stewart and Sespe companies, which had reached a peak of 26,000 barrels monthly in February had fallen to 15,000 barrels in November. Instead of a marketing problem, Mission Transfer was having difficulty meeting its commitments. One customer, Pacific Rolling Mills, sued Mission Transfer early in 1889 because it could not supply oil of the gravity contracted for. Lyman Stewart told his brother, "We are having an oil famine"; to a friend he wrote, "There is a regular *howl* for oil."[20] Consequently, when the *W. L. Hardison* made its first voyage early in January of 1889, Mission Transfer had limited use for it. The 3,600-barrel ship was on only its seventh trip when it burned at the wharf at Ventura on June 25, 1889. A careless mate had let down a lantern to determine the amount of oil in one of the tanks.[21]

The embarrassment of the Southern Californians was a windfall for PCO, which had turned to the southern end of the state following the *Julia* disaster, fearing that restrictions on fuel oil would shrink the San Francisco market. In April of 1888 it stepped up operations at the

Newhall refinery and in May for a first time established a Los Angeles sales office. Within three months, however, PCO closed the sales office after its anxiety over conditions in the north proved groundless. The Newhall refinery continued to fill occasional orders from gas companies in Southern California and Arizona until March, 1890, when it was shut down permanently.[22]

But PCO was having no easy time. Like the companies of Hardison, Stewart, and Bard, it had suffered a sharp decline in production. Its minimal drilling program, which had maintained the output at Pico remarkably well for several years, began to fail in the latter half of 1887. From just under 500 barrels daily in July, production fell off to 350 barrels at the end of the year and in April, 1888, to little more than 300—an amount that was considerably below the needs of the Alameda refinery.[23]

As the storm over the *Julia* subsided, PCO felt the challenge of the gas and fuel trade. Ventura crude was not the equal of Pico, but in November, 1888, it brought $2.00 a barrel at Santa Paula, and gas oil $3.20.[24] These prices were no temporary phenomenon, for they continued high over the next three years. Stimulated by so lively and profitable a market, PCO started to rebuild its production. Beginning in 1888, it embarked on a drilling campaign that surpassed the early eighties. At the same time it strengthened its hold on the Pico district, patenting oil claims, locating new ones, and gathering in other properties and rights through purchases. Together with the old, the new lands would encompass the total drilling territory of the company for the balance of the century.

3

As late as 1888, only the 160 acres belonging to California Star had gone to patent; the properties that PCO had drilled elsewhere in the Pico district still had the less secure status of mining claims. In September, 1888, Felton at last moved, through the Occidental Asphalt Company, to patent four claims comprising 453 acres that included virtually all of these drilling sites as well as those originally assigned Hardison, Stewart & Company. Six months later, PCO started its 92-acre Wiley claim, where it had wildcatted, on the route to patent. Meanwhile the company had begun locating new claims adjacent to these properties, annexing about 2,000 additional acres over the next decade.[25]

Purchases were another means by which PCO built up its land stake. To help meet the payments for Mission Transfer, Hardison and Stewart relinquished their two wells in Pico Canyon during 1888 and 1889, closing out the only producing interest in the district that was not in PCO's control. At about the same time California Star bought the refinery site at Newhall, a transaction it had failed to complete during the crisis in its affairs a decade earlier. California Star paid $750 to the Newhall Land and Farming Company for 12.88 acres in October, 1888, just as the refinery was reaching the end of its service. The site was still valuable, however, for storage and for its carloading facilities. Another purchase redolent of the past occurred in December, 1893, when PCO paid the widow of Dr. Gelcich $7,000 for a quitclaim to whatever rights he had retained when he sold Felton a part interest in his numerous claims in January of 1879.[26]

PCO reached out in a new direction early in 1889 when it took up three mining claims in Elsmere Canyon, where evidence of oil had been found in several waterholes. These claims were located in the San Gabriel Mountains about two miles southeast of the Newhall refinery and on the opposite side of the valley from the Pico wells. A decade later the company acquired two mining claims in Grapevine Canyon, south of Elsmere, and made a number of purchases and leases near the two canyons. In these ways it piled up southeast of Newhall about 1,500 acres, of which in 1899 it patented 470 previously held under mining claims.[27]

The drill, of course, was the test for all this territory, old and new.

4

The search for oil had heartening results. Between 1888 and 1892 PCO completed thirty-two wells, more than it had drilled in all its past history. By 1893 there were thirty-seven producing wells, and PCO's production had increased by better than half.[28] Two years later, after a sustained program of well deepening, the yield from the Pico district reached 173,000 barrels, which was not far below the record years of 1884 and 1885. This achievement, with roughly comparable figures for the Union Oil Company and for California, is shown in Table 4.

On October 1, 1888, just as the new campaign was gathering momentum, PCO shook up its Pico team. M. R. Craig was replaced as manager by the accountant and office manager, Edward North, an appointment that probably suggests a greater concern over costs. At the same time Alex Mentry was put in charge of all drilling, being elevated to superintendent from his former position of foreman of the wells. Other changes were less important. The job of foreman of pipelines was abolished and the refiner at Newhall for many years, James Morrison, was replaced by his helper.[30]

Table 4: Crude Oil Production (Barrels) in California—1888-1895[29]

Year	PCO	CSOW	TOTAL PCO-CSOW	Union†	State of California
1888	51,335*	50,020*	101,355*	—	404,762
1889	48,626	46,300	94,926	—	303,220
1890	68,453	44,760	113,213	—	307,360
1891	83,174	48,636	131,810	157,388	323,600
1892	72,378	49,531	121,909	179,570	385,049
1893	100,311	55,068	155,379	183,287	470,179
1894	127,848	44,632	172,480	156,311	705,969
1895	102,527	70,213	172,740	188,657	1,208,482

*The figures for 1888 contain estimates for the first three months, which are missing.

† Union's fiscal year ended Oct. 31, except 1895, when it was extended to Dec. 31.

Mentry's drillers concentrated primarily on the Pico patent and the adjoining land to the east. They peppered this territory, about a mile long and a half mile wide, with twenty-three new wells, of which few were dry holes. Several recorded initially fifty barrels or more daily.

In Wiley and Elsmere canyons the drilling was more wildcat in character. Elsmere seemed a likely prospect for heavy crude suitable for fuel, but only one of the four wells there proved a fair producer. It gave about fifty barrels a day of heavy black oil for the first four days before settling down to approximately eight barrels. PCO's success was hardly greater in Wiley Canyon, where two of the six wells yielded about thirteen barrels daily of 30° gravity oil. This was lighter than the Elsmere product but heavier than Pico's crudes of from 35° to 42°.[31]

During the summer of 1889, PCO let a contract to the Western Prospecting Company of Denver for two wells to be put down with a diamond drill. The Pico drilling, as earlier in the 1880's, had continued to be a somewhat dreary experience of caving, crooked holes, fishing for tools, and, occasionally, shutting off water. PCO was ripe for an experiment. Diamond drilling, a rotary process, was used principally to prospect for coal and metallic ores and, at times, for water; it had never been used in the West for oil.[32]

The Denver company was able to finish only one well, for its drill, a thin circular tube edged with industrial diamonds, could not pierce the cobbles near the surface at the other location. Mentry found that diamond drilling gave a straighter hole than cable tools. In most other respects, however, he considered the new method a "stupendous failure." For one thing, it provided a small hole, 3½ inches in diameter in this case, in comparison with holes for cable tools that ranged from 9⅝ inches at the top to 4½ inches at the bottom. An even greater shortcom-

C A L I F O R N I A   S T A R   O I L   W O R K S   C O.

C.S.O.W. WELL No. 19.

Aneroid elevation 1930 ft.

PROFILE

Scale
30 ft.
to 1 inch

R O A D   and   G R A D E.
   Commenced
   Finished
   Cost

R I G.
   Commenced hauling Material
   Cost of Hauling
   Commenced building Rig
   Finished   "   "
   Cost, including material, hauling, etc.

W E L L.
   Commenced drilling   **Sept 23,1889.**
   Finished   "   **Apr.29,1890.**
   98 days   "
   20 days fishing
        days idle
   TOTAL COST OF WELL
      Labor   3687 75
      Fuel (at $2.00 per bbl.)   16 92
      Water (at $2.00 per day)   226 --
      Total cost of hole   6376 09
      Cost, per foot including fishing   7 97
      Cost, per foot excluding fishing

C A S I N G
        ft   from   to
        ft   from   to
        ft   from   to
        ft   from   to
        ft   from   to
        ft   from   to
      Total Value of Casing
        ft 2" Tubing
        ft Sucker Rods

R E M A R K S.
      Drilled originally by the diamond drill process
by the Western Prospecting Co. of Denver,at the contract price of $3.50 per foot,we to furnish fuel,
water and casing. Drilling was done entirely by
steam from Boiler House No.2,which accounts for
small amount of oil used. Western Prospecting Co.
completed their contract Nov.30,1889. We had to put
up a pumping rig after they got their rig out of the
way,and being greatly hindered by weather,did not
get ready to pump till Jan.9,1890. Well did not
                                        (Over)

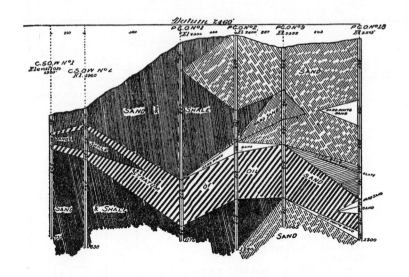

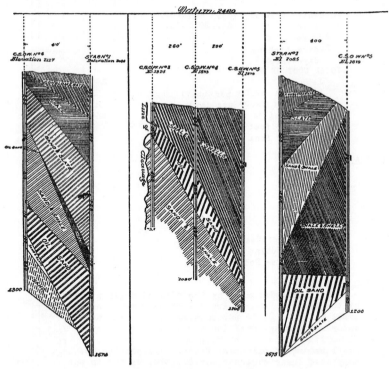

SCALE 600 FEET TO ONE INCH.

10th Ann. Rpt. of the State Mineralogist
(Sacramento, 1890), pp. 292 and 295.

Cross Sections of Pico Structures

ing was the tendency of the shale cuttings to be forced by the "pressure of water used in drilling into the oil sand rock, cementing it up and preventing the oil oozing into the hole. . . ." Consequently, the PCO superintendent redrilled the well with cable tools, quadrupling its production. The diamond drill was used thereafter merely to try to straighten a few holes.[33] The pounding of cable tools continued to resound in Pico Canyon and elsewhere in California for almost twenty years before effective rotary equipment made its appearance from the coastal oil fields of Texas and Louisiana.

But the experiment had an important auxiliary outcome. As the diamond drill cut into the rock, it left standing a central core which, when jerked out with clamps, let the driller know the nature and thickness of the strata. Western Prospecting used this information to prepare a "profile," on a scale of 80 feet to one inch, showing the width of the various strata penetrated and the location of oil sands. Such a procedure was apparently customary in exploring for coal or metallic ores, where profiles supplied data for mapping the subsurface structures. Edward North, the PCO manager, quickly adopted the practice, ordering Mentry to prepare profiles for new wells and to reconstruct profiles for older wells as best he could from surviving records and from memory. North used the profiles to draw subsurface cross-sections, charting the depth and thickness of the oil sands throughout the Pico field. Eleven of the cross-sections, along with the original profile prepared by Western Prospecting, were published in 1891 in a report of the state mineralogist, to which North also contributed an article analyzing PCO's past drilling experience. The company's use of these cross-sections in locating new wells was a notable early attempt to put drilling on a more scientific basis.[34]

Figures on the cost of the Pico drilling between 1888 and 1893 are as elusive as those for the earlier eighties, though an average cost of $7.50 a foot probably continues to be a reasonable estimate. Along with the companion expenditures for roads, tanks, gathering lines, and the short pipelines from Wiley and Elsmere canyons to Newhall, the total investment must have been about $375,000.[35]

For a time, the Panic of 1893 caused a change in drilling policy. To avoid the greater cost of new wells, the company deepened and cleaned twenty-three wells, chiefly in 1893 and 1894. The program brought a handsome return in the discovery of a rich sand a few hundred feet lower down. But deepening, of course, could be only a short-term answer to the problem of production; new oil sands were not always to be discovered, and PCO found no third sand.[36]

When the company again prepared to start wells, it at least briefly considered shifting its emphasis to the prolific new Los Angeles City field, where President Felton was an interested observer on several visits during 1895. This aroused the attention of Bard, who wrote Lyman Stewart in September of 1895, "I . . . am curious to know what Felton's plans are in respect to going into the Los Angeles field as a producer."[37] Meanwhile, at Pico, Edward North had been reduced in rank from manager to accountant and his salary cut. He feared his job was running out.[38] If Felton had led the company into the Los Angeles field, its history over the next few years would surely have been different. Instead, he finally decided not to venture into a territory so overrun with oil hunters.

PCO continued to rely solely on its old domain, where it drilled thirty-eight wells during the five years after 1895. The company had its successes, especially in Elsmere Canyon, where thirteen of the new wells were located. In general, however, the results were unexciting. PCO still found oil on the Pico patent and the adjoining lands, but not in the former quantity. For that light crude, the growing production from Elsmere was a poor substitute. The yield from Wiley Canyon continued to be small, and the attempts to develop other neighboring canyons were failures.[39]

Standard Oil scouts passing through the Pico early in 1899 commented, "Lately have been drilling dry holes; think they have drilled about all their territory. . . ."[40] Except for Elsmere, by the turn of the century PCO's oil lands were playing out.

Table 5: Crude Oil Production (Barrels) in California—1896-1900

Year	PCO-Pico	PCO-Elsmere	CSOW	TOTAL PCO-CSOW	State of California
1896	78,374	1,723	82,911	163,008	1,252,777
1897	73,798	961	70,469	145,228	1,903,411
1898	70,106	—	65,420	135,526	2,257,207
1899	70,439	28,074	54,788	153,301	2,642,095
1900	61,758	50,153	44,808	156,719	4,324,484

Dash denotes statistics not available.
Sources: Newhall Division monthly statements; US Geological Survey, *Mineral Resources of the United States, 1901*, p. 199.

5

The refinery at Alameda, which received all of the Pico crude after the closing of the Newhall works, changed little in physical appearance during the last dozen years of the century. There was no reason to build

George Loomis

Eric A. Starke

Laboratory at the Alameda Refinery

Alameda refinery about 1898. Kerosine bleaching house is in the right foreground, agitators in the center, and lubricating house to the left rear

it up, for its capacity was fully adequate to handle the Pico production.

But refinery operations were affected by PCO's changing market. No longer was the company seeking primarily to produce a quality illuminating oil. Gas and fuel oil, as we have seen, had become prominent items on the sales list. PCO had a good market, too, for its lubes, especially its engine and car oils. An increase in the number of tar stills, from six to eight, to turn out more lube oils was one of the few additions at Alameda after 1888. The company also found a ready sale among paint manufacturers for its gasoline and benzine, two highly volatile products that had to be removed before the oil could be sold to the gas companies. Kerosine continued on the roster, but much of it was blended with high-quality eastern kerosine for domestic sale or was exported unblended to Mexico and other low-grade markets.[41]

Another change of the nineties was a permanent switch from coal and coke to fuel oil to heat the stills. Jets had been placed under the stills as early as 1883, with steam or air being used to atomize the oil to get a more even heat, but the fires did not always burn steadily. Market opportunities also affected the use of fuel oil. When the lube market was good, PCO had more to gain from distilling the residuum for lubes instead of burning it for fuel. By the middle nineties, however, the technical problems in using fuel oil had been solved, and the rapid increase in California production assured an ample supply at low prices.[42]

The most meaningful development in refining, by far, was an emphasis on research. Previously there had been experiments with refined oils, but most of them had been carried on by George Miller, the refinery manager, who was the closest approximation to a chemist that the company had. "In his sanctum under the water tower were the inspection devices he used—a test cup for taking the flash and burn of kerosine, a viscosimeter for testing lube oils, hydrometers, beakers, a shelf of chemicals, several racks of samples in four-ounce bottles, and test lamps," recalled one old-time employee. Miller used his equipment not to develop new products or processes, but for testing PCO oils and, occasionally, crudes and refined oils from other sources. Late in 1892 PCO hired a professional chemist, Walter B. Price. When Price came, PCO replaced Miller's cubbyhole with a well-outfitted laboratory on the refinery grounds.[43]

In hiring Price, PCO was following a trend in the industry. The success of the chemist, Herman Frasch, in producing a good illuminating oil from Ohio's sulfur-laden crudes was already well-known. His achievement in 1888 could certainly have been suggestive to westerners beset with their own special problems. And in 1889 the Standard Oil Company (Ohio) hired Dr. William M. Burton, who years later would revolutionize the manufacture of gasoline with the process for cracking crude that bears his name. In the West, Union was the pioneer. Its leaders, after having been excited for months by the prospect of finding new and more valuable products in their Ventura crude, hired a Swiss chemist, Dr. Frederick Salathe, in January, 1892, at the "fabulous salary" of $10,000 a year. Bard and the Stewarts looked forward to a large increase in the value of their crude, perhaps to as much as $10 a barrel, if it could be made to yield the aniline dyes and other special products they hoped for. Salathe proved a disappointment, however, for he made no important discoveries during the two years he worked at Santa Paula.[44]

PCO's chemist, Walter Price, followed in the track of Frasch rather than Salathe. By the end of 1892, he was working on the old problem of getting a good kerosine and was attempting to discover why the PCO product smoked and stank and clogged lampwicks. The Pico crude, he found, contained a little sulfur and considerably more carbon than did Pennsylvania crude. Price considered the sulfur to be the main trouble. Eventually, in September, 1893, he applied for a patent to remove the sulfur by treating the kerosine distillate with fuming nitric acid.[45] But the new process, unfortunately, resulted in little improvement.

At this juncture the abler mind of E. A. Starke was brought to the problem. Starke was a twenty-nine-year old chemist whose experience had been almost wholly in the explosive powder industry. Fifteen years earlier he had gone to work as a cartridge folder in the plant of the Giant Powder Company on San Francisco Bay. The superintendent of the plant, who was attracted by his intelligence and diligence, encouraged Starke to enroll in the University of California, where he took a few courses in chemistry beginning in 1888. When he returned to the explosives industry, his fellow employees bestowed on him the title of "Doctor," after the fashion of the time. By 1893 Starke had become chemist for the U.S. Smokeless Powder Company, in which George Loomis, Charles N. Felton, Lloyd Tevis, and Gordon Blanding were important investors. His special task was to improve the stability and safety of military and sporting powders.[46]

Starke's introduction to the oil industry, however, came through the Golden City Chemical Works, a producer of industrial acids which also employed him as chemist. In October, 1893, George Loomis offered to buy sulfuric acid for the Alameda refinery from the Golden City company if it would carry away the refinery's acid sludge. This arrangement deepened Starke's interest in oil, for he had been experimenting with a petroleum derivative to coat and stabilize grains of powder. The Golden City chemist used the sludge to try to discover an easy way to produce benzol for the powder company.[47]

His research proved to be far more important to oil than to either the chemical or powder industries. Starke made his first significant contribution early in 1894 when he attempted to treat kerosine distillate, not with sulfuric acid at normal temperatures, as was customary, but heated to a temperature of 212° F. or more. This "hot-treat" method removed some of the highly carbonaceous properties, causing the kerosine to burn more brightly than under any prior process. Starke permitted Walter Price to seek a patent on the method in July of 1894. The kerosine was not the equal of eastern oil, but it was a considerable improvement. Lyman Stewart, Union's president, soon noted the difference. "The P.C.O. Co. have been making a fair quality of illuminating oil of late," he wrote Milton early in 1895. Starke's success may have been one reason why the Standard Oil Company (Iowa) contracted in April, 1895, to market the refined oil output of the Alameda refinery, an agreement we shall note again later on. Even after the turn of the century PCO was using the "hot-treat" method.[48]

Starke continued his experiments with kerosine. In 1896, he made his great discovery. By adding another step and treating the distillate with fuming sulfuric acid, he found that he could totally remove the "excessive quantity of refractory bodies and matters of carbonaceous nature" and produce a kerosine "fully equal in quality and illuminating power to the best grades and brands of Eastern . . . illuminating oils. . . ." This time Starke applied for the patent himself.[49]

The discovery brought Starke onto PCO's payroll. Gordon Blanding, PCO's new president, was so impressed that he hired Starke as a consulting chemist to fill the position that Price had relinquished a year or two earlier. In February, 1897, Starke was employed for four years at a salary of $4,000 per year on condition that he assign his patent to the company.

It was also understood that Starke would give his attention to the manufacture of lubricants and to the problem of disposing of the sludge acids. In the spring of 1898, with the aid of James Eaton, the refinery's chief mechanic, PCO's new chemist constructed an acid recovery plant. By heating the sludge in a retort, he separated the acid from the aromatic oils. PCO sold the retort acid to a fertilizer company and burned the aromatic oils, which were too impure to be of commercial value.[50]

Starke's efforts by 1900 had placed PCO far in front, technically, in the treatment of California oils. But his patent as yet had no commercial value. His process was feasible solely on a laboratory basis, for the sulfuric anhydride crystals used in making fuming sulfuric acid were available only in limited quantity and at high cost. Starke's supply had come from Nordhausen, Germany. Before his patent could fulfill its promise, the chemical industry had to increase its output of these crystals and lower the cost, goals that were not achieved until after 1900.[51]

6

The year 1893, when Starke first became interested in oil, marks the principal divide in the history of the California industry between 1887 and 1900. The panic and depression beginning in 1893 constricted the market at the very time new sources of production were opening up. Peruvian oil was threatening to invade California, and the first small production of the Los Angeles City field was making its appearance. At about the same time, or a little earlier, there were stirrings in Coalinga, McKittrick, Sunset, and Summerland, to mention four other fields that were to brighten the state's oil future.[52]

The panic and depression in the nineties rank with any in the nation's history except 1929. California felt their full impact, for, as the economist, Ira B. Cross, has noted, "by the '90s, the industries and financial interests of the state had become more and more interwoven with those of the Middle West and the East. . . ." By mid-June of 1893, six weeks after a great stock market crash in New York, the depression lay heavy upon the state. "Numerous mercantile failures occurred, banks in the central and southern part of the state were forced to the wall, and unemployment and uncertainty reigned on all hands." Bank failures in California were more numerous than in any other state except Kansas. Five of the seven national banks in Los Angeles temporarily closed their doors. In San Francisco the banks got along better, but clearings in 1893 were fully one-seventh less than they had been in the previous year.[53]

Both PCO and the Union Oil Company were hit by the sharp reduction in business. During the spring of 1893, even before the panic, low coal prices were slowing the shift from coal to fuel oil. Firms that were considering switching to oil delayed the change. With the onslaught of depression, Union and PCO received fewer and smaller orders from many of their regular fuel and gas oil customers. The diminished market also affected the sales of lighter oils and lubes.[54]

Of the two companies, PCO was in better condition to ride the storm, for it had the stronger marketing position. For one thing, PCO could turn out a full line of salable refined products, from gasoline to lubes, in contrast to the gas distillates and marginal lubes of Union's refinery. For another, its PCO production was not enough to supply the San Francisco market with fuel and gas oil. If PCO needed customers, moreover, the stature of its leaders gave it an edge in San Francisco over its southern rival. Late in 1893 it gained a valuable contract from the San Francisco Gas Light Company, which Union had formerly supplied.[55]

Union was more vulnerable because of its greater dependency on the fuel trade and because of the intense competition in its less populous home area. Its position in the Los Angeles market had deteriorated, as Puente's production rapidly increased and the first production of the Los Angeles City field came in. Oil began to pile up in its tanks. In June of 1893 Union was forced to suspend dividends. By the end of the year, with its sales of fuel and gas oil off 30 per cent from their record in 1892, Union cut sharply its price for fuel oil.[56]

Union, in fact, was pushed to extreme efforts to find customers. In the spring of 1893 it hired George M. Smith, a fuel oil expert and former superintendent of the Smith & Wesson Arms Company, to prod the market. During 1894, E. A. Edwards, the veteran Ventura oilman, and A. M. Hunt, a prominent engineering consultant on fuel oil matters, were added to its staff. They canvassed the state, talking to brewers, vintners, power companies, sugar beet refiners, iron and steel firms, brick and pottery works, cement companies, government agencies, an ice company, a laundry—wherever they thought there was a chance for their product. They worked chiefly, however, in the area around San Francisco Bay. From the autumn of 1893 Union's directors were considering how they might reduce costs and invade this market more effectively by substituting marine for rail transportation, but their plans for a steamer or barge proved impractical because of the company's already heavy indebtedness.[57]

Apart from San Francisco, Union based its greatest hopes on capturing the railroads for fuel oil. The coal bill of the Santa Fe in California alone amounted to $35,000 a month, and the Southern Pacific's was much larger. Stewart began to discuss fuel oil with officials of the Santa Fe's Southern California Railway in July of 1893. He pointed out that oil had been used for years on locomotives in Russia and Peru, to which the railroad's general manager, K. H. Wade, replied that he was "very anxious to introduce the use of oil" and suggested that they investigate how the change might be made.[58]

These discussions led to a series of experiments in October, 1894, which Union, the Southern California Railway, and the Southern Pacific jointly sponsored on a strip of Southern Pacific track near Santa Paula. The Santa Fe subsidiary supplied the engine, and the Southern Pacific the engineer; Union's mechanics installed the fuel tank and burners. From the very beginning the experiments gave promise of success, and the engineer took his locomotive all the way to Los Angeles without difficulty. The experiments also showed that fuel oil was more economical than coal, permitting savings of more than 25 per cent.[59]

K. H. Wade soon was negotiating with Union for fuel oil. To Milton Stewart, in Titusville, the situation seemed to offer an opportunity to strike for preferential rail rates: ". . . . wouldn't it be well to make quite a little concession in price, providing they will agree to make a corresponding concession in rates—say 20 or 25 cents per bbl.—on the oil shipped by us over their road to San Francisco?" he wrote Lyman early in 1895. The negotiations went far from smoothly, however. Rumors were current that Peruvian crude was to be laid down in California for about $1 a barrel. When Wade and Union signed a contract, it lasted but a month. The railroad executive decided that he could buy more cheaply from producers in the Los Angeles City field. Two years later the Santa Fe was itself in the oil business as a producer.[60]

The possibility of imports from Peru and the burgeoning production in the Los Angeles area were hardly less disturbing to PCO than to Union. The new oil, if in sufficient quantity, would endanger PCO's position in the San Francisco market. More than to a depression, PCO was vulnerable to new sources of cheap oil.

7

A few years earlier the small and remote Peruvian industry would have been an unlikely threat, but by the early 1890's English capital was beginning to develop the oil region along the northern Peruvian coast where the Incas had dug tar long before the days of the Spaniards. The London & Pacific Petroleum Company, organized in 1889, soon began to get a light crude from shallow wells north of Talara Bay. Even though Peruvian production in 1893 was only a minor fraction of the 3,000 barrels per day cited in the press, the news was arousing interest among both marketers and producers in California.[61]

The development in Peru coincided with a decline in California production after 1888 when the ex-Mission and Sespe properties of Hardison & Stewart began to slip. For several years thereafter sufficient production was not found to offset their reduced yield. High oil prices in California made bringing Peruvian crude north seem an attractive possibility.

W. R. Grace & Company, the great American mercantile firm operating in Peru, was the first to act. Late in 1893 it chartered a British steamer, the *Bawnmore,* for seventeen trips between Peru and the West Coast of the United States. Grace outfitted the ship with tanks capable of carrying 19,000 barrels, which was more than five times the capacity of the ill-fated *W. L. Hardison.*[62] An added attraction was the strong possibility that a 20 per cent duty on foreign petroleum would be removed, for at the request of President Cleveland a Democratic Congress had turned to revising the tariff.

The threat of foreign oil admitted free from duty did not escape the watchful eyes of American oilmen, especially in Standard Oil circles. Even more than imports from Peru, they feared Russian imports. In December of 1893 Iowa Standard's president, W. H. Tilford, telegraphed W. S. Miller, his chief western executive, that "free petroleum might let Russian oils into California" and told Miller to ask the Southern Pacific, Tevis, and Scofield to "oppose putting petroleum on the free list." Miller quickly gained their support. "Loomis . . . telegraphed ex-Senator Felton, who is in Washington, D.C., to see all members and Senators from this State," he wired Tilford. "Lloyd Tevis will do all he can. . . . Scofield will see Union Oil Company and Puente Oil Company at Los Angeles tomorrow." A few weeks later, in reply to a letter from Lyman Stewart, Loomis wrote, "It is of course to the advantage of all of us to keep as heavy a duty as possible on all foreign oils. Please advise me what you propose to do, and in what way our company can assist in the good work."[63]

Meanwhile the oilmen had lost their battle in the House, but they had greater hopes in the Senate. In February, 1894, W. S. Miller was ordered once more to enlist the support of Tevis, Scofield, and the Southern Pacific. They could do the most good, Miller was told, if they stressed to senators the harmful effect of duty-free Peruvian oil on the Pacific Coast industry. In Washington, Felton worked closely with the Standard Oil lobbyists, and toward the end of June the oilmen gained their victory. The Senate accepted an amendment providing for a duty of 40 per cent in cases where a foreign country levied a tariff on American oil products. Both Russia and Peru were hit by this provision. In Peru's case the former duty was doubled.[64]

The Peruvian threat was not at an end, however. If anything, it appeared even greater to the Californians during the fall of 1894. In September, W. L. Hardison, who had left Union following a quarrel with Bard, joined with Sutherland Hutton, another California oilman, to draft an immense contract with the Peruvian producers. Hardison and Hutton let it be known that they could deliver oil at San Francisco for 80¢ a barrel and that they had a five-year contract for up to 105,000 barrels a month. There was a vast difference between an occasional cargo brought by the *Bawnmore* and this huge amount. California's average monthly production in 1893 was less than 40,000 barrels. Bard heard a rumor that the first cargo was due to arrive in January, 1895.[65]

Hardison's project caused turmoil, especially in the Union Oil Company, which dispatched a young engineer, R. W. Fenn, to Peru to check upon the scheme. At about the same time Stewart began negotiating with Hardison over a proposal that Union buy part of the stock and market through Hardison's new United Oil Company. In return, Hardison was to give Union's oil "first call" in all sales and keep Peruvian oil out of Southern California.[66]

This plan was being considered by Union's board when Fenn returned late in March of 1895. Perhaps at some future time Peru would be able to supply 100,000 barrels monthly, Fenn reported, but at the moment its production was little more than one-tenth of that amount. The young engineer also discovered that the Hardison and Hutton contract had never been signed. Hardison had "cut his swath, as usual . . . a wide one for a short distance. . . ." Such, at least, was Bard's caustic comment when he responded to an inquiry from Felton a few weeks later.[67]

By the end of 1895 Peruvian oil had completely disappeared from California. In August W. R. Grace lost the *Bawnmore* off the coast of Oregon with only three of its voyages completed.[68] Thereafter, for more than a decade neither Grace nor any other West Coast shipper brought in oil from Peru.

An enormous leap in oil production within California, starting with the Los Angeles City field in the middle nineties, was the reason.

8

The Los Angeles City field, the largest producer among California fields in the nineteenth century, was about two years in gaining stature. The field started many a new career in oil, and none more remarkable than that of its discoverer, a miner from Colorado named E. L. Doheny. This was his first of several great oil developments in California and Mexico that ultimately brought him a fortune estimated as high as $75,000,000.[69] In November, 1892, Doheny and his partners, Sam Connon and C. A. Canfield, sank a shaft not far from the Second Street

Park to a depth of 155 feet, using pick and shovel and a hand windlass to lift the dirt. As they dug, a heavy oil exuded from the walls. This outcome enabled them to finance a small rig, which they used to drill the first of many profitable wells later in the same month.[70]

Their success brought others to the scene. The shallow wells, some of which were no more than 500 feet, could be put down with an ease not possible at Pico and Puente or in Ventura County. Many cost less than a dollar a foot. By June of 1894, the Second Street men were producing around 115 barrels a day, about one-quarter of the yield from Pico. Five months later no other California field was producing so much oil. In 1895 the Los Angeles production, estimated at 729,000 barrels by the State Mining Bureau, dwarfed that of all the other oil fields combined. It came from about 300 wells, for the most part bunched tightly together in an area totaling hardly more than 160 acres. "Wells were as thick as the holes in a pepper box," was the reminiscence of one old oilman.[71]

Location, rather than quality, gave the Los Angeles field its great importance. The best of its crude was not more than about 20° gravity, which was considerably heavier than the production of the older fields. Too heavy to refine, it did make good fuel.

The excessive production began playing hob with the southern market toward the end of 1894, sending oil prices at Los Angeles from $1 a barrel in October to less than 30¢ about a year later. Union and Puente were hard hit. Union found that a price cut in December, 1894, to 50¢ a barrel at Santa Paula did little to help its fuel oil sales in Los Angeles.[72]

As a way out, Union attempted to organize the Los Angeles producers and to dispose of their surplus elsewhere. Lyman Stewart proposed this tactic to Union's board along with the price cut, offering a pattern of operations which he said was "based partly on the rates and methods employed by the Standard Oil Company." He suggested that Union could market the surplus crude, or it could establish a separate company to do so.[73]

Within a month the proposal was submitted to the Los Angeles producers of oil of 16° gravity or lighter, representing about one-quarter of the field's output which could be most readily sold for fuel. Union told the oilmen:[74]

> Southern California is producing now, perhaps 40 per cent more fuel oil than the local market requires. This surplus will necessarily have to be marketed elsewhere. To reach other markets, cars, pipe-lines and boats will be required. To provide for the surplus production, storage will be necessary, and to insure safety in taking large contracts, as well as

to supply the periodic requirements of the sugar factories and wineries, large stocks will need to be accumulated and carried the greater part of the year. If the producers of 80% of the fuel oil not below sixteen degrees gravity in the City of Los Angeles will unite, the Union Oil Company of California will undertake to provide for all these requirements, and will handle all their oil up to an accumulated surplus of 7,500,000 gallons.

Union's offer came to nothing, for the Los Angeles producers would not get together. Perhaps some of them balked at the charge the company intended to levy as their marketing agent: 7 per cent, or 9 per cent if Union guaranteed payment of the account. Others probably preferred the risks of running their own business. Instead of accepting Union's proposal, the oilmen set up two lightly financed companies: Producers Oil Company, organized by Doheny and others, to sell most of the heavy crude, and Los Angeles Oil Company to handle principally lighter crude.[75]

These events of January, 1895, were not lost on the management of the Pacific Coast Oil Company, for metropolitan San Francisco was the most likely destination for the surplus oil. Moreover, Union, frozen out of Los Angeles, would undoubtedly turn with greater vigor to find outlets to the north. If the Los Angeles production continued to rise, the pressure to dispose of it would increase. In the circumstances, it seemed wise for PCO to protect itself by seeking an alliance with Union.

The thinking of the PCO leaders must have been about as follows: The market for fuel and gas oil in San Francisco was larger than PCO could supply. The most lucrative part was the gas trade, which was the company's prime interest. The needs of the gas companies were also greater than PCO could meet surely and comfortably. By inviting Union to share in the use of a barge or boat, PCO could employ cheap marine transportation to bring north a needed supplement to its own Pico production of almost 15,000 barrels monthly. It could sell at a lower price than formerly and the market would be more adequately supplied, discouraging additional shipments to San Francisco. "Incidental to the transportation," Bard wrote some months later, "we have in view the possibility of preventing the Los Angeles producers offering their oil at ruinous prices."[76]

PCO began to plan along this line at the end of January, 1895. Scofield asked George W. Young, Union's San Francisco sales representative, whether his company would join PCO in building a 10,000-barrel barge. At the same time, PCO was considering a pipeline from Pico to the coast. In March, Felton and Scofield came to Los Angeles to select a terminus for the pipeline and to discuss their ideas with Stewart and Bard.[77]

As the discussion progressed, the negotiators agreed that PCO should build and own a tank steamer of about 6,000 barrels capacity capable of making a round trip between Ventura and San Francisco every five days. Felton offered Union up to half (16,000 barrels) of the monthly capacity. A figure of 13¢ a barrel was fixed for 16,000 barrels. If Union shipped less, the rates gradually increased to a maximum of 26.75¢. On the other hand, if PCO did not need its full half, Union could use the excess at progressively lower rates. The minimum charge for 25,000 barrels or more monthly was 10¢ a barrel. The 13¢ figure, which presumably would be the usual rate, was a good bargain for Union. It was about one-fourth of the prevailing rail rate and about one-third of the marine rate to San Francisco.

But the bargain was by no means one-sided. PCO gained from the economies of operating a larger vessel than its own production required. There were other gains, too, which Stewart and Bard accepted reluctantly. For example, Union could not use the vessel to ship naphthas or illuminating oil. With respect to gas oil, the two sides entered into a compromise that PCO hoped would leave the trade in its hands. Union could transport up to 30,000 barrels of gas distillate annually if its sales of fuel oil at San Francisco amounted to no more than 15,000 barrels monthly, but such shipments had first to be offered to PCO. The price fixed—$1.60 a barrel at Ventura—was fairly low. If PCO refused to buy, Union could enter the market. Only in this case, however, could Union sell distillate to a gas company north of a line 100 miles south of San Francisco. In return, PCO made a much less meaningful promise not to sell fuel oil south of the same line.[78]

Despite the agreement, signed in mid-April of 1895, the almost explosive growth of the Los Angeles City field continued to give the two companies many anxious moments. Felton was frequently in the south during 1895 to watch developments. As crude plunged toward 40¢ a barrel in July, the Los Angeles producers set up an Oil Exchange with a dual purpose: to facilitate buying and selling, and to find new markets for the wild flood of oil. This move caused Felton to talk with Bard and Stewart about expanding their agreement to channel oil north and to limit competition in that end of the state. With prices so low, he believed they would have no difficulty in building a larger fuel trade in the San Francisco area. He suggested that they jointly finance additional transportation and storage facilities.[79]

Felton found Union lukewarm. Bard, for one, counseled his company against the new scheme, arguing that it did not seem "good policy . . . to be the tail of his [Felton's] kite." Bard was moved by reasons of prestige, but that was not all. He also believed that Felton was more interested in the profits to be made from transporting and marketing than in maintaining the price of fuel oil. Because of its light gravity crude, PCO had much less fuel oil to sell than did Union. Consequently, Bard urged his company to make its own offer to the Oil Exchange to handle the production, provided that Union could raise funds through a bond issue for a barge, tankage, and for a pipeline from Los Angeles to tidewater.[80]

Some action was urgently needed, for there were well substantiated reports that other parties were dickering with the Oil Exchange. Union's proposal, made in mid-September of 1895, was a somewhat shadowy affair, the best the company thought it could make in the circumstances. Its offer indicated in a general way that Union and PCO would co-operate in marketing oil for the Exchange, but on this point it was not specific. Union proposed to transport at least 20,000 barrels a month to San Francisco at a maximum charge of 27.5¢ a barrel and to erect tanks and store the oil for 1.25¢ a barrel monthly. The company also suggested that the price for selling the oil would be "based largely on the relative value of coal. . . . The relations and negotiations of the Union Oil Company with the Pacific Coast Oil Company are such," the company concluded, "that it cannot make a more definite proposition until it shall have an opportunity of submitting these suggestions and the reply of the Oil Exchange to the Pacific Coast Oil Company."[81]

Like Union's proposal of January, 1895, this one also failed. The producers decided that their interests would be better served by keeping clear of the larger marketers. Instead of dealing with Union and PCO, they made an arrangement with the Arctic Oil Works, a well-known San Francisco whale and refined oil firm, to be their northern outlet. They also set up a corporation, the California Oil and Transportation Company, to convert a thirty-eight-year old sailing ship, the *Enoch Talbott,* to carry the oil. This vessel, outfitted with tanks for 7,000 barrels, made a few trips to San Francisco beginning in February, 1896, before it became unseaworthy after a severe storm.[82]

Along with these events, the gradual rise of oil prices in the south reduced the threat to the San Francisco market. In May of 1896 crude oil at Los Angeles was worth more than $1 a barrel for the first time in eighteen months. The advance was helped by falling production, improved sales in Southern California, and more storage facilities.[83]

Meanwhile, Felton and Scofield had spent a busy time. Neither construction of the pipeline nor of the steamer went smoothly. The 44-mile line to Ventura, which was started in July, 1895, consisted about equally of two-inch pipe for the mountains and three-inch for the flat country beyond. It was designed to carry by gravity at least 600 barrels daily, which was as much oil as Pico had ever produced. The pipe was inferior and soft, however, and it was laid by an unskilled crew headed by a driller. The upshot was a line that leaked oil all over the countryside. At the end of 1895 it was still unfinished, being about a mile from Ventura and the 20,000-barrel tank PCO had erected.[84]

The building of the steamer, named the *George Loomis* for PCO's late president, was begun in May at San Francisco's Union Iron Works, but its completion was delayed well beyond the scheduled delivery in October. Problems of tanker construction probably caused the delay. Unlike the earlier West Coast oil carriers, which had been equipped with tanks fitted into the hull, the *George Loomis* was a true tanker. Its skin served as one big tank divided into six smaller tanks by one long and two transverse bulkheads. No yard on the West Coast had constructed such a vessel, and few had been constructed elsewhere. The earliest American tanker, the *Standard,* had been built by Standard Oil on the East Coast only seven years before. Perhaps the novel nature of the *Loomis,* a vessel of 691 tons, explains why it could carry about 6,500 barrels, 500 more than the builders had planned.[85]

When completed late in December, the *Loomis* had cost PCO $96,188. Along with the pipeline, the company had spent about $180,000 to protect its market.[86]

9

As an oil carrier, the *Loomis* fully met the hopes of its sponsors. Its maiden voyage to Ventura in the second week of January, 1896, was the first of sixty trips that year with cargoes totaling 371,500 barrels. This included Pico's entire production and by far the bulk of Union's oil. Union, the larger producer, supplied about three-fifths of the oil. Together, the two companies loaded the *Loomis* with almost as much crude as was produced in the whole state three years before. The shipments also provided the San Francisco market with nearly all of its California oil, for, as they had planned, the veteran companies continued to dominate the northern fuel trade.[87]

But the relations between PCO and Union were far from harmonious. From the beginning, differences arose concerning the use of the *Loomis.* Felton found fault with the loading time at Ventura on the first two voyages and forced Union to put in a larger delivery line, a change that Stewart regarded as unnecessary.[88]

Other and more serious disputes were to follow. When Union signed the agreement for the *Loomis* in April, 1895, it had no refinery on

San Francisco Bay; in fact, the decision to build a refinery at Oleum was not reached until the next month. Undoubtedly, the opportunity to use the *Loomis* strongly influenced Union's decision. And undoubtedly PCO was not pleased to see a competitor established so close to its Alameda works. By the terms of the agreement PCO had to deliver to Oleum, but it refused to consider Oleum as the equivalent of San Francisco in determining rates. Instead, it charged approximately two cents a barrel more for the additional twenty-four miles. Lyman Stewart argued that while "technically correct," PCO's additional charge was "certainly not in accordance with the spirit of our understanding." A complaint by Scofield that fog at Oleum would delay unloading nearly a third of the time added to Union's discomfiture.[89]

PCO's refusal to unload crude at Moss Landing to serve Union's customers among the Pajaro Valley sugar refiners, about one hundred miles south of San Francisco, was even more disturbing. The PCO leaders claimed that the *Loomis* would have to stand offshore better than half a mile, too far for efficient delivery through a line, and that the weather was too uncertain. Consequently, Union was forced to receive the oil at Oleum and to pay an additional twenty cents a barrel for rail freight to fill these large contracts.[90]

PCO was most sensitive about its gas trade. The *Loomis* agreement had been drafted with the clear intent that any gas distillate shipped by Union would pass through PCO's hands. At that time PCO had apparently failed to realize, however, that some of Union's lighter crude could also readily be used in manufacturing gas. When Felton sought to buy some of this crude early in 1896 for resale to the San Francisco Gas Light Company, Stewart rebuffed him with a price higher than he wanted to pay. A few weeks later Scofield became concerned over a sale of crude to San Francisco's other gas company, the Pacifiic Gas Improvement Company. He challenged Union. Stewart replied, saying ". . . we have never, since the making of the transportation agreement . . . quoted a barrel of either crude oil or distillate to any of the gas companies. . . ." He also pointed out that his company had refrained from selling crude, not because of any restriction in the agreement, but "simply out of good will toward you. . . ." The sale that had aroused Scofield, it developed, had been made by independent Los Angeles producers using the *Enoch Talbott*.[91]

The matter of selling crude for gas again became an issue in November, 1896, when PCO asked Union for four cargoes of light crude at $1.40 a barrel for the Pacific Gas Improvement Company. The refinery manager at Oleum made a counter-offer of $1.50 a barrel, canceled it, and then arranged for Union to make a direct sale to the gas company. Blanding, PCO's excitable president, charged Union with having "openly declared war against us" and with having "invaded our territory." He claimed that the sale was a "violation of the spirit and intent of the agreement" for the use of the *Loomis*. In reprisal, he instructed Mentry to offer to purchase crude from "the various outside producers" along Union's pipeline in Ventura County. If Union would not sell to PCO, Blanding was willing to attempt to annex the production of the several small independents who were selling to Union.[92]

A compromise of this high-spirited argument was reached at a conference held late in February, 1897, between Blanding, Scofield, Stewart, and Bard. The Union representatives would not guarantee to sell light crude to PCO, but they promised not to deal with the gas companies. They also agreed to help PCO meet the demands of its gas trade by an offer of 1,000 barrels of distillate monthly for two years and such stocks as the Oleum refinery might accumulate at six-month intervals. The price, $1.60 a barrel plus the cost of transportation from Ventura, conformed to the terms of the agreement of April, 1895. For its part. PCO ceased dickering for the oil of the Ventura independents.[93]

The two parties were once more at odds in July, 1897. Blanding complained that Union was loading the *Loomis* with a mixture of oils so heavy as to endanger the ship and to reduce its carrying capacity. Water and other foreign matter in Union's cargoes, he asserted, had also contributed to overloads. The PCO president asked for a conference to consider revising the agreement of April, 1895.[94]

When the conferees met, Blanding and Scofield revealed that PCO's other major grievance, apart from a jealous concern for its gas trade, was its gross underestimate of the cost of operating the *Loomis*. Instead of $2,720 a month, the base from which PCO had constructed its rates, the cost had averaged $4,440. This was an error highly favorable to Union. Blanding argued that the rates "should be readjusted upon a new basis . . . as actually ascertained by experience. . . ." Stewart and Bard regarded the charges concerning the character of Union's cargoes as trumped up and false, but to mollify PCO they did agree to load the tanker with slightly lighter crude in the front and rear tanks.[95] They also came to terms on rates. The readjustment was a mild one, for PCO's bargaining power was weak. It had in prospect no other customer who could supply cargoes so readily and of sufficient size to keep the tanker busy.[96]

Union, meanwhile, was rapidly outgrowing the *Loomis*. An intensive drilling campaign was enlarging production in Ventura County, long the company's home base. But Union was also moving into the oil fields of Los Angeles and Orange counties, both as purchaser and producer, and was eying the prospects at Coalinga in the San Joaquin Valley, where it put in a short pipeline to the railroad. By 1898 its own production was running about 400,000 barrels annually.[97] Union was marketing aggressively, too. In 1898 it was supplying the sugar refineries near Moss Landing with about 100,000 barrels of crude yearly, and it had a considerably larger trade around San Francisco Bay. Needing additional marine capacity badly, Union began to plan for a tanker or barge.[98]

These plans prompted PCO early in 1899 to offer to build a tanker for Union one-third larger than the *Loomis* if satisfactory rates could be worked out. Perhaps Blanding believed that the offer would be attractive because of Union's weak financial condition and that Union's acceptance would give PCO a certain leverage, as well as profit, on the trade of its southern rival. But Union chose to build a 7,500-barrel wooden barge, the *Santa Paula,* which was launched in November of 1899.[99]

PCO, by contrast, was drifting. As we have noted, it took no significant part in the vast expansion of California production in the later nineties. Its position in the San Francisco market was also becoming precarious, for its relatively small production could no longer mean much to a community using ever more fuel oil, and cheap oil at that. At the turn of the century San Francisco's consumption was estimated at 100,000 barrels monthly, with Union and the independents supplying the lion's share.[100] In 1898 and 1899 PCO was still reporting a profit, but there was no guarantee that it would stay in the black much longer.[101]

Perhaps PCO could have preserved an important place in the industry through forceful leadership, but such leadership it did not get. Lloyd Tevis and Charles N. Felton continued to be its largest stockholders and PCO directors until 1899. Tevis resigned as director in March, 1899, four months before his death. He was succeeded by his son, Hugh Tevis. Felton resigned in December to be succeeded by his son, Charles N. Felton, Jr. The three remaining directors held their qualifying shares from the Tevis family.[102] Only one man on the board, D. G. Scofield, had been with PCO from the start, and his role was more managerial than policy making.

The future belonged to the companies and men who scrambled successfully for opportunities in such new fields as Coalinga, Kern, McKittrick, Whittier, and Fullerton.[103] Chief among them was Union. But there were many others, some of which would supply roots for later great western oil corporations, like the Associated and the American arm of the Royal Dutch-Shell, the Shell Oil Company.[104]

There was one organization, the Standard Oil combination, to which the future belonged even more. By the later 1890's its New York leaders were perceiving bright prospects in handling California crude and refined products. In following this vision, they would depart from their earlier exclusive emphasis in the West on marketing, a field in which Standard was clearly pre-eminent.

VII

IOWA STANDARD GROWS

The Standard Oil Company (Iowa), founded in 1885 through the merger of Ohio Standard's western stations with those of the Continental Oil & Transportation Company, was the corporate window through which the great Standard combination viewed the Far Western landscape. Like Standard's other marketing units (of which there were seventeen in 1885), the Iowa company had its own geographic domain. At the start, its stations were all located in California and Oregon, but within the next fifteen years the company set up outlets in Washington, Arizona, Nevada, Idaho, the Hawaiian Islands, Alaska, the Yukon Territory of Canada, and, until 1898, in British Columbia. This great expanse was lightly peopled. Its population at the time of the organization of Iowa Standard was no more than 1,750,000; by 1900 it had grown to perhaps 3,250,000. Despite the difficulties caused by the vast distances and relatively few large population centers, the Iowa company was to score a major marketing triumph during these years.

Like all other important subsidiaries, Iowa Standard was supervised and administered to a large extent from the famed Standard headquarters at 26 Broadway in New York. This august address was the home of the Trust and of such key units as the Standard Oil Company (New York) and the Standard Oil Company (New Jersey). Information on operations flowed there from E. A. Tilford, president of the Iowa company, in San Francisco; instructions flowed back.

Tilford's line of communication in the 1880's ran straight to the bailiwick of two other Tilford brothers, the Southern and Western Domestic Trade Department of New York Standard. This department was headed by the most brilliant of the Tilfords, Wesley Hunt, who in 1887, at the age of thirty-seven, was appointed one of the seven trustees of the Standard Oil Trust. In the same year his youngest brother, Henry Morgan Tilford, joined the department and in 1893 became manager of the split-off Western Domestic Trade Department. Earlier, Wesley, and later, Henry ruled on requests for new stations in Iowa Standard's territory. They also placed orders for products sold by the Iowa company and passed upon requests for price changes. The New York Tilfords, especially Henry, made frequent trips to the West. There can

162

be no question as to the importance of the hard-driving Tilford brothers in developing the Far Western market.[1]

The administrative efforts of the Tilfords in New York Standard were guided by a series of committees at 26 Broadway, particularly the Domestic Trade Committee. This committee, formed in 1886 at the suggestion of Wesley H. Tilford, shaped policies governing such matters as new stations, prices, quality and range of products, sources of supply, and methods of distribution. It made recommendations and suggestions on the basis of reports from the marketing subsidiaries and on its general knowledge of Standard's total operations. In lesser degree, other integrating committees, such as the Lubricating Oil Committee and, more rarely, the Cooperage and Case and Can committees, affected the operations of the western company. The Executive Committee controlled the purse strings. This committee, situated at the very heart of the Standard organization, reviewed all appropriations for plant investment in excess of $5,000 and salary increases for employees earning $600 or more a year. In general, the Executive Committee accepted recommendations from the West that had been endorsed by the New York Tilfords, but it could exercise a veto when it chose.[2]

Because it was technically a company, Iowa Standard had its own five-man board. The members representing the Standard organization were usually from one or another of the committees that influenced its operations, chiefly Domestic Trade. E. A. Tilford, president and director of the company from 1885 to 1891, was an exception. So was George H. Vilas, auditor of the Trust, who served as director from 1885 to 1888 and as secretary-treasurer for two years thereafter. The other Standard men, like Vilas, were all top executives at 26 Broadway. W. H. Tilford was a member of the Iowa board until 1907 and president after the resignation of his brother. H. M. Tilford took the directorship vacated by E. A. Tilford in 1891 and became vice president in 1895. Both of the New York Tilfords were members of the Domestic Trade Committee, though at different times. John D. Archbold, a member of the Executive Committee and the most versatile man in Standard's management, served on the Iowa board from 1885 to 1888 and again from 1893 to 1903. Colonel W. P. Thompson, chairman of the Domestic Trade Committee, was a director for the year 1888-89, and Orville T. Waring, chairman of the Lubricating Oil Committee, succeeded him. Another Domestic Trade Committee member, Charles M. Pratt, joined the Iowa board in 1888. Lloyd Tevis, representing a minority interest of 40 per cent, was the director from outside the Standard family. Because the corporation was hardly more than a convenient legal fiction, its board was far less important in shaping western affairs than were the decisions of the various committees at 26 Broadway or of New York Standard's Trade Departments. The board met mainly to take care of matters requiring formal action, such as the declaration of dividends or, in February, 1892, the increase in capital stock from $600,000 to $1,000,000 through a stock dividend.[3] But the names of the members, in conjunction with their committee assignments, suggest the high level of talent that shared with the Tilfords in directing Standard's activities in the Far West.

In the fall of 1892, shortly after the stock dividend, Standard gained total ownership of the Iowa company. Standard paid Lloyd Tevis $475,000 for his stock, which was in line with a policy several years old of wiping out minority holdings in the marketing companies.[4] For Tevis, the purchase ended a very profitable association. Over a period of seven and one-third years, his interest had received $173,000 in dividends on an investment initially valued at $240,000. Together with the capital gain from the sale of stock, Tevis had obtained an average return of almost 25 per cent a year. This was a generous reward, indeed. Tevis had bothered to attend only two board meetings and had avoided altogether the meaningless gesture of voting his shares.[5]

The Tevis shares went to the Standard Oil Company (New Jersey), which had taken over the majority interest in Iowa Standard from the Standard Oil Trust after the Rockefeller organization had sustained its first important defeat in 1892 in an antitrust suit before the Supreme Court of Ohio. The Iowa company thus became a subsidiary of Jersey Standard, which for seven years after 1892 was one of twenty holding and operating companies jointly designated as the "Standard Oil Interests" on the books at 26 Broadway until, during 1899, the unity of the Standard combination was restored when Jersey Standard became the central holding company.[6]

2

In the West, the San Francisco headquarters was the regional equivalent of 26 Broadway. San Francisco was the point of consolidation and of immediate control. Standard's agents could expect frequent visits from that location, and to it they made their reports. Since the men at the stations were in direct contact with the customer, the San Francisco headquarters was especially concerned with their zeal in drumming up trade and the quality of their service.

The San Francisco office was also a station, being Standard's outlet for the city. The office had grown substantially since 1878, when E. A.

Tilford and two assistants had been the whole staff. By 1895 its roster numbered about thirty. Four years earlier, it had moved from its original location at 123 California Street to more commodious quarters at 308 Market Street. In the spring of 1896 the office moved again, to the Sheldon Building at 421 Market, where it remained until 1903.[7]

The intervening years had seen many changes in personnel. E. A. Tilford resigned as president in December, 1891, but stayed on in San Francisco for most of the next year watching over transportation rates.[8] When he left, 26 Broadway sent no one of the same stature to replace him. During his fourteen years as Standard's regional executive, the main outlines for the development of marketing in the Iowa territory had been laid down and the market itself largely won. Presumably, the eastern headquarters believed that there was no need to send a prominent executive to play an agent's role.

The man who became the ranking officer in the West, at half Tilford's salary of $10,000, was William S. Miller, the Iowa Standard treasurer. The forty-seven-year old Miller, a former sales manager for the Acme Oil Company at Syracuse, New York, had been transferred to San Francisco in September, 1890. Miller had switched to oil in 1875 after having been a conductor on the Oil Creek Railroad in northwestern Pennsylvania. He was beginning a career in the West that would run for almost thirty years and would be capped by his election as chairman of the board of the Standard Oil Company (California). A tall, lean, and brusque man, he was little prone to decisions that required the spending of money.[9]

In the fall of 1891, 26 Broadway made a second appointment that suggests an emphasis on careful, conservative management. William M. Hall, an auditor from Cleveland, was sent out to join Iowa Standard's staff. Like Miller, Hall would later serve as a director of the Standard Oil Company (California).[10]

H. C. Breeden, who arrived in San Francisco in March, 1895, was the last of the important newcomers. Breeden was a young protégé of the Tilfords. His vigor and assertiveness contrasted sharply with the cautious, conservative temperament of Miller, whose assistant he became. Breeden had a capacity for rubbing people the wrong way, but where vigor was an asset he did well.[11]

Of the old guard, none was more important than Charlie Watson, the former right hand to E. A. Tilford. The sharp-tongued Watson continued to hold the title of chief clerk, but his duties ranged far beyond the office. He was a frequent visitor in the field, where his most important task was supervising the construction of new stations.[12]

MARKETING STATIONS & SUB-STATIONS · 1900

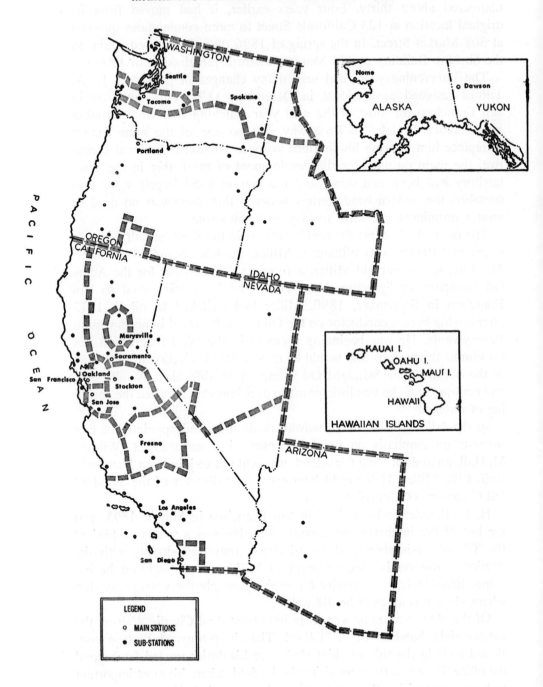

WASHINGTON

Seattle

Tacoma
Spokane

Portland

OREGON
CALIFORNIA

IDAHO
NEVADA

Marysville

Sacramento

San Francisco   Oakland
            Stockton
        San Jose

Fresno

ARIZONA

Los Angeles

San Diego

PACIFIC OCEAN

Nome
            Dawson
ALASKA   YUKON

KAUAI I.
    OAHU I.
        MAUI I.

HAWAII

HAWAIIAN ISLANDS

LEGEND
○ MAIN STATIONS
● SUB-STATIONS

Iowa Standard spent these years saturating its territory with outlets and improving its marketing techniques. At its start, the company had a nucleus of five stations: San Francisco, Stockton, Sacramento, Los Angeles, and Portland, and a depot at Oakland. Each could be served by water as well as by rail. By 1900 these "main" stations had grown to fifteen, mostly established during E. A. Tilford's day. Before the year 1885 was over Iowa Standard had acquired the outlet of Yates & Company at San Jose, some fifty miles south of San Francisco, and opened a new station at the terminus of the Northern Pacific Railroad at Tacoma on Puget Sound. San Diego and Seattle were added in 1886, and Oakland was made a main station in 1887. Another new station, Spokane, pierced through the wilderness of eastern Washington in 1888. In 1889, Marysville, north of Sacramento, and in 1890, Fresno, south of Stockton, joined the list. Vancouver, British Columbia, followed in 1893. The Vancouver station remained with Iowa Standard until 1898, when it was transferred to the British Columbia Oil Company.[13] In the same year, the Iowa company opened its last main station of the nineteenth century, the so-called Alaska station.

The establishment of this distant outpost shows the flexibility and resourcefulness of Standard's organization at its best. In July of 1896 for a first time the San Francisco office sent north a traveling salesman, J. C. Fitzsimmons, to canvass opportunities for oil production and for marketing in that land of long nights and deep cold. It was, by chance, just a few weeks before gold was discovered on the Klondike, a tributary of the Yukon, in Canada's Northwest Territories. The excitement which broke out the next year after the first gold shipments put 60,000 eager gold-seekers in motion. They ranged down the Yukon into Alaska and by 1899 were working the rich gold sands at Nome.[14]

Well before that time Iowa Standard had made its entry. In the spring of 1898, for $39,500 it had purchased and outfitted at Seattle a stern-wheel river steamer, which it renamed the *Oil City*. With Fitzsimmons in charge, the steamer made a two-month voyage beyond the Inland Passage to the old Russian village of St. Michaels at the mouth of the Yukon. Charlie Watson was already there, building a warehouse for the candles, lamps, lanterns, kerosine, naphtha, and lubricating oils he had brought by sailing ship. Meanwhile, in July, 1898, Marshall D. Rainbow was appointed special agent at Dawson, Yukon Territory, more than 2,000 miles away. Rainbow came down the Yukon, building storage depots of corrugated iron at Dawson and of logs at Circle City and Eagle. For six years, when the weather permitted and so long as the traffic warranted, the *Oil City* traveled back and forth between St.

Michaels and Dawson exchanging the products of the Iowa company for the miners' gold dust. In 1900, after Nome had become the chief center of the gold stampede, Iowa Standard split off Nome from Dawson and made it a separate main station.[15]

Although Iowa Standard had no station in Honolulu, its kerosine sales to the Hawaiian Islands supply additional evidence of its enterprise. Charlie Watson was also a pioneer in this trade, for in 1887 he had taken 10,000 cases by sailing ship to the tropical paradise. It was a trip he liked to recall. While in the Hawaiian capital Watson had played poker with Kalakaua, last of the Hawaiian kings, and had "skinned" him. In Honolulu, Standard dealt with one of the large factoring houses, Castle & Cooke. This arrangement was highly satisfactory, for it permitted the company virtually to monopolize the Hawaiian trade without having to maintain a station. In most years, sales to the Islands were larger than those of any of the smaller main stations, including Alaska.[16]

Stations varied considerably in size and equipment. The two largest, located in San Francisco and Los Angeles, by 1896 represented investments of about $53,000 each. The smallest, at San Diego, was valued at about $5,500. Each station had one or more plain brick warehouses containing an office and storage for cased goods, and several tanks ranging up to 7,000 barrels in size for bulk storage. They were also equipped with a pumphouse, barreling plant, and a stable. They kept on hand a thirty- to sixty-day supply.[17]

The principal stations had fairly large staffs. At Portland, for example, there were nineteen in 1894: the special agent (manager), a cashier, two clerks, and an office boy; two traveling salesmen; eight warehousemen, three teamsters, and a man who served as both pumper and cooper. Only seven, including George Flanders, the special agent, who earned $2,700, appeared on the roster at 26 Broadway with salaries of $600 or more per year. Most of the warehousemen were probably paid a daily wage, and the teamsters may have worked on commission. They all put in a six-day week, consisting of nine hours a day for the office force and ten hours for the plant employees.[18]

Iowa Standard supplemented its main stations with depots or substations. The storage depot established in 1883 at Oakland was a forerunner. By 1890 the company was operating eleven substations and twelve main stations. A decade later, when there were fifteen main stations, the number of substations had grown to fifty-eight. Some were sizable, like the $4,200 plant at Bakersfield, consisting of a warehouse and tanks; others were just a small tank and perhaps a warehouse located on a spur track near some hamlet like Nampa, Idaho, or Elko, Nevada. They were usually staffed by no more than one or two men, who were paid a commission.[19]

Because the substations were scattered and frequently remote, Iowa Standard tried to watch over them closely. San Francisco used the special agents to help with the supervision. Each agent was frequently on the road making certain that the substations in his territory were up to the mark. He kept track of all sales, including those of competitors, and reported his findings monthly to the San Francisco headquarters. A detailed rulebook governing such matters as safety, the unloading and return of tank and box cars, reports of oil shortages, sales ("for CASH only," except for a credit list approved by the Home Office), correspondence with customers, and the care and maintenance of stocks, was also distributed to guide the men at the substations.[20]

The substations gave Iowa Standard better coverage of its market, for they helped serve the growing population within each main station territory. They made possible direct deliveries to retailers in or near communities too small to merit a main station, thus eliminating the need for a jobber. They also permitted freight savings and more extended use of the cheaper method of bulk deliveries by tank wagon as opposed to delivery of oil in tins.[21]

One of the important marketing developments, in fact, was an increasing reliance on tank-wagon delivery in the kerosine and gasoline trade. The Iowa company turned to the tank wagon in the more populous areas as the most economical means of distributing oil except for a large delivery direct from a tank car. For the merchant, too, there were advantages. He could retail bulk oil more easily from a tank filled regularly by tank wagon than from an unwieldy barrel, and he was no longer troubled by possible damage from leakage to goods stored near his oil. Nor was he faced with the problem of returning empty barrels.[22]

This mutual convenience to both company and merchant is reflected by a rapid increase in the use of the rumbling vehicles. Standard's wagons first appeared on the streets of San Francisco in 1883; by 1890 they had been adopted at all the main stations except Marysville. In that year the Iowa company delivered about one-seventh of its kerosine by tank wagon. Soon the practice also became common at the substations. By 1900 the tank wagons were handling about one-third of the kerosine sales. Together with barrel deliveries, they reversed the sales pattern existing a decade earlier; only one-third of the kerosine was sold in the more costly five-gallon tins, compared with two-thirds in 1890.[23]

Iowa Standard was also alert for economies in marketing its cased oil. Freight costs were higher for cased oil than for oil in bulk. Moreover, many tins coming to the West Coast, especially by water, were damaged en route and required retinning and recasing before they could be sold. To reduce costs and the risk of damage, the Iowa executives late in 1894 arranged for Ohio Standard to send some used can-making machinery from Cleveland and men to operate it. By the summer of 1895 this machinery was at work in San Francisco in a rented building near Iowa Standard's bayside tanks. Two years later the company bought a six-acre tract at Seventh and Irwin streets, where it located a can factory and built additional storage for the San Francisco station at a cost of $138,000. In 1895 it had also set up can-filling machinery at each of the main stations so that oil, sent in bulk, could be tinned and cased with cans supplied from San Francisco.[24]

3

While Iowa Standard was perfecting its marketing system, it was also extending its product line. In 1885 it was a wholesaler mainly of kerosine. Fifteen years later it had an even greater share of the kerosine trade, but the combined sales of allied products ($2,569,000) amounted to almost as much as the sales of kerosine ($3,151,000). In 1900 the naphthas, including gasoline, were second in value to kerosine, followed closely by lubes and specialty products, and then by a group of painters' supplies comprised of linseed oil, turpentine, and white lead.[25] The painters' supplies were appropriate trade items because hardware merchants stocked them as well as oil. They may have been more important to Iowa Standard than to other marketers in the Standard empire, however, because of the company's long battle with the paint and oil firm of Whittier, Fuller & Company.

The Tilfords supplied the Iowa company to the greatest extent possible from refineries of the Standard combination. At first Cleveland was the chief source of oil, but smaller amounts also came overland from refineries in the Pittsburgh area and around Cape Horn from Bayonne, New Jersey. Later the big Whiting works, which were opened in the fall of 1890, took over as the main supplier. Whiting, located just outside Chicago, was closer to the West Coast than any other Standard refinery. The painters' items were also stocked from Midwest sources.[26]

During its first years Iowa Standard owned many of the cars used for delivering oil and other supplies to its marketing stations. This came about largely because of the nearly 100 three-compartment combination cars it had inherited from the Continental Oil & Transportation Company of California. Bulk deliveries, in fact, were handled almost exclusively in these cars. Deliveries of cased goods, which in the later 1880's amounted to more than three times the volume of bulk oil, were made mainly in box or cattle cars belonging to the railroads.[27] As the bulk trade increased, Iowa Standard expanded its fleet, buying 187 new combination cars between 1890 and 1893. It was on the way to becoming about as much a transporter as a marketer, for at the end of 1893 its investment in rolling stock ($314,260) was greater than in stations and land ($309,081). A year later, however, the Iowa company sold its 273 cars to the Union Tank Line Company, which was the specialized carrier for the Standard companies, and thereafter engaged solely in marketing.[28]

The kerosine sold by the Iowa company was principally a water white oil of 150° fire test marketed under either of two historic brand names, Pearl or Pratt's Astral. This oil always accounted for more than 90 per cent of the kerosine sales. The balance consisted of Elaine, a blue ribbon Pennsylvania kerosine; Eocene, the premium product of the Whiting refinery; Headlight, an oil of high fire test used especially for railroad locomotives; and small quantities of a cheap oil of 110° fire test called Standard White.[29]

Sales of gasoline, the most important of the naphthas, increased more than fourfold during the last decade of the nineteenth century. Earlier, gasoline had been a lightly valued by-product of the manufacture of kerosine. At times it was burned at the refineries, though it had a limited market mainly as a cleaning solvent and as a thinner for paints and varnishes. During the 1890's this market was greatly expanded. The gradual introduction of small stationary engines powered by gasoline was partially responsible, but an energetic advertising campaign stressing the comfort of cooking with gasoline was also a contributing factor. No splitting of wood, no hauling of wood and coal, no soot, no ashes to be removed from the grate, a fire that could readily be turned on and off, these were among the advantages put forth for its use.[30] Many housewives were converts to the new fuel, especially in the warm climate of Southern California and in the San Joaquin and Sacramento valleys. Standard's principal brand was its Red Crown Deodorized Stove Gasoline. *"Red Crown* does not gum the burner, is nicely deodorized, and is always uniform," proclaimed an advertisement of 1892.[31] This Cinderella among oil products was in its humble kitchen phase.

Lube oils and greases had almost no place in Standard's western trade until after 1886. Once started, however, the Iowa company pushed their sale with increasing vigor, for they usually yielded a higher rate of profit than did kerosine. "Luminants are to lubricants as milk is to cream," was the pithy comparison of one old oilman. A wide range of lubes was marketed, including such famed Standard brands as Capitol Cylinder Oil, Renown Engine Oil, Eldorado Engine Oil, Atlantic Red Oil, Extra Signal Oil, and Dynamo Oil. There was also a good sale of Eureka Harness Oil, Boston Coach Axle Oil, and Mica Axle Grease for the horse-drawn vehicles of the era, and of Electric Cycle Oil for bicycles.[32]

Late in 1892 a Lubricating Department was set up at San Francisco to supervise the marketing of lubes, greases, and such specialized lines as candles, wax, and "petroleum hard oil" (petrolatum). Colonel E. H. Merrill, a former traveling salesman for the Portland station, became its chief. One colorful battle waged during these years was against the animal, fish, and vegetable oils—lard, neatsfoot, dogfish, castor, cottonseed—that were among the early competitors of Standard's lubricants. Colonel Merrill once gained a customer by giving a sample of a Standard lube to the superintending engineer of a steamship company that had been using lard oil. He had similar success on another occasion with a large Puget Sound lumber mill that had been using dogfish oil. When a customer insisted, Merrill was willing to supply non-mineral oils, for Iowa Standard also stocked them.[33] But his greater competition came, of course, from the lubes of the independent eastern and western refiners.

Because of 26 Broadway's keen interest in lubes, the New York headquarters controlled this trade more rigorously than any other. At times Colonel Merrill received almost daily instructions from the meticulous Silas H. Paine, who was in charge of lube sales west of the Alleghenies. Merrill's general cost-price book gives a clear picture of the drive with which Paine pursued new customers. *"Get right down to naked cost,"* Paine wrote Merrill on one occasion. *"Get Tubbs biz at all hazards and regardless of cost,"* he wrote another time. During the nineties Paine appears to have sought a 5 per cent profit. When Iowa Standard, at Paine's urging, took less to get an order, he frequently promised to restock the company at a cost sufficiently low to restore the 5 per cent margin. The success of his efforts was striking. The value of kerosine sales grew by half between 1893 and 1900, while lube sales grew by 150 per cent and sales of specialty products increased nearly fivefold. In 1900 lubes and specialty products accounted for about 15 per cent of all sales.[34]

As the Merrill cost-price book indicates, special prices were offered to preferred customers to build up trade. Occasional discounts were made to keep trade from a competitor and for large orders. At times prices were shaved if a large purchaser agreed to buy the company's

Sales in Far Western Marketing Area
1893 ⚬ 1899

MILLIONS OF DOLLARS

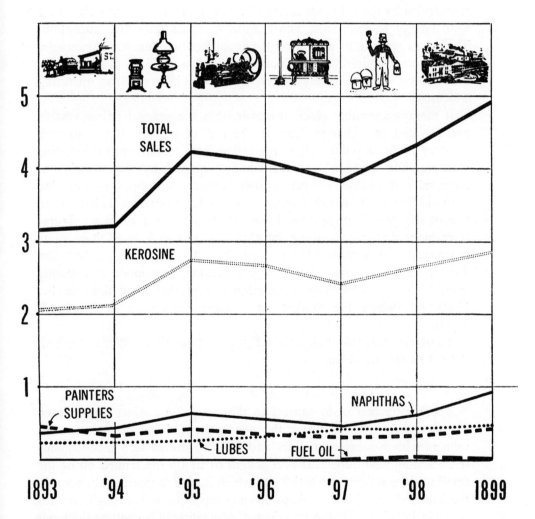

SOURCE - ANNUAL SALES STATEMENTS, 1891-1922.

NOTE - BARRELS OF PRODUCTS SOLD ARE TABULATED IN APPENDIX.

products exclusively. In one instance a reduction was granted a manufacturer of engines on condition that he urge his customers to use Standard's gasoline.[35]

Variations in prices between communities are more notable. Freight rates were one factor, for they favored Pacific Coast terminal cities over the interior towns. Bakersfield, at the southern end of the San Joaquin Valley, maintained the highest wholesale price for kerosine in 1900 of any station or substation in California; undoubtedly, the local rates levied by the railroads for hauling oil from Stockton to Bakersfield were largely responsible.[36] The hazards of trade were also important. The prices and profits per barrel for supplying the Yukon, for example, were extremely high, but the Yukon trade was small, unpredictable in its duration, and relatively costly, both for plant and for operating expenses.[37]

It seems reasonably clear, however, that the general policy was to make a slightly higher markup on the cost of refined oil and to seek a larger profit at points where there was little or no competition. For example, San Jose, which was wholly supplied by the Iowa company, almost always yielded a higher profit per barrel of kerosine than did San Francisco or Oakland, fifty miles away (see Table 6). In five of the years between 1892 and 1900 the San Jose profit figures were more than double those for Oakland, and in four of these years more than double those for San Francisco. The Bay cities, unlike San Jose, always had some degree of competition, and more was readily possible. Profits were also proportionately greater at stations in the Northwest, where the market was almost completely in Standard's hands.[38]

The Iowa company had little liking for competitors. When it could, it tried to remove them.

4

There were two main aspects to the campaign against competitors. The company tried to break the connections of independent eastern refiners with western marketers and to keep the eastern independents from finding new outlets. It also sought to tie up the refined oil of the small western refiners, an activity to which it gave increasing attention in the later 1890's. This struggle to down competition was a rough one, far more in keeping with the practices of the nineteenth century than our own.

In dealing with competitors, Iowa Standard drew strength from several sources. The efficiency of its marketing organization was cer-

Table 6: Kerosine Per Cent Markup and Net Profit Per Barrel at San Jose, San Francisco and Oakland Agencies, 1892-1900

| | Per Cent Markup | | | Net Profit per Barrel* | | |
	San Jose	S. F.	Oakland	San Jose	S. F.	Oakland
1892†	18.8	7.7	18.9	$ .66	$(.03)	$ .11
1893	20.6	9.8	16.6	.61	.16	.02
1894	18.4	7.4	12.4	.51	(.04)	(.18)
1895	36.8	32.0	34.9	1.59	1.28	1.41
1896	28.4	20.2	22.5	1.16	.66	.77
1897	23.8	18.5	15.3	.77	.36	.22
1898	23.6	25.3	17.5	.72	.75	.33
1899	31.2	27.4	23.5	1.17	.95	.67
1900	24.0	19.4	24.1	.98	.70	.80

*Variations in selling expense and in the quantities sold of the different grades of kerosine (lumped in a single "cost of goods sold" figure for each of the cities) were other factors affecting the profit margin. San Jose generally ranked lowest both in cost of goods sold and in selling expense. Freight rates from the East were identical for all three cities.
†2nd half of 1892.
Source: SO(Iowa) Special Statements.

tainly one important factor. The financial resources of the Standard organization, which gave flexibility and scope to Far Western operations, were also significant. And so was Iowa Standard's favored position in regard to rail transportation. This latter advantage has been the subject of much debate, but it was a pattern of nineteenth century competition by no means limited to the Rockefeller companies.

Standard's chief advantage in getting more favorable transportation rates than its rivals was the large size of its shipments. One railroad was played against another. Some trade was also given to competing ship-owners. The traffic was so large that railroads were eager to bid for it and to give rebates from published rates that they would not give smaller shippers. When rebates were declared illegal in 1887 by the Interstate Commerce Act, for several years the company still found ways to maintain a preferred position.

The close ties with the railroads meant that after 1885 no independent eastern refinery was successful in establishing a major outlet in the Iowa company's territory. Only a trickle of independent oil came in. When it did, Iowa Standard was quick to notice. Occasionally it offered a dealer a better buy, usually through a discount, or it might attempt to purchase his business.[39]

An agent might also "make a fist." In 1894 George C. Flanders, special agent at Portland, sent a tactless letter to a retailer in South

Bend, Washington, where a jobber had started cutting into Standard's market with kerosine purchased from the American Oil Company of Titusville, Pennsylvania. Flanders wrote:[40]

> We will state for your information, that never a drop of oil has reached South Bend of a better quality than what we have always shipped into that territory. They can name it 'Sunlight,' 'Moonlight,' or 'Starlight,' it makes no difference. You can rest assured that if another carload of 'Sunlight' oil arrives at your place it will be sold very cheap. We do not propose to allow another carload to come into that territory, unless it comes and is put on the market at one-half its actual cost. You can convey this idea to the young man who imported the carload of 'Sunlight' oil.

John D. Archbold later disavowed this letter before the United States Industrial Commission as a "foolish statement by a foolish and unwise man," but it undoubtedly dulled the desire of the young jobber for independent oil.[41]

Years later the federal Bureau of Corporations uncovered other examples of rough play. George W. Arper, a sizable wholesaler at Oakland who had switched his business from Standard to a refinery in Pennsylvania, reported a visit from Charlie Watson in 1891, warning him, "If you bring oil in here, we will see that you can't sell it, we will drive you out of business." A small jobber and retailer in the East Bay, John Goldstone of Alameda, told an investigator of a similar threat in 1896 when he had refused to sell out. "You may be glad later to come to terms," was the grim comment of Standard's emissary. Both Arper and Goldstone continued to buy independent oil, but others were not so bold. H. R. Slayden, a wholesaler in Pasadena, recalled that in 1896 he had ceased to purchase from Scofield, Shurmer & Teagle of Cleveland because a friend, R. J. Keon, the assistant special agent at Los Angeles, had advised him, "Our orders have been, if you do not stop shipping [sic] goods to break you up." Another merchant, H. S. Walker of Pomona, by 1897 had transferred most of his trade from Standard to two eastern independents, Arnold, Cheney & Company and the Penn Refining Company, who maintained outlets at San Diego. He reported a conversation with E. S. Sullivan, the special agent at Los Angeles: "Walker, remember there have been others like you before. The Standard takes good care of its friends. Those who are not its friends never remain in the oil business a very long time." When Standard bought up the two San Diego outlets in 1900, Walker was out of the oil trade for about two years because Standard would not sell to him.[42]

Both Arper and Walker spoke of the low quality of Standard's oil

Inside Iowa Standard's Head Office at 123 California St., about 1889

216,506. OIL-CARS. M. Campbell Brown, Cleveland, Ohio. Filed Jan. 7, 1879.

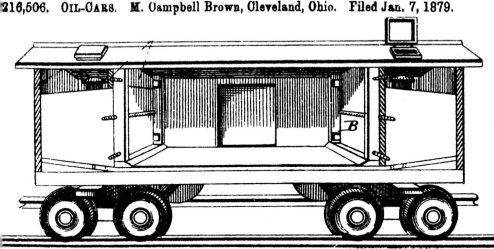

Claim.—A car subdivided into two or more compartments, each end compartment containing an oil-tank, said tank constructed with an inclined or self-draining bottom, and resting upon a floor formed in counterpart thereto, said tank also having a tapering or inclined top, with a filling-opening placed at or near its highest point and in line with a filling-opening in the car-top, and there being a removable partition separating said tank from the next adjacent compartment, all combined substantially as set forth.

The "Campbell Brown" combination car used by Iowa Standard

Note Price of Refined Oils and Gasoline.

STANDARD OIL COMPANY

SAN DIEGO, CAL., MAY 20, 1897.

GENTLEMEN:

We quote you the following prices, F. O. B. San Diego, subject to change without notice :

MICA AXLE GREASE

3 dozen tin boxes to a case, $2.80 per case.

3 dozen wood boxes to a case, $2.25 per case.

25 lb. wood pails, $1.15 each.

BOSTON COACH AXLE OIL,   ASK

ELECTRIC CYCLE OIL,   FOR

CYCLE LANTERN OIL,   PRICES

SEWING MACHINE OIL,   ON

EUREKA HARNESS OIL,   THESE.

Paraffine Wax, in cakes, @ 7c. per lb.

CANDLES

OUR CANDLES ARE FRESH FROM OUR OWN FACTORIES.

Electric Light, 6, 10, 20, $1.15 per case,   Granite, 6, 10, 20, $1.30 per case.

"   "   6, 12, 20, 1.30   "   "   6, 12, 20, 1.45   "

"   "   6, 14, 20, 1.40   "   "   6, 14, 20, 1.55   "

"   "   6, 16, 20, 1.50   "   "   6, 16, 20, 1.70   "

Paraffine, 1s, 2s, 4s and 6s, $3.24 per case.

Our Granite Candles are especially adapted to Mining Purposes.

REFINED OILS

Kerosene, in barrels or drums, @ 10½c. per gallon.

Pearl, Astral or Star, @ $1.65 per case.

Eocene, $1.85; Extra Star, $2.05; Elaine, $2.15.

NAPTHA AND GASOLINE

Deodorized Stove Gasoline, in barrels or drums, @ 11c. per gallon.

74° Naphtha, in barrels or drums, @ 12c. per gallon.

Gas Machine Gasoline, in drums, @ 20c. per gallon.

Red Crown Gasoline, in cases, @ $1.65.

Benzine, or 63° Naptha, in cases, @ $1.65.

86° Gasoline, in cases, @ $2.50.

LUBRICATING OILS, &c.

	BLS.	CASES.		BLS.	CASES.
600° W. Cylinder,	70	75	Extra W. S. Lard Oil,	59	64
Capitol Cylinder,	50	55	No. 1 Lard Oil,	49	54
Renown Engine,	28	33	Union Thr'd Cut'g Oil,	35	40
Eldorado Castor,	26	31	Pure Neatsfoot Oil,	60	65
Eldorado Engine.	25	30	Extra Signal Oil,	55	60
Atlantic Red,	24	29	Dynamo Oil,	28	33
Golden Machinery,	22	27	Black Lubricating Oil,	15	20

STANDARD OIL COMPANY.

as one reason for refusing to deal with the great eastern organization. This may have been true. At the time of Arper's defection, the goal of a good kerosine from Ohio's sulfurous crudes had been only partially achieved. As Arper reported a conversation with W. S. Miller, ". . . the [Ohio] oil was all that I would be able to get. . . . I could not get Pennsylvania oil because they were not making enough to send it out west." Miller claimed, "We [Standard] can't get enough for our Eastern trade. . . ." And by the later 1890's Standard was blending refined oil from the small California refiners with its imports from Whiting, turning out for some localities a kerosine that was undoubtedly inferior to that from Pennsylvania.[43]

Nevertheless, competitors who established ties with the eastern independents and who resisted Standard's blandishment and harassment usually survived. At times they felt persecuted by price cutting, by exorbitant freight charges, and by delays when their cars traveled by roundabout routes or were damaged.[44] It was easy for them to attribute to Standard what Standard may have had nothing to do with, and to see themselves as victims of its power. But their oil did get through and found a market. The greatest danger for these marketers was that they would be left high and dry if their eastern supplier folded or was purchased by 26 Broadway.

5

Iowa Standard experienced its most vigorous new challenge from outside oil when a Colorado competitor tried to enter the western market during 1892 and 1893, putting to the test the company's powerful leverage on the railroads. A few years earlier Colorado oil would have offered little competition. The picture changed in the later 1880's, however. Crude production in Colorado amounted to 76,000 barrels in 1887; three years later it climbed to 369,000 and in 1892 to 824,000, which was more than double the figure for California. Moreover, the crude yielded about 40 per cent kerosine, half again as much and of better quality than the yield from California crude. Standard's executives were not caught napping. When the first important Colorado producer and refiner, the United Oil Company, was organized in July, 1887, Isaac E. Blake, president of the Continental Oil Company, was among its founders. The next year Continental acquired a minority interest in the new concern and signed a contract to market its oils.[45]

As production soared, a few of the United stockholders, led by Daniel P. Eells, a prominent capitalist of Cleveland, Ohio, joined with others, including the Cleveland steelmaster, Charles Otis, in organizing the

Rocky Mountain Oil Company in 1890. The company put down wells at Florence, the site of the only important Colorado field, and within two years became the state's leading producer. Apparently, like United, Rocky Mountain hoped to ally with the Continental Oil Company. "Early in 1891 . . . Mr. Daniel Eells came to our office," H. M. Tilford testified in 1907, "and had an interview with W. H. Tilford and myself in which he stated that he and some friends proposed to build a refinery . . . and asked if the Continental Oil Company would take their output. He was told the Continental . . . was getting . . . all the oil they could market in that vicinity." Nevertheless, Rocky Mountain went ahead with its plans, building north of Pueblo a refinery which it connected with the wells at Florence by a thirty-mile pipeline. The refinery was equipped to manufacture everything from gasoline to paraffin and had a still capacity of 2,400 barrels, which was considerably larger than that of PCO at Alameda. Early in 1892, Rocky Mountain again attempted to get Continental to take its products or to have Standard market them elsewhere. Failing in this, the company prepared to challenge Standard all the way to the Pacific Coast.[46]

In April, 1892, the New York Tilfords apprized their San Francisco brother of the new threat. Shortly, E. A. Tilford wrote Wesley that 26 Broadway had nothing to fear at cities on or near the Pacific Coast, for rail rates to the Coast were lower from Cleveland and Whiting than from Pueblo. They were, in fact, much lower: 78¢ a hundred pounds on oil from Whiting and 96¢ from Cleveland in comparison with $1.60 from Pueblo, with the low eastern rates being justified because of the competition of waterborne shipments around Cape Horn. The rate from Whiting gave Iowa Standard an insuperable advantage along the Pacific Coast of nearly 5.5¢ a gallon over kerosine from Pueblo. In Arizona and Nevada, however, the advantage lay with the Colorado company. "Will you kindly advise me whether the Rocky Mountain Oil Company will amount to much[?]," E. A. Tilford asked his brother. ". . . if so, I had better see what can be done to have the rates from Colorado to these various intermediate points equalized with . . . the rates . . . from Chicago and Cleveland."[47]

Tilford's strategem was to get the railroad to remove oil from regular tariff schedules and make it a special item of commerce. Should this be done, he wrote Wesley, "I do not think there will be much difficulty thereafter to shift rates at any point at any time to a figure that would be agreeable to us. . . ." To J. A. Munroe, the General Freight Agent of the Union Pacific, Tilford pointed out that his scheme would free a railroad from embarrassment in adjusting rates "as the situation might warrant. . . ." But try though he did, he could not get the necessary unanimous consent of the western railroads.[48]

Meanwhile, Tilford heard rumors that negotiations between Rocky Mountain and the Union Pacific might open the Coast to competition from Colorado, after all. The Union Pacific had its own track into Portland. Disturbed, on June 10 he prevailed upon Richard Gray, the General Traffic Manager of the Southern Pacific, to send Munroe of the Union Pacific a stiff wire that Tilford had drafted: "I hope you will do nothing to affect our joint relations with that company with regard to Pacific Coast business. Have you observed the large tonnage you have lately been handling for them? I think it is so great you should be careful how you jeopardize your own interest in this direction."[49]

Tilford's fears were soon justified, for within a few days he learned of a circular the Union Pacific had issued in October, 1891, fixing rates from the Missouri River to the Pacific Coast as the maximum for all traffic originating on its lines west of the river. Gray, of the Southern Pacific, had agreed to this ruling but had forgotten it until June 15, when the Santa Fe brought it to his attention by asking his company to join it in a similar arrangement. He quickly turned down this proposal.[50]

The Union Pacific circular was a troublesome matter, for the oil tariff from the Missouri River was identical with that from Chicago. Rocky Mountain thus was promised the same 78.5¢ rate to the Pacific Coast that the Whiting refinery received, a situation that caused a flurry of wires and letters. Because the Union Pacific had published its circular after an understanding with the Southern Pacific, E. A. Tilford wrote Wesley, "it would embarrass them [the Southern Pacific] more or less if the Union Pacific accepted tonnage on the basis of the circular in question. . . . Therefore they think if Munroe can be brought into line and withdraw the circular . . . through influence brought to bear on him in a quiet way, it would be much the best way."[51]

But the Southern Pacific continued to work in harness with the western Tilford. Gray wired Munroe that his road could not accept less than $1.60 for oil from Pueblo. In a long letter he urged the withdrawal of the circular, lest it cause the Interstate Commerce Commission to re-examine the pattern of rates between the Missouri River and the Pacific Coast to the detriment of both roads. Gray also stressed their good relations with Standard, which for a first time was sending no oil West by water. "The Standard Oil Company has been treating you very nicely," he went on. For Munroe's reflection, he pointed out that in addition to sharing in the traffic to California, the Union Pacific was carrying about half of Standard's shipments to the Pacific Northwest. Standard could easily divert this traffic to other roads. "In view of the fact that some of the Standard Oil people are in the Northern Pacific directory . . . I think you should appreciate the amount of Portland business you are receiving."[52]

The Union Pacific soon buckled under this pressure. On June 20, Munroe notified Gray that he was withdrawing the 78.5¢ rate to California. For a time, he continued to hold out for 78.5¢ to Portland, but in little more than a month that figure, too, was raised to $1.60.[53]

When a Rocky Mountain representative named Gaylor came to San Francisco early in August to talk with the Southern Pacific, he was able to accomplish nothing for his company. Gray refused to consider a tariff from Pueblo equal either to 80 per cent of the Missouri River rate, as Gaylor first requested, or to the full Missouri River rate. Gaylor suggested that Rocky Mountain could ship oil back to the Missouri River and then to California for less ($1.28½) than the $1.60 figure. Gray replied that the Southern Pacific would allow no such subterfuge. Learning of Gaylor's threat, Tilford wondered briefly whether Standard should try to have the Missouri River rate raised lest some oil slip in by this roundabout route, but he soon decided that the effort was neither desirable nor necessary.[54]

Rocky Mountain, nevertheless, continued to attempt to crash Standard's barricade. It made headway by gaining the assent of the Santa Fe for a 78.5¢ rate between Pueblo and the railroad's Pacific Coast terminal at San Diego. But the new company still had to reckon with the competitive disadvantage that came from using cylinder tank cars as opposed to the combination cars of Iowa Standard, for sending an empty cylinder car back to Pueblo added about two cents a gallon to Rocky Mountain's transportation costs. And shipping oil from San Diego to San Francisco by water cost 25¢ per hundred pounds, or an additional 1.6¢ a gallon.[55]

Late in 1892 Rocky Mountain seized an opportunity to strike a blow at Iowa Standard's preferred position with the railroads after persuading William C. Bissell, the former assistant chief clerk of the Iowa company, to resign and set up a partnership to market its oil at San Francisco. Bissell's firm, the Great Western Oil Company, established its office at 123 California Street, Iowa Standard's former home. The defection of Bissell was especially important, for in addition to his personal knowledge of Iowa Standard's operations he had brought along a good deal of E. A. Tilford's correspondence, which he had thoughtfully filched from the files.[56]

Bissell lashed out at Iowa Standard in December by filing a complaint against some thirty railroads before the Interstate Commerce Commission. Citing numerous dates and rates, he showed the company's winning ways since 1885. He spent little time with rates that were no longer current. His heaviest fire he reserved for the favored treatment the Iowa company received for using combination tank cars, to which the company claimed patent rights. These cars, Bissell asserted, had "no advantage whatever" for the railroads over cylinder tank cars. The combination cars, in fact, were "less advantageous and more expensive," weighing more and carrying less. Yet the railroads charged less to transport oil in these cars to several points in California's interior valleys. And, far more important, they made no charge for hauling them East while levying $105 for an empty cylinder car. The justification commonly offered that the space between the tanks in a combination car could be used by a railroad to carry freight on the return run, Bissell denounced as "a mere pretense and sham. . . ." He claimed that they were returned empty about as frequently as cylinder cars, for the space between the tanks was so small and "so saturated with petroleum oil" as to be "unfit for the transportation of nearly every kind of merchandise." Bissell asked the Interstate Commerce Commission to order the railroads to refund all charges paid for the return of empty cylinder cars. Standard's renegade concluded his complaint by denying that the oil rate from Chicago, which discriminated so sharply against the petroleum industries of Colorado and Wyoming, could be justified by the theory of water competition around Cape Horn. Bissell argued that the rates from "Colorado common points to Pacific Coast Terminals, in order to be reasonable and just," should be proportionate to the Chicago rate.[57]

In rebuttals that were frequently lengthy, the railroads entered categorical denials of Bissell's accusations, which the Secretary of the Interstate Commerce Commission passed on to S. C. T. Dodd, Standard's counsel at 26 Broadway. For nearly two years the case dragged through a series of postponements, requested chiefly by Bissell as he sought to buttress his arguments. Finally, in November, 1894, he asked that his complaint be dismissed.[58] By that time neither he nor the Rocky Mountain Oil Company was in business. Rocky Mountain had suffered heavy losses in marketing, and early in 1894 had agreed to a merger of its producing properties with those of Standard's affiliate, the United Oil Company, leaving its refinery idle.[59]

6

The deeply rooted western firm of Whittier, Fuller & Company proved to be Iowa Standard's leading antagonist after 1885. This pioneer partnership in lead, paint, glass, and oils had been dealing in oil products at least as early as the Civil War. Until the 1880's, however, it was solely a marketer in central California, with outlets in San Francisco, Sacramento, and Oakland. Then, about the time of its purchase of the paint and oil business of Scofield & Tevis in 1883, it began to expand. Within a decade it had added branches at Portland, Los Angeles, San Diego, Marysville, Stockton, and Seattle. Most of its oil came from the Bear Creek Refining Company in Pittsburgh and from Lombard, Ayres & Company in New York, but it also bought some on the West Coast from PCO and, occasionally, from the Union Oil Company. Its Star kerosine and premium Extra Star were well known.[60]

One indication of the growing stature of Whittier, Fuller & Company was its inclusion late in 1884 in the talks at 26 Broadway between CO&T of California and Standard that led to the formation of the Standard Oil Company (Iowa).[61] Apparently, Whittier, Fuller had planned to make its oil business a part of the merger, but backed out. Nevertheless, a period of relative peace and stable kerosine prices followed the formation of Iowa Standard, enduring for almost a year before PCO was forced to resort to an auction house to dispose of kerosine that Iowa Standard had refused to accept under a purchase contract. Efforts of certain eastern independents, especially the Beacon Light Oil Company of Cleveland, to develop a larger trade in the San Francisco market also contributed to the price collapse.[62]

The contest between Iowa Standard and Whittier, Fuller went on for almost a decade. Whittier, Fuller proved resourceful in the hard fight, but the advantage lay with the Iowa company. Prior to the Interstate Commerce Act, both companies received rebates from the railroads. Standard, with its heavier traffic, was able to gain the larger margin; usually, its rebates ranged from 15 to 30 per cent of the published rates. Iowa Standard moved to improve upon this advantage after 1885 through the use of the patented combination tank cars it had acquired from the Continental Oil & Transportation Company. In the minds of the Standard executives, the patent rights to these bulk and case oil carriers were undoubtedly considered a principal gain from the merger with CO&T. Whittier, Fuller protected itself by designing a combination car which had a single large center tank and which, like the car of its rival, the railroads also hauled East free of charge. Iowa Standard viewed this evidence of ingenuity as a patent infringement, though for some years it took no action.[63]

The companies battled on other fronts. Iowa Standard extended its competition in the paint trade, cutting sharply the price of white lead, which Whittier, Fuller manufactured, "as a club to bring the San Francisco firm to terms."[64] Kerosine prices also fell off. Between June, 1886 and June, 1887, the price at San Francisco of the chief 150° brands dropped from 26¢ to 18.5¢ a gallon, though apparently the Beacon Light Oil Company was more responsible for this decline than either Iowa Standard or Whittier, Fuller.[65] In the autumn of 1887 the San Francisco firm struck out at Standard when it hired Charles J. Woodbury, the onetime manager of CO&T's Lubricating Oil Department, to appear before the Oakland City Council and Fire Department officials and conduct tests of the major kerosine brands. The tests showed that the kerosines of Whittier, Fuller were considerably safer in their burning temperatures than those marketed by Standard, results that the San Francisco firm publicized widely. For several years Whittier, Fuller also vexed Standard's close ally, the National Lead Trust, by sending East occasional shipments of its high-quality white lead at cut-rate prices.[66]

As the struggle dragged on, Iowa Standard hoped that its opponent could be induced to yield. Late in 1888, the thirty-two-year old Henry M. Tilford arrived from New York to make a new attempt to be rid of a troublesome competitor. Tilford found, however, that the asking price of Whittier, Fuller was too high. It could hardly have been the million dollars later cited in the press, but it was more than Standard cared to pay.[67]

While the negotiations with Whittier, Fuller were going on, the Iowa Standard executives were also at work on another plan to build up their position in the West. They were discussing freight rates with the Transcontinental Association, an organization of railroads west of the Mississippi River, which was holding a convention in St. Louis. They were deeply interested in these meetings, for, in wiping out rebates, the Interstate Commerce Act had increased rail charges, and they wished to recover as much of Iowa Standard's former advantage as possible.

The railroads, especially the Southern Pacific, had reason to want to cooperate, for the Iowa company was sending a good deal of its traffic around Cape Horn to offset the higher rail charges. In the year beginning September 1, 1888, according to the Interstate Commerce Commission, approximately 23 per cent of the 9,178,000 gallons received by Iowa Standard in California made the four-month sea voyage. The railroads were anxious to reverse this trend. Before J. C. Stubbs, the general traffic manager of the Southern Pacific, left for the meetings, he and E. A. Tilford worked out a plan they hoped would be mutually satisfactory. It was a simple one: The Transcontinental Association would reduce rates briefly when Iowa Standard notified the Association that it wished to replenish its stocks; at other times competitors like Whittier, Fuller would have to pay the higher rates.[68]

Stubbs encountered little difficulty in selling the plan at St. Louis. After talking with other traffic managers, he wired his assistant, "Say to Tilford that association will probably consent to following agreement: Oil rate from Cleveland to be $1; at this rate he can stock up; after doing so he to notify Chairman Leeds, who, after giving necessary notice, will advance rate to $1.25, and continue that rate until such time as Tilford notifies him of reduced stock, when he will again reduce it to $1 to enable him to stock up."[69]

Tilford argued that $1 was too high. He maintained that Iowa Standard could afford to pay only 85¢ per 100 pounds, "owing to water competition." The argument led Stubbs to visit Wesley H. Tilford late in November at 26 Broadway before a compromise of 90¢ for points between Chicago and Pittsburgh was agreed upon. In addition, Stubbs had promised E. A. Tilford, "Clipper competition will be taken care of." And it was. Even though Iowa Standard's sea traffic declined, rates for waterborne oil shipments rose from 50¢ to 62.25¢ per 100 pounds in 1888 and from 62.5¢ to 81.25¢ in the following year.[70]

Meanwhile, with Iowa Standard fully stocked, on January 1, 1889, the rail rate was raised to $1.25, which gave the company an advantage of nearly 2¢ a gallon over the oil brought in by competitors at the higher figure. E. A. Tilford was delighted. "I think we have managed this freight business pretty well," he triumphantly wrote his brother.[71] In 1889, in response to his request, for a time the rates were again lowered, and apparently in 1890 as well.[72]

Whittier, Fuller felt the pressure of its rival more overtly in December, 1889, when Iowa Standard decided to test its patent rights to the combination cars. It did so in an unusual way, taking advantage of its friendly relations with the Southern Pacific to make the railroad its target instead of Whittier, Fuller. In a quiet suit that was virtually uncontested, a federal circuit court at San Francisco granted an injunction against the Southern Pacific for hauling the cars of Whittier, Fuller which Iowa Standard charged infringed its patent. Whittier, Fuller did not learn of the injunction until two of the cars failed to arrive from Pittsburgh. Its attorney remarked acidly that the Southern Pacific was "about as agreeable a defendant as any complainant could wish . . . for a running mate." In all, fourteen cars bound for San Francisco were stranded by the injunction.[73]

Before it could be made permanent, the court agreed to hear Whittier, Fuller as obviously the true defendant. In May, 1890, it dissolved the injunction on grounds of hardship pending a decision. Whittier, Fuller agreed that its cars were similar to those of Iowa Standard, but it argued that a combination car was "a mere aggregation of parts" and not patentable. The attorney for Whittier, Fuller pointed out that the patent Iowa Standard acquired in 1885 had been preceded by a number of others. One of these the United States Supreme Court had declared void in 1880 as "[without] exercise of the inventive faculty" and "frivolous." Iowa Standard's case was dismissed in October, 1891, and the company lost an appeal seventeen months later.[74]

Nevertheless, by 1890 Whittier, Fuller was gradually losing its fight. It was, in fact, purchasing a good deal of its kerosine and naphtha from the Standard companies. Some it bought in New York; it took more from Iowa Standard on the West Coast. By 1891, the San Francisco firm was getting almost half of its oil from Standard. In that year Standard had about 85 per cent of the western trade in kerosine and naphtha, if its sales to Whittier, Fuller are included. The relative positions of the two companies is clearly shown in Table 7.

Table 7: Kerosine, Gasoline and Naphtha Sold in Iowa Standard's Territory in 1891 (Barrels)

	Kerosine	Per Cent of Sales	Gasoline & Naphtha	Per Cent of Sales
Iowa Standard	267,231	74.0	37,153	75.0
Whittier, Fuller (Standard Oil)	39,197	10.9	4,822	9.7
Whittier, Fuller (competing oil)	42,764	11.9	4,714	9.5
PCO	2,680	0.7	2,287	4.6
35 small wholesalers (competing oil)	8,970	2.5	—	—
4 small wholesalers (competing oil)	—	—	643	1.2
Total	360,842	100.0	49,619	100.0

Source: Refined Oil, Naphtha and Gasoline Sales for 1891, McClanahan Records.

Even in turpentine, the Iowa company outsold Whittier, Fuller four to one.[75]

Whittier, Fuller also continued to suffer from a disadvantage in freight costs. The pattern of special favor to Standard sanctioned by the Transcontinental Association late in 1888 had been abandoned, but the new rate structure served the Iowa company almost as well. In March, 1891, just as Standard's Whiting refinery, near Chicago, began to supply the West Coast, the railroads changed their former practice of a single blanket rate for points between Chicago and Pittsburgh to a system of fixed rates. The new rates ranged from 78.5¢ per 100 pounds from Chicago to Pacific Coast terminals to 96¢ from Pittsburgh.[76] It cost Whittier, Fuller about 1¢ a gallon more to bring oil from Pittsburgh than it did Iowa Standard to ship from Whiting under the new arrangement.

Whittier, Fuller, as an alternative, could buy oil in New York and ship it around Cape Horn, a route it favored far more than did the Iowa company. But here, also, the firm was hurt by its competitors' powerful leverage on freight rates. E. A. Tilford, at the end of 1891, made clear to J. C. Stubbs of the Southern Pacific that the clippers must avoid low rates around Cape Horn in 1892 if the railroads were to receive all of the traffic of Iowa Standard. He urged Stubbs to get Sutton & Dearborn, the chief clipper operators to California, to agree to a rate of at least 50¢ a case (60¢ per 100 pounds) in return for a promise of 100,000 cases over the sea route. Stubbs was glad to make the effort. In 1891 Whittier, Fuller had shipped more than 200,000 cases by water, E. A. Tilford wrote Wesley, of which nearly half came from Standard. He thought, therefore, that he could promise the clipper companies 100,000 cases (Whittier, Fuller's oil!) without requiring Iowa Standard to send any at all.[77]

When oil arrived at a West Coast port, Whittier, Fuller faced additional freight charges unless the cargo could be sold at the port city. Local rates were high; for example, the charge paid from San Francisco to Bakersfield was nearly as much as from Pittsburgh to San Francisco. Here again the Iowa company held an advantage. In California the Southern Pacific gave the company preferential rates; in Washington the Northern Pacific did so.[78] Iowa Standard could ship from San Francisco to Sacramento and Los Angeles for less than half the published rates, and to Stockton and Marysville at lesser savings. This advantage was ended for a time in California in 1892 when the railroad canceled its special rates, at the suggestion of Tilford, before responding to an order from the State Railroad Commission for a statement of all its oil rates. "I did not want these net rates to become open for everyone," E. A. Tilford wrote his brother, "as I had in view the distribution of Horn Oil that could be brought here and sent to better advantage from San Francisco . . . if the net rate was made an open one. . . . After awhile, when this matter blows over, I can arrange to secure our old net rates from time to time as we may desire to use them."[79]

Still other pressures gradually helped to wear down the resistance of the western competitor. For one thing, Whittier, Fuller & Company suffered great internal stress following the death of the senior W. P. Fuller in 1890, for W. F. Whittier and W. P. Fuller, Jr., proved an incompatible team. The upshot was that the Fuller family bought out the Whittier interest early in 1894 for $400,000. This large sum was a heavy burden for the new firm, reorganized as W. P. Fuller & Company.[80]

Standard's western rival was also in danger of losing its tie to the Bear Creek refinery, owned by the Mellons of Pittsburgh, who were competitors of Standard overseas, especially in France. To remove them, in August, 1893, 26 Broadway took an option on stock of the Bear Creek Refining Company and of other Mellon oil companies. It delayed the purchase until November, 1895, but in the meantime Fuller had learned of the negotiations.[81] The western firm faced the bleak prospect either of scrambling to find another supplier or of purchasing nearly all its requirements from Standard. If Fuller bought solely from Standard, it would have to buy at a figure fixed by its rival and meet the market price of its rival's comparable brands.

Fuller's outlook for profits in any case was limited, for Iowa Standard was intensifying its competition. During the fall of 1894 the price of Pearl and Astral kerosine was reduced at San Francisco and Oakland to 17.5¢ per gallon, a price so low that Iowa Standard lost money.[82] Such prices must have been disheartening to Fuller.

Early in 1895 the western firm decided to end the contest. The negotiations with Iowa Standard's W. S. Miller and H. C. Breeden resulted in an agreement late in March divesting Fuller of its kerosine and naphtha business, apparently for $550,000. Standard's price included a bonus of $325,000. Later an additional $41,000 was written off as overvaluation. Fuller continued as an oil firm solely as a marketer of lubes.[83]

The transaction was a good one for Fuller. It gave the family sufficient funds to pay off Whittier and, if they chose, to expand the remaining three-quarters of their business. After the sale, Fuller was in a better position to develop its trade in lead, paints, varnishes, wallpaper, and glass.[84]

Standard also had reason to be pleased with the outcome. The last major western competitor was removed just before Pennsylvania crude shot to $2.66 a barrel, its highest price in more than two decades. Simultaneously, Ohio crude rose to $1.15 a barrel.[85] The improved market for crude helped trigger increases in refined oil prices throughout the nation, but the rise was especially steep in cities of the West where

Fuller formerly had sold oil. Within three weeks of Fuller's exit, San Francisco wholesale prices for kerosine and stove gasoline had increased by 5¢ a gallon. The cased brands, Pearl and Astral, jumped from 17.5¢ to 22.5¢, and Red Crown from 18.5¢ to 23.5¢, causing anguished outcries against the "Great Oil Trust."[86] Earnings of the Iowa company spurted from $177,000 in 1894 to $703,342 in 1895, the company's largest profit to that time. The high earnings were only partly due to the elimination of Fuller, for 1895 was a year of business revival following the panic of 1893. But they were more than enough to pay off the bonus and write-off on the Fuller property within nine months.[87]

Iowa Standard kept alive the Fuller brand names of Star and Extra Star that had held a loyal group of customers for so long. It sold Pearl and Astral under the Star label and the premium Eocene as Extra Star.[88]

7

The capture of W. P. Fuller's light oil trade helped Iowa Standard acquire control of the kerosine and naphthas of the Pacific Coast Oil Company some three weeks later. Fuller and its predecessor had been a valuable outlet for PCO oil.[89] After Fuller stepped out, PCO had either to struggle for new sales among the few independents, or to seek to do business with the Iowa company.

PCO found that Iowa Standard was willing. The negotiations with PCO were by no means so important as those with Fuller, but the Iowa company had even stronger representation at the bargaining table. H. M. Tilford, who was on the Coast from 26 Broadway, shared in the talks, along with Miller and Breeden. Charles N. Felton and D. G. Scofield represented PCO. Under an agreement, signed on April 11, 1895, Iowa Standard contracted to purchase annually up to 1,000,000 gallons of water white kerosine, 350,000 gallons of the lower quality standard white kerosine, 500,000 gallons of naphtha, and as much benzine as it could sell. PCO agreed to market none of these oils, with the possible exception of benzine, to any other party so long as the contract was in force. The prices, 8¢ a gallon for water white, 7.5¢ for standard white, 9¢ for 74° naphtha, and 8.5¢ for 58° benzine, promised PCO a gross income amounting to at least $150,000 a year, which it could supplement by sales of lubes and gas and fuel oils to other parties. The term of the contract, for one year from May 1, 1895, renewable annually, suggests that PCO's bargaining power was weak. The western refiner could never be sure that Iowa Standard would take its goods the following year, though, in fact, the contract was regularly renewed.[90]

The figures specified in the agreement indicate that PCO at this time was able to put through its refinery about 350 barrels daily. Theoretically, Alameda could handle almost half again as much, but even with "hot treating" the manufacture of kerosine required redistilling and treating to a degree not known in eastern practice. During the early years PCO presumably was able to furnish the maximum quantities to Iowa Standard, for the Pico production, though declining, was well above refinery capacity. After 1898, however, as the production of light crude continued to fall, PCO deliveries dropped off. A light crude production averaging 282 barrels daily provided only four-fifths of the kerosine and four-sevenths of the naphtha permitted under the agreement during the last eight months of 1900.[91]

Iowa Standard blended its PCO kerosine with oil from Whiting in the ratio of 30 per cent western to 70 per cent eastern. It found that the mixture gave a satisfactory burning oil for its volume trade under the labels of Pearl Oil, Astral, and Star. In the year following the agreement the Iowa company was able to reduce its receipts of kerosine from Whiting by about 8 per cent and to make appreciable savings in rail freight.[92]

PCO's naphtha was even more useful. Western naphtha was fully as good, if not better, than eastern. And the naphthas, including gasoline, were in growing demand. The San Francisco Bay region, unlike Southern California, used few gasoline stoves, but it shared the mounting enthusiasm for the internal combustion engine. These one-cylinder stationary "explosive vapor engines," ranging up to ten horsepower and more, were being used in increasing numbers to power pumps for irrigation and for other simple tasks. "It looks to me as though there is no business in Los Angeles thriving like that of the gas engine man," wrote one contemporary. "You meet engines on all sides going to various sections of the country. One hears of new plants being put in on every ten acre ranch. The traffic in this article is simply astounding." In 1896 PCO's naphtha supplied Iowa Standard with nearly one-seventh of its needs.[93]

The agreements with Fuller and PCO caused Lyman Stewart to observe that Standard had " 'coopered' things on this Coast so far as illuminating oils are concerned. . . ." He had reason to know, for Union's Santa Paula works was the only other California refinery that had manufactured light products. Probably because of that fact, and at Standard's request, PCO wrote a provision into the *Loomis* agreement of April 18, 1895, forbidding Union to use the tanker to ship kerosine or naphtha to San Francisco Bay. Even without the prohibition, Union could not have shipped much. Its crudes yielded very limited quantities of naphtha and of low quality kerosine. Earlier, in 1891, Standard had sought to buy Union's naphtha output only to be refused. By April, 1895, the Santa Paula refinery was producing nothing; it was so dilapidated that it had been shut down.[94] At San Francisco, a few small firms were importing a little eastern oil, but far less than Fuller had done.

When Union opened its Oleum refinery at the beginning of 1896, western oil again came into the San Francisco region. The company began to sell to jobbers, who mixed its kerosine with eastern for their wholesale and retail trade. Oleum was one reason why 26 Broadway considered purchasing Union in the summer of 1896, though undoubtedly a greater motivation was Standard's growing interest in California oil lands. When these negotiations failed, Standard offered to buy the lighter oils manufactured at Oleum. Lyman Stewart was tempted, but he was also wary. "In making a deal of this kind," he wrote the Oleum manager, "it is important that we keep in mind the fact that at the expiration of the proposed contract we would have no market for our goods until we again built one up, and having abandoned our customers to the mercy of the S. O. Co. they would be slow to tie up with us again."[95]

A brief price war ensued. "They [Standard] are giving more attention to the cutting of our illuminating trade than formerly," Lyman wrote his brother. "But we think we can stand it if they can. . . ." Union shipped some kerosine to Los Angeles, where it was sold for 8¢ and 9¢ a gallon. Union also took the necessary step of negotiating for combination cars and eastern oil so that it could improve the Oleum product through blending.[96]

In March, 1897, however, the two companies ended their strife with an agreement roughly paralleling the one with PCO. The document no longer exists, but it provided for a longer term, two years, and was twice renewed, running until February, 1904. Union agreed to sell "all grades of refined illuminating oil" as well as its naphthas exclusively to Iowa Standard.[97] Occasionally, it also sold lubes to the Iowa company, as did PCO.[98]

The agreements with the western refiners benefited Iowa Standard around San Francisco Bay, enabling the company to tie up competing oil at a low price and to make freight savings through blending. In conjunction with declining prices for eastern crude, they also helped bring about a marked reduction in kerosine and gasoline prices, influenced, too, perhaps by the company's efforts to get at the remaining small importers in the Bay area. The 22.5¢ per gallon charged through much of 1895 for the cased brands of kerosine and the 23.5¢ for gasoline in cases had declined to 15.5¢ and 16.5¢, respectively, late in 1897. And the Iowa profits, if not as high as in 1895, were nevertheless considerably higher than they had been prior to that eventful year.[99]

8

Later, the Iowa company also contracted for the light oil of Puente's new refinery at Chino. The Iowa Standard executives, as usual, were alert to this development in Southern California. In January, 1896, before the refinery went on stream, they arranged for a sample of Puente kerosine to be delivered to their Los Angeles agent. The first attempt at negotiations collapsed because the two companies could not agree on the life of a contract, for the one-year term Miller proposed Puente regarded as "suicidal." Instead, the Puente company invested about $30,000 in land, buildings, tanks, tank cars, and other equipment for a Los Angeles outlet and began to import eastern kerosine for blending.[100]

It was not long before Puente became a vexatious competitor. Puente's sales of kerosine and naphtha were largely responsible for a sharp dip in the volume and profits of the Los Angeles station. By 1897, Iowa Standard's total sales at Los Angeles had declined to $635,000 from a peak of $835,000 two years before. The reduction in profits per barrel was even more notable. Earnings of $1.95 on kerosine and $2.02 on naphtha during the last six months of 1895 had become only 36¢ on kerosine and 21¢ on naphtha during the last half of 1897. "We are costing the Standard Oil Company a whole lot of money—how much they can undoubtedly tell you," J. A. Graves of Puente wrote his friend and Iowa Standard's counsel, E. S. Pillsbury. The situation caused Miller to resume negotiations early in 1898.[101]

On March 31 the two sides signed a two-year contract. Iowa Standard agreed to pay 7¢ a gallon for as much as 600,000 gallons of water white kerosine and 360,000 gallons of 67° naphtha annually, which proved to be more than the refinery could make. The Iowa company also offered to pay 7¢ a gallon for all the 58° benzine from the Chino works that it could sell in the Los Angeles territory. Since Puente no longer needed so elaborate a marketing set-up, Iowa Standard bought its tank cars, horses, wagons, iron barrels and its inventory of kerosine and gasoline for approximately $24,000. As frequently happened in transactions of this kind, the Puente property was overvalued by about $2,000. For its part, Puente promised to sell none of the products mentioned in the contract to other parties except at the site of the refinery. The contract placed no limitation on the manufacture and sale by Puente of distillate for internal combustion engines, which became the southern company's chief refined product.[102]

Puente's success with distillate was so marked that late in 1898 W. S. Miller moved to correct this oversight. The Puente leaders, who knew they had a good thing, chose to bargain. To get the distillate, Miller had to pay 8¢ a gallon for up to 600,000 gallons a year and to raise the price of 67° naphtha to the same figure. Puente also gained an extension of the contract to April 1, 1904 and sold the balance of its marketing facilities to the Iowa company for $16,000.[103]

The effect of the Puente agreement was apparent almost at once. Kerosine in Southern California jumped from 1.5¢ to 2.5¢ a gallon and continued to rise; sales of kerosine and naphtha increased, and profits climbed even more rapidly. Profits per barrel for kerosine and naphtha at the Los Angeles station were up more than threefold during the last six months of 1898 from the lows established early that year. The revised agreement had barely been signed in January, 1899, before distillate also became a noteworthy sales item. During the balance of the year the Los Angeles station sold 778,000 gallons, which was almost 200,000 gallons more than the company had agreed to take. The value of all products sold at Los Angeles grew from $635,000 in 1897 to $1,004,000 in 1899.[104] Other factors may well have played a part in this remarkable increase, but there can be no doubt of the importance of the Puente contract for the Iowa company.

9

Iowa Standard's few remaining competitors were confined principally to the two major markets, the San Francisco Bay area and Los Angeles. Around San Francisco there were a few small importers. At Los Angeles the competition was of a different order and more difficult to deal with. Because of the oil fields nearby, new refineries appeared toward the turn of the century. The Franklin works, established by Union's former refiner, Franklin H. Dunham, was in operation in 1898, as were four others by 1900. The crude they processed was heavier than that handled by Puente, and their main product was usually asphalt. But they also manufactured small quantities of naphtha, kerosine, distillate, and lubes. They produced enough so that the contest in Los Angeles continued to be the most severe in Iowa Standard's marketing domain.[105]

After 1898 the Iowa company carried on what closely approached a "mopping up" operation around San Francisco Bay. In little more than two years it purchased four small concerns that had been importing eastern oil in their own tank cars. Two of them, F. B. Joyce & Company of San Francisco and George W. Arper of Oakland, had also been former customers of Union's Oleum refinery. Arper, the longest lived of these competitors, was finally forced to sell out in January, 1900, after 26 Broadway bought and shut down his eastern suppliers, the Manhattan Oil Company and the Oil Creek Oil Company. The other firms were the Golden Gate Oil Supply Company, a San Francisco wholesale and peddling house, and the King-Keystone Oil Company of San Francisco and Oakland, which sold only its refined oil business. Iowa Standard spent about $57,000 in these four transactions. In each case the company later wrote off a fraction of the purchase price, indicating that it may have paid a small premium.[106]

Three of the four purchases the Iowa company liquidated, but F. B. Joyce it kept alive. Renamed the F. B. Joyce Oil Delivery, it became the means first used by Standard to deal directly with consumers in San Francisco. Joyce took over the routes and equipment formerly used by the Golden Gate Oil Supply Company and carried on a peddling trade. By 1902 it was selling about 7 per cent of the kerosine marketed by Standard in San Francisco. It was a "hidden" company; that is, Standard tried to keep the public from learning that Joyce was its property. Even earlier the company had been carrying on a similar hidden operation in the East Bay, where in 1896 it had picked up the Penn Oil Company, an Oakland concern that was in debt to Standard for its oil. After the purchase of Arper, the Penn Oil Delivery became prominent as a retailer in Oakland and Alameda, and with the purchase of some small companies in Southern California, entered Los Angeles and San Diego. Both Joyce and Penn at times were operated at a loss; they were obviously intended to serve as a new competitive weapon.[107]

10

By 1900, because of its vigorous expansion and its successful battle against competitors, Iowa Standard virtually controlled the western trade in light oils. In kerosine, for example, it had competition at only five stations (Los Angeles, San Francisco, Oakland, San Diego, and Seattle), and its share of the total market had grown from an estimated 84.9 per cent in 1891 to an estimated 96.5 per cent in 1900. In the naphthas, its climb was equally impressive, from 84.7 to 96.4 per cent.[108] In lubes the company's position was not as strong, but it far surpassed any competitor. The company had also a substantial trade in painters' supplies.[109]

Financial statistics supply additional evidence on the extent of Iowa Standard's achievement. Its total sales in 1900 ($5,720,000) were nearly double those for 1893 ($3,174,000), the first year for which dollar figures are available. The company's gross assets had grown from

$828,000 at the end of 1885 (after the first six months of operation) to $3,039,000 at the end of 1900. It had also paid dividends of $2,432,-000, of which $2,000,000 were declared after 1895.[110]

A comparison with the other domestic marketing subsidiaries and affiliates of 26 Broadway is likewise revealing. During the period from 1895 through 1900 Iowa Standard never ranked lower than third in earnings per barrel on all products among the fifteen or more main marketing divisions. It was surpassed only by the Continental Oil Company, the nearest to a monopoly among Standard's subsidiaries, and less regularly by the Waters-Pierce Oil Company. The ratio of the per cent of the nation's population in the Iowa company territory to the per cent of Standard's marketing profits earned there underscores further the high earning power of the western subsidiary. In 1900 the Iowa territory included a little more than 4 per cent of the population of the United States; between 1895 and 1900 it had provided from 5.6 per cent to 10.2 per cent of Standard's net earnings from domestic marketing.[111]

In one part of the western trade, however, Iowa Standard had little place. This was in fuel and gas oil, the main outlet for California's rapidly growing crude production. It was the prospect of profits in this trade, joined with the belief that the problem of manufacturing a good kerosine in commercial quantities was not insoluble, that finally brought Standard into all aspects of the California industry in the fall of 1900.

VIII

26 BROADWAY
MAKES A DECISION

The entry of 26 Broadway into all phases of the California oil industry was merely one link in a chain of events dating from the middle and later 1880's when Standard reversed its earlier policy of leaving producing to others and began also to extend its crude purchasing beyond the old Oil Regions. For these moves, there was a dual stimulus. To offset declining Pennsylvania production and to serve growing markets, Standard needed larger supplies of crude; to maintain its dominance, it also needed to keep the light crude of new territories from falling into the hands of other refiners. Within a few years, 26 Broadway bought or organized a series of producing companies, including the South Penn, Forest, Carter, and Ohio oil companies, and assembled a skilled staff to operate them.[1]

The discovery in 1885 of the great Lima field in northwestern Ohio was the prelude to these changes. By 1886 Ohio accounted for nearly 4 per cent of the nation's output of crude oil. Two years later its share had grown to 35 per cent—9,700,000 barrels. Ohio produced a light crude yielding a somewhat smaller proportion of refined products than did Pennsylvania crude, and its kerosine was smoky and foul-smelling.

In spite of these shortcomings, 26 Broadway did not linger on the sidelines for long. In March, 1886, it organized a pipeline company, under the leadership of Calvin N. Payne, to purchase, pipe, and store the crude of the new region. The same year Standard hired a distinguished chemist, Herman Frasch, to work on the problem of turning out a good kerosine and erected a refinery at Lima to skim off the light distillates. With these volatile fractions removed, the remainder could be sold as fuel—a use the former Californian, E. A. Edwards, had pointed out when he started an Ohio fuel trade in 1885 with his lightly financed Edwards Oil Burner Company. Standard distributed its fuel oil chiefly through a 200-mile pipeline which it laid from Lima to Chicago in 1888. Later that year Frasch had his first success, leading to the building of the great Whiting refinery during 1889 and 1890. While the Whiting refinery was being constructed Standard's Ohio activities were completely integrated, for 26 Broadway plunged into producing and bought

195

the Ohio Oil Company. Over-all, by 1891 more than $32,000,000 had been invested in this Ohio venture.[2]

Further to the West, 26 Broadway was attracted by other, less explosive oil regions. In 1895 it bought a number of the early wells and leases in Kansas. Prior to 1900 the annual Kansas crude production topped 100,000 barrels only once, but the oil was readily refinable, prompting Standard to build a refinery at Neodesha in 1897.[3] That year also witnessed Standard's entry into Texas. Through Calvin N. Payne and Henry C. Folger, Jr., it formed a partnership with a leading operator at Corsicana, the first commercial oil field in Texas, and helped finance a refinery. Crude production in Texas as late as 1900 was under 1,000,000 barrels annually, but Standard's entry there, as in Kansas, marked a continuance of its westward march.[4]

In areas still more distant, 26 Broadway investigated but did not act. By the turn of the century, its scouts had roamed to the West Coast and around the margins of the Pacific as far as Alaska, Peru, the Dutch East Indies, China, and Japan.[5] The scouts, who were usually leaders of Standard's producing companies, collected samples and made their reports to John D. Archbold, head of the Producing Committee and Rockefeller's successor as chief at 26 Broadway after the middle nineties. Archbold, in turn, consulted with H. C. Folger, Jr., of the Manufacturing Committee to determine the products that could be derived from the various oil samples. The vision of Standard's executives had grown, for in examining the possibilities of production in these remote regions they were looking toward the more effective development of markets around the world.

2

At first, their interest in the California fields was casual and intermittent.

Toward the end of 1886, nearly a decade after Rockefeller had turned down the pleas of Scofield and Cyrus Angell to join them in developing California oil, 26 Broadway briefly considered purchasing the Pacific Coast Oil Company. Presumably, the lure for the New York headquarters was the possibility of reducing freight costs in supplying Iowa Standard. I. E. Blake, a PCO stockholder and president of the Continental Oil Company, Standard's Rocky Mountain marketer, was one who urged the purchase. To aid negotiations, in the spring of 1887, PCO sent two barrels of Pico crude to the Acme Oil Works at Olean, New York, so that William M. Irish, one of Standard's top refiners, might work with it.

His inability to turn out a good kerosine helped shelve whatever plans 26 Broadway may have had for California at that time.[6]

A few months later Standard was offered a more limited opportunity. In September of 1887 Charles S. Gilbert, a resident of Los Angeles, arrived in Cleveland to try to interest Standard executives in the wildcat activities of a group of small-time Southern California promoters and oilmen in the Coalinga region. Gilbert was one of a group who had staked Colonel William M. Leete, an old mining man, for a prospecting trip over the desolate country along the western border of the San Joaquin Valley. Early in 1887 in Oil Canyon, which within a few years would be the center of the first Coalinga oil rush, Colonel Leete dug some shallow pits and found oil. He filed claims on several sections of government land under the placer mining laws and collected samples of both green and black oil, which Gilbert took to Cleveland. Standard examined the samples but refused to bid for the properties or to supply the promoters with additional capital.[7]

In the spring of 1891, for the first time on record, 26 Broadway sent out a scout of its own. J. L. McKinney, an executive of the South Penn Oil Company, was an old-time producing man—"owned by the Standard, body and breeches," said one Titusville acquaintance who had not made his peace with the Rockefeller organization. McKinney's destination appears to have been high on the coast of northern California in the Humboldt area, which for a year or two enjoyed a revival of interest after a long quiet since the middle 1860's. The Standard scout may also have extended his journey to include other California oil regions, but his report, whatever it was, could hardly have been favorable.[8]

There is little evidence, in fact, of any deep interest on Standard's part in any California oil territory or company prior to the great outpouring of the Los Angeles City field during 1895. Until that time, California's oil production had been relatively small and static for almost a decade. Suddenly, as a result of the Los Angeles boom, production shot to 1,208,000 barrels in 1895, nearly triple the figure of two years before. This rapid climb did not level out, for the search for oil went on with renewed vigor and optimism. Summerland, about one hundred miles up the coast from Los Angeles, Coalinga, on the west side of the San Joaquin Valley, Whittier-Fullerton, in the Los Angeles district, and Kern River, McKittrick, and Sunset, near Bakersfield, were all becoming well-known fields by the turn of the century. Their output helped bring California production in 1900 to a new peak of 4,320,000 barrels, which amounted to nearly 6 per cent of the nation's oil.[9]

Two of the fields, Coalinga, beginning in 1896, and Kern River, beginning in 1899, gave promise of duplicating, if not surpassing, the startling development at Los Angeles earlier in the decade. Each owed much of its early growth to one of the discoverers of the Los Angeles field. At Coalinga, C. A. Canfield, in partnership with J. A. Chanslor, was the most successful operator.[10] At Kern River in July, 1899, two months after James and Jonathan Elwood had sunk a shaft and discovered oil, E. L. Doheny, with a partner, bought the territory surrounding the discovery site and by September had brought in the first of their many wells.[11]

These developments, which elevated California to the status of a major attraction, led 26 Broadway to send out several scouts to make detailed surveys in the years following 1895. Archbold and his associates directed many inquiries to Iowa Standard, which supplied a ready-made fact-finding organization. And the flow to the East of oil samples increased.

Archbold also noticed that much of the new oil, though little suited for refining, was readily marketable as fuel. This burgeoning trade had already attracted Iowa Standard. In 1895 the Iowa company began to buy crude from small producers in Los Angeles and to sell it for fuel at its Los Angeles station. A year later the company had fuel oil tankage at both Los Angeles and San Francisco. Its sales of fuel oil prior to 1900 were never large—in 1899 they amounted to little more than 35,000 barrels—but they pointed to a potentially valuable new trade.[12]

Standard's executives studied California carefully and without haste. They had the resources to move whenever they believed such a step would serve their cause. The volume of production, the range of products that could be derived from the crude, the extent of the market—these were the factors that governed their decision. They could pick their moment.

3

While 26 Broadway was viewing California with mounting interest, California producers were eying Standard with more varied feelings. Its scouts could be seen and talked with, and its probable course of action was a matter of frequent discussion. Some of the gossip carried a note of alarm; California, some oilmen said, would be "gobbled up" by the eastern giant. Others took a more optimistic view, holding that Standard's resources would provide a powerful stimulus for the industry. There were hopes, too, that Standard would buy up or into western companies, enabling their owners to cash in on their years of effort. Such hopes led to a number of offers and promotional schemes after 1895.

Standard's attraction to California probably was a greater concern to Lyman and Milton Stewart, the owners of a controlling interest in the Union Oil Company, than to any other western operators. The Stewarts had been embattled independents in Pennsylvania during the formative years of the Rockefeller combine. They still harbored a good deal of the feelings and prejudices of that bitter era. They had a special reason to fear any added competition from Standard, for, burdened by debt, they were in poor shape to take on their old adversary. Almost all of Lyman's interest (roughly, one-seventh of Union) was pledged for debts as late as the end of 1898.[13] Milton, who for all these years had stayed on in Titusville except for occasional trips West, was also intermittently under a severe financial strain.

Strife within Union was another factor contributing to the Stewart uneasiness. The Stewarts clashed with Thomas R. Bard, the holder of a large minority interest, on a variety of matters. In their eyes, Bard was "too conservative to be progressive." In Bard's view, Lyman was a "most impractical man; unmethodical . . . , visionary, and speculative."[14] The fact that Union's monthly dividends were suspended in 1893 and were rarely paid for several years thereafter intensified the feelings of bitterness.[15] As a consequence, through most of the nineties both Bard and the Stewarts were looking for ways to help Union gain additional financial strength or to sell out. For either alternative Standard frequently seemed a logical answer.

Union first approached 26 Broadway in 1891, the year after the company was organized. At that time its directors were considering selling Standard a minority interest in a company they planned to organize to hold all of the Union properties. After a preliminary attempt to interest 26 Broadway in this fund-raising scheme, their banker reported that Standard "would not have anything to do with it." The "Old House" would consider nothing less than a clean-cut acquisition, a tender Union did not care to make.[16]

By the summer of 1895 the Stewarts were again turning their thoughts to selling all or part of Union. A false rumor in June that 26 Broadway had offered Union a million dollars led Milton to raise the question with his brother. The production of the Los Angeles City field had surely been noticed by the Standard executives. "They are bound to control the oil business of the world and will buy out or freeze out competition. . . . I would advocate selling at anything like a fair price."[17]

The idea, which appealed to Lyman, caused him to confer with his son, W. L. Stewart. His desire to unload at least a portion of the Stewart holdings became even more keen after Iowa Standard entered the fuel oil trade at Los Angeles in October, 1895, but he hesitated to make a direct approach for fear of weakening his bargaining position. Instead, Lyman selected a cousin, Rufus H. Herron, the president of the Los Angeles Oil Exchange, to act as an intermediary. Just prior to Thanksgiving he furnished Herron with a summary of Union's holdings: 60,000 acres of oil land, owned or under lease; a production of 17,500 barrels of crude monthly; 100 miles of two-inch and four-inch pipeline; 51 tank cars; storage tanks with a capacity of 185,000 barrels; and a refinery under construction on San Francisco Bay.[18]

Lyman told Herron that the Stewart family was willing to sell 51 per cent of the stock of the Hardison & Stewart Oil Company, a Union predecessor and subsequently a holder of Union's stock, for $510,000. The Hardison & Stewart Oil Company, he pointed out, owned about 44 per cent of Union in its own name and nearly 30 per cent more through its interests in the Sespe and Torrey Canyon oil companies, the two other stockholding predecessors. Thus 51 per cent of the Hardison & Stewart Oil Company would control the whole of Union. "Our purpose in selling in this way," he explained, "is to form a stronger and more aggressive combination and avoid ruinous competition. Also to avoid care, etc. . . ." To his brother he volunteered a more poignant reason, "To tell the truth, Milton, I have been so long under pressure of debt that I fairly loathe the sight of a note. . . ."[19]

When Lyman's approach through Herron failed to bring a response, he swallowed his fears and on December 18, 1895, "put the proposition directly" to W. S. Miller, Iowa Standard's chief executive in the West. But 26 Broadway, sphinx-like, made no reply. In mid-January, 1896, the Union president withdrew his offer and spent the next few months in futile efforts to raise funds through a bond issue.[20] Though there had been no response, Lyman's offer had alerted the New York headquarters to the fact that Union would probably be "willing" if Standard cared to negotiate.

A few months later, in May, 1896, the hopes of the Stewarts were buoyed from another quarter. Their old friend, I. E. Blake, was trying to get back on his feet after suffering disaster in the Panic of 1893. His love of speculation had led him into a series of unwise mining and railroad ventures, costing him most of his fortune and, in August, 1893, the presidency of the Continental Oil Company. When Blake left Denver that year, he owed its banks nearly $200,000. Among his losses were his PCO shares, amounting to nearly one-fifth of its stock, which went to his creditors at the end of 1894.[21] Blake's plan, devised in association with a New York promoter, F. L. Underwood, was to gather in PCO,

Puente, and Union and "go into the market prepared to offer a consolidated company controlling the output of the Pacific Coast," with Standard as the likely purchaser. Their San Francisco agent, a mining man named Oliver O. Howard, Jr., dickered first with Lyman Stewart for an option to buy out Union, and intended to seek at least a controlling interest in the other companies later on.[22]

One outsider who got wind of the scheme was D. G. Scofield. It held no lure for him. Prior to the Panic of 1893 he had been associated with Blake in his mining and railroad projects, and Blake considered Scofield partly responsible for his downfall. Thereafter Blake would have nothing to do with his former colleague.[23] If Blake and Underwood could carry their plan through, Scofield would surely lose out.

Early in June, perhaps as a counter-move, Scofield attempted to push a merger of his own. He enlisted the aid of Albert Gerberding, a San Francisco grain merchant, who wrote his brother-in-law, Thomas R. Bard:

> Schofield [sic] and I are to secure the P.C.O. Co., Union Co. and Puente Co. and sell the three outfits to the Standard Co. . . . Schofield says he can secure the P.C.O. Co. if I can secure the 'Union' and 'Puente' and that if we had the three . . . the chances of success will be good, and that while the Standard would not pay an exhorbitant [sic] price, they would pay what the property was worth.

Bard replied that nothing could be done at the moment, presumably because of the discussions with Oliver O. Howard, Jr. He did, however, hold out to Gerberding the possibility of a short-term option on Union's stock at a later date.[24]

Though nothing came of either of these proposals, they reveal clearly the widespread belief that Standard was about ready to enter the California industry. In July, 1896, 26 Broadway made its first overt move.

4

On July 13, Lyman Stewart received a telegram from H. C. Breeden at Iowa Standard's San Francisco office. Acting on instructions from H. M. Tilford, Breeden invited the Union president to San Francisco, where Stewart soon discovered that Breeden had been authorized to negotiate for the control of the Union Oil Company. Ten days later, after conferring with Breeden and counseling with Bard and others among his Union associates, Stewart offered Standard one-half of Union at $30 per share ($750,000), or 65 per cent at $40 ($1,300,000). "If they deal," he wrote Milton, "I will be out of debt. If not, I will have to struggle along."[25]

Breeden pledged that Standard was negotiating "in thorough good faith," though, he noted, "it seems to me $1,300,000 is a large sum for 65%. . . ." Accompanied by his chief, W. S. Miller, Breeden went to Southern California at the end of July to make a nine-day inspection of Union's books and properties. "They are evidently well satisfied," Stewart wrote at the end of their survey, "and ask only till September 10th to give us an answer." As the time drew near, however, Breeden requested an additional ten days. "Seems . . . that our friends do not want to break off negotiations entirely, and I'm inclined to think they are playing for a reduction," commented W. G. Hughes, a Union director.[26]

The delay was indeed a bad omen. On September 19, the day before the extension expired, Breeden informed Stewart that 26 Broadway had decided not to accept the Union offer. The price, he reported, was too high.[27] Archbold and his associates may well have considered that if half the stock was worth $750,000, it was too much to pay $550,000 for an additional 15 per cent to give Standard control.

This decision, nevertheless, was almost as great a disappointment to Breeden and Miller as to Union, for both men had become thoroughly convinced of the value of the southern company. The Stewarts, of course, were deeply grieved. Debts still weighed heavily upon them. Milton came to believe that the Standard men were "simply spies looking over our lands to see what we had and how we were situated," and Lyman volunteered the bleak opinion that Standard would negotiate again after it "has subjected us to the usual squeezing process."[28]

Standard did resume negotiations late in 1898, but only after Lyman had made the first move. With Bard's consent, the Union president again offered Standard a controlling interest. By 1898, Union's property, owned or under lease, had increased to 120,000 acres, and its production had grown to more than 30,000 barrels a month. As before, 26 Broadway delegated the fact-finding to Iowa Standard. Early in December W. S. Miller appeared in Los Angeles to bring his earlier report up to date. Miller told Stewart that his report would be "very favorable," but added that the decision to purchase rested with John D. Archbold. If Archbold approved, Standard would send experts to examine the Union properties before taking final action.[29]

The outcome of Miller's visit was the same as in 1896, however. In mid-January, 1899, he wrote Stewart that "our Eastern people . . . [do] not desire to negotiate further. . . ." Miller made no further explanation, leaving the Stewarts harboring "a slight soreness" over the abruptness with which the negotiations had ended.[30]

5

Standard's discussions with Union were by no means its only tentative reach into California during these years. Beginning in 1898, Archbold sent West a number of topflight oilmen, some of whom had authority to commit Standard by leasing oil lands.

One such high-powered team invested with leasing authority was in the state in February, 1898. William Fleming, its senior member, was an old Pennsylvania operator and an outstanding producer who had gone into Ohio for Standard in the later 1880's, first with the North Western Ohio Natural Gas Company and then as president and general manager of Standard's top producing company of the nineties, the Ohio Oil Company. To assist Fleming, Archbold sent along K. Robey, a younger scout who had recently returned from a survey of southeastern Alaska.[31]

The two men traveled California from one end to the other. They visited Humboldt County and Moody Gulch, where hopes still flickered, the Pico region, and Ventura County. They also examined carefully the newer fields that were the current centers of excitement, Summerland, Coalinga, and Los Angeles.

Fleming did no leasing; instead, he submitted a severely factual report to Archbold without specific recommendations.[32] That he took no leases was in itself an indication of his thinking. He evidently believed that the wisdom of seeking California production was still moot, and that Standard could well afford to wait.

Two fields Fleming described with special care: Coalinga, to which Robey returned for a second look, and Los Angeles. Archbold was particularly interested in the Oil City area at Coalinga, the earliest of the Coalinga fields, because the Manufacturing Committee reported its crude yielded an extremely high percentage of naphtha and other distillates. The Committee also noted, however, that the kerosine was impossibly smoky from excessive carbon, a characteristic that caused chemists later to label the Oil City crude as "freak" or "poison" oil.[33] At Coalinga, Chanslor & Canfield had eight wells with a daily yield of about 200 barrels, which they shipped to San Francisco by tank car. The Los Angeles production Fleming estimated at around 3,500 barrels a day from some 800 wells jammed close together, but the field, he thought, had passed its peak and was not likely to recover.

On marketing, Fleming made little comment beyond reporting a conversation with J. B. Treadwell, an oil expert for the Southern Pacific Railroad. Treadwell said that the Southern Pacific could afford to pay $1.50 a barrel for fuel oil and still save money over the cost of coal, a statement Archbold may well have found interesting.

Fifteen months later, in May, 1899, Archbold sent out C. F. Lufkin, Fleming's right hand and manager of the Ohio Oil Company, and John F. Eckbert as Lufkin's assistant. Lufkin, like Fleming, had had a long career in producing. He had served as an oil scout for Standard on an important mission to the Dutch East Indies in 1892, an area to which he returned in 1897. Eckbert, who would later become the first manager of the producing department of the Standard Oil Company (California), was superintendent at Titusville for The Carter Oil Company, another of Standard's producing companies.[34]

The two scouts repeated much of the tour of their predecessors, eliminating the areas Fleming and Robey had found unimpressive, and adding Puente and the new fields of Whittier and Fullerton. Since both men far surpassed the semi-literate Fleming in fluency, they provided Archbold with a much more detailed report on specific fields and on the state as a whole.

Lufkin and Eckbert estimated that California contained about 1,200 producing wells located on no more than 1,000 acres of proven territory. Production amounted to a little less than 7,000 barrels a day. They attributed an increase over 1898 of about 1,000 barrels daily chiefly to Whittier, Fullerton, the Ventura fields belonging to Union, and, above all, Coalinga, a field they found "laboring under a high pressure excitement." At Coalinga, production had climbed to about 1,400 barrels daily. The Los Angeles City field, by contrast, had justified Fleming's prediction, declining to about 2,200 barrels a day.

Standard's scouts estimated that no more than 2,000 acres had been drilled since the beginning of the California industry. This meager record they ascribed to the oil not being a "good refiner" and the tendency of westerners to drill in "precipitous cañons" where seepages from sharply tilted strata gave visual evidence of the presence of oil. The two men believed that the lands already developed were no more than "a 'drop in the bucket' of the probable oil lands of the State," and that much oil would probably be found "in some of the valleys."

Lufkin and Eckbert capped their report with a number of conclusions and recommendations. If Standard desired to develop solely a fuel oil business, they believed that a sizable investment in lands and plant probably would be required before the company could produce and handle enough oil to make money. On the other hand, they told Archbold, "if the refined products, as you now find them in the California oils, should be the attractive feature . . . and the fuel business be considered as only secondary, then we can see no reason to hesitate. . . ." They warned him, however, that setting up a producing organization would not be easy. Conditions were "very unlike anything your men have had to deal with in the East." If Standard entered California, moreover, its men would not be able to draw readily on the experience of the total Standard organization because of their remoteness from the older Oil Regions.

For these reasons, the scouts advised purchasing a California company. They suggested Union or Puente, for each company had large and well-located holdings of oil lands and seemed willing to deal. Puente stock, they reported, had recently sold at $50 a share, indicating a value of about $1,000,000 for the company. Lufkin and Eckbert made no mention of PCO, a concern whose lands they believed were well on the way to exhaustion.[35]

The departure of the two scouts late in May to survey prospects further east scarcely reduced the flow of information from California. In mid-June W. B. Webber, a salesman from Iowa Standard's San Francisco office, returned to Coalinga and wrote Miller a long report, which was forwarded to H. M. Tilford and then to Archbold. Two months later H. C. Breeden informed Tilford of an offer to lease Standard 10,000 acres in San Benito County, northwest of Coalinga. In forwarding the proposal, Tilford told Archbold that "a great many people" were coming to Iowa Standard with offers of potential oil lands and asked for a general statement of policy.[36]

Excitement in California was mounting ever higher during the last half of 1899; Coalinga was its greatest center, but other new fields, including McKittrick and Kern River, were coming in for their share. "Companies are being organized on any kind of property, and stocks are being sold and everybody seems anxious to get hold of them," Lyman Stewart wrote Milton. In October a California Oil Exchange was established at San Francisco, offering investors a market for oil securities in the West's financial metropolis. The Exchange numbered among its members many prominent local capitalists and important outsiders like W. L. Hardison of Los Angeles and J. J. Mack of Bakersfield.[37]

While traveling in the East, W. L. Stewart picked up news that would arouse further the imagination of western oilmen. Standard "is going to locate permanently" in California, the young Stewart reported, and John Eckbert and John H. Fertig would head the advance. Fertig, a former Titusville refiner, had led the Forest Oil Company, one of

Standard's important producers, into Kansas in 1895. Two years later, with C. F. Lufkin, he had gone on a scouting mission to the Dutch East Indies, where he had stayed until the summer of 1899.[38]

Fertig arrived in California late in October accompanied, not by Eckbert, but by Charles H. McCready, one of his superintendents from Kansas. The two men opened an office in Los Angeles. Through Fertig and W. S. Miller, Archbold renewed negotiations to take over Union, but again nothing came of them. The failure may have been due to the fact that the Stewarts sought a higher price than formerly in view of the booming market in oil stocks but, more likely, it was their desire to retain an interest in Union, contrary to the wishes of 26 Broadway, that wrecked the negotiations.[39]

Fertig and McCready were also busy on other matters. The two scouts roamed California, especially the San Joaquin Valley, looking for oil lands. They were less interested in Coalinga than were their predecessors, for a number of dry holes in the Oil City district late in 1899 suggested that the field was reaching its limits.[40] Kern River and McKittrick, on the other hand, were in the glow of their first feverish development. At both places the two oilmen found J. B. Treadwell drilling for the Southern Pacific Railroad. Fertig was sufficiently impressed that he called upon Julius Kruttschnitt, the general manager of the Southern Pacific, to ask if the railroad would be willing to allow Standard to develop its extensive holdings in the Valley. In this bold pitch he also failed.[41]

Like Fleming before him, Fertig had authority to take leases. He concentrated on larger endeavors, however, like the acquisition of Union and the lands of the Southern Pacific, rather than a scattering of leases. Fertig had taken none before he was ordered to Japan early in 1900 to set up a producing company.[42]

Meanwhile, McCready stayed on through the spring informing 26 Broadway of developments in Kern County and elsewhere. McCready watched Kern River and McKittrick most carefully, but on one of his trips he also visited the Sunset field, south of McKittrick and about thirty-five miles southwest of Bakersfield. At this desolate outpost he found W. E. Youle, the veteran driller, who had been working the field for ten years and had been getting a little heavy oil. In May, 1900, McCready's tour came to an end when he was sent to Japan to join Fertig.[43]

By that time 26 Broadway had determined to take a hand in the Valley fields. It had no plans to enter producing, but it had decided to build storage for the mushrooming production at Kern River and McKittrick. At Kern River everything pointed to a tremendous field. By the end of August 134 wells had been drilled to depths of rarely more than 1,000 feet with hardly a dry hole, and production was approaching 1,000 barrels a day. The crude was black and heavy, ranging between 14° and 17° in gravity. About fifty miles west lay McKittrick, which had impressed Fertig still more favorably. In this area of little water, of salt grass and greasewood, there were in August a total of seventeen wells, drilled usually to depths of less than 1,000 feet. From these few wells McKittrick was turning out about half as much crude as Kern River and of a little higher gravity. Together, the two fields had about 40,000 barrels of tankage, which was far from enough to handle the production. The decision of 26 Broadway to handle this heavy oil must have been influenced by the prospects for a profitable fuel trade, a business it had known since 1886 when it went into Ohio to purchase and store the rocketing production of that new region. Nationally, in 1900 fuel oil was in short supply; in California, the trade was reported in excess of 300,000 barrels monthly and was growing rapidly. Storage and transportation seemed to be the main hurdles in the West to its further growth.[44] While crude of such low gravity offered little opportunity for refining, 26 Broadway may have considered that the discovery of light crude in an area of such prolific production was also a reasonable gamble.

Late in August, 1900, at Bakersfield, Charles Watson made a limited announcement of Standard's intentions. His was an appropriate voice, for since 1882 he had led Iowa Standard into many a new community and trade. "We are not coming to produce any oil or buy any land or oil, for that matter," Watson stated. "We are in the storage business, and we see an opportunity for good business and we are coming after it like any others who understand the business. Your production here is going to be enormous, and somebody has got to help you handle it, and we are prepared to do it. It's going to cost lots of money, about a million dollars."[45]

The news set off a wide range of comment. "John D. Rockefeller is reaching out to control the petroleum business of California," was the ominous prediction of the *San Francisco Examiner*. "The situation today comes to this: The Standard Oil Company will forthwith establish tanks in Kern County and go in to obtain control of the output of the Kern petroleum fields, the most productive and promising fields in the State. This will be the thin edge of a wedge, and not so very thin either, when you come to consider [it] carefully."[46]

As tankage began to move from the East, not all of California was viewing the matter so darkly. W. L. Hardison's *Los Angeles Herald*, which had learned of the attempt by Fertig to secure the lands of the Southern Pacific, summarized much of the feeling in this way:[47]

> The Standard, with an eye to business, as is its habit, has waited until California has proven itself an oil producing state of no small degree before showing any desire to have a hand in the business. That the Standard Oil company will be doing business in the state on an extensive scale within the next two years, both as a buyer and producer, there seems no doubt. Opinions differ as to the effect it will have. Some prominent oil men in the state stand in mortal terror lest the entire business be gobbled up and the poor producer ground out of existence. Others, and especially the Kern River operators, see no cause for worry. Certain it is, that for the best interest of the industry, there should be some system in the way of marketing the product, whether the Standard Oil company furnish the system or some other large corporation with equal facilities. As a general proposition, the producers in California are indifferent, acting on the assumption that the state is large enough for even the Standard Oil company to do business in, without injuring the prospects of every individual well owner.

Shortly, the voice of another prominent independent, Lyman Stewart's cousin, Rufus H. Herron, was heard from. Following a trip East, he forecast that Standard's entry would make the California industry increasingly attractive to eastern investors. "They now realize that this is proven oil territory. The coming of the Standard Oil Company this way is good, for it encourages faith in the East in our oil resources and at the same time helps to make a market for the producer. I am not a Standard man, but I know these to be plain facts."[48]

6

Over these same months another action was taking place that received no publicity. When 26 Broadway had attempted to acquire Union, in line with the recommendation of Lufkin and Eckbert, it had failed. Late in February, 1900, however, the opportunity to buy another company had presented itself, for the Pacific Coast Oil Company indicated a desire to sell out.

D. G. Scofield, the vice president and general manager of PCO, was the principal agent. He had watched the rising tide of production with growing concern, for PCO was active in none of the new fields. The Tevis family, it is true, had incorporated the Western Minerals Company in December, 1899, as an adjunct to its Kern County Land Company to buy up claims of oil locators under the placer mining laws. Scofield himself was one of its incorporators, having joined a few months earlier

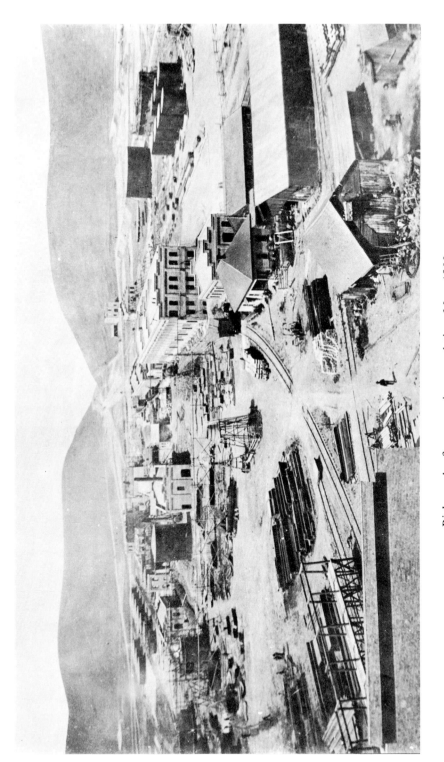

Richmond refinery nearing completion, May, 1902

Richmond refinery during first expansion, probably January, 1904

Coalinga pump station, 1912

with members of the Tevis family, its employees and friends, in filing numerous claims in an area that Lloyd Tevis had contemptuously dismissed as "jack-rabbit land" less than three years before. But Western Minerals was a purely speculative enterprise in no way tied to PCO.[49]

When PCO held its annual meeting of stockholders on February 20, 1900, Scofield made known his misgivings. He told the stockholders, he later recalled, "that in order to remain in business and successfully compete with the new companies . . . it would be necessary . . . to enlarge the business by furnishing additional facilities, which would require . . . a large amount of new capital. . . ." If they did not wish to put up additional funds, Scofield believed they ought to try to sell out to Standard at a fair price. Stockholders voting 81,892 shares (held almost wholly by the widow and children of Lloyd Tevis and by C. N. Felton and his son) preferred the latter course. The balance of the shares, which were outside California in the hands of creditors of I. E. Blake, were not voted.[50]

Scofield, accordingly, discussed a sale with W. S. Miller and H. C. Breeden. They, in turn, carried the proposal through H. M. Tilford to John D. Archbold. Probably at Miller's suggestion, Scofield advised the PCO board in March to revalue the company assets so as to give a more accurate valuation of its property. In the past PCO had rarely deducted losses, whether from depreciation or from any other cause. It may have written off a dead horse or worn-out equipment, but it wrote off little else. The figures on its books for wells, the Alameda refinery, pipelines, tank cars, and real estate, represented close to the total investment from the time of the organization of the company.[51] In this first major effort to make its assets square with reality, the board agreed to reduce the well account by $245,000 for non-productive wells and to write off an additional $16,000 for depreciation of other plant. As a result, on April 30, 1900, the company's stated assets stood at $1,218,000. Early in May, Scofield submitted a balance sheet to W. S. Miller, along with itemized statements showing the productivity of the wells and the value PCO placed on its plant, lands, and oil inventory. Shortly thereafter, Standard took an option at $8 a share on the 81,892 shares that had been voted in February with the understanding that the sale, if made, would be retroactive to April 30. The PCO board held no meetings after March while waiting for Miller's superiors to act.[52]

Meanwhile, 26 Broadway moved unhurriedly. In mid-June, John Bushnell, comptroller of the Standard Oil Company (New Jersey), recommended that the Scofield statements be checked carefully against the PCO books and that an appraisal be made of the property. Two prominent executives, Calvin N. Payne and Theodore M. Towl, left for the West Coast about September 10 to serve as appraisers. Payne, who had helped lead 26 Broadway into Ohio in the 1880's and later into Texas, ranked third below H. H. Rogers and Daniel O'Day in Standard's pipeline operations, and Towl was manager of the Real Estate and Tax Department at the New York headquarters.[53]

The two men, joined by Breeden and Scofield, inspected PCO's properties from Pico northward, pausing for several days late in September to arc south through Kern County from Kern River to McKittrick on their way to San Francisco. The press correctly reported that their purpose was to size up the Kern fields and the probable need for tankage. Their departure from Bakersfield preceded by but a day the return of Charlie Watson, who had come down from San Francisco to lease lands for oil tanks at Kern River and McKittrick.[54]

Payne and Towl mailed their report to Bushnell early in October.[55] On the whole, they were well pleased. The figure fixed by PCO for its pipelines ($165,626) they believed a fair valuation, and the *Loomis,* carried at $80,195, they considered worth at least $100,000. They were far less impressed with the value which PCO had assigned its producing properties ($533,395). This figure they cut to $181,432, but they believed, contrary to the opinion of Lufkin and Eckbert, that at Pico "an acreage equal to what [has already been] developed is certainly good. . . ." Much of the producing equipment, moreover, they regarded as "first class." The Alameda refinery, "an old plant, and yet . . . in a fair working condition," Payne and Towl scaled down from $206,671 to $125,000. PCO's inventory of materials and merchandise ($90,462) they accepted without question. These main property items, along with others of lesser consequence, were appraised at a total value of $756,402.

The two executives believed that the whole capital stock of PCO could be acquired for this sum. Recently, they had taken an option from two Denver banks on 14,764 shares at $5.50 a share which, along with the $8.00 figure authorized for the stock voted at PCO's annual meeting in February, would require an outlay of $736,338. The remaining 3,344 shares, held by other creditors of Blake, they estimated could be bought for about $20,064, or $6.00 a share. "The acquiring of this property gives as strong a hold on the [California] business as could possibly be obtained at this late date," the easterners concluded, "and we strongly advise the purchase."

Archbold approved their report. On October 17 the PCO board, except for Scofield, resigned. Hugh and Harry L. Tevis, the sons of Lloyd Tevis, Gordon Blanding, the son-in-law, and Charles N. Felton, Jr., were replaced by four interim directors headed by Evans S. Pillsbury, Blanding's former law partner, while documents were signed and the remaining shares were acquired.[56] Evidently, rounding up the last shares cost a little more than Payne and Towl had forecast, for, according to the PCO books, Standard paid a total of $761,427 for the company.[57]

With the acquisition completed, on December 18 three of the interim directors resigned in favor of H. M. Tilford, W. S. Miller, and H. C. Breeden of Iowa Standard. Two weeks later W. M. Hall, Iowa Standard's auditor, succeeded to the directorship that E. S. Pillsbury had held briefly. H. M. Tilford became the new president, and D. G. Scofield, the only holdover from the old board, continued as vice president and general manager.[58]

The transaction had been a well-kept secret. Not until the second week in December, almost two months after the resignation of the PCO board, did the press pick up the news, though Union had gotten wind of the event a little earlier. "I would suggest that you call on Mr. Miller," Lyman Stewart wrote his manager at Oleum after the news was out, "and state that we are congratulating ourselves that we now have first-class, practical oil-men to deal with. . . . We cannot help ourselves so far as the situation is concerned and it is much better I think to be *pleased* with it."[59]

7

Two lesser matters connected with Standard's entry into California carried over into the next year. PCO's majority interest in the California Star Oil Works Company posed a problem of what action Standard should take with respect to the minority holdings. And Standard executives also briefly considered the possibility of acquiring the Puente Oil Company.

By 1900 California Star was a company of the past. Its property consisted of the 160-acre Pico patent and the old refinery at Newhall, which had not been operated since 1890.[60] Twenty of its wells were still producing, but several of those drilled near the end of the century (including the two put down in 1899) were dry. In the first nine months of 1900 the average daily production from the CSOW wells was 124.61 barrels. This was a little less than PCO got from its own wells in Pico Canyon (139.84) and considerably less than the total PCO production (292.29), including the wells in Elsmere and Wiley canyons.[61]

For nearly fourteen years after the compromise of 1879 the CSOW shares had been held three ways. PCO held four-sevenths; the balance was divided equally between General Edward F. Beale and his partner,

Colonel Robert S. Baker. For a number of years, especially in the middle 1880's, the CSOW stock gave a lucrative return. During the 1890's, however, the dividends fell off, as competing production drove crude prices downward and CSOW's own production began to decline.[62] When Beale died in 1893, his shares passed to his widow. Following the death of Baker a year later, Mrs. Baker received about two-thirds of his shares, with the balance being distributed among other heirs. By 1900 PCO had picked up nearly 300 of the Baker shares to boost its total holdings to 6,011 $2\frac{3}{36}$.[63]

Standard decided to gather in the minority holdings and to liquidate California Star. It was willing to pay a fair price, but it did not want to be gouged. To avoid being held up, Standard engaged in a ruse. In November, 1900, it transferred the shares held by PCO to J. S. Severance, the secretary to Timothy Hopkins, a capitalist who was the adopted son of Mark Hopkins and who had been an occasional business associate of Felton and Tevis.[64] The price quoted Severance, $9.33 a share, indicated a valuation of $93,333 for the company. It was probably arrived at by the common practice of estimating the future recoverable oil at a price per barrel of the current production, with the addition of a smaller amount to cover the Newhall refinery and grounds. John Bushnell, the Jersey Standard comptroller, had valued California Star's oil reserves a few months before at $638.63 per barrel of the current daily output, which made its Pico property worth about $80,000. On January 8, 1901, Severance succeeded D. G. Scofield as president of California Star with a new board of directors.[65]

Meanwhile on December 18 Iowa Standard had advanced $20,000, which Severance used to pay Mrs. Beale $9.33 a share for her interest (2,138 shares). Acquiring Mrs. Baker's interest proved more difficult. Scofield urged her to sell at the same price, pointing out that "The new owners . . . [with] over 8/10 of the capital stock . . . have decided to liquidate. . . ." Reluctantly, at the end of January, 1901, Mrs. Baker acquiesced. Over the next seven months, Severance gathered in the balance of the Baker shares with funds advanced by Iowa Standard, and then, on August 30, turned back the shares he had received from the PCO in November, 1900.[66] At the end of September 1901, in a purely bookkeeping transaction, PCO closed out California Star, taking over the Pico patent, including the wells and other property, and the Newhall refinery.[67]

While these transactions were going on, Standard also briefly looked over the Puente Oil Company. H. C. Breeden went to Los Angeles on this mission in mid-January, 1901. At his request, J. A. Graves, the business manager of Puente, sent to San Francisco financial statements and other data for the years 1899 and 1900. Although smaller than PCO, Puente was aggressive and profitable. It produced about 350 barrels daily in the Puente Hills and bought additional crude at Coalinga in order to turn out from the Chino refinery more engine distillate, a product much in demand. Its dividend in 1899 amounted to $52,250 (compared to $25,000 for PCO) and was $95,000 in 1900. Evidently, Breeden believed that Puente wanted too high a price. Graves replied to one letter, in which Breeden questioned some of Puente's figures, "From the tone thereof, I hardly think we will be able to do business."[68]

If Standard had purchased Puente, its position around Los Angeles would have been somewhat similar to that in the San Francisco Bay area after the take-over of PCO. Its hand would have been strengthened in the southern end of the state, especially in the first decade of the new century. But 26 Broadway apparently decided that Puente was no bargain.

8

In any case, PCO seemed adequate for Standard's entry. The San Francisco company had been a respected organization since 1879, and D. G. Scofield, its fifty-seven-year-old manager, had accumulated more than a quarter-century of oil experience in the West. Chartered with broad powers, it was a fully integrated operation. Through PCO, Standard became more than a marketer in California; it gained at least a toehold in the other phases of the industry—producing, transporting, and refining.

26 Broadway valued PCO chiefly as a vehicle for the future. While the negotiations were being completed, M. F. Elliott of Jersey Standard's legal department was checking the pipeline powers in the PCO charter. Calvin N. Payne, shortly after his return to Titusville in October, 1900, told Milton Stewart that Standard planned to develop a fuel oil business in California on a grand scale and to erect perhaps a million barrels of tankage. He also indicated that water in the oil could be removed by steaming and that the oil could be piped, statements that made Milton believe Standard was preparing to build a pipeline from the Kern County fields to San Francisco.[69]

A few weeks later, after visiting New York, Payne had more to tell of Standard's plans. He found that H. C. Breeden had been summoned to 26 Broadway and had brought with him a list of California refineries, their capacities and products. Breeden reported that 117

IX

PCO EMBARKS
ON NEW VENTURES

No doubt, Calvin Payne sketched accurately the plans of the executives at 26 Broadway. But these veterans of other bonanzas were prudent men. They were unwilling to invest large sums in permanent installations until their plans were tested. For nearly a year PCO operated tank stations at Kern River and McKittrick on leased land before the sites were purchased. And the capacity of PCO's tankage, though large compared with neighboring facilities, was modest for fields of any consequence. Before Standard's leaders authorized many more tanks and a long pipeline to San Francisco Bay, they studied the production potential of the fields of the San Joaquin Valley and the feasibility of piping the Valley's heavy crudes. Similarly, Standard men operated PCO's old Alameda refinery the best part of a year, learning the characteristics of California crude, before they built a new plant.

Standard's principal new venture was to build a large fuel oil business in California. To help win a place in this highly competitive trade, the eastern executives counted on their great financial resources and their extensive marketing organization for refined products. Independent operators and companies, notably I. E. Blake, the Union Oil Company, associations of producers, and the railroads, had other ideas for developing the fuel oil business. These rivals were not to be pushed aside easily.

A secondary venture was a new refinery on San Francisco Bay at the end of the proposed pipeline. PCO looked chiefly to the light crude of Southern California to produce refined products for the West, but in some measure it also planned to draw on the heavy crude from the pipeline. The residuum from the refinery it could mix with heavy crude for sale as fuel.

These plans soon would be substantially modified, as the discovery of larger quantities of light crude opened up great new opportunities for the refiners. But in 1900 fuel crude was the chief lure, and 26 Broadway's preparations to break into the western fuel oil trade provide the principal theme of this chapter.

2

The tour of Payne, Towl, Breeden, and Scofield in late September, 1900, started the translation of plan into reality. S.O. (Iowa) leased tank station sites at Kern River and McKittrick from the Southern Pacific, paying $50 a month for each of the two eighty-acre tracts. It is odd that the marketing company leased the tracts; PCO undoubtedly was the chosen instrument for the new venture. However, the details of PCO's purchase by Standard were not quite complete. The site selected to serve the Kern River field was two miles north of Bakersfield, a town of nearly 5,000 situated on the eastern margin of the San Joaquin Valley. The tract was well-chosen, for it lay at the edge of the field and on the Southern Pacific's branch line. Just a few weeks earlier, the railroad had reached the oil field, providing an eagerly awaited signal for a boom in production. Heretofore, oil had been brought out by wagon. A typical thirty-barrel tank wagon, drawn by ten mules, made two round trips every three days over routes of seven to twelve miles through jumbled hills to the railroad. The charge was about 50¢ a barrel, compared to 42¢ a barrel for rail transportation from Bakersfield to San Francisco. Short gathering lines from wells to the railroad soon put an end to the tedious and costly wagon hauls.[1]

The other lease adjoined the northwestern corner of McKittrick, a hamlet forty-eight miles by rail west of Bakersfield. Here, wrote a visiting journalist, men were "trying to pump a useful commodity out of the heart of a blasted world . . . a dumping ground for refuse, covered over with alkaline shale, sprinkled here and there with little stubby sage brushes writhing and twisting in fitful gusts under a scorching sun. . . ." The McKittrick field, fortunately, lay near a railhead. In 1893 the Southern Pacific had built a line from Bakersfield to Asphalto to serve asphalt quarries. About 1900 the track was shifted from Asphalto through the newly plotted McKittrick townsite and extended a short distance to the oil field, ending near Iowa Standard's lease. Clearly, the two tank station sites were well-located at promising new fields with rail connections to the major western markets.[2]

During the next few months PCO spent $200,000 on the two tank stations and the gathering lines that connected them to producing properties. The Kern River station consisted of five 35,000-barrel tanks, a loading rack, a switch to the railroad, and a camp of frame buildings: office, bunkhouse, dining room and kitchen, boiler and pumphouse, and half a dozen minor structures. The McKittrick station was smaller, having only three tanks and less extensive gathering lines.[3]

This construction was carried on under the direction of Standard veterans from the East. Shortly after the work got under way, William V. Miller, an assistant to Calvin Payne in the National Transit Company, was sent to Kern River in January, 1901, to take charge of field operations, including the Newhall producing division. He won praise from Payne for building at Kern River a well-designed net of gathering lines. Also in January, George M. Brown, experienced in another Standard enterprise, the Forest Oil Company, was transferred from Kern River to the McKittrick project, which he directed to the end of 1903. Brown has left a revealing description of his duties: "I had charge of putting in the pipe lines, and . . . all construction, and the loading of cars, and the billing, and the hiring, and discharging of employees, and the reports on the West Side fields from the Devil's Den to Maricopa." His monthly reports to Miller and Breeden showed the thoroughness of PCO's intelligence system. Each month Brown tried to visit the superintendent of every oil property in his territory, collecting data on production and pipeline runs, number of wells producing, wells drilling and their depth, new rigs put up, and any changes in ownership. He prepared maps showing the producing wells. Brown reported, too, on new companies entering the fields and old ones withdrawing, land for sale, and new mineral locations and their locators.[4]

About March, 1901, the basic plants were completed. The Kern River gathering system had been delayed somewhat by landowners who feared the "gigantic trust" might take advantage of them. The *Bakersfield Californian* cautioned its readers against a phrase in the right of way agreements which it reproduced in capital letters, "the said grantor, heirs or assigns to fully use and enjoy the said premises, EXCEPT FOR THE PURPOSES HEREIN BEFORE GRANTED." This exception, the paper thought, might mean the owner was giving up his right to lay pipelines on his own property. The Bakersfield correspondent of the *Los Angeles Herald* scoffed: "Some of our citizens seem to think that because it is the Standard Oil Company they must be very careful in their dealings lest forsooth the monster gathers them in and places them on the market at 15 cents each." Evidently, the wary ones were assured; the delay was not serious. At McKittrick, the construction period had been extended a little because the Southern Pacific added two and a half miles to its spur, paralleling the belt of oil wells and ending at a station named Olig. Brown put one of his three tanks there.[5]

As the plants neared completion, the PCO directors authorized Breeden to make crude purchases for the company. Scanty evidence suggests, however, that only a limited buying program was planned.

A Kern River producer said that he offered a contract to PCO but was refused on the ground that there was more than enough oil on the open market. On another occasion, Breeden told his interviewer that "the oil being so coarse, we do not care to handle any more . . . than we can find a ready market for." Indeed, it would have been unwise to contract for oil on a declining market. As it turned out, even Breeden's cautious purchases at Kern River and McKittrick were too much, for when the crude inventory was revalued at the market price at the end of June, 1901, it showed a net loss of $21,000. Prices had begun to slide as soon as the railroad spur approached the Kern River field and a new drilling campaign got under way. It was to be expected. When thirty-four producers in Bakersfield were looking for buyers in September, 1900, Lyman Stewart predicted: "The Tank Wagons having been tied up by those Companies that had sold their Oil, these other Companies are expecting an outlet for theirs when the Railroad Spur is completed. I expect to see Oil sold there within the next year at 25¢ per barrel." Breeden, too, must have seen the trend and prudently restricted his purchases.[6]

In fact, the market became demoralized just as PCO was preparing to enter it. Although falling prices were turning more and more industrial users to fuel oil, this additional demand did not improve prices in the field because of a transportation bottleneck. Production increased before the railroads obtained enough new tank cars to handle it. At the end of March, Breeden tested the crude market in the field by calling for offers of 25,000 barrels. Producers priced their oil low enough to draw from him this encouraging comment: "I think that the offers made were such that we can take much more than the 25,000 barrels that were called for and that the price is such that the oil can be sold in competition with coal. This is the competition we must meet."[7]

Nevertheless, PCO was not yet ready to buy in really large quantities —for storage as well as immediate sale. Despite press reports that the company intended to add twelve or thirteen tanks, Breeden stated that no more tankage was planned. However, within a few weeks PCO showed signs of changing its mind. In May, when the company was paying less than 20¢ a barrel, W. S. Miller of Iowa Standard stated publicly that the price of oil was too low and would soon rise. To provide storage while oil was still cheap, PCO began work in June on ten more tanks at Kern River. At the end of July, the *Bakersfield Californian* reported that PCO was interested in contracting for oil, which suggested an impending advance in price. W. S. Miller let it be known he hoped the price of oil would rise. He said that Standard did not believe in discouraging the producer; that would be "killing the goose that laid the golden egg." Meantime, the three McKittrick tanks were filled, and plans for more were rumored. In the Los Angeles City field, PCO negotiated for the production of a newly formed Producers Association only to have 26 Broadway call off the negotiations, claiming that it would take months to build the necessary storage.[8]

Following these beginnings, 26 Broadway reached a crucial decision. Sometime in the summer of 1901 the New York headquarters decided that the Kern River field promised enough production at low prices to warrant a major marketing effort and, to support it, a heavy investment in more tankage and a pipeline to the sea. Evidence of the decision is first seen in the purchase, on August 30, of nearly eighty acres adjoining the original eighty leased the previous year. About the same time, work began on a $6,000 office building, and fifteen more tanks were ordered. Perhaps as early as mid-September PCO contracted for the production of one of the most prolific quarter sections in Kern River, that of the Peerless Oil Company. An observer in Ohio reported that Standard had taken down sixty tanks in Wood County for transfer to California. By the end of September the whole story had leaked out—PCO would build a pipeline to San Francisco Bay and a refinery there. From this point on, Breeden's goal had to be an ample supply of crude, preferably under long-term contracts at prices low enough to insure a profit. To supplement the big Peerless contract, he added an even larger one in December with the Monte Cristo Oil & Development Company for 5,400,000 barrels over a five-year period. At the end of 1901 PCO was said to be receiving 3,000 barrels daily from these two companies at 25¢ a barrel. To store this oil pending completion of the pipeline, tank after tank was built at Kern River.[9]

In November, Standard's intentions were summarized by Breeden in a curious mixture of fact and fancy:[10]

> The main feature of our Point Richmond developments will be the building of a pipeline from Bakersfield to Point Richmond, for the purpose of transporting oil at a low rate. . . . We shall of course require a big plant, not only for storage but for shipping purposes, as we have already made plans to make Point Richmond the shipping center for the Standard Oil Company for the whole Pacific Coast. The trade already is large, but it is nothing to what we contemplate, when we are prepared to handle all that is now [offered].
>
> We shall not operate the refinery at Alameda Point any longer. At Point Richmond there will be a plant that will undoubtedly reach great proportions soon after it is started. . . . Within a year this refinery will

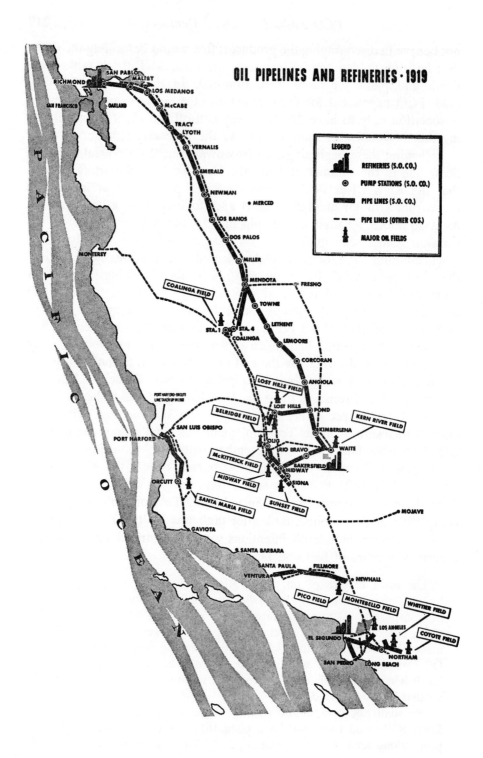

OIL PIPELINES AND REFINERIES · 1919

LEGEND
REFINERIES (S.O. CO.)
PUMP STATIONS (S.O. CO.)
PIPE LINES (S.O. CO.)
PIPE LINES (OTHER COS.)
MAJOR OIL FIELDS

be in active operation and perhaps even earlier, as orders have been issued to begin work at once in the transportation of a nucleus of this plant from the Alameda Point refinery.

We have our agents in all the Pacific territory, and from the Hawaiian Islands we have received very flattering reports of the favor with which oil has been received by the planters. In the Philippines those millions of natives will very soon learn to appreciate the labor-saving elements of oil, both as light and fuel. . . .

We intend to take care of that territory from Point Richmond and shall establish a regular line of steamers between the Hawaiian Islands and the Point, just as soon as we are able to handle the business. . . . We cannot find any better locality than Point Richmond for transacting our business and we have decided to centralize all the many elements of our trade right there.

Breeden was wrong in predicting the old Alameda plant would supply the nucleus for the new refinery, and Standard did not have the overseas market in hand. But the pipeline and the construction at Richmond were under way. The preliminaries were over; Standard had committed itself heavily.

3

Charlie Watson had stated an obvious fact when he told Kern River producers in August of 1900, "Your production here is going to be enormous, and somebody has got to help you handle it. . . ." Who was that somebody to be? None of several hundred companies in Kern River and the West Side of the San Joaquin Valley was as well qualified as Standard to balance production with demand, a balance that could be achieved only by a company with a large marketing organization and large storage facilities to hold surplus oil until the market could absorb it. But there were others that grappled with the problem before Standard did, and their achievements limited Standard's role.

The first to attempt to bring stability to the crude oil market was Isaac E. Blake. Late in 1899, Blake again turned his creative mind to the petroleum industry. Taking leave from railroad promotions in the Northwest, he planned a major campaign—the organization of the entire fuel oil business of the West. First of all, he satisfied his obligation to 26 Broadway, incurred when he sold his share of the Continental Oil Company, by offering Standard an opportunity to participate in his enterprise. He was told that Standard had not decided as yet to enter the fuel oil business; it was not sure there was enough oil. So Blake was free to go ahead on his own.[11]

He outlined his plan to Lyman Stewart:

> The first thing is to get the producers to cooperate in . . . piping, storing and selling their oil as a unit, so that the best rates of transportation can be obtained, and the best markets for fuel oil consumption could be supplied and those customers first served who are willing to pay the best prices; afterwards if there should prove to be a surplus the larger customers who are in a position to command lower prices could be served.
>
> The very quality of the California oil indicates that it should be handled as a unit and the R.R. should do the carrying so that the pipelines might be as short as possible, reducing the difficulties in piping heavier oil.

This proposed organization, Blake warned, should be made strong enough to cope with the possibility of rich oil strikes by amateurs who might otherwise break the market by a too rapid development of their properties. For the present, refiners would be left out, but later they, too, would be brought into the scheme. If the producers agreed to his plan, their first goal should be fresh capital to lay pipelines to rail connections and to establish more storage at central distribution points. Diplomatically, he proposed that Stewart manage the combine.[12]

Stewart did not rise to the bait. His own company was well-situated for transportation to market; its oil fields near the coast were served by pipelines to the sea and by cheap marine transportation. However, he considered contributing his production in the interior at Kern River and Coalinga, not only for the benefits to be derived, but also to prevent Blake's combine from soliciting his own customers.

Blake's proposals interested other prominent oilmen without convincing them. He signed up no major producer, and his grand design was never executed. The best he could do was to put together a marketing company, called United Oil Producers, which by the end of 1900 was building stations at San Jose, Stockton, and Alameda. By this time Standard had announced its entry into the fuel oil business, causing Stewart to suspect that Blake might be working for Standard despite denials by both Blake and W. S. Miller. Independent or not, the skeptical Stewart thought, Blake would have "a nice plant to sell to the Standard when they absorb this coast."[13]

His business eventually did pass to Standard, but without his consent. Harassed by litigation and a shortage of tank cars, in April, 1902, Blake sold the United Oil Producers to the Peerless Oil Company. Both of his problems he blamed on his onetime employer. He charged that Standard had caused the car shortage by withdrawing its cars from the Southern Pacific rail lines, a matter that will be discussed later on, and that Standard had instigated the lawsuit brought against him by one of his suppliers, the Kern River Oil Company.[14]

Comments from others suggest, however, that Blake hardly needed a push from Standard to fall on his face. John Baker, Union's sales manager, wrote of Blake:[15]

> Whereas he may be hustling, there are not many people who are willing to do business with him and as a matter of fact, one company from whom he has been securing Oil informs us that he owes them between $6,000 and $7,000 which is long overdue. . . . His former assistant, Mr. Howard, also tells a woeful tale of his financial loss during his connection with Mr. Blake.

The litigation implies, too, that in addition to being short of capital, Blake had misjudged the trend of crude prices. In December, 1900, United contracted with the Kern River Oil Company for crude at 52.5¢ a barrel. The price fell to 38¢ by February 1, and United repudiated its contract. When the Kern company sued, the judge awarded it the difference between the market and contract prices. Since the company called Standard men for expert testimony at the trial and had turned to Standard to take its oil, Blake believed that Standard had prompted the suit.[16]

In any event, Blake sold out to Peerless, which began operating a large and growing fuel oil business at San Francisco, Stockton, San Jose, and Sacramento. Peerless was also a PCO crude supplier. As the time for the expiration of its contract with PCO drew near, Peerless had won a strong position. It was a high-volume, low-cost producer which was marketing 1,000 barrels of fuel oil daily. Looking toward the future, it had bought a refinery site adjacent to PCO's Kern River tank farm. But after prolonged negotiations with Breeden, Peerless accepted a package deal. In November, 1902, it sold Iowa Standard its marketing contracts and stations and agreed to supply PCO with 9,000,000 barrels of crude over the next five years at 20¢ a barrel, the largest crude oil contract yet made in California. John M. Wright, the president of Peerless, said that he had found the storage and distribution of fuel crude so troublesome he decided "those who made money at it earned it, whether the Standard Company or anybody else." He was "very glad" to sell the business to Standard.[17]

For Peerless, this was the end as an independent fuel oil marketer, but the resourceful I. E. Blake returned for another round the next year. With characteristic optimism, he formulated another bold plan. He proposed that the Stewarts join him in leasing lands in the undeveloped

Sunset and Midway fields. To move the oil, he was promoting a railroad to run from the Sunset to the coast at Port Harford. To market the oil, he drew an offer from the Shell Transport & Trading Company. Shell wanted to establish a Pacific Coast base to supply its Far Eastern fuel oil depots; Sir Marcus Samuel, Shell's principal owner, was enthusiastic over the future of fuel oil, especially for steamers. Shell told Blake that it would sign a twenty-one-year contract to advance money to producers on their oil, handle the oil at cost, and then split the profits.[18]

While Blake was seeking support for his plan, PCO was reported to have offered to tie the Sunset field into its pipeline system if the producers would agree to sell 1,000,000 barrels at 17¢. Perhaps the offer was to counter Blake's project but, judging from the price, PCO was making a purely business proposition. The producers refused, so sure were they that Blake's railroad, the Midland Pacific, would be built. On the strength of the prospective railroad and the Shell contract, Blake drew some of his old Titusville friends, including Milton Stewart, into a small oil company operating in Sunset and Santa Maria. Once again, Blake had to settle for a crust instead of a loaf. The railroad was never built, and the Shell contract never materialized. Milton Stewart ruefully admitted that Blake was "extremely visionary." Yet one can wonder what Blake might have achieved if Standard, with its capital resources, had allied with him in 1899, just as Kern River and McKittrick began to boom.[19]

4

There was one California-born company that could have provided the fuel oil storage and marketing service that Blake envisaged. It was the Union Oil Company, led by that apostle of fuel oil, Lyman Stewart. Union was already a major marketer as well as the major producer in California. It was alive to all oil developments in the West. In addition to its base in Ventura county, it had a promising property in the Fullerton field, a little production in San Benito County, and a small pipeline serving the Oil City field at Coalinga. But when Kern River and McKittrick became active, Stewart was not ready to plunge into those Valley fields. He was absorbed in increasing the production of his own properties and in a plan to handle crude produced in the Whittier-Fullerton district. Moreover, he thought the "large gambling excitement" over the two Valley fields made them doubtful investments. When W. L. Stewart, Lyman's son and Union's general manager, visited them in January, 1900, he found little territory available for lease. Kern River did not impress him; McKittrick, he thought, would take time to develop. Consequently, he felt Union was safe from serious competition from those fields in the near future.[20]

A month later, however, Lyman was warning that their company should follow eastern practice and hedge against a possible flood of oil by securing some properties in Kern River and the fields on the West Side. Then, if these fields did develop a large production, Union could compete with oil from the same fields, shutting in its properties elsewhere until the flood subsided. The same day, W. L. Stewart, after listening to the talk among oilmen, wrote his father:[21]

> I gathered that Mr. Blake's, or some other scheme providing for the handling of the production of the state will be essential to the welfare of the business; therefore, I beg to most respectfully urge that you devote some of your thoughts to the development of some plan for the taking care of the production by us if possible, if not by some one we can interest.

Lyman hedged by taking an interest in the Green and Whittier property at Kern River, but he continued to avoid a heavy commitment in the interior fields. He reasoned, "The Coalinga field is barely holding her own, and the Bakersfield country is such heavy oil that it can never be piped a long distance, so that we have a great advantage in all our Southern California fields . . . as we can reach water transportation with comparatively little expense."[22]

Stewart edged closer to leadership of the industry when he took on the responsibility of marketing for the Coalinga producers on Section 28. By mid-August, growing evidence of the tremendous potential of the Valley fields convinced him that 1900 was a year of crisis for his company, that California's oil industry was "being revolutionized" as it had been five years earlier by the Los Angeles City field. And Kern River was clearly much larger than Los Angeles. Fortunately, large contracts to supply the Spreckels sugar refineries assured a market for Union's own production, but lower prices were certain to come. He advised his son to have a man quietly gather production statistics in the Kern field and, if the oilmen could produce one-quarter of the amount they claimed, Union should try to tie up as many fuel oil consumers as possible with long-term sales contracts. Producers would then have to go to Union to sell their oil. This policy, he added, might seem cold-blooded, but most new producers were trying to seize a market they had not built. "The only way possible for us to help them is to protect the market as far as possible from their devices and thus compel them to cooperate with us." He further suggested that the Mc-Kittrick and Sunset producers should be signed up to use a pipeline which Union would lay to Port Harford.[23]

While the Stewarts were considering filling the vacuum in the industry, Standard moved in. The Stewarts could hardly believe Charlie Watson's announcement that Standard was offering its services to the producers. But their fears were confirmed when Mrs. Calvin Payne told Milton Stewart she was accompanying her husband to California on a business trip. Milton wrote:[24]

> Am very sorry those fellows are arranging to get a foot hold in California production for it means control of the business, just as in this country, I fear. Am sorry also we are not in better shape to meet them as well as the new conditions developing. . . . In the main I agree with you in your proposed policy, but the Standard coming in, will no doubt render much of it inoperative. . . . Perhaps, under the circumstances, it would be well to sell them the control in case they care to buy.

Not only had Union failed to forestall Standard's move, but its ability to recapture the initiative was severely limited. The Bard faction among Union's stockholders had long doubted the competence of the Stewarts. In 1900 it balked at a Stewart scheme to raise new capital, and late in the year sold its holdings to a group of Los Angeles men.[25]

Short of capital though he was, Lyman wrote W. L. Stewart, "Let us play a strong hand." What matter if they could not afford a pipeline to the coast? Spend a few thousand dollars on a right of way and tie up the light oil producers of the West Side from Sunset to Coalinga. Then there would be "no Pipe Line proposition left open for the Standard unless new Fields are opened and they will have to come to us if they want to do business."[26]

Milton Stewart's advice was to fight back by furnishing the California oilmen with Henry Demarest Lloyd's *Wealth Against Commonwealth* to open their eyes to the character of their "prospective master." Nevertheless, when Payne returned from California and suggested to Milton that the two companies "work along the same lines without antagonizing each other," the Titusville Stewart wrote, "Looks as though we had better fall in line with Payne's suggestion." Milton thought Standard's capital resources were too immense for Union to fight.

Still another view of the Standard-Union relationship was held by J. S. Torrance, a leader in the group that had bought out Bard. He believed Union should seek contracts to pipe and transport the oil of other producers. "Having the production tied up as far as may be and the contracts for the sale of the product, and a large production of our own, if the Standard then comes into the field they will purchase our property at a much higher price possibly." At this time, a sale of Union was being discussed with General Greene of the American Asphalt Company. Lyman Stewart was sure that Greene secretly represented Standard.[27]

This view of Standard as the irresistible cannibal led Lyman to suspect that Standard's "gloved hand" was behind Union's difficulties with the railroads in getting tank cars and a spur to a tank site at Bakersfield. After PCO sold out to Standard, he warned John Baker at San Francisco to enforce safe loading practices on the barge *Santa Paula* because, he said, Union was competing with men whose secret agents had once built a competitor's refinery so that it would blow up. It is true that three Standard executives and H. B. and C. M. Everest of the Vacuum Oil Company were indicted for this crime, but Lyman did not mention that the indictment against the Standard men was quashed and that the rights and wrongs of the suits and counter-suits, nearly twenty years before, were very unclear. Nevertheless, he believed that if Standard would try to blow up a competitor's refinery, it might also try to blow up a competitor's ship. He urged Baker, too, to charter a tug for the barge *Santa Paula* lest Standard embarrass Union by chartering all the tugs on the Bay. Curiously, eight months later, his tone had changed completely. Commenting on a news dispatch concerning a war between Standard and Union, he wrote Milton:[28]

> The newspapers are so lawless and so utterly unreliable that we do not pay any attention to these matters now. There is no real conflict between the Standard and us, or, rather, we are on very friendly terms, and we do not anticipate any particular trouble with them.

In the interim, in March, 1901, S.O. (Iowa) had renewed its contract for Union's light products, and Union had gone ahead with its expansion without opposition, ordering a tanker and securing a right of way from McKittrick to Port Harford. Lyman Stewart had troubles: he had too much high-priced oil in storage and lost on a falling market just as Blake and Breeden did; the sale of new stock to pay for expansion lagged; producers were slow to sign up for the pipeline; a number of new wells pumped so much sand as to be nearly useless. These reverses could not be ascribed to the Standard Oil Company. "Confidentially," wrote the pious Lyman, "I sometimes feel that the Lord is having a controversy with us because of our Sabbath work and also because of our employing intemperate men. . . ."[29]

In fact, if Standard was the lion among oil companies, Union was not afraid to give its tail a good, hard twist. W. L. Stewart worked very closely with W. S. Porter, who in 1901 was organizing the Associated Oil Company. The young Stewart told Porter that Union was "heartily in accord with your scheme to consolidate the fuel oil interests of the State under one ownership and management." He offered Porter Union's fuel oil properties, contracts, pipelines and marketing facilities, though when the showdown came virtually nothing belonging to Union went into the Associated. In addition to encouraging Standard's competitors, Union also did not hesitate to invade Hawaii, where Payne had told Milton Stewart that Standard intended to market fuel oil. It snatched fat contracts from under Standard's nose. When a group of four Hawaiian companies decided to convert to fuel oil, they gave their 100,000 barrels a year business to Union at $1.40 a barrel, although Standard had bid $1.37½ and Blake, $1.15. Lyman Stewart attributed his company's good fortune to Claus Spreckels, whose Pacific Coast sugar refineries had long been Union's customers.

Standard promptly sent Charlie Watson to Honolulu to corral any other business that could be developed. Apparently it had hopes of salvaging some of the trade because, in discussing PCO's future a few months later, Breeden indicated that PCO was planning a shipping line to the Islands. But Union was following up its advantage. John Baker, its sales manager, visited the Islands to pick up other accounts and to start construction of a station. Lyman Stewart immediately began to enlarge Union's fleet. "If Mr. Baker succeeds in securing all the business over there, the Standard will have no use for any large tankers on this coast, and I think our policy should be to provide all the necessary water transportation that may be required." So far as the Hawaiian trade was concerned, his strategy was successful; Standard did not establish tanker service there for a decade.[30]

On another front, Union sought to checkmate Standard by making a five-year contract to pipe the light crude of the Caribou and Sauer Dough companies to the railroad at Coalinga. Union made an effort to organize the entire Coalinga field and went so far as to survey a pipeline route to the coast, but suspended its plans when it could not tie up the producers. Besides, Lyman Stewart had come to believe that his company might do better to invest its limited capital in exploring its new lands near the ocean around Santa Maria.[31]

In Kern River, Union let its interest in the Green and Whittier property go into Associated toward the close of 1901. Otherwise, Union remained active on its own account, taking contracts, building an asphalt refinery near PCO's tank farm, and even buying property. As Lyman Stewart wrote his brother: "The situation is becoming quite interesting. We now have the Associated Oil Company, the Standard Oil Company and the Union Oil Company each of which is trying to absorb the production of the other producers."[32]

5

Though Blake, Union, and Standard aspired to organize transportation and marketing for the San Joaquin Valley producers, many oilmen preferred to control their own destinies. To be strong enough to influence the volume of production and sales, they had to combine. They made two attempts to combine without destroying their individual identities before some of them finally agreed to a merger. Their new instrument, already mentioned, was the Associated Oil Company.

The oilmen's first attempt at self-help took place before Union and Standard made their moves. On July 9, 1900, fourteen companies issued a manifesto:

> . . . realizing the necessity for the well-being of the industry that the prices of petroleum be sustained and that the marketing thereof should be accomplished by the producers, and thus eliminate the middle man, [we] do hereby call a meeting of all producers of petroleum of Kern County . . . for the purpose of organizing the petroleum industry. . . .

Among the sponsors were such prominent producers as B. F. Brooks, E. L. Doheny, Chanslor & Canfield, and Jewett & Blodgett. J. J. Mack of the Bank of Bakersfield, an oilman himself, forecast that the meeting would lead to a statewide organization.[33]

Their plans called for a marketing company owned by the producers in the proportion of $100 of stock for each producing well. Each producer would lease his property to the new company. Then he would be employed to develop his property and, as compensation, receive 90 per cent of the sales receipts from his oil. When Charlie Watson came down to Bakersfield to announce Standard's entry into the storage business, he was asked his view of the embryonic combine. He said that Standard had encountered such organizations before and had not been defeated. But, the interviewer told him, this association had corrected the usual tendency to disintegration by requiring its members to join for a term of years, renouncing the privilege of withdrawing. In that case, Watson replied, the scheme was dead before birth; few producers would yield control of their lands and their identity.[34]

Watson's prediction was a shrewd one. The Producers' Oil Storage and Transportation Company was born, but it did not long survive. Actually, the numerous sponsors had dwindled away until it was no more than a marketing outlet for five companies organized by B. F. Brooks. The only other partner in Producers' Oil Storage was Chanslor & Canfield, which did not even use the company's facilities. Agencies were established throughout California and Arizona, notably in San Francisco and Los Angeles. According to J. M. Wright of Peerless, Producers' Oil Storage began operations by cutting prices in an attempt to force independents to join up, which was a sure way to alienate them. It failed to become a major influence in the market.[35]

Although the Producers' Oil Storage and Transportation Company came to nothing, the need for some organization to stabilize prices became ever more clear as prices continued to drift lower. The leaders in cutting prices were not necessarily the most efficient producers; more often they were the weakest financially. Too many leases in the Kern River field were signed in a fever of speculation, calling for a cash bonus, a certain amount of drilling each year, and a one-third or three-eighths royalty. These provisions pressed the operator to drill and to turn his oil into cash. Yet there was a bright side to the picture. Lyman Stewart described it: "The low prices . . . will be a great blessing in the end, for oil will be pushed out into so many new channels that I think it will be difficult to supply the demand when the reaction sets in."[36] Meantime, however, in the absence of a single dominant company, price competition was the only way of balancing supply and demand.

When prices of crude dropped below 20¢ a barrel in the spring of 1901, fresh interest in a combination developed. In May the Combined Petroleum Producers Association was established to try to force the price up to at least 50¢. The Association avoided the leasing technique of the Producers' Oil Storage and Transportation Company. Instead, its members agreed that, save for filling their existing contracts, they would turn over all their oil to the new organization, and it would be the sales agent. It planned to charge 10 per cent, or less, for the service. To test the practicality of this arrangement, the period for the agreement was set at two years. But even this much weaker union failed to win sufficient support to be effective. Lyman Stewart concluded dismally, "The very best thing for the business now is to allow prices to remain depressed until all the producers come to their senses." Nevertheless, he let his son work with W. S. Porter in still another attempt at unity, the most binding of the three, "a trust to control all the fuel oil on the coast."[37]

Porter, an energetic promoter and pipe salesman, had been invited by several prominent producers to lead this effort at combination, which matured into the Associated Oil Company. At least half the leaders in its formation had also been sponsors of the earlier Producers' Oil Storage and Transportation Company. Their goal, as defined in the prospectus for the Associated, was:[38]

> . . . to secure to the producer a legitimate return for fuel oil. . . . The actual value of fuel oil today is what it can be sold for in competition with coal, which is not less than $1.30 per barrel f.o.b. San Francisco. Under conditions of overproduction and destructive competition the product has been for some months past sold for from 60¢ to 65¢ a barrel f.o.b. San Francisco, or 15¢ to 20¢ per barrel f.o.b. Kern River Fields, or a loss to the producers from 65¢ to 70¢ a barrel.

The initial publicity in July, 1901, was most impressive. The twelve founding companies were reported to represent 65 per cent of the Kern River field, and the Associated's probable capitalization was put at $75,000,000 to $100,000,000. A pipeline to San Francisco was forecast as a part of the program unless the railroads cut rates. The founder companies took as strong an approach as possible to the problem of maintaining unity; they sold their properties to Associated in exchange for stock and bonds and also turned over their sales contracts. In other words, they formed a big new corporation which, through its ownership of the oil rights, would be permanent and would permit a strong management. Associated, incorporated on October 7, began to operate on January 1, 1902, with Charles A. Canfield as the first president and Porter as general manager.[39]

PCO's plan for a pipeline to San Francisco became known in September, 1901, after the organizing drive for Associated was already well under way. It would appear that a clash was inevitable. However, there does not seem to have been an overt battle for adherents. There was also some idle speculation that Associated was controlled by Standard. The *Los Angeles Express* was positive that Standard would not invest so heavily in Kern River if it did not control the "Producers' combine." The *Bakersfield Morning Echo* scoffed at the idea: "We do not believe the Standard has the Kern River field in its grasp, nor has it, in the opinion of many operators, any serious intentions in that direction." Lyman Stewart suspected Standard "was running a tremendous bluff or else they have an arrangement with the combination."

An English publication, *Petroleum Review*, contributed a more judicious estimate to the discussion. It saw two well-defined schools of thought over the wisdom of the Kern River organization. It cited

Oil, Copper and Finance, representing investors, as approving the consolidation for the sake of more effective management without altering the ownership. Small producers, on the other hand, using the *Pacific Oil Reporter* as their mouthpiece, argued that a producer who joined Associated "was bartering away his birthright for a mess of pottage" and that the Standard would make a market for California oil as it had for Ohio oil. The *Review* concluded, "The Standard Oil Company has come to be looked upon in the American oil world—and outside, for that matter, as a professional 'pacifier' in all difficulties pertaining to the industry, and if any attempts at grand strokes of Independence are made at all, they are generally abortive." Standard was moving in "its usual quiet and competent way" to control the oil industry in California. In doing so, it would save the producers.[40]

As a matter of fact, the Associated people had their eyes fixed on solving the price problem, not fighting Standard. A spokesman for Chanslor & Canfield answered those who feared Standard would crush Associated by saying that the combine was not trying to compete with Standard but to secure a market at a reasonable price. It would sell to Standard if the price was fair. A few years later, C. A. Canfield, looking back, did not polarize the attitudes of the producers into pro-Standard and anti-Standard, as the press tended to do. He said:

> Our oil field . . . was composed of saloon men, ministers of the Gospel, farmers, grocery men, everything. Some of them had good contracts, and those who had contracts wouldn't go [into the Associated] because they thought they were protected by their contract for a few years anyway. Many of them . . . had an idea they could run their business a little better than anyone else could, and many people object to putting trust in anyone.

Canfield himself obviously believed in the efficiency of large-scale enterprise, as Associated's experience proved. Field operating costs were cut by two-thirds, and marketing expense by three-fourths.[41]

W. G. Kerckhoff, one of the founders of Associated and subsequently president of the San Joaquin Light and Power Company, recalled that at first all the oilmen planned to join Associated, but later some thought they could rely on Associated to hold the price up while they disposed of their production more rapidly for a little less. Gradually, men of this mind dropped out of the project. When the company finally began operation, its share of production was too small to control the price. The only virtue of the combine was that it could take large contracts and guarantee delivery. By the end of the year 1902, Associated had issued

$20,000,000 in stocks and bonds for properties that were certainly far overvalued. It claimed 50 per cent of the wells in Kern River and 90 per cent in McKittrick. Perhaps these percentages were correct for the number of wells, but they did not represent Associated's share of production. It was less than 30 per cent.[42]

Associated's role as champion of the producers became less convincing when it sold at low prices and made an alliance with the Southern Pacific. Before the first year of operations was over, Porter had offered a half-interest to E. H. Harriman, the master railroad financier who had bought control of the Southern Pacific after Collis P. Huntington died. Harriman borrowed the services of C. F. Lufkin, probably through H. H. Rogers, to evaluate Associated's properties. Lufkin found that Associated had made sales contracts at prices which, after allowing for transportation, were below the cost of production. Porter had acted on the theory that cutting prices would secure a large volume of sales and thus he would have a large volume of freight to use in bargaining for lower rail rates. If necessary, he believed he could use a guaranteed volume of freight as the basis for financing a railroad or pipeline by Associated's owners and friends. Lufkin was unimpressed. In his view, Porter was "carrying the matter along strictly on the lines of a promoter, and between his ignorance and his interests, sees much larger financial results than the situation seems to warrant." Porter thought the company was worth $8,000,000. Lufkin estimated $6,000,000, although he admitted a reduction in transportation costs would increase profits and, therefore, the value of the company. The upshot of the negotiations was that during 1903 the Southern Pacific bought 10,000,000 barrels of crude in a five-year contract and acquired a minority stock interest of 4,000,000 shares. These transactions made Associated financially secure, but it could no longer be considered an independent company.[43]

While failing to control the Valley fields, Associated had also effectively denied control to any other company. In the period from 1902 through 1904, it sold three times as much fuel oil as S.O. (Iowa), mainly of its own production. So another big corporation, a home-grown giant, took its place with Standard and Union as a major force in the fuel oil market.[44]

6

There were two other strong competitors for Valley crude oil, the Southern Pacific and Santa Fe railroads. They were gluttons for fuel oil, for they had found it cheaper and easier to use than coal.[45] Their need for an assured supply led them to produce a part of their own requirements, but they were major purchasers, too. In another very important way the railroad companies were significant; they were the principal arteries of the oil business. Their capacity to carry oil automatically limited the production that could be marketed.

Since the middle 1890's, both railroads had been interested in oil development. In 1896 the Santa Fe had joined E. L. Doheny in developing the Fullerton field and later purchased his interest. The following year the Southern Pacific hired J. B. Treadwell to develop production on lands it acquired near Santa Barbara in the Summerland field. In 1899 Treadwell and Doheny were both pioneering in the Valley fields. Doheny again agreed to supply the Santa Fe, this time for its line under construction from Bakersfield to Point Richmond. In 1902 the railroad, compelled by their agreement to pay 96¢ a barrel for oil that cost 10¢ to produce, bought him out. Meanwhile, Treadwell was examining and drilling on Southern Pacific lands—that is, those that remained. The Southern Pacific, to its chagrin, saw oil derricks sprouting on some properties that it had sold at grazing land prices.[46]

The railroads were important to some producers as a market, but they were important to nearly all producers as carriers of their production. Naturally producers, hurt by low prices and overproduction, criticized the railroads for high rates and inadequate service. There was some suspicion that the Southern Pacific was leagued with Standard to restrict the supply of tank cars so that producers would have to sell their production at distress prices. Standard's withdrawal of Union Tank Line cars late in 1901 lent substance to this view. Although the car shortage did work to Standard's advantage, enough is known to suggest that Standard's action resulted from defeat rather than design.

The facts appear to be, roughly, as follows. Sometime prior to 1899 the Southern Pacific had leased Union Tank Line cars from 26 Broadway, for the railroad did not want to invest in such expensive equipment until an adequate volume of traffic was assured. When, in 1899, the Southern Pacific decided to build and operate its own cars, someone in the Standard organization objected. Julius Kruttschnitt, the Southern Pacific's general manager, was not willing to yield. He temporized, stating that the cars being built were hardly enough for the railroad's own needs. Thereupon Standard, which was nationally the principal supplier of tank cars, offered to buy the Southern Pacific's cars. Kruttschnitt passed the offer along to Collis P. Huntington, the railroad's president. To give up the tank cars would be a "very dangerous precedent," Kruttschnitt thought, and the only reason for considering it was the "very large earnings" that came to the railroad from hauling

Standard's products. Huntington gently refused to accept Standard's offer in this philosophical vein:[47]

> . . . I would not think it wise for the company to part with its tank cars at this time. . . . the Standard Oil people are very excellent people, and have been, and are, doing much good to the people of this country in giving to them a very excellent quality of lubricating oil and also burning fluid, and at prices much below what they could have been bought at if the business had been in a thousand hands instead of mostly in theirs, as it has allowed them to experiment and get the very best at the minimum cost. Because of these reasons I would do more for them than I would do for any other people in this country. . . . if we can do anything with the Standard Oil people that is not against our interest and to the interest of the public it will give me pleasure to do business with them.

At this time, January, 1900, the Southern Pacific owned nearly 150 tank cars and had 325 under lease from the Union Tank Line. Before the end of summer, the railroad placed an urgent order for several hundred more, as the spur to the Kern River field neared completion. A few months later, in February, 1901, the Southern Pacific asked Standard to help out by leasing an additional 100 U.T.L. cars, only to get a cool response. Standard offered 50 to be used for Standard Oil business exclusively, but the railroad demurred at handling cars it could not control. Shortly, Standard countered by asking that 125 of the U.T.L. cars be returned. To end this tug-of-war, W. H. Tilford and Charles M. Hays, the Southern Pacific's new president, worked out a compromise. Tilford agreed to let the railroad keep the 325 leased cars until September 1, 1901, when they were to be returned to Whiting. In the meantime, the Southern Pacific could build up its own tank car fleet (which it did by ordering 500 cars from American Car & Foundry), and Standard would ease the demand for the leased cars by supplying whatever additional cars were needed for its own business. To this agreement, Tilford attached two subordinate conditions: The leased cars had to be used solely in California except when serving the railroad's own needs, and Standard would control the movement of cars used for Standard Oil shipments. The foregoing chain of events does not support the theory that Standard and the Southern Pacific plotted a car shortage for Standard's benefit. Rather, it suggests that Standard retreated in the face of the Southern Pacific's determination to enter the tank car business.[48]

The Southern Pacific was not moving fast enough to suit the producers. In March, 1901, nineteen oil companies complained to the State

Board of Railroad Commissioners that the railroads had done little to keep pace with the rapid growth of the fuel oil industry. Hays stated that the 500 cars on order for the Southern Pacific should end the complaints. In a light riposte, he also suggested that the oil companies had an obligation to provide enough tankage so that wells need not be closed down while waiting for cars. The *Railway Age* added that too many shippers of oil were using the tank cars as storehouses.

During August, 1901, the Southern Pacific began to return its leased U.T.L. cars to Whiting. Standard must have needed them, for by the end of the year the shops at Whiting were busy manufacturing cars. In Standard's extensive operations, the cars from California could readily be absorbed; they amounted to about 5 per cent of the U.T.L.'s fleet. They may have been sent to the Beaumont field in Texas, where in September shipments of fuel oil were exceeding 100,000 barrels daily. Despite the withdrawal of the cars, the upward trend of shipments from Kern River continued. In December, 1900, 960 carloads were shipped; in July, 1901, 1,700; and in September, a record 2,000.[49]

At the end of 1901 the cry of a tank car shortage was heard again. A correspondent of the *Los Angeles Herald* claimed that the shortage arose from the failure to return cars promptly, although producers ascribed the situation to a different cause, namely, "the influence of the Standard Oil Company over the Union Transport [sic] Line." This was obviously a baseless assumption, for nearly all of the U.T.L. cars were gone.

President E. P. Ripley of the Santa Fe confirmed the *Herald's* explanation. His company had put into service nearly 500 new cars, each of which had a capacity virtually double that of the older cars. Ripley found that too frequently companies which had always stocked a two- or three-month supply of coal would build a fuel oil tank holding only a few days supply, demand a car a day, and use the car as a storage tank instead of releasing it promptly.

It may be, too, that the railroads' need for tank cars to supply their locomotives limited their ability to serve the oil companies. Of the 2,364 carloads shipped from Kern River in November, between 800 and 850 were for the Southern Pacific and nearly 300 for the Santa Fe. Some cars may also have been drawn off for the Southern Pacific's Atlantic Division. In July, 1901, the Southern Pacific planned to assign 150 of its 670 cars there, and at that time the company was not sure it would have enough cars "to handle all our own oil and the commercial oil besides." The following month, the *Railway Age* reported that the company had ordered 500 tank cars to be used in substituting oil for coal on its Atlantic Division.[50]

Although Standard apparently had nothing to do with the shortage at the end of 1901, the company did reap at least one advantage from it. For lack of cars, the Monte Cristo Oil & Development Company, a large producer and a strong advocate of the Associated Oil Company, turned to PCO to take over its contracts and buy its crude shortly before the Associated began operation. Some years later one of its representatives told the federal Bureau of Corporations that the Southern Pacific had claimed that the withdrawal of the U.T.L. cars had caused the shortage. But nine months had elapsed after the Tilford-Hays agreement before Monte Cristo sold to PCO; the railroad, surely, was well forewarned. The huge Monte Cristo crude purchase contract, mentioned earlier, was an important factor in getting Standard's fuel oil venture under way.[51]

The railroads, it is abundantly clear, were a vital force in the life of the oil industry. They were large producers and still larger consumers. Making their living outside the industry, they were too strong to bow to any oil company or association. They rendered less feasible the organization of the industry under any single control. In another respect, they affected the industry because most oilmen had to use rail transportation to reach their markets. However, the stronger oil companies could provide cheaper transportation in the form of pipelines and tankers for themselves, if they chose, and thereby gain an advantage over other oilmen.

7

The foregoing pages have described Standard's bid to handle the oil of the Kern River and McKittrick fields and the factors that limited its success. These factors are sufficiently numerous to warrant a brief summary. Basic to the situation was the magnitude of the fields, which completely upset the equilibrium between supply and demand for fuel oil in the West. Probably most oilmen believed that a single dominant storage and marketing company would be the most effective instrument to increase demand by displacing coal, and to control the supply in order to prevent overproduction and price wars. But a majority of the producers could not be brought into agreement by any one organization. Blake won little support. The Stewarts were too interested in other fields and too short of cash to make a serious effort. The Associated was slow to take shape and never gained the wide support it had hoped for. The biggest consumers, the railroads, bought and stored oil for their own needs but did not seek to organize the industry.

Of all the candidates for leadership, Standard was the best qualified in terms of capital and organization. It began to move about the same time as the Stewarts and the producers but was not aggressive enough to control the Kern County fields. In fact, Standard's limited purchases and its failure to buy out key producers while the market was demoralized indicate that its goal was simply to buy oil that it could sell profitably in a competitive market. Undoubtedly, Standard men believed that both their company and the industry would be better off with a stable market directed by themselves. The *Mining and Engineering Review* seems to have shared their view when it hailed the news of PCO's pipeline with grandiloquent optimism:[52]

> It requires a large capital to handle large industrial enterprises and the producer will benefit by the entrance of the Standard Oil Company into California. At a single stroke the questions of transportation and market have been settled and by one wave of the magic wand of Capital the pessimist and his objections have been swept away.

But Standard's actions do not reveal a determination to force a dictatorship upon the industry. If it did entertain such an ambition, it was doomed to disappointment. Union was favored by geography; its fields were close to cheap water transportation. The Los Angeles producers were located in one substantial market and were near the sea. The Associated, though failing to realize the hopes of its sponsors, was rich in production and had gained strength financially through its alliance with the Southern Pacific.

Theoretically, an alternative to tying up producers would have been for Standard to sign major consumers to long-term contracts, and to use that leverage to control the producers. But it is unlikely this technique could have been successful in an expanding market. For example, the Hawaiian consumers deliberately favored Union. And the railroads did their own buying and storage. However, Standard held one high card that could give it at least a temporary advantage and increase its share of the market—the pipeline to Point Richmond on which preliminary work began in the fall of 1901. Despite the extra costs of pumping heavy crude, Standard expected pipeline transportation to prove cheaper than rail. More than that, the line would enable Standard to guarantee delivery, something companies dependent on tank cars could not do. Uncertain deliveries had forced some consumers to return to coal and had frightened away some other potential customers.[53] The ultimate outcome of Standard's venture in fuel oil awaited completion of its pipeline.

8

Standard raised its stake sharply when it decided on an eight-inch pipeline from the Kern County fields to San Francisco Bay. The $3,-000,000 to be spent on a trunk line was twice the value of the plant and equipment of the PCO and S.O. (Iowa) combined. There was risk, too. Large amounts of oil would have to be bought and sold before the investment could be recovered. So viscous an oil had never been piped for so great a distance. And the line would be far from its suppliers, the mills and shops of Pennsylvania, where the pipe and pumps were manufactured.

Before 26 Broadway committed itself to the line, it wanted the technical problems explored. In the summer of 1901, the New York headquarters sent a man to California to find a way to pipe heavy oil. He was thirty-eight-year-old Forrest M. Towl, a civil engineer trained at Cornell and son of Theodore Towl, the manager of the Real Estate and Tax Department at 26 Broadway. Heavy the oil certainly was! One producer said, with pardonable exaggeration, that a barrel of Kern River crude would take a week to ooze down a flight of stairs, and that a fly could trot over the surface without wetting its feet. Experienced men, like Lyman Stewart and Isaac Blake, thought that the oil could not be piped profitably. Before Towl arrived, some experiments had been made mixing water with the oil. The mixture gradually turned into an emulsion which was even harder to pump. Towl took another tack. He recommended heating the oil to reduce its viscosity, a procedure that had yet to be tried with a long-distance line.[54]

In October, 1901, Theodore Towl sent a crew of right-of-way men to California. They spread out over the desert lands of the west side of the San Joaquin Valley, frequently jouncing in a buckboard over fifty miles of rough road to find an owner of land along the pipeline route. Two of the principal landowners were the railroads, for which a pipeline spelled lost business. But they did not prove hard bargainers. E. P. Ripley, president of the Santa Fe, later explained that, although the pipeline would seriously affect his company's business, he could not make a rate low enough to stop its construction. Therefore, he thought it best to be cooperative and share in the freight generated by the line and the facilities at Point Richmond. PCO's right of way agreement with the Santa Fe included a proviso that the railroad could use the spur line the company was building across the marshes to the site of the pipeline tankage and the refinery. In addition, the Santa Fe had the right to build a parallel spur. The Southern Pacific, too, won certain privileges.

It evidently had in mind offsetting the Santa Fe's Point Richmond marine terminal with one of its own. The Southern Pacific owned a tract of land on the bay shore just north of PCO's. It obtained the right to use PCO's spur and to run a line north through the PCO tract. In turn, PCO could operate a spur to its wharf off the Southern Pacific's line. Of the railroads' cooperative spirit, Daniel O'Day wrote Archbold, "As a general thing [they] are inclined to recognize . . . that crude oil should be transported by pipelines."[55]

A substantial part of the right of way was acquired in a few weeks, but it took longer for work to begin. Pipe from the National Tube Company at Pittsburgh did not arrive until March, 1902. Meanwhile, the construction of tanks at Kern River continued. Following the Monte Cristo contract, this work was speeded, especially after William Ogg, a foreman from National Transit, arrived in January from the East with thirty or more workmen to erect second-hand tanks shipped in from Ohio. Forrest Towl, assisted by his brother, Allan, prepared to get pipeline construction under way. As a preliminary, he let contracts to the Risdon Iron Works of San Francisco for boilers and heaters, and for five 55,000-barrel tanks for Point Richmond. About the same time Theodore Towl was selecting pump station sites, locating tank sites at Point Richmond, and arranging with Western Union and Postal Telegraph to carry the Pipe Line Department's telegraph wire on their poles over much of the route. Calvin Payne joined Forrest Towl at Kern River, where the two observed heated oil being pumped without difficulty. They were sure the problem of handling Kern crude had been solved.[56]

When the pipe was delivered, the joints could not be screwed together because tools from the East had not yet arrived. On April 9, 1902, the first joint was bucked up with borrowed tools. After this inauspicious start, the work moved rapidly until the stock of pipe on hand was exhausted. The eight-inch pipe was unloaded from railroad cars at "yards" which contained as much as twenty-five or thirty miles of pipe and were located as conveniently as possible to the right of way. If the haul was short, ordinarily six men could string—lay out—pipe for the tong gang at the rate of a mile or two a day. During the record day, two gangs strung four and a half miles. On the other hand, when handicapped by bad weather in hilly country, it sometimes took a six-horse team to deliver a single joint of pipe. The stringers managed to keep the pipe moving, never holding up the two tong gangs bucking up the pipe so long as there was pipe in the yards. Over most of the route, the pipe was wrapped in a five-eighths-inch blanket of asbestos and felt and buried three feet underground. Towl hoped this insulation would keep the heated oil flowing freely.[57]

Labor turnover was high during the first few months. The construction superintendent wryly said he had three gangs—"one coming out to work, one working and one coming in to be paid off." According to one story, on a scorching day in the Valley a foreman short of men persuaded the local justice of the peace to release some of his prisoners on condition they help unload several cars of pipe. On another occasion, a foreman was reported to have played the same game in reverse. Hearing that his men were planning a spree when the line reached town, he persuaded the constable to lock up the ringleaders early in the evening. He wanted them able to work the next day.[58] Of course, a job like this used many nomadic pipeliners and casual laborers working under company supervision. In general, however, labor was not a problem.

To heat and boost the oil through the line, Towl built ten pump stations spaced 28 to 30 miles apart. This spacing was substantially closer than was typical in the East, where 40 miles was common. The 205-mile line from Lima to Chicago, in fact, operated originally with a single jumbo pump. But Towl had to keep the oil hot to move it. Each station consisted of a brick boiler house, a brick pump house, and two frame cottages, built by E. R. Smith, a San Joaquin Valley contractor. The stations were equipped with four boilers and two high-pressure, compound, duplex National Transit pumps to force oil into the line at 600 pounds pressure. Exhaust steam from the pumps passed into a heater containing two-inch tubes through which the oil flowed and picked up heat, raising the oil's temperature from 60° F. to 180° F. Towl designed the line to carry 10,000 barrels a day, about twice the amount PCO planned to move initially.[59]

As 1902 drew to a close, the completion date was put off into 1903 because of pipe shortages. Meanwhile, Kern River crude continued to pour into the tank farm, filling some eighty tanks before the line began operation. PCO's W. V. Miller suggested building earthen reservoirs holding 350,000 barrels each. True, there would be a loss from seepage, but a reservoir could be built at a cost of only ten cents a barrel. A circular hole was scooped out of the ground, the earth diked around it, and then was roofed over. Healy, Tibbits & Company completed the first reservoir in January, 1903. Short of space, PCO bought a nearby quarter section in December, 1902, and pocked it with reservoirs.[60]

As the line neared Point Richmond, testing began at Waite, the pump station at the Kern River tank farm. Water was pumped through the line to find leaks and, incidentally, to flush out snakes, lizards, and the like that had crept into the pipe during construction. On March 19 Towl started pumping oil, but because of pump trouble he was forced to shut down. When he tried again, he was pumping against a plug of oil lying stiff as molasses in the winter-chilled earth. With 600 pounds pressure, oil moved into the line at a rate of only 1,000 barrels a day. J. B. Treadwell, of the Southern Pacific, heard "from very good authority" that after pumping five days the oil had traveled only nineteen miles and had burst the pipe. He predicted costs of piping would exceed the railroad's costs.

The pipe may not have burst, but the hot oil had certainly cooled by the time it had gone fifteen or twenty miles. Towl treated the oil like the proverbial balky mule by building a fire under it. The line was tapped, letting the oil drain into a trench beneath the pipe and then set afire. Towl thus managed to move as much as 3,000 barrels a day but only for brief intervals. For a time, news of the difficulty was withheld from O'Day and Archbold. When O'Day learned of it, he insisted that he be told all the news, good or bad. Though disappointed, he wrote Forrest Towl, "You must not feel discouraged. . . . The elements of success are there I am sure, and that you will overcome all difficulties in good time I am also sure." Calvin Payne, too, sympathized with Towl. He recalled a Pennsylvania pipeline, and another in West Virginia, that had failed to pump satisfactorily during the first sixty days.[61]

At last, on July 18, 1903, oil reached the tanks at Richmond, four months after it had entered the line. But to build the volume to a satisfactory level, some additional action seemed necessary. An obvious remedy was to double the number of stations. Since this would cost both time and a half-million dollars, Towl tried to find another answer. One was the "water cure." Towl had turned down a water and oil mixture originally, but he agreed to try a mixture in the ratio of one part hot water to three parts crude. The pipeliners had found that cold oil lay in the bottom of the line and warm oil rode over it, though in limited volume. Hot water, it was believed, would float the cold oil to the top, where it would gain heat. To test this idea, an extra tank was put in at Pond, the second station on the line. Towl also set up a tank at Kimberlena, fourteen miles from Waite, to study the effect of pumping just half the distance between stations. He planned to use the tank to suggest the effect of an intermediate station or, by withdrawing half of the crude into the tank, to simulate a second line from Kimberlena to the next station—in other words, "looping" the line. These tests proved helpful. Eric Starke volunteered a different possibility. By heating the Kern River crude under pressure, he broke its viscosity so that 12.5° gravity oil flowed as freely as a 19° gravity oil. However, if this oil came in contact with water, it formed an emulsion that was hard to pump and to separate.[62]

As an expedient, Towl settled on still another method for hurrying the oil along—mixing lighter oil from the Coalinga field with the Kern. Fortunately, he had begun a branch line from the Mendota station to Coalinga early in 1903, about the time he started oil into the line at Waite. On July 10 Coalinga oil began to move toward Mendota, located 115 miles north of Waite. In a month, deliveries to Richmond reached 3,000 barrels a day, meeting the refinery's need for heavy crude, and, with the residuum from refining, supplying sufficient fuel oil for the Iowa Standard marketers. Once the line was operating steadily, Towl thought he could run nine or ten thousand barrels a day of a relatively light Kern oil, 16° gravity, without water. Some of the heavier oil he believed would probably require water, though if the oil could be pumped to Mendota, the addition of Coalinga crude would make the rest of the trip easy. Satisfied with the rate of flow, Towl shifted his attention from the line to tankage, for the five 55,000- and three 30,000-barrel tanks at Richmond would soon be filled. A conference with Payne and the PCO executives led to a recommendation for five more tanks.[63]

Already pipeliners and refiners were feeling cramped in the 150-acre tract they shared at Richmond; neither had room to expand. The refinery superintendent suggested that the pipeline locate elsewhere, turning over its tanks to the refinery. Towl agreed, and as his farewell task tentatively located a new site for a tank farm nearby in San Pablo Canyon. His successor, John Page, another engineering graduate from Cornell, had been working with him since June to get the line operating smoothly and to set up a permanent pipeline organization. On September 15, 1903, Towl departed for the East to become general superintendent of Standard's trunk lines in New York and Pennsylvania. He left behind an impressive monument to his ingenuity and tenacity.[64]

9

While Standard's principal venture in 1900 was the handling of fuel crudes from Kern River and McKittrick, the company was also alert for lighter crudes that could be refined profitably. As yet the production of refinable crudes was too small to be exciting, but in a petroleum province the size of California prolific light oil fields could well exist. If Standard contemplated refining in the future, it was sensible to begin at once because, as Lufkin had warned Archbold, "it will be an exceedingly slow operation to get systematically established," for conditions in California were very different from those in the East. In buying PCO, Standard acquired the largest refiner of light products on the West Coast, and unexpectedly, through the ingenuity of Eric Starke, an outstanding innovation in manufacturing kerosine. From Pico Canyon, it had also gained one of California's best refining oils, but in so limited a quantity that the throughput of the Alameda refinery could scarcely be maintained. If refining were to increase at all, a new source of supply was essential. Even as the negotiations for PCO were going on, Standard had Herman Frasch, conqueror of the Lima crude, working on the peculiar light crude of the Oil City field at Coalinga. Though a high gravity oil, it did not make good kerosine. On the other hand, it yielded quantities of good engine distillate. In fact, Puente was buying it and selling distillate made from it to Iowa Standard. Frasch developed ways of separating out the smoke-producing aromatic hydrocarbons, but his techniques, even if practical, soon were irrelevant as less difficult crudes became available in quantity.[65]

It fell to the operating refiners to unlock the secrets of the California crudes. After purchasing PCO, Standard sent its own men to run the Alameda refinery. The new superintendent, William S. Rheem, was a tall, handsome man of thirty-nine who had worked for Standard since 1887. He had served first as an inspector for the Atlantic Refining Company at Franklin, Pennsylvania, and later as a foreman and a superintendent at the Whiting refinery. Rheem arrived by special train in the spring of 1901, along with his second-in-command, J. P. Smith, who had been a night superintendent at Whiting, and a considerable number of operating men, who brought their families. Some of the men went to work at Iowa Standard's can factory in San Francisco, but most followed Rheem to Alameda.[66]

Shortly, Rheem began to overhaul the refinery. The steam still condenser was rebuilt, the office and Starke's acid restoring plant enlarged, the fire protection system extended, and two 35,000-barrel storage tanks erected. The sources of crude oil handled by Alameda were also increased. In addition to oil from Pico and Elsmere, crudes were brought in from Fullerton, Coalinga, McKittrick, and Kern River. As early as January, 1901, Breeden bought the production of W. L. Hardison's Columbia Oil Company, the principal light oil producer at Fullerton, and of the neighboring Fullerton Oil Company. PCO shipped Fullerton crude by rail to Redondo Beach for storage until the *Loomis* could carry it to Alameda. At Redondo, the company purchased a three-acre plot and set up a 28,000-barrel tank, connected by pipeline with the wharf of the Los Angeles and Redondo Railway.[67]

PCO tried several crudes from the Valley fields. It bought a little Oil City crude but soon gave up trying to make a good kerosine from that refractory oil. Crude from the new Eastside field at Coalinga was also tested. Within two years it would become extremely important to the company, but at this time it may have been considered a little heavy. As late as mid-1902, Rheem thought crudes of less than 25° gravity were too heavy for refining. He was willing to make an exception only for heavy crude from Kern River and McKittrick, which was run primarily for lube oils in Alameda's "tar stills." Elsmere crude had previously been the principal lube stock, but no shipments were received after April, 1901. No doubt, the *Loomis'* full capacity was needed to take care of the Fullerton oil.[68]

Rheem and Smith, who was an experienced paraffin oil treater, were eager to see what lubes they could make. Smith was chiefly responsible for adding lighter lubes to Alameda's line, including some bearing eastern brand names, like Diamond Paraffine and Atlantic Red. The refinery gained additional skills in August, 1901, when Luther D. Dimm, Assistant Superintendent of Whiting's Grease and Lubricating Compounding Department, arrived. Soon Alameda was supplying S.O. (Iowa) with Mica Axle Grease, Arctic Cup Grease, and several other oils.[69]

Within a few months, Rheem began scouting for a new refinery site and pipeline terminal. Alameda's eight acres were inadequate and the adjoining land expensive. Moreover, the Bay waters off Alameda were too shallow for sizable ocean-going vessels. Three sites were selected, two of which were on Suisun Bay in the Sacramento River estuary and the other on San Francisco Bay proper, a mile north of the Santa Fe's new marine terminal at Point Richmond. The planners at 26 Broadway had in mind a fifty-acre tract, but when Scofield protested that the business would grow and more land would be required, this limitation was removed. On September 14, 1901, PCO paid $15,000 for 118 acres of hills, tidelands, marshlands, and a little flat ground north of Point Richmond, which was soon increased to 149 acres. The land was part of a peninsula formed by the Potrero Hills, a five-mile range of low hills rising from the Bay, parallel to the mainland and joined to it by a marsh. The bulk of the tract lay on the mainland side, but an arm flung across the hills pointed toward deep water a third of a mile offshore.[70]

The *Bakersfield Californian* reported the initial transaction in an extravagant story, stating that the third largest refinery in the world was to be built at a cost of three to five million dollars. The refinery would run principally on Kern County crude, the paper said, and would end

Standard's dependence on eastern products. Speaking for PCO, Breeden denied that the company planned more than a small venture. He admitted it would erect quite a number of large tanks, explaining, "We intend to establish a shipping station there more than a refinery, although a refinery may be erected soon." Nevertheless, a substantial refinery, large for California, was indeed under consideration. Rheem went back to Whiting to talk over the project, and on to 26 Broadway to discuss it with the Manufacturing Committee. He took with him a set of lube oil samples made at Alameda. The New York headquarters finally approved a refinery that would use Pico, Fullerton, and Kern River crudes to manufacture a wide range of products, including 10,000,000 gallons of kerosine a year—650 barrels a day. Its cost was estimated at about $650,000.[71]

A representative of the Manufacturing Committee, John W. Van Dyke, vice president and general manager of the Solar Refining Company at Lima, Ohio, and a distinguished inventor, was selected to work with Rheem. Estimates of costs were prepared at Solar under Van Dyke's direction as well as at Alameda. The Whiting refinery was also deeply involved because its shops would fabricate most of the equipment for assembly at the site. It was to Whiting that Rheem wired on October 26, 1901, for eight crude stills, ten tar stills, a steam still, ten boilers, fifty-one tanks, eight agitators, lube-compounding and grease-making equipment, and other items.[72]

Monday morning, October 28, Rheem, J. C. Black, the twenty-one-year-old chief engineer, and E. J. Garrard, the mason foreman, swung off a Southern Pacific train, climbed into a surrey and drove out a winding ranch road to the refinery site. They took over the vacant tenant's cottage as their home and office for the busy months of construction. A grading contractor was already setting up his camp. The fill for the railroad spur across the marsh was well under way. The spur was to be the axis of the refinery; as it neared the cottage, it curved and approached a pass in the hills leading to the Bay. Along the north side of the track, the buildings were to rise, and behind them, on the hill slope, the storage tanks. Along the south side of the track, the refining equipment would be installed. On the Bay side of the hills, a wharf would reach out to deep water.[73]

The first buildings—a bunkhouse and a carpenter shop beside the cottage—were temporary. Meanwhile, the grading contractor prepared sites for the buildings and tanks, built roads, and constructed three earthen dams to save the winter rainfall for drier months. When Garrard put his masons to work, they located the front wall of each permanent building by measuring 12 feet 8 inches from the center of the railroad track. Each corner formed by a side wall they squared up by measuring 8 feet along one wall, 6 along the other, and then forced the hypotenuse of the triangle to measure 10 feet.

The first of these red brick structures, a one-story storehouse, was finished by the close of 1901. It was followed by a two-story brick stable at the end of the track; next, beside the storehouse, a long one-story building for boiler, machine, and pipe shops was completed. Along the other side of the track the masons built a boiler house, the foundations for stills and their condenser boxes, and the receiving houses. Rheem did not press work on the ten 350-barrel tar stills of Battery #2, for they would not be needed until the pipeline was ready to bring heavy crude from Kern County. The crude stills, on the other hand, could be put to work just as soon as light oil could come over the wharf from Southern California. The push was behind Battery #1—eight 1,000-barrel crude stills which were located toward the end of the track. The supporting walls for the condenser-boxes were almost finished when, in February, rain and high winds tumbled much of them into rubble. Last in priority were the barrel house, the acid recovery works, and, apparently least necessary, the office and laboratory building. The barrel house was the most impressive of all. Two and a half stories high, 245 feet long and 53 feet wide, it housed equipment for compounding lubes and mixing greases, making boxes and barrels, and filling the containers for shipment.[74]

Building materials were, of course, bought locally. Pre-cut metal sheets and equipment came largely from the East, principally from Whiting, but pumps are known to have been drawn from National Transit at Oil City, Pennsylvania, and from Galatea, Ohio. All in all, the equipment was shipped expeditiously and the work moved smoothly. Occasionally, Rheem prodded his old associates for some failure in planning. His sharpest protest came in mid-February, 1902, when he wrote W. M. Burton at Whiting, "I suppose there is a very good reason for it, but it is rather unfortunate for us that the tops of the tanks reach us before the bottoms." Rheem seems to have been a hard-driving man, but this trait was tempered by reason and a dignified friendliness. He was well-liked and respected.[75]

While the refinery was going up, a grading contractor was cutting a pass through the hills, later known as the "Scofield Cut," for a road and pipelines to the Bay. Out into the Bay, solid fill was dumped for 1,300 feet and extended with 450 feet of trestle and wharf. Another installation on the Bay side of the hills was the salt water pumping station. When drilling failed to develop an adequate water supply, Rheem and Van Dyke were forced to ask New York to let them use Bay water for cooling. Rheem pointed out an incidental benefit from building a pump station near the wharf—the pumper could protect the copper covering on the piles from the "many thieves that infest the bay and river above us."[76]

Late in June, 1902, the *Loomis* began to deliver Southern California crude over the Richmond wharf; the long awaited day of operation neared. On July 7 Rheem wrote Scofield, "For your information and as a matter of record, the first oil run at the Richmond Refinery came into the Receiving House at 12 o'clock today. The crude charged was Fullerton, 13 parts, Pico, two parts." The refinery began operating a year before the pipeline delivered its first oil to Richmond. By that time, refining, the junior partner in the initial expansion of the PCO, was well on the way to becoming the company's principal business.[77]

X

EXPANSION
AND CONSOLIDATION

Although the fuel oil venture would prove somewhat disappointing, this disappointment was more than offset by PCO's marked success with what originally had been its secondary objective— a modest attempt to refine California crudes. In this endeavor, the company was fortunate to be in the right place at the right time with the right refining process. The refinery had barely been completed before the new Coalinga Eastside field began to produce large quantities of refinable crude. Located some thirty miles off the pipeline, Coalinga was the nearest to Richmond of the major oil fields. About a year later, a second new field came in near the coast at Santa Maria. Its light crude could readily be shipped to Richmond by tanker, a technique Standard knew well.

With factors so favorable, 26 Broadway nonetheless made its way rather cautiously, uncertain of the size of the fields and of the western market. To John Page, successor to Forrest Towl as pipeline manager and the most independent-minded of the California executives, the New York leaders frequently seemed to move all too slowly. His voice was ever urging them on, especially at Coalinga. But it is easy to exaggerate the eastern temporizing, for it never lasted long. On the whole, Richmond's growth was sound and continuous. Soon Richmond replaced Whiting as the principal supplier for Iowa Standard's West Coast markets. And as markets and crude supplies increased, PCO's continued expansion was inevitable.

2

The Richmond refinery provided a sound base for a growing enterprise. From the beginning, among West Coast refineries it was the colossus. Its eight 1,000-barrel stills and ten 350-barrel stills far surpassed Union's Oleum refinery of four 150's and six 125's, and its own predecessor at Alameda, which had one 900, one 190, and eight 38's. The nearest rival in point of size was the Sunset Oil Refining Company at Los Angeles, which had sixteen 150-barrel stills. These were physical capacities; no one knows the actual operating capacities. The evidence suggests that in 1902 Richmond was expected to process about 3,000 barrels a day, eight times as much as Alameda had been running. On the other hand, Richmond's throughput of 3,000 barrels was puny compared to Whiting's 22,500 barrels daily. Few would have dreamed that Richmond would match the Whiting figure in four years.[1]

Richmond was also remarkable in the California industry for its production of highly refined products. Only six among the thirty other refineries were making kerosine; most were simple plants which turned out asphalt, distillate, and lubes. Probably none matched Richmond in its variety of heavily treated oils. Its line of lubes was further diversified when in May, 1902, Standard bought the remaining business of the Arctic Oil Works of San Francisco. Arctic, which had been gradually selling out, had already disposed of its whaling fleet, salmon canneries, and canning steamers. To Standard, it sold its business in refining whale and sperm oils, manufacturing lubes, and distributing eastern kerosine. By this purchase Standard also acquired the services of A. B. Brooks, later a director of the Standard Oil Company (California), and his brother, J. F. Brooks, later the general manager of refineries. A. B. Brooks' first task was to build a two-and-a-half-story whale oil plant at Richmond to house Arctic's former equipment. This plant, plus the storage tanks taken over from the Pipe Line Department and other extras, raised the cost of the Richmond refinery to a million dollars.[2]

More fundamentally important to expansion than a large new refinery was a process to make a salable, inexpensive kerosine from California crude. Fortunately, when Standard bought the PCO, it also acquired Eric Starke's fuming sulfuric acid process for removing the aromatic hydrocarbons that caused California kerosine to smoke. This process, H. M. Tilford later testified, "made it a merchantable article, which it was not before." Heretofore, S.O. (Iowa) sold refined oil that had been blended, 30 per cent Californian and 70 per cent eastern. Curiously, Rheem does not seem to have been impressed with Starke. Of course, Rheem came from the great Whiting refinery, where the superintendent was W. M. Burton, a Ph. D. in chemistry from Johns Hopkins. The chemist at little Alameda was largely self-taught; his formal education had been merely four one-term courses at the University of California. Though Rheem knew that Starke's "hot-treat" method for kerosine and his acid-recovery process were the basis of Alameda's operations, he had faint praise for Starke when answering Burton's offer of a chemist: "The man we have at present is making such an effort to fill the bill, I feel disposed to let the matter rest as it is, for a time at least." Rheem was slow to adopt Starke's most important discovery, the fuming acid treatment, either because of skepticism or the high cost of acid. Starke recalled, thirteen years later, that numerous processes were tried before his was finally installed.[3]

It was a stroke of good fortune that fuming acid became available at a reasonable cost while the Richmond refinery was under construction. Acid was the most expensive single item in refining; for example, in 1901 Alameda spent $7,800 for labor and $28,200 for acid. Up to this time, fuming sulfuric had to be imported and was too expensive for commercial use. But a noted gunpowder chemist, William C. Peyton, with financial assistance from Eugene du Pont, his father-in-law and president of E. I. du Pont de Nemours & Company, had recently built a new kind of acid plant at Martinez, some twenty miles from Richmond. It was probably the second plant in the United States to use the German-developed "contact" process. Finished in 1901, the plant was intended to serve the California Powder Works, in which the du Pont firm had a minority interest, but because of a dispute this did not occur. So a source of fuming sulfuric became available at the very time Rheem was learning to handle California oil. To Scofield, Rheem wrote this revealing summary of his success:[4]

> Since the Peyton Chemical Co. have been supplying us with Fuming Acid we have made several very interesting experiments, which show conclusively that we shall be able to make a much better oil and at less cost by the use of Fuming Acid than Sulphuric Acid, either of the ordinary 93% to 94% or the 98% Sulphuric Acid. These experiments have been made in a large way, that is, treating in batches of 128 barrels.
>
> These experiments show that the net cost of refining 100 gallons of crude oil that will yield 30% Water White Oil, such oil as we are now using to mix with the Eastern Oil, is $ .27. To make the same grade of oil from a Crude that will yield 40% Water White Oil will cost 30.8¢ per 100 gallons Crude Oil run. To make a satisfactory refined oil entirely from California Crude Oil will cost $ .40 per 100 gallons Crude Oil run, giving a yield of 30% Water White Oil, and 48.8¢ per 100 gallons Crude Oil run for an oil that will yield 40% of Water White Oil.
>
> These experiments were all made using a mixture of Pico and Fullerton in the proportion of one to one.

A refinery, a process, and plenty of crude; those were Rheem's three principal requirements. As the refinery neared completion, PCO turned to the Fullerton field for more light crude. Early in 1902, the company considered laying a pipeline from Fullerton to Redondo, the port through which PCO was carrying the crude north to Alameda. In March Theodore Towl spent a week looking over a route, but the line was not built. H. M. Tilford suggested that a small refinery in Southern

California would be more economical than transporting the oil to Rich-mond and then carrying part of the products back for sale in Southern California. Rheem killed this idea. He pointed out that Richmond already had the capacity to supply the southern market, and the more Fullerton oil he ran at Richmond, the more kerosine distillate he would have to mix with and upgrade the distillate from Kern River crude. The latter point he re-emphasized after Richmond was in operation: "My experi-ence has been that the best practice to get the greatest yield of Refined Oil [kerosine] from both crudes is to work the distillates together." Rheem went on:[5]

> In preparing myself to recommend a policy for the running of the Refinery at Richmond as concerns the consumption of the two different grades of Crude, I have kept before me these points: The cost of the two different grades to the Refinery, the yield of Refined Oil from the same, the earning power of the pipeline as affected by the policy adopted at the Refinery, and the cost to produce the Refined Oil. After considering the above points carefully, I think we should run as much Kern River as possible in connection with whatever Southern California Crudes it seems best for us to purchase, considering the possibility of other persons re-fining the less refractory Crudes of Southern California if we refuse to purchase the same.

For more Fullerton oil, PCO contracted with the Santa Fe's Petroleum Development Company and the Brea Canon Oil Company of Dan Murphy, a well-known producer. To receive the additional purchases, it built a spur and loading rack at Olinda and a four-inch line to nearby Brea Canyon. Although Union laid a pipeline to bring out Fullerton crude, PCO continued to use tank cars to move its oil to Redondo. Perhaps the Santa Fe was responsible for PCO's foregoing a pipeline. The company's activities in Fullerton were directed by a rising young man, H. M. Storey, who, after coming to Kern River from the Eureka Pipe Line Company in West Virginia in 1900, had become field super-intendent in Southern California.[6]

One thing more was necessary to get the oil to Richmond—another tanker. The *Loomis* was too small to satisfy Richmond's need for crude, leading the company in May, 1902, to buy a collier, the *Asuncion*, for conversion into a tanker. It was a symbolic purchase, for the West was gradually changing from coal to oil for its principal fuel. Captain G. E. Bridgett was transferred from the *Loomis* to the *Asuncion*, which was remodeled at the Union Iron Works in San Francisco at a cost of $357,-000. It would carry 21,000 barrels of oil compared to the *Loomis'* 6,500. In January, 1903, the *Asuncion* began transporting crude to Richmond and fuel oil to Portland and Seattle; thereafter, the cargoes of the *Loomis* were kerosine and engine distillate.[7]

3

Even as PCO was preparing to rely on Fullerton crude, the Coalinga Eastside field began to demonstrate its potential. The development there was led by the California Oilfields, Limited (COF). This company owed its existence to William Graham, a veteran Pennsylvania and California oilman, and to Balfour, Guthrie & Company, the San Francisco branch of Balfour, Williamson & Company of London, to which Graham had turned for help in the spring of 1901 to develop seven sections of land of which he was a part owner. Graham, as general manager, operated the company. His first well, begun in July, 1901, was followed by many others. In October, Lyman Stewart offered to pipe COF's oil to the railroad at Ora and to sell it, but Graham, who had decided to operate independently, built his own pipeline.[8]

As early as January, 1902, samples of the COF crude were tested at Alameda. The first sample on record was a 19.6° gravity oil yielding an unimpressive 20.5 per cent kerosine. Three months later Rheem had Starke test a mixture of Kern River and Coalinga crudes to see what would happen to the light hydrocarbons in Coalinga crude if the two crudes were mixed for easier pumping in the pipeline to Richmond. Starke found that the light hydrocarbons would be lost. Many more tests of COF oil followed. Finally, a month after Richmond went on stream, Breeden asked Rheem to take a batch of 2,000 barrels. This may have been a more attractive refining crude, about 28° gravity, that had been discovered in deeper wells. Cryptic statements by Calvin Payne to Milton Stewart suggest that PCO had arranged to buy part of COF's production by October, 1902, an important turning point in the history of both companies.[9]

Once again Union sought to check PCO's advance. In September, W. L. Stewart devised a scheme to control Coalinga production, apart from California Oilfields, by offering to combine with producers on Sections 22 and 28 in a new company. He planned for this company to take over the producing properties and build a six-inch pipeline to the coast to handle its own production and that of any other producers who wanted to use the line. He also believed the line could be extended to serve the McKittrick and Sunset fields. Not only did Stewart expect good profits from piping the oil but, he thought, "The great value . . . in having the privilege and control of such an enterprise would be the assurance it gives us for doing business and the monopoly it gives us of so large a production." When some of the producers backed out, Lyman Stewart guessed that this was due to the influence of Standard. He may have been right, for within a few months at least two producers on Section 28 were selling crude to PCO. Later Lyman, writing his brother of a big COF well and the Coalinga field, commented simply, "Had we gone on with our pipe scheme, we would have controlled this oil but it was too big a proposition for us at the time."[10]

Still another potential competitor for the job of handling the Eastside's oil was the Southern Pacific. Although tank cars were in short supply, it considered building a nine-and-a-half-mile spur into the Eastside district before PCO's entry with a pipeline changed its mind. Nevertheless, the Southern Pacific was bound to be a factor in Coalinga; it owned sections checkerboarding the Coalinga region.[11]

By the end of 1902, PCO was grading tank sites on the COF properties and at the Mendota pump station on the trunk line. Forrest Towl designed the gathering system, with two big storage tanks on top of a hill overlooking the plain in which the trunk line lay. He set pump stations in both the Eastside and Westside fields to pump the oil to the hill tanks from which it flowed by gravity to Mendota. The fact that a gathering line was laid to the Westside field showed that Standard was interested in Coalinga's heavy, as well as refinable, crudes. Work on the twenty-seven mile, six-inch branch line was completed May 19, but the pump stations took a little longer. It was July 10 when 20° gravity oil finally began flowing to Mendota for mixing with the slow-moving Kern oil. Late in August, after mixing had proved a success, Towl shut down the line south of Mendota and put through a batch of 30,000 barrels of 28° gravity Coalinga crude to Richmond.[12]

Coalinga's crude and an effective refining process made the next step inevitable. In April, 1903, Rheem was authorized to double the refinery's production of kerosine to 20,000,000 gallons a year, which was enough to supply the needs of Iowa Standard without help from Whiting and the East. To reach this goal, Rheem added seven 1,000-barrel crude stills to Battery #1, set up a new battery of six 350-barrel "Kern Crude" stills, and installed two 600-barrel reducing stills for rerunning lube oil distillate to specifications. All the other related facilities had to be expanded, too. The new stills went into operation in January, 1904.[13]

After one more essential addition, an acid plant, the refinery showed little significant change until the latter part of 1905. For lack of acid, Richmond had nearly strangled at birth. At one point, in October, 1902, the supply of acid had been so inadequate that Rheem predicted he would have to shut down the refinery if more were not forthcoming immediately. Greatly concerned, he urged Scofield to have Peyton's plant investigated and, if enough production were not in view, to ask 26 Broadway either to buy the plant or make some other arrangement.[14] Toward the close of 1903, Richmond was again short of acid to treat the mounting stocks of distillate. This time Rheem asked for a plant of his own, and got it. In November, 1903, 26 Broadway, through its Bergenport Chemical Works, bought a license to the process of the Verein Chemischer Fabriken of Mannheim, Germany.[15]

Shortly, Rheem started work on a site on the northeastern side of "Acid Hill," breaking out of the little valley that had cradled the original refinery. An impressive brick plant costing $375,000 began operation in January, 1905. It housed sixteen acid-making units, each capable of producing three and a half tons a day. The raw material, iron pyrites, was roasted to give off sulfur dioxide which was changed to sulfur trioxide, partly in chambers containing burnt ore cinders and partly in chambers of asbestos mats impregnated with platinum. The sulfur trioxide was then drawn through "absorption towers" filled with stones through which sulfuric acid trickled and was recirculated until its sulfur trioxide content reached 15 per cent.[16]

As the refinery expanded, it soon was in danger of running short of space. In September, 1903, Scofield laid the matter before H. C. Folger, Jr., of 26 Broadway, who wrote O'Day, "We expect this Plant to grow largely and we will need every available plot of ground." Coalinga crude had wrought a striking change in 26 Broadway's original view of the size of the refinery. The immediate answer, as noted earlier, was for the pipeline to surrender its tankage and terminal at Richmond. For a new site, the pipeliners chose San Pablo Canyon, about five miles away, where 154 acres for forty tanks were purchased in October. The pipeliners planned to store Coalinga crude there, rather than in the field. The refiners, seeing the price of land skyrocketing, also bought 117 acres of land and marsh north of the refinery in anticipation of their future requirements.[17]

4

The question of whether to enlarge the capacity of the pipeline was a more difficult one. John Page, the new pipeline manager, was a persistent and ardent advocate of expansion. His letters betray the frustration of the good soldier who is sure his superiors, far from the scene, are wrong. In September, 1903, the pipeline was handling 5,500 barrels of Coalinga oil daily. Page warned Payne that the Coalinga six-inch branch line would reach its capacity of 7,000 barrels in December. Why not build up the capacity of the Coalinga branch, he asked, by replacing the six-inch pipe with eight-inch drawn from the downstream end of each of the four sections of the trunk line between Waite and Mendota? The gaps in the trunk line could then be closed with ten-inch pipe, increasing the capacity of that line. In the larger pipe, the Kern oil, chilling and thickening as it approached the end of a section, would flow more easily. North of Mendota, Coalinga oil could be mixed with the Kern to help it along; a half-and-half mixture could be pumped at four times the rate of Kern oil alone. The experiment in pumping to Kimberlena, half-way between the first two pump stations, soon proved Page's point, for the heat loss was not great during these first fourteen miles. Increase the size of the pipe toward the end of each section, Page argued, and the difficulty from cooling would be largely offset.[18]

But the eastern management hesitated, unsure of the future. While Breeden was in New York, he and H. M. Tilford met with the pipeline men—O'Day, Payne, Forrest Towl, and John Bushnell—to consider the pipeline in the context of the West Coast business. They decided to shut down the Waite-Mendota part of the trunk line, storing the Kern River crude in reservoirs. The refiners wanted straight Coalinga oil, and Breeden had contracted for enough to supply Richmond and to fill the San Pablo tankage. The eastern executives were not convinced that the Coalinga field and the western market justified further expansion.[19]

At Coalinga, competition was another factor with which the executives had to reckon, along with the usual uncertainties concerning the size and life of a new field. The Southern Pacific was taking an interest in Coalinga as a supplier of fuel oil. A number of the producers were operating on the Southern Pacific's land, and their leases required both a royalty and an option offering the railroad the opportunity to buy their production at the market price. With this option in mind, Page recommended that PCO set a sliding scale of prices for the lighter oils based on gravity, so that the Southern Pacific would exercise its option only for the fuel grades. Breeden did so, and the strategy seems to have worked. The Southern Pacific laid a pipeline late in 1903 from the Westside to the railroad at Ora, but it did not try for the lighter production of the Eastside. Union, which would have been a serious competitor if its plans for a pipeline to tidewater and a combination of producers had not collapsed, still controlled 460 acres of proven property and was planning a line to Ora. Associated invaded Coalinga and was seeking to sign up producers. Also, a new and powerful combination was forming under the leadership of Captain William Matson, a shipowner and oilman, to build a pipeline from Coalinga to the coast. According to W. L. Stewart, Matson believed that the railroads, Associated, and Standard were all working together. Matson was interested in three Coalinga companies which he wanted to free from dependence on rail transportation, and he thought that a pipeline would add to their value. Before long, PCO heard that Balfour, Guthrie, together with the Spreckels sugar interests and other strong firms, were supporting Matson, who was reported to have already enough fuel oil contracts to make the line pay. This array of capable competitors must have contributed to 26 Broadway's indecision.[20]

While the New York executives hesitated, Page was facing a storage crisis at San Pablo. He wrote O'Day that unless the tanks for San Pablo were erected more rapidly, he would have to pump Coalinga oil to Kern River for storage. It was a week or two before more tanks were shipped from the East, but, fortunately, the refinery used more oil than anticipated. Meanwhile, Page pumped water into the line from Waite to Mendota to clear out the Kern oil before it congealed from cold. The following month, in November, Breeden received word to take all the Coalinga crude he could get. Beginning December 1, 1903, he expected to buy an average of 7,500 barrels a day, of which the enlarged refinery would take 5,700. One drawback to substituting Coalinga for Kern crude was eliminated by a decision to run all Coalinga oil through the refinery and to make its flash test for fuel oil as safe as the Kern-Coalinga mixture which Richmond had sold earlier. To handle the additional Coalinga purchases, Page proposed that eight-inch pipe be pulled out of the idle trunk line south of Mendota and used for a second line to Coalinga. He pointed out that chill weather had reduced sharply the capacity of the six-inch Coalinga line; it was necessary to mix light with heavy oil to continue pumping 6,000 barrels daily. Page's argument was further strengthened when Scofield revealed that the refinery was hoping 26 Broadway would authorize another round of expansion.[21]

The persistence of the PCO pipeline manager caused O'Day to reply that 26 Broadway did not want to increase its pipeline investment because of uncertainty concerning the size of the market for the refinery's products. But O'Day did ask Forrest Towl to prepare a technical report on the proposals Page had made. Towl supported Page up to a point. He agreed that the trunk line would have been more successful if it had been laid originally with half eight-inch and half ten-inch pipe, but thought a change at this time was impractical. In his view, it was better to rely on water to help along any Kern oil that might be run.

For the Coalinga line, he recommended looping with six-inch pipe and increasing the length of the loop as the need grew for a larger capacity. Page wrote back to O'Day, agreeing that Towl's recommendations were probably adequate to meet current needs. He continued to argue, however, that in the long run his plans would prove more economical. "The oil business is in its infancy yet . . . and . . . the time will come when you will wish you had a larger main line." At least, he pleaded, let the Coalinga loop be eight-inch pipe.[22]

Calvin Payne sided with Page, writing O'Day, "I have great faith in the stability of the California oil production and I think the growth of production and consumption is beyond what any of us expected." He anticipated that demand would exceed the trunk line's capacity by the spring of the next year. With some diffidence, he endorsed Page's proposal of inserting ten-inch pipe at the end of each section in the trunk line because he had suggested this plan before the line was built, only to be talked out of it by his subordinates. In fact, Payne went beyond Page in recommending that ten-inch pipe be substituted for a full half of the line between Waite and Mendota, and that the salvaged eight-inch be used to loop the line north of Mendota to equalize the line's capacity for heavy oil over its entire length. Payne believed that eventually a double line from Mendota to Richmond would be desirable in order to keep the light and heavy oils separate. An alternative—doubling the number of stations—would reduce the cost of extra pipe, but he pointed out that the cost of operating the extra stations would gradually eat up these savings. Whichever plan was adopted, he urged that work should begin soon so that the pipeline could handle the prospective volume of business.[23]

O'Day had barely received Payne's letter before Page was writing of an inquiry from Scofield and Breeden, who wanted to know whether the pipeline could deliver 3,500 to 4,000 barrels daily of fuel grade crude to the Southern Pacific, mostly at Richmond, in addition to 8,000 barrels daily for the refinery. A million barrel contract with the Southern Pacific was under discussion. Page had to say he could not pump that much crude through the line during the winter months. Since this incident spoke volumes, he contented himself with telling O'Day that anything that could be done to enlarge the capacity of the main line would be helpful.[24]

The contract with the Southern Pacific was never signed, but in anticipation of some growth in demand, Page was summoned to New York to help plan for delivering to Richmond an average of 8,000 barrels daily from Coalinga during the first six months of 1904, and 10,000 from Coalinga and Kern County during the remainder of the year. The principal new construction proposed was a ten-mile loop of eight-inch pipe on the Coalinga line. On January 7, O'Day sent the estimate to H. H. Rogers, his superior at 26 Broadway, along with a recommendation for the purchase of an additional 150 acres to expand the San Pablo tank farm. The Manufacturing Committee was asking that the Coalinga and Kern oil be tanked separately, O'Day told Rogers, and for efficiency the pipeliners would need to pump Kern oil in large batches, a practice that would require more tanks. O'Day raised another point. At the time, PCO was buying no more than 6,000 barrels of Coalinga oil daily, but Page reported that the field's production was already well above that figure. PCO thus was failing to provide the producers with an adequate outlet. "I would urge," O'Day warned, "that we make special efforts to care for the Coalinga oil, as that field is within about 100 miles of the coast, and it is probable if we fail to take care of the oil, a pipeline would be laid to the coast. . . ."[25]

Within a month, the marketers handed PCO a new set of requirements which called for the pipeline to carry an average of 10,000 barrels a day during the first half of the year and at least 15,000 during the second half. After June, 1904, at least 6,000 barrels daily of Kern oil would be traveling through the line, and the refiners had emphasized that this oil should be piped separately. Faced with these conditions, 26 Broadway agreed on February 3, 1904, that it was time to go ahead with the oft-discussed plan for building nine new stations at the midpoints between the original ten. These stations, plus heavier pumps at all stations, would raise the line's capacity above 20,000 barrels a day. A million barrels more tankage would also be needed. Theodore Towl came West to negotiate for the necessary land, and in April construction of the stations began. The debate over the handling of Kern crude had been settled at last. For a brief moment, Page had reason to be satisfied.[26]

5

The decision to build up pipeline capacity had hardly been made when PCO was instructed to cut its offer for heavy Coalinga oil from 20¢ to 12⅔ ¢ a barrel late in February, 1904. Page regretted this blow to the Westside producers. Two months earlier, he had written O'Day that because eastern prices were rising, the Coalinga oilmen felt they should be receiving a little more money. They were getting restless. One had jokingly told Page that his oil cost 25¢ to produce and that "he was willing to work for the Standard Oil Company and board himself, but it was hard to be obliged to pay five cents per barrel to hold his job."

Page had also passed on to O'Day, with an eloquent absence of comment, an experience with Breeden reported by two young lawyers. These men controlled 2,500 barrels a day of 19° gravity oil, which in December, 1903, was about one-fourth of Coalinga's production. When they asked Breeden to renew their contracts at a little higher price, he turned them down, saying that Kern River oil was as valuable to PCO as Coalinga and could be pumped as cheaply. The men thought Breeden's statement was untrue and an affront to their intelligence.[27] Perhaps Breeden meant only to say that the refiners considered a 19° gravity oil a fuel oil, and Coalinga had to meet the competition of Kern oil. But Breeden was not noted for tact, and he undoubtedly irritated two men whom the Pipe Line Department knew as friends.

However interpreted, the price cut of February clearly showed 26 Broadway's lack of interest in Coalinga's fuel grade crudes. It may have reflected the intention to rely on Kern oil after the pipeline was improved. Also, the rapid rise in production of Coalinga light crude—PCO was taking 6,000 barrels daily by the end of February—and a large new contract with Union for light crude and distillate may well have convinced the eastern executives that Richmond no longer had sufficient still capacity to run the heavy crude. Perhaps, too, a shortage of tankage was a factor.[28]

There can be no doubt of the distress the price cut had caused the Westside oilmen. They reduced production and looked more sympathetically on the Matson pipeline, though many of them hesitated to sign up because the line was offering only long-term contracts at the current market price. The rumor that the Spreckels interests were behind the line added to their concern because they feared Spreckels might sell out. Producers were grateful to PCO for its aid in opening the field, but they were hurt by its cut in price; their costs of production were too high to permit them to operate profitably. Some planned to either stop producing or to store their oil. "It looks as though the cut in price is going to be very effective in . . . keeping the pipe line from getting Coalinga oil," Page reported with a touch of asperity. Indeed, because of the growing threat of water damage to the oil sands of Kern River, he believed that 26 Broadway was making a mistake in not basing its operations on the Coalinga field and forestalling competition by keeping the producers happy.[29]

Page kept a steady flow of letters to O'Day telling what PCO's competitors were doing. From a producer he learned that the Southern Pacific planned to exercise its option to buy its lessees' production at the market price and that the Associated was endeavoring to bring the Coalinga producers into a new combination. In April, one of the Matson companies was shipping oil by rail, and another had called for bids on a 108-mile, six-inch pipeline to the coast at Monterey. When Breeden asked Page to locate the route planned for the line through the Coast Range, he suspected that Breeden was thinking of having friendly parties buy land across the route, but there is no evidence that anything of this sort took place.

The newly organized Coalinga Oil & Transportation Company, which built the line, began work in May. Matson was its president; on its board was Captain John Barneson, later the moving spirit in the General Petroleum Company, who superintended the construction. Although the pipeline was primarily intended for heavy crude, it posed a partial threat to PCO's light crude supply because Coalinga Oil & Transportation planned to buy enough Eastside oil to raise the gravity of its oil to 20° for easier pumping. As the line neared completion in the fall of 1904, Lyman Stewart commented, "These people are getting to be factors to be reckoned with in the future. They are our competitors in the Hawaiian Islands and are not at all scrupulous in their business methods." Page heard that Coalinga Oil & Transportation was lending money to oil companies to drill and would accept oil in repayment. Clearly, a vigorous competitor had entered the fuel oil market, facilitated by 26 Broadway's reluctance to commit more capital to its California venture. A year later, in 1905, the Matson pipeline and other interests in the Coalinga and Santa Maria fields, along with an asphalt refinery at Gaviota and four tankships, were sold to Associated.[30]

26 Broadway's indifference to the fuel crude production in Coalinga became even more apparent on May 19, 1904, when it instructed Breeden to buy no more Coalinga oil under 22° gravity. This meant no more contracts in the Westside field and even shut out PCO's old supplier, the Peerless Oil Company of Kern River, which had developed production just under the gravity limit in the Eastside field. Page was dumbfounded. He knew the order was none of his business, but he could not resist writing to O'Day and Payne that it would cost PCO loyal friends who had looked to the company to handle their oil. At least, if the limit had been set at 20° gravity, he could have retained all of the Eastside field. This new policy, the pipeliner felt sure, would increase competition for S.O. (Iowa), because the oil PCO did not take would find other outlets. O'Day talked Page's letter over with Tilford and answered:[31]

> The fact is that the situation in California is entirely different from what it was in Ohio and in Pennsylvania; in the latter we had a market for all the oil we could get, and consequently we took and are now taking it, but in California we have a limited market, and can only take as much

oil as the refiners and distributors can market, and we must be governed by them in that regard. . . . I feel sorry with you from the pipeline standpoint that we cannot take everything that is offered, but . . . we have immense stocks of oil in California, and the prospect of a market is a long way in the future. . . . Between ourselves, the best thing the producers could do would be to stop producing so much oil until a market is secured.

Three months later, PCO shocked the Kern River producers as it had those at Coalinga earlier. On August 13, 1904, Breeden cut the company's offer from 15¢ to 11⅔¢ and a few days later ceased buying, regardless of price, stating that the company had all the Kern oil in storage or under contract that it wanted. However, many producers were of another opinion. Since W. S. Porter followed Breeden's cut with an offer to buy oil at 15¢ on two- and three-year contracts, they concluded that Standard had clubbed the market to help Associated.

PCO's action not only earned ill-will, but it brought into being a new competitor. On August 23, the *Bakersfield Echo* published an interview with a prominent producer, H. H. Blood, who urged the producers to organize, not for a fight, but to facilitate the sale of oil and to prevent indiscriminate competition. That evening a group of men decided to call a meeting of independents, which led to the formation of the Independent Oil Producers Agency. Incorporated on November 3, 1904, the Agency leased the lands of members for five years and, in turn, licensed each member to operate its own land. The Agency had the exclusive right to handle and dispose of the oil. Its original directorate, one man from each company, consisted of thirty-five, but by the time the Agency started to operate, it represented only nineteen companies. Nonetheless, the Agency controlled an important part of the independent production at Kern River.[32]

PCO's withdrawal from the market in August puzzled the producers, who could not reconcile PCO's statement that it needed no more oil with the fact that it was building tankage at San Pablo and reservoirs at Kern. Actually, there was no mystery: PCO had to store Coalinga oil in excess of refinery runs at San Pablo; it had to provide storage to handle pumpings in large batches from the two fields; and it had to store the Kern oil already contracted for. Stocks of fuel oil at Richmond so far exceeded the demands of the marketers that in mid-August PCO was forced to shut down pumping Kern River crude altogether. In September the company was still receiving under contract 12,700 barrels daily at Kern River, adding to the 8,500,000 barrels already in storage.

The circumstantial evidence for the charge that Associated and Standard Oil were working together is certainly subject to a more prosaic interpretation. Intracompany correspondence uniformly suggests that PCO did not expect or desire to be the principal buyer of fuel crude. Rather, it bought what it thought could be sold at a profit. O'Day's letter, quoted above, regarding Coalinga oil testifies to that. In fact, Breeden seems to have been adjusting his purchases to a reliance on refinable crudes at Coalinga and Santa Maria and to have been de-emphasizing fuel crudes. PCO had not received any McKittrick oil after October, 1903, though the plant there remained in place and idle. In August, 1904, Breeden sold it to the Associated and traded the oil in the tanks for Kern crude. These transactions were interpreted as evidence of an Associated-Standard alliance, but they are hardly conclusive. About the same time, PCO was also withdrawing from the Fullerton field, which had been supplying about 700 barrels daily, an amount that had ceased to be important after Coalinga boomed. When the contract with Dan Murphy's Brea Canon Oil Company expired in March, 1904, it was not renewed. The company also ceased receiving oil from the Santa Fe's Petroleum Development Company about August. Subsequently, PCO sold Murphy all its property in the Fullerton field.[33]

A week after PCO withdrew from the Kern River market, it re-entered, offering 12.5¢ a barrel. There were few takers because that price was below the cost of production. No doubt, a number of producers were waiting to see what their efforts at combination could achieve. Perhaps PCO set the price for the crude so low it would not be accepted, for just to hold the Kern River production already under contract, Page was busy buying more land for reservoirs.[34]

In October, Rheem visited New York to talk over plans for enlarging the Richmond refinery. It seems certain that he discussed a major new opportunity to manufacture kerosine for the Oriental market; the first cargo had left the refinery the previous month. During a conference with O'Day, Payne, Bushnell, and Rheem, H. M. Tilford forecast a need for 10,000 barrels daily of Coalinga oil in the spring of 1905 after the refinery's capacity had been increased. Presumably, he referred to converting the "Kern River" stills of Battery #2 from batch distillation of heavy crude to continuous distillation of light crude, for this change was soon begun. Tilford and Rheem also told the pipeliners that they would require 5,000 barrels of Kern River crude daily, of which about half would be shipped by rail to buyers in the interior.

Tilford said he expected to receive instructions to buy all the Coalinga oil he could get above 20° gravity. In view of the Eastside's rising production, this would force the Pipe Line Department to store part of the oil at Waite. The Coalinga oil would have to be put in steel tankage to avoid the loss of valuable light hydrocarbons by evaporation, and the heavy oil already in the tanks transferred to new reservoirs. The reduction in the gravity limit was most welcome to Page. He noted, philosophically, that the change came too late to get Peerless' 1,500 barrels a day, but so much drilling was going on that more oil would undoubtedly become available.[35] He must have been pleased to see Coalinga at last receiving the attention he believed it deserved.

6

To accommodate more Coalinga oil, Page was allowed to relocate pump station #2 in the Eastside field, moving it out of a narrow canyon down onto the flat and placing there the storage tanks that Towl had originally set upon a hill. Under the new arrangement—an idea attributed to H. M. Storey, who had become the field superintendent at Coalinga—oil run by producers would flow by gravity to the station. At the larger station site, there was room for large storage tanks which could also be used as working tanks, and, in addition, room for camp buildings. Page had first sought land from the Southern Pacific, but the railroad asked a rental of $750 a year for twenty acres. Outraged at so high a rent for desert land, the pipeline manager went a little farther from the field, where he bought twenty acres for $2,000.[36]

Page won a round in his fight for more pipeline capacity when he pointed out that during the winter the Coalinga line might be unable to handle all the oil offered over 20° gravity. He suggested extending the existing eight-inch loop all the way to Mendota with six-inch or, preferably, eight-inch pipe. At 26 Broadway, O'Day, J. A. Moffett, and H. M. Tilford won approval to spend $95,000 for laying nineteen miles of eight-inch line only to be assailed by second thoughts. They questioned whether the additional capacity was really needed. Page reassured the doubters. Seventeen wells were drilling, and ten others were rigged up in the Eastside field. Moreover, PCO needed ample capacity to handle the new production because Matson's Coalinga Oil & Transportation Company was actively competing for crude. The Matson pipeline company was already taking 2,300 barrels a day of Eastside oil, compared to PCO's 9,700. Recently, it had made an unsuccessful attempt to contract for oil from California Oilfields, Limited, which had just brought in a well producing 1,200 barrels a day and was drilling four more. Page summed up the situation: "The production is steadily increasing and it seems to me if we want the greater part of the light oil produced, we should be in shape to handle it and not allow the competing pipe line to take it away from us." Evidently Breedon supported him, and he was allowed to go ahead.[37]

The decision to concentrate on Coalinga's Eastside field and store the surplus at Waite was, no doubt, the reason for a new loss of interest in Kern River production. About November, 1904, the Independent Oil Producers Agency sent a committee to Breeden, hoping for a contract at 22.5¢ a barrel. Their hope was based on a request Breeden had made earlier that the Agency offer its oil to PCO when ready for business. At that time Breeden had said the company could not pay the 25¢ the producers wanted, but they guessed that it would pay 22.5¢. When the committee called on him, Breeden curtly told the members that he had instructions not to buy oil at any price. Matson, Southern Pacific, and Santa Fe also turned them down. So the Agency was forced to sign with Associated. Porter gave the producers 18¢ for part of their oil and agreed to rent storage to them for the rest.

Disappointed, the Agency companies concluded that Standard was playing Associated's game. No conclusive evidence of an agreement between Standard and Associated has ever been found, and one can wonder what Standard would have gained by restricting its freedom of action. It seems more likely that PCO's retreat from the fuel crude market was governed strictly by what seemed to be Standard's own best interest. PCO was certainly turning out more fuel oil at Richmond, as it increased its runs of Coalinga crude. And at the end of November it had 9,812,000 barrels of fuel crude stored at Waite, which was around a three-year supply at Iowa Standard's current rate of sale. In December PCO again cut its takings of Kern River oil. During the first eight months of 1904, it had averaged between 17,000 and 18,000 barrels a day. After the August price cut, its takings had dropped to 13,000. In December they fell to 9,000 and continued at that rate for the following year.[38]

As 1904 drew to a close, Iowa Standard suddenly demanded more fuel oil, to the embarrassment of Page. It asked for 12,000 barrels of fuel oil daily, 7,000 more than the refinery was producing. Page was caught unprepared. Believing that enough fuel oil was coming from the refinery and enough fuel crude accumulating from the final contract deliveries at Coalinga to satisfy the marketers, he had turned late in the year to repairing the pipeline. In several spots it was badly corroded, at least twenty miles in all. The wrapping Towl had used to hold the heat had acted like a poultice, absorbing moisture even in relatively dry soil and encouraging corrosion. Page had two gangs of thirty men each uncovering the pipe, flooding the ditch with Kern crude, and then pushing the dirt back into the ditch so that a mass of oil-impregnated earth would jacket the line and shut out water. He expected to finish the worst of this job by January 1, 1905.

The new intermediate stations and the second line to Coalinga would have helped, but neither were ready. North of Mendota, the stations would take another thirty days; those to the south, two months. The new Coalinga line would not be finished until mid-February. At Coalinga, the heavy oil on hand could not be pumped effectively because un- usually cold weather had cut sharply the capacity of the existing line. As a recourse, Page mixed light oil with Coalinga heavy, raising the gravity from 17.5° to 20° and increasing pumpings to 10,000 barrels daily. He also pumped light Coalinga oil to Waite, where it was mixed with the heavy Kern oil and pumped north. This meant a loss of valuable light hydrocarbons, but there was no help for it.[39]

Fortunately, the squeeze was temporary. The new facilities soon pushed the capacity of the line to about 16,000 barrels of Kern oil daily in the six warmest months and to half that in the six coldest. In view of PCO's shift from Kern to Coalinga oil, this capacity probably was excessive, but the fact that the line could be started up at will, regardless of the weather, and a sizable block of oil put through quickly, must have been reassuring to the pipeliners. Of Coalinga oil, the main line could handle 25,000 barrels a day during the summer and 20,000 during cold weather. The new eight-inch line at Coalinga could pump 18,000 to 20,000 barrels daily. After these improvements, no other additions to the Valley line were needed until a branch line to the Midway field was built in 1907.[40]

A fitting close to 1904 was the signing of a new contract with California Oilfields that called for 4,400,000 barrels over a two-year period, or about 6,000 barrels a day. PCO paid prices ranging from 20¢ for oil of 20° gravity up to 45¢ for 27° gravity or more. December was notable, too, as the month in which receipts of crude at Coalinga first exceeded those at Kern River, offering conclusive proof of the shift in emphasis from fuel to refined oils in 26 Broadway's California venture.[41]

7

Coalinga had scarcely taken over from Kern River as PCO's chief supplier of crude oil when a rival field appeared close to the coast. Breeden first showed interest in Santa Maria, the new field, in September, 1903, but in an offhand way. He had been impressed with the ease of pumping a mixture of Coalinga and Kern River crude and had suggested to H. M. Tilford that they try to buy a fairly light oil within reach of Waite. Breeden had the Midway and Sunset fields primarily in mind, but he also mentioned Santa Maria farther west, where some 20° to 26° gravity oil was being produced. To get Santa Maria oil to Waite would require a 95-mile pipeline over a range of mountains, which Forrest Towl believed would be no problem. However, Breeden admitted that a line would not be warranted unless production increased. Less useful, he thought, would be a shorter line to the coast at Port Harford. Without making a firm recommendation, Breeden suggested that Tilford consider encouraging Santa Maria production. Evidently, Tilford reacted favorably. Breeden signed a three-year contract, November 12, 1903, with the Pinal Oil Company for 120,000 barrels at prices ranging from 75¢ for 23° gravity to $1.11 for 32° gravity or higher. Pinal bore the cost of shipping by tank car to Port Harford, where PCO set up a tank and began accepting oil in December.[42]

Obviously, an oil in this range of gravities and prices would never be used to help heavy crude through a pipeline. The sole analysis of Pinal's oil in the records suggests that it was purchased for its naphtha content. Starke reported that it could not be made into kerosine economically. While it yielded 32 per cent kerosine distillate, fully a third was lost in chemical treatment. It yielded 18 per cent naphthas, or if run solely for engine distillate, about 33 per cent. By 1905, when PCO signed large contracts for Santa Maria oil, a satisfactory yield of kerosine undoubtedly had been achieved, but engine distillate probably was the initial attraction. The likelihood of an interest in engine distillate is reinforced by the fact that after a lapse of several years, PCO was again buying crude from the Oil City field at Coalinga. In July, 1903, PCO signed a five-year joint contract with the Home Oil Company and the Coalinga Oil Company, the two firms that controlled practically all of the little field. This production, about 300 to 400 barrels daily of clear green oil, was shipped by tank car from Ora to Richmond and distilled for engine distillate. Presumably, Santa Maria crude was bought for the same purpose, or perhaps for gasoline, which was also showing a growth in sales.[43]

Late in 1903, Standard was offered an opportunity to tie up the major production in Santa Maria and other coastal fields when Lyman Stewart proposed an alliance. He had bought 72,000 acres in Santa Maria and the nearby Lompoc area, which showed thick oil sands. But, land-poor and fearful of a contest with the "Old House" for markets, Stewart hoped to cede Union's manufacturing, transportation, and marketing activities to Standard in exchange for an assured market for crude and for capital to develop his company's properties. On October 7, he wrote John D. Archbold at 26 Broadway:[44]

> I will say to you very frankly . . . that notwithstanding our strong position, I do not covet an 'endurance contest' with your company, and believe that fair-minded business men can come together and adjust the questions that may be at issue between them on a fair business basis, without wasting time and money in the usual preliminary tactics.
>
> The Union has more territory than it can even hope to operate during this generation. Its Board, therefore, contemplates subdividing and selling or leasing some of its lands. Some of our local refiners have been looking for light oil territory in order to insure the future of their business. It would doubtless be easier to arrange with one party than with many.
>
> I am writing to you very candidly, as an old-time friend, without the knowledge or consent of any member of the Company. As the Stewarts indirectly control the Union, I am in a position to make this advance to you and trust that it may receive your company's favorable consideration.

In a subsequent letter, Lyman listed Union's resources, eliciting a warning from his brother that "writing to the S. Oil Co. or any of its officials is not just the thing to do. They don't put themselves on record by letter, consequently they always expect to have the advantage on their side. Friendship cuts no figure with those cold-blooded fellows." Archbold asked Stewart to take up the proposal with Breeden and added, "It will be a matter of great satisfaction to me if some amicable and mutually satisfactory agreement with your company can be agreed upon." The thought of negotiating with Breeden cooled Stewart's enthusiasm. He hoped to deal with W. S. Miller, "a very candid, fair-minded sort of a man." But from Breeden he felt less sure of a satisfactory outcome.[45]

Nevertheless, negotiations began about November 20. In a month of give and take, a tentative agreement was worked out. Stewart could not decide whether to be gloomy or gay. He described the terms this way: He was selling Union's pipelines and ships; he was abandoning transportation, storage, marketing, and refining, except for asphalt; he was accepting a ceiling on production. In return, Standard would pay the market value of the materials for pipelines and storage facilities and practically the cost of the ships. Standard would get Union sales contracts at less than half their "real value" and would pay low prices for crude for ten years. Taking a more cheerful view, Stewart noted that Union would receive $2,000,000 in cash and an outlet for all production up to 11,000 barrels daily for ten years at a considerable advance over current prices. Its stock should jump quickly from about $50 to $200 and quadruple its dividend. Moreover, if oil prices rose and increased the value of oil property, he could sell off some land at a substantial profit, permitting Union to declare large extra dividends. In short, Stewart regretted relinquishing parts of a business built by hard work and giving up big potential profits, but he would be greatly relieved to have money at hand to develop production and the assurance of profits for ten years. What was the view of Standard's negotiators? All that is known is Stewart's statement that Breeden and Miller were anxious to close the deal, but that the decision was up to 26 Broadway.[46]

For some reason, the New York executives turned down the proposal. Perhaps their original conservative attitude toward California lingered, especially in view of Coalinga's expanding production and their heavy investments in the Valley fields. Perhaps they thought a ten-year contract too long in an industry full of surprises. Milton Stewart was pleased at the outcome. He wrote Lyman, "Am sorry on your account negotiations with the 'Old House' have fallen through—but on the whole think it decidedly better for our Co. to have no affiliation with the brigands, if only in shape to raise money to meet pressing demands." Although he called Standard "the worst soulless and grinding monopoly that ever disgraced the face of the earth," Milton was not unwilling to seek its aid. He recalled that "Thede" Barnsdall, an ambitious eastern producer, had borrowed from Standard frequently, sometimes as much as a million dollars. Perhaps Lyman could borrow the $250,000 he needed so badly. On second thought, he urged Lyman to mortgage and sell property to tide their company over. Union was much more favorably situated in its crude sources than was Standard. "With the advantage of ocean transportation, we can surely hold our own with them. It is a very different proposition from interior transportation . . . , and most of our oil being light can be easily, or comparatively so, gotten to the ocean." If Union could gain financial strength, "I doubt not it [won't] be many years before they . . . come to us instead of our going to them, and on the basis of better terms than they now propose."[47]

Through PCO, Standard soon did supply Union with considerable relief. About three weeks after the sweeping contract was turned down, Breeden and John Baker, Union's San Francisco manager, agreed on a more limited arrangement. PCO agreed to take from Ventura, Santa Barbara, and San Luis Obispo counties up to 50,000 barrels of light crude a month for two years, paying from 95¢, f.o.b. steamer, for 25° and 26° gravity oil up to $1.25 for 32° gravity and lighter. Union had the right to substitute as much as 10,000 barrels a month of distillate of 45° or more gravity, for which PCO would pay 4.5¢ a gallon delivered at Richmond. This provision superseded Iowa Standard's earlier arrangement by which it had been taking refined oil, gasoline, and engine distillate directly from Union; henceforth, Union distillate would be turned into finished products at Richmond. In return for PCO's purchases of crude and distillate, Union agreed not to manufacture or sell any gasoline or kerosine or other products lighter than 38° gravity in Contra Costa County, which was the location of its Oleum refinery. This provision, in its ultimate effect, changed nothing; it merely continued to bar Union from marketing the lighter refined oils and to channel these products from Union to Standard.[48]

PCO was offered more Santa Maria production by Pinal in July, 1904, but Breeden turned it down pending completion of Richmond's Mannheim acid plant. In November the two companies came to terms on an option. Shortly, John Page arrived at Santa Maria to assess the field for 26 Broadway. He reported its production at 2,000 barrels a day, mostly of 27° gravity. There were signs, too, that the field would grow. Union was planning a pipeline to Port Harford, and some other companies were planning lines to connect with the Southern Pacific. Competition of Santa Maria's heavy oil in the fuel trade appeared to be in the offing. Page judged that Santa Maria would develop slowly but in time would become a considerable field. When production became large enough, PCO would have to decide whether to lay a pipeline to Port Harford and tanker the oil to Richmond or lay a longer line to the Valley trunk line. The longer line, Page pointed out, could also serve the McKittrick, Midway, and Sunset fields.

Less than a month after his survey, Union's Hartnell #1, "Old Maud," blew out and flowed out of control at 12,000 barrels a day. It was the greatest producer that California had seen. On December 7 Page reported it flowing at least 7,500 barrels daily of 23° gravity oil, just a trifle heavier than PCO was obligated to take under its contract with Union. Page was convinced that the Santa Maria field would be one of the most important in the state. Again he discussed the pipeline question. Although Breeden was sending PCO tanker captains to look for a site near Point Sal, south of Port Harford, for a shipping station and terminus for a Santa Maria pipeline, Page doubted that the company had sufficient tanker capacity to handle the 10,000 barrels daily which could be put through a six-inch line. The alternative favored by Page, a line to Bakersfield, would cost a million dollars, but it would enable PCO to use two and a half million barrels of tankage there and to tie Santa Maria and practically all of the fields in the San Joaquin Valley into one continuous pipeline system.[49]

The prospects for big production in Santa Maria did not hurry

Breeden along. In fact, he allowed his option on Pinal's production to lapse without comment. When Pinal pressed him, he asked that the contract be delayed until March when PCO would receive an additional tanker and barge from the East. Finally, on February 28, 1905, he sent Pinal a contract reducing deliveries by 10,000 barrels a month and fixing a price of 5¢ a barrel less than under their earlier tentative agreement. Breeden explained the price cut: "Owing to the reduction in prices of oil in the Orient, this is about all we can pay at present." He added that some of Pinal's neighbors were willing to accept this price.

After negotiating for a week, the two companies signed a three-year contract providing for a million barrels of oil at a maximum rate of 35,000 barrels monthly. Save for 500 barrels a month, Pinal could sell only to PCO. Prices began at 22.5¢ a barrel for 23° gravity oil and ran up to 45¢ for 27° gravity or lighter. This was a sharp reduction in price from the November, 1903, contract, but it was at least as much as PCO was paying California Oilfields, and better for some of the heavier oil. For Pinal, there were two redeeming features. Since PCO would lay a pipeline to its property, Pinal no longer had to pay rail freight. Second, the contract was a large one. According to one of the owners, they accepted its terms because PCO offered the only substantial market, and if they did not produce the oil and sell it, their property would be drained by Union's neighboring wells.

A few days earlier PCO had signed a contract with the Western Union Oil Company, which owned lands about a mile away from Pinal. Except for the quantities of oil, the terms of the two agreements were identical. Western Union contracted to supply 2,000,000 barrels at a maximum rate of 75,000 barrels a month.[50]

The sharply reduced prices galled the producers. Pinal had its oil chemically analyzed and concluded that refiners "could pay 75 cents at least a barrel and make an enormous profit." For example, Pinal claimed its oil yielded nearly five gallons of gasoline to the barrel and that gasoline was wholesaling at 25¢ a gallon. To be sure, the company was operating profitably, but it could make a greater return from higher prices or from a market for more production. When a Pinal director asked Breeden why prices in the new contract were fixed so low, Breeden was said to have replied:

> There is a very much larger production now than [formerly]. At that time we could handle the oil here and dispose of it, but now we can't. . . . We must . . . spend large sums of money, and it is impossible for us to pay you more than we are paying for the reason that we have got to make a market for this oil, the market isn't in the United States.

In other words, Breeden was saying that Richmond had begun to make a low-priced kerosine for the Orient. To compete in that market and provide an outlet for Santa Maria crude, it could not afford to pay much. The question in the producer's mind was whether the low prices were the natural result of market forces. As one of the Pinal owners put it:

> [If Breeden's statements as] to the overproduction at the present time of refined products of petroleum, and as to the expenses of increasing the market are true, the producer has no ground for complaint and the present conditions are due to natural causes. But if, on the other hand, his representations are untrue, then the producer has ground for complaint; and the producer is not in a position to know of his own knowledge whether these representations are true ar not.

Many producers were not so judicious in temperament.[51]

After the agreements with Pinal and Western Union had been signed, the decision over a pipeline could no longer be delayed. The contracts contained a clause that required the pipeline to be ready in four months. A PCO agent, H. G. Morrow, immediately began to secure a right of way to Port Harford. Morrow found it hard going. An indignant Page reported to O'Day in March:[52]

> He has secured about twenty-three miles . . . for reasonable prices. He will probably secure one-half of the remainder on reasonable terms, but he will have about a half dozen property holders at the wind-up who will undoubtedly hold us up for all they can get. . . . One man asked $5.00 a rod. We will have to pay big money to four or five others. You will understand these men have no regard for justice. . . . We will leave these cases until the last and try to bring what influence we can to bear on them, but I do not hope for much. Believe we will simply have to do as we usually do in such cases, viz.: pay a nominal sum for a right of way and the balance for damages.

Page transferred J. M. Atwell, later general manager of the Producing Department, from the Valley to Santa Maria to construct the line. Atwell built a pump station just outside the little town of Orcutt and from there to Port Harford laid thirty-eight miles of eight-inch pipe, finishing the work in July, 1905.[53]

8

The contracts for Santa Maria crude caused adjustments in other PCO departments. In addition to a pipeline, more tanker capacity was required to carry the crude to Richmond. PCO's ocean-going fleet grew to four vessels with the purchase from New York Standard of the *Atlas* and *Barge 93,* which enlarged the fleet's capacity from 27,500 to 74,000 barrels. The 17,000-barrel steel tanker cost PCO $120,000; the four-masted 29,500-barrel barge, $197,000. At the time, an ocean-going barge was favorably regarded as a means of transporting oil, for a tanker could drop off a barge at one port, continue on to another, and pick up the barge on the way back. The tanker and barge arrived from the East Coast at the end of February, 1905, after a 13,135-mile trip, the longest tow on record to that date. As soon as they reached San Francisco, they joined the *Asuncion* in bringing crude to Richmond from Ventura and Port Harford.[54]

The growing volume of light crude from Coalinga and Santa Maria was reflected in refinery runs at Richmond that grew from an average of 9,450 barrels daily in 1904 to 12,058 in 1905. As mentioned earlier, Richmond's capacity was boosted by converting the original ten tar stills to continuous distillation. Authorized in November, 1904, the first unit was ready for operation by May, 1905. Santa Maria crude became the staple of the tar stills, which were hooked together in two sets of five. In each set, one still acted as preheater, and the others dis-tilled the crude into its principal components. Under the batch method, oil was heated in a single still, and the temperature increased to distill off hydrocarbons with higher and higher boiling points. In the con-tinuous method, several stills were joined together by pipes and oil run through them continuously. Each still was held at a different temperature, so that each distilled off hydrocarbons with a different range of boiling points.

The continuous method was no new idea. Rheem had talked about trying it as early as July, 1902, but the conversion of the tar stills marked its first use at Richmond. These stills were increased in charging capacity from about 1,700 barrels of Kern crude daily to about 4,600 of light crude. The conversion proved so successful that within two or three months Rheem was authorized to increase the number of 1,000-barrel stills in Battery #1 from fifteen to twenty and to put ten into continuous operation.[55]

9

In the course of four years, the manufacture of refined products had far outstripped the purchase and transportation of fuel crude as the primary mission of PCO. More significant, PCO's success with California crude enabled it to take over as the principal supplier for Iowa Standard. This shift became permanent, as enough light oil was found in California to support a large and sustained refining effort. Because of these developments, 26 Broadway decided in 1906 to administer its West Coast business through a single integrated company.

The consolidation of PCO and Iowa Standard was preceded a year earlier by a consolidation within PCO itself which seems to have grown out of a minor clash between Breeden and Page during construction of the Santa Maria line. When O'Day suggested that Page should consult with the traffic manager under Breeden before routing pipe, Page was stung by the implication that he had been uncooperative. He guessed at the incident lying behind the suggestion and explained his part in it to O'Day. Breeden had asked Page to ship pipeline materials from Bakersfield to Santa Maria over the Santa Fe through Richmond and by steamship to Port Harford, rather than over the Southern Pacific to a point near the Santa Maria field. Page did not question the reduction in freight costs to be achieved by following Breeden's recommendation, but he pointed out that this was not the sole issue. He had used the Southern Pacific to transfer heavy pumps in order to avoid the danger of damage from extra handling in rail-and-sea transportation and had sent three cars of tank iron by rail so that his men would not be idle while waiting for a ship to arrive.

Page bluntly accused Breeden of recommending the Santa Fe route because Breeden had an interest in the Richmond Belt Railway, which connected the Santa Fe to the dock used by the steamship company. At the time Page wrote, about 2,000 tons of pipe had been at Richmond nearly three weeks waiting on the steamship company. He stated heatedly, "We have no time to dally with a steamship company that has already more business than it can do promptly, and it would be madness on my part to load them up with a lot more freight when . . . I can get prompt shipments, and keep our men in work and things moving." Page added, "I could call your attention to other matters on the above line."[56]

This incident may have brought home to the New York headquarters that the Pipe Line Department was operating very much as a separate company with its line of authority running through O'Day to H. H. Rogers, who, of course, was a member of the Executive Committee at 26 Broadway. The remainder of PCO reported to H. M. Tilford, who seems to have reported to his brother, W. H. Tilford, and to J. A. Moffett, who were also members of the Executive Committee. These men of the Big Board decided that in the future Page should advise Scofield on pipeline matters, and Scofield should write O'Day. No explanation was given except that Page was informed it was desired, "for many reasons, that you have closer and more immediate contact with Mr. D. G. Scofield." O'Day knew Scofield thought well of Page and was sure they could work together. Scofield was an "old experienced man, wise in all branches of the business, more so perhaps in all others than in the pipeline branch, but on that subject you [Page] can post him. . . ." Scofield was told, "We have for some time past given very careful consideration to . . . your being in closer touch with Pipe Line Dept."

This decision may have been reached more easily because the period of heavy expenditure on the California pipelines seemed over, and 26 Broadway no longer needed to hold so tight a rein. Very likely, too, the directors believed that Scofield had proved himself over some five years of association, and they preferred to have a single voice speaking for PCO. Symbolic of the change was a new name for the Pipe Line Department. By the end of October it was known as "Division B." Page stayed on as head of Division B for a little more than a year, before he returned to 26 Broadway's principal pipeline company, National Transit, at Oil City, Pennsylvania.[57]

The consolidation of PCO and Iowa Standard was being considered at least as early as March of 1906. PCO, the larger of the two companies, was chosen by 26 Broadway to carry out the consolidation, preserving for the future the broad powers of its California charter. As a preliminary, on July 23 its name was changed to the Standard Oil Company. A second step was to increase its authorized capital. For PCO, this represented the third increase since 26 Broadway had taken over in 1900: from $1,000,000 to $3,000,000 in May 1902, to $6,000,000 in April, 1903, and now, to $25,000,000 on October 2, 1906. The additional capital was used partly to purchase the marketing business of S.O. (Iowa). On October 15, after twenty-one years, Iowa Standard left the field, turning over to its successor, S.O. (California), its eighty-three stations and substations and other assets for $4,500,000. A part of the increased capital was also used to reduce the debt of California Standard to its parent company, Jersey Standard, by $6,500,000, and the remaining $8,000,000 was left unissued to take care of future growth.[58]

The merger of the two managements raised no problems. Ever since 1900, four of the five PCO directors—Miller, Breeden, W. M. Hall (to 1905), and H. M. Tilford—had been S.O. (Iowa) men. Tilford, the vice president of S.O. (Iowa), was president of PCO. In this shuffle, there was actually little change. Rheem had risen in PCO, replacing Hall as director in February, 1905, and, following Breeden's resignation in May, 1906, took over as secretary and treasurer. In the consolidated company, he and W. S. Miller, who held the corresponding posts in S.O.

(Iowa), split their titles. Rheem became secretary and Miller, treasurer. Their major duties, of course, continued as before, with Rheem in charge of refining and Miller in charge of marketing. Rheem also picked up Breeden's responsibility for marine operations. To help him, 26 Broadway sent out twenty-seven-year old John C. Rohlfs, secretary to R. C. Veit, who managed Standard's marine affairs. The team of Scofield, Rheem, and Miller, directed by H. M. Tilford, was already accustomed to working together, and it remained the executive group until 1911.[59]

After these arrangements were completed, the western executives were heading up a consolidated business with assets amounting to $22,533,000 at the end of 1906. Total sales that year amounted to $11,707,000, which was slightly more than double the figure for 1900. At Richmond, California Standard's refinery was feeling the stimulus of both the domestic and the Oriental trades, a matter that will be discussed in the following chapter. Crude runs, averaging about 25,000 barrels a day in December, 1906, made Richmond one of the largest refineries in the world. The company's network of pipelines in 1906 was handling a daily average of nearly 26,000 barrels of crude, run either to storage or to the refinery; the receipts of crude oil, the result almost wholly of purchases, were about 29 per cent of California's production. Only in producing was the company weak—⅕ of 1 per cent of the state's production in 1906—but it could plunge deeply there, too, if doing so was desirable. Assured of the continuing support of 26 Broadway, California Standard could look to the future with confidence.[60]

The period of trial after the take-over of PCO was clearly at an end.

10

The events of consolidation and the accompanying change of name make 1906 a memorable year in the history of Standard of California. For Standard, the year is also memorable, as for the West generally, for the great earthquake and fire that shortly preceded the consolidation and made a ruin of much of San Francisco. The Standard companies, like most everything else in the city, were caught up in the tragedy, but their business operations were only lightly and temporarily affected. The significance of the disaster lies less in its effect on the business of the companies than in the response of their leaders to human needs in communities with which they had long been identified.

Early in the morning of April 18, 1906, the earthquake struck for 350 miles along the northern California coast from Humboldt Bay to Monterey, but its impact was greatest in San Francisco. Water and gas mains were broken, pavements split, cornices toppled, and the brick facing stripped from numerous steel-framed buildings in the stricken city. Worst of all, the quake also touched off fires, which proved shortly to be the real disaster. When the fires had run their course, the whole of 490 blocks and parts of 32 others had been laid waste, causing property damage estimated as high as $500,000,000. Within seventy-two hours, 452 persons died, 1,500 were injured, and thousands were made homeless.[61]

PCO and Iowa Standard were among the many companies that lost their headquarters to the fire. The Rialto Building at Mission and New Montgomery, which had housed both companies since 1903, was scarcely damaged by the quake. But as the office workers began to arrive, the fire edged near. Among those who came early that fateful morning were two pipeline employees, William H. Berg, a young stenographer, and Albert Shulte, a clerk. They snatched up pipeline ledgers and financial records and fled through a shower of cinders. The records they saved were among the few that survived for either company.[62]

Later that morning Scofield arrived from Oakland to see the top of the building aflame and the fire advancing beyond it. He recrossed the Bay to the refinery, where he was relieved to find damage limited to the collapse of four or five brick chimneys, the shattering of a fire wall, the springing of a number of tank seams, and the snapping of a wharf line or two. At Richmond he gathered together some of the executives, but W. S. Miller was on the train coming back from New York and Breeden stayed on in San Francisco, concerned with his personal affairs and the work of the relief committee. Since normal business operations were disrupted, Scofield and Rheem decided to cut back refinery production for the domestic market to the level of actual need. The next day, payday, Scofield wired to New York for money to meet Richmond's payroll. Pending its arrival, he borrowed $20,000 from the Central Bank of Oakland on his own signature to pay the refinery workers half of their wages. Within two days, the confusion began to subside. Shipments were resumed to the Bay area and to interior points, and in five days the office staffs were quartered in two rented houses close to downtown Oakland. When this resettlement was over, Scofield wrote: "Today is the first time I have had a place to sit down outside of when I have been at Richmond."[63]

In addition to their own problems, the Standard men showed a deep concern for the general human suffering. They supplied fuel to boats bringing in supplies, to gas and power plants around the Bay, and left two tankers, PCO's *Atlas* and New York Standard's *Seminole*, adjacent to San Francisco to house refugees. On the morning of the quake, Colonel

E. H. Merrill, manager of Iowa Standard's Lubricating Oil Department, had gone to Mayor Eugene Schmitz to offer the use of the *Seminole* to pump water into the city's lines. But the mayor was unable to accept, for he had no hose and the water mains were broken.

Shortly, the western executives were entrusted with some substantial relief funds. The day after the quake Scofield received a wire from John D. Rockefeller, "You may draw on me as needed up to one hundred thousand dollars to be expended by yourself in consultation with our attorney Pillsbury for relief of homeless and destitute poor." The letter that followed read in part, "I trust this will not be too severe a burden for you. I have preferred to render such aid as may be needed through you and our attorney, Mr. Pillsbury, to sending funds through channels with which I am unacquainted. . . . I prefer to have the funds used in behalf of [those] who have no powerful influences to aid them and who could offer no returns of any kind to anyone." Two members of another prominent Standard Oil family, Charles W. and Edward S. Harkness, each added $10,000. W. H. Tilford authorized the expenditure of $100,000 of Iowa Standard's funds. And H. H. Rogers sent a wire to Scofield announcing that he was sending some provisions to be "distributed as your judgment feels best." By April 20 four freight cars, loaded in Butte, Montana, were sped on their way by passenger train.[64]

Scofield and Pillsbury placed $70,000 with the Finance Committee of the Relief and Red Cross Funds, of which James D. Phelan, a former mayor of San Francisco, was the chairman. They also gave smaller sums to relief committees in other communities around the Bay. Immediate relief needs, however, they regarded as being reasonably well taken care of by the heavy flow of funds from all over the nation. The two men came to believe that the best use they could make of the remainder of the money was to help several classes of people who faced long-term problems of readjustment. As Scofield explained to Rockefeller:

> These comprise the superannuated clerk who had in many cases been practically on pension, and whom former employers will be unable to further care for. Such are unfitted for hard labor, and must be cared for until some provision is made for them in homes or institutions. The widows and the orphans, deprived of the husband and the father, will also have to be taken care of until some plan is perfected for their future support. It is therefore our intention to render such aid in all cases as seems most fitting and expedient, until employment is obtained by those who are able to work, and homes offer[ed] to the little ones.
>
> We find in some cases that widows who had supported families by keeping little stores and utilities have been rendered helpless, and where

we find worthy cases of that nature we have designed to offer them the needed help to make them again self-supporting—always having in view the desirability of keeping together little families, if possible.

There is still another class that appeals to us—the young woman stenographer or clerk without kindred or friends, who has been deprived of a position by the loss of business of her employer. She must be taken care of until . . . her condition can be bettered by restored business conditions.

Accordingly, Scofield and Rheem picked out a tract of thirty-six acres near Richmond as a site for a semi-permanent camp, which they called Camp Rockefeller. Within ten days housing was ready for 1,000 people in a series of long, low buildings constructed of lumber and corrugated iron. Each room was 8½ x 14 feet in size and contained three beds. A recreation hall in a nearby Catholic church served as a hospital under the direction of a local physician. Three weeks after the fire, between 300 and 400 persons were living at the camp.[65]

In San Francisco, Colonel Merrill set up a relief bureau to handle more of the money. Besides gifts to institutions, much was spent on individuals. He gave nothing to able-bodied men except tools. Merrill and his assistants followed the advice of clergymen, bankers, businessmen, doctors, and other trusted people in distributing aid, principally to women—kitchen utensils, groceries, bedding, sewing machines, stoves, shoes, dress goods. Some of the elderly ladies lamented most the loss of their Bibles, of which Merrill bought and handed out a supply. All in all, he provided for 355 families, 303 women, and 25 men, exclusive of the clergy. "It made no difference to us whether a person was a Protestant, Catholic, Infidel or Jew, black, white or yellow."

Clergymen were one of Merrill's special concerns. Since "a clergyman's weapon of offense and defence and of making his living is really his books," he gave a number of them book orders of $100 each as well as groceries, clothing, and other necessities. One incident seems almost too good to be true, although Merrill reported it as the truth. Meeting with four clergymen whom he planned to help, he harked back to a protest Congregational ministers had made in 1905 over a gift by Rockefeller to their Board of Foreign Missions as "tainted money." He told them that he wanted it distinctly understood that they were receiving tainted money, "tainted through and through, and that if they had any conscientious scruples . . . , I would not feel hurt if they declined to accept it." One of the clergymen replied, "The taint wears off the moment it passes from your hands into ours." Another stated, "It's the motive that makes money tainted or not." The third one commented, "All money is tainted." The fourth said, "Taint 'nough!"[66]

Five days after the quake, before these relief activities were fully developed, Scofield was able to write, "I feel from all the expressions heard from every side during the past few days, that there will hereafter be less harsh criticism of our people than has been the case in the past."[67] For Standard, this favorable public response had supplied an early lesson on the value of identifying the company with community welfare.

XI

REFINING
FOR NEW MARKETS

The story of 26 Broadway's California venture after 1900 is one of a careful and calculated response to new opportunities. At first, as we have seen, the great opportunity to displace coal with fuel oil was the chief lure; then refined oils to take care of the growing Pacific Coast market, when large light crude fields were discovered. Soon the sheer size of these fields offered another vision—the possibility of supplying kerosine from California for the Orient. It was a vision Californians had wistfully entertained ever since the days of Benjamin Silliman, Jr., and the oil boom of 1864-65; 26 Broadway made it a reality. In doing so, the Standard Oil combination created a market for millions of barrels of California crude that badly needed an outlet.

The decision to make Richmond a major base for the Oriental trade was reached as early as 1904, when the first shipments of a cheap kerosine, called Petrolite, were sent to Standard of New York's Far Eastern marketing agencies. To get sufficient volume, Richmond was greatly enlarged. In 1906, while this expansion was going on, Standard put through its stills around 4,500,000 barrels of crude—an average of 12,300 barrels daily—in manufacturing slightly more than one million barrels of Petrolite for export. Petrolite, clearly, had become the refinery's chief product.

Richmond's position as a supplier for the Orient, however, was not as secure as its position in the Pacific Coast trade. Its opportunity to manufacture Petrolite depended upon an adequate volume of low-priced crude. When the New York executives considered it advantageous to reduce Richmond's output and to provide more Petrolite from other refineries, they were quick to do so. Indeed, in 1910 it appeared that Richmond's role as a supplier of Petrolite was drawing to a close, and that henceforth the refinery would depend almost entirely on its lucrative and steadily growing domestic market, especially for gasoline and lubes.

2

During the early years of the century, the New York executives could look hopefully to California for help in the marketing struggle going on in the Orient. For almost a decade they had been undergoing a serious challenge from rivals who were selling kerosine refined from the crudes of Russia, Borneo, and the Dutch East Indies. The three leading contenders, the Shell Transport & Trading Company, Royal Dutch Petroleum Company, and the Rothschilds pooled their interests in June, 1902, by forming the Asiatic Petroleum Company. To their challenge, 26 Broadway had reacted in various ways. It had established its own marketing agencies through Standard of New York, tried unsuccessfully to find a crude oil supply in the Far East, and had even bought and sold some cheap Russian kerosine as a competitive weapon. One abortive effort occurred in 1900 when John H. Fertig was transferred from California to Japan to help organize the International Oil Company and to direct its producing activities. Unfortunately, he found little refinable crude. Another action taken by Standard after 1900 was to refine and market a lower grade kerosine of its own manufacture, Petrolite.[1]

The possibility that California oil could eventually help in the Far Eastern struggle undoubtedly counted for little or nothing in 26 Broadway's purchase of PCO in 1900. Within another year and a half, however, this idea had come alive. Even before Rheem moved from Alameda, he was experimenting with the manufacture of kerosine which would meet export specifications. Soon after Richmond began to operate, H. M. Tilford was asking what an export oil would cost and whether such an oil could be made from straight Kern River crude. Rheem replied that he could use Kern oil, but he believed it would be a better practice to blend the surplus "lighter fractions" from Southern California crudes with Kern distillate in making kerosine. One record of an experiment shows that Rheem charged a $24.7°$ gravity oil and took a broad cut of the distillates, between $57.5°$ gravity naphtha and $13°$ gravity fuel oil, which gave him 32 per cent of the crude as an export oil at a cost of 52¢ per 100 gallons of crude. Neither the yield nor the cost satisfied him.

Gradually, as crude prices declined, the prospects for an export oil brightened. An inspector's record hints of production for export as early as June, 1904, with the name "Petrolite" appearing before the close of the year. In September, the *Housatonic*, a tanker belonging to 26 Broadway's Anglo-American Oil Company, departed for Shanghai with 31,000 barrels of kerosine. It must have pleased Scofield, who could recall that thirty years earlier he had gone to Japan on an unsuccessful mission for F. B. Taylor & Co. It pleased other California oilmen, too, who were hoping to expand their market. Union's John Baker reported, "I have been making an effort to get aboard the Steamer, without a permit from the PCO's office, but so far have not been successful. . . . It would seem that the market for Light Crude is no longer confined to supplying the local demand for Refined Oils, which is certainly very cheering to say the least."[2] Before 1904 was over, PCO had provided Standard of New York with 73,000 barrels of kerosine.

To move Petrolite from Richmond in quantity, more shipping facilities were needed. Standard of New York and Anglo-American could provide the ships, but Richmond's wharf could not handle the extra traffic, especially loading cased goods on sailing vessels. A slow-motion effort to remedy this deficiency started in April, 1905, with an appropriation for a new wharf, and in September PCO acquired a thirty-acre tract two miles up the coast from Richmond. It was given the name Point Orient, an apt suggestion of its mission.[3]

By the close of 1905, construction was under way. A wharf was begun, and a can factory and a box factory laid out. These big, two-story brick buildings, plus a corrugated iron structure for filling and casing cans, were crowded into a niche in the hills along the bay. The filling and casing shed was connected by a covered conveyor with a storage shed on the north end of the "T" wharf. From the south end, an electric trolley car carried tin for cans and shook for cases to the factories. The can factory's capacity of 20,000 five-gallon cans a day was sufficient for 10,000 cases. On the target date, June 1, 1906, the plant was still incomplete. J. F. Brooks, the superintendent at Point Orient, hurried the new can factory along by ordering the tins to be hand-soldered until machinery arrived. Though tankers commenced using the wharf in June, it was August 13, 1906, before Anglo-American's white-hulled ship, *Radiant,* tied up at Point Orient after discharging coal from Newcastle. On September 5, it set sail for China with the first cargo of cased goods.[4]

Early in September the can-making machinery from Iowa Standard's San Francisco can factory was moved over to Point Orient, and the plant was soon in full operation. Petrolite was canned under two brand-names, Victory and Cock. Victory kerosine, the name adopted during the Russo-Japanese War, was sent to Japan. Of the less common Cock brand, two shipments went to the Philippines and one to China between 1906 and 1908. Otherwise, oil for China was carried in bulk by tanker. Tankers also began to serve Japan and India. A fragmentary record for Point Orient from October, 1906, through July, 1907, shows seventeen tankers leaving for China, two for Japan, and four for India. One sailing vessel carried cased oil to China, while six went to Japan and one to the Philippines.

Point Orient was graced by many sailing vessels of Anglo-American and Standard of New York, including big four-masted steel barks built especially for the case-oil trade and named for Standard's famous brands: Anglo-American's *Comet, Brilliant, Daylight, Arrow,* and Standard of New York's *Astral* and *Acme.* The *Daylight* carried the largest cargo of them all, 154,000 cases, the equivalent of nearly 37,000 barrels. In 1908 the sailing vessels ceased to call, save for the tanker bark *Calcutta.* They had been forced to yield to the more prosaic steam-powered tankers of Anglo-American's fleet, on charter to Standard of New York.[5]

The can factory was something of a headache. Aside from the unforeseen problems of a new plant, an embarrassing number of complaints of leaky and rusted cans came back from New York Standard's agents. Usually, Superintendent Brooks could only say helplessly that the cases were in good shape when they left. He had support from the inspector of Meyer & Company, a New York firm that New York Standard employed to test the oil and to examine tanks and cases. Point Orient's procedure was to set a can aside long enough after filling for a leak to become evident. Cases, too, sat in storage on the dock before loading, and leakers were pulled out. But the handling in the Orient must have been rough. Indeed, returning captains suspected that sometimes rough handling was deliberate because damaged cases were sold at auction at low prices. Point Orient also received numerous complaints from domestic stations to which it supplied empty cans.

The principal problem, apparently, was the brittle quality of some of the tin-plate provided by the relatively new American tin-plate industry, to which Standard was giving about 40 per cent of its business. The balance was better grade English tin, but at least one shipment arrived badly rusted from salt water. Point Orient also suffered on another occasion from an insufficient supply of pine shook for boxes. Spruce was substituted, but its coarse grain split more easily. In view of these difficulties, there must have been a widespread sense of relief when the decision was reached in 1908 to ship all Petrolite in bulk. The can factory continued to make cans for domestic marketing, but box-making and can-filling were transferred to the refinery. Thereafter, a major part of Point Orient's noisy operation fell silent, and the fragrance of newly sawn wood competed no longer with the odor of kerosine.[6]

3

Spurred by the requirements of the Oriental trade, 26 Broadway in the early part of 1906 authorized a new expansion at Richmond to nearly double the refinery's capacity. The continued inability of the International Oil Company to supply sufficient crude for its refinery at Naoetsu, Japan, may have helped inspire this decision. At Richmond, the plans called for converting all crude stills, except those making lube oil distillate, to continuous operation and for fifteen more 1,000-barrel stills. Complementing the crude stills, another steam still to finish naphtha distillates was part of the expansion. This "fractional steam still" was an unusual structure, 6 feet, 4 inches in diameter, that rose in a column 55 feet tall. A continuous stream of crude naphtha was pumped to the top and trickled down through three sections of broken quartz; beneath each section, a steam coil vaporized the lighter hydrocarbons, gasoline in the top section, naphtha in the middle, and engine distillate in the bottom. The new stills and related facilities, costing about half a million dollars, were completed by the end of the year. They were expected to boost Richmond's capacity to 28,000 barrels a day, making the refinery the third largest in the Standard family. Following the expansion, Richmond promised to be equal to its twin tasks of supplying almost entirely Standard's needs in the West and a substantial share of the Oriental kerosine market.[7]

One matter remained to be arranged, an increase in crude to match the growth of the refinery. The Coalinga Eastside field was still developing, and Santa Maria was thought to be far from its potential. Beginning in January, 1906, the small refiners in Kern River were a minor source. Their 20° to 25° gravity distillate, which was equivalent to a refinable crude, furnished a supplemental supply that peaked in 1907 at 100,000 barrels. On the other hand, PCO lost an important source of crude and distillate in February, 1906, when its contract with Union expired. The company undoubtedly refused to go on paying 95¢ a barrel for crude when newer contracts called for 40¢. Union chose to go on its own. In a confident, expansionist mood, it almost tripled the crude capacity of its Oleum refinery to 2,000 barrels daily and began making refined oil again. As an alternative, PCO developed new and greater plans for Santa Maria. H. G. Morrow, the Pipe Line Department's land man and coordinator of oil field intelligence, prepared a complete survey of the Santa Maria and Lompoc fields. He reported to Scofield that if all the shut-in wells were opened, the current production of 10,000 barrels a day would shoot up to 40,000. Some time in the spring of 1906, Scofield initiated negotiations with Santa Maria producers for an increased supply of crude on five-year contracts.[8]

Evidently, Scofield thought he had been successful because, in July, 1906, Tilford authorized construction of a pipeline from Santa Maria to Coalinga capable of carrying 20,000 barrels daily. The cost was estimated at $1,242,000 for five pump stations and 110 miles of 8- and 10-inch pipe. Obviously, John Page had finally won his point that it was wise to use larger pipe on the downstream end of each section. The route surveyed ran northward from Santa Maria through San Luis Obispo, Santa Marguerita, Creston, and Shandon to Coalinga. Suddenly, in October plans for the line were canceled. This astonishing news Page brought down to Coalinga just as the survey party reached the camp.[9]

The Santa Maria producers had refused to sign their contracts. Undoubtedly, the reason lay in the course of events at Coalinga, where PCO's principal supplier, California Oilfields, Limited, had filled its contract in August. The two sides had deadlocked over a substantial increase in price, which COF demanded for a new contract. If the newly named Standard Oil Company (California) hoped that the projected Santa Maria line would bring COF to terms by suggesting that it could get oil elsewhere, it was disappointed. Just the opposite occurred, for the Santa Maria producers followed COF's lead. They had oil yet to deliver on their old contracts and could afford to wait on COF's success or failure, while refusing to commit themselves to Standard's plans for the future. From COF, the company received a decreasing amount on day-to-day purchases until October, and nothing thereafter. Three smaller Coalinga producers, the 28 Oil, Oil City Petroleum, and Sauer Dough Oil companies, followed COF's example. Standard's receipts of crude over 20° gravity were halved, dropping from 19,000 barrels a day in July, 1906, to less than 10,000 in December.[10]

To effect their boycott, these producers had to shut down at least part of their wells. Standard was not immediately under the gun; it had in storage about three and a half million barrels of Coalinga oil, which was nearly a six-month supply for the refinery. While living off its reserves, Standard set out to prove it did not need COF's crude. To increase the company's bargaining strength, 26 Broadway early in November called in John Eckbert of The Carter Oil Company and sent him to California to organize a Producing Department. The department was established on January 1, 1907, but, as will be noted in a later chapter, it did not soon become a significant influence. Meanwhile COF showed it meant business by buying two and three-quarter sections on the outskirts of the Eastside field, and acquired in the process some of Standard's suppliers. In competition with Associated, it was also dickering for the Oil City Petroleum and the 28 Oil companies, located on Section 28 in the heart of the field.

To strengthen itself, Standard bought these companies for cash from under the noses of both COF and Associated, and purchased the Independence Oil Company as well. It induced the Sauer Dough again to deliver to the pipeline and in February picked up a contract from Associated for an additional 100,000 barrels of Sauer Dough's crude. Standard also re-entered the Westside field. It revived drilling there by signing a one-year contract for 1,755,000 barrels at 30¢ with Stanley W. Morshead, the agent for ten small companies.[11]

While these maneuvers were occurring, the Santa Maria producers were carrying on their own campaign for higher crude oil prices and were looking forward to the completion of the Western Union and Pinal contracts by about August of 1907. In January, after visiting Balfour, Guthrie, who were the managers of COF, Tom Hughes of Western Union reported that Standard was in dire need of crude. He had heard that the company was getting less than 3,000 barrels daily from Coalinga, and that its light oil stored at Kern River was gone. But he was wrong. Actually, Standard was receiving over 6,000 barrels a day of 20° gravity or lighter oil, and had over a million barrels of Coalinga crude at Kern River and another million elsewhere. Hughes felt his hopes confirmed when he discussed prices with Scofield for the oil of a smaller Santa Maria concern, the Rice Ranch Oil Company. Scofield offered only 40¢, the current contract price for 26° gravity oil, but Hughes came away with the impression that the price would soon be raised.

After several talks with Hughes, two of Pinal's directors wrote, "We are almost thoroughly convinced that W.U. [Western Union], B.G. [Balfour, Guthrie] and ourselves are to a considerable degree (if not) masters of the situation, as far as refinery oil is concerned." They were impressed with Hughes' categoric statement that Western Union would not settle for less than 75¢ a barrel.[12]

The producers were outflanked, though they did not seem to have realized it immediately, when on February 1, 1907, Associated agreed to sell Standard the distillate from Santa Maria crude run through its refinery at Alcatraz Landing near Gaviota in northern Santa Barbara County. This refinery had passed from the Alcatraz Asphalt Company to the National Oil & Transport Company, and through it to Associated in the deal by which Associated had acquired the Matson interests in 1905. Associated lacked sufficient light oil to enter the refined products market, but it was actively wildcatting and was using the refinery to "top" crude for a salable fuel oil. Associated provided Standard with about 500 barrels daily of distillate ("tops") which Richmond split into naphtha and kerosine.

After selling the tops to Standard, Associated withdrew an increase in price it had offered the Santa Maria producers. They could have turned to Union, which held out hopes of 60¢ or more a barrel. But Union's second and larger pipeline was not yet ready, and Pinal was not favorably impressed with Stewart's terms. Instead, Western Union, Pinal and its ally, the Brookshire Oil Company, formed the Santa Maria Oil & Transportation Company and announced they would build a 10,000-barrels-a-day pipeline to the sea and buy ships to carry their oil to market. The new company went so far as to buy land at Pismo for tankage and a wharf.[13]

The letters of Marks Fleisher, the president of Pinal, suggest that the Pinal group—Pinal, Brookshire, and New Pennsylvania—was not so anxious as Western Union to break with Standard if Standard would grant a substantial price increase. In January, 1907, Pinal offered to sell out for nearly $2,000,000, a far higher price than Standard would pay. W. M. Weller, Standard's agent at Santa Maria, kept in touch with Fleisher and late in March talked with him again. Fleisher said he would consider selling 5,000,000 barrels at 60¢. When Weller suggested 45¢ as a more reasonable price, Fleisher told him not to waste time thinking of so low a figure.

The deadlock at Santa Maria was broken at the end of March after Brookshire agreed to sell to Standard at 45¢ all oil in excess of its contract with Associated. Very likely the news that Balfour, Guthrie had thrown in its hand caused Brookshire to come to terms. On March 27, 1907, California Oilfields had signed a three-year contract under which it promised to deliver 15,000,000 barrels by the end of 1909, the largest crude oil purchase, Scofield believed, ever made. The new price of 50¢ was a sharp increase over those in the old COF contract which, using a sliding scale of 20¢ to 45¢, depending on gravity, had averaged 25¢ in 1906.

Within a few weeks, Standard negotiated new agreements with Brookshire, Pinal, and New Pennsylvania at 50¢ for a total of 5,000,000 barrels over a three-year period. Deliveries were to begin immediately, and the monthly maximum for Pinal was raised from 35,000 to 75,000 barrels. The 50¢ price gave Pinal a modest increase over the sliding scale in its earlier contract, which had brought the company about 40¢ in 1906. At the same time, the old contracts with Pinal and Western Union were renegotiated to eliminate the clauses giving Standard the option of taking any excess production or requiring the producer to store it. Undoubtedly, the size of the new contracts and the freedom from restrictions on production powerfully influenced the Pinal group of companies to accept a lower price than they had hoped for. Capacity production, they believed, would spell profits.[14]

Reminiscent of the 1905 Pinal contract, which was delayed for the arrival of the *Atlas* and *Barge 93,* deliveries on the new contract were limited temporarily to 45,000 barrels a month until the *Colonel E. L. Drake* arrived from the East Coast. This vessel, with a capacity of 38,000 barrels, was a major addition to Standard's small tanker fleet. Already it had made its mark in the nautical world. It had twice towed an oil barge from New York to London, the first vessel ever to do so. In January, 1907, Standard bought it for about $400,000 from Standard of New York, though the *Drake* did not depart for California until May, perhaps awaiting the outcome of the Santa Maria negotiations. Meantime, a coastal tanker, the *Catania,* was chartered and in March began carrying crude from Port Harford to Richmond.[15]

When the Pinal group signed, the Santa Maria Oil & Transportation Company lost its mission. Western Union alone was too small to carry the project. The fact that Standard renegotiated Western Union's contract, along with Pinal's, suggests that Standard hoped to keep that producer, too, in the fold. Instead, Western Union, in June, signed a three-year contract for 3,000,000 barrels with the Graciosa Oil Company, bringing into alliance "by far the two best properties" in the Santa Maria field, according to Standard's scouts. The contract was effective in October, a date which seems related to the completion of a refinery by Graciosa's sister company, California Petroleum Refineries, Limited, at Oilport, two miles south of Port Harford. The refinery was an integral part of a bold new venture that could have developed strong competition for Standard. The prime mover was the Graciosa Oil Company, which listed among its stockholders Isaac and Ben L. Liebes (H. Liebes & Company), Henry Crocker, and Louis Phillips of San Francisco.

In 1905, Graciosa's principals had bought a small, fire-damaged refinery of four 150-barrel stills located at Rodeo, about ten miles from Richmond. The following year, with the assistance of English capital, they began at Oilport a new and modern refinery, second in size in California only to Richmond. Construction began in May, 1906, and was completed late in August, 1907. Its builder was a Russian engineer from the Baku who had become familiar with California-type crudes in Java. He set up crude oil batteries consisting of thirteen 250-barrel stills hooked up for continuous distillation and two 300-barrel stills. Beside each battery stood a steam super-heater and a fractionating tower 75 feet high. There was also a battery of four steam stills. The refinery, which was reported to have a capacity of 8,000 barrels a day, was designed so that it could be easily enlarged. Eric Starke examined it and commented:

It is quite unlike anything here and radically new to California. . . . It is the intention to distill the oil first by continuous process with the aid of steam and then to carefully fractionate the distillates so as to obtain a product that will not require an acid treatment for purification, but only a small acid wash for color, etc. It seems to me inconceivable that the above stated method of refining is to be adopted as it has been tried by scores of people, and it has always failed.

To serve the refinery, the California Petroleum Refineries group laid a pipeline from Santa Maria with a capacity of about 10,000 barrels a day. A steamer was bought, too, probably the *Catania,* which Standard kept busy for about two years.[16]

Strangely, the Oilport refinery was never operated. One explanation was that it lacked crude, which may have been true. Standard's reports showed Western Union and Graciosa producing 194,000 barrels of light oil in June, 1907, falling off to 52,600 in December, but the two companies were believed to have an additional production shut-in of at least 50,000 barrels. Another contributing factor to the stillness at Oilport may have been a contract Graciosa signed late in 1907 to supply crude to Toyo Kisen Kaisha (Oriental Steamship Company), a Japanese company controlled by Assano & Company. Assano's plan was to import California crude and split it into fuel oil for ships and kerosine for the Japanese and mainland trade. The crude contract with Graciosa was believed to call for 2,000,000 barrels a year at 42¢ a barrel. But this market evaporated. Only a small refinery was built at Yokohama, and within a year it was turned over to a large oil firm, Hoden Sekiyu Kabushiki Kaisha. Meanwhile, discussions with Henri Deterding of Royal Dutch–Shell matured into an agreement with Hoden to supply crude from the Asiatic Petroleum Company. The Japanese were glad to make the new arrangement, partly because their refiners were unable to deal effectively with the high sulfur content of Santa Maria crude. Graciosa's plans obviously had proven no threat to Standard.

With Pinal and COF delivering oil once more, Standard was fairly well supplied with light crude. The producers had learned, too, that Standard could not be bluffed. Confidently, Scofield wrote Tilford in the spring of 1908, "We do not think that the producers in . . . these fields [Coalinga and Santa Maria] will again, in light of their past experience, shut down their wells in order to force us to pay an extreme price."[17]

4

During the tug-of-war between Standard and the light oil producers, one major development occurred in the heavy crude industry: Standard made possible the growth of the Midway field by connecting the field with its Valley trunk line at Waite. The reason it did so is not clear. The possibility that Midway oil might be substituted for Coalinga oil is most obvious but least likely, for Midway at this time was a heavy crude field. If there was a connection between the impasse at Coalinga and the opening of Midway, it may have been that reduced refinery runs meant less fuel oil. The simple way to make up the deficiency in fuel oil was to buy fuel grade crude. A more compelling reason, one strong enough to warrant investment in a pipeline, was that the price of heavy oil was going up. When a five-month deadlock between Associated and the Independent Oil Producers Agency ended in November, 1906, Associated agreed to boost its price from 18¢ to 27.5¢ a barrel. Another consideration that could have influenced Scofield was the decline in production of his Kern River suppliers. By the close of 1906, Peerless was behind 385,000 barrels on its contract, which would expire at the end of 1907. Still another factor was a renewed interest in the Valley fields shown by Union, which was buying Kern River oil and building a 500,000-barrel reservoir alongside Standard's tank farm. And the Southern Pacific was planning an active drilling campaign. Moreover, the trend of Standard's fuel oil sales was upward. Some combination of these factors is the likely explanation why Standard turned to the Midway.[18]

The Midway lay atop the foothills of the west side of the San Joaquin Valley, some thirty-five miles southwest of Bakersfield. Geography gave the field its name, for it was halfway between the developed fields of McKittrick and Sunset. Both of these older fields were served by rail, but Midway remained neglected, needing transportation and higher prices. Its potential was known. Back in December, 1902, the Standard scout, C. F. Lufkin, had reported as "exceedingly promising" Tim Spellacy's Mascot property in the hills behind what is today the town of Taft. Spellacy, a jovial, elegantly attired ex-driller, proved the Mascot property was productive the next year. Toward the end of 1906 Standard ran right-of-way surveys to the Midway, and on January 3, 1907, Tilford authorized Scofield to spend $440,000 on a thirty-three-mile, eight-inch pipeline, gathering lines, and two pump stations. For oil, Standard turned to Spellacy and some of his associates, offering 25¢ a barrel. This was not a bad price in view of the Associated-Agency contract and the cost of putting in a line, but Spellacy wanted 30¢. He got it in a three-year contract, signed February 4, that called for 3,500,000 barrels. Standard also lent him $70,000 to start drilling. With a few smaller contracts, the line seemed assured of 5,000,000 barrels of crude.[19]

H. M. Storey, who succeeded John Page in charge of pipelines, assigned an able, self-educated pipeliner, Henry A. Forsburg, to handle the construction, which began in March. Four months later Spellacy's oil flowed into Standard's tanks. It was a 15° gravity oil, like most of the Midway production. Operation of the pipeline, however, awaited Standard's success in putting down a water well; good water was necessary for boilers powering the pumps.

Lack of water had also restricted drilling. An incident in the neighboring Sunset field, where water was being shipped in from Bakersfield by rail and sold for 25¢ a barrel, suggests its importance. When a levee along the Buena Vista Lake burst and disrupted rail service, the only remaining supply was a spring back in the hills. Water went up to a dollar a barrel at a time when Sunset oil was worth only 20¢. In the Midway, Standard's well found water, but the quality soon fell off. Consequently, oil development continued to be restricted until a producer brought in a good water well later in the year. Meanwhile, Standard was pumping in boiler water from Waite and joined the producers in buying fresh water that the Santa Fe transported from thirty miles away. By September the pipeline was completed, but no oil was pumped for another four months. The early deliveries, amounting to about 1,000 barrels a day, were disappointingly small; Standard merely tanked the oil while it awaited a larger volume.[20]

An inexplicable bit of byplay accompanied construction of the Midway line. In March, 1907, three years after Standard had spurned the McKittrick field, it appropriated $225,000 for a sixteen-mile line connecting McKittrick with Midway. Friendly relations with Associated, indicated by contracts between the two companies in Coalinga and Santa Maria, did not prevent this obvious threat to Associated's hold on the McKittrick field. Standard bought a forty-acre pump station site at Olig from the Southern Pacific. But the principal producers stayed with Associated, and Standard apparently made no move to bid for their oil. The line, which was completed in October, 1907, lay idle until 1914, when Standard at last started taking oil from McKittrick.[21]

While the company was extending facilities to the Westside fields of Kern County, a rival pipeline system began to be developed by the Southern Pacific. In March, 1907, rumors got out that the railroad was planning to lay a line from the Kern River field to San Francisco, another to Mojave, and another to San Luis Obispo by way of Midway and McKittrick. It was the line to San Francisco—or rather, Port Costa, about fifteen miles northeast of Richmond—that became a reality.

This line employed a new engineering principle to ease the heavy crude through the pipe. In Standard's line, Forrest Towl had heated the oil to lower the viscosity and, on occasion, had injected hot water. In the railroad's line, friction was reduced by keeping a layer of water between the oil and the walls of the pipe. This layer was maintained by using pipe with rifled walls so that the water, with its core of oil, revolved slowly as it moved along. In 1906 trials using rifled pipe showed that 12,000 barrels a day could be pumped over a thirty-two-mile stretch of eight-inch line from Kern River to Delano. When the full-length line was laid, the Southern Pacific spaced the pumping stations just twenty-four miles apart to provide a capacity of 25,000 barrels daily. The route selected followed the railroad right of way, along the east side of the San Joaquin Valley to Fresno and then over to the west side, where it paralleled Standard's line. The Southern Pacific joined with the Associated late in August, 1907, to form the Associated Pipe Line Company to build the line.

Obviously, the prospect of lower operating costs for oil shipments was one factor that prompted the railroad to construct a pipeline. But another compelling factor was the recurrence of a tank car shortage which was especially acute early in 1907. An inquiry by the Interstate Commerce Commission revealed that the Southern Pacific owned 1,400 cars employed largely in its own service; it consumed 25,000 barrels a day. It had also an additional 625 cars on order. Meanwhile, Standard was operating over 700 Union Tank Line cars and thus was able to supply consumers when other oil companies were pinched.

Even Associated was running into difficulty. A San Francisco power company executive, C. W. Walker, reported in February, 1907, that Associated had attracted customers with a "very low price" and then failed to deliver, making it necessary for consumers to turn to Standard and frequently pay double the contract price. Walker stated, "It is thanks to the Standard Oil Company that the towns of Oakland, San Francisco and several other towns in California have not been out of gas for several days." When E. E. Calvin, a Southern Pacific vice president, appeared before the Interstate Commerce Commission, he expressed the belief that the new tank cars would take care of the shortage. And the pipeline, with a capacity equivalent to the service of 700 or 800 cars, offered additional protection for the future.

The 300-mile line from Kern River began operation in September, 1908. Unfortunately, in subsequent years, as water broke into the lands of the companies at Kern River, it formed an emulsion which was made worse by the lubricating water in the line. Eventually, the Associated Pipe Line had to resort to the hot oil principle and increase the number of pumping stations, as Standard had done earlier.[22]

Kern River was the scene of two moves made by Standard during 1907 to protect its position in heavy crude while the outcome of its gamble at Midway remained uncertain. Early in the year Scofield took up with Peerless the question of extending its contract. A draft was drawn up in April. It recited the facts that Peerless had mortgaged its property to Standard as a guarantee of performance and that, with undelivered oil amounting to 1,817,000 barrels, Peerless could not fulfill its contract before expiration on January 1, 1908. The draft stated, therefore, that the contract would be extended for eighteen months. It appears that Standard was in a position to force acceptance. However, the company improved the price to Peerless in return for a promise to deliver double the amount of oil owed under the earlier contract. After January, 1908, Peerless received 30¢ a barrel, compared to the earlier rate of 20¢—a concession that was also extended to Monte Cristo, even though its contract did not expire until April, 1909.[23]

5

Far more than for heavy crude, Standard had reason to be concerned over its light crude supply in 1907 and thereafter. When the company had compromised its differences with the Coalinga and Santa Maria producers, it had scheduled deliveries so as to permit Richmond to run close to capacity. But almost without exception, the producers fell short of their promises. Instead of five million barrels, California Oilfields delivered less than two million in 1907, when its manager, William Graham, failed to develop the 15,000 barrels a day he had predicted. Disillusioned, Rheem forecast Richmond's output for 1908 on the basis of 15,000 barrels daily from all Coalinga suppliers and 5,000 barrels daily from the coastal and southern fields.

It was not easy to locate new sources of light crude. One move Standard made was to build up its arrangements for distillate as a light crude equivalent. It added to its supply from the little asphalt refineries in Kern River, and in January, 1908, contracted for all tops from the refinery of Associated's affiliate, Amalgamated Oil, at Los Angeles. 26 Broadway helped, too. The New York headquarters bought crude naphtha in Sumatra for Richmond to finish into gasoline. The first shipment, 53,000 barrels, arrived in October, 1907.[24]

Richmond received its greatest relief, however, from a contract Standard signed with Union in January, 1908, for 3,000,000 barrels of Santa Maria crude to be delivered over the next two years. The price, 85¢ a barrel, was a substantial increase over the 50¢ other producers had accepted just eight months earlier. Because of the Union contract, Richmond's receipts from Santa Maria rose by 5,300 barrels daily to 8,300 during 1908. Standard was hoping Union would give the refinery still more help. In March, 1908, Scofield advised Tilford that Union was disappointed in its effort to refine and market part of its crude, and that he was negotiating for tops from 11,000 barrels of crude daily at Oleum. But nothing came of these negotiations.[25]

The shortage of light crude gave rise to a spectacular vision on the part of J. A. Moffett. He wrote Scofield confidentially—the scheme was "in the nature of a chimera"—asking for advice on constructing a 1,500-mile pipeline from Caney, Kansas, to Albuquerque, and from there along the route of the Santa Fe Railroad to Bakersfield. Caney was the terminus of the gathering lines 26 Broadway's Prairie Oil & Gas Company had thrown into Oklahoma to such prolific oil lands as the Glenn pool. At first, Caney served Standard's refineries at Neodesha, Kansas, and Sugar Creek, Missouri. Later, after Forrest Towl built an eight-inch line from Kansas City to Whiting in 1905, Caney was connected by pipeline all the way to the Atlantic Coast. Moffett envisioned a line connecting Oklahoma with the Pacific—a pipeline system spanning the nation. In Oklahoma, Praire Oil & Gas was paying 41¢ a barrel for crude oil of 32° gravity and above, and was tanking millions of barrels of it. Why not pipe this oil to Richmond and refine it for the Oriental trade? He specified one important pre-condition—that another field be discovered along the route, for which, he thought, the new Virgin River field in southwestern Utah might qualify.

Scofield replied enthusiastically that "consumption on the Pacific Slope will double within the next ten years, and the Oriental demand will practically be unlimited." The western executive also saw railroads, mines, and irrigation works along the pipeline as customers for fuel oil. Moffett had talked the matter over with H. N. Kuechler of California Standard's Pipe Line Department, who happened to have been in New York at the time, and asked whether that "bright, vigorous young man" could be spared to search out a route for the western end.

Before taking this step, however, Moffett wanted a report from John Worthington, 26 Broadway's chief scout, on the Virgin River field, from which Scofield had already sent East an analysis of a crude oil sample. Worthington returned from Virgin River to tell Moffett that the production there was extremely small, and that the formation was too broken to permit the development of an important field. His report seems to have tipped the scales against the proposed line. Nothing more was done to make California an outlet for Mid-Continent crude, and so ambitious a scheme has not been realized to this day. Instead, 26 Broadway organized the Standard Oil Company (Louisiana) in April, 1909, built a refinery at Baton Rouge, and connected it with the Oklahoma fields.[26]

There is evidence, scant to be sure, that suggests 26 Broadway wrote off Richmond as a major source of Petrolite and decided to rely on its eastern refineries and Mid-Continent crude. In April, 1909, Rheem warned oilmen seeking a 25¢ increase in crude prices that California kerosine was already suffering in the Oriental market from competition from the Mid-Continent and other fields, and that the proposed increase would take California out of the running. The advantage of the Oklahoma fields became more pronounced in June and July of 1909 when Prairie Oil matched the 35¢ price of its competitors for 32° gravity oil and lighter. By contrast, in California, Standard was using principally a 22° gravity oil costing 50¢. Despite the shorter haul from Richmond to the Orient, eastern refiners were able to overcome this disadvantage in transportation with a cheaper, higher yielding crude. Shipments to the Far East from Richmond fell off by half during the last six months of 1909. In March, 1910, Tilford warned Scofield that Richmond could expect to ship 1,000,000 barrels of Petrolite during 1910, but none thereafter because of large stocks of kerosine in the East. 26 Broadway was also considering building a pipeline for kerosine from the Gulf of Mexico to the Pacific.[27]

Though Richmond was denied Oklahoma crude, it soon found a partial alternative in crude from Peru. In September, 1909, G. H. Mayer of California Standard's Marketing Department and W. O. Todd of the Producing Department left San Francisco for Peru, by way of New York, to examine the property of the London & Pacific Petroleum Company. London & Pacific, which was an enterprise of William Keswick, a partner in Balfour, Williamson & Company, had become the leading Peruvian producer because of the rapid growth of the Negritos field. Previously, in 1904, Mayer had stopped briefly in Peru to examine crude prospects while on a trip to the Straits of Magellan. Back again in 1909, he and Todd made an extended visit to oil fields in both the north and south, collecting data and photographs before Todd returned with their findings toward the close of the year. 26 Broadway sent out John Worthington and H. P. Chamberlain to consider further the purchase of Peruvian properties, but Worthington was doubtful: "It will be more profitable to buy production than to hunt for it."

Accordingly, some kind of agreement was reached with London & Pacific to supply Richmond with distillate from the Talara refinery and probably also with crude. Crude oil was purchased, too, from Lobitos

Oilfields, Limited. Three cargoes of crude and one of distillate came from these firms in 1910, beginning in April with 45,000 barrels of 33.8° gravity crude. The crude was high in gasoline and kerosine content; Richmond also valued it highly for lubes. These arrangements with the Peruvian companies led to the formation in April, 1911, of the West Coast Oil Fuel Company, which was owned 70 per cent by Jersey Standard and the balance by Balfour, Williamson and Lobitos Oilfields. West Coast was set up to bring high gravity crude to California and take back fuel oil to sell along the west coast of South America. Actually, after 1910, Richmond benefited more from shipments of Peruvian crude naphtha than of crude oil because of the disproportionate surge in the Pacific Coast demand for gasoline.[28]

6

As the prospects for Petrolite paled, California Standard's interest in fuel oil quickened. Whether there was a casual relationship or a coincidence cannot be established. Evidence of this renewed concern for heavy crude is to be seen as early as February, 1909, when Standard began taking oil from the Monte Cristo's property in the Sunset field. In the absence of a pipeline, the oil was shipped by tank cars. About April, Standard also contracted for an additional 3,500,000 barrels of Midway crude, of which a million was scheduled for delivery in 1909. Runs from the Midway increased steadily, from 55,000 barrels in January to 109,000 in April, and to 273,000 at the year's end.

The headlines in the trade journals, however, were usually made by Standard's powerful competitors, Associated, Union, and the two agencies, the Independent Oil Producers Agency in the Kern county fields and the Coalinga Oil Producers Agency, which had been formed at Coalinga in 1907 by a group of heavy oil companies. In April, 1909, Associated warned the Independents, whose oil it handled, that their increasing production could not be disposed of without an aggressive campaign for foreign markets, which would mean lower prices. The Agencies agreed to curtail drilling. There was also talk of merging the Agencies, which finally did occur the following spring.[29]

Early in May, 1909, the press announced a $25,000,000 bond issue put on the market by Associated that clearly registered its confidence in the future. Associated sought the new money for a pipeline from Coalinga to Port Costa, for another from McKittrick to Gaviota, for at least one tanker, and for additional storage and distributing stations. The company was overextended and hard-pressed for cash, paying for oil only after sixty to ninety days, while Standard paid on delivery. As-

sociated was also counting on renewal of its contracts with the two
Agencies at the end of the year. Suddenly, a bombshell burst on May
26, when the Agencies voted to build their own pipeline.[30]

This astounding action was part of an agreement engineered by
W. L. Stewart. Lyman Stewart described his son's coup in this way:[31]

> For some time W. L. has had negotiations pending with the repre-
> sentatives of the independent producers for a ten year agreement for
> handling their oil. The Union's hand has not been disclosed in this, but
> suspicion has become so strong in the past few days as to increase the
> market from $101 for Union up to $107.50. The pipe line will be
> eight inches in diameter, will connect the Sunset and Coalinga fields,
> and will have its outlet at Port Harford. About 20,000 barrels per day
> from 5,000 acres of land are already signed up.

In another letter, he went on:[32]

> The producers' pipeline agreement has been closed, the pipe bought,
> some tanks already on the ground for storage of surplus; now comes the
> interesting problem of financing the scheme. The company is capitalized
> at $7,000,000, and will issue $3,500,000 five per cent twelve year
> bonds. . . .
> The Union will guarantee the bonds, turn in its contracts—covering
> 20,000,000 barrels of oil, aggregating in value $13,000,000—and will
> make the price of its fuel oil at coast points the same as that in the
> San Joaquin Valley. . . . For doing these three things, and furnishing the
> $3,500,000 cash for the construction of the pipe line and storage system,
> we get all the stock and all the bonds. We also get a liberal price for
> water transportation, and ten per cent of the net amount realized for
> the oil at the wells for the use of our terminal facilities and expense of
> marketing. This latter item will doubtless net us $1,000 per day.

When Union's role was revealed, the *California Oil World* called the
agreement "the biggest thing in oil in the West today. . . . For the first
time in the history of oil in the West there is an absolutely dominant
hand at the head of the business." It explained that of the state's production of 160,000 barrels daily, 30,000 was consumed by the railroads
on long-term contracts, 30,000 was refined, and 100,000 was available
for the fuel oil market. Of the fuel crude, Union controlled 30,000 and
the Agencies 20,000. This estimate of the strength of the Union-Agencies
combination was undoubtedly exaggerated, but the combination was
obviously destined to play a strong hand in the crude market. Its pipeline project called for 240 miles of pipe and fifteen pump stations,
drawing oil from all of the San Joaquin Valley and carrying it over
the Coast Range to Port Harford. The combination immediately ordered

tanks and pipe and set up the Producers Transportation Company as its pipeline company. Nevertheless, Associated refused to be counted out; it went ahead with its Coalinga–Port Costa line. Even though it had lost the Agencies' contracts, Associated had substantial reserves in undrilled land.

Early in July, California oilmen had still more to think about when the *California Oil World* reported that Standard would build a new pipeline paralleling its old one, and that after two years the company was planning to contract again for crude in the Coalinga Westside field. It reported, too, that Standard marketers had thrown themselves whole-heartedly into selling fuel oil. The oil journal speculated that Associated was to be tied more closely to the Southern Pacific and that Associated's oil would be held in the ground for the railroad. Consequently, the assumed agreement between Standard and Associated, long accepted as real by the *California Oil World* and many oilmen—for Associated to dominate fuel oil and Standard refined oils—was at an end. Standard was not only free to push fuel oil more strongly, the oil journal be-lieved, but actually felt impelled to do so to prevent the Union-Agencies alliance from dictating the price of crude.[33]

But Standard's actions fail to substantiate any such powerful counter-stroke. Its pipeline project consisted merely of looping the line from Mendota to San Pablo, laying about ten miles of eight-inch pipe on the far side of each pumping station. The most likely stimulus for the looping was the rising Midway production and the hope of major production there, a hope stirred by the drilling of several promising wells in the flat ground east of Midway. There was ample capacity for Midway and Kern River crude as far as Mendota, but beyond Mendota the heavy crudes had to be pumped speedily to San Pablo so that the line would be available for the all-important refinable oil from Coalinga. As for the report that Standard would take oil from Coalinga Westside, this did not come to pass.

The contention that an agreement between Standard and Associated to split the market had been abrogated is susceptible to a simpler and more likely explanation. Historically, Standard's primary interest was in refined products. It had the know-how, capital, and marketing organ-ization to pursue this profitable line. Associated was born in the heavy oil fields; it had neither the men, capital, light oil production, nor market for refined oils. And the forecast of a battle between Standard and the Union-Agencies alliance for the power to set prices is doubtful, too. A study of Standard's contracts does not reveal an aggressive effort to tie up crude production. The company made several contracts in Midway in April, 1909, and more at the end of the year, as the looping of the pipeline neared completion. But it would have been odd for Standard not to have been active in Midway. The company's pipeline had brought the field to life, and it was a vigorous wildcatter there.[34]

At the time the Union-Agencies alliance was formed, Standard openly affirmed that overproduction existed. In fact, the company's April contracts adopted each day's market price as the formula for paying for deliveries in place of the former fixed-price policy. To buy more oil meant building more storage, and Standard had no desire to buy high-priced oil for storage. In August the company emphasized this point by cutting its price for oil on daily runs from 50¢ to 40¢. The *California Oil World* lamented that ex-President Roosevelt's "unexampled display of strenuosity . . . against the Standard" had not had a permanent influence, and called the cut "a duplicate of the old time raids this company has made upon other people's property." Judging from the record of Standard's runs and stocks, it appears more plausible that the rapid increase in receipts on contracts with Midway producers caused the company to discourage daily runs until it was ready to handle them. If, on the other hand, the price cut was meant to force producers into signing contracts, it failed; the first new contract after the cut was not signed until more than three months later.[35]

Late in 1909, when the enlarged pipeline capacity was almost ready, Standard went after more contracts in Midway and Sunset, offering 50¢ for heavy oil and 65¢ for light. From November 19, 1909, to April 2, 1910, it signed two- and three-year contracts for a total of over 12,000,000 barrels. It had hopes, too, for its own wildcatting, which were rewarded in January with a well flowing 3,700 barrels the first day. To handle the additional oil, the company laid a second eight-inch line out of Midway, extended service to Sunset with a line and a pump station, and built two more half-million barrel reservoirs at Waite. Undoubtedly, Standard was preparing to meet the challenge of Producers Transportation and also Associated, which was extending its Coalinga line south to McKittrick and was considering continuing on into Midway if it could sign up enough light oil producers at 75¢ a barrel.[36]

Standard's western executives were not worried. Early in March, 1910, in a letter to Tilford, Scofield wrote that they thought it would be "only a question of time" before the Associated Oil Company was subordinated to the fuel oil needs of the Southern Pacific Company, which would limit the ability of the Associated "to do a general commercial business." They looked for the Union–Agencies combination to provide Standard with its principal competition in the near future, but their judgment "of the management of the former, and the characteristics of some of the prominent members of the latter," led them to believe that the combination could not last.

The westerners urged, therefore, that Standard should take the long view and be prepared to handle a portion of the Agencies' oil after the combination broke up in order to forestall competition and the probable construction of another trunk line system. Scofield argued:[37]

> Our eagerness in this matter is based upon our belief that the production and business upon this Coast will grow, that our representation in it is too small proportionately, and we cannot . . . see our percentage of the whole grow gradually less and new competitive interests grow up which will menace us in more ways than one, without our striving to prevent it.

Rising prices and the optimism engendered by the Union-Agencies alliance contributed to overproduction more rapidly than anyone could have dreamed. All over the Midway, men had been pricking the earth and drawing forth great gushers of oil. The most spectacular, Union's Lakeview gusher, began to spout March 15, 1910, at the rate of 125,000 barrels a day. "My God, we've cut an artery down there," the driller yelled, or so the story goes. After April 2, Standard made no new contracts for almost five months, though it did accept oil on daily runs. Especially significant was the fact that some of these new Midway wells produced refinable oil. Their productivity reversed the upward trend of prices. By the fall of 1910, Standard was looking forward to an assured light crude supply and was planning a new and greater growth based on the Midway field.[38]

7

From 1906 to 1910 the refiners were particularly hampered by the uncertainties and inadequacies of the crude supply. They were harassed, too, by shifting patterns of demand. Meeting the mounting demand for gasoline in the West was one vexatious problem, but far more troublesome was Petrolite, for which New York fixed the production figures from year to year.

For 1907 the planners at 26 Broadway, assuming there would be enough crude, called on Richmond to supply 2,000,000 barrels of Petrolite. This huge order at once gave rise to concern over the adequacy of the supply of acid, a problem for which J. C. Black, Richmond's chief engineer, provided an answer. Black, who had had some formal training in engineering at Columbia University, was a gifted innovator. Late in 1905, he had begun to experiment with the gas, sulfur anhydride (SO_3), in treating kerosine distillate in place of fuming acid (H_2SO_4, plus 15% SO_3). His experiments showed that this gas removed the smoke-producing aromatics from unheated distillate as effectively as fuming acid did from heated distillate and was even more effective in removing sulfur. He found, too, that the gas would treat more than twice as much distillate as the equivalent liquid acid. But in gas treating, little acid was recovered from the sludge, compared to the substantial amount salvaged when fuming acid was the treating agent. The tests were so promising that the refiners decided to erect near the Mannheim acid plant a battery of ten 48,000-gallon agitators and two wash tanks, of which the first units were ready in April, 1907. Thereafter, sulfur anhydride production from the Mannheim plant was diverted to the new facilities, and for fuming acid Richmond relied wholly on the Peyton Chemical Company. The fuming acid treatment of heated distillate continued to be the principal one for Petrolite, however, possibly because gas treating took more time.[39]

Although the problem of providing sufficient acid was solved, the refiners were deeply troubled by a shortage of crude oil. During 1907, instead of the 2,000,000 barrels of Petrolite 26 Broadway had called for, Richmond was able to manufacture only 1,150,000, plus 443,000 barrels of domestic kerosine. In 1908, the costly contract with Union for Santa Maria crude seemed to promise the necessary relief, but water, breaking into the Santa Maria field, turned Union's production into an emulsion with a high sand content which was difficult to refine. Much of it Standard refused to accept, and the crude it did take slowed the distilling process. Tilford suggested that heat exchangers be installed to separate the water from the oil. J. P. Smith, the assistant superintendent at Richmond, dissented. He believed that eastern experience was not applicable in this case; too high a heat would be required to break the emulsion. Richmond developed its own technique. On the first still of each continuous battery, the refiners placed a tower into which the crude was fed from the top and, as it descended, the heat of the vapors ascending from the still removed the water. After this device was adopted, Richmond stepped up its takings from Union. Nevertheless, the search continued for a better method. In September, 1909, Rheem came very close to building a special battery of 262-barrel stills for emulsion crude, patterned after a Roumanian process of which Tilford had sent him the plans. J. C. Black proposed continuous fractional distillation with conventional equipment as another alternative before the problem finally faded away when Union suspended shipments and new sources of crude were developed.[40]

While the refiners strove to increase production of Petrolite, New York Standard's agencies were successfully pushing sales across the seas. Their most effective promotional device was a little lamp called "Mei Foo," meaning "Good Luck." New York Standard offered the lamps at the low price of 7.5¢ as a means of attracting customers for kerosine. During the first year 875,000 were sold. The company's aggressive marketing campaign raised its share of kerosine deliveries in the Far East from 34 per cent in 1903 to 46 per cent in 1908. Richmond's contribution of Petrolite for this trade peaked in 1908 and 1909, and then fell off gradually to a rate of 300,000 barrels annually late in 1910 before reviving the next year. When Richmond lost its place in supplying the Orient in 1910, the domestic market briefly became almost the sole target for its products.[41]

Unlike the rise and decline of Petrolite, the domestic trade in light products was at least steady. Kerosine sales grew slowly, and gasoline added a powerful impulse to Richmond's development, too powerful for a balanced growth. Between 1906 and 1910 gasoline sales nearly doubled, climbing from 290,000 to 548,000 barrels. The rate of growth for engine distillate sales was even greater, but their volume was not as large. The demand for this heavy naphtha or light kerosine did not outrun the refinery's capacity.

The demand for gasoline did. Shortly after the contract with Union for light crude and tops expired in 1906, a shortage of gasoline appeared likely. Tilford wrote Scofield in April, 1906, that it was "very desirable to provide all the gasoline required on the Pacific Coast, even if it is necessary to cut off some of the lube oil shipments to the East." He wanted to avoid the freight costs involved in shipping gasoline from refineries in the East and Midwest. Lube oil production was not affecting the output of gasoline; rather, it was a lack of crude with a high gasoline content. More Santa Maria crude would have helped, for it yielded 5.61 per cent "stove gasoline" compared to about one per cent from Coalinga crude. But Standard's plans for large purchases and a pipeline system from Santa Maria came to nothing.

In his laboratory, Starke worked with heavy crudes to determine whether they could be made to yield appreciable amounts of gasoline. He obtained from 2.5 to 5 per cent of naphtha, partly by cracking the heavier hydrocarbons with heat, but the cracked naphtha, even when redistilled, smelled like turpentine. Because of the odor, Starke believed it could not be sold for use in the home. But, he told Scofield, "There is no doubt that for automobiles and gas engines it will fullfill all requirements, and in this way it may fill a gap which now exists."[42]

The gasoline shortage of 1907 was surmounted, not by Starke's efforts, but by purchases of tops from other refineries and of crude naphtha from Sumatra. The Sumatran naphtha came from the Shanghai-Langkat Company, owned by George McBain, an independent old Scotsman who refined his production primarily for the Far Eastern kerosine market and had surplus naphtha for sale. 26 Broadway had bought from him for its European refineries, and for a time had considered buying him out. Around June, 1907, Tilford contracted for up to 35,000 tons of naphtha, with the first cargo arriving at Richmond in October, 1907. To the refiners' dismay, the naphtha produced a gasoline of a lower gravity than they were accustomed to. Tilford responded that "this question of gravity is not as important as consumers seem to think. It is our opinion that the efficiency of gasoline should be judged by the boiling points instead of the gravity." In this judgment, he was correct. Shipments from the Shanghai-Langkat, totaling 333,685 barrels, were completed in 1908. Along with Santa Maria crude under the new contract with Union, they helped make gasoline a plentiful product once more. When the gasoline tankage at Richmond proved inadequate, Tilford arranged for relief in the summer of 1908 by having the Continental Oil Company take 40,000 barrels.[43]

In 1909, as gasoline stocks again dwindled, Smith obtained Rheem's approval to cut gradually the gravity of gasoline from 65.8° to 63.0° in order to increase production. Again Tilford came to the rescue with Sumatran naphtha. The first cargo arrived early in October aboard the *Cowrie,* a tanker that belonged to the Anglo-Saxon Petroleum Company of the Royal Dutch–Shell Group. Standard bought from its rival at least part of the more than 400,000 barrels received in the next twenty months. Meantime, Shanghai-Langkat's McBain died, and in June, 1910, his son sold the company to the Royal Dutch–Shell Group. After relations between Standard and the Group became strained in 1910, Tilford wired Scofield late in July that he could obtain no more Sumatran naphtha.[44]

Since Peruvian naphtha had not yet begun to arrive and Peruvian crude shipments had been small, the refiners at Richmond were thrown back on their own resources. As a stopgap, they turned to cracking light crude for a greater gasoline yield. Anticipating their need, they had begun experimental cracking of residuum from Coalinga crude early

Point Orient in June, 1907. Can factory in the foreground; box factory to its left. The SONY bark *Acme* is to the left; Anglo-American's bark *Arrow* is to the right, and the *Brilliant* behind it

Rialto Building after earthquake and fire

in 1910. Their cracking was by heat alone, not by the combination of heat and pressure in special stills, as cracking later came to imply. The stills were heated as hot as possible and the residuum run down to tar or coke. By this technique, Coalinga crude could be made to yield about 3 per cent gasoline, 2 per cent more than by normal distillation. The cracked product contained slightly more sulfur and had a poor odor, but the experimenters thought it would prove satisfactory. Their main concern was the length of time cracking took, reducing the refinery's throughput. To run more than 5,500 barrels a day of Coalinga crude all the way to tar or coke would require additional stills. In October Tilford authorized fifteen for Richmond, which proved to be the start of a new round of expansion.[45]

Like the naphthas, production of lubricating oils for the domestic market also doubled, stimulated primarily by the demand for lighter engine oils. One advantage the lubes possessed over the naphthas was a national market. Unfortunately, this advantage cannot be measured for lack of sales statistics beyond the Pacific Coast, though it is known that some shipments were being made to the Continental Oil Company and to other Standard companies further East at least as early as 1906. The next year Richmond started to send small quantities of lubes to The Imperial Oil Company, the sister company in Canada. However, during this period Richmond was primarily concerned with the lube market along the Pacific Coast.

Both the New York and western executives hoped to enlarge the market for Richmond's lube sales. In 1905 Tilford asked what the refinery could provide in the way of heavy engine oils if a permanent foreign market could be secured. When the refiners replied that their throughput would be cut 1,200 barrels a day, the idea was dropped. Another example of 26 Broadway's interest in broadening Richmond's market was an inquiry in March, 1906, by H. C. Folger, Jr., regarding a light engine oil with a zero cold test. Richmond could not meet the specifications he laid down. Nevertheless, J. P. Smith undertook several experiments with lighter oils and sent samples on to New York.[46]

Kenneth R. Kingsbury, California Standard's agent at New York, played a large part in stimulating Richmond's lube oil production. He wrote Rheem in February, 1907, "There is quite a demand throughout the country for an oil of low cold test and having a good viscosity which can be used for automobile lubrication, but to be acceptable must be of fairly pale color. . . . An oil of 200 vis [cosity] at 100 [degrees F.] would be good enough." Soon Kingsbury brought about a related and broader investigation of Richmond's capabilities when he had the Whiting refinery ship Rheem a case of samples of trademarked engine oils. Curiously, Richmond had been working with standards set by Colonel Merrill of the Marketing Department, who relied on his memory. Compared with the samples, Richmond's oils were all too dark. There was a feeling, moreover, that California's oils could not meet the color of eastern oils. After J. F. Faber took charge of the Treating Department in the spring of 1907, heavier applications of acid were used to lighten the color and a little acid-treated tar was added to provide a good bloom (fluorescence). With these adjustments, Richmond's engine oils came very close to matching the samples from Whiting.[47]

A number of new lubes were turned out during this period of re-examination. The first was Calumet Engine Oil, a heavily treated oil of probably 450 viscosity that was designed for automobile lubrication. Developed by Luther Dimm, the refinery superintendent, it went into commercial production in May, 1907. A second oil with a much greater future was produced in September by Henry Hulin, who had come to Richmond from Franklin, Pennsylvania. Its viscosity was around 335, and it was even more heavily treated—130 pounds of acid per fifty-gallon barrel, compared to 75 for Calumet. Kingsbury thought well enough of this oil to accept it as a substitute for the Mobil oils turned out by the Vacuum Oil Company, Jersey Standard's renowned affiliate specializing in lubes. He named it "Zerolene," perhaps influenced by Swan & Finch's "Zerol Engine Oil." In addition to having the West Coast marketers adopt the oil, he proposed selling some of it to Vacuum as "Pale Viscous Oil No. 10." There is no evidence that Vacuum became a customer, but Richmond soon was shipping Zerolene regularly to Jersey Standard's Eagle Works and Ohio Standard's Cleveland No. 2 refinery.[48]

While Zerolene was being developed, Tilford asked the refiners in June, 1907, for a lube to compete with Russian oils in the United States and Europe. These were made from a crude similar to California's and could not be duplicated from eastern stock. They had become a serious threat to Standard's position in Western Europe. The lube Tilford wanted duplicated was the Russian No. 1 Pale Oil sold in England, which apparently resembled Calumet Engine Oil. Rheem and J. P. Smith determined that the oil could be made but requested that production be delayed until two new reducing stills were finished. Toward the end of the year Tilford wired that he had sold 30,000 barrels to be delivered in bulk in London during the summer of 1908, by far the largest lube order yet placed with Richmond. Production began immediately. Then word came that the tanker *Housatonic*, scheduled to carry the oil, had been lost. Before another tanker could be substituted, Tilford ordered production stopped and thus brought to an end Richmond's prospects for a substantial lube export trade.[49]

Nevertheless, the market in the eastern United States was open for the whole range of Richmond's engine oils. These California lubes were desired for their low cold test, but their color was against them. Late in October, 1907, Rheem told Dimm that Richmond's prestige with the lube trade in both East and West depended on improving the color of the oils. He wanted no expense spared in getting it right. After tripling the acid used in treating, the refiners sent East a new set of samples that brought high praise from Kingsbury. He called them beautiful oils that compared favorably with the best made from eastern crude, but wondered whether Richmond could guarantee uniformity in color. The refiners were satisfied they could. The heavy use of acid brought a protest from Tilford, who was alarmed at the cost. But Kingsbury backed up the refiners, saying that if Richmond was going to market lubes in competition with eastern oils, its products had to meet eastern standards. Perhaps as a concession to Tilford, Richmond began in March, 1908, to make its Diamond, Zone, and Ruddy Harvester lubes by both methods—the severe acid treatment and the old one. There was a substantial difference in cost. The "Old Diamond" took 0.52 pounds of acid a gallon and cost 0.5¢ a gallon to treat; the new "Diamond" required 1.9 pounds of acid and cost 1.3¢. Evidently, many customers were satisfied with the older products, for the refinery continued to follow both processes.[50]

Beginning in August, 1908, Richmond started using a different crude for lubes—Kern River or possibly a Kern River–Midway mixture, for oils from the two fields were not yet recorded separately. The refiners actually increased their lube output by running the Kern crude through continuous stills; Coalinga crude had been distilled in batches. The Kern oil had another advantage, the important quality of a low cold test. On the other hand, its color was too dark. In July, 1909, the refiners began to mix some Coalinga crude with the Kern. Coalinga's color was good, but its cold test was high. In making Zerolene, no more than 25 per cent Coalinga crude could be mixed in if a zero test was maintained. A few months later straight Midway crude was tested. Its color and cold test were good, but its flash test was poor. Whether Midway oil became the mainstay of Richmond's lube production at this early date cannot be told, but the rising receipts from Midway and, some years later, the segregation of certain Midway crudes for lube stock suggest that by 1909 the field may already have become a contributor to Standard's lube production. At any rate, Richmond had ample low gravity crude for lubes and, with plenty of acid, could turn out a merchantable product. In fact, by 1910 thirty to forty per cent of its highest priced engine oil, Zerolene, was being sold to Standard companies in the East.[51]

Clearly, the years between 1906 and 1910 were a time of rapid growth in refining for the domestic market, especially gasoline, engine distillate, and lubes. The refining of Richmond's principal product, Petrolite, by contrast, waxed and waned. By the close of 1910, however, California Standard was on the threshold of a new era, for a flood of light Midway crude was about to offer greater opportunities at refining than the company had yet known.

XII

THE RISING TIDE
OF COMPETITION

Standard's oldest activity in the West was the sale of oil products, in which by 1900 it had achieved an outstanding success. Seemingly, 26 Broadway's heavy investments thereafter in other phases of the western industry, especially transportation and refining, should have further strengthened the marketers. These investments undoubtedly did contribute to a gratifying increase in sales between 1900 and 1910 of more than threefold, from $5,720,000 to $18,870,000. But except in fuel oil, which in 1910 accounted for $6,769,000 of these sales, Standard's relative position declined. And there is reason to question whether the company ever competed so seriously in the fuel trade as in marketing refined oils. In the latter trade, its virtual monopoly gradually eroded away, as more and more companies with access to light crude began to refine and entered the market. In short, the decade after 1900 for Standard was one of substantial growth and of relative decline.

2

As the twentieth century opened, Iowa Standard dominated the Far Western market for refined products with an unmatched network of seventy-three stations and substations that were served by rail from Whiting and other refineries of sister companies in the eastern United States. But 26 Broadway gave the western marketers a new product and a new pattern of supply when it bought the Pacific Coast Oil Company and, through it, ventured into the fuel market and built the Richmond refinery. Heretofore, Standard's fuel oil business had been insignificant. In 1896, after the Los Angeles City field began producing, Iowa Standard had set up tanks for fuel oil in San Francisco and Los Angeles. Its sales, which were never large, dwindled until they ceased to be particularized on the semi-annual sales statements to New York.

Late in 1900, the purchase of PCO automatically put Standard in the fuel trade in a small way because of PCO's heavy Elsmere crude. Beginning in November, about 100 barrels a day were diverted to the Los Angeles agency. The next year, when PCO stopped shipping Elsmere production to the Alameda refinery, the oil began to flow to the San Diego area as well as to Los Angeles. Curiously, at the start of 1902

Elsmere's declining output was diverted almost entirely to Arizona, and in April production was halted for the rest of the year. By this time PCO was buying Fullerton crude for Alameda, some of which was a little heavy. It seems to have first supplemented and then supplanted the Elsmere oil.[1]

Elsmere was an insignificant contributor to the industry's campaign to convert coal users to fuel oil. For Iowa Standard to play a major role in the fuel trade, PCO had to supply it with crude from Kern River. In this booming field, PCO began to purchase substantial quantities during 1901. Tanks erected at the Alameda refinery provided a storage center for the Bay area, but in the pre-pipeline period much of the crude was shipped direct to consumers without passing through Alameda. Perhaps there was some overlap in sales effort between PCO and Iowa Standard. At any rate, in December, 1901, when PCO turned over to Iowa Standard its sales contracts acquired along with the production of the Monte Cristo Oil & Development Company, it set a policy of transferring any future fuel oil sales contracts as well. During 1901, Iowa Standard's San Francisco district sold more than 200,000 barrels, nearly all in the latter half of the year, and over 900,000 in 1902. Sales by other districts were negligible.[2]

While fuel oil added another product to Iowa Standard's line, revolutionary changes in its marketing pattern awaited completion of the refinery and the pipeline. Thereafter, Richmond took over from Whiting as the chief source of refined products and largely replaced Kern River as the chief source of fuel oil. Richmond's special advantage, indeed a major reason for its construction, was its ability to employ marine transportation. The first step toward realizing this potential was PCO's purchase and conversion in 1902 of the collier *Asuncion* to transport crude from Southern California to Richmond and fuel oil from Richmond to stations up and down the coast. A second step was changing the mission of the *Loomis* to carrying refined products. To receive its cargoes, PCO's crude oil station at Redondo was enlarged, making Redondo the primary supply point for distributing refined products in Southern California. At the other end of the Coast, at Seattle, Iowa Standard spent $55,000 for a site on Elliott Bay, where in 1903 it constructed a marine terminal and bulk station.[3]

Around San Francisco Bay, PCO was also beginning to utilize low-cost water transportation. In competitive bidding with shipbuilders, Rheem won for his boiler makers the opportunity to build *Barge No. 1*. Perhaps "building" exaggerates their accomplishment. Working on the shore of a cove near the whale oil plant, they constructed eight tanks to the specifications of J. C. Fitzsimmons, the burly ex-marine engineer who had taken the *Oil City* to the Yukon in 1898. The tanks were floated to a wooden barge and installed like two rows of fat sausages. For $37,000, PCO had a 4,500-barrel barge that netted a $20,000 profit in 1903, its first year of operation.[4]

Meanwhile, the fuel oil venture was growing rapidly. Purchase of the Peerless Oil Company's marketing contracts and facilities helped build Standard's sales by the end of 1902. The Peerless plant at Stockton and probably its San Francisco plant became outlets for Iowa Standard. More volume was acquired in May, 1903, through the purchase of the statewide fuel oil jobbing business of King-Keystone Oil Company, the same firm whose refined oil business Iowa Standard had bought in 1900. The King brothers were forced to sell because their suppliers could not get enough tank cars, while Standard was well taken care of with cars of the Union Tank Line. Fred King blamed both Standard and the Southern Pacific. However, Henry King accused only the railroad, claiming that it had tied up cars for several weeks while filling its fuel tanks in Arizona, Texas, and New Mexico. He also declared that Santa Fe cars were available, but the Southern Pacific would not switch them to the King-Keystone siding. Whatever were the facts of the matter, the result was that the King brothers sold Standard their contracts for 40,000 barrels of fuel oil monthly. Still more important to the success of Standard's fuel oil business were the completion of the pipeline and the expansion of Richmond to use Coalinga crude. These new facilities meant that Kern crude would be available at a cheaper price and that Richmond would drown in residuum from the refining process if Iowa Standard did not aggressively sell the residuum as fuel oil. To stimulate sales, J. C. Fitzsimmons was appointed manager of the newly created Fuel Oil Department, to which he would devote his keen mind and abounding energy for many years.[5]

The expanding business inevitably required more fuel storage. For Iowa Standard, PCO laid an eight-inch line at San Francisco running from a dock at 16th Street to two 10,500-barrel fuel tanks at the main station. One of these tanks was transferred from Los Angeles, which was abandoned as a fuel oil storage point. At Redondo, during the winter of 1903 and 1904 two fuel tanks with a combined capacity of 55,000 barrels were set up to serve Southern California and Arizona.[6]

To ship fuel oil from Richmond to Southern California was like carrying coals to Newcastle; the Los Angeles City field, the neighboring Salt Lake field, and even the Whittier-Fullerton fields had a marked advantage in transportation costs. But Iowa Standard was pressing hard for markets.

Late in 1903, it agreed to channel most of its sales effort through a local man, Edward Strasburg of the Oil Storage & Transportation Company. From Strasburg, W. L. Stewart learned that the arrangement called for Standard to supply 40,000 barrels a month at 65¢ and to sell no more than it already had under contract. Stewart concluded that Standard believed 40,000 barrels monthly was all the market could absorb and that it was[7]

> . . . more economical for them to place the oil at the price they get from Strasburg, 65 cts., in a lump, rather than throw it on the market and compete with Southern California oil; or, in other words, they are long on oil and are endeavoring to dispose of it to the best advantage possible without making new investments in the shape of transportation and terminals.

Stewart's observation was a shrewd one. Standard's Los Angeles station reported a low profit on fuel oil, but at least a substantial amount of oil was moved without a costly price war.

Standard's position in Southern California was seriously menaced by local oil, as an active drilling campaign in the Salt Lake field boosted production by 30,000 barrels monthly between October, 1903, and May, 1904. To meet this new competition, Breeden obtained a cut in freight rates from the Santa Fe on the Redondo–Los Angeles run; on fuel oil, the reduction amounted to 25 per cent. Subsequently, a representative of the federal Bureau of Corporations asked Breeden if PCO had threatened to build a pipeline to Los Angeles. Breeden referred his questioner elsewhere, but for PCO to have considered such a project was certainly reasonable. The Bureau publicly criticized the cut as a secret rebate, although Breeden had defended it on the grounds that it was necessary to meet local competition and that the Santa Fe had told him the rate would be published. He claimed that any other shipper from Redondo would have received the same rate, and that the Southern Pacific had established a comparable charge from San Pedro to Los Angeles.[8]

Competition became even more intense in 1904 when Associated set out to capture the Los Angeles market. That year it bought out Strasburg and, presumably, acquired Standard's contract to supply him. Associated was blamed for cutting prices to pick up contracts, notably with the Pacific Electric Railway. The veteran fuel crude producer, E. L. Doheny, speaking generally of the California situation, explained Associated's advantage over Standard in the fuel trade by saying that Associated had made profitable contracts before competition existed and thereafter had only to break even on new customers. This may have been Associated's policy in Los Angeles. On the other hand, an Associated man blamed the development of the Salt Lake field as the basic reason for falling prices and explained Associated's low bid to the Pacific Electric as a response to a very low bid by Union. Union was well-placed to compete in the Los Angeles market because of its pipeline from Fullerton and cheap water transportation from Santa Maria. Associated improved its position by leasing the best part of the Salt Lake field, after which it stopped shipping in oil from Kern River. To operate the Salt Lake holdings, it organized the Amalgamated Oil Company. Iowa Standard was not so aggressive, although it supplied a sizable trade through an independent oil dealer, Mrs. E. A. Summers. In mid-1905 Amalgamated's secretary estimated Standard had a fourth of the business, and that the balance was divided between Associated and Union.[9]

Clearly, Standard and Associated stopped short of fighting each other in a fuel war because on May 1, 1905, PCO bought a million barrels of crude from Amalgamated. The contract called for delivery at 30¢ a barrel over a two-year period. It also contained an unusual option that allowed PCO to buy an additional quantity equal to the number of days between the date the option was taken up and the expiration of the contract, multiplied by 800 barrels. Deliveries could be stretched out as late as May 1, 1909. The price on the option crude was 30¢, with a proviso that if Amalgamated sold to another at 30¢ or less, the price to PCO would be reduced to 2.5¢ under the sale figure to the third party. PCO exercised its option in January, 1906, and until April, 1909, it received crude and some residuum from Amalgamated. One of PCO's obligations in the contract was to deliver only Amalgamated crude and Richmond residuum in Southern California, except in San Diego County. At San Diego, where Iowa Standard was building a fuel oil depot, PCO could deliver Kern River crude if it wished to do so. But the San Diego station's fuel trade was minor; two cargoes a year by the *Asuncion* would have handled it.

This contract with Amalgamated gave rise to rumors that PCO and Associated were exchanging oil, with PCO taking Salt Lake oil at Los Angeles and giving Associated fuel oil at San Francisco. By economies in transportation, it was said, they were thus able to undersell their competitors. So far as the contract is concerned, there is no hint of an exchange, but something of the sort may have developed. Later in the year, in September, Richmond began to load an Associated barge with fuel oil about every other day. However, there were other practical reasons for the contract between the two companies. Amalgamated's leases contained stiff drilling requirements that in a new and prolific field undoubtedly forced it to look for an outlet. As for PCO, it was probably a case of "if you can't lick 'em, join 'em." PCO's sources of fuel oil were not well situated to compete with low-cost production in Southern California, and Amalgamated offered oil at a price low enough to be profitable. In the first six months of 1905, during which PCO drew fuel oil from both Redondo and Amalgamated, it lost $5,600 on the Redondo operation and made $22,900 on Amalgamated's oil. Moreover, so long as PCO sent a tanker to Redondo to pick up refinable crude, it cost little more to send a cargo of fuel oil. But when PCO withdrew from the Fullerton field in 1904, these voyages were no longer necessary. There was one other result of the contract, or at least a coincidence, the transfer of the Redondo depot from PCO to Iowa Standard. It was a logical step, for Redondo's sole remaining function was to serve marketing, and Iowa Standard was already operating several marine terminals.[10]

During the expansion of fuel oil facilities in 1903 and 1904, Iowa Standard made a few other moves. Fuel oil equipment was installed at San Jose, even though it was not a port city. A small station was set up at Knights Landing north of the city of Sacramento, and a wooden tank was placed at Angels Camp in Calaveras County. And a daring reach was made overseas when George H. Mayer was sent to Chile in November, 1904, to plan a fuel oil station at Punta Arenas for bunkering ships plying between Hawaii and Europe. Before the station could be built, however, the construction of a railroad across Mexico diverted this traffic from around Cape Horn.

Apart from its efforts around San Francisco Bay, Iowa Standard's campaign in the Northwest was especially important as time went on. In 1904, fuel oil facilities were completed at Portland and Seattle and plants authorized at Tacoma and Astoria. The Astoria plant may have been set up to service a contract with the Portland & Astoria Railroad, which was Iowa Standard's only fuel contract with a railroad.[11]

The company's two chief rivals, Associated and Union, differed in the extent of their activity along the northern Pacific Coast. Associated viewed that territory dimly because coal was cheap there. Union, on the other hand, bought terminal rights at Portland in 1904 and within a year had tanks at Portland, Astoria, and Seattle. It also invaded British Columbia, the home ground of the coal industry, where it was selling oil late in 1905. Union's life depended on fuel oil sales, and it had its own crude supply close to water transportation.[12]

Throughout the West, in fact, throughout the world, Union pushed hard in 1905 to make room for its flush Santa Maria production. It took away from Standard the business of the American-Hawaiian Steamship Company, amounting to 500,000 barrels yearly, and considered a pipeline to Arizona to capture Standard's contracts with Arizona mining companies. Union's enterprising sales manager, John Baker, visited New York and London on a marketing expedition. Back in the United States, Baker saw a Seattle newspaper article stating that Union had joined Standard and Associated in a combine. This he branded as false and probably an attempt to scare consumers into contracts for fear of a price advance. He surmised that "it came directly from the enemy and was circulated for the purpose of influencing buyers . . . , as the enemy realize we are in earnest and they are endeavoring to secure as much business as they can at present quotations, fearing the decline in market prices forced by us."

Lyman Stewart blamed his competitors for a San Francisco ordinance placing a flash test on fuel oil. The ordinance shut Santa Maria crude out of the market until Union built earthen reservoirs so that the crude could "weather," permitting the light hydrocarbons to evaporate. Late in 1905 the Union executives began to speak more cautiously, as fuel crude production outside Santa Maria declined. W. L. Stewart wrote, "We have already secured a very considerable amount of extremely cheap business that we have got to take care of during the next few years, and we have already discovered that we were unable to buy oil against it at a price that will even let us out whole."[13]

Union's suspicions of unfair competition probably were unwarranted, but obviously the rivalry was keen. And the fuel oil sales of Standard grew, especially in the San Francisco Bay area and the Northwest, as Table 8 shows.

Table 8: Standard's Fuel Oil Sales in Major Sales Districts and Total Sales, All Stations
(Barrels to nearest 1,000)

	1902	1904	1906	1908	1910
San Francisco	932,000	1,597,000	3,532,000	3,310,000	3,463,000
Oakland	4,000	84,000	124,000	519,000	622,000
Los Angeles	8,000	893,000	674,000	381,000	474,000
Portland	0	74,000	446,000	1,036,000	451,000
Seattle	0	69,000	302,000	803,000	1,596,000
Total, all Stations	1,004,000	3,015,000	5,380,000	6,087,000	7,663,000

Source: Annual Sales Statements.

Sales in Far Western Marketing Area
1900 — 1910
MILLIONS OF DOLLARS

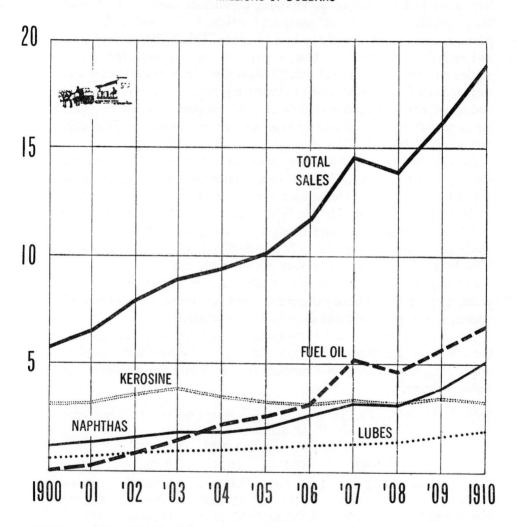

SOURCE - ANNUAL SALES STATEMENTS, 1891-1922.

NOTE - BARRELS OF PRODUCTS SOLD ARE TABULATED IN APPENDIX.

Yet, despite this impressive rise in sales, it is possible to exaggerate the vigor with which Standard battled in the fuel trade. The high ratio of Richmond's residuum to the total fuel oil sales strongly suggests that after Standard's initial venture in fuel-grade crude, the company's primary concern was disposing of the residuum from refining. After Richmond began running Coalinga crude, rail shipments of fuel-grade crude from Kern County dropped off. From 1904 through 1909, they averaged only about 2,000 barrels a day. In 1910 they climbed to nearly 4,000 barrels daily, influenced in part by a contract with the Western Pacific Railroad. To serve this new railroad, Standard built a shipping station at Lyoth, which was also located on the tracks of the Southern Pacific, 212 miles up the pipeline from Waite and about twenty miles southwest of Stockton. Lyoth began operating in June, 1910, and soon rivaled Waite as a shipping point. Nevertheless, the refinery continued to be the primary source of fuel oil. During the years for which profit figures are available—1901 through 1905—PCO barely broke even on its sales of fuel oil to Iowa Standard, and the marketer's profit was small, considering the large quantities handled. In the peak year, 1905, fuel sales contributed only 17 per cent to the net profits of the Iowa company. There is no doubt that refined products were always the chief breadwinners.[14]

3

When Richmond replaced Whiting as the principal source of refined products, it might have seemed that Iowa Standard's near monopoly of the western market would be impregnable. The PCO–S.O. (Iowa) combination linked together high-volume crude purchasing, cheap pipeline and marine transportation, the largest refinery in California, an excellent kerosine refining process, and by far the most extensive marketing network in the West. Ironically, as PCO's facilities were completed, Standard's share of the market began to decline, although its sales volume continued to rise. From 1900 through 1910, its estimated share of the kerosine trade declined from 96.5 per cent to 82.7, and of the naphtha trade, from 96.6 to 67.5.[15]

As the decade opened, Standard was tightening its grip in its traditional way by buying out competitors. In 1902 it purchased the Arctic Oil Works, a manufacturer of lubricants and one of the few remaining large independent dealers in refined oils on the Coast. This pattern proved no longer effective, however, as light crudes were discovered which small refiners could process for nearby markets. At the time Richmond was completed, PCO counted twenty-nine other refineries in California with an estimated capacity of 11,000 barrels a day. Within two years, the number of refineries had grown to thirty-eight with a capacity of 16,000 barrels a day. Most were simple affairs designed merely to boil off the lighter fractions for the sake of road oil or asphalt residuum. The distillate from the heavy crude of the Los Angeles City and Kern River fields was largely used for stove distillate (a household heating oil), fuel oil, and some lubricants. But from the less heavy crude of the Whittier-Fullerton and Salt Lake fields, some refiners also turned out gasoline, engine distillate, and kerosine. So long as these refiners manufactured only the heavy products, they were not in conflict with Iowa Standard. Competition among themselves was limited by the California Asphaltum Sales Agency, an association of the larger refiners which pooled sales and maintained uniform prices. Most of the Los Angeles refiners sold their stove distillate to a local concern, the Diamond Oil Company.

S.O. (Iowa) did not sell asphalt and did not seriously compete in the stove distillate market. However, the company did have most of the market for light products and intended to keep it. Competition became intense and broke the market, especially in Southern California. According to H. M. Tilford, the asphalt refiners took any price they could get for their gasoline, engine distillate, and kerosine, which were really by-products. To some extent, Tilford's statement was an oversimplification, for a few refineries were operating on light crude that Tilford once had under contract and later let go.[16]

The principal competition developed in the Los Angeles area, as indicated in Table 9.

Table 9: Estimates of Competitors' Share of Kerosine Market

Year	Los Angeles District	S.O. (Iowa)'s Total Marketing Area
1901	13.9	3.9
1902	13.4	4.4
1903	23.4	6.0
1904	33.4	8.4
1905	28.2	8.1
1906	21.6	6.5

Source: *US* v. *SONJ*, Petitioner's Exhibits 388 and 390, VIII, 918, 921.

Obviously, Iowa Standard's hold on the kerosine market in Los Angeles was slipping in 1903. And the company's position in the engine distillate trade was probably worse because of the ease with which that product could be manufactured.

In 1904 an Iowa Standard ally turned into an opponent, small but formidable. Since 1898 Iowa Standard had been taking under contract the Puente Oil Company's refined oil, gasoline, and engine distillate. These purchases in 1903 supplied more than one-fifth of Standard's sales in the Los Angeles district. Because Puente's refinery was operating below capacity, its potential competition was even greater. Puente initiated the break with Standard. In February, 1903, more than a year before the contract expired, Vice President J. A. Graves suggested to W. S. Miller that it be renewed; otherwise, he wrote, Puente would need time to prepare to market its products again. Perhaps this canny executive was probing the significance to his company of a new factor, for the *Loomis* was beginning to bring Richmond's products to Southern California. When Miller refused to be drawn out, Graves agreed to postpone the discussion, but warned that Puente had a standing offer for its distillate from another company. Late in 1903, Breeden offered Graves a one-year contract for distillate at 5.25¢ a gallon. Graves asked for a five-year contract at 7¢. Translated into terms of crude prices, he was seeking an increase in the price of crude at the very time PCO was planning to rely on low-cost crude from Coalinga.[17]

The possibility of compromise faded when Graves resigned and Puente's merger with the Columbia Oil Company put new, adamant directors on its board. As the expiration date for the contract drew near, the *Bakersfield Californian* headlined, "Will Fight Rockefeller, Corporation at Chino Once in Conflict With the Octopus Again Clashes With It." Considering the disparity in their size, one may wonder at Puente's temerity. But with an assured crude supply that included some of California's lightest production, it was in a strong position. In addition to crude from the Puente Hills, the company had Columbia's light oil from the Fullerton field and a five-year contract with the Fullerton Oil Company. Early in the decade, both Columbia and Fullerton had sold crude to PCO, but their contracts were not renewed when Breeden proposed, as in the case of Puente, to reduce the price. To process this highly refinable crude, Puente had a $60,000 refinery capable of charging 600 barrels a day. Located at Chino, about thirty-nine miles east of Los Angeles, it was well situated to deliver engine distillate to irrigation works in Southern California.

Puente had been out of the market for six years. Could it break in again? Within a few months, the *Fullerton Tribune* reported that Puente was prospering, as its engine distillate trade grew. The paper claimed that a war was on between Standard and Puente, although neither would admit it. A Puente executive was quoted as saying, "We are going ahead selling our products at the market price and trying to make money for our stockholders. I know of no fight and look for no cut in prices. It is true that refined petroleum has declined about 3 cents in the east, and as our market price is regulated by eastern prices, of course, we are affected to some extent."[18]

Table 10 makes clear that the loss of Standard's patronage, effective April 1, 1904, did not seriously damage Puente's ability to move its goods.

Table 10: Comparison of Sales of Puente and S.O. (Iowa)

	1903		1904	
	PUENTE (bbls.)	*S.O. (Iowa)* *L.A. Dist.* *(bbls.)*	*PUENTE* (bbls.)	*S.O. (Iowa)* *L.A. Dist.* *(bbls.)*
Crude receipts	125,000	—	197,000	—
Crude refined	100,000	—	111,000	—
Sales of:				
Kerosine	15,000	65,000	8,000	65,000
Gasoline	5,000 ⎫		8,000 ⎫	
	⎬ 92,000		⎬ 119,000	
Eng. Distillate	16,000 ⎭		24,000 ⎭	
Stove Distillate	0	0	5,000	600
Residuum	55,000 ⎫		39,000 ⎫	
	⎬ 48,000		⎬ 893,000	
Crude	20,000 ⎭		50,000 ⎭	

Sources: For S.O.(Iowa), Annual Sales Statements; for Puente, Bureau of Corporations file #3323, National Archives.

Even though Puente's kerosine sales nearly ceased after the contract ended, falling to 65 barrels in April, 1904, by December they had climbed back to 968, which was more than half the figure for the same month the year before.

In January, 1905, H. E. Graves, Puente's secretary and the brother of J. A. Graves, made an optimistic report to the Puente stockholders despite some unfavorable market conditions. He admitted that the profitable market for light crude had disappeared. Prices of distillate had steadily declined, and Standard was, he said:[19]

> . . . entrenching itself strongly by placing storage tanks in centers of greatest consumption, with a view to delivering directly to consumers.
>
> The small Refiners in their efforts to dispose of their products are doing more to demoralize the market than the Standard.

The prospect for selling our share of the goods, in fact more distillate than last season seems to be good the coming season. . . .

The Coal Oil and Gasoline trade is very good. . . .

We are not losing any trade but seem to be gaining customers on the merits of our refined products.

The last official figures for Puente, for May, 1905, indicate that its sales volume of refined products was up 20 per cent over December, 1904. At that time, H. E. Graves described Puente's marketing activities as follows: It had tank stations at Los Angeles, Anaheim, and the Chino refinery. It shipped products all over Southern California and even a little to Arizona and San Francisco. It had broadened its appeal by bringing in Pennsylvania kerosine and gasoline and was preparing to sell Pennsylvania lube oils.

A later glimpse of Puente's progress, revealed by a Standard report on wholesalers for August, 1907, shows that Puente was leading all of Standard's competitors in the Los Angeles area and had more than doubled its sales of light products since August, 1904. Much later, in 1922, when the Shell Company of California bought the Puente-Columbia properties, it used the Puente marketing organization as a start for its own organization in Southern California. The old refinery it used briefly, too. Obviously, Puente was an effective challenger.[20]

Iowa Standard did not remain passive. In 1904 and 1905 it put in substations at Moneta, Anaheim, Colton, Azuza, and Corona in Southern California, which accounted for virtually all of its construction outside port cities for those years. Undoubtedly, the competition from Puente and the Los Angeles refiners was responsible for the new outlets.

Another aspect of the rivalry was a decline in prices. H. E. Graves told a Bureau of Corporations investigator, "After we began selling distillates last year they began reducing the prices wherever we went. The Standard invariably made the cuts. . . . They want all the business. They had nearly all of it before we began distributing." He saw no use moving into towns where prices were high: "The Standard would charge the full price until the day we got our wagons in there, and on that day the price would be reduced." He suspected that Standard sent the Penn Oil Delivery into Riverside, peddling house-to-house, to undersell grocerymen handling Puente's products. A Puente marketing executive, T. W. Okey, relayed a charge that an S.O. (Iowa) salesman told ranchers it would undersell Puente regardless of price.

When Breeden was asked if any salesman was authorized to make such a statement, he said "No." Asked if he was aware such statements had been made, he replied:

Well, I would like to say, in connection with the price in Southern California and vicinity of Los Angeles, that almost all of our competitors at that point are selling refined oils and distillates at less price than we are asking today [May 20, 1905]. In other words, they are cutting our open prices.

Breeden maintained that this had been going on for two or three years and that the original reductions had almost always been made by competitors. "Not invariably?" he was asked. "No, not invariably," he replied. "It is very hard to tell at all times who is the first to make the cut."[21]

In addition to charging Iowa Standard with cutting distillate prices, Okey blamed the company for initiating price cuts in kerosine from 9¢ to 7.5¢ a gallon and in gasoline from 15.5¢ to 14.5¢ during 1904. He explained that the price of gasoline did not decline as much because little gasoline was manufactured on the Pacific Coast. Standard could afford to let competing gasoline enter the trade at high prices in order to protect profits on its large trade. This is good logic. But, carrying it a little further, would Standard not have been reluctant to initiate price cuts on its other products, too, unless it was confident of driving the competition out of business in short order? Unfortunately, this possibility was not discussed. Breeden admitted selling kerosine below cost but explained simply, "We did this in order to stay in business; if we had not, the competitors would have taken the trade and we would have been out of the business."

The real leader in price cutting is hard to determine. Government investigators found the changes shown in Table 11 in Iowa Standard's kerosine "tank-wagon prices," and Puente's prices "to the Retail Trade, for lots of 1 to 5 bbls. or more" during 1904.

Table 11: Los Angeles Kerosine Prices per Gallon

	S.O. (Iowa)	Puente
November, 1903	10¢	selling to S. O. (Iowa)
March 2, 1904	9¢	under contract
April 1, 1904		9¢
June, 1904	8¾ ¢	
July, 1904	8½ ¢	
July 2, 1904		8½ ¢
July 12, 1904		7½ ¢
August, 1904	7½ ¢	

Source: Bureau of Corporations file #3323, National Archives.

Discussing Puente's figures, taken from its sales books, an investigator noted that he "had to depend on Bookkeeper that these prices were directly comparable owing to variety of prices to different sellers." A further uncertainty in establishing the price leader is the absence of any record of prices for the Los Angeles refiners. H. E. Graves had blamed these refiners in his report to the stockholders, though not in his statement to the Bureau of Corporations, for demoralizing the market.[22]

Moreover, while the price changes in Table 11 seem to show a relationship between the expiration of the Puente contract and a cut in price by Iowa Standard, the decline was actually part of broader trends. A comparison by the Bureau of Corporations of kerosine prices at Los Angeles and San Francisco shows that a gap of two cents a gallon was opened in mid-1901, and Los Angeles prices were not so buoyant thereafter. By the fall of 1903, while J. A. Graves and Breeden were still discussing a new contract, the gap in prices between Los Angeles and San Francisco had widened to five cents. This difference persisted throughout 1904, as prices in both districts declined. The decline that year was nationwide. For example, on March 2, 1904, the day Iowa Standard cut its Los Angeles price one cent, the Whiting refinery cut the price of 120° Water White kerosine to the Waters-Pierce Oil Company, 26 Broadway's marketer in the Southwest, by half a cent and by June 9 had made further cuts amounting, in all, to two and a half cents a gallon. If the whole story could be developed, it would probably show the market to have been a mêlée, a struggle for every customer, each company arguing price, transportation costs, quality of goods, availability, personal relationship, and so on, while a general decline in prices intensified the worries of oilmen and the satisfaction of consumers.[23]

Iowa Standard's competitors had grievances other than low prices. A Los Angeles refiner stated that whenever an independent set up a tank station in order to save on carload lots, the Iowa company would promptly put in one of its own and go after the business. Asked about his experience, he said, "Oh, I don't come in competition with them [S.O. (Iowa)]. I have to follow the Standard prices and I keep out of the field where they are very low." Another refiner stated that Iowa Standard salesmen used price cuts to persuade customers to cancel orders placed with other firms. More than that, he thought a man discharged by Iowa Standard for drunkenness whom he had hired and let go and who then was rehired by Iowa Standard, had been a spy. Investigators of the Bureau of Corporations did not secure confirmation of these charges.[24]

The most vocal critics of Iowa Standard were the house-to-house peddlers. Some complained that the company sold to customers at the same price it charged the peddler. Others continued to fire away at

Standard's so-called hidden companies, F. B. Joyce Oil Delivery, which carried on a peddling trade in San Francisco, and the Penn Oil Delivery, which peddled in Oakland, Los Angeles, and San Diego. Their contribution to Iowa Standard's sales was modest. In the last half of 1904, Joyce accounted for 2 per cent of the kerosine sales in the San Francisco district, while Penn made 7 per cent of the kerosine sales in the Los Angeles district and 16 and 18 per cent, respectively, in the San Diego and Oakland districts. Usually, these peddling outfits lost money on kerosine but made it back on other products. As mentioned earlier, H. E. Graves said that Penn was used as a competitive weapon to force grocers to buy from Iowa Standard. His charge indicates that by 1905 there could not have been much secrecy about its ownership. In fact, Graves said that both purchasers and sellers of oil generally knew that Penn belonged to Standard.[25]

Peddlers of independent oil resented these Standard peddling concerns. One Riverside peddler blamed Penn for forcing him out of business. He claimed that in February, 1904, shortly before Iowa Standard cut its price and Puente re-entered the market, the Iowa company stopped giving him a rebate. When he said he would buy elsewhere, Penn Oil wagons rolled into town and soon began selling at cut-rate prices. He bought from Puente, but its promise to help him meet Penn's prices proved empty. Another Riverside peddler managed to stay in business. His recollection was that Penn did not cut prices immediately. However, many people had the idea it was a Standard company and refused to buy its products until Penn reduced its price by a penny a gallon. This man met Penn's price, although Puente failed to protect his profit margin. In July, 1906, at the time he was interviewed, he was buying from both Standard and Puente. He wanted to take more from Puente, but Puente gave priority to supplying its own wagons. Meanwhile, the Penn name had been withdrawn about December, 1905, when Iowa Standard substituted its own as a part of a nationwide movement by 26 Broadway abolishing hidden companies.[26]

Price cuts in the Los Angeles area caused Iowa Standard's Los Angeles district to lose money on its kerosine business from 1904 through 1906, the last year for which figures are available. But these losses were made up on gasoline and other refined products. Investigators from the Bureau of Corporations concluded that Standard's price policy in Southern California was "mainly designed to exterminate competition," although Iowa Standard, from its point of view, was fighting a defensive battle, trying to protect its share of the market.

Whatever may have been the truth and ethics of the competitive situation, it is plain that the Iowa company lost its near-monopoly of refined oils irretrievably, as other refiners moved their products into the market. Puente, relying on light Fullerton crude, was by far the most successful. Others were Densmore-Stabler, running Whittier crude and distillate from Amalgamated's topping plants; Southern Refining, running Fullerton crude that PCO had let go; Union Consolidated, running Whittier-Fullerton and Ventura crudes and Amalgamated distillate; and Union, running its own Santa Maria and Ventura crudes.[27]

Of all Standard's competitors, Union had the greatest potential, primarily because of its production in the Santa Maria field. Prolific wells, high-gasoline content crude, and proximity to marine transportation provided Union with a low-cost product. Unlike Puente, Union was not limited by a small field and costly rail transportation. Its crude production rose sharply during 1907 and 1908, and in 1908 the company doubled the capacity of its Oleum refinery. For distribution purposes, Oleum was as well placed as Richmond. Moreover, Union had been selling fuel oil widely for years. It was marketing kerosine in Seattle and Portland at least as early as 1908, when it converted a steamer to make bulk deliveries to both of these ports and to San Pedro.

In March, 1908, Union's Seattle manager accused Standard of trying to drive his company out of business with deep price cuts in gasoline and kerosine. In four months the price of gasoline had declined 3¢ in San Francisco and 4¢ in Seattle, while kerosine fell off 0.5¢ in San Francisco and 1.5¢ in Seattle. These changes can be interpreted too simply, however, for statistics covering San Francisco and Seattle show that kerosine prices were in a long, slow decline, and that gasoline prices were fluctuating.

When Union published its *Annual Report for 1908*, it made no reference to the charge by its Seattle manager. "The prices of refined oils [kerosines] have been generally maintained along the coast," it stated, "[but] gasoline prices . . . have been reduced . . . owing to large importations of benzine from Sumatra." Although the report did not mention Standard as the importer, certainly the naphtha Standard brought in from Sumatra enabled Richmond to increase the flow of gasoline to its marketers. Nevertheless, Union was obviously undismayed by Standard's competition. It forecast that in 1909 all the production of its enlarged refinery would be sold at satisfactory prices.[28]

During these years Standard's own marketing plant was being substantially increased. Its facilities for tanker transportation in the Northwest were built up in 1906 and 1907 by additions at Portsmouth (Portland) and Seattle and by a marine terminal costing $80,000 at Tacoma.

The days when Tacoma received tank cars from Whiting and redirected them throughout Washington were gone forever. The old plant was sold to the Paragon Oil Company, which was later taken over by Union.[29]

During 1906 Standard also began construction of a marine terminal at Honolulu. The company for years had sold refined products, principally Star kerosine, through the Honolulu firms of C. Brewer & Company and Castle & Cook. In June, 1905, W. S. Miller sent George Mayer to Honolulu to establish the company's own agency. Miller had been aroused by Union's competition in light products and by the fact that another competitor sold most of the lubes in the Islands. He was dissatisfied, too, with a law requiring Standard to store its products in a government warehouse, consisting of a roof and a wire fence. Standard paid more of a fee than he liked, and the goods were pilfered. So Mayer was asked to secure the right to store products in the company's own warehouse. By the time the new station was ready, he had gained this permission from the Legislature.

One other hurdle for Standard was a vaguely worded statute, enacted in 1878, which apparently prohibited the sale of petroleum products with a flash test of less than 100° F.—in other words, gasoline. Though the law was ignored by all, E. S. Pillsbury, Standard's legal counsel in San Francisco, thought it imperative to have a written opinion from the Territorial Government. The Governor, pointing out that no one had ever been sued for selling gasoline, suggested to Mayer that the law be ignored. But Mayer, acting under Miller's instructions, refused to market any more gasoline except f.o.b. San Francisco. Subsequently, the Territory's Attorney-General offered a verbal opinion that the law did not apply to pure gasoline. Pillsbury refused to be satisfied until a test suit was arranged. In 1908, after the territorial Supreme Court had overruled a lower court to hold that pure gasoline was exempt, Standard's sales of gasoline at Honolulu promptly revived.[30]

Standard continued to use private sailing vessels to deliver packaged goods to Honolulu, but for its growing trade along the Pacific Coast it used an enlarged fleet of company-owned vessels to carry bulk oil. In October, 1906, the company paid Standard of New York about $250,-000 for the 12,000-barrel tanker, *Maverick,* and the 23,000-barrel *Barge 91*. Three months later these vessels docked at San Francisco after an eighty-two-day voyage from New York via the Straits of Magellan. California Standard used the *Maverick* primarily to carry products to the Northwest and *Barge 91* for crude and fuel oil deliveries. Shortly after they were acquired, the company also purchased the *Colonel E. L. Drake,* a 38,000-barrel tanker that was put to work transporting crude oil. With the addition of these vessels, Standard had five tankers and two barges in its ocean-going fleet, which remained unchanged until 1911.[31]

The company's river and harbor fleet was also expanded. Between 1905 and 1910 Standard added four more barges, a stern wheel steamer for river traffic, and two launches. The largest was the 7,600-barrel self-propelled steel barge, *Contra Costa,* built in 1908, but the most interesting was the launch, *Petroleum.* Constructed like a miniature tanker, it carried 20,000 gallons of kerosine, gasoline, and distillate around San Francisco Bay and the neighboring rivers. Its designer, R. L. Hague, Standard's newly hired marine architect, later left the company during World War I for the U.S. Shipping Board and, in time, became manager of Jersey Standard's Marine Department. One other little craft deserves mention as the first based away from Richmond. *Barge No. 6,* with a capacity of 650 barrels of fuel oil and two deck tanks for kerosine, was bought in 1909 for San Pedro just as the station there was relocated across the harbor at East San Pedro.[32]

By 1910 Standard was operating a total of eight river and harbor craft which, along with most of the ocean-going fleet, was directly tied into marketing operations. The increased use of waterborne transportation, despite the decline of crude purchases in the Santa Maria field, is clearly shown in Table 12.

Table 12: Water Transportation (Barrels)

Year	Coastal	Coastal—except Santa Maria	Harbor	River
1908	5,944,000	3,004,000	1,665,000	442,000
1909	5,440,000	3,502,000	1,504,000	554,000
1910	4,715,000	3,821,000	1,732,000	671,000

Source: Rohlfs to Rheem, Apr. 6, 1911, California Shipping Co. records.

Between 1900 and 1910, Standard's new plants were built primarily to take advantage of water transportation from Richmond, but late in the period there was also expansion inland to provide fuller coverage of the market. The company established a number of new substations, moved others, and made increases, too, in storage capacity. In these years, gasoline and engine distillate sales were rising, stimulated in large measure by an increasing number of consumers and motor vehicles, as Table 13 suggests.

Table 13: Substations and Sales of Naphthas[33]

Year	Appropriations for Substations		Sales of Naphthas (bbls.)		Auto & Truck Registration	Estimated Population as of July 1
	New	Re-located	Tank Wagon	Total	5 Western States	5 Western States
1908	4	3	186,000	514,000	25,670	4,058,000
1909	6	9	247,000	656,000	38,090	4,290,000
1910	9	6	334,000	833,000	58,040	4,519,000

The new stations were scattered throughout the West from Anacortes, Washington, to Bisbee, Arizona. Earlier, in 1906, the company's Idaho outlets had been transferred to the Continental Oil Company, but in this surge Standard set up stations as far east as Ely, Nevada, and Clifton, Arizona. Most of them were in smaller communities located between cities with older stations. The stations were, of course, essential to the tank wagon method of distribution, which was continuing its steady growth. A horse-drawn tank wagon normally served a territory twelve to fifteen miles in radius from a station, but in some cases it served customers as far as twenty miles away and traveled as much as forty or fifty miles in one long workday. Regardless of weather, the tank wagons made their routes because customers depended upon them. At times, this meant hitching up six horses to plow through mud, or substituting a sleigh with an improvised tank to get over snow-drifted roads.

A new mode of transportation, the motor truck, appeared just at the end of the decade. The first purchase was made toward the close of 1910, when the Oakland station bought a $3,500 truck (probably a Kelly) that was guaranteed to carry 8,400 pounds. A bed in back of the cab was used for transporting packaged goods; behind the bed was an eight-foot tank divided into compartments that held 100, 300, and 450 gallons. One day in the Oakland hills this truck emulated its horse-drawn contemporaries, rearing into the air as the heavily loaded tank pulled the back end toward the ground.[34]

Standard's sales of naphthas rose impressively in the latter part of the decade, but its share of the market declined from an estimated 84.6 per cent in 1906 to 64 per cent in 1908 before recovering slightly to 67.5 per cent in 1910. Perhaps the additional investment in stations arrested the decline temporarily. The increasing competition in naphthas was ominous because gasoline, and not kerosine, was the great oil product of the future. An evidence of gasoline's growing importance is to be seen in W. S. Miller's instruction to Rheem in the fall of 1906 that hereafter all Stove Gasoline should be delivered to the marketers under the brand name Red Crown. In 1908, for a first time the sales of all naphthas exceeded kerosine sales in volume, and in 1911 Red Crown sales alone outstripped those for kerosine.

Nevertheless, Standard's hold on the naphtha market was steadily weakening, probably because it ceased to buy out able rivals and failed to control the supply of refinable crude. The antitrust campaign may have caused the company to refrain from purchasing competitors. As for control of refinable crude, the company does not seem to have tried. Perhaps it despaired of success. In 1905 C. A. Canfield, one of California's foremost producers, had commented, "I think they [Standard] realize . . . that the conditions in California are entirely different from what they have been up against in other fields. . . . They can't control, nor no other corporation, the oil industry in California. There are too many fields easy of access to market that can be developed by individuals every day." Where there was refinable crude, there was bound to be a refiner, and his products were sure to find purchasers, especially when demand outran Standard's supply.[35]

4

Standard's competitive position in the lubricating oil market cannot be evaluated with certainty. Throughout the decade there were ten or twelve refineries in California making lubricants. Most of them produced merely the cheaper, heavier lubes. In 1908 Union, which had been selling residuum for skid oils, built four stills to enter the refined lube trade. At Los Angeles, Densmore-Stabler made the heavier engine lubes; it sold all its production to W. P. Fuller & Company. One of the few refineries turning out light oils was King-Keystone, which the King brothers had built at San Francisco in 1904 to manufacture lubes and asphalt from Kern River crude. The brothers also bought eastern stock for cylinder oils. In addition to these California rivals, Standard met with some competition from the highly refined oils of independent eastern companies.[36]

In Standard's western business, oils from Richmond displaced the company's eastern imports whenever possible. By 1906 Richmond produced enough oil to meet the marketers' needs except for a few special grades. The lube oil business differed from other oil lines because the variety of lubes was infinite. There were so many uses—cylinder oil, wool oil, floor dressing, harness oil, ice machine oil, and so on. Moreover, many were blended to the needs of the individual customer. Colonel

Merrill, manager of the Lubricating Department, seems to have asked Richmond once too often for a special oil, one of many lube matters over which 26 Broadway kept close control. Kenneth R. Kingsbury, who by 1905 was sharing in this control, admonished Merrill:[37]

> I hope you will appreciate my request that you will refrain from asking the Pacific Coast Oil Co. to make for you any special oils or products that are being offered by your competitors. It is against all rules and regulations, and I write to ask that you will hereafter refer all such matters to me.
>
> There is no objection to your submitting [a] sample or samples to Mr. Scofield, he, in turn to have same analysed and advise me specifications of such samples; but it will rest entirely with me as to whether we can or cannot furnish you duplicates or oils that would answer the same purpose as the samples submitted.

In one class of oils, Iowa Standard was ordered out of competition when it was told in October, 1903, to leave the trolley and street car trade to the Galena Signal Oil Company, 26 Broadway's principal supplier of railroad lubes. Since Galena was not quite ready to undertake the selling job, the westerners were asked to continue soliciting new business so long as their efforts were "not out of harmony with the desire of the Galena-Signal Company." Iowa Standard helped Galena's distribution by receiving and storing oil and delivering it to customers.[38]

The lube oil trade differed a little in structure from that for other products. Standard marketed kerosine primarily through retailers; gasoline, fuel oil, and lubes it commonly sold directly to the consumer. But in lubes Standard also dealt with jobbers, some of whom were compounders of specialized oils.

A sampling of instructions from New York suggests that the jobbers' business was secondary, wooed or spurned depending on the shifting balance of supply and demand. In January, 1901, Silas H. Paine, the long-time Manager of the Lubricating Oil Western Sales Department at 26 Broadway, told Merrill that his policy was to sell to jobbers only when doing so did not interfere with the company's direct sales to consumers. H. S. Morton, who eventually took over Paine's post, wrote in January, 1903, not to sell to jobbers and then modified this injunction, so long as jobbers paid the same prices as did consumers. In 1904 he reversed this rule. In January, Morton was writing that to meet competition from the East, Iowa Standard's marketers could buy from Richmond for as little as 10 per cent above manufacturing cost, and in June his instructions, briefed down, read, "Want biz of every oil jobber. Willing to sell right down to cost, or, if necessary, away below cost. Are willing to sell on 5 to 10% margin, exclusive of marketing expenses —in re Neutral Oils, Paff [Paraffin] Oils & Cyl. stocks to consuming trade, think 3 or 4 over net cost sufficient."

During 1905 Morton changed his tune again. In October, he ordered that selling eastern lubes to jobbers should stop when the stock on hand was exhausted. Subsequently, he specified, "Please make no further sales . . . of Eastern Neutral Oils to jobbers without first submitting the matter to me." Obviously, jobbers were of only marginal concern.[39]

The relationship between 26 Broadway and San Francisco in marketing lube oils is somewhat clearer than for other products because a few price policy books have escaped destruction. The lube oil business seems to have been more strictly controlled from New York than the trade in other products. Yet a measure of flexibility was allowed, at least in pricing. Morton's letters regarding sales to jobbers, mentioned above, are evidence on this point. On another occasion, he described a list of prices as the "lowest prices at which you can take any business." Similar instructions were given by C. E. Bedford concerning the sale of Vacuum's Atlas Engine Oil for the marine trade. He urged Iowa Standard to strive for a price equal to 35¢ a gallon, f.o.b. New York, but to accept not less than 24¢. If a sale was made at a substantial reduction, Bedford wrote, "We shall expect an explanation in detail."[40]

In other aspects of the lube business, New York laid down the law firmly. Morton wrote in 1903, "All printed matter of whatever nature should first be submitted to me. This covers not only advertising circulars or cards, but applies to price books, envelopes bearing advertisements, any change in letterhead, all matters of this nature." Kingsbury wrote on another occasion:

> The characteristics, individual tests and formulae of the different marine oils are such that, in no instances, and under no conditions, would you be warranted, through shortage of one brand in substituting another brand for it under the same name. . . . To attempt to deliver a Swan & Finch brand as Vacuum No. 1 Marine is most undesirable, is misleading, affects our reputation for stability and our general standing.

And, as noted above, Merrill was told to stop asking Richmond to make up special oils. Some months later he asked Morton if on minor matters, such as the packing of Mica Axle Grease for special business in an emergency, he could settle the matter with the PCO directly without going through New York. Otherwise, the business might get away. To this, Morton agreed.[41]

Over-all, the performance of the Lubricating Department was one of steady growth, with lubes regularly contributing about 10 per cent of the total sales income. The most notable new lube was Zerolene, a high priced oil for automobiles. Also known as Polarine, it was enjoying a wide sale by 1911 and was being shipped East in substantial quantities. But the principal demand for lubricants still came from industrial plants. Standard's leading districts for lube sales were San Francisco, Seattle, and Portland, although Los Angeles had led all others in naphtha and kerosine sales since 1908. Los Angeles did not take the lead in lubricating oils until 1918, when the demands of the automobile age on the company and the industry were already well advanced.[42]

XIII

WILDCATTING
FOR SECURITY

The clash between Standard and the Coalinga producers late in 1906, just as Richmond's capacity was doubled, pointed up the danger of relying almost entirely on purchased crude. 26 Broadway sought protection against this threat of starvation by establishing a producing department in the California company and giving it money to develop its own production. Curiously, the company's executives did not seem to welcome this assistance, at least not in the form of aggressive, free-spending, and perhaps arrogant, producing men. From 1907 through 1910, the story of the Producing Department is the clash of wills of determined men and the growing pains of an inexperienced organization. Though Standard's usually effective executives stumbled for a time, they gradually laid the foundation for a large and successful department. It must be admitted, however, that producing activities scarcely influenced the fortunes of the company until after 1910.

2

While 26 Broadway pumped millions of dollars into PCO to build crude oil storage, pipelines, a refinery, and a tanker fleet, one function of PCO atrophied. Production of crude declined in importance relatively and even absolutely. PCO's refinery runs increased from 358 barrels a day in 1901 to 17,502 in 1906, but crude production fell off from 485 barrels a day in 1901 to 267 in 1905 and, crippled by a brush fire at Pico, to 167 in 1906. At that time the investment in producing lands and wells amounted to only $480,000. Three years earlier Scofield had made one hard-luck effort to expand Pico Canyon production, ordering CSOW #32 drilled 500 feet off the apex of the anticline along which the old California Star wells had been strung. From February, 1903, to March, 1905, the drillers fought water, caving formations, hard strata at steep angles, and inferior casing down to 3,090 feet. The completed well made sixty barrels a day, a "disappointment" Superintendent Walton Young called it, compared to the big wells other companies were getting in the Santa Maria field. Next year, when Scofield set Young to deepening the well, he ran into a new problem. The casing parted,

333

leaving in the hole debris that had to be drilled out of the way. Tiny production and little prospect of more—that was the state of PCO's oil lands when negotiations for a new contract with California Oilfields, Limited, its principal crude supplier, deadlocked late in 1906. When other Coalinga and Santa Maria producers also proved uncooperative, 26 Broadway had to think of turning to producing for itself. But there was no skilled executive in the California organization who could head an active campaign of land acquisition and drilling. A new man and new capital had to be provided.[1]

The man 26 Broadway chose was John F. Eckbert of The Carter Oil Company, a prominent Standard affiliate in West Virginia and Ohio. Eckbert had been well-schooled in producing by Colonel John J. Carter, with whom his fortunes would continue to be linked during much of his stay in California. His mentor, the redoubtable Colonel, had one of the most attractive oil success stories of the later nineteenth century. Carter had been brought to the United States at the age of five as a penniless Irish orphan. When he was twenty, he won the nation's highest honor, the Congressional Medal of Honor, at Antietam and came out of the Civil War a brevet colonel. A dozen years later in the Bradford fields in Pennsylvania he made his first venture in oil, and from that time on he was never out of the oil game. To gain capital, Colonel Carter in 1894 sold 26 Broadway a majority interest in his company, which he continued to manage. Both the company and the Colonel were highly regarded at the New York headquarters.

Eckbert was a Carter favorite and a man of merit in his own right —"the best man in his line the S ever had," wrote Milton Stewart. As we have noted, in 1899 Eckbert accompanied C. F. Lufkin to California and the following year turned down a permanent assignment there. In November, 1906, he accepted his new commission after a visit with John D. Archbold and others at 26 Broadway. It happened that Colonel Carter was in New York preparing to leave on a mission to Japan when his lieutenant was summoned. The Colonel, who was an inveterate diarist, penned a warm entry: "Another of my boys fixed."[2]

After arriving in San Francisco about the first of December, Eckbert set out for the oil fields looking for properties yielding refinable oil that might be leased or purchased. He reported favorably on the Santa Maria, Coalinga, and Midway fields and was told to see what could be acquired. In Santa Maria, he found that Pinal could be bought for about $2,000,-000. Eckbert was authorized to offer a little over half that figure on condition that Standard be allowed to test the wells for thirty days, but Pinal turned him down. In Coalinga, he did better, purchasing three companies—Oil City Petroleum and 28 Oil for $855,000, and Independence Oil for $133,000. These companies were operating 480 acres on Section 28 in the heart of the Eastside field, producing over 2,000 barrels of light crude daily. Although the properties were poorly equipped and required an additional outlay for repairs, they offered an opportunity for further development. Standard ordered five more wells drilled as soon as the purchases were completed. The first well, using casing purchased locally, was finished in 1907, but the others were delayed by tardy deliveries from the East. At the end of the year, production was actually down a little. A second group of five wells was delayed because of a lack of housing for more drillers. It was hardly an auspicious beginning for the new Producing Department.[3]

Save for the purchases at Coalinga, Eckbert's other recommendations went unheeded, probably because the pressure for crude seemed off after California Oilfields and the Pinal group of companies signed new contracts in the spring of 1907 and Standard began opening the Midway field. Indeed, it is conceivable that Scofield and Rheem viewed Eckbert's mission more as a hedge against failure in their contract negotiations than as a substitute for crude purchases. Their primary concern was to keep the refinery operating regardless of whether crude oil was bought or was their own production. Eckbert and Carter, by contrast, thought solely in terms of producing. Carter wrote, after visiting Eckbert on his way to Japan, "They have a fine field open for their labors; if they get in there now, money will be made. . . . The business of oil producing here with the S.O.C. yet is in an indifferent state. They may clear it up, but they must work. It seems to me the S.O.C. do not realize the importance of the business."[4]

Early in 1908, Eckbert listed for Carter some of his rebuffs. His recommendation to buy the E. E. Jones properties in the Midway was not acted upon, nor was his recommendation of the Kreyenhagen and other lands south of Coalinga. Rheem had talked agreeably of asking for $100,000 to spend in leasing and developing land south and southeast of Coalinga, but no action was taken. In the Coalinga Eastside, Eckbert sought to lease seven sections from the Southern Pacific. In June, 1907, E. E. Calvin, the railroad's vice president, offered to lease them at a ⅛ royalty, provided that the royalty oil be delivered to the Southern Pacific at its option and wells be drilled to offset wells on adjoining properties. Although Eckbert thought Calvin's terms too high, he proposed without success that the matter should be discussed with 26 Broadway. Eckbert also urged the purchase of the Pleasant Valley Farming Company in the Coalinga Westside field for $768,000. Part of its property had been leased to companies which were producing about 1,700 barrels a day of heavy crude in the spring of 1907. Again he was turned down. When Eckbert called for an active campaign for oil land in the Los Angeles area, he was told that Standard was not interested. To have his recommendations so regularly rejected could hardly have improved his temper, which was not the best anyway. "John has many kindly traits . . . ," Carter noted in his diary, "[but] at times he gets the 'cusseds' for a season when he is exasperating and mean." It is not surprising that Eckbert soon fell out with the California management; he and Rheem, particularly, were at swords points.[5]

One move took place in the spring of 1907 that may have been designed to limit his authority. On May 15, J. M. Atwell was appointed general superintendent under Eckbert. Atwell was a long-time friend of Rheem. He had run the warehouse at Richmond, held various posts in the Pipe Line Department, and most recently had helped out in the Marine Department after Breeden resigned. Though his varied experience had not included producing, he was a fair and friendly man who was liked and respected and who knew something of the oil fields through his work on the pipelines. But one wonders if Eckbert chose him in preference to bringing out an experienced producer.

Eckbert's judgment was also checked upon by a frequent practice of sending other advisers on tour with him. On one important trip in the fall of 1907, Eric Starke, chemist in Rheem's department and Scofield's counselor on petroleum lands, accompanied Eckbert. H. M. Storey, the general superintendent of the Pipe Line Department, went along, too. In October, the three men spent eleven days inspecting by auto and mule team the ranches of Truxton Beale and William S. Tevis, sons of General Beale and Lloyd Tevis, in the mountains between the Sunset field and Fort Tejon. They agreed that oil might be discovered there, but time and money would be required to find it.

Following this trip, Storey proposed a fundamental change in exploring for oil. He wrote to Scofield:

> A hasty survey of territory so extensive as we have just seen, while in some instances [it] might be of value, depending upon the territory, in this case has been largely lost energy. . . . With what knowledge I have of California and its broken surface conditions, I feel convinced that an engineer with some idea of rocks and . . . the ability to discern between igneous, sedimentary, and altered rocks, could do much toward producing the results desired. I do not claim that the application of scientific principals [sic] to surface structure will develop oil, but I do claim that careful study by the means suggested will reduce the percentage of failure and consequently increase the percentage of success.

H. M. Tilford

Col. J. J. Carter

Eastern directors at Coalinga office, November, 1910. Front row seated: J. M. Atwell, W. W. Richardson. Center row seated: Unknown, W. S. Rheem, J. C. Donnell. Standing: W. C. Teagle, Unknown, J. J. Carter, H. C. Folger, Jr., A. C. Bedford, H. M. Storey

Well #2, Section 30, Midway, March, 1910

View of "Twenty-Five Hill" and Standard's Jameson camp from Fourth Street in Taft, 1910

In Storey's opinion, the company could well afford to employ such a man to study California's anticlines and indicate the most likely prospects. "I feel . . . that the condemning of miles of territory for oil purposes by hurried glances at the country is absurd."[6]

Storey's suggestion may have been an implied criticism of the producing manager, but it is possible, too, that he got his idea from Eckbert. Eckbert wrote Carter in December that he had "again" advised setting up a "bureau of information." Perhaps Storey was reflecting a Carter practice described by Eckbert, or perhaps he was influenced by Starke's great respect for science, as well as his own experience. At this time nothing came of Storey's proposal, but his letter has been accepted by later generations of Standard men as a landmark in the gradual acceptance of geology in the company's operations.[7] Subsequent developments suggest that probably Storey was unimpressed with both Eckbert and Starke.

3

As 1907 wore on, it became apparent that neither California Oilfields nor the Santa Maria producers could live up to their promised deliveries. Richmond was distressingly short of crude. Perhaps this explains why late in the year Eckbert was allowed to start a major wildcatting venture in Monterey and San Benito counties. With the concurrence of Starke, he picked up over 30,000 acres in the Peachtree and Topo valleys. In December ten wells were authorized. Rank wildcats they were, but a seepage of 42° gravity oil provided a basis for hope.[8]

It is hardly a coincidence that in January, 1908, Archbold sent a cablegram to Colonel Carter, who was still in Japan trying to save the International Oil Company: "Very important that you at the earliest possible moment be in California with a view to extending producing operations there. Will you undertake their direction?" Carter's long record of success in exploration and producing was reason enough for the offer, but the fact that he had made a scouting trip to California for 26 Broadway in the spring of 1905 undoubtedly was also in Archbold's mind. At that time, the Colonel had been especially favorably impressed with the Santa Maria–Lompoc area and had come away "fully satisfied" that a number of other large fields lay undiscovered. Carter decided to accept Archbold's proposal.[9]

A month later he sailed through the Golden Gate and stepped off the ship to a warm welcome from Eckbert. He paid a quick visit to the headquarters, where he talked over the problems of California Standard, and then went home to Titusville and on to New York for instructions. Armed with what Eckbert had told him, Carter advised the Executive

Committee of the conditions in California, including the "want of harmony between the different parties." Perhaps he repeated a criticism noted in his diary:

> The objection to the organization in California is: It is not well organized; there is too much division of authority, no one is responsible to some one—except to Scofield—and he delegates his authority to men who are clerks and not operators—or business men of experience. The men are not responsible to the man above, but to anyone who chooses to command.

Carter's view may have been true, if lacking in sympathy for Scofield. Scofield had come to Standard when PCO was a small company. As 26 Broadway poured money into PCO after 1900, it grew rapidly. Doubtless, Scofield relied on the department heads, well-schooled in Standard's methods, to carry on the bulk of the company's business, while he personally handled a miscellany of items in an informal fashion. Colonel Carter, imbued with military principles, could hardly have approved.[10]

The Executive Committee told Carter to set a goal of 20,000 barrels a day for 1908. Since California Standard's current production amounted to no more than 2,800 barrels daily, this was a staggering request. In the circumstances, Carter asked for full authority to act, subject only to H. M. Tilford's approval. He got it. To keep the record straight, Carter wrote out his understanding of his mission: "To push operations to a finish and if possible obtain new production for the use of your refinery, either by drilling or purchase, which may aggregate 20,000 barrels of oil per day in 1908." To achieve this goal, he was authorized

> . . . to buy material, employ men, drill wells, and organize the Producing Department . . . to purchase oil producing property if same can be had at prices that should warrant their purchase, submitting the proposition and the purchase price to you [Tilford] for your approval. . . . To have complete control of the Producing Department . . . subject only to your control and orders, *always* ready and willing to be in harmony and perfect accord with the gentlemen having charge of your company in California, but not subject to their orders.

Carter went on to note that the expenditure on the Monterey County wildcats would probably be high and the outcome uncertain. Coalinga, too, would require immediate heavy drilling expenditures in order to speed crude production. "I am to push *this work* for *oil*, not *economical results*." Carter specified that he would take men with him to California and listed the companies from which he planned to buy equipment.

He seemed to have covered all the possible sources of disagreement save one—the possibility that Tilford would not support him. When the Executive Committee approved his statement, J. A. Moffett remarked, "We would not give such authority to many men . . . [but] we know you will use the authority properly." In a single sentence, Tilford replied that it would be "satisfactory" for Carter to take charge of the Producing Department on the basis outlined. Hindsight suggests that Tilford agreed without enthusiasm.[11]

Even before leaving for California, Carter approved Eckbert's recommendation to buy out the Hanford Oil Company's Section 28 for $500,000. The purchase would save the royalty on the leases Standard had bought from the Oil City and 28 Oil companies and would complete its ownership of the section. Shortly after he reached the Coast, he plunged into a tour of the oil fields. Carter was sixty-five and lame in one knee, but his enthusiasm was inexhaustible. After examining a suite of offices in the Sheldon Building in San Francisco, to which the company was returning from Oakland, he commented, "I don't think the Producing Department will occupy the rooms very long, as it is my purpose to go into the field instead of staying in San Francisco." The third day after his arrival he ordered 20 drilling rigs and the fourth day, at 7:17 A.M., Sunday, March 29, he boarded a train for Los Angeles.[12]

With Eckbert and Starke, he began his whirlwind tour by inspecting the properties of W. H. Murphy, of Detroit, in the Whittier field and the Coyote Hills nearby. He made a cursory examination partly at the request of J. A. Moffett, who was a friend of Murphy, although Carter was potentially interested in any oil lands. The condition of the Murphy holdings he found unimpressive. At Whittier, the wells were producing about 700 barrels a day, but they were poorly maintained, badly equipped, and menaced by water which the field management did not know how to handle. The Coyote Hills property had two deep wells that were producing about 500 barrels a day, but quite erratically. "In short," Carter wrote, "it has been an expensive plaything, and an unprofitable undertaking."

The day before Carter sent his report to Moffett, he mailed the same report to Archbold with some further remarks. Obviously, there was a considerable difference in his mind between what the properties were and what they might become. Carter told Archbold that $1,500,000 "would not be *unreasonable,* and might be *cheap*" for the Murphy lands. He wanted Archbold to take an option so that he could make a more careful examination with the idea of purchasing because "first, it is well located; second, because it is a splendid acreage, and last, because it has a present production which we need in our business. . . . Don't let it get away from you."[13]

Eckbert and Starke held similar views. Starke contended that the wells had been drilled too near the fault lines on both properties and that deep drilling on the sides would bring a large production. He gave as another reason that buying the Murphy lands would ward off competitors: to "remove from the Los Angeles market a large amount of easily refinable oil."[14]

Late in April, when Murphy was in New York, he offered to sell his holdings for $6,000,000, a price 26 Broadway regarded as too high. Murphy then asked on what terms Standard would be willing to take a lease. Carter agreed that $6,000,000 was indeed too much, but suggested a lease for a one-third royalty on the existing wells and a sliding scale ranging from one-tenth on new wells producing 100 barrels a day or less to one-quarter on wells producing over 500 barrels. Although this would have made a liberal offer, either Murphy or 26 Broadway refused to consider it.[15]

After less than a day at Whittier and the Coyote Hills, Carter and his party had hurried on. He stopped briefly at the Salt Lake field west of Los Angeles, which he had visited in 1905. He decided to secure land near there, for he believed that Salt Lake was part of the same line of deposits as the Murphy properties. Next he crossed the mountains to Kern River in the San Joaquin Valley, where he listened to stories of the pipeline men concerning the field. In 1905 he had predicted that Kern River would be dead in a year or two because of water infiltration. Carter recognized that his prophecy had been clearly disproved and that the field would last because "the oil seems to be forced to its present bed by water pressure."[16]

In Bakersfield the party picked up Elmer E. Jones, a convivial, openhanded speculator in oil claims on government lands. Over a year earlier a recommendation of Eckbert that Standard buy one section in the Midway field and half of two others from Jones had been rejected. On the way to McKittrick, they looked over the Jones holdings in the flat land east of Midway. When Starke offered to show Carter seepages and gas outcrops, Carter was satisfied, saying that was all he wanted to know. Starke knew the territory well. About 1897 he had recommended it to Lloyd Tevis as oil land and had spoken highly of it ever since.[17]

Standard's scouts had been over the Midway area more than once. In 1900 Charles H. McCready had traveled there. In the winter of 1902, C. F. Lufkin, a veteran oil property appraiser from the Ohio Oil

Company, visited the territory while reporting on the Associated Oil Company for E. H. Harriman of the Southern Pacific. Lufkin examined a Midway company, undoubtedly Chanslor & Canfield, and wrote Archbold that it might be worth $1,500,000, just half the price its owners were asking. Carter did not visit the Midway in 1905, but Eckbert's first recommendation, in December, 1906, was favorable to the field. Possibly he was influenced by Starke. Eckbert volunteered what would later prove to be a significant guess: the possibility "of getting good wells of lighter gravity East of the present production by deeper drilling." Standard showed its interest in Midway oil by laying a pipeline in 1907, but it remained for Colonel Carter to put the company into the field as a producer. After seeing the Jones land, Carter and his party stopped for the night at a sheep camp and saloon near McKittrick. There, on April 1, 1908, Carter made a fateful decision, taking an option from Jones on the Big Four Oil Company's Section 30 on the flank of the field, just three miles from Standard's pump station.[18]

The arrangement Carter made was a shrewd one. In return for an option, he agreed to advance the Big Four as much as $10,000 for a well up to 2,000 feet deep. If it should be a producer, yielding 50 to 100 barrels a day, Standard could buy the quarter section on which it was located for $150 an acre, or, if it produced over 100 barrels, for $250. It was agreed, too, that Standard thereafter would finance a well on each of the other three quarter-sections under the same option arrangement. The purchase price, however, was not payable until the Big Four received a patent from the government on its oil claim and had transferred to Standard a clear title. This was not just a routine precaution; the status of government lands was very uncertain because of squatters' claims. To Tilford, Carter explained:

> If we attempt to take title from the government, we have to fight the squatter, and incur public condemnation as—a rapacious monopoly whose sole aim is to get rich on the patrimony of the poor. If we take title from the squatter, we have to pay all the bills, give the squatter a big profit; and incidentally and financially stand behind the squatter, while he fights his rapacious neighbors to a finish and a patent. . . . In either case it takes time, patience, and money. These [considerations] . . . are given, not to show the lion in our pathway, but to indicate the time and money required to brush him out of our way in order to produce oil in California. . . .
>
> The good thing about this is—if we got the section from the government or the squatter, we would have to drill the first well, which would cost from $10,000 to $25,000: this well costs us only $10,000. There are

wells on both sides of Section 30, so that, the chances are more than even, we will have to pay the $160,000 for the whole section; and thus get a splendid property at a minimum price. . . . I consider the deal a good one!

Colonel Carter, it must be confessed, was less than candid in describing the location. To say that there were wells on both sides of Section 30 was stretching the truth. The belt of wells along the hills from Maricopa to Fellows ran diagonally across one corner of the section, and on only one side had there been substantial drilling. Actually the property, which edged out into the flat ground, was something of a wildcat proposition. But better than Tilford, of course, Carter knew that risks had to be taken to win production, and he had ably protected Standard against excessive costs.[19]

After stopping at Midway, Carter drove on to Coalinga and crawled into a filthy bed at Standard's camp. The next morning he decided to build twenty cottages, a machine shop for repairing equipment, a blacksmith shop, and a large stable. He wrote Tilford, "We must provide for housing our men better. Good men will not stay. . . ." And he added, "In the extreme warm weather of this section, the men cannot get the necessary rest, they break down and have to go away, or quit before breaking down; in either case the company loses the man." As for the oil property itself, he thought it "fine."[20]

From Coalinga, Carter pushed on over rough mountain roads to Peachtree Valley in Monterey County, where Union, the Lone Oak Oil Company, and Standard were drilling. Topo Valley, nearby, impressed him more. He sent Archbold photographs of a great outcrop of asphaltum along with a rhapsodic comment:

> This bed of asphaltum is up against the granite wall—the plutonic rock of the ancient world—behind which the hydrocarbons could not pass, so at the base of the granite barrier the bitumen found a resting place, while the lighter products resolved themselves into their original forms. These airy products did not take their flight until they demonstrated their chemical strength by dissolving the granite barrier into the original constituents. By going a little deeper, oil in its liquid form, oozes from the open wound and points to the reservoir beyond—the Topo and Peachtree valleys. . . .
>
> The company has gathered together 50,000 [acres] of as desirable wildcat land as I ever saw with earmarks to capture the most skeptical oil smeller. The future alone can tell the story of the hidden rocks. We have now three wells drilling in the Peachtree Valley, so that before the snow of another winter, we should be able to say what our harvest in this section would be. I look for nothing but good tidings and profitable results, and yet I am neither a prophet nor the son of one.

Carter wound up this initial, swift review of his domain by locating five wells on the Topo leases. At midnight, Sunday, April 5, just one week after his departure, he was back in San Francisco.[21]

4

More exciting prospects lay ahead. Shortly after his return Carter learned from William Graham, the manager of California Oilfields, Limited, at Coalinga, that its property might be for sale. The next day he was invited to spend a week end there, an invitation which he hailed as the "Big Thing." "Of course," he wrote Tilford, "I apprehend the price will be prohibitive; but I shall not pale before anything nor refuse to buy the earth, if the 'fulness thereof' be thrown in as an inducement."[22]

Before leaving, he mailed to New York reports on his field trip, took an option on the Talara Oil Company lease near the Big Four property, and issued "General Order No. 1," which established a structure for the Producing Department. Carter designated Eckbert as general manager, Atwell as superintendent, and Starke as chemist and geologist. In the accompanying "Special Order No. 1," he distinguished between the types of communications that should be directed to himself, Eckbert, and Atwell. With these chores completed, he and Eckbert were on their way. Carter had visited the California Oilfields property in 1905, when he admired it as "the cream of the territory." By buckboard, auto, and shanks' mare, he again inspected the COF holdings, which he called "the finest in California." It was a rugged outing for a man of his age. "Climbing over rocks," he admitted, "was not easy for the lame soldier." But, "if S. O. Co. could only be induced to buy [the property], it would be the biggest card ever played for it in California." Back in San Francisco, he conferred with Scofield and Rheem over the prospects for oil. He told them there were three ways to supply the refinery, "1st buy production, which would cost millions; 2nd buy the land and drill; and 3rd wildcat, which would not yield oil immediately and might not at all." Carter thought the first two were the practical choices, although either would "cost many millions." COF was, of course, a rare opportunity. Carter also mentioned his keen interest in the Southern Pacific lands at Coalinga that Eckbert had gone after a year earlier. The railroad held the alternate sections there. These, plus COF's holdings and Standard's Section 28, nearly blanketed the Eastside field, which produced a prime refining oil. Scofield agreed to arrange a conference with E. E. Calvin of the Southern Pacific.[23]

When Carter talked with Calvin, he tried to win Calvin's approval for a leasing arrangement under which Standard would operate the lands and supply the railroad with fuel oil. The railroad executive replied, "Our present policy is to neither lease nor sell any of our lands—particularly any lands likely to produce fuel oil." Calvin was supported by Professor E. T. Dumble, the geologist who managed the railroad's oil properties. Dumble said they did not think it wise to lease oil lands, particularly at "nominal royalties." Asked what "nominal royalties" meant, he responded that Coalinga owners were being offered one-third, a prohibitive figure to Carter's mind. When Carter asked if there was any way by which he could get six sections on the Eastside, Calvin stated that he was preparing to drill on three of them but would entertain an offer. Obviously, he was less inclined to deal than he had been a year earlier when he had offered the land at one-sixth royalty. One-sixth, Carter wrote Archbold, he would willingly pay if he had to. But he saw little hope in Calvin's new position. "Here, then, is a closed door, unless you can do something in New York that will grant the boon I seek. . . . I want these sections, cannot you get them for me?"

Carter also urged Archbold to name a price for an option he hoped to get on the California Oilfields, Limited.[24]

> It has never been my good fortune to see a better equipped property!
> . . . If I could buy it at $12,000,000, I would recommend it strongly; but I
> fear I cannot get it at any price, certainly not less than $15,000,000,
> maybe $20,000,000. Would you entertain it at any of the prices named?
> . . . What I want is that property and the railroad lots. . . . In such an
> event . . . [the] pipelines and refinery will be safeguarded to a finish! . . .
> I think I have pointed the way to success. Will you follow the light thus
> given, or take your chances in following the uncertain wildcatter?

While waiting for a reply, Carter bought the Sonntag property at Coalinga, approved plans for the Coalinga camp, sent Atwell to Midway with instructions to put together a block of eight or ten sections that would include Section 30, and set out again for Southern California. Poor weather and absent owners thwarted him, but he went on to King City and bought more land in the Topo Valley on Starke's recommendation. Then bad news came in a letter from Tilford:[25]

> You are doubtless aware there is still due from the California Oil Fields,
> Ltd. . . . about 12,000,000 barrels. . . . On account of this, in connection
> with certain other reasons we do not think it advisable to consider the
> question of buying their producing property. There might be an oppor-
> tunity from time to time to purchase at a reasonable price some existing
> producing property, but outside of this . . . we will have to devote our
> efforts to developing new fields, and it is along these lines we would sug-
> gest your devoting your efforts.

It was a furious Carter who read the concluding lines of the letter. So he was to settle down to the life of a wildcatter! A letter drafted in his diary, though evidently not sent, described his predicament in California. Wishful thinking had led producers to overvalue their properties and led the company's refiners and salesmen to believe that rivers of oil would flow from the mountain sides at the touch of a drill. It was a delusion that he himself had entertained in 1905. He now realized that territory which might have been purchased earlier at reasonable prices could not be had except for the expenditure of millions. But it was better to buy before costs pushed prices still higher. In 1907 the company had spent, including depreciation, 60¢ a barrel to produce oil at Coalinga and $2.44 at Pico Canyon. Other producers were making only a little profit, and those with contracts at low prices were producing at a loss.

Carter marshaled the reasons why the company's best hope was to buy producing property: It needed oil for the refinery and pipeline, it would be cheaper and quicker to buy than to wildcat, purchasing crude would cost more as prices rose, and the amount of refinable oil and oil territory within reach of the pipelines was limited. Elaborating on the cost of wildcatting, he pointed out that the crude deposits were scattered; consequently, it was necessary to buy or lease large tracts before entering upon the search for production. Transportation, timber, and labor were expensive. Pipelines had to be installed. All these costs built up the cost of opening new territory. Carter concluded that it was "cheaper, better, and safer to buy a bird in the hand than go gunning for one in the bush."[26]

He discussed Tilford's letter with Scofield at length and stated he would do all he could "to retrieve the error of judgment of New York." The Colonel noted that Scofield was glad he was staying to help them out, saying that his "presence was worth lots . . . in moral effect." Nevertheless, Scofield did not share Carter's views.

Even as Tilford's admonition to wildcat was traveling West, Scofield sent Tilford a personal letter denying that the COF and Southern Pacific properties offered the only sure way of supplying sufficient crude for the refinery. Since Carter had talked of going to New York to correct Tilford's erroneous conclusions concerning California producing matters, Scofield and his associates evidently wanted their views before Tilford. They rejected a gloomy view of the future. Even if COF could not be bought (and they were sure the price would be too high), and the Southern Pacific lands could not be leased, the company was in no more trouble than it had surmounted before. There were 20,000,000 barrels still due on contracts in the Coalinga and Santa Maria fields, and the producers had learned the risks involved in shutting down wells "to force us to pay an extreme price." There was no other company in California prepared to handle refinable crudes on a large scale. Moreover, enough drilling was going on so that additional light crude would surely become available. The western executives agreed that "a substantial production of our own, as a balance of power and factor in regulating the price of refinable crude" was desirable, but they did not think an extravagant price should be paid.

Scofield concluded:[27]

> Mr. Miller, Mr. Rheem, and myself have discussed very fully this entire subject. . . . As you are aware we have been here many years and are pretty familiar with the general situation. . . . We have had confidence in the views of Mr. John Page and many of our field men, like Mr. Storey and Mr. Atwell, also Dr. Starke, and we think that our combined judgment as to the future . . . is entitled to material weight. . . . Colonel Carter has been in California about one month; he has spent about three weeks . . . in the field and covered as much ground as it was possible for him to do in that time, and his conclusions are naturally based upon . . . the country he has visited. We believe, however, that there are along the great oil belts of California, great possibilities of future production. . . .

Along with his letter, Scofield sent Tilford a copy of a seven-page summary on California Oilfields, Limited, which he had prepared for Carter. It took a skeptical view of the potential of the COF lands. Carter flatly contradicted the memo: "In all my experience I never saw as compact a production, with as much fine drilling territory in sight, sure to produce large quantities of good oil."[28]

The Colonel was not a man to knuckle under. On April 30, he sent his resignation to Tilford, saying he was not qualified to lead a wildcatting campaign. The day this letter was posted, a telegram from Tilford rubbed salt into his wounds. It pertained to the option Carter had taken on an eighty-acre lease in Midway belonging to the Talara Oil Company. The lease, which had a single well producing 120 barrels a day of 20° gravity crude, could be had for $75,000 and a royalty of one-eighth. "Price seems high . . . ," Tilford wired. "Is the crude refinable? What do you estimate property will produce . . . ? Do you mean ⅛ royalty to be paid for all crude oil produced? What is your estimate of how long it will take to pay back purchase price?" To these "irrelevant questions," Carter replied curtly, "The price is not too high in my opinion, or I would not have presented it. . . . I approve the purchase and that is as far as I can go in justice to the Standard Oil Company and myself."[29]

To Archbold, Carter then wrote a brief, frank note, enclosing copies of his correspondence with Tilford. "It is unnecessary for me to add anything . . . to convince you that I can not fill your expectations with the conditions surrounding me. . . ." He told Archbold that he was determined to leave California. Carter's state of mind is reflected in an entry in his diary for May 1:[30]

> I am satisfied, no one with sufficient knowledge of the business, can run the producing department under Mr. Tilford. He is not large enough for the business. I am as well, yes better pleased, for I am weary of these bosses who know nothing of the business.
>
> It has been my purpose to organize the oil department on broad lines with substantial properties to draw from which would protect the investment here; but Tilford cut all that off early—so I give up the battle.

As he awaited word from 26 Broadway, he recorded this poignant note regarding his mission to California:[31]

> If Jno. [Eckbert] but knew it, I came here to save him. . . . I owed as much to one of my pupils, but it is a question if he appreciates it. I don't care; it was my duty. . . . Friendship with me is an abstract of love, if not the same so I can't do otherwise than perform the duty of a friend to the boys I have.

Tilford promptly accepted Carter's resignation with a polite expression of appreciation for his efforts. Archbold merely replied he would like to talk to Carter in New York. Good soldier that he was, Carter went on working, and along the lines Tilford laid out. He leased from E. E. Jones, with an option to purchase, the mining claims to Section 20, which lay out in the Midway flat away from the proven oil lands in the hills. He set the company engineers to collecting data on all wells and every squatter's claim in the Midway, McKittrick, Devil's Den (north of McKittrick), and north Coalinga areas. With this information in hand, he could campaign for drilling lands within reach of the company's pipelines. Back to the oil fields he went. At Coalinga, he selected a new and roomier camp site on Section 28; the new buildings would have so crowded the old site that a fire could have swept through them all. For a first time, Carter visited the Pico field, where he was appalled by the contorted strata and poor equipment: "The whole field is one junk pile of miserable proportion." Eckbert, Atwell, and Starke agreed with Carter that CSOW #32 should be drilled only 75 feet more, to 3,500 feet. It had already cost nearly $100,000 and in two trouble-filled years of deepening had showed only slight traces of oil. On his way back to San Francisco, he drew up plans to assign a man to each of nine producing areas to investigate likely oil properties.[32]

Following his return, Carter sent off a proposal to Calvin to lease four sections of Southern Pacific land on the Coalinga Eastside at royalties ranging from one-tenth on wells producing less than 100 barrels daily to one-third on those producing over 900 barrels. Again he returned to Coalinga, this time to lay out the new camp and engage a contractor. While he was there, Graham inquired what Carter thought the COF property was worth. Carter violated his usual practice and gave him a figure, but added he did not know if Standard would buy at any price. After leasing from Jones 1,920 acres more in mining claims at Midway, Carter's land acquisitions ended.[33]

In a second and final "General Order," he established a "Bureau of Information," with Starke as its chief, "to provide information of an exact character . . . of the possible oil and gas producing areas of California." As Starke's assistants, Carter named John B. Terry, the head chemist at Richmond, and H. Norman Snively, geologist and chemist. Snively, who had been hired just that day, was a graduate in economic geology at Stanford, with postgraduate training at Columbia and a few months additional study under Professor John C. Merriam at the University of California. He was the California company's first trained geologist.[34]

On May 26, Carter's final day at his desk, he sent Tilford his "valedictory." He reviewed the history and accomplishments of his three-month mission: In Coalinga, enlarging of the company's holdings and planning a new camp; in Midway, acquiring a major wildcatting opportunity on 3,520 acres, principally under lease with options to buy; in Topo Valley, acquiring an additional 2,063 acres and locating the wildcat wells; improving drilling practices; collecting data on all California fields; determining the cost of producing; "Raising the standard of the Producing Department . . . from being a *trailer* to that of a *leader,* so that oil producers look upon your department as a business institution, which will lease, bargain, and buy when it finds conditions to its liking, and, last, organizing your employees into an active force, with eyes and ears in the service of the company."[35]

When Carter reached New York, just before he reported to the Executive Committee, he had a few minutes with Archbold. He asked Archbold what he should say to the Executive Committee. Archbold answered, "Say to it what you have said to me—free, full, and fair; the Committee should know all there is to know." Carter wrote of the session that followed:[36]

> I pointed out where the company's holdings were weak, and showed
> that the California management . . . was not equal to the requirements

of the producing end. . . . Scofield and Rheem were good men but no oil producers. . . . The company interests might be better served by separating the management of the Producing Department from the Pipeline and Refinery. . . . I showed the Committee where it erred in . . . refusing to consider the California Oil Fields property and indicated [that] . . . the company should . . . purchase every good piece of property offered at a fair price.

After two hours of discussion, Archbold put the matter up to a subcommittee, consisting of J. A. Moffett, A. C. Bedford, and H. M. Tilford. The next afternoon Moffett laid its decision before Carter. He explained that "the question of the independent management of the Producing Department" was "impossible." Moffett spoke as if there was no question of following some of the proposals Carter had recommended, but these proved to be minor. For example, Starke, whom Carter thought underpaid, was granted a higher salary. No conclusion was reached on a policy governing properties to be purchased, but Carter's withdrawal from the field left Tilford, Scofield, and Rheem in command. Carter, although shaking his head over the outcome, took his reverse calmly. "The Standard Oil are not sure of its footing in California and therefore do not show me its full hand. I have done my full duty. The company must do the rest."[37]

Within three weeks, Eckbert was in Titusville discussing the likely loss of his job. Carter suspected that in order to get rid of Eckbert the California executives had accused him of arranging to share with Jones in the returns from the Midway lands deals between Jones and the company. Carter did not press Eckbert as to the accuracy of the charges but advised him to go to New York and answer frankly any questions that might be asked. Shortly thereafter, toward the end of July, Eckbert's retirement was announced. The terms of the "retirement" are obscure. Eckbert turned down an offer from Union in October, saying that he was on a six-month furlough and looking after some matters for Standard; over a year later, he told J. C. Donnell of the Ohio Oil Company that he was still waiting for 26 Broadway to put him to work. As a matter of fact, Eckbert had obtained an interest in the mining claims which Jones leased to Standard and eventually joined Jones in dealing in oil lands. With this cloudy episode, the disciple followed the master out of the California company.[38]

What was the impact of Colonel Carter's brief but meteoric career in California? In three months time, Carter had placed Standard firmly in the Midway field, which within a few years became one of the twin pillars of Standard's producing strength. He recommended the other pillar, the Murphy properties, which Standard finally leased in 1913. He firmly established the scientist in the role of adviser in evaluating oil properties. And his recommendation for an independent Producing Department must also have been recalled when after two and a half years of fumbling, 26 Broadway sent to California a more diplomatic man, F. H. Hillman, with a broad grant of power to make the company a major producer.

5

With Carter and Eckbert out of the way, Scofield's and Rheem's optimistic view that wildcatting would locate inexpensive oil was put to the test. The company desperately needed experienced oil scouts. It had only Eric Starke, who was still a novice, and H. Norman Snively, who was just beginning his career as a petroleum geologist. Probably this explains why Standard employed two University of California men as consulting geologists. One was Professor John C. Merriam, an eminent paleontogolist and president of the Carnegie Institution later on. The other was G. Clark Gester, a graduate of the university and an instructor in geology who, after almost a decade, would join Standard permanently.

Beginning in June, Merriam and Gester, accompanied by Starke and Snively, reviewed at least five territories: the Peachtree and Topo valleys, an area near Livermore, the Pico-Elsmere fields, the area from McKittrick to Coalinga, and the Midway field, including Buena Vista Hills. In the Midway study, R. W. Pack, who later served with the U.S. Geological Survey, helped, too. The assistance given by the consultants was not constant, but rather when they could take time from their university duties. It ceased altogether in the spring of 1909. Gester's final assignment was to report, with Starke, on the Murphy property in the Coyote Hills. They agreed that it was a promising property. Starke again urged unsuccessfully that it be purchased. A few months later Gester joined the Kern Trading & Oil Company, and there is no trace of further work by any consultant. However, Starke could and probably did confer with Merriam informally; they were neighbors in Berkeley. Starke, who was transforming himself into a professional geologist, undoubtedly benefited from the association with Merriam and Gester. During 1908 and 1909 he and Snively were out in the field much of the time, not only with their consultants, but also on ventures of their own to other possible oil lands in California, Oregon, Washington, and Idaho.[39]

In addition to the use of geology, a second innovation of the post-

Carter period lay in the technique of drilling. Heretofore, with the exception of an unsuccessful attempt at diamond drilling in 1889, all of California Standard's wells had been drilled with cable tools, using a heavy bit on the end of a cable to pound the strata to pieces. But in Texas and Louisiana, drillers had been rotating a string of pipe with a bit on the end, flushing the cuttings to the surface with a stream of mud pumped down through the drill pipe and up the outside. The mud plastered the sides of the hole, helping prevent caving in soft formations; it also, in the opinion of prejudiced cable tool advocates, sealed off the oil sands. In March, 1908, J. R. McAllister, an ex-rotary driller who was Rheem's foster brother and foreman of the pipe shop at Richmond, talked to Carter about using rotary equipment. No agreement was reached, but after Carter left, probably through the influence of Rheem, McAllister won the chance to try. This was more of a gamble than a later generation can suspect. Rotaries "made hole" fast in the fields along the Gulf of Mexico, but California contained hard strata and layers of cobblestones as well as the soft formations. In 1902 the Western Union Oil Company had experimented with a rotary in Santa Maria, and Union had used one in Fullerton, but these were isolated instances. The Lockwood Oil Company tried rotary drilling for several hundred feet in the Midway during 1907 before running into a stratum too hard to penetrate. The next year, after a rotary had proved successful at Coalinga, McAllister went to the Gulf Coast in July. He bought three rotary rigs and hired six drillers, including Cyrus Bell and L. B. Little, who later became Standard executives. McAllister had known Bell some years earlier when they both had been drilling in Alabama. The men and equipment arrived in California in August for trial in the Midway, Coalinga, and Peachtree fields. In the Midway, Standard's first rotary-drilled well, Jameson #2, was spudded in on September 20.[40]

It was the Midway that held the key to the Producing Department's future, for nowhere else did the drillers meet with success. The great hopes for the Peachtree and Topo valleys died, as the drill penetrated to the granite basement rock without discovering productive sands. In fairness to Eckbert and Starke, Standard's was not the only failure. The Union Oil Company and E. L. Doheny were others who plunged at Topo and Peachtree. Doheny said, "There are miles of oil strata in Monterey county. I feel certain of it and base my conclusions on an exhaustive personal examination." He backed his judgment by forming the American Petroleum Company to drill on several thousand acres. When American Petroleum pulled out in the middle of 1908, Standard doggedly kept on. It got a show of oil early in October, but that was all. As one observer put it, there was "not enough oil to lubricate the running gear of a jack-rabbit." The company suspended most of its operations in November, 1908, though limited activity continued for two more years.

Meanwhile, another area was being explored east of Livermore near the town of Altamont. This was wildcat land, presumably recommended by Merriam and Gester. The rotary outfit shipped to the Peachtree area was diverted to Altamont and, on November 2, 1908, Bell and Little spudded in Leonardo #1. A year later it was abandoned. Still another strictly wildcat territory was completely outside the area served by the pipeline. Contrary to Starke's advice, the company commenced drilling just east of Los Angeles in the Repetto Hills in March of 1909, but to no avail.[41]

At Midway, Standard had run into a thorny problem almost before drilling began. E. E. Jones had confidently asserted his possessory rights to these as yet unpatented lands, and the company's lawyers had approved the contracts with him. However, part of the lands were claimed by others, leading to suits in the courts. Scofield told Eckbert to keep Standard-owned material off the lands until these disputes were settled. To Tilford, Scofield wrote that he had

> . . . always been averse to . . . attempting to develop . . . mineral locations made by other parties where no title except mere possession was attached . . . based on my own old experience in clearing such titles in the Newhall District . . . , but as our attorneys had advised [Carter and Eckbert] that they could make legal agreements along the lines of the Jones agreement, I did not wish to . . . appear captious, and made no further opposition.

To the public, Scofield announced that the company would back no faction and wanted only clear titles. Nevertheless, in July, 1908, Oscar Lawler, the U.S. District Attorney for Southern California, arrived in Bakersfield in behalf of one of these claimants and stated that he "wanted to see if the Standard Oil Company . . . and Jones could steal Sections 10 and 14 from the rightful locators." H. M. Storey promptly asked a mutual friend to assure Lawler that Standard was not taking sides. Except for the wells of the Big Four on Section 30, which were directed by Standard's superintendent, the company postponed drilling on the Jones properties until early 1909.[42]

6

The first purely Standard drilling in the Midway was on the Jameson lease, formerly the property of the Talara Oil Company, about which

Tilford had questioned Carter so closely. Carter finally turned the deal down because of a lien against the property, but a few weeks later Scofield made the purchase, in June, 1908. The lease lay on the slope of the hill running down to the flat where the city of Taft now lies. It was on the edge of proven production and already had one well producing about eighty barrels a day of 20° gravity oil. Here Standard built its main camp, wooden buildings painted white and trimmed in green. One rotary and five cable tool rigs were set to drilling on the Jameson, while three more wells were begun on Section 30. Soon it was evident that the vaunted rotary was going down more slowly than the cable tool outfits, as the drillers ran into cobblestones—the formation most feared. Fishtail bits could whirl through shale two or three times as fast as cable tools, but they could not chew up boulders. The rotary took 110 days to drill 1,720 feet before Jameson #2 came in as a small producer during January, 1909. Though the drilling had been slow, the rotary did have the advantage of requiring fewer strings of casing. The company still was not prepared to say which was the better and ordered more rotaries. It put one of these on Section 30 in well #1, where cable tools had been pounding on sand without making much progress. The rotary showed what it could do, drilling 614 feet in February and 1,037 feet in March.[43]

As the rotaries came into use, a rivalry developed between rotary and cable tool men that went as far as bare knuckle battles. The "swivel necks," "hard heads," "long horns," or "big hats," as the rotary men were called, were sure that rotaries were the drilling tools of the future. The cable tool men, known as "jar heads," "up and downers," or "mail pouchers," ridiculed their rivals and claimed the rotaries mudded off the oil sands. Actually, they were beginning to fear that their jobs would disappear. To keep the peace, the rotary and cable men ate separately and lived in separate bunkhouses. Rheem brought Bell and Little from the Altamont well when their work was interrupted by heavy rains and sent them to Midway to damp down the rising tempers. In February, 1909, McAllister moved up from his job as Superintendent of Rotaries to Assistant General Superintendent of the Producing Department, and Bell, soft-spoken but firm, became Assistant Superintendent of Drilling under F. A. Fether, a cable tool man.[44]

The *California Oil World* commented on Standard's support for the rotaries:[45]

> Although it has not been popular with most of the oil operators, the rotary seems to be growing in favor with the Standard. The main difficulty

with the companies which previously tried the revolving drill, and abandoned it, seems to have been with the drillers. There is a deep-seated jealousy and half-hatred which exists between rotary and standard [cable tool] drillers, much like the feeling between cattlemen and sheepmen, and the standard operators who were put on the rotaries generally neglected the work, while genuine rotary men were hard to find.

The Standard seems to like the rotaries, however, and more will probably be added soon.

Fether had been in charge of drilling barely six months when his feelings flared. According to a story that reached the press, Fether had been ordered to use rotaries in the Repetto Hills when he wanted cable tools. When a bit broke in his first well and fishing for it failed, he substituted cable tools. With a second well going slowly, he switched to cable tools there also. These troubles and the rapid progress with cable tools on a neighboring well of the Rowland Oil Company led Fether to write a letter severely criticizing the rotaries. Rheem called Fether to San Francisco. After a heated discussion, Fether quit, and his foreman at Repetto was fired. Fether was not replaced. McAllister controlled all development and production, with Bell as his assistant in charge of rotaries. The company was thoroughly committed to rotary drilling, a fact that was illustrated again when lessors complained to Rheem that the rotaries mudded up the formation. Rheem called for Bell, who explained to the doubters that the cable tools pounded the shale back into the formation, sealing it off more than mud did. Moreover, cable tools could not drill all the way through an oil sand when there was substantial gas pressure. Rheem made his position crystal clear: "We've got these rotaries and we're going to put them over if I break the Standard Oil Company."[46]

In two or three years, the controversy began to die out, as drillers realized there were circumstances that favored each type of tool. A rotary could make hole faster and, possibly, fight gas pressure better. The latter point was still debatable because heavy muds for use in the wells had not yet been developed. Most wells made their own mud, though some from the slough at Richmond was being shipped to Midway as early as 1909. On the other hand, rotaries, for lack of power, could not handle long strings of casing as well as cable tools did. For a time, cable tool drillers started and finished the rotary wells, set the pipe, and cemented. But after the rotary men gained experience and acceptance, their crews did the whole job.[47]

Standard's use of rotaries may have helped stimulate development of the Perkins process of cementing, which was an outstanding advance in drilling technique. Almond A. Perkins joined Standard in June, 1909, after thirty-eight years as driller, operator, and pipeline builder in the oil fields of Pennsylvania, Peru, Wyoming, and California, to take charge of the camps and tankage in the Midway. When he arrived, cementing was a matter that greatly disturbed the drillers. They were having trouble shutting off water, which ran from water-bearing sands down between the walls of the hole and the casing into the oil sand unless something was done to prevent it. In using rotaries, the customary technique was to drill down to the point of water shut-off, then rig up cable tools, drill a few feet of small hole below the casing, and drive the casing into the hole for a tight fit. By February of 1909 Standard had turned to using cement on some wells at Midway to fill the ring between the casing and the walls, a practice begun in 1903 by Frank Hill of the Union Oil Company.

The method favored by Standard's men was to dump cement into the bottom of the hole with a dump bailer, pull the casing up 20 or 30 feet, fill the casing with water and screw a plug on top of it, then lower the casing. The cement was squeezed up around the casing. In three weeks, the cement would harden; that is, the driller hoped it would. In the Midway wells, however, the cement failed to set because of carbonates in the water. Starke and Snively put their knowledge of chemistry to work on the problem. They found that gypsum would harden despite the water and that mixing in calcium chloride would speed the process. They also discovered that adding sodium silicate to water and cement helped the cement to set. It is not known to what extent their findings were used.

In October, 1909, Perkins, together with Edward Double of the Union Oil Tool Company, applied for a patent on an improved mechanical technique. A plug, similar to a pipeline scraper, was inserted in the casing and cement pumped down on top of it. On top of the cement, a second plug was inserted and driven downward by water pumped upon it, keeping the cement uncontaminated by water and mud. When the bottom plug dropped below the casing, the cement was squeezed upward between the casing and the walls of the hole. The favorable outlook for his process caused Perkins to leave the company shortly after applying for a patent and to go into business. Before long, Standard was hiring the Perkins firm to do all of its cementing in exchange for a discount. His process soon was widely used throughout the oil world.[48]

7

Early in the autumn of 1909, 26 Broadway sent J. C. Donnell, the president of the Ohio Oil Company, its biggest producer, to California. Donnell's primary mission was to examine for possible purchase two oil companies that were opening up new territory on the southeastern edge of the Coalinga Eastside field. But he was also asked to make a general report on California. Donnell was not impressed. The Coalinga wells he went to see were so deep, 3,000 feet, that he believed they would not pay. Standard's Section 28, which the Producing Department had been developing intensively, looked very profitable. However, after investigating, he learned that though the number of wells had been doubled since the property was purchased, production had increased only 500 barrels daily for a total of a little more than 3,000 barrels a day. The property was $900,000 short of paying for itself, with no allowance for interest. In the Midway field, where the company had discovered some oil on the Jameson lease and on Section 30, Donnell visited two wells being drilled, both of which were having trouble. At Pico Canyon, he noted that wells were cheap to operate but very expensive to drill. He also visited the Murphy Coyote property, where he found a flowing well 3,700 feet deep. "Most people," he wrote "are afraid to tackle territory where they have to go deeper than 2,000 feet and I do not blame them." In the Repetto Hills, both Standard wells were poor prospects. From Tim Spellacy and other oilmen, he heard that many California producers were barely breaking even. Donnell concluded, "From my general observation of the entire situation in California, unless they get some other prolific pools that are shallow, they cannot produce oil below the present price at a profit."[49]

After his tour was finished, Donnell heard his first exciting news, though it obviously failed to influence the generally pessimistic tenor of his report. On October 10, Standard's discovery well on Section 26 had come in flowing an estimated 7,000,000 cubic feet of gas daily. This section was rank wildcat territory in the Buena Vista Hills, a ridge paralleling the Midway and forming the eastern wall of the valley that contained the Jones properties. In February, 1909, Standard had purchased mining claims there to half of both Sections 22 and 26, which Starke had recommended because of extensive gas and bitumen outcrops and because the same formation was productive at McKittrick. When the well on Section 26 was started in April, 1909, the *Bakersfield Californian* said that it represented "about the wildest wildcatting which John Rockefeller has been . . . guilty of," but the well's huge gas production changed this tune. Standard's gas well was called bigger and stronger than a Honolulu Oil Company gas producer in the southern end of the hills that had been hailed for months as the largest gas well in California and one of the greatest in the world. Although Standard was not especially interested in gas, the sands thrown out with the gas on Section 26 showed traces of petroleum. Little more than a week later, on October 19, the company began pumping its first well on Section 14 at 150 barrels a day. Perhaps there was hope for Standard in the Midway after all.[50]

Following a trip through the fields, Starke made a rather optimistic report to Rheem early in November and also defended himself vigorously. His job was in danger because the oil discovered on Section 30 was not as light and refinable as Standard wanted. The company had gone so far as to employ a Stanford-trained geologist, Robert B. Moran, who did not report to Starke and who was given an office with the pipeline's chief engineer. Perhaps this was on Starke's mind when he wrote of the severe criticism his recommendation of the Jones lands had received from "most producers and geologists." But, he reminded Rheem, he had been told to look for light oil property, of which California had little. All the likely lands had been taken up, and "when Mr. Jones offered us the flat territory it was because he could not get others to take it." Starke pointed out that no large shallow light oil wells had ever been discovered in California in anticlines (strata folded upward), and he believed oil was in the Midway syncline (strata folded downward). He hoped for good production there and from the sands laid down in the Miocene period, the principal source of California oil so far. While Starke was not wrong, he failed to guess that the great light oil production would come from Pliocene strata in the Buena Vista Hills anticline. He was certain that oil would be found in the Hills because of the evidence of gas, but his great hopes were for the wildcats in the syncline.[51]

Time would prove him a minor prophet rather than a great one. The Midway section with by far the greatest future, the McNee, may have been bought without his specific recommendation. The Standard executives were jarred in September, 1909, when President Taft ordered a sweeping withdrawal of oil lands on the public domain from entry and sale, for the order made doubtful the status of much of the Midway flat and the Buena Vista Hills. Thereafter, William Edwards, who was in charge of land purchases, took the precaution of looking for "school lands," that is, the Sections 16 and 36 in each township which under federal law had passed to the state and had been sold for the support of its schools. Title to these lands, Edwards thought, would be safe. In November, he arranged to buy the McNee section in the Buena Vista Hills, and the Tupman section and 480 acres of the Hay section in the Elk Hills a few miles to the northeast. The McNee cost about $100 an acre; the others cost less. In March, 1910, Edwards agreed to buy the Packard section on the edge of Elk Hills. He appears to have viewed these school lands as "protective acreage" rather than as lands for immediate drilling, and only with difficulty persuaded the directors to support him. If this is true, he can be credited with a most rewarding prudence, as a later chapter will reveal.[52]

The first convincing show of oil in the Midway came on January 22, 1910, when well #3 on Section 30 began to flow and the next day gushed 3,683 barrels of 21.3° gravity oil. It was proof that the Carter-Starke gamble on the Jones lands was not futile. Twenty years later, Starke recalled that a few days after the strike he visited Rheem expecting to be complimented, but " all Rheem had to say was while the well was alright it did not help his department any for the oil was 17° gravity and the company had no use for heavy oil." Unfortunately, Rheem was right. Although the first gush was lighter, it came from a rather heavy oil field.

The petroleum press was much more enthusiastic. Seventeen months earlier, the *California Oil World* had crowed over Standard's wildcatting:

> It is the irony of fate that the biggest thing on earth can't get what it wants with all its resources and must scratch gravel like any other chicken, or go down in the struggle for existence. When, in the bad old days, it swung into Kern River, cracked its whip and ordered the common people to come in and leave their profits with it, things looked bully for the Standard. It had everything its way and made the princely offer of fifteen cents the barrel. That made oil worth just exactly fifteen cents the barrel, no more. The mills of the gods, grinding slow, have turned round just once. The Standard stands a beggar at the back gate asking for the poor chance of a whack at the woodpile.

Now, a note of admiration crept into its congratulations for the discovery on Section 30:

> This is really its first success, a success worth while. Of course, it has attained some production in Midway before this big strike but at such a heavy cost that it did not boast of the size of it. Several well known operators of the great West Side field in speaking about the Standard's production in the locality have been heard to declare that it has cost at least $5 a barrel. However, the Standard has the nerve to go to it and the courage to go from it when it finds that it is mistaken. The Standard's experts are now of the opinion that the Midway field will prove the greatest oil field in the world.[53]

More and more, Midway became a center of oil enthusiasm. Standard soon had two other wells on Section 30, each of which gushed above

6,000 barrels a day. Another in the flat, three miles to the southeast, was Union's incredible Lakeview #1, which averaged over 60,000 barrels daily during the first three months. Over in Buena Vista Hills, the Honolulu Oil Company pumped clay, manure, and sawdust into its big gas well on Section 10 to halt the gas and drilled down to the oil sand, developing a flow of 500 barrels daily of 29° gravity oil. According to the *California Oil World,* Standard was willing to give Honolulu a million dollars for this light oil section, but Captain Matson demanded an offer of $1,500,000 before he would call together his board of directors. Standard may or may not have made an offer to purchase, but it did contract for the production. Honolulu's discovery of this valuable refining crude set off a rush of claimants to lands in the Buena Vista and Elk Hills, accompanied by the threat of claim jumping and gun play. In the Buena Vista Hills, Standard began drilling McNee #1.

About a mile from the McNee, Standard's second well on Section 26 blew out one night in May, 1910, and caught fire from the "stink pots" lighting the rig, making a giant torch that burned for weeks and was visible from the bluffs east of Bakersfield, some thirty miles away. Finally, the fire was smothered with steam and the well capped three months after it broke loose. Its pressure of 2,000 pounds per square inch, H. N. Snively believed, "probably broke the world's record. . . ."[54]

8

This well quickened Standard's already mild interest in natural gas. Two years earlier, Scofield had commissioned a mining engineer to study dry gas fields (in which the gas is not associated with oil) in the Central Valley of California, especially around Stockton. The next year a gas strike near Suisun, northeast of San Francisco Bay, caused Starke to assign Snively and Gester to study the geology of that territory, a study later broadened to include gas possibilities elsewhere in Northern and Central California.

No action followed until the huge Buena Vista wells raised the question anew. The company used some of the gas for fuel in its field operations but had no other use for the remainder. To discuss the problem, Atwell went to New York, where he found the executives reluctant to enter the gas business in California, even though they were heavy marketers of natural gas in the East and Midwest. Not long after Atwell's return, Starke prepared an optimistic report on the prospects for gas in the San Joaquin Valley, which he considered the only geologic area in California favorable to large accumulations, especially in the anticlines at Buena Vista Hills, Elk Hills, Kettleman Hills, and Lost Hills. The Buena Vista gas wells already discovered, Starke pointed out, were among the largest producers in the world.[55]

Scofield, who shared Starke's optimism, forwarded his report to Tilford and wrote that some eastern gasmen had recently described the Buena Vista territory as "the largest possibility . . . they have ever seen." The western executive suggested that a company be set up to serve the Bakersfield area and, eventually, Los Angeles, the San Francisco Bay area, Stockton, and Sacramento. He started a market survey of all these areas and recommended that the proposed company sell to existing gas companies at a rate cheaper than gas could be manufactured. By working with the existing companies, instead of competing with them, he believed that Standard would avoid conflict, and the influence of the companies with local regulatory boards would probably result in rates that would allow Standard more profit than if it distributed the gas itself.

Tilford accepted Scofield's proposal. On September 20, 1910, the California Natural Gas Company was incorporated as a subsidiary of the Standard Oil Company (New Jersey), but it did not get under way until the following year.[56]

9

Despite the excitement over the gas wells and gushers, the Producing Department had not yet achieved its objective of discovering large quantities of light, refinable oil. Finally, in mid-September, 1910, a second, deeper well on Section 14 struck a productive sand. The well flowed 1,550 barrels a day of 21° gravity oil. This was a creditable showing, even though the oil was not as light as the refiners desired. The *California Oil World,* commenting on Midway's great growth, said it was now "a poor week" when a gusher was not reported, and awarded Standard the palm for pioneering in the Midway flat:[57]

> It is a common saying that the Standard never goes out to seek oil itself; it lets others take all the risks and then comes in and reaps the harvest. However true this may be elsewhere, no candid person can bring this charge in the present instance. The honor of opening the great Midway flats is the Standard's and no one desires to deprive it of the credit it deserves.

The new well came at an auspicious time. Early in November a party of top-ranking eastern executives stopped in California during one of their annual tours of inspection. The party included Colonel Carter and J. C. Donnell as its experts on producing. What they saw at Midway, Carter felt, had vindicated Starke. Subsequently, he wrote to his old subordinate, "Be happy my good friend; it took two years to turn the tables; but the spirits of knowledge and justice, crushed to the earth, for a season, triumphed. . . . Injustice may blind 26 Broadway *some* of the time; but not *all of it* much of the time."[58] Yet, Carter's complements to Starke notwithstanding, Standard's production at the close of 1910 still fell far short of giving the refiners an assured supply of crude.

Table 14: S. O. (California) Production, December, 1910

Field	Barrels per Day	Gravity, to Nearest Degree
Midway	480	15
"	2,925	20
"	1,072	23
Coalinga	3,030	21
Pico Canyon	354	33
Elsmere	37	14
Total	7,898	

Source: Field Operations reports, Economics Department.

During the four years since the Producing Department had been established Standard had developed outside Pico Canyon and Elsmere a production of about 7,500 barrels daily, most of which could be refined. But the company needed to do better. Its requirements had grown steadily, and plans for the future, notably for a Southern California refinery, called for still more oil. The company faced a further problem, the likelihood of more effective competition for crude purchases. In October, the shaky finances of the Union-Agencies alliance had been strengthened when a third participant, the Associated, joined up—a move which caused the *California Oil World* to declare that Standard had been "completely eclipsed in this state." At the close of 1910, it appeared that Standard was going to have to reconsider its producing policy and intensify its efforts.[59]

XIV

INDEPENDENCE
THROUGH ANTITRUST

The affairs of the great Standard organization controlled and directed by 26 Broadway came to a crisis during the first decade of the twentieth century. The crisis arose from no loss of mastery in the oil industry; rather, it was due to a hostile public opinion that buffeted the Standard headquarters and many of its subordinate units with gale force. As a result, Standard companies came under legal attack at both state and national levels, and finally the unity of the organization was destroyed.

Much of this story is relevant to the history of Standard of California in only its broadest outlines. Unlike many other prominent subsidiaries of Jersey Standard, the western company during these years endured no important suit brought by a state government. But the company could not escape the wave of popular feeling, nor an examination of its activities and those of its predecessors in the federal antitrust case. Ultimately, of course, the federal case cut loose the western executives from 26 Broadway and started Standard of California on its independent way. It also gave the company, along with other former Standard units, an enduring respect for the force of public opinion.

2

The judicial ordeal began on November 15, 1906, for on this date in the Circuit Court for the Eastern District of Missouri the United States government filed suit under the Sherman Antitrust Act against the Standard Oil Company (New Jersey), its subsidiaries and affiliates, John D. Rockefeller, and six other directors. The Standard Oil Company (California), New York Standard, Indiana Standard, and the great pipeline company, National Transit, were among the most important defendants of some seventy subsidiaries and affiliates listed in the case. This suit, the most famous of all antitrust actions, dragged on for four and one-half years before the United States Supreme Court spoke the last word in mid-May, 1911.[1]

The indictment had a long public prelude and was, in fact, a "natural" for the times. It followed a period during which many a new huge combination of capital had joined earlier giants like Standard Oil, the

American Tobacco Company, and the American Sugar Refining Company as examples of "monopoly" in the public mind. During the early years of the century United States Steel and Amalgamated Copper were organized in the metal industries; the Northern Securities Company and International Mercantile Marine appeared in the transportation industry; International Harvester in the farm implement industry; the National Biscuit Company in the baking industry, and so on. Between 1900 and 1904 the number of industrial combinations in the United States increased from 185 with a total capital of $3,000,000,000 to 318 with a capital in excess of $7,000,000,000.

The formation of many of these giants was front page news. Much of the public reaction was by no means favorable. Deep in the American consciousness was a sentimental yearning for an earlier day when virtually all companies were small, when markets were local or regional rather than national, and when the very size of a business permitted a personal relationship between employer and employee, between company and customer, hardly possible in the new day. The earlier times, enshrined in memory, had not been especially distinguished either for virtue or efficiency, but the comforting evidence of multiple sources of supply had usually been conspicuously present and breaches of ethics or the law had generally had only a limited impact on society.

The new giants had become large mainly because of the efficiencies of bigness. But the gains for society were mixed. Many a competitive practice that had been both legal and tolerable when there were many firms, and none of them huge, became no longer so tolerable as the number of firms was reduced and the giants emerged. Such weapons as price cutting and restrictive contracts, for example, took on new characteristics. In an earlier day a man might enlarge his business, if he could, by price cutting, even if by so doing he wrecked a competitor; society, indeed, esteemed him for his low prices. There were always more competitors, so that the public need not fear domination. In the new day, price cutting by a giant could deprive the public of this protection. A number of competitive practices had to be modified and laws changed, as the public sought to regain its old sense of security. Great power could not be irresponsibly used. This process of adjustment was already going on; it was hastened by the appearance of so many new huge corporations.

One of the chief forces making for change early in the century was a popular literature dealing with the abuse of economic power. It was the product of a group of able journalists, the so-called muckrakers. They included such skilled writers as Ida Tarbell, Burton J. Hendrick, Ray Stannard Baker, Lincoln Steffens, Samuel Hopkins Adams, Thomas

W. Lawson, and David Graham Phillips. They found a ready market for their articles in such family magazines as *McClure's, Collier's, Everybody's,* and *Cosmopolitan.* In fact, many of the articles were commissioned. Some muckrakers made use of the novel as a medium, like Upton Sinclair, whose famous book, *The Jungle,* effectively exposed unsavory practices in the meat packing industry, or Frank Norris, who indicted the Southern Pacific Railroad with his realistic story, *The Octopus.* Like most writing that has had wide popular success, sensation was an ingredient. The books and articles of the muckrakers were not notable for calmness, for reasoned argument and balanced presentation; rather, they tended to be boldly drawn from partial evidence, with the blacks and whites all too clear if, indeed, the coloring was not more vivid. They helped create a mild popular hysteria.

Whatever their deficiencies, the muckrakers aroused public opinion to such a pitch that big business was forced, through governmental sanctions and self-interest, to accept new rules for business behavior. The pace of change was quickened. New statutes were enacted at both the state and national levels designed to ensure standards of fair competition, to protect the worker, and to look after the interests of the consumer and the investor. And an old statute, the Sherman Antitrust Act, was proved at last a formidable instrument in the hands of the federal government for breaking up organizations that were approaching monopoly.

Inevitably, Standard Oil became a chief object of public scrutiny. It made a useful focal point for progressives like Theodore Roosevelt, "the Trust-Buster," who needed to whip up popular support for the extension of governmental authority in the economic realm. Standard was old enough to have endured prior waves of popular feeling cresting in the later 1870's and again in the 1890's, when a decision of the Ohio Supreme Court in 1892 had forced the break-up of the Trust established ten years earlier. The company was especially vulnerable because of a long-standing policy of secrecy in public relations. This policy was common business practice, for traditionally business had been considered a private matter. It was another example of a policy requiring change, however, in the new day. Secrecy had been a grave error because it had long permitted the public to suspect the worst of Standard and to accept as wholly accurate the broadsides of such attackers as Henry Demarest Lloyd, whose *Wealth Against Commonwealth* (1894) Milton Stewart had recommended to his brother Lyman on more than one occasion as a useful weapon in the battle against Standard in the West. Milton wanted the book circulated among California producers so that they would learn to be wary of the "sweet-scented thieves."[2]

The journalist who dealt a much more damaging blow was Ida Tarbell. Her *History of the Standard Oil Company,* which began appearing in *McClure's Magazine* in the fall of 1902, was published in two volumes in 1904. It had been prefaced by years of research and represented the most thorough study yet made of an American company. But it was not an objective and balanced account. Miss Tarbell was a daughter of the Oil Regions of Pennsylvania; her father had been an antagonist of the Standard in the bitter battles fought there. Her story, probably in consequence, dealt for more than half its length with events occurring prior to 1880, and her emphasis throughout was on the misdeeds, proven or suspected, of the Standard organization. Only one chapter had to do with what she called the "legitimate greatness" of the Standard Oil Company.

The impact of her work was deep and immediate. Some commentators, like the reviewer for *The Nation,* considered her study incomplete and one-sided and believed it designed to intensify "popular hate." Others, perhaps, may have taken it as a lesson in success, as did John Baker, manager of the Union Oil Company's manufacturing and sales department. Baker saw no ethical problems involved, merely sound policy. He wrote, after reading the first two articles, that "the simplicity of the S.O. Co's plans appeal to me. As I see it, their success is due to their getting the railroad officials interested with them and thereby making it possible for the railroad officials to be helping themselves when helping the S.O. Co." In general, however, the *History* was received as a devastating document. It was acclaimed as "absorbing, . . . masterly," and as marked by a "judicial spirit." The Tarbell *History* became at once a best seller, and it has had an enduring influence on public opinion.[3]

The Tarbell volumes had been published only a few months when a storm broke out in Kansas. Beleaguered producers, oppressed by declining prices as production soared in that state and even more in Indian Territory to the south, lashed out at Standard's Mid-Continent pipeline and storage subsidiary, the Prairie Oil & Gas Company. In March, 1905, the Kansas attorney-general filed a suit against Prairie that later matured into an antitrust case. It was a forerunner of numerous suits in various states that were to harass Standard executives. During the next few years Standard subsidiaries were ousted from Texas and Tennessee and, for a time, 26 Broadway feared the same result in Missouri.[4]

3

The furor in Kansas also carried over to the national level, for in mid-February, 1905, Congress requested the Bureau of Corporations in the Department of Commerce and Labor to investigate Standard's position in the Kansas oil fields. The Bureau was itself an outgrowth of the new popular feeling. It had been established two years before, at Theodore Roosevelt's request, to serve as a fact-finding agency on business. Since an investigation of conditions in Kansas could hardly be carried on without reference to the whole oil industry, Commissioner of Corporations James R. Garfield broadened the scope of his inquiry to include all phases of oil activity throughout the nation. In the process, Kansas receded far into the background.

For over a year investigators roamed the nation, checking the files of Standard at 26 Broadway and in the field, searching for data in the files of the railroads, and interviewing literally hundreds of people conversant with the oil industry. The Bureau's *Transportation of Petroleum,* published as a 500-page special report on May 2, 1906, was a bombshell. It came at a critical moment, just when the President needed some powerful force to blast through Congress the Hepburn bill, the most important extension of federal authority over interstate commerce since the passage of the Interstate Commerce Act nineteen years before. The report thus, in effect, served a larger purpose. By mobilizing public feeling against Standard, it facilitated the passage of legislation that otherwise might not have made the statute books.[5]

In its report, the Bureau conceded that Standard enjoyed significant advantages over its competitors "by reason of its vast resources, its efficient organization, and its extensive facilities," but the Bureau claimed these advantages grew at least in part from railroad discriminations favorable to Standard that had gone on in the past and in some measure were still in being. In 1904, according to the Bureau, Standard had "unfair" access to many communities, from Vermont to California. The report, in fact, dwelt for more than one-fifth of its length on conditions existing in California, where railroads vied for traffic and companies negotiated for rates in a manner reminiscent of the national scene prior to the passage of the Interstate Commerce Act. Railroad regulatory legislation in California was extremely weak, and the state's Railroad Commission was notoriously ineffective.[6] The Bureau found that in 1904 railroads, chiefly the Southern Pacific and the Santa Fe, were making over eighty variations from published rates on oil shipments to various locations within California. In more than half of these cases, Standard was either the sole or a chief beneficiary. The Bureau estimated that these concessions to shippers and consignees in 1904 amounted to about $200,000, with Standard receiving about half of this amount. The government agency noted with satisfaction, and as evident proof of its

charges, that the California railroads had made their public rates conform to the former secret rates in more than thirty cases after the Bureau
had begun its investigation.[7]

These accusations brought forth angry denials from 26 Broadway.
John D. Archbold and H. H. Rogers denounced as "untruthful and unjust" "any assertion that the Standard Oil Company has been or is now
knowingly engaged in practices which are *unlawful*," a word the Bureau
had not used.[8] They declared that the situation within California, in
particular, was due to the explosive expansion of the oil business there,
and that Standard was the recipient of no favors not available to other
shippers. A few days later Charles M. Pratt, secretary of Jersey Standard,
reinforced the statements of Archbold and Rogers in a letter to the
stockholders. Pratt commented on the Bureau's main allegations, one by
one, and claimed that the federal agency had been unable to show a
single rebate on the company's interstate shipments. Standard's achievement, Pratt maintained, was "not traceable to illegal or reprehensible
methods, but to its economic and elaborate industrial organization, covering as it does every detail of transportation, manufacture, and administration."[9] But the Commissioner of Corporations refused to back down,
and the public, in general, accepted the assertions made by the Bureau.
They led directly to the suit against Standard in mid-November, 1906,
for violation of the Sherman Antitrust Act.

While the suit was still in its early stages, the Commissioner of Corporations put forth more findings in two additional volumes: *The
Position of the Standard Oil Company in the Petroleum Industry,* published in May, 1907, and *Prices and Profits,* published three months
later. The Commissioner pointed out that in 1904 Standard transported
nearly 90 per cent of the crude in the eastern fields and 98 per cent in
the Mid-Continent. It refined and sold nearly seven-eighths of the
nation's kerosine, gasoline, and lubricating oil. This remarkable achievement was documented and analyzed in great detail. Standard's extraordinary position, the Bureau finally concluded, was "not due to superior
efficiency alone," as its defenders contended, but to "highly unfair
competitive methods." These included Standard's refusal to operate
pipelines as common carriers or, in the "rare cases" where it had done
so, its charge of extortionate rates; railroad discriminations ("the cornerstone on which the Standard first built up its power"); price discriminations between communities, designed to stifle independents with their
more limited markets; the use of "bogus" independent companies to
capture the trade of those bitterly opposed to Standard and to permit
Standard to offer special prices to customers of independents while main-

taining its general price structure; and espionage on the operations of its competitors.[10] These charges by the Bureau, and the information it had compiled, the government used extensively in preparing its antitrust case.

The two reports published in 1907 announced a third, an examination of the oil industry in California that had grown out of the Bureau's larger investigations.[11] When the agents of the Bureau, led by Commissioner Garfield, came into the state late in April of 1905, they had found an acute discontent among the producers. Most of the oilmen maintained, according to Luther Conant, Jr., the economist who headed the California probe, that they were the victims of a combination of railroads and a few other large producing interests, particularly the Standard Oil Company and the Associated Oil Company:[12]

> They contend that the effect of this combination has been to depress the price of crude oil far below its fair value and on the one hand to enable the Standard and Associated Oil companies to dominate the general fuel oil market of the Pacific Coast and on the other to permit the railroads to acquire valuable oil properties at unreasonably low cost.

The Bureau's agents quickly turned to exploring this charge. Over the course of nearly nine months they collected an immense mass of information from more than two hundred individuals. Except for Charles N. Felton, they missed hardly an important figure conversant with the affairs of the California industry during more than forty years, but they concentrated especially on events since the turn of the century. They relied heavily on interviews with producers and with such prominent executives as H. C. Breeden, D. G. Scofield, Lyman Stewart, W. S. Porter, the general manager of the Associated, H. E. Graves of Puente, G. W. Luce of the Southern Pacific, and E. P. Ripley, president of the Santa Fe.

Standard's western leaders were among the first to be interviewed. They proved willing witnesses. During two long sessions Breeden gave much information on Iowa Standard's marketing. In answer to a question concerning fuel oil sales to the Santa Fe or the Southern Pacific, Breeden replied that neither Iowa Standard nor PCO supplied fuel oil to either road. Breeden defined the relationship of Iowa Standard to PCO as that of a purchaser and distributor of PCO refined oils and of crude oil for fuel. To specific questions on freight charges, total sales, selling costs and prices, he responded by promising to check the records and provide answers. In a brief preliminary interview Scofield seemed equally frank and assured Conant that he would collect data on PCO's plant investment, refining yields and costs, prices paid for crude, and other matters.[13]

When Conant returned for another round toward the middle of May, however, he found "considerable demurring and hesitation" in place of the earlier frankness. Alarmed at the course the inquiry was taking, 26 Broadway had instructed Breeden and Scofield to refer questions pertaining to finance and operations to New York. Scofield would not even admit to Conant that Jersey Standard (or its agents) owned the stock of the PCO company. The New York headquarters believed, so one of its counsel wrote Garfield, that the investigation was going far beyond its original focus on transportation in seeking information concerning costs, prices, and profits and details of a business that was largely intrastate in character. Only on general questions did the western executives feel free to speak out. Scofield told Conant, for example, that the low crude prices were the result of excessive production and that there was no other reason. And he denied that PCO had ever been a party to any agreement or understanding that was designed to depress those prices.[14]

At 26 Broadway, the Bureau's agents also ran into difficulty in pressing their quest. In mid-June, 1905, Garfield was told that John D. Archbold was "out of the city," H. H. Rogers was away, and H. M. Tilford, the chief figure in Standard's western enterprises, was about to sail for Europe "for a much needed rest." Not until Tilford's return toward the close of July were Bureau representatives permitted to comb through the bulky freight records of the Far Western subsidiaries, which had been forwarded to New York. On most other matters, especially those pertaining to costs, profits, and the terms of contracts for crude purchases, the New York headquarters was even less cooperative.[15]

Conant and his subordinates found a freer flow of information elsewhere. In California a parade of aggrieved producers were willing, even eager, to speak of what they knew or believed concerning tank car shortages, rate favoritism, and other forms of discrimination.[16] Lyman Stewart of Union and Graves of Puente made available a great deal of data concerning their operations, including detailed cost figures on refining. Executives of the Santa Fe, the Southern Pacific, and the Associated (in which the Southern Pacific had a large stock interest) were also interviewed at length.[17]

By June of 1906, after reviewing all this evidence, Conant had drafted a 300-page manuscript. He concluded that while "natural conditions were in part responsible" for the decline in prices, "the independent producer had also suffered severely from artificial causes introduced by some of his powerful competitors." These artificial causes, said Conant, included special rates and other forms of discrimination by the railroads in favor of the Associated and Standard Oil, "particularly an unfairly large allotment of tank cars to the Associated" by the Southern Pacific. The resultant sharp decline in crude prices in turn diminished the value of oil lands, permitting the Associated and the Santa Fe to extend their holdings at low cost and to give "the railroads and the Associated Oil Company complete control of the principal fuel oil fields of the Pacific Coast."[18]

Standard's contribution to this state of affairs Conant viewed as largely negative. It consisted of a set of circumstances that he considered highly suggestive and sinister. PCO's ceasing to buy crude in 1904 in the heavy oil fields of Kern River and McKittrick and its purchase of no heavy crude at Coalinga, along with the absence of any fuel oil sales by the Standard companies to the railroads, were among the principal reasons causing him to believe that Standard had conspired to turn over the fuel trade to the Associated and the railroads. Conant also noted that 26 Broadway was represented on the boards of the Southern Pacific and the Santa Fe. H. H. Rogers was a Santa Fe director, and apparently Conant believed that James Stillman, president of the National City Bank of New York, was the Standard representative on the board of the Southern Pacific.[19]

Following completion of his report on the fuel oil industry, Conant extended its scope to include a chapter on refining and the marketing of refined oils that focused more sharply on Standard. As a preliminary, a Bureau agent was dispatched to collect more material on Iowa Standard's marketing practices through interviews with the small refiners and wholesalers around Los Angeles who handled oil from outside the Standard combination. Conant finished his 67-page addition in February, 1907. The Bureau had found, he stated, that in 1904 Standard had refined about 3,300,000 barrels of crude at its Richmond refinery, or more than three times the entire amount for its nineteen competitors. He conceded that Standard's large resources and its efficiency in transporting crude by pipeline and tanker and in processing the crude at the new refinery had contributed substantially to this achievement. So had the extent and efficiency of its western marketing net of stations and substations. But these, Conant indicated, were not the only factors. There was a darker set: crude oil purchase contracts that were intended to deny refinable oil to competitors; purchase contracts with independent refiners that removed the competition of their goods; unduly favorable railroad rates; cutthroat prices; threats to customers of competitors; and the refusal to sell to retailers who bought any oil from competing refiners. Conant, nevertheless, ended on a hopeful note: "While . . . these practices have greatly limited the operations of its rivals, some of them have been able to remain in business, and at the present time the appearance of several important new competitors promises to seriously disturb the Standard's substantial monopoly of the refining industry on the Pacific Coast."[20]

This draft report on the California industry is rich with quotations giving a keen insight into business practices around the turn of the century. It was never revised and published, however. The raw material quoted from interviews and other sources shows clearly that the oil game was played hard, with strong companies frequently taking advantage of weaker parties. The quotations from Standard's contracts with competing refiners and with certain oil producers are especially informing. But much of the testimony is more difficult to evaluate. A good deal relating to Standard was opinion, influenced by self-interest, and some was false. The charge that in March, 1905, PCO had bought 5,700 acres in the Santa Maria field when crude oil prices were low, for example, was one false item picked up by the Bureau.[21] Nor was the report always fair. It is a curious fact that the patented Starke process, which gave Standard's kerosine so important a market advantage over the inferior kerosines of other California refiners, is nowhere mentioned.

At times, too, in various ways the report seems highly speculative. That Standard deliberately ceased to purchase Kern River crude late in the summer of 1904 and withdrew from McKittrick so that the Associated Oil Company could buy the heavy oil of the producers at a lower price is certainly dubious. As we have noted earlier, by August, 1904, Standard had nearly nine million barrels of heavy crude backed up in storage near Bakersfield which it was as yet unable to pump through its pipeline.[22] Moreover, from Coalinga, almost a hundred miles closer to Richmond, the company was getting nearly all of its refinable light crude, which supplied large quantities of residuum. In these circumstances, more heavy crude held little lure for Standard. And the two major railroads hardly offered a ready prospect for Standard's fuel oil, for each road had other and more likely sources of supply. The Southern Pacific had its wholly-owned subsidiary, the Kern Trading & Oil Company, and its affiliate, the Associated; the Santa Fe owned two prominent producing companies, the Petroleum Development Company, in which E. L. Doheny had once been the railroad's partner, and the Chanslor-Canfield Midway Oil Company, which in 1902 Standard's scout, C. F. Lufkin, had praised so highly.[23]

It is possible, too, to read too much into the presence of the New York banker, James Stillman, on the board of the Southern Pacific and of H. H. Rogers on the board of the Santa Fe. Rogers had been a

Santa Fe director only since February, 1905. The stock he represented apparently had been acquired the year before. Stillman's association with Standard derived principally from his connections with Rogers and John D. Rockefeller's elder brother, William, whose two sons had married the Stillman daughters. Standard usually maintained a sizable deposit in Stillman's bank, but it was a practice John D. little approved. In fact, according to Allan Nevins, Rockefeller mistrusted Stillman. Rockefeller also viewed with disfavor a number of the outside interests of H. H. Rogers. In his personal investments Rogers was something of a maverick among Standard's top leaders, and his membership on outside boards did not mean that he represented 26 Broadway.[24]

Conant's endeavor to determine the relative efficiency of the Richmond refinery and those of independent refiners is a speculation of a different order. He had not seen the PCO accounting records. Prefaced to a later section on PCO's profits from refining, he himself wrote, "I question the advisability of printing these figures, which are largely estimated." The last sentence of his report, which mentions "the appearance of several important new competitors," is also doubtful. At the time Conant wrote, California Petroleum Refineries, Limited, was building its ill-starred refinery at Oilport, near Santa Maria, which never operated. There were no other important new refiners in California until Associated and Shell entered the field six to eight years later.[25]

It may have been a recognition of some of these weaknesses that caused the Bureau to shelve its California study early in 1908. The manuscript was placed in the files bearing a note, "Material . . . to be preserved until after oil trials."[26] Like the Bureau's published reports, however, the manuscript served as a resource for the government prosecutors in the antitrust case.

4

The trial finally got under way in mid-September, 1907, at New York before Franklin Ferriss, a former St. Louis judge whom the Circuit Court had appointed its special examiner. Each side had assembled a formidable team of lawyers. The government placed its case in the hands of Frank B. Kellogg, a St. Paul attorney (who later became Secretary of State in the Coolidge administration), and Charles B. Morrison, the federal District Attorney for the Northern District of Illinois. Standard's counsel included M. F. Elliott and Martin Carey of its own staff, John G. Milburn of New York, John G. Johnson of Philadelphia, and Moritz Rosenthal of Chicago. Over the next fifteen months Judge Ferriss conducted hearings in New York, Washington,

Cleveland, and Chicago, at which more than four hundred witnesses testified. The resulting transcript was, as Chief Justice White later wrote, "inordinately voluminous, consisting of twenty-three volumes of printed matter, aggregating about twelve thousand pages, containing a vast amount of conflicting testimony relating to innumerable, complex and varied business transactions, extending over a period of nearly forty years."[27] It was truly an extraordinary mass of information, of claim and counterclaim, the largest body of data that had ever been collected about an American corporation.

In spite of the work of the Bureau, Standard's western operations were accorded but a minor place in the trial. The Pacific Coast was far removed from the main markets of the nation and from the historic centers of production. Although Standard had sold in the West even prior to 1880, the market area of California Standard as late as 1910 contained less than 6 per cent of the nation's population.[28] California had been an important oil producer for less than a decade, and Standard's own prominence in the state, except as a marketer, had been of even briefer duration. The first units of its Richmond refinery were not in operation before July, 1902. The long pipeline up the San Joaquin Valley was not completed until the spring of 1903, and Standard had no formally organized producing department until January, 1907. California's oil, moreover, in contrast to most of the other oil regions, was marketed principally for fuel, a product in which Standard had only a secondary position and interest.

Nor was the West aroused by the antitrust proceedings to the same extent as the older oil regions. Western sentiment, as revealed in the press, was mainly hostile to the company, but the trial itself received very little notice. The filing of the suit, for example, was rarely the subject for an editorial, and as a news item usually failed to make the front page.[29] When in the fall of 1907, Kellogg questioned W. H. and H. M. Tilford on Standard's western operations, their statements reached the West in brief and garbled press dispatches that inspired no editorials, and the extensive testimony of H. M. Tilford as a defense witness in December, 1908, passed almost unnoticed.[30] Even the sensational report of the Bureau of Corporations on transportation in the petroleum industry, which had dealt in such detail with rebates and special preferences in California, failed to strike much fire. While the San Francisco papers took the report as additional evidence of Standard's "villainy," the *Los Angeles Herald* gave the story a local twist with its headline: "Union Oil Company Found Guilty of Accepting Rebates."[31] California was far more anti-railroad than anti-Standard, and local followers of Theodore Roosevelt had the Southern Pacific Railroad as their target. When they thought of Standard, they viewed it as a national issue. A contemporary chronicler of progressivism in California records no reference at all to Standard Oil during the years of the trial, and the narrative of a recent historian of the movement shows conclusively that the California progressives centered no attack upon the western subsidiary.[32]

Clearly, the West was marginal to the antitrust case. It provided a hunting ground for the government's attorneys and, at times, created problems for Standard's counsel in fashioning their defense, but it rarely occupied the center of the stage. Aside from the Tilfords, the only New York executive to be interrogated about Standard's western activities was John D. Archbold. His testimony was brief and general. The only man brought from the West was Hugo Wasmann, a defense witness and Standard Oil salesman at Los Angeles.[33]

Kellogg and Morrison attempted to use Standard's western operations primarily for evidence relating to marketing. The government attorneys were particularly on the alert for any benefits to Standard in transportation. The prosecution noted, as had the Bureau of Corporations earlier, that the railroads in the spring of 1891 abandoned their former practice of charging a common blanket rate for all oil shipments to the Pacific Coast from Chicago and points east, just as Standard's new refinery at Whiting, on the outskirts of Chicago, became the main source of supply for the West. The government claimed that the new higher freight charges for points east of Chicago had deprived independent eastern refiners of Pacific Coast business, and that pressure on the railroads from 26 Broadway had forced this change.[34] The government, however, was unable to produce any evidence of such pressure. It was self-evident, as even the Bureau conceded, that the western railroads had a direct interest in ending the former practice, for no longer did they have to share revenues from a common rate on oil shipments with eastern lines. Standard was also able to cloud the government's contention by showing that for years the company had transported its blue-ribbon kerosine, Elaine, from Franklin and Pittsburgh, Pennsylvania, at the higher rates and had experienced no difficulty in selling in Pacific Coast markets. Between 1902 and 1905, for example, it had sold up to nearly 300 cars annually on the West Coast.[35]

The government attorneys, again following the Bureau of Corporations, were particularly interested in Standard's trade in fuel and refined oils in Southern California. They argued that in Los Angeles and San Diego the company had been guilty of unfair competition against

Southern California producers and refiners. Special preferences and rebates from railroads, along with price cutting, they asserted, had been the weapons Standard used in attempting to deprive the southern oilmen of their home markets. Armed with secret rate agreements from the Santa Fe, Standard had pushed its campaign vigorously, especially after 1903. It brought both crude and refined oil by tanker to Redondo, located on the coast about twenty miles from Los Angeles, and from this point received special rates to supply its southern stations. The rate it paid on refined oil from Redondo through Los Angeles to San Diego in 1904, for example, was less than one-third that paid by the Los Angeles refiners for the shorter haul, and on crude oil shipments for fuel its advantage was substantial, if not quite so pronounced. The government also placed heavy emphasis on the sharp decline in kerosine prices in Southern California following Standard's failure to renew its purchase contract in the spring of 1904 for the refined products of the Puente Oil Company. From July, 1902 through 1906 Standard's tank wagon sales of kerosine in Los Angeles and San Diego were almost always made at a loss, and from one-half to five cents a gallon cheaper than at San Francisco, immediately adjacent to Richmond. And July, 1902, marked the opening of the Richmond refinery.[36]

The defense, for its part, argued that there was no California law requiring that rail rates be published, and that there was "nothing illegal in the shipper getting and using such a rate as it could secure. . . ." If freight rates had not been made sufficiently low to be attractive, Standard could have built a pipeline from Redondo to Los Angeles. Even more easily, it could have supplied San Diego by tanker. H. M. Tilford, as a defense witness, also supplied useful testimony. Standard had always found marketing in Southern California highly competitive, he stated, because of the large number of small asphalt refiners that produced gasoline and kerosine as by-products and sold at cut-rate prices. Instead of being the leader in price cuts, the company had actually been forced to make cuts to hold its trade. Tilford was supported in this testimony by Standard's salesman, Hugo Wasmann, who had formerly worked for Puente and for the Southern Refining Company of Los Angeles.[37]

The government contended that Iowa Standard's several contracts after 1895 to purchase the refined output of the independent western refiners (Pacific Coast Oil, Union, and Puente) were intended to remove these companies as competitors, and that some of PCO's contracts after 1904 for the purchase of crude for Richmond were unduly restrictive. Tilford replied that California kerosine, unless manufactured under the

Starke process, even in 1908 was not competitive with eastern kerosine. It was marginally marketable and was capable of a wide sale only when mixed with kerosine of a higher quality. The restrictive provisions in some of the crude purchase contracts requiring a producer to store any oil not sold to PCO for the life of the contract, he said, were intended merely to make certain that the Richmond refinery received the quantity and quality of crude which had been agreed upon.[38]

Standard's final defense in regard to these contracts was abrupt and total. Whenever the government pressed Tilford, the New York executive responded that he had no way of re-establishing their contents. The documents, he stated, had been kept at the San Francisco headquarters. The memoranda on the contracts prepared for his use he had thrown away when the contracts expired, and the documents had been destroyed in the fire following the San Francisco earthquake. The other parties, it is true, may have retained their originals, but if so, they did not rush forward. Lyman Stewart, for example, had earlier permitted the Bureau to transcribe Union's contract with PCO of March, 1904, which continued the arrangement to keep Union out of the trade in lighter refined oils. The government attorneys, anticipating a challenge of the authenticity of their copy, wrote Stewart asking for the original, but the Union president thought it tactically wise to deliver the document only if served with a subpoena. For some reason, the government did not take this step.[39]

And so the argument went. Standard maintained it had not dominated the western industry; rather, it had helped mightily to develop the industry by pouring capital into the Pacific Coast Oil Company, by building a pipeline and a large refinery, and by turning out a merchantable kerosine, which it sold not only on the Pacific Coast but also in the Orient. In 1907, of the state's crude oil production of 40,000,000 barrels, Standard produced but 681,000 and purchased 8,500,000. There were, moreover, twenty-two competing refineries in California.[40] This hardly seemed monopoly.

5

The outcome of the case, of course, depended to only a minor degree on the western story. The arguments over Standard's western activities, however, were typical of the "opposing contentions" so "numerous" and "irreconcilable" with which the courts were faced.[41] Both the judges of the Circuit Court and the Supreme Court justices, to whom the decision of the lower court was appealed, took the only possible way out. Instead of becoming deeply involved in the specific data offered at the trial, they based their decisions on more general grounds. On November 20, 1909, the Circuit Court found in a unanimous decision that the Standard Oil Company (New Jersey), the seven named individuals, and thirty-seven subsidiary or affiliated corporations were truly a conspiracy in restraint of trade within the meaning of the Sherman Act. The case against thirty-three other subordinate companies it dismissed. In a key sentence the court held: "The defendants and their associates acquired the control of a majority of the stock of more than 30 corporations, many of which were potentially and naturally competitive, prevented their competition by means of the ownership, and then by the transfer of the stock of 19 of them to the principal company in exchange for its stock, placed in that company the control and management of all of them." Standard's counsel had argued that the companies were not competitive prior to 1899, the date Jersey Standard had become the holding company for the combine. But the court believed, nonetheless, that "the power of the principal company after the transfer of 1899 to fix the prices at which they dealt . . . and all the infinite details of their vast operations in which they might compete . . . was greater, more easily and quickly exercised, and hence more effective, than it could have been in the hands of 3,000 scattered stockholders." And the attempt to monopolize had been a main characteristic of Standard's entire history. The court ordered Jersey Standard to cease its control of the thirty-seven subsidiaries, with its decree to take effect in thirty days unless appealed.[42]

Eighteen months later, on May 15, 1911, the Supreme Court upheld the decision of the lower court. It agreed with the findings of the Circuit Court that the transfers of stock of subsidiaries and affiliates to the Jersey company had operated "to destroy the 'potentiality of competition' which otherwise would have existed. . . ." "We think no disinterested mind," Chief Justice White also asserted, "can survey the period in question [since 1870] without being irresistibly drawn to the conclusion that the very genius for commercial development and organization . . . soon begot an intent and purpose to exclude others . . . from their right to trade and thus accomplish the mastery which was the end in view." In affirming the decision of the lower court, the Supreme Court construed dissolution "not as depriving the stockholders or the corporations . . . of the power to make normal or lawful contracts or agreements, but as restraining them from . . . recreating directly or indirectly the illegal combination which the decree dissolved." The only modification made by the Supreme Court was to extend the time for dissolution to six months.[43]

Almost as widely noted as the dissolution itself was the court's elaboration of the famed "rule of reason." A large part of Chief Justice White's lengthy opinion, in fact, was concerned with establishing this principle. After a long review of British common law doctrine covering restraint of trade, the Chief Justice concluded that the proper criterion in determining whether violations of the Sherman Act had occurred was "the rule of reason guided by the established law and by the plain duty to enforce the prohibitions of the act. . . ." He held that the court was looking for "undue restraint." The "rule of reason" was the one portion of the opinion that caused controversy within the court, for it inspired a spirited dissent from Justice Harlan. Harlan argued that the court was reading into the Sherman Act something that was not there and was changing the law from a "simple, definite rule that all could understand" to something far less precise. This process of "judicial legislation," Harlan asserted, was a usurpation of the law-making functions of Congress and a threat to the constitutional structure of the government.[44]

The California press preserved its relatively detached attitude to both decisions. The findings of the Circuit Court were frequently carried solely as a news story. When editorials were written, they usually took the pessimistic view that Standard would "find a way out."[45] The decision of the Supreme Court received a far greater play. The pleasure generally expressed at the government's victory, however, was frequently restrained by dissatisfaction at the court's statement of the rule of reason. The new doctrine, it was widely held, had made the victory hollow. "It does not appear that there is anything now to prevent trusts doing about as they please and finding refuge in protracted litigation, with the encouragement to hope they can show no 'unreasonable' act has been committed," said a Los Angeles newspaper.[46]

But the press mentioned California Standard hardly at all. In the dispatches and editorials the company and its executives were almost ignored. The judicial decisions the West viewed primarily as a national, not a regional, matter.

6

Throughout the long ordeal the western executives had been faithful subordinates of 26 Broadway. The Californians kept the New York headquarters especially well informed about any matters meaningful to the antitrust case. They offered counsel, when requested; they took counsel. They watched their business behavior with a careful regard for any possible repercussions. Their stake in the outcome of the case differed from that of 26 Broadway, however, and there is good reason to believe that they viewed dissolution as no catastrophe. Their carefully considered business actions, moreover, conditioned in part by the trial, gave California Standard a more secure popular base in the West on which to build in the years of independence.

Publicity was one matter to which the Californians became increasingly attentive. When hearings held in San Francisco before Interstate Commerce Commissioner Franklin K. Lane in the fall of 1907 revealed numerous special rates by the Southern Pacific Railroad on various commodities, including oil shipments within California by the Associated and California Standard, one of the few specific allegations reported against the oil companies was that the Associated paid no charge for having its cars switched at San Jose.[47] W. S. Miller, treasurer of California Standard, was quick to point out to the eastern headquarters that his company did pay a charge. A month or two later, at the request of 26 Broadway, D. G. Scofield circularized producing and pipeline superintendents in the field, asking that they send to San Francisco "all articles which attack the Standard Oil Company . . . in the newspapers of your vicinity," so that a reply could be made if desirable. A clerk was set to work in the San Francisco office looking in newspapers and magazines for material unfavorable to the company, which was then screened and sent on to New York.[48]

In the conduct of business, especially producing, the western leaders also worked to achieve a more positive popular feeling. Their more genial attitude toward the producers, for example, marked by a greater willingness to adjust terms of Standard's purchase contracts in hardship cases and to supply information on its drilling activities, pipeline runs, and storage, helped change the image of the company in the minds of many oilmen. The *California Oil World*, which was rarely friendly to Standard, spoke favorably of these developments in a lengthy editorial:[49]

> Standard Oil is no longer a creeping, crawling black monster in California. It is easy to bargain with . . . and generally seeks the light of publicity in all of its operations. . . . So much in justice to the great octopus which has, in the past, done deeds that have brought upon it the wrath of an outraged nation. [In] a democracy such as ours the wrath of the people is the wrath of God. Standard Oil, viewed from the west, no longer invites that visitation.

Standard's more careful concern for public opinion paid out in other ways. When the Cartwright Act, an antitrust statute modeled after Ohio's stringent law, was enacted in California in the spring of 1907, the company found it had little to fear. Its name was mentioned rarely, if at all, during the period the bill was under consideration, and it was later subject to no suit.[50] E. S. Pillsbury, Standard's local counsel, after an examination of the company's marketing and oil purchase contracts, reported that very few were in any degree questionable under the act.[51] The terms of contract found so objectionable by the Bureau of Corporations two or three years earlier were no longer in force, and contracts with similar provisions were no longer written.

The company's executives were equally at ease over rebates when a case broke early in 1908 affecting the Santa Fe Railroad and the Associated Oil Company. The State Board of Railroad Commissioners reported that for most of 1906 the railroad had given the oil company a rebate of about one-third on crude oil shipments from Kern County to San Francisco Bay. Pillsbury wrote Tilford that he was willing to institute an investigation through the State Railroad Commission to see if the Southern Pacific had granted the Associated the same or a similar rebate. "I am satisfied," he commented, "that this action will have a salutary effect upon the treatment of the S.O. Company by the Railroads in the future." But the New York executive, understandably, had little liking either for publicity or public agencies. Instead, he suggested that the Southern Pacific be approached directly. This step apparently satisfied Pillsbury that the Southern Pacific had not been granting a special rate, and the matter was dropped. Standard merely filed a claim for overcharge with the Santa Fe in June, 1908, seeking the same rate the Associated had received while the rebate was in effect.[52]

In the same year, to aid the eastern executives and Standard's lawyers, D. G. Scofield wrote a long statement tracing California oil history from the time of his arrival in the West in 1870. He stressed particularly the heartbreaking years of experiment by California refiners trying to manufacture a good kerosene, a period finally brought to a close by Starke's patented process which was available solely to California Standard. His analysis of the history of the California industry during the early years of the century differed markedly from that of Conant. The western executive vigorously denied that Standard was responsible for the decline of crude prices in California in the early years of the century; rather, he asserted, overproduction was responsible. Standard, in fact, had supported the market, being the purchaser of many millions of barrels for which it had no need at the time and no prospective market outside the Pacific Coast states. "By its large investment and facilities to refine oil, to store and carry millions of barrels pending extension of markets, by providing an export outlet for the surplus of production over domestic wants of the Coast," Scofield stated, "it has really been the factor that at many times has prevented the utter demoralization of the oil business in California and saved many producers from ruin." Far from inviting censure of the company, he wrote, these accomplishments "should entitle it to the greatest praise. . . ."[53]

Scofield and his associates, loyal though they were, nevertheless were far less disturbed at the prospect of a government victory than were the residents of 26 Broadway. "A few years ago one of them would nearly jump out of his chair if a door slammed," E. S. Pillsbury later wrote, with pardonable exaggeration.[54] The executives at the New York headquarters were bearing the brunt of the trial. If they lost, their sphere of authority would be very much cut down. But for the Californians a government victory would have its positive side. It held forth the promise of independence. No longer would the westerners clear through 26 Broadway; they would become their own court of last resort.

The prospect was not unpleasing. For years the California executives had made their recommendations to H. M. Tilford or to Kenneth R. Kingsbury, his chief assistant, at 26 Broadway. At the New York headquarters the recommendations were considered along with those from other subsidiaries and in terms of Standard's world-wide program. Usually the California executives got their way, but not always. Inevitably, there was some delay caused by the necessity of referring almost any matter for the approval of the higher headquarters. There could also be a sense of exasperation among the Californians at being turned down. The western team believed that it was capable of seeing and seizing opportunities in what had become during the early years of the century the nation's most prolific oil center.

The annoyances were many. For example, the marketing executives could not build a new substation without drawing complete plans and submitting written arguments to the New York headquarters. At times, months would pass before approval was granted for what was, after all, but a small expenditure. In the meantime, a competitor might have moved in, especially in Southern California, the most sharply contested area in California Standard's domain. Similar delays and problems were experienced in expanding refinery capacity. The nature of the product line and the quantities manufactured were determined at 26 Broadway, and the quantities at times were subject to change on short notice. And while the several rebuffs to Colonel Carter in 1908 obviously pleased the other western executives, they also had to reckon with the will of 26 Broadway in producing matters.[55]

This feeling of intermittent frustration shows clearly in a strong letter that Scofield addressed to H. M. Tilford in the spring of 1910. He pointed out that during the decade, California Standard had paid more than $12,000,000 in dividends on a capital of $17,000,000 and showed a surplus of almost $15,000,000 at the end of 1909. Scofield wrote:[56]

> We do not think we will be misunderstood in stating, without particular recapitulation, that if some of the policies recommended by your California officers had been carried out at the time they were suggested, we would have shown a much larger earning power, and have also prevented the major competition we have encountered and are now meeting. We state this as an inducement and argument for you to sustain us in a present policy of looking ahead and providing ample facilities, even if they may appear at a distance somewhat in advance of actual necessity.

A year later, when Scofield was traveling to New York, W. S. Rheem asked him to take up the question of giving the western subsidiary greater authority in making fuel oil contracts. Jersey executives had recently expressed surprise, Rheem said, that California Standard's share of the Pacific Coast fuel trade was no more than 17 per cent; on the other hand, they burdened the California company with unnecessary restrictions. Rheem felt keenly about the matter, for a few days earlier Kingsbury had forced the company to turn down a profitable contract in Southern California for 100,000 barrels annually. Rheem continued:[57]

> I think it is possible that many instances of this kind might be mentioned, with parallel results extending back over at least ten years. . . . I do not feel that there will be any risk in giving us a little more of a free hand in carrying on the everyday transactions of the business here. There are enough of us, we have been in the business long enough, and have given it sufficient careful study . . . to safeguard its [Jersey's] interests. . . .

Scofield was successful in getting from James A. Moffett, California Standard's new president, the freedom of contract Rheem wanted. He also scribbled at the bottom of Rheem's letter a note indicating that he had gained Moffett's assent to a little greater freedom in another area: "Hospital donations, etc.," he wrote, "use judgment of Committee when amounts are not over $50."[58]

While detailing these evidences of feeling and friction, we must also recognize, however, that increasingly (and in important matters) the western executives were getting their way. The strikes of light, refinable crude in 1910 at Midway, as we have noted, caused the New York headquarters to begin to share the western excitement and to loosen purse-strings. That year, principally in the search for oil, California Standard's Producing Department spent a record $1,500,000. The outlay for additional pipeline and storage facilities was almost as large.[59] At Richmond, too, there was a leap forward. To help meet the growing demand for gasoline, 26 Broadway late in 1910 approved the construction of fifteen new 1,000-barrel crude stills costing a quarter-million dollars, the first substantial expansion in the size of the refinery since 1906. It was also considering building a refinery in Southern California.[60]

Before making further large investments, 26 Broadway dispatched a team of top eastern executives to California for an intensive inspection visit. Three Jersey directors made the trip: Alfred C. Bedford, a specialist in natural gas and Jersey's treasurer; Henry C. Folger, Jr., chairman of the Manufacturing Committee at 26 Broadway; and the brilliant thirty-two-year-old Walter C. Teagle, whose experience had been primarily in marketing, foreign and domestic. J. C. Donnell, president of the Ohio Oil Company, and the redoubtable Colonel J. J. Carter joined the tour to advise on producing matters. The visitors checked in at San Francisco early in November; then, accompanied by W. S. Rheem, H. M. Storey, and J. M. Atwell, the Producing Department's manager, they went down the Valley. They stopped at Coalinga, Midway (where they observed the Lakeview gusher), and Kern River. Later they crossed into Southern California, inspecting various sites for a refinery and several oil fields, including historic Pico and the promising Murphy property in the Coyote Hills.[61] Although we have found no formal report made by this high-powered team, the events of 1911 are eloquently suggestive of their conclusions, for the year is memorable not only for independence but also for the extraordinary growth in California Standard's operations.

It ran the gamut. The year 1911 witnessed the completion of a second pipeline from Waite to Richmond and, when even the two lines seemed dubiously adequate to handle the gushing production from the Valley fields, 26 Broadway authorized the building of about seventy-five miles of loops, mostly of 12-inch pipe, north of Mendota. Nearly 8,000,000 barrels of new storage were also provided in a series of large reservoirs near Bakersfield.[62] Manufacturing, too, came in for its share. The new Southern California refinery was located and almost completed at El Segundo, some ten miles west of Los Angeles on the California coast. A short pipeline was built connecting the refinery with the oil fields near the La Habra Valley.[63] At Richmond the fifteen new stills, authorized in 1910, were put on stream and asphalt added to the line of products, just after the California legislature had made its first large appropriation ($18,000,000) for paved highways. In other departments the events of 1911 were not quite so striking, but in each case the company's expenditures for new plant were greater than in 1910.[64] This sudden surge caused the *California Derrick* to remark, "It begins to appear that the great company [has] jumped as . . . from a leash unfastened. . . ." In its year-end review, the same journal again spoke of the company's "phenomenal activity . . . in every department of the oil . . . business." At that time Standard's plant account stood at $34,047,000, an increase over 1910 of $9,219,000, which was nearly as much as had occurred during the preceding five years.[65]

Even though this pouring of capital into California Standard went far toward meeting the hopes of the western executives, it diminished little, if at all, their pleasure at the prospect of freedom held forth by the antitrust decree. They recognized, of course, that the same stock-holders would control the company as was true before dissolution, but the stockholder relationship would become direct. The western executives viewed stockholder control as a lighter check upon their aspirations than control by a higher headquarters busy with the affairs of a world-wide empire. The decree, in short, brought a feeling of release, a belief that because of it their destiny would be brighter and the road ahead easier.[66]

7

The dissolution process took from May until December of 1911. On July 28, H. C. Folger, Jr., secretary of Jersey Standard, announced that the company's holdings in thirty-three subsidiaries would be distributed among the Jersey stockholders in accordance with the Supreme Court's decree. Each Jersey stockholder would receive his proportionate interest in each of the disaffiliated companies.[67] On September 30 Jersey's stock transfer books were closed. Within three weeks thereafter D. G. Scofield was in New York to sign in his meticulous way the new stock certificates of the Standard Oil Company (California).[68]

When the certificates were distributed, John D. Rockefeller, with 24.85 per cent, became the western company's largest stockholder. The estate of Charles Pratt ranked next with 5.37 per cent, and Charles W. Harkness was third with 4.41 per cent. Fourteen of Standard's great names, their companies and philanthropies, owned just under 52 per cent. This was the same proportionate interest that they held in Jersey Standard and all other of Jersey's former wholly-owned subsidiaries. Because of this continuing body of large stockholders, for a number of years many observers considered the antitrust decree ineffective, though in time a high degree of competition did emerge among many of the old Standard companies. The balance of the stock was scattered among approximately six thousand smaller holders, some of whom held less than a share. Many of these very small holders soon liquidated their interests, causing the company's stockholder list to shrink by several hundred.[69]

The distribution was completed by December 1. On that day J. A. Moffett, California Standard's president since February, 1911, resigned to stay at 26 Broadway as a Jersey vice president. Four days later D. G. Scofield succeeded him. The choice, forecast by Scofield's designation to sign the new certificates, inspired universal approval. It seemed especially appropriate both because of the loyal and effective service he had given as vice president and chief of Standard's western operations for more than a decade and because no living man had had a longer experience in California oil.[70]

His company was the fourth largest of thirty-three disaffiliates emerging from the dissolution. It ranked after New York Standard, which was half again as large; National Transit, the chief pipeline company of the old combination; and J. C. Donnell's producing organization, the Ohio Oil Company. Jersey, of course, led them all. The former parent, with a net value of $285,000,000 at the end of 1911, was more than seven times as large as California Standard (net value, $39,213,195). In 1911 none of the nation's so-called independents, like Pure Oil, Gulf, The Texas Company, or Union surpassed these five in size.[71]

Comparing California Standard with the other disaffiliates in the range of generally recognized oil industry functions is also informing, for by this yardstick the western company stood first among the old family except for the group that Jersey continued to head. In 1911 California Standard was a well-integrated organization committed to producing, refining, domestic marketing, and pipeline and marine transportation. In two other activities, natural gas and foreign marketing, it was not directly engaged, though it was a supplier. California Standard sold gas from its Midway wells to the California Natural Gas Company, which stayed with Jersey following the dissolution. And it had long furnished a large volume of refined oil and other products to companies engaged in foreign trade, chiefly New York Standard and the Vacuum Oil Company. Of the other disaffiliates, New York Standard alone approached the western company in the number of functions, being engaged in refining, domestic marketing, foreign marketing, and marine transportation.[72]

As President Scofield took over, he was heading an organization broadly experienced in the oil industry. This experience, combined with the soaring production and rapid population growth in its home territory, augured well for California Standard in the years of independence.

XV

A LOOK AT 200 BUSH

While the dissolution process was going on, California Standard took a step of symbolic significance. Late in May, 1911, the month of the Supreme Court's decree, in fact, the company revealed plans to build a home of its own in San Francisco. It bought property for a million-dollar headquarters located in the city's financial district at the northwest corner of Bush and Sansome streets, where construction began in March, 1912. The cornerstone, laid in June, reflected both past and future, for photographs of John D. Rockefeller, John D. Archbold, and Henry C. Folger, Jr., of 26 Broadway, were deposited there alongside those of the board of California Standard.[1] After another year, in June, 1913, Standard's 420 home office employees left their crowded quarters in the Sheldon Building on Market Street for 200 Bush. A ten-story, steel frame structure, sheathed in limestone and pressed brick, with a spacious and richly ornamented marble lobby, wide halls and commodious offices, the new headquarters was "quite a contrast" to the upstairs office on nearby California Street where the Tilford brothers had set up Rockefeller's first western outpost in 1878.[2] It symbolized thirty-five years of progress and the independence the company had recently achieved.

200 Bush, which one oil journal called "as fine a building as there is in San Francisco," gave Standard impressive headquarters in the city that was still clearly the western oil capital. Some sixty companies, mostly producers in the oil-rich San Joaquin Valley, were neighbors. Standard purchased crude from many of them. Two of its largest suppliers, Captain William Matson's Honolulu Consolidated Oil Company and the Southern Pacific's Kern Trading & Oil Company (to which Standard frequently traded heavy crude for light), had their offices nearby.

So had its foremost rivals. The Union Oil Company's northern headquarters was housed in the Mills Building next door to 200 Bush. Across Market Street near the Palace Hotel was the Associated Oil Company. Two blocks north on Sansome Street was a new competitor, named the General Petroleum Company in 1912 by a group of San Francisco promoters led by Captain John Barneson and Eugene de Sabla. The American Gasoline Company, organized the same year, which was the spearhead of the Royal Dutch–Shell's American invasion, was located three blocks away in a small suite of rooms in the Kohl Building.[3]

When Standard entered its new home, it was leading its rivals by a considerable margin in most phases of the western oil industry. Even in producing, it was edging to the fore. But, as we shall note, California's huge production in combination with the booming population of the West meant for the industry surging growth and change. For Standard to maintain its position, its executives needed to be alert, flexible, and resourceful in meeting the challenges and opportunities thrust upon them. Let us look briefly at the Big Seven at 200 Bush who shaped the destiny of the company during the early years of independence.

2

The directors and high administrative officers who guided California Standard after 1911 were a combination of executives long experienced in the West and of some relative newcomers.[4] None, of course, came close to the record of President Scofield. Three of the group, W. S. Miller, W. S. Rheem, and H. M. Storey, the manager of the Pipeline Department, had worked for the company ten years or more. F. H. Hillman and R. J. Hanna, the manager of the El Segundo refinery, on the other hand, had served less than a year, while K. R. Kingsbury had known the company's affairs mainly from New York, where he had been its agent since 1906.

All of Scofield's associates held him in high regard, as did the large stockholders, who could so readily have chosen another as president if they had doubted his leadership. Sixty-eight years old at the time he became the chief executive, Scofield was a long way from his flamboyant youth, when some of his actions were fully in accord with the speculative Comstock mining era in San Francisco's history. The Scofield of later years, his subordinates recall as conservatively dressed and somewhat reserved in manner, but calm and kind. He usually kept an open door, would take time to chat, and always put visitors at ease. Over the years he had developed a capacity to delegate and to listen. And despite his age, he was not strictly a desk man. As late as 1915 Scofield led his board on a tour of the company's oil lands in Southern California. In the period immediately following independence Scofield was a persuasive spokesman in getting the approval of the eastern stockholders to major programs of expansion that required additional capital. He was also ever alert to public opinion, striving constantly to improve the relationship between company and public.

W. S. Miller, the gruff, leonine giant who ranked next to Scofield in length of service, continued as director of sales, though he shared his responsibilities increasingly with a young executive recently brought in from the field, H. T. Harper. Miller's cautious, conservative temperament fitted better to the past than to the future when the gamble for production was to be the company's foremost concern. He was a Main Street merchant type, distinguished more for frugality, punctuality, and industry than for imagination. "Spending any sizable sum of money frightened him," said one who knew him well.

To a far greater extent, Scofield leaned on W. S. Rheem, the able and gregarious refiner who, at forty-nine, was almost twenty years his junior. The two men had been close friends since the construction of the Richmond refinery and had developed an abiding regard for each other. When Scofield became the chief executive, Rheem became vice president and heir apparent. He continued to spend a day a week at the refinery, but he also had an influential voice in many matters outside manufacturing. Since 1906 he had supervised the company's Marine Department. Another forte of Rheem was employee relations. This friendly, hearty man, "handsome as a matinee idol," said a secretary, was usually conspicuously present at any social function sponsored by the headquarters.

H. M. Storey matched Rheem in years of service, having come to California in 1900, but he was a dozen years younger. His work in the Pipeline Department brought him a directorship in April, 1913, to which he added the next year the secretary's office and the exacting responsibility for the company's crude oil purchases. Storey, a tall man who stood "straight as an arrow," spent most of his time in the field, where he had an inspector's keen eye and a deep interest in employee welfare. Like Rheem, he possessed a quick and active mind and great human warmth.

During the teens Fred Hillman was probably the most notable new member of the board. Coming from the Ohio Oil Company in January, 1911, with instructions similar to those given Colonel Carter three years before—to build up production—he accomplished his mission with phenomenal success. Within eight years the company was to move from a position far back in the pack to become the nation's top producer, a success due to a happy combination of skill, teamwork, a reputation for "fair dealing" with lessors, and luck. Among Hillman's talents was a diplomacy of a high order. A practical oilman who had come up through the ranks, he gradually came to recognize in California the contributions of geologists and other technical men and helped blunt the prejudices of other old-timers against the new techniques. This short, rotund man, with a head crowned by a shock of iron-grey hair, had a capacity for inspiring loyalty and devotion, so much so that his department became almost a family affair.

Richard J. Hanna, formerly the superintendent of the Eclipse refinery at Franklin, Pennsylvania, traveled West about the same time as Hillman to undertake the building of the refinery at El Segundo. This refinery, of which he became the manager, went on stream late in November of 1911, just before the company cut its ties with 26 Broadway. Like Hillman, Hanna was to play primarily a specialist's role. As Rheem's responsibilities broadened, Hanna became the chief figure in manufacturing. In April, 1913, along with Storey, he was elected a director, and the next year, in June, 1914, he took over the office of treasurer from W. S. Miller. Hanna, called the "Old Gent" by his immediate subordinates, was a big man, somewhat florid in appearance, slow in speech, and rather crusty in manner.

Youngest among the Big Seven was Kenneth R. Kingsbury. Although only thirty-five in 1911, for more than five years he had been intimately acquainted with the company's affairs, first as assistant to H. M. Tilford and later to J. A. Moffett. Marketing had been his special interest. Kingsbury was elected second vice president and director in December, 1911, and came to San Francisco the following June. He had the unique distinction on the board of being a college man, having studied for four years at Princeton with an additional year in mining engineering at Columbia. Kingsbury was an impressive figure, forceful, strong-willed, and decisive in manner, gifted with imagination and ability. He was a hard driver, usually the last among the executives to turn off his office lights, a man who could lose himself in his job. Like Rheem and Storey, he was to play a larger and larger role in shaping policy. He handled the "external relations" of the company. Drawing up contracts with other former Standard units, marketing products outside the home market, and attending to arrangements for rail transportation were mainly his responsibility. He also had a strong hand in advertising and public relations. Along with Scofield, Kingsbury was especially important in gaining approval for programs of expansion from the big eastern stockholders, for he had won their confidence while at 26 Broadway.

There were also, of course, a number of veterans at 200 Bush supporting the Big Seven. The secretary of the company, William Edwards, who was in charge of oil purchases until his abrupt departure late in 1913, worked closely with Scofield, Rheem, and Miller. R. C. Warner, by 1914 manager of the credit department and later comptroller, also played a prominent supporting role. In the early years Warner headed a small office called the "clearing department" that gathered and analyzed statistical data on all phases of company operations for the guidance of the directors. An even more important adviser was the brilliant Oscar Sutro, a partner in Pillsbury, Madison & Sutro, who gradually took over Standard's legal work from his firm's aging senior partner, E. S. Pillsbury.

In each of the operating departments there were a few key subordinates who cannot be overlooked. Hillman, for example, relied especially on two quite dissimilar men: his department manager, happy-go-lucky Joe Atwell, an explosive yet friendly sort, a practical oilman far less experienced than Hillman, and the hypersensitive Dr. E. A. Starke, who headed the company's geological staff until he resigned in July, 1917. H. M. Storey looked chiefly to two skilled engineers, the somewhat aloof and determined Henry N. Kuechler, who succeeded Storey as pipeline manager in April, 1913, and the coolly efficient H. H. Hall, the department's chief engineer. J. C. Rohlfs, since 1906 the soft-spoken young manager of the Marine Department, reported first to Rheem and later to K. R. Kingsbury. In manufacturing, Rheem's three top aides at Richmond—L. D. Dimm, the manager, J. P. Smith, the superintendent, and J. C. Black, the chief engineer—reported to R. J. Hanna following Hanna's appointment as director of manufacturing in 1913. Subordinate to Miller and Harper in marketing were three home office veterans— Charlie Watson, manager of Real Estate and Construction, Colonel E. H. Merrill, manager of the Lubricating Department, and J. C. Fitzsimmons, manager of the Fuel Oil Department.

There never was any question where power lay, however, for important decisions were almost always made at the directors' level. Following a practice of 26 Broadway, the directors met every morning in the board room to discuss matters informally. About once a month they gathered at the refinery at Richmond, the legal home of the company until April, 1917, for a formal board meeting.[5] The morning sessions frequently were little more than a talk fest, for each director expected to handle his own responsibilities. The board, moreover, was made up of strong men who had faith in themselves, and who would have resented intrusions for too light reasons into their areas of jurisdiction. In day-to-day affairs, each man was apt to have his own way. Hillman, the most independent of the directors, sometimes acted solely on his own judgment when speed seemed essential. On one occasion he wrote Scofield, after buying some oil lands at Coalinga, "I feel sure you would have agreed with me in this purchase if I could have consulted you."[6] From time to time delegations of directors, ranging from two to the whole board, would go on trips of inspection to Southern California or to the Northwest. And if it was an important matter concerning finance, a director, usually Vice President Kingsbury, was likely to go East to consult with the big stockholders.[7]

Most problems confronting the directors, such as the search for oil, oil purchases, additional pipeline and refining capacity, new marketing facilities, and so on, fell within the bounds of the operating departments. A few of the most crucial, however, like raising new capital and public and governmental relations, were of an overarching character, and for that reason President Scofield, aided by Rheem and Kingsbury, made them particularly his own.

3

Securing new capital to continue the spectacular round of growth was the most serious problem facing the company in 1911. Earlier it had looked to 26 Broadway, where Jersey Standard had acted as banker, advancing funds on open account and buying the notes and treasury stock of its western subsidiary. As the time for dissolution approached, 26 Broadway moved to tidy up this arrangement. Late in July, 1911, when the company's indebtedness to Jersey amounted to $5,603,000 on open account and $6,600,000 in twenty-year notes at 6 per cent, the New York headquarters ordered California Standard to sell Jersey the last $8,000,000 of its treasury stock (bringing its capital to the authorized limit of $25,000,000) and to use the proceeds "in payment of your debt and part payment of the notes." But this was purely a bookkeeping transaction. At the end of August, California Standard still owed Jersey $4,200,000 in twenty-year notes and a more modest $650,000 on open account.[8]

It was inevitable that when Scofield visited New York in October to deal with the dissolution he should discuss this indebtedness and future capital requirements. At the time of Scofield's visit, the open account had grown to nearly $2,000,000, in addition to the balance of the twenty-year notes. The western executive told 26 Broadway that his company would require about $13,500,000 in new capital during 1912 if it paid off its debt to Jersey and continued its scheduled expansion. He estimated that the company would earn around $5,000,000, leaving about $8,500,000 to be raised from other sources.[9]

Perhaps because of the myriad of problems attached to dissolution, 26 Broadway came up with a short-term answer. Jersey Standard, obviously, could hardly maintain its banker role for long without arousing the interest of the federal government, but while California Standard developed new means of financing, the lawyers believed that Jersey could continue to help. It was decided that, for the moment, the balance of the twenty-year notes could remain outstanding and, in addition, Jersey would take $8,000,000 in new 6 per cent notes, converting its open account into a short-term fixed debt and supplying more than $5,000,000 in new money. Of the notes, $2,875,000 would run for one year, a like amount for two years, and $2,250,000 for a three-year term.[10]

This arrangement provided an even briefer breathing spell than at first appeared, for by February, 1912, Scofield was writing James A. Moffet that California Standard had already allocated $4,750,000 of the new loan. Since this sum represented all of the three-year money and the bulk of the money Jersey Standard had offered for two years, what remained was mostly for a one-year term, scheduled for repayment in 1913. Scofield also informed the Jersey executive that his earlier estimate of the company's needs for the year was short by nearly $2,000,000, for the cost of 200 Bush and some prospective pipeline expenditures had been inadvertently omitted.[11]

An obvious answer was to ask the stockholders to supply additional capital. This possibility was first discussed informally, for among the nearly six thousand stockholders the Rockefellers and eleven other great interests, including members of the Harkness, Pratt, Payne, and Flagler families, controlled a majority of the stock. Finally, toward the middle of May, 1912, they approved a proposal to double California Standard's authorized capital, making the new limit $50,000,000.[12] E. T. Bedford, a former Jersey director and member of its Executive Committee, who had recently been to California, gave Scofield an insight into what had gone on: "I was consulted in reference to this increased capitalization and found there was some difference of opinion. I urged the amount be made the maximum . . . which I am pleased to note has been agreed upon." The friendly words of this respected counselor of the big stockholders, especially the Pratt family, must also have delighted the westerner:[13]

> I believe in the California Company for I believe in its people and in its . . . conservative management, its valuable assets and its possibilities for the future from the growth in consumption. It will be strange indeed if you do not get your share of it. I feel, as I have often expressed to you, that years ago you were denied a chance [at] some of the good future that should not have been denied you and which was so generously granted to all other subsidiaries. Now you have to make up for lost time.

After receiving the welcome news Scofield wrote a long letter to Kingsbury in New York concerning the amount of new stock the company should issue. The California president stated that he expected outlays for the remainder of 1912 of nearly $8,000,000:

Marine Department (2 tankers)	$1,143,250
Pipeline (extension and expansion of the Valley system)	1,101,793
Sales Department (2 new terminals in the Northwest, etc.)	588,300
Office Building (200 Bush)	452,078
El Segundo (completing the refinery)	297,310
Richmond Refinery (a general expansion)	1,510,300
Producing Department	2,825,000
Total	$7,918,031

And the company's debt to Jersey had grown to $10,350,000, making a total need of more than $18,000,000. As Scofield saw it, California Standard had two options. It could issue $15,000,000 in stock and use its net earnings for the last eight months of the year—estimated at $3,333,333—to make up the difference, or issue $18,000,000 and resume the payment of dividends. Since February, 1910, California Standard had paid no dividends but instead had plowed back its profits into the business, a policy that had recently brought inquiries from stockholders like Moffet and E. T. Bedford. They hoped that the company would resume dividends on a "conservative" basis. "Would it not . . . place the Company in a better position with its stockholders generally," Scofield asked Kingsbury, "to offer the $18,000,000 and commence the payment of dividends as soon as the funds were available . . . ?"[14]

It was to take until August before the legal technicalities connected with the increase in authorized capital were surmounted. By that time California Standard realized that it would need the full $8,000,000 of the Jersey loan and, in fact, would borrow $450,000 more. In these circumstances, the board decided to sell $20,000,000 of the new shares. Stockholders of record at the end of August were offered rights at par ($100) amounting to 80 per cent of their current holdings. The offer was extremely attractive, for between late May, when the prospective issue became publicly known, and the end of August the market price of the company's stock had jumped from $155 to $215 a share.[15]

The returns from the issue, along with a rate of earnings running fully 40 per cent above Scofield's estimate, gave an unusual feeling of financial ease. During November and December the directors placed $6,500,000 with the New York brokerage house of Jessup & Lamont to profit from high interest rates in the call money market. They also used a portion of their ample funds in mid-December to pay a dividend of $2.50 per share, which became for nearly a decade a regular quarterly practice, plus an occasional extra dividend in the war years and after.[16]

Money at hand, Scofield and his associates quickened the pace of the company. In 1913 they built up the great Richmond plant to a capacity of 60,000 barrels daily, enlarged El Segundo, and laid a second short pipeline to the Southern California refinery. Two fine new tankers, the *Richmond* and *El Segundo,* were added to the fleet, and a third ordered. Marketing facilities were also expanded.[17]

But the principal drive was for more production. During 1913 Standard was extremely active, drilling 72 wells, of which 63 were in the San Joaquin Valley. It was in Southern California, however, that the company made its great gamble, when in December, 1913, it took a forty-year lease on the highly prized Murphy properties in the Coyote Hills near Whittier. The terms, $5,000,000 and 2,500 shares of stock (valued at $200 per share), plus a large royalty on the oil produced, suggest the scale on which Standard was doing business. The shares of stock and the first million were paid at the time the lease was signed. A second million was due four months later, and the balance at intervals through 1918.[18]

This big deal capped a year in which Standard's new investment reached $13,908,000. In addition, the company had paid dividends totaling $4,493,000. Offsetting these expenditures, it showed earnings of $19,386,000. Of this amount, however, $8,475,000 represented a write-up in the value of the producing properties, leaving only $10,-911,000 as profits from the general business of the company. The rate of spending for new plant, along with the dividends, in the course of 1913 had changed the financial condition of the company from ease to stringency.[19]

Once more Standard turned to its owners, offering each stockholder early in January, 1914, a 10 per cent increase in his holdings at the par value of $100. The sale went through without a hitch, for Standard's oil strikes in the Coyote Hills adjacent to the Murphy lease, in addition to the lease itself, had caused a very favorable response in the stock market. In the three-month span before the beginning of February, 1914, when the warrants were issued, the company's stock climbed nearly 90 points to a peak above $280 a share. The new financing, completed on March 10, gave Standard a little more than $4,500,000 to meet its obligations and for new investment.[20]

Because this transaction would leave the treasury with fewer than 3,000 unissued shares, simultaneous with the January offering Standard asked its stockholders to approve a second jump in authorized capital from $50,000,000 to $100,000,000. The proposal was approved on March 16, 1914, only to run into an embarrassing technicality. The meeting, held at 10 o'clock in accordance with the board resolution and the legal notice published in the press, did not correspond with the noon hour specified in the announcements mailed to the stockholders. Out of "prudence," the stockholders met again in July, and not until August was the increase effective.[21]

Meanwhile, in May Scofield made what was to be his last trip to New York. Probably, among other things, he discussed a stock dividend with some of the large holders. At the end of 1913 the company's balance sheet showed a surplus of $35,089,000; in March, 1914, its stock touched $350 per share.[22] Large surpluses and high stock prices had caused several of the old Standard companies, including Indiana, to issue stock dividends.[23] For Scofield to have favored such a move, moreover, would have been in keeping with his past. In April, 1909, just after California Standard had paid a dividend of $6,600,000 in the form of twenty-year notes to its Jersey parent, Scofield urged that in the future 26 Broadway issue treasury stock against the surplus to the full limit of the authorized capital. His argument had a public relations cast: "It would seem that by this method our capital stock would more fittingly represent our investment. There would be no large surplus showing in our books and current earnings available for dividends would look better in the way of percentage of current earnings to capital stock." Less "adverse criticism" of the company would occur, he maintained, because no longer would the ratio of dividends to capital appear so high. The western executive enclosed a clipping from a San Francisco newspaper to buttress his point. Tilford replied in a brief note that "we have already given consideration to . . . increasing the issued capital stock . . . and had reached the conclusion it would not be advisable. . . ."[24]

Presumably, President Scofield's ideas had not changed. His annual report to the stockholders for 1914 reveals that the board had been thinking of a stock dividend, but, because of the mix-up in approving the new shares, World War I had begun before they became available. The war's demoralizing effect, including a precipitate decline in stock values, caused the board to shelve its plans. "We could not and cannot foresee what possible effect a long . . . war might have on our business," Scofield wrote, "and we felt that it was far better for all of our stockholders that we should not declare a stock dividend until the general business situation had changed."[25]

Shifting their attention, during the spring of 1915 the directors considered offering the stockholders one new share at par for each ten already held in order to raise about $5,000,000 in new capital to enlarge the refineries and to extend and improve the pipelines.[26] But this idea was soon dropped, probably because of falling production in the Midway and of a concern for the future of the Oriental trade during these war-wracked years. One expenditure that could not be delayed, however, was for an addition to 200 Bush, where nearly 600 employees were crowded in quarters that had housed 420 two years before. In September of 1915 Standard made an appropriation to add two more floors costing $184,000. The company's total new investment that year was $3,778,-000, the lowest figure since 1909. It was easily handled, along with the quarterly dividends, by the net earnings, which amounted to $9,530,-000.[27]

During 1915 the recession following the outbreak of World War I yielded to a boom, marked in the oil industry by improved demand and higher prices. Scofield, in his annual report, summarized 1915 as "very satisfactory," and forecast "a very prosperous year for 1916." The company's balance sheet and the price of its stock supported his optimistic outlook. At the end of 1915 its surplus had grown to $44,852,000; its stock in December had reached almost $400 per share.[28] A survey at the beginning of 1916 credited Standard's total shares with a market value of $192,500,000, a larger figure than that for any member of the old combination except Jersey ($550,695,000). Standard of New York ranked next after the California company, with a market value totaling $172,500,000. The New York company, however, had issued stock with a par value of $76,000,000, compared to California Standard's approximately $50,000,000.[29] To Scofield and his associates it seemed a good time to dust off their plans for a stock dividend.

In January, 1916, 200 Bush announced that all stockholders of record on March 4 would receive one additional share for each two shares held. The effect of this action was to reduce the surplus by $24,843,000 and to increase the capital stock from $49,687,000 to $74,530,000. To correct a possible misconception that the dividend represented a huge disbursement of earnings of special benefit to a few large stockholders, the company carefully pointed out that surplus represented earnings that had been reinvested in the business rather than paid out to the stockholders. The purpose of the stock dividend, 200 Bush stated, was merely to recognize that the portion of the surplus converted into stock would remain permanently in the company and that the stockholders, as owners, should receive dividends upon it.[30] Financially, of course, the company could have served its stockholders about as well by maintaining the former amount of stock and by paying a proportionately larger cash dividend. But this higher rate of return on a smaller number of shares would have made the company vulnerable to the sort of criticism against which Scofield had warned in 1909.

The trend of Standard's business in 1916, fulfilling the Scofield forecast, influenced the board to declare a second stock dividend in January of 1917. The year 1916 was "most prosperous . . . in all of the Departments of our business," declared Standard's president in his annual report. In December, 1916, the market price of Standard's stock was once more approaching $400. With net earnings of $17,605,000, the company had more than met the sizable new investment for that year, amounting to $9,834,000, and the dividends of $6,832,000. Standard's surplus stood at $30,782,000. "In view of the accumulation and reinvestment over a period of years of the Company's surplus earnings in lieu of their distribution as dividends, [we] deem it only just to the stockholders that stock should be issued to them to represent surplus earnings," the directors stated. The stock dividend of 1917, payable at the rate of one new share for each three shares held, raised the capital stock issued by the company to $99,373,000, just short of the authorized limit of $100,000,000.[31]

This move had one astonishing outcome; in par value, the capital stock of California Standard slightly surpassed that of Jersey Standard ($98,300,000). These figures, it is true, supply an inaccurate comparison of financial strength, because the old parent, ever conservative, had stood firm against all arguments for capitalizing its huge surplus, which at the end of 1916 amounted to $300,472,000. Nevertheless, the new amount of capital stock on California Standard's balance sheet was probably not inappropriate in suggesting both the optimism of its leaders and, with some exaggeration, the pace of its growth. The company had been surging forward rapidly, as the following statistics show:

Table 15: Comparison of Total Assets (In Millions of Dollars, December 31)[32]

	1911	1916
California Standard	$ 48.9	$109.4
Jersey Standard	367.5	505.3
Ratio—California to Jersey	13.3%	21.6%

During its first five years of independence the western company had raised $24,686,665 in new capital and had issued $49,686,665 in stock dividends. It had earned $53,221,225, retaining $30,937,799 (58 per cent) in the business and paying out $22,273,426 to the stockholders. In addition to the cash dividends, during 1915 and 1916 the earnings had easily handled the new investment, which during the whole five years had amounted to $45,878,490. California Standard had come far from the capital-starved operation that gave Scofield and his board so much anxiety at the moment of dissolution.

4

The other major overarching problem of these years, building better relations between California Standard and its public, was more nebulous and, over the long run, proved more difficult than securing adequate capital. Unfortunately for the company, the name "Standard" carried a dual connotation: it signified business efficiency and quality products; it also suggested to many people economic power ruthlessly used. This latter popular feeling, enduring from pre-dissolution times, was inevitably a matter of concern for the men at 200 Bush.

"You have not a monopoly and you have a chance to grow as no other subsidiary I know of has," E. T. Bedford wrote Scofield late in the summer of 1912.[33] And yet, along with all other Standard units, California Standard had been scarred in some measure by the long argument that had gone on around the old Trust. The company had this legacy to live down. It was a vexatious burden, for Standard's officers had to consider public response to their actions far more seriously than did executives of other western companies. They also had to be especially circumspect in their relations with government, for clashes with public officials had supplied many damaging moments for 26 Broadway. At times prudence dictated that they avoid taking a public stand on legislative matters important to them, even when other companies felt free to do so. In these circumstances, good counsel was imperative. The company relied especially on its able legal advisers, E. S. Pillsbury and his younger colleague, Oscar Sutro.

Among the most disturbing matters confronting the company in 1911, was the possibility that California's major pipelines might fall under the jurisdiction of the Interstate Commerce Commission. Standard had no desire to see its pipelines transformed into common carriers subject to the will of a governmental body. Sutro advised the company to protect itself by continuing to use the lines solely to move crude to its refineries, which was clearly intrastate transportation. In no event, he warned, should Standard permit the pipelines to perform any marketing function, because marketing could so readily come within the definition of interstate commerce.[34]

Early in 1913 the threat of public regulation became greater when the independent California producers brought pressure simultaneously at both Washington and Sacramento to make the lines common carriers. Indirectly, an action by Standard had spurred this compaign. In September, 1912, having 21,000,000 barrels of heavy oil in storage, Standard ceased purchasing crude of less than 18° gravity. Most heavy oil operators, hard hit by this decision, were forced to restrict production and to shut down wells. As a way out, they wanted the pipeline companies to transport their crude at rates low enough to permit them to enter directly into the main fuel markets of the state, an opportunity denied them by the high railroad rates.[35] A few oilmen, including Mark Requa, later head of the Oil Division of the Fuel Administration during World War I, doubted the efficacy of this plan. Instead of relief, Requa foresaw a greater demoralization of prices if numerous small operators entered the fuel trade and destroyed such stability as the major companies were able to create because of their vast storage facilities. To him, overproduction was the heart of the problem. It could be solved only if the independent producers were willing to combine into a few large companies so that the flow of oil could be regulated to correspond more closely with demand.[36] But more oilmen preferred what seemed an easier and quicker solution.

The producers desiring to force common carrier status on the pipelines pointed out that the federal government had a weapon at hand, for the major lines all traveled in part through the public domain without authorization. To ward off this threat, early in 1913 Standard sought an amendment to extend to California an act of Congress that had granted rights of way to private pipelines passing through federal lands in Arkansas. Oscar Sutro was the leader in this maneuver. Nevertheless, for reasons of public relations he felt that Standard had to keep in the background, leaving lobbying for the amendment to others. "It seems unfortunate," he wrote, "that active participation on the part of the Standard Oil Company in any such movement should be an obstacle to its success, regardless of the merits of the case—but such seems to be the temper of the public at this time."[37]

Sutro's interest in this effort waned rapidly, however, after the producers won a victory at Sacramento, where they had introduced several bills in the legislature during the spring of 1913. One bill spelled out a pattern of regulation by the State Railroad Commission; another, a bludgeoning measure, provided that pipelines not serving as common carriers should pay fifty cents a barrel for oil transported beside or across a public highway as a license for the right of way.[38] Standard took no part in the hearings, for to have done so would have been self-defeating.

Instead, it watched unhappily as both producers and pipeline companies tried to make emotional capital from its name. Common carrier status for pipelines was essential, the producers claimed, to keep Standard from monopolizing the California industry. They claimed that Associated, which had a pipeline running from Kern County to San Francisco Bay, was an ally of Standard, and that the General Petroleum Company, with a pipeline from the San Joaquin Valley to Los Angeles and an option to purchase control of the Union Oil Company, was itself under Standard's control. These oil companies, for their part, unequivocally asserted their independence. They also argued, according to a Progressive Party chronicler, that the effect of the bills "would be to fill the pipelines of Standard's competitors . . . with low gravity oil, unfit for refining, and thus prevent successful competition with the Standard in the gasolines and other distillates." The Producers Transportation Company, in fact, professed to fear that Standard would force its own huge stocks of heavy oil into the lines of its rivals.[39]

For several years after the bills were enacted, Standard followed the strategy of leaving opposition chiefly to others. Among the pipeline companies it alone conformed, filing under protest with the State Railroad Commission rates and regulations for the use of its lines that were little intended to please the producers.[40] But it shipped no oil. An injunction secured by the Associated soon suspended the operation of the laws, and the State Railroad Commission made no effort to enforce them while the nation was at war.[41] By that time the California Supreme Court had ruled that the Associated could not be forced to serve as a common carrier because the company had constructed or purchased its lines for its own use. Presumably, Standard was protected by the same argument. Early in 1919 Standard entered the fray to strike a last blow. Using the device of a stockholder suit against the company, it got a decision in the federal courts declaring unconstitutional the fifty cents a barrel levy on private pipelines running beside or across a public highway.[42]

200 Bush again endured an unhappy experience as "whipping boy" when gasoline prices fell precipitately and then rose quite as rapidly during the years 1914 to 1917. As the largest western company, Standard usually played the role of price leader. When the company lowered prices early in World War I because of the overproduction of light crudes, heavy stocks of gasoline, and unsettled world conditions, some small refiners charged Standard with a "cut-throat game" designed to "crowd us out of business."[43] When gasoline rose sharply a year or more later, induced by the war boom in the United States, a declining

STANDARD OIL COMPANY

INCORPORATED UNDER THE LAWS OF CALIFORNIA

ANNOUNCES
EFFECTIVE DECEMBER 7, 1911
ITS OFFICERS ARE AS FOLLOWS:

D. G. SCOFIELD	PRESIDENT
W. S. RHEEM	VICE PRESIDENT
K. R. KINGSBURY	SECOND VICE PRESIDENT
W. S. MILLER	TREASURER
WM. EDWARDS	SECRETARY
W. M. HALL	ASS'T SECRETARY AND ASS'T TREASURER
R. C. WARNER	ASS'T SECRETARY AND TRANSFER AGENT

BOARD OF DIRECTORS

D. G. SCOFIELD   W. S. RHEEM

F. H. HILLMAN   W. S. MILLER

K. R. KINGSBURY

SHELDON BUILDING
SAN FRANCISCO
CALIFORNIA

Announcing independence

D. G. Scofield, July, 1912

W. S. Rheem, July, 1912

K. R. Kingsbury, July, 1912

F. H. Hillman, July, 1912

W. S. Miller, July, 1912

H. M. Storey, July, 1912

R. J. Hanna

200 Bush in 1914

production of light crudes, and the heavy demands from belligerents, a Los Angeles newspaper stirred up a hornet's nest of accusations. It charged the company with "reaping exorbitant profits" and, joined by some public officials, including the mayor, helped stage two public mass meetings early in 1916. Appeals were sent to Sacramento asking that the State Railroad Commission regulate gasoline prices or, at the very least, investigate the causes of the "arbitrary and unwarranted" price increases. But the state's Progressive governor, Hiram Johnson who took no part in the hysteria, calmly replied that the State Railroad Commission had no authority even to conduct an investigation.[44] This turmoil, coming at a time when gasoline cost as little or less in California than in any other section of the country,[45] suggested how readily popular feeling could be manipulated against the company. For 200 Bush, it was a matter to ponder.

In other situations, especially those to which government was a party, the company could more easily chart a course to avoid trouble. Guided by its attorneys, it negotiated new agreements with some members of the old Standard Oil group that would not run afoul of the dissolution decree, putting its business with these companies on the same basis as with any outside firm.[46] Union Tank Line, the tank car company of the old combination, to take a minor example, paid for the right to use Standard's telegraph line up the San Joaquin Valley after 1911. And when the suggestion was made that Zerolene be advertised by painting signs on the UTL cars under contract to the company, it was not done lest it be viewed as a special favor.[47]

There was hardly a matter more harassing to the California industry and to Standard during the second decade of the century than the fight over the rights of oil producers on government lands withdrawn from sale by President Taft's executive order of September, 1909. Standard vigorously supported the position of the industry, as we shall see, but it also tried to keep the company's name from becoming a target in the contest. Taking the advice of its counsel in determining its own conduct, the company recognized the action of the President as valid. Regardless of what its competitors did, Standard attempted "to keep well inside the law. . . ."[48]

Many more examples could be given. In 1913 California followed a number of other states in enacting a "one-price" law, requiring that companies sell their products at uniform prices throughout the state, except for costs of transportation and distribution, or to meet the prices of competitors. This measure, which Standard had not opposed, attempted to strike at the ugly tactic of selling below cost in localized markets in order to drive smaller and weaker competitors from the field. Vice President Kingsbury was determined that Standard should not come under attack. "It will be necessary for us to very carefully go over all of our selling prices in this State to see that they conform strictly to the new law," he wrote Standard's attorneys.[49]

Even when no law was directly involved, the company was cautious. In 1912 Standard refused a sizable contract for gasoline because the foreign marketer placing the order wanted the gasoline put up in tins of 4¾ gallons instead of the customary 5 gallons without noting the fact on the label. Although the tins would have borne the name and brand of the other company, Pillsbury advised Standard to be party to no such deceit, "even indirectly." Its reputation, he pointed out, was far too valuable to risk in such a transaction.[50]

Beyond trying to keep free from controversy, 200 Bush also courted public favor. It involved little things, like identifying the company with the West. "Incorporated in California" its new letterhead proclaimed immediately below "Standard Oil Company." Standard began to distinguish many of its products from those of other Standard companies by using the prefix "Calol" (California oil) and the grizzly bear for its trademark.[51] And, led by President Scofield, it sought to destroy the reputation for secrecy, earned in an earlier day, which had caused so much suspicion.

Because of the rapid growth of its capital, Standard was a likely candidate for the numerous rumors sweeping California concerning purchases or mergers among the large oil companies. In 1911 Standard was reported to have bought the Associated, a story that would crop up again a year or two later.[52] Late in 1912, when the General Petroleum Company picked up an option from the Lyman Stewart family for control of the Union Oil Company, some oilmen thought that General must be a stalking horse for Standard, for they doubted that General could raise the many millions the deal would require. General, in fact, could not raise the money, and the efforts of an English syndicate, to which General turned for support, also failed.[53] In 1913 an even wilder rumor had California Standard buying the Ford Motor Company.[54]

The company could have ignored such baseless stories, but to have done so Scofield felt would have been an error in times so sensitive to the charge of monopoly. Instead, he responded to the rumor of 1911 concerning the Associated by asking that the *San Francisco Chronicle*, which had started the story, give equal publicity to his denial.[55] When the news broke of the deal between General and the Stewarts, he ordered paid advertisements inserted in the San Francisco newspapers stating that Standard was in no way involved. He did the same thing a few weeks later in the case of another rumored purchase of the Associated. The frequently hostile *California Oil World* gave Scofield high marks for these actions. "No concealment, no attempt at secrecy, no 'none of your business' attitude had been maintained," said its editor. "His frankness has generally disarmed suspicion, as it ought to, so that even the papers usually distrustful of anything with a Standard label . . . have not ventured to cast doubt on Mr. Scofield's word. . . ."[56] By 1914 the public was becoming convinced that the best source of news on Standard was the company itself.[57]

Such experiences helped lead the company to what was probably its most important decision in public relations during these years, the establishment of a monthy house organ, the *Standard Oil Bulletin*. This little magazine, which first appeared in May, 1913, was the brainchild of Vice President Kingsbury. Before long its statement of purpose was riding below the masthead: "The aim of the STANDARD OIL BULLETIN is to furnish first hand . . . to the Company stockholders, employees, and patrons, as well as the general public *facts* concerning the Company's business and its methods." Scofield regularly used the *Bulletin* to supplement the annual balance sheet with a clear and informing analysis and a detailed report on the events of the year, an uncommon practice in that day. Its editorials, usually written by Oscar Sutro, forcefully presented the company's point of view on a host of public matters. The *Bulletin* also early began to give authoritative data on production in the California fields and the prices Standard was paying for crude. Because of its contents, this pioneer oil company magazine was widely quoted almost from the start. Standard soon enjoyed the compliment of imitation when other companies, like Jersey Standard, began to publish their own house organs.[58]

The company also won friends among the several millions who visited the Panama Pacific International Exposition at San Francisco in 1915 commemorating the opening of the Panama Canal. At this first world's fair held in the West, Standard set up four separate exhibits, the handiwork of J. C. Fitzsimmons, the imaginative manager of the Fuel Oil Department. The main exhibit, housed in the Palace of Mines, was an eye-catcher. Enclosed by a "fence composed of models of the derricks of famous wells," it contained, in addition to the customary displays of products, models of various phases of the oil industry: miniature wells actually pumping oil beneath blackened derricks, the Richmond refinery, and tank steamers, tank cars, and tank wagons. Fossils from oil producing formations were placed under miscroscopes for public viewing.

Most impressive of all, according to the oil journals, was a replica of Standard's famed McNee section in the Midway, which showed the wells and underlying strata and the techniques used to keep water from seeping into the oil sands. A model of its gas trap, which saved natural gas for fuel, was also on display as another evidence of its interest in conservation.[59]

The Exposition jury awarded Standard a number of gold medals for its products, but the medals that pleased Scofield and his associates most were those which had public relations overtones. Sutro wrote his partner, E. S. Pillsbury, "Everyone here is very proud of the awards to the S.O. Co. 'Grand Medal of Honor' for its work and policies; also Medal[s] of honor for Conservation of Natural Resources and for the 'Bulletin.' " "Work and policies," so Kingsbury informed the press, referred to "the manner in which our company has dealt with its employees, its customers and the public, and for the methods it has developed in producing, transporting, refining and selling petroleum."[60]

5

While the Exposition was going on, Standard's board determined on a gesture to one of its own members which had incidental public relations value. Taking a suggestion from A. C. Bedford,[61] they decided to name a tanker for D. G. Scofield, who was entering the twilight of a long career.

To honor Standard's venerable president, nearly five thousand people gathered for the launching on June 3, 1916, at San Francisco's Union Iron Works. His granddaughter, Miss Rosamond Boynton, christened the vessel. Twenty-one years earlier at the same shipyard Scofield had witnessed a similar ceremony, the launching of the *George Loomis*, a vessel with less than one-tenth the tonnage of Standard's new flagship. It was fitting that Captain George E. Bridgett, the first skipper of the *Loomis*, was still around to take command of the *Scofield*, which, with a capacity of 81,000 barrels, was the largest tanker on the Pacific Coast and one of the largest in the world.[62]

Scofield's thoughts that day must have been of the past. He could look back at the milestones in the history of the company as he read the congratulatory messages from such old friends as John D. Archbold and A. C. Bedford of Jersey Standard; H. C. Folger, Jr., and H. I. Pratt of New York Standard; J. C. Donnell of the Ohio Oil Company; and C. N. Payne, formerly of the National Transit Company, who had retired in Titusville.[63] For at some signal point in his career and that of his company, each of these men had played an important part. But perhaps most of all he was touched by the words of William K. Flint of Alameda, the father-in-law of one of his daughters. Flint recalled, in a letter embellished with detail, how "the little craft of the Pacific Coast Oil Co. has with your guidance . . . and wise management become one of the great fleet of the Standard Oil Co." Scofield thanked his old friend, so "familiar with all my early struggles in the oil industry of California. It is a great satisfaction to me," he wrote, "to have lived to see the outcome which has far exceeded the most optimistic forecast made by me many years ago."[64]

Even at the time of the launching, his health had begun to give way. For two weeks prior, he had been ill, and his condition did not improve. For a while he managed to attend the monthly board meetings at Richmond, but he was away from 200 Bush much of the time. More and more the burdens of the top office fell upon Rheem and Kingsbury. On September, 26, 1916, Scofield's attendance at the monthly meetings came to an end.[65]

Aware that he was failing, Standard's chief realized that the time had come to step down. Late in October of 1916 he made known his decision to John D. Archbold and A. C. Bedford, and to John D. Rockefeller shortly thereafter. "You will always be associated in the minds of your friends with the name of the Standard Oil Company of California," replied Archbold and Bedford in a joint letter, "for you have been so identified with it from its earliest history that to think of that Company is also to think of you." They wished him a speedy return to health and strength, as did Rockefeller in another letter of cordiality and concern.[66]

The formal transfer of power at 200 Bush occurred at the annual meeting held on March 8, 1917, when William S. Rheem took over as the new president. But both the directors and the stockholders were loathe to sever completely the patriarchal tie. In graceful tribute, they gave their former leader the newly created and purely honorific title of chairman of the board. Scofield did not long survive this event. Bowed down by physical infirmities, including failing eyesight, and suffering the shock of the death of a beloved daughter, on July 30, 1917, he took his own life.[67]

XVI

PRODUCING
COMES TO THE FORE

The return to 26 Broadway of A. C. Bedford, H. C. Folger, Jr., Walter C. Teagle, J. C. Donnell, and Colonel Carter from their western inspection swing in the fall of 1910 heralded a new day for the Producing Department of Standard of California. Impressed by what they saw, they felt the time had come for the western company to build up its producing interest. California's oil output that year was up more than 30 per cent over 1909, with nearly three-fourths of the increase being light crude chiefly from Midway. The eastern executives believed that the rapid increase in the supply of light oil offered an opportunity to expand refining capacity. And they also recognized that if the company plunged deeply into producing, organized independents could no longer hope for a whip hand by cornering the refinable oil.[1]

Prior to November, 1910, when 26 Broadway accepted these recommendations, the record of the Producing Department had been outstanding solely in the Midway field. In 1911, the year of transition, Standard of California ranked a poor sixth among the state's oil producers:

Table 16: Average Daily Production in California, 1911

Company or Agency	Barrels	Per Cent of Production
Independent Oil Producers Agency	28,242	12.3
Associated	27,371	11.9
Union	21,123	9.2
Southern Pacific	12,152	5.3
Atchison, Topeka & Santa Fe	11,725	5.1
Standard Oil (California)	8,695	3.8
Others	120,128	52.4
Total	229,436	100.0

Source: Appendix Table III

Over the next three years Standard began to make rapid headway. Its production passed that of Union, the Southern Pacific, and the Santa Fe in 1913. A year later the company took the lead over Associated and the Independent Agency. Thereafter, Standard's hold on first place was never in danger. In spite of the entry of two new majors, Shell and General Petroleum, its production by 1919 had grown to more than one-quarter of the state's total, a figure which was almost equal to that of its next three rivals combined.

Table 17: Average Daily Production in California, 1919

Company or Agency	Barrels	Per Cent of Production
Standard Oil (California)	71,415	25.8
Southern Pacific	26,158	9.4
Union	24,693	8.9
Associated	24,460	8.8
Independent Oil Producers Agency	24,381	8.8
Shell	18,549	6.7
General Petroleum	11,165	4.0
Atchison, Topeka & Santa Fe	10,325	3.7
Others	66,174	23.9
Total	277,320	100.0

Source: Appendix Table III

A comparison with the nation's leading producers in 1919 offers yet another measure of Standard's achievement. That year Standard produced 25,485,000 barrels. Its nearest rival was Gulf with 21,486,000 barrels. Other national leaders were The Texas Company, 16,957,000, Jersey Standard, 16,812,000, and the Ohio Oil Company, 14,833,000. The crude output of Standard of California, in fact, was not a great deal less than that of its former parent and the chief producer of the old combination, the Ohio Oil Company, put together.[2]

This notable period in Standard's producing history lends itself to no simple statement. It has many aspects. One, clearly, is the company's growth in production in the San Joaquin Valley, especially at Midway, the greatest of the Valley fields; another is its move south in the Los Angeles basin, which by 1919 had become its principal center of producing strength. Failures, too, dot the record, along with the moments of high success.

But the story is much more than of oil fields and oil wells. It is of advances in conservation, brought about by self-interest on the part of the company and by public pressures upon the industry. Linked to these advances is the gradual rise of the technically trained, especially the geologists, which at times caused sharp conflicts with executives whose petroleum schooling had been limited solely to the oil fields. Another aspect is the continuing uncertainty concerning the transfer of public lands to private ownership for oil development after the withdrawal order of 1909, a matter that will be treated at length in the following chapter.

And certainly it is a story of leadership, for the great advance in the company's position in producing between 1911 and 1919 was achieved under F. H. Hillman. There can be no question of his central importance to the events of these years.

2

In sending Hillman to Standard of California, 26 Broadway provided the western company with one of the outstanding producing executives of the old Standard combination. Forty-eight years of age when he came to California in January, 1911, Hillman had worked for thirty-two years with Standard companies in Pennsylvania, Ohio, Indiana, and Illinois. For most of this time he had served under J. C. Donnell, whose Ohio Oil Company for more than a decade had been 26 Broadway's leading producer. Hillman had been a director of the Ohio company since 1900 and for several years had been head of its operations in Illinois, which in 1910 was a strong third among the nation's oil states. In February, 1911, he was elected to the board of Standard of California, but the primary support for his great authority in the producing area even after 1911 lay in the unusually broad grant of power with which he had been sent West by the New York headquarters.[3]

Hillman must have found the Producing Department of Standard of California a sorry contrast to the Ohio Oil Company. The vigorous spirit that had pervaded the young department during the brief tenure of Colonel Carter had long been gone. Strange as it may seem, the department in 1911 was being run by men who had only minor producing experience. The general superintendent, J. M. Atwell, and the assistant general superintendent, J. R. McAllister, were originally Rheem's men from the Manufacturing Department. In the field, only Walton Young at Pico was an old hand, and the superintendents at Coalinga and Midway were more of the office-manager type.

It did not take Hillman long to shake up the department. Atwell was kept on as general superintendent because of his knowledge of Standard's operations and his ability to get along well with men, a trait that Hillman highly prized. But Atwell and his office assistant, W. H. Berg, were shifted to Bakersfield, near Midway, in March, 1911. They remained there until the headquarters at 200 Bush was completed in

1913 and Standard's producing properties no longer were limited almost wholly to the San Joaquin Valley. McAllister, who was moved out of the chain of command, within a year or two was back again with the Manufacturing Department. The superintendents at Midway (Taft) and Coalinga were replaced by Cyrus "Cy" Bell, formerly the assistant superintendent of drilling, and W. S. "Bill" Smullin, a cable tool driller who had gained his early experience in the Bradford field in Pennsylvania. Both superintendents were able leaders.[4]

One specialized skill, that of a lease man, Hillman soon learned was not to be found on Standard's payroll. He turned to D. F. Martin, formerly of the Ohio Oil Company, whom he stationed in Los Angeles to sign up oil lands to supply the new Southern California refinery. Hillman, who had a passion for fair and honest conduct in all human relationships, was especially determined that Standard live up to high standards in leasing. He insisted, for example, that neighboring lessors be treated the same; if he had to pay more for a lease than he had planned, he was known to adjust the terms of other leases in the same vicinity. Over the years, Hillman was to build an enviable reputation for Standard with its lessors.[5]

For another skill, that of geologist, Hillman at first had little use. The three geologists on the roster, E. A. Starke, H. N. Snively, and R. B. Moran, he soon reduced solely to Starke, who probably was retained because of his long and varied experience. In Illinois, Hillman had been successful without geologists, and he expected to do as well in the West. But he quickly learned that California's soft and deformed formations presented much more difficult problems. It was part of Hillman's strength that he could change his mind. Within a year he was permitting Starke, the staunchest proponent of applied science around the headquarters, to begin once more the slow building of a geological staff.[6]

To oversee the work and to keep production mounting, Standard's producing director was on the road much of the time. He preferred to leave the swivel chair to others. Each year he traveled thousands of miles, building up an unrivaled personal acquaintance among men in the field. He liked to stop at a drilling rig, to greet the crew by name, to exchange a story or two, and to talk shop. Men admired him because he was a leader, not a driver. His practice was to ask a subordinate for recommendations and, unless there was a compelling reason to the contrary, to let the man follow through. Because of his fairness and great human warmth, Hillman had an extraordinary talent for drawing men to him and infecting them with his own enthusiasm for the search for oil.[7]

3

During Hillman's first years, the Producing Department continued to emphasize the Midway field as its principal target. Standard's holdings there of nearly 6,500 acres in mining claims and school sections alone held forth the promise of a large increase in the volume of light crude. The Coalinga lands of the company were past their peak, and the Pico and Elsmere fields offered little to hope for. Consequently, thirty-three of the forty-two wells completed by Standard in 1911 were at Midway, compared to ten out of twenty-two the year before. The company's investment there during 1911 was around $1,350,000, which was almost half again as much as the total amount spent earlier. And its Midway production showed a gratifying spurt: from 1,377,000 barrels in 1910 to 2,075,000 the next year, for which a single well, McNee #1, was largely responsible.[8]

Standard's McNee property was a school section, lying in the Buena Vista Hills north of Taft where for more than a year large volume, high pressure gas wells had made news. When it appeared that the first McNee well would also come in as a great gas producer, drilling was suspended early in the fall of 1910. Standard's allied company, California Natural Gas, already had in prospect more gas than it could handle, and a fresh expenditure for another gas well seemed hardly warranted. About February, 1911, when Hillman was on an early visit to Midway, he decided to gamble that the deeper formations underlying the McNee contained oil. On July 27 he was rewarded when the well came in at 2,455 feet with a daily production of 5,000 barrels of 25° oil. By the close of the year it had produced 365,677 barrels. Hillman was jubilant at this, the first of many gushers he would know in the West. Every day the well also blew away many million cubic feet of gas which at that time Standard knew no way to save.[9]

So big a strike increased the lure of the Buena Vista Hills. Shortly, three more wells were spudded on the McNee. And before July was over, Hillman pushed to a conclusion preliminary terms for leasing 8,320 acres (13 sections) for which he had been dickering with the Kern Trading & Oil Company, the oil arm of the Southern Pacific. Hillman's interest was oil, but California Natural Gas was also hoping for a sufficiently large increase in gas production to permit extending its lines to Los Angeles. KT&O's terms were stiff: an oil royalty of one-sixth; a drilling commitment requiring Standard to start a well on each section within 120 days and, where oil was discovered, to keep as many as four rigs working on that section until thirty-two wells had been drilled;

a gas royalty of approximately two-fifths (2¢ per thousand cubic feet); and a requirement that three-fourths of the gas marketed by Standard should come from the KT&O sections. Except for the gas royalty, Hillman was satisfied. He wanted the land, which would have given Standard control of more than half of the Buena Vista Hills.[10]

A transaction of this size required the approval of 26 Broadway, one of the last major decisions before dissolution that affected the western company. In October, 1911, A. C. Bedford, who was especially interested in the prospects for gas, sent Martin B. Daly, president of the East Ohio Gas Company, to investigate. Daly's judgment proved a cautious one. Some of his concern revolved around "the irregularity of the gas or oil bearing formations" and the expense of separating the gas from the oil. An additional unsettling factor was the chance that the Los Angeles market might be supplied more cheaply from some less distant point—the Whittier-Fullerton field, for example. John G. Pew, another Standard gas executive from the East, voiced similar views. The heavy drilling commitment may also have disturbed 26 Broadway, particularly at a time when the federal government was challenging the title of the Southern Pacific to land-grant oil lands in the San Joaquin Valley. At any rate, the KT&O negotiations were dropped.[11] Fifteen years elapsed before Standard finally acquired these sections through a merger with the successor to KT&O, the Pacific Oil Company.

Although Hillman was disappointed, Standard's Midway lands nonetheless furnished plenty of opportunity for achievement. In the eighteen months following McNee #1, Midway provided Standard with six more gushers, each on a different section, that produced above 1,000 barrels daily. The largest, McNee #4, came in at a record 30,000 barrels a day in April, 1912. Within a week it sanded up, but four months later it was flowing at about an 1,800 barrel rate. There were some tremendous gas wells, too. The giant of them all, Derby #1, also made April, 1912, a memorable month. It blew out with a daily flow of gas that rose to an estimated 63 million cubic feet before the pressure fell off. Later, the Derby lease, which was located southeast of the McNee, became a valuable oil property after deeper drilling.[12]

By the end of 1912 Midway's production of 16,000 barrels a day was supplying almost four-fifths of Standard's crude oil output. It was a record not lost upon the company's large stockholders, for while the Midway wells were coming in, President Scofield was sending the news to New York. At last his confidence in wildcatting appeared vindicated, and the company was finding itself where he had hoped it would be before 26 Broadway dropped the reins. Scofield found a ready listener in E. T. Bedford. "Have always felt you did not get the support here at New York, say in the early days, you should have . . . to have helped you increase your strength and position by your larger holdings in producing property," Bedford wrote approvingly in September.[13]

Shortly, Scofield received a second letter from Bedford bearing testimony to the soundness of company-owned production. "Think that is the key to the whole situation. Here we are all troubled for want of crude. The Vacuum Oil Company is not getting their requirements and the Standard Oil Company of New Jersey is using 27,000 barrels a day out of reserve. The Texas Oil Company is stronger than any competitor, because of having its own production. Any increase in this direction means strength, and the very best kind of strength." In 1912 Jersey, stripped of its crude producers except for Carter Oil and Louisiana Standard, had averaged only about 7,500 barrels daily.[14]

The leaders of California Standard continued to be delighted over their remarkable record at Midway, where the McNee, in particular, kept on its spectacular course. McNee #9 opened the year 1913 with a blow out, producing an estimated 35,000,000 cubic feet of gas daily. In its wake, the drillers brought in a flowing oil well each month. The number in July rose to three, of which the greatest was another extraordinary gusher, #10. It came in on July 24, at 2,480 feet, flowing 10,000 barrels a day. "Can you match it, or do I take first place?" was the wire an elated Hillman sent his old chief, J. C. Donnell, at Ohio Oil. Two days later the well broke loose, at least doubling its output and daubing the earth's surface for nearly two miles around. Two hundred men worked day and night for more than a week throwing up embankments and carving out temporary sumps to handle the flow before the well, capped with four tons of fittings, gates, and nipples, was finally brought under control. Not long after, Standard got another runaway well that was almost as large, McNee #6, which flowed nearly 20,000 barrels daily for about three weeks before sanding up. The two gushers pushed Standard's September production at Midway to an average of 35,763 barrels daily, its all-time peak for the field. Fully three-fourths of this amount (26,940 barrels) came from the McNee, which had proved itself the most valuable 640 acres in California's oil history.[15]

Apart from Midway, where legal clouds over land titles made expansion difficult, and Coalinga, where Standard's production was averaging less than 3,000 barrels a day, Hillman's chief efforts in the San Joaquin Valley were spent wildcatting in two regions, Lost Hills–Belridge and Kern Front. At Lost Hills, in the low ridges between Midway and Coalinga, independent operators had discovered oil in the summer of

1910. A year later Hillman made his entry, buying 1,000 acres in the first of several purchases and leases. Standard got its first well in April, 1912, at 2,100 feet and by the end of 1913 had completed thirty more for a total investment of above one million dollars. The oil was light in gravity but production was not large; in December, 1913, it was averaging about 1,800 barrels daily.[16]

Kern Front, located northwest of the old Kern River field where Hillman had acquired 3,900 acres on Starke's recommendation, proved even less rewarding. A well completed in July, 1912, found a little oil but it found water, too. Starke and the drillers were baffled by an underground structure, originally a river delta, in which oil and water sands were separated by only a thin and weak rock stratum. Several years were to pass before the water problem was solved and Standard finally could build Kern Front into a profitable field.[17]

Meanwhile, Hillman's prime interest had shifted away from the San Joaquin Valley to Southern California, the scene of many of the company's greatest triumphs. For years, Standard's production there had been limited to the scant output in Pico and Elsmere canyons. Starting virtually from scratch, by 1917 the company was drawing the bulk of its production from new fields in the Los Angeles basin.

4

Hillman's first attempt to find oil in Southern California took place in the La Habra Valley, where in 1911 D. F. Martin painstakingly put together around 1,700 acres in forty-five leases. The valley, which lay between good wells in both the Puente and Coyote Hills, was attractive wildcat territory. Its chief shortcoming was the depth of drilling that appeared necessary. Three strong operators already in the territory had put down wells around 4,000 feet—a slow and expensive job for that day.[18]

Using a rotary rig, Standard spudded in its first well in June, 1911. Nine months later, as the well was being cemented at 3,870 feet, Hillman told the press that it had passed through "a most prolific sand." But water broke in, and the well had to be redrilled. After a production test, the well, still troubled by water, was abandoned. One by one, work also ceased on four other wildcats. Standard had spent more than $500,000 on this series of failures.[19]

Fortunately, there were better opportunities ahead. One was the eighty-acre Emery lease in the West Coyote Hills, for which Martin had negotiated nearly a year before reaching an agreement in March, 1912. Standard bound itself to begin drilling three wells at intervals of sixty days to a depth of 4,000 feet, if necessary. Further, if oil was discovered, the company agreed to keep two strings of tools working until ten wells—"one for each 8 acres"—were completed. In December, 1912, Emery #2 came in at 1,250 barrels, followed by four other gushers in 1913 on what soon became known as the "Big Bonanza Lease." The largest, #7, which roared in late in October with 10,000 barrels of 31.5° oil, was hailed as "the greatest . . . ever" in Southern California.[20]

This success on the Emery lease helped bring about organizational changes in the Producing Department. In May, 1913, a Southern California District was set up for a first time. W. S. Smullin, who had been in charge at Coalinga, was made its general superintendent. Simultaneously, Cy Bell at Taft was appointed general superintendent for the San Joaquin Valley fields. J. M. Atwell, whose office was returned to San Francisco, received the new title of manager.[21]

The Emery success also spurred Hillman to seek additional land in the Coyote Hills. During the spring and summer of 1913 he took up three eighty-acre parcels that either adjoined or were close to the original Emery lease.[22] Then late in the year, far overshadowing these deals, he acquired the holdings of the Murphy Oil Company, which were unquestionably among the richest and most extensive in Southern California.

Standard, it may be recalled, in 1908 had considered buying the Murphy lands in the Coyote Hills and East Whittier after Colonel Carter had recommended their purchase. Later it kept them under a watchful eye, but the presence of water in the wells had caused the company to view the properties somewhat skeptically. Nevertheless, in October, 1911, Standard signed a contract with Murphy for 3,000,000 barrels of crude to help supply the soon-to-be-opened El Segundo refinery.[23]

This contract was still in effect when in June, 1913, Hillman learned through a Los Angeles broker that the Murphys were planning to sell out. The upshot was that he began negotiations almost at once with W. H. Murphy. Before drawing up terms, Hillman had several Standard experts go over the property. W. S. Smullin, the general superintendent, O. O. Allen, the pipeline superintendent, and P. W. Thompson and R. C. Stoner, geologists, all gave glowing reports, especially on the Coyote Hills tract, where only seven wells had been drilled on more than 2,700 acres. They were confident that Standard possessed the technical knowledge to seal off the water. Smullin believed that at least 1,000 of the Coyote Hills acres were proven and another 1,000 were likely oil territory. Calling this property "the most desirable . . . in Southern California," he prophesied a daily production of 10,000 to 30,000 barrels. The company's experts were less impressed with the Murphy holdings in East Whittier, where 28 wells had been drilled on about 500 acres in a 2,700-acre tract, but Smullin thought a production of about 1,000 barrels daily could be maintained for eight or ten years. "If this Property could be handled on a price basis of Five Millions of Dollars," he concluded, "I would recommend the purchase, as I feel confident that by operating 10 Strings of Tools, at the end of Five years the amount of investment plus Ten Per Cent Interest and cost of development work would be repaid."[24]

Shortly after these reports, a meeting was set for October 23 at the Blackstone Hotel in Chicago, where Hillman and W. H. Murphy were joined by Rheem, who was on his way home from New York. The terms agreed upon provided for Standard to take a forty-year lease on all the Murphy holdings in West Coyote and 1,100 acres in East Whittier as of December 1, 1913. In exchange, the company offered a first payment of $1,000,000 in cash and 2,500 shares of stock valued at $200 a share; a second $1,000,000 four months later; $3,000,000 more spread over a five-year period; and a royalty of one-fourth of the crude produced above 730,000 barrels annually during the first five years, and on all crude thereafter. Further, Standard agreed to keep ten strings of tools drilling until a production of 10,000 barrels daily was developed, and five strings until a 20,000-barrel goal had been reached.[25]

In all of Standard's history, there had never been so large a transaction. Two of the company's directors, it is said, thought Hillman had lost his mind. Yet future events thoroughly confirmed his judgment. In less than five years, Standard had more than recovered its investment and operating costs, and its share of the Murphy production in 1917 was averaging above 13,000 barrels daily. The West Coyote field, moreover, was almost wholly a Standard operation, which it could develop economically without the competitive drilling and close well spacing so common in most California fields.[26]

By 1917 Standard had brought in another great Southern California field, the Montebello. Located in the Baldwin Hills, ten to twelve miles northwest of the Coyote Hills, it lay on the old Rancho La Merced, which in 1876 F. P. F. Temple had lost to the Comstock Lode millionaire, E. J. "Lucky" Baldwin, after the Temple bank failed. Following Baldwin's death in 1909, a small portion of the rancho made its way back to the Temple family through a sale to Walter Temple, F. P. F.'s son, but the bulk of the estate went to Anita and Clara, the two Baldwin daughters.[27]

Late in 1914 a Los Angeles broker first called the Montebello to Hillman's attention. The next spring the geologist, R. C. Stoner, reported that the structure, an elongated anticlinal fold, was "very favorable," and Starke added, "The surface indications for oil here are equally good as those of the Murphy property." Leasing Walter Temple's 58 acres proved easy, but almost eighteen months were required to work out an arrangement with Anita Baldwin for 712 acres.[28]

Drilling got under way at the end of November, 1916. The colorful Anita christened the drilling bit with a bottle of California wine. And the Baldwin luck held, for the discovery well came in three months later at 350 barrels a day. In October, 1917, Baldwin #3 touched off a wild rush to the field when it pierced a deeper sand at 3,755 feet with a flow of 7,500 barrels of 24° gravity oil. Two years after the discovery Standard was getting better than 21,000 barrels daily from 32 wells; its Montebello production for 1919 was worth almost $12,000,000. The Montebello joined West Coyote as one of the principal fields in the Los Angeles basin.[29]

Elsewhere in Southern California, Standard was not so fortunate. Two wells started early in 1916 west of the Santa Maria field were down almost 4,500 feet after eighteen months without oil. Three wells south of Santa Maria that were begun a little later had the same outcome. In all, the company lost around $500,000 in this effort to find new production in northern Santa Barbara County.[30]

Within a decade, other promising locations noted by Standard's geologists in the Los Angeles basin would become famous oil fields. R. C. Stoner in 1915 recommended three likely areas—Signal Hill, Dominguez Hill, and Sunnyside Hill (Rosecrans)—in a low range running northwest from Long Beach to Inglewood. Signal Hill appeared to offer the best bet, but the territory surrounding it was broken into many small holdings, none larger than twenty acres. Developing an oil field there inevitably meant costly "town lot" drilling in order to prevent neighboring wells from draining away oil from under each small parcel. Such excessive drilling Hillman abhorred; moreover, he did not like the prospect of a flood of damage claims if a wild well should spatter the neighborhood. For a test, he chose instead the lightly settled Dominguez area, where a well was spudded in during September, 1916. It was abandoned at 2,800 feet and a second well, put down to 5,005 feet, just missed the structure which the Union Oil Company would find a few years later.[31]

Standard also lost out on the discovery of Santa Fe Springs, lying between Montebello and West Coyote, which both Starke and Stoner had

urged upon Hillman. The company leased 320 acres at the beginning
of 1917, but Hillman's ardor soon cooled when Stoner told him that
Standard would probably have to drill more than 4,000 feet to find oil.
So far the company had drilled no good well that was so deep, and there
was already an expensive deep wildcat under way at Dominguez. Hillman decided to let the opportunity go.[32]

But despite such failures, which inevitably accompany the search for
oil, Hillman had reason to be proud of the company's record in the
southern end of the state. By 1917 Standard's Southern California
production, averaging 27,556 barrels daily, had come a long way toward
supplying a daily throughput averaging 30,588 barrels at the El Segundo
refinery.[33]

5

World War I, with its heavy drain on oil in storage, marked the beginning of a third phase in Standard's producing history under Hillman.
The company stepped up the development of its proven oil properties.
Its efforts were particularly successful at Montebello and West Coyote,
where the jump in production more than offset a decline in the San
Joaquin Valley and helped boost the company's daily average production
from 50,000 to 71,500 barrels between 1917 and 1919.[34]

A great surge of wildcatting was Standard's other response to the
critical oil need. For a first time the company put down wells outside
California, though it continued to concentrate primarily on the Los
Angeles basin and the San Joaquin Valley.

As far back as 1913, Hillman and Starke had canvassed the Pacific
Northwest, with Starke going on to Alaska, but no drilling had followed.[35] It took a more likely opportunity, conjoined with the threat of
an oil shortage, to cause Standard to go outside California's borders.
The area chosen was in the high and desolate Rangely basin country
of northwestern Colorado, where since 1901 oil prospectors had intermittently been producing small quantities of very light crude. A sizable
acreage had been patented and bought by the Southern Pacific's Kern
Trading & Oil Company, which later sold the property to one of its
executives, A. C. McLaughlin. To evaluate these lands, Hillman sent
out a party of geologists in March, 1917.[36]

Following a favorable report, Standard paid McLaughlin $200,000
for 5,000 acres and prepared to drill the next spring after the rigors
of winter were over. Using a subsidiary, the Richmond Petroleum Company, it put down fourteen shallow wells in little more than a year's time
and drilled two more further east on leased land at Devil's Hole, near

Meeker. Results were discouraging: dry holes at Devil's Hole, and a total production at Rangely during 1919 that amounted to less than 2,100 barrels. By the end of 1919 the Rangely wells were shut down. The Colorado ventures by that time had cost the company almost $600,000, including the land. But Standard kept the Rangely property, which a quarter century later would more than fulfill Hillman's expectations at the time of World War I. During and after World War II Rangely became the second largest field in the Rockies and one of the largest in the nation.[37]

In Southern California during 1918 and 1919 Standard was not a great deal more successful than in Colorado. Late in the summer of 1918 it got an eighty-barrel well and five more the next year on its Kraemer lease near Richfield, southeast of West Coyote, but this lease was two or three miles away from the prolific sands that made Richfield one of the principal finds of 1919.[38]

The San Joaquin Valley, Standard's third theater for wildcatting, for several years had been subordinated to the Los Angeles basin in the company's scheme of things. Standard's sole discovery in the valley after Kern Front was the McKittrick Front, where in July, 1916, it brought in a ten-barrel well of very light crude. A dozen successor wells were hardly larger. In the San Joaquin Valley, in fact, purchases of already developed properties were the principal means by which the company gained more oil. Beginning late in 1915 Hillman picked up twenty-two properties, chiefly in Kern River, Midway, Coalinga, and Lost Hills, that were adding about 6,000 barrels daily to the company's production at the end of 1917.[39]

But greater fortune was in store when Standard began to drill in Elk Hills, a few miles northeast of the Buena Vista Hills, in the summer of 1918. Since 1910 the company had held 1,780 acres there in three sections which under federal law the State of California had sold earlier to private parties to raise funds for schools. Whatever hopes the company may have had for these properties were shadowed by the failure of several competitors to find commercial production nearby. In Standard's opinion, the region was not prime territory. Nevertheless, because of the "dire need for oil," as G. C. Gester, the company's chief geologist, later phrased it, "we were told to take chances that we had not taken before."[40]

The gamble paid off, for in January, 1919, at 2,500 feet Standard got a 250-barrel well of 37° oil on its 480-acre Hay property. In April two more wells came in, of which the larger gave 750 barrels. By this time Standard was also preparing to drill on most of the remainder of the Hay section, which it had leased from Frank J. Carman at a 50 per cent royalty, and on its two other school sections in Elk Hills.[41]

Suddenly the Hay property seemed reminiscent of the McNee, located six miles to the south, when two great gas wells blew in. The second, Hay #7, on July 25 began producing an estimated 187,000,000 cubic feet daily, the largest gas well California had ever seen. Almost at once it caught fire, creating a torch that could be seen for eighty miles. Ten days passed before the fire was finally snuffed out by a charge of dynamite. Late in September Elk Hills caused further excitement with its first big oil well—a 5,000-barrel gusher on the Carman lease.[42]

As yet Elk Hills was in its infancy, but its demonstration in 1919 more than compensated for the disappointing course of events at Rangely. At that time, too, few, if any, foresaw the long battle with the federal government over ownership of the Hay and Carman section that, begun in 1921, would continue for nearly two decades.[43]

6

A companion development to this notable producing record was Standard's more careful and effective use of oil and gas resources. During the teens the idea gained greater currency that the nation's reserves of oil and gas were not inexhaustible, and it was a wise policy for both industry and government to see that they were prudently used.[44] The idea drew strength from a number of groups with overlapping interests: from conservationists, from government scientists in the U.S. Geological Survey, U.S. Bureau of Mines, and numerous state bodies, and, certainly, from enlightened oilmen. No company could be the leader in a movement so broadly based, but in many of its aspects Standard of California ranked toward the front.

One area of advance was in the conservation of natural gas. For decades gas had been a lightly valued by-product of the search for oil, even a nuisance in the judgment of many oilmen. Many operators, not all of them small, let the gas blow away or burned it at the well. This lax attitude had not been typical of the old Standard combination, which had recognized early the importance of natural gas as fuel. Rockefeller himself in 1885 was encouraging his associates to "pursue the gas business earnestly." Starting in Ohio and Pennsylvania, these gas ventures were later extended into West Virginia. And, especially in the years just prior to 1911, the gas business became highly profitable, contributing approximately 10 per cent in 1908 and better than 7 per cent in 1910 to the combination's earnings. Evidence of the value of natural gas was also reflected in public policy. Beginning in the 1890's, a number of the older oil states, like Indiana, Ohio, and Pennsylvania, passed laws forbidding the burning off of gas at the well or permitting its wasteful escape. California enacted a similar statute in March of 1911.[45]

In California 26 Broadway had a subsidiary, the California Natural Gas Company, already in the field at the time of Hillman's arrival. Organized the preceding autumn, as we have noted, the company had been planned to market the Midway gas production that Standard had developed beyond its own fuel needs. California Natural Gas was primarily a wholesaler to a Kern County utility company, but to a lesser extent it also made direct sales to oil producers and refiners and to ranchers along its lines. The price Standard charged the gas company was a low one—5¢ per thousand cubic feet. "In the spirit of conservation," Hillman wrote later, "we set about . . . to market all of the gas . . . possible . . . in the hope that through education as to its use we could develop a valuable product to the consumer and one that would eventually be profitable to us."[46]

Not all the gas produced was readily marketable, however. In some wells it poured forth mixed with the oil. This "wet" gas could not be distributed safely until the natural gasoline was liquefied and removed in a gas-oil separator; otherwise, it would liquefy and plug the gas lines. And high pressure wells could not be handled by an ordinary cylindrical separator, which would soon be destroyed by the blast of the sand-laden gas. McNee #1, which came in during July, 1911, producing 8,000,000 cubic feet of gas along with 2,000 barrels of oil daily, was such a well. How to save this gas worried Hillman. In September, he wrote of his dilemma: "There is no way known . . . by which this natural gas could be conserved or used, nor any way . . . whereby we could produce the oil without wasting the gas."[47]

C. C. Scharpenberg, a perceptive twenty-seven-year-old engineer who had joined Standard from the Ohio Oil Company in April, 1911, supplied the answer Hillman needed. With a master's degree in engineering from Rose Polytechnic Institute, Scharpenberg was an early example of the technically trained specialists who more and more would gain prominence in the company. His invention, modified by E. A. Starke to make use of materials readily available in the oil fields, became known as the Starke gas trap. It was the first of a number of inventions, including a tank-type low-pressure gas trap and an early turbo-drill, that would come from Scharpenberg's fertile mind.[48]

The Starke trap consisted of two parallel pipes of different diameters that ran for several hundred feet down a slight incline and were con-

Emery #7, October, 1913

Two styles of Starke's high-pressure gas trap, probably Murphy-Coyote property, 1914

nected by arch after arch of one-inch pipe. Gas, oil, and sand jetted from the well into the larger pipe, with the gas rising and descending through the arches into the smaller pipe. Sufficient time was provided by the length of the trap for the bulk of the natural gasoline to liquefy and separate from the permanent gas. In some cases, a third separator pipe was used to permit a still more complete separation from the gas. The natural gasoline was thrown in with the crude oil for piping to the refinery, while the nearly "dry" gas was delivered to the gas company. The relatively small diameters and absence of flat surfaces in both pipes permitted the trap to handle high pressures without difficulty, and the fairly high pressure within the trap prevented the sand from blasting the walls. This ingenious device was also used by the company for its gushers in Southern California, especially in West Coyote.[49]

Wherever Standard found gas, Hillman sought earnestly to avoid waste. Early in 1914 he was instrumental in bringing about a conversion from oil to gas of the original twenty-three-mile pipeline from Northam to the refinery at El Segundo, where the boilers and stills were altered to burn gas from West Coyote. As production continued to mount, Hillman arranged a sale in November, 1914, of a minimum of 2,500,000 cubic feet daily to Dan Murphy and Richard Dillon, two Southern California oil and gas men with whom the company long enjoyed friendly relations. The amount they took was later increased, and they also became the outlet for Standard's lesser gas production at Montebello and Kraemer (Richfield). Beginning in 1915, the Southern California Gas Company, too, became a customer, taking gas from West Coyote.[50]

In 1917 Hillman proudly reported that "our system of conservation as now developed is replacing . . . 5,000 Bbls oil per day over and above what I use for fuel. . . ." This was equivalent to sales for the year of almost 13 billion cubic feet worth $650,000, or more than one-fourth of all the natural gas sold in California. Standard's own use of gas for fuel in producing and refining amounted to at least another billion cubic feet. The preceding year more natural gas was estimated to have been wasted in California than was saved and marketed. Hillman was pleased to have his company aligned on the side of the conservationists, even though the gas business had brought little profit because of the low price at which the gas was sold.[51]

7

During the teens Standard's interest in natural gas broadened. Earlier the company had viewed natural gas solely as a fuel that required treatment at times to remove natural gasoline. Gradually, as gasoline became the principal oil product, natural gasoline took on greater importance, for it offered a significant supplement to the gasoline turned out at the refineries. This was another aspect of conservation in which the company joined under Hillman's direction.

The idea of utilizing natural gasoline, like natural gas, arose first in the older oil regions. Beginning prior to 1905, some small operators in West Virginia and Pennsylvania began compressing "casinghead gas" (flowing between the casing and tubing of oil wells) to extract its gasoline content. Invariably, the gas that was richest in gasoline came from older wells, in which the pressure was low. By 1911 the first compression plant had appeared in the West in Brea Canyon near Fullerton.[52]

Standard made its first move to conserve natural gasoline by extraction late in the summer of 1913 when it installed at Newhall an experimental Bessemer compression plant to work with the rich gas associated with the high-gravity Pico crude. To condense the natural gasoline, the gas was compressed and then refrigerated at 20° below zero. From the start, the plant ran into difficulty. The gasoline was of extremely high gravity, so light, it was said, "that a cupful . . . thrown into the air would almost entirely disappear before any of it touched the ground." It was so volatile and wild, so dangerous to handle, that after about a year of effort Standard decided to shut down the plant. Several California companies at the time were blending natural gasoline with engine distillate to increase their output of gasoline for motorists, a practice Standard refused to follow because of concern for the uniform quality of its Red Crown gasoline and because it viewed such mixtures as hazardous. When a natural gasoline explosion at Ardmore, Oklahoma, took nearly fifty lives in the fall of 1915, the company pointed to the closing of the Newhall plant the previous year as evidence of its concern for public safety.[53]

Nevertheless, natural gasoline was potentially too valuable a product for Standard to ignore very long. In fact, the company never stopped producing it, at least as a by-product. Early in 1914, while the Newhall plant was still operating, Standard installed a compressor plant on the Emery lease to boost the pressure in order to deliver gas through the line to fuel the El Segundo refinery. The natural gasoline liquefied by the compressor was thrown into the crude oil for piping to the refinery. Within two years the company was showing a more direct concern when it set up a simple absorber plant at Emery to capture some of the light hydrocarbons that compression and cooling had failed to remove. The gas was passed through crude oil, which, acting as an absorber, picked up some natural gasoline and carried it away. At the beginning of 1916 Standard also reopened the Newhall plant, where it devised means to take off the wildest vapors so that a more stable product could be shipped to El Segundo.[54]

At Midway, the company's other great gas territory, Standard built during 1916 on its McNee section a large compressor plant capable of handling 22,000,000 cubic feet daily and reputed to have cost $750,000. Apparently, the boosting of gas pressure for delivery to the Valley Natural Gas Company (successor to California Natural Gas) was one purpose, but the natural gasoline was also valued for itself. As at West Coyote, the natural gasoline was run into the crude oil for piping to a refinery. Within a year or two, another simple absorption plant using crude oil was added to the McNee installation to bring about a more complete recovery of the light hydrocarbons.[55]

Standard shortly extended its experience with the absorption process after C. C. Scharpenberg persuaded Hillman to build on the Derby lease a small and efficient plant that used mineral seal distillate, instead of crude oil, as the absorber. To save this relatively expensive oil for re-use, the natural gasoline vapors were distilled off and condensed. Some of the very light fractions were sent by truck to Richmond, where a number of early experiments were carried on to discover new uses for butane and propane, which at the time were of little commercial importance.[56]

All this activity is underscored by statistics that show clearly the rapid rise of natural gas as a source of gasoline. The Producing Department's production in 1919 amounted to 36,372 gallons daily, which was equivalent that year to 6.3 per cent of a total gasoline output with a refinery value of $37,547,000. Six years earlier, the experimental plant at Newhall had yielded little more than 150 gallons a day. Standard's achievement in this area of conservation is impressive, too, when compared to the rest of the California industry. In 1919 its ten plants were producing approximately half as much natural gasoline as the fifty plants operated by all other companies.[57]

8

Another significant aspect of producing history in the decade of World War I was the gradual rise in status of the geologist, both inside and outside the company. "Oil geology and technology are comparatively new sciences, largely developed within the last ten years," wrote Ralph Arnold, a distinguished petroleum geologist, in 1920.[58] Within Standard, as within the industry generally, these technically trained specialists first gained prominence examining and reporting on likely oil territory, but gradually they also began to acquire authority over the actual producing of oil. Their rise was aided by the work of the U.S. Geological Survey, U.S. Bureau of Mines, and the California State Mining Bureau, whose studies supplied a base for the more specialized efforts of company geologists and engineers.[59] As they learned more about the subsurface formations, companies were able to reduce the chances of failure in wildcatting and to bring about a larger recovery where oil had been discovered. The companies were enlisting science to aid both oil exploration and producing.

Standard was not the leader in this movement. For it to have been so would be surprising because producing was long the least important of the company's major activities. Union, which in 1899 hired W. W. Orcutt, a young Stanford graduate, was the first western company to put a geologist on its permanent payroll.[60] But the first company to use geologists in a large way was the Kern Trading & Oil Company, organized by the Southern Pacific in the spring of 1903 to develop the railroad's oil lands.

There were at least two reasons why geology made such rapid headway in KT&O. Most important was its general manager, Edwin T. Dumble, a well-known geologist with great faith in the contributions his profession could make to the oil industry. For nine years, from 1887 to 1896, Dumble had been the State Geologist of Texas before he came to the Southern Pacific as consulting geologist concerned with the development of its mineral lands. When KT&O was set up, Dumble was given a free hand, which he exercised until about 1910. The fact that KT&O was a new organization meant, too, that Dumble was not faced with the resistance of entrenched practical oilmen, wary of geologists as a threat to their status, as was so frequently the case in old, established companies.[61]

To a large extent, Dumble recruited geologists and mining engineers from among the young graduates of Stanford University, where a friend, John C. Branner, was a professor and vice president. Economic geology was also one of Branner's interests; he had been State Geologist of Arkansas from 1887 to 1893 and had occasionally served as a consultant to mining and oil companies. In tribute to his talents, a professional organization of petroleum geologists and engineers at Los Angeles later took as its name the Branner Club.[62]

If Dumble had used geologists solely in the search for oil, his record would not have been so unusual, for other companies, including Standard, were also beginning to follow this practice. Geological surveys and maps of the Southern Pacific lands were an important part of Dumble's program, to be sure, but they were not all. His special contribution was his reliance on geologists in oil producing. These technically trained men, known first as development or resident geologists and later as petroleum engineers, studied the samples brought to the surface when a well being drilled was bailed. The KT&O geologists correlated the samples from neighboring wells to draw subsurface cross-sections, which they used to determine locations for new wells and where the casing should be set to keep water out of the oil sands. In the oil industry, they were playing a pioneer role. KT&O and Rio Bravo, the sister company Dumble set up for the Southern Pacific in Texas, in time became a recruiting ground for other oil companies. In addition to a few KT&O veterans acquired in this way, Standard gained the whole California organization, including M. E. Lombardi (who would succeed F. H. Hillman), in the landmark merger with KT&O's successor, the Pacific Oil Company, in 1926.[63]

In E. A. Starke, as we have seen, Standard had its most ardent advocate of technically trained men. This chemist-turned-geologist got a second chance to build a geological staff after Hillman's early experience with the difficult California formations had caused him by 1912 to reverse himself on the value of geologists. In hiring young geologists, Starke looked to the University of California and to his friend and neighbor, Professor John C. Merriam. There were others on the faculty who were also interested in oil. One was George D. Louderback, who led a geological expedition to China for Standard of New York in 1914. The next year the University made a great stride forward in petroleum studies when Lester C. Uren, a young instructor in its college of mining, drew up a specialized curriculum in petroleum engineering, the first in the West. But Starke's link to Merriam was Standard's important tie.[64]

During 1912 and 1913 Standard employed two of Merriam's students, Percy W. Thompson and R. C. Stoner. Both were exceptionally able men. Until Thompson's death in 1920, he seemed destined to go to the top of the Producing Department, a peak Stoner did reach with his appointment as general manager in 1931 and director in 1938. An important early assignment for both men was their evaluation of the West Coyote field. Later, after Thompson was drawn off into producing operations, Stoner continued to report on potential oil lands.[65]

As the geologists proved their worth, Starke was able to expand his staff. During 1915 two more University of California graduates were hired, and H. N. Snively was restored to the payroll. The next year

Standard added S. H. Gester from KT&O and J. O. Nomland, and in 1917 Omar Cavins and E. M. Butterworth before Starke's career with the company came to an end. A renewal of the dispute over patent rights to which Starke asserted ownership, contrary to the rules of the company, appears to have been responsible. On earlier occasions Scofield had been successful in heading off a crisis, but Rheem, who had little liking for Starke, had succeeded Scofield as president. Starke resigned. There is no question that Starke was a highly sensitive and difficult man, but, considering his outstanding contributions to the company, it seems that he deserved a better fate.[66]

His resignation was merely a personal matter, however, free from any overtones of hostility to geology. In fact, the hiring of geologists was stepped up. By the end of 1919 there were twenty-two responsible to W. H. Berg, Atwell's onetime office assistant, who since 1916 had been in charge of the Land and Lease Division. This large number could do much more than follow the earlier pattern of merely reporting on lands that had been offered to the company. They began to range widely throughout the West and even into Mexico and Central America looking for likely oil property. Exploratory geology was becoming an increasingly important function.[67]

To replace Starke, Hillman hired a thirty-three-year-old geologist of broad experience, G. Clark Gester, whose brother was already on Standard's payroll. Gester graduated in geology in 1908 at the University of California, where he stayed on for a year as an instructor and occasionally worked for Standard as a consultant, along with Professor Merriam. But his greater experience came from KT&O, which he served for five years in exploration and producing. Gester had been KT&O's Chief Development Geologist for two years when he resigned in 1914 to take charge of exploration work in Peru and Ecuador for New York Standard. After completing this mission, he went as a consultant for Hillman to Rangely, Colorado, early in 1917 before joining Standard permanently.[68]

Gester's experience as chief development geologist undoubtedly was one of his attractions for Hillman. In linking geology to oil producing, Standard had not gone so far as had KT&O. And, probably in consequence, Standard's practical oilmen were frequently clashing with geologists of the State Mining Bureau, who were trying to protect the oil fields from water damage. The state geologists at times may have been too officious and all-knowing; the practical oilmen, surely, were all too willing to downgrade the contributions geologists could make to good oil field practice. A little more than a year after his employment, Gester was given the task of reconciling the two sides.[69]

The background of this dispute sheds much light on the transition going on in the conduct of oil producing within both the company and
the California industry, for it had much to do with the evolving specialty
of petroleum engineering.

9

Early in California's career as a great oil state, a number of its fields
began to be faced with a serious water problem. In the East and the
Mid-Continent the situation was different. Oil wells there generally
pierced through strong strata of limestone, sandstone, and slate, which
permitted drillers to seal off water readily by resting casing on the overlying strata. In California, however, the geological formations were
frequently poorly consolidated, soft and friable. Water was hard to keep
out. At first, in the delight of finding a new field, it was easy to mini-
mize the problem and, in any case, the anarchy of many independent
operators, each seeking his own gain, made concerted action difficult,
if not impossible.[70]

But water encroachment could not long be ignored. A careless operator, or one who was unable to effect a water shut-off, both damaged his
own well and threatened the oil recovery of neighboring wells. Another
danger was the operator who ran out of cash and quit before plugging the
hole properly. Kern River, California's first great field, was the earliest to
suffer serious damage. "No matter what the production . . . was or what
the hopes of the producer are," Colonel Carter wrote in 1905, ". . . *death*
and *destruction surrounds that field,* and it will only be a year or two
at most, when it will be numbered with last year's snows and forgotten. . . ." Carter's judgment was too extreme, as he himself later
recognized, but his comments on Kern River (and also Santa Maria)
in 1905 reflect the initial impact of the state's water problem on one
discerning eastern visitor.[71]

During the first fifteen years of the century California oilmen tried to
solve the problem in two different ways: by setting up a cooperative
organization to combat water encroachment or, swallowing their fears
of government, by enlisting the police power of the state to the same
end. Simultaneously, geologists and practical oilmen were making
progress in understanding the California formations and in devising
new and better means for barring water from the oil sands.

California made its first attempt at legislation in 1903 when, at the
behest of some Kern River oilmen, a law was passed making it a mis-
demeanor to fail to shut off water above and below the oil-bearing
strata or to abandon a well without securely filling the hole for at least
100 feet above the oil sands. Unfortunately, machinery for enforcing

the act was almost wholly absent. A successor statute, enacted in 1909, which required the keeping of oil-well logs and the appointment of a county commissioner to supervise water problems if requested by three or more producers, was not a great deal stronger. Evidently, many operators, including Standard, were not yet ready to accept a law with teeth.[72]

Operators at Midway moved to improve on the California statute in the spring of 1912 by establishing a Kern County Oil Protective Association. It was an advisory body, staffed by a deputy county commissioner and a geologist, to whom the companies furnished their well logs, records, and drilling information. Peg models and numerous cross-sections were prepared, so that the smaller operators, who could not afford a resident geologist, would have a better idea of the subsurface structure and have skilled advice in sealing off water. Hillman, apparently for legal reasons, felt unable to enroll Standard as a member, but he cordially agreed to supply the association with "any . . . information at our command" and to advance $150 monthly in order to help defray its expenses.[73]

Two years later a second association was set up at Coalinga. The Coalinga arrangement was more than advisory; its representatives could enter the property of any member to enforce a water shut-off. This time Standard signed up.[74]

Such a progression, field by field, might have continued, but operators who were able to agree to go so far as at Coalinga were helping to make a case for an effective, statewide organization. Moreover, some fields needing the benefits of cooperative action were too small to organize under the Kern or Coalinga pattern. A regulatory agency operated by the state seemed more and more an appropriate answer. Its chief protagonists were within the State Mining Bureau: Fletcher M. Hamilton, the State Mineralogist, and his assistant, Robert P. McLaughlin, a former geologist for the Associated Oil Company who had been campaigning for years for a state agency. Some companies, notably KT&O, were also vigorous advocates of the idea, and Hillman himself had come round to state regulation as the only way to police the wells of fly-by-night operators.[75]

The measure, which passed unanimously and became law in June, 1915, provided for setting up in the State Mining Bureau a Petroleum & Gas Department staffed by technically trained specialists and headed by an Oil & Gas Supervisor. Wells could neither be drilled nor abandoned without first informing the Department, which reviewed the plans of the operator and later checked on the effectiveness of his water shut-off. The functions of the Department were partly advisory. But in cases where it found that water had not been satisfactorily sealed off, it could order the operator to do such remedial work as the Department believed necessary, subject to review, at the operator's request, by a board of his fellow operators. R. P. McLaughlin, the first Oil & Gas Supervisor, zealously entered upon his new duties, aided by three geologists and a mining engineer who were located in the oil fields.[76]

One result of the water legislation was to encourage Hillman early in 1917 to follow belatedly the lead of KT&O and some other companies in adding resident geologists to the Producing Department's job roster. R. C. Stoner was appointed in the Northern District (San Joaquin Valley), and a little later S. H. Gester received the same assignment in the Southern District. They took up a considerable range of duties: preparing histories and graphic logs of old and new wells, correlating data to determine the location of the oil sands and sources of water, and standardizing drilling and producing reports. They used this data to recommend the location, depth, and points of water shut-off for new wells.[77]

In so doing, the resident geologists frequently touched off sparks. Operating men who were used to asking for advice only when they wanted it were apt to resent what was, in their view, an unwarranted attempt to invade their sphere of authority. Cy Bell, who had become the Producing Department's assistant manager, pointedly told Stoner that he did not think much of geologists; he would rather rely on a string of tools. The superintendent at Montebello, who had struggled upward in the oil fields since the age of twelve, contemptuously commented that geologists were as useful to an oil company "as tits to a boar pig."[78]

Practical oilmen were not soothed when a resident geologist proved them wrong. On one occasion, a drilling crew continued on below the depth Stoner had advised until the appropriation for the well had been exhausted. As they started to abandon the hole, he persuaded them to perforate the casing at the point he originally suggested. They found oil. Stoner also provided a solution for the water problem at Kern Front, where the impervious clays capping the oil sands were so thin and soft that they broke down repeatedly and let water through. He recommended that the casing be cemented at the top of the overlying clay strata in addition to the customary cementing at the bottom. With Hillman's approval, this was done. Occasionally the geologists made mistakes, which the operating men eagerly pounced on. They were not anxious to share their hard-earned power.[79]

The feelings of Standard's practical oilmen ran even higher against the Oil & Gas Supervisor and his subordinates. McLaughlin, a single-minded devotee of applied science, was not always the most tactful of men, and Standard's field superintendents resented his frequently blunt criticisms of their drilling practices and methods of water shut-off.[80]

In January, 1918, a conference was held at Whittier, which both Atwell and McLaughlin attended, to try to make peace and to achieve better cooperation. McLaughlin quickly went to the heart of the matter by asking if Standard's geologists, like those of KT&O, had authority to determine the point of water shut-off and the depth of hole. Atwell replied that Standard's plan was to have the resident geologist make recommendations, frequently after consultation with the deputy Oil & Gas Supervisor in the field, but that final authority rested with the field superintendent. McLaughlin argued that this was not good enough: "I am confident your method . . . will not work. . . . There are two phases to the question. The mechanical superintendent will say to the geologist: 'What do you know about it—you never carried a dinner bucket?' while the geologist will say: 'What do you know about it—you never went to school?' If you put this system in force, and insist that the mechanical superintendent shall have the last word, this department will not know anything about it. We want to be referee." He meant on the side of the geologist, of course.[81]

But it is easy to judge too harshly the practical oilmen. Their confidence in themselves was based on the fact that they were producing a great deal of oil, and they had made many a water shut-off without benefit of geological advice. On occasion, too, they were not unwilling to look to men of technical training for help. For example, Cy Bell, while superintendent of the Northern District, appointed Scharpenberg as cementing engineer in January, 1915, to develop quick-setting and stronger cements to seal off water. Standard's field executives, along with Starke and Stoner, also tried hydraulic lime and various muds. However, they tended to view these experiments more in terms of their meaning for Standard than in any broader perspective. Not easily influenced by the written word themselves, they did not foster the systematic collection of data and its publication.[82]

And at times they correctly evaluated the suggestions of the Department of Petroleum & Gas as impractical. For Standard to have followed the Department's advice in combating water at the Murphy-Whittier property, according to S. H. Gester, would have cost millions of dollars which never would have been regained. Moreover, Standard's field leaders refused to exalt water shut-offs above the efficient use of drilling crews. Instead of holding a crew for a water test, they put it to work on another well. If a water shut-off failed, they could try again.[83]

The great merit of the state geologists was their broad view. In systematically collecting data and publishing their findings, in encouraging others to experiment and to publish, in holding conferences and promoting the free interchange of information, they were helping to transform producing from a rule-of-thumb activity to one disciplined by science. At the same time, they were making a case for advancing men of technical training from advisory into executive roles.[84]

Conflict between the operating men and the state geologists came to no sudden end, but by the close of World War I it had begun to wane. Under Hillman's quiet prodding, the two sides gradually resolved their differences. One clear evidence was Clark Gester's appointment, some months after the Whittier conference, to the newly created post of Chief Development Geologist with authority to report directly to Hillman. Although Gester made headway as a peacemaker, he much preferred exploratory geology to wrangling with field men. No doubt, he was glad to be relieved in 1920 by Earl Wagy, who soon was given the significant title of Chief Petroleum Engineer. Wagy, a mining engineer from the University of California, had worked for KT&O until 1917, when he resigned to join the U.S. Bureau of Mines, which was the nation's chief center of research in petroleum technology.[85]

The gradually improved relationship between geologists and operating men is also to be seen in the reports of the State Oil & Gas Supervisor. Writing in mid-1918, McLaughlin had sharply criticized Standard and two other large operators as laggard in adopting "modern scientific methods of directing their drilling work. . . ." Standard's record of water shut-off, he charged, was poorer than that of any other large operator, and water had become a serious menace at Montebello. Two years later, however, McLaughlin found Montebello in "excellent condition." "The Standard Oil Company . . . ," he went on, "merits special commendation for the manner in which it has harmonized speedy production of oil with the public interest in conservation. . . ."[86]

10

What, in summary, may be said of Standard's producing achievement during these years? For one thing, the decision of 1910 in favor of building a strong producing organization ushered in a period of heavy investment in this hitherto lightly regarded area. Between 1910 and 1919 Standard's cash investment in producing grew from $5,860,000 to $49,989,000, which represented a jump in ratio to the company's total cash investment of from 17.2 to 41.6 per cent.[87]

This effort, which Hillman so ably directed, greatly strengthened the company. It gradually changed Standard from an organization producing 27.5 per cent of its refinery throughput in 1911 to one producing 75.8 per cent of a throughput in 1919 that was more than three times as large. This enlarged throughput, supplied almost wholly with Standard's own crude, required crude purchases that were scarcely larger than those for 1911.[88] The great increase in production also proved immensely profitable, especially during the war years. Surviving figures beginning with 1916 show that producing was providing from 33 to 45 per cent of Standard's net income before taxes:

Table 18: Ratio of Producing Department Earnings to
Company Earnings—1916-1919

	Producing Dept.	Company	Ratio
1916	$ 5,864,075	$17,955,907	32.7
1917	10,076,050	24,479,746	41.2
1918	15,276,097	36,333,469	42.0
1919	18,297,718	40,390,107	45.3

Source: Directors Annual Statements, Comptroller's Records

It appears that more than to any other cause the company owed its rapid growth following independence to its producing victories.

One matter remains to be noted—the shift in producing from an activity carried on almost exclusively in the light of practical experience to one illumined by applied science, a transition that would become ever more meaningful. By the end of World War I men of scientific training were beginning to win a larger place in producing operations. Within another few years, Ralph Arnold would warmly endorse Standard's corps of geologists under Hillman and Gester as "one of the best . . . in the world." It was a judgment he could not have made a decade earlier.[89]

XVII

A STUDY IN POLITICS

One important aspect of the producing story in the crowded, lively second decade of this century is not to be found in the oil fields but in the national political arena, where a change in policy governing oil development on public lands was being hammered out fitfully and painfully. It was a decade of turmoil for the western industry, marked by costly court battles and contests over land legislation before Congressional committees and in the Congress which provoked bitter cabinet wrangling and even involved the White House. Standard's involvement arose from the importance of the Midway field as the Richmond refinery's chief crude supplier after 1909. At issue was the ownership of some 4,000 acres for which the company had signed development agreements between June, 1908, and February, 1909, and, much more important, the rights of numerous small companies in the Midway who sold their oil to Standard.[1] Throughout the long controversy, Standard's executives looked to their legal counsel for guidance. They tried to steer a cautious course consistent with Standard's interest, and at the same time kept an attentive eye on how their company looked both to the government and to the public.

2

The controversy had its roots in the conservation movement early in the century. Far-sighted conservationists were preaching that for generations Americans had been despoiling the land while subduing it, that natural resources were being plundered right and left. This point of view President Theodore Roosevelt advertised and dramatized. The headlong destruction of the nation's forests was his first target; his next was coal. Oil was largely ignored, although in a message to Congress in May, 1906, just before publication of a report of the Bureau of Corporations critical of Standard Oil, Roosevelt made an early reference to the conservation of public oil lands. Forecasting the future lines of debate, he declared, "The fee to such lands should be kept in the United States Government . . . and the lands should be leased only on such terms . . . as will enable the Government to keep entire control thereof." Several bills to accomplish this end were introduced in both House and Senate, but they were buried without discussion.[2]

By the end of the Roosevelt years, proponents of oil conservation began drawing strength from a new quarter, as the Navy gradually shifted its battle fleet from coal to oil fuel. The advantages of oil—easier fueling, more compact storage, greater cruising radius, greater cleanliness, a lesser need for manpower in the engine room, etc.—had been noted since the days of the early experiments with the gunboat *Palos* at the close of the Civil War. And yet there was a concern over how long the nation could have an oil-burning Navy if its oil resources were wastefully developed. One of the leading experts, David T. Day, estimated in 1908 that the nation's reserves ranged between 10 and 25 billion barrels, which might last less than half a century. Others viewed the future even more darkly. The great bulk of the reserves were in private hands, but a portion, notably in California, underlay lands to which the federal government still held title. In order to meet future demands of the Navy and to meet them economically, George Otis Smith, the director of the U.S. Geological Survey, recommended in February, 1908, that the government retain its California lands.[3]

At the time, his recommendation brought no action but, resubmitted and amplified in September, 1909, during the Taft Administration, it got a more favorable hearing from Richard A. Ballinger, the new Secretary of the Interior. Ballinger made Smith's argument his own in forwarding it to the White House. The Secretary also shared Smith's concern over an historic pattern for the "disposal of public petroleum lands at nominal prices" that encouraged overproduction and "unnecessary waste"; they jointly urged "the enactment of legislation that would provide for the sane development of this important resource." Such a law, they suggested, should be phrased in terms of the "disposal . . . of barrels of oil rather than acres of land." While legislation was being formulated and passed, they asked the President to withdraw temporarily public oil lands from entry and sale.[4]

Conforming to their request, on September 27, 1909, Taft withdrew 2,871,000 acres in California and 170,000 acres in Wyoming. The withdrawn area in California cut, to some extent, into Coalinga, Lost Hills, Belridge, McKittrick, Kern River, Whittier, and Olinda, but its principal impact was on the Midway-Sunset field of western Kern County in the San Joaquin Valley. According to one estimate, the withdrawal covered at least a quarter of the productive territory in Valley fields.[5]

The Presidential order brought to a sudden halt a pattern of acquisition of public oil lands that had evolved from the days of the petroleum mining districts in the California oil boom of 1864-65 and had been validated by the Department of the Interior under the Placer Acts passed at the beginning of the 1870's. This legislation, we have seen, had come under attack by conservationists as not compatible with the public interest. From the standpoint of the wildcatter, it also had grave deficiencies. Notably, in limiting an oil patent to no more than 160 acres, the placer laws permitted too small an acreage for an efficient, economic operation and for the risks involved in the search for oil. Operators had supplied their own remedy, making neighboring "paper" locations with nominal or "dummy" entrymen while they drilled for oil. It was a subterfuge that was legally vulnerable, though it had been used at least as early as the California oil revival of the 1870's. A further concern was that a right to patent depended upon the discovery of oil, which was a time-consuming and expensive proposition. Pending discovery, a locator's hold on his land was merely the insecure one of a mining claim.

The effect of the Taft order, in breaking with the past, was to increase the insecurity of the oilmen. The withdrawal had "caught a large number of operators in every conceivable stage of development, from those who had made only "paper" locations to those who had drilled almost to the oil sands." It placed at risk a total investment running into millions of dollars.[6]

3

When news of the withdrawal reached California, Standard turned to its legal counsel, Pillsbury, Madison & Sutro, for advice. Much of the company's investment in Midway, amounting to around $510,000, seemed threatened. Also the order began to cloud crude purchasing, for the future of many Midway well owners who sold crude to Standard appeared doubtful. If they should be forced to suspend or curtail operations, Oscar Sutro believed a considerable number of them eventually would be bankrupted. Through a Washington, D.C., law firm, Britton & Gray, he set out to get the Taft Administration to modify the order and to release lands "upon which . . . substantial work . . . [had] been done." The eastern lawyers discussed this view with the Secretary of the Interior late in October, but he was not won over. Ballinger said the withdrawal was a "direct order of the President" and would have to stand, "subject to action of Congress."[7]

Finding themselves blocked, the Washington attorneys suggested to Sutro that the matter be taken directly to the President. "Possibly you can find some strong aid . . . which would insure his giving his personal and careful consideration." As it happened, there was—Sutro himself, for as a young lawyer in Manila he had known the President in the days when Taft was Governor-General of the Philippines. He telegraphed the President:[8]

If strict compliance is intended order will work enormous injustice and hardship. . . . Literally the order seems to include . . . cases where large investment has necessarily been made prior to discovery . . . and if order were carried out many crews would have to be disbanded to the consequent destruction and deterioration of partially completed wells and materials. I respectfully suggest that the order be modified . . . to allow entrymen who have recorded proper notice prior to September twenty-seventh to proceed with development work for discovery.

President Taft promptly called on Ballinger for a report and recommendation. The Secretary acknowledged that the effect of the order was "to absolutely withdraw all lands . . . upon which no actual discovery had been made," but he did not agree with Sutro's proposal for modification. Ballinger argued that it would be difficult to exclude the lands being drilled and at the same time include lands covered by "paper" locations. He suggested that those who had been working in good faith should look to Congress for relief when legislation was enacted governing the withdrawn lands. It was all the comfort that the Administration was willing to offer.[9]

This decision placed Standard in a dilemma. Sutro's advice was for the company to observe strictly the withdrawal order. The question whether oil had been discovered prior to the withdrawal became the factor that governed Standard's actions. Where no discovery had been made, rigs were closed down, and the company refused to finance further the development agreements it had with owners of mining claims. Standard's crude buyers also turned down offers of production from claims where the discovery had occurred after the withdrawal.

This curtailed activity gave rise to a good deal of idle chatter. The *California Oil World* in January, 1910, dryly observed: "It is said the great company, which has bumped so many legal bumps during the past few years, proposes to conduct itself in a faithful, punctilious manner."[10]

In a business way, the Sutro policy put Standard at a disadvantage with competitors who chose to disregard the order. Some of the large companies, Sutro noted, were proceeding "with apparently increased vigor in 'locating' the Government lands." A good many of the smaller firms were doing the same. In February, 1910, Standard relaxed its strict policy and began to drill again on acreage covered by the development agreements it had negotiated a year or more earlier, but it took on no new lands.[11]

Actually, Standard's rivals were acting on the advice of lawyers who believed, quite sincerely, that Congress alone had authority over the public domain and that the Taft order was unconstitutional because it had not been authorized by Congress. Unlike Standard, these companies were unwilling to take a conservative course. President Taft, who was a constitutional lawyer, had himself expressed serious doubts as to his powers. These doubts were in keeping with a message sent to Congress on January 14, 1910, in which he said: ". . . it is the duty of Congress now, by a statute, to validate the withdrawals which have been made . . . and to authorize the Secretary of the Interior temporarily to withdraw lands."[12]

More than two stormy months elapsed before a bill was introduced by Representative Charles E. Pickett of Iowa to meet the President's request. In the meantime, tempers had grown thin and conservation sentiment was running high as a result of a bitter feud between Chief Forester Gifford Pinchot and Secretary Ballinger over the disposal of some Alaska coal lands. When Pinchot carried his attack on Ballinger to the public, Taft had curtly dismissed the Chief Forester and provided the conservationists with a martyr. The Pickett bill, as it emerged from the House Committee on Public Lands, contained an amendment recognizing the "legal rights" of wildcatters "initiated prior to the withdrawal," but the amendment did not survive the onslaught of eastern conservationists. "Eastern sentiment," Sutro was told, "runs on 'conservation,' without adequate knowledge, and without desire to protect any existing rights."[13]

The defeat caused a stir in the California industry. Meetings were held at Los Angeles, Bakersfield, Coalinga, and San Francisco, and a hastily organized "California Producers Committee" was sent off to Washington. In May the committee won a victory before the Senate Comittee on Public Lands when an amendment was added to the House bill protecting the rights of the oil claimants. It was less than the oilmen desired but, in Sutro's view, it was more than they deserved. The Standard attorney objected to a provision declaring that nothing in the measure should be "construed as a recognition, abridgment, or enlargement of any asserted rights or claims initiated . . . after any withdrawal . . . prior to the passage of this Act." Sutro argued that an explicit ratification of the withdrawal would have been "fairer" to those who had respected the Taft order. At least, he told Britton & Gray, Standard wanted no stronger concession to arouse the conservationists and to threaten the bill's enactment. As it was, after passing the Senate, the amended bill had hard going in the House, which finally concurred on June 21.[14]

Four days later Taft signed the Pickett Act.[15]

4

However viewed, the Pickett Act left a good deal to be desired. For one thing, it set up no policy for the future disposal of the public lands. The act gave Congressional approval to the withdrawal principle, but that was all. Another problem involved the wording of the relief provision: ". . . the rights of any person who, at the date of any order of withdrawal heretofore or hereafter made, is a bona fide occupant or claimant of oil or gas bearing lands, and who, at such date, is in diligent prosecution of work leading to discovery of oil or gas, shall not be affected or impaired by such order. . . ." There was plenty of room for different interpretations, which eventually led to hairsplitting legal discussion. For example, did "work leading to discovery," refer to producers who were engaged in preliminaries, like building roads, as well as those actually drilling? No one, at this juncture, seemed sure.[16]

And, as Sutro had foreseen, the Pickett Act strengthened those who had maintained that the Taft withdrawal of September, 1909, was not valid and that entries were legal until the land was properly withdrawn by authorization of Congress. When the President confirmed the earlier withdrawal by another order on July 2, 1910, covering approximately the same territory, many oil lawyers hailed his action as proof of their contention. So most producers who had gone onto the withdrawn lands after the original order continued their work of development, confident that the courts eventually would sustain them.[17]

Regardless of what others might do, Sutro continued to insist that Standard follow a conservative course. The company purchased no land. With respect to crude oil purchases, Scofield asked for an opinion in September, 1910. Suppose, he said, the company bought crude from producers who had begun to drill prior to Taft's second withdrawal order. Would Standard be in danger of being sued later by the government? Sutro replied that what Scofield proposed would be legal, but that Standard should be extremely careful:[18]

> Your company is peculiarly exposed to demonstrations of governmental activity and to the exploitation of the various theories of conservationists. It is safe to say that the Government would not hesitate to sue for the value of oil sold to you and which was taken from land withdrawn by the President and not in the bona fide occupation of your vendor at the time of withdrawal. . . . For these reasons, where practicable, in contracts of any magnitude for oil taken from unpatented lands, where there is any doubt as to the facts, the vendors should be required to exhibit their title, so that we may determine whether or not the oil comes from land which they lawfully hold and may lawfully claim.

Even while Sutro was writing, a new storm was in the air. The Department of the Interior, by imposing on oil locators for a first time a
regulation of the previous year called the "Yard Decision," was maintaining that claims transferred by locators to other parties before a
discovery of oil could not be patented. This meant many producers could
not gain title to their land, even if they had brought in wells, and it
reversed a practice decades old in western oil development. A wave of
protest swept California. Meetings were held at Los Angeles and Bakersfield late in August. Led by a Fresno attorney, Frank H. Short, oilmen
drew up plans to upset the ruling by legislation. Sutro recommended a
more moderate approach, for he believed that the Midway field could
be shown to be "discovered territory" within the meaning of the mining
laws, and therefore the Yard decision was not applicable. He counseled
the oilmen to seek redress before the Department of Interior and the
courts instead of risking another Congressional battle. But more operators held to the contrary view, and Standard agreed to lend its support.
Their bill, called the Assignments Act, met surprisingly little opposition.
It was signed by the President in March, 1911.[19]

The turmoil over titles by no means had died away, however. While
the agitation over the Yard decision was going on, the government was
taking its first steps to recapture oil lands from the Southern Pacific
Railroad in California. The land grant act of 1866 under which the
railroad had gained title had expressly reserved to the government sections known to contain minerals, except for coal and iron. Around 6,000
acres in Elk Hills the railroad had patented as recently as December,
1904. By 1910 conservationists, including Gifford Pinchot, were arguing
that any oil lands belonging to the Southern Pacific should be recovered
for the public domain. Appearing before the American Mining Congress, meeting in Los Angeles in September, Pinchot declared, "The
Government will not be doing its duty unless it . . . restores these lands
to the people. . . ."[20]

When the Mining Congress adopted a resolution to this effect, Taft
asked Ballinger to conduct an investigation into the railroad's holdings.
The Secretary's report soon became public knowledge. Ballinger pointed
to a possible recovery of many thousands of acres in Midway and elsewhere. Though the issue was not to be settled in Taft's time, the approaching battle sent a chill through the ranks of producers who had bought
lands from the railroad. In December, 1910, the first suit was filed to
regain the acreage in Elk Hills; six others were entered later for an
additional 160,000 acres in the San Joaquin Valley. "Chaos!" said the
California Derrick, in meditating on the struggle. "That is the word
which best represents the condition of the minds of oil men whose lands

are in the balance. They do not know and cannot know exactly where they stand."[21]

5

On the Congressional front, matters drifted after the passage of the Assignments Act in 1911. There was no law to reopen the withdrawn lands to entry. Congress grew cool toward any bills dealing with the problem. Meanwhile, lawyers talked and wrote of test cases over the withdrawals, although the government itself made no move in that direction. And during this time Midway producers became more firmly entrenched, drilling more wells and offering more oil. In a year's time, Standard's share of their production had climbed to 43 per cent, averaging 38,000 barrels daily in 1911. William Edwards, who was handling the company's crude oil purchases, would gladly have taken more. In September he asked Scofield if the company would not be "reasonably safe" in doing so. But Standard's attorneys were adamant. In advising Scofield, E. S. Pillsbury wrote: "I do not overlook the fact that some of your competitors . . . are buying oil without giving much heed to the kind of title, if any, which the sellers may have. . . ." He counseled, however, that Standard could not afford to observe the "doctrine of chances," for it was much more vulnerable to governmental attack than were other companies.[22]

In the face of this warning, Standard continued to buy solely from producers who could furnish substantial evidence that they had a good title. The task was difficult and time consuming. A flaw in a location or in the work done—not always readily uncovered—might easily cloud a title to oil. These were hazards the company tried hard to keep to a minimum.[23]

Toward the close of 1912, the government took a step that carried to a logical conclusion one aspect of the thinking behind the withdrawals. In September, Taft set aside an oil reserve in California for the Navy Department, which was building its first two battleships, the *Nevada* and *Oklahoma*, that were designed to burn oil exclusively. His order affected 38,969 acres in Elk Hills, of which nearly one-third was held under patent by private parties. Except for two school sections, virtually all the rest of the patented lands were at issue in the Elk Hills suit between the government and the Southern Pacific Railroad. There were also numerous mining claims, but few operators, notably the Associated Oil Company, had carried on development work to an oil discovery. California oil circles generally showed no great concern over the establishment of the Elk Hills reserve. If Elk Hills met the Navy needs, said some Midway operators, it would "be a feat quite as great as the Panama Canal."

In December, the oilmen had more to think about when the President unexpectedly added another reserve (Naval Reserve #2) covering 29,341 acres in the Buena Vista Hills, the center of an oil boom that had been going on since shortly before the withdrawal of 1909. Around five-eighths of this land had been patented, of which 15,360 acres had been held by the Southern Pacific since the mid-1890's. Some operators, like Standard on its McNee section, were drilling on patented land, but usually they had no such protection. Their operations were principally on placer mining claims. A fortunate few had made oil discoveries prior to the 1909 withdrawal and could confidently look forward to patents unless charged with fraud because of dummy locators. Others, whose rights were less sure, were covered by the Pickett Act; still others had come onto the land after the withdrawal of 1910.[24]

The establishment of Naval Reserve #2 was a jolt, for it indicated that the government was determined to construe the Pickett Act narrowly and to institute suits against operators who had entered the withdrawn lands after September, 1909. Sutro had picked up the news a little earlier. Of one statement by an agent of the Department of Justice made in August, 1912, Sutro had noted, "This announces a government program which we thought *might* be put into effect. . . ."[25] The fight, it was obvious, would have calamitous effects on the industry, which had millions tied up in disputed lands. It threatened not only the industry but also the financial interests which had supplied the funds. Underlying everything was the ultimate fact that the end-victory or end-defeat lay far in the future in the hands of the courts. Meanwhile many producers, already hard pressed by falling prices in a period of flush production, faced a struggle for survival.

The first legal blow fell in January, 1913, when a supplier of Standard, the Midway Northern Oil Company, was called into court. Midway Northern maintained that predecessor locators were at work on its lands prior to the first withdrawal and that it had discovered oil in paying quantities prior to the signing of the Pickett Act; the government claimed that the company was a trespasser, having entered the withdrawn lands after September, 1909. Standard, which had received 136,000 barrels of Midway Northern's crude, was named a co-defendant. Shortly, two other suits were instituted against Midway operators and the purchasers of their crude, leading to conferences between the federal attorneys and the defendants. Much of the discussion centered around how to keep the producers in business while the litigation ran its lengthy course. The companies were not likely to find crude purchasers if the buyer ran the risk of having to pay twice for the oil—first to the producer and second to the government—if the government won its suit and could not recapture the value of the oil from the producing company. Both sides agreed that the purchasers should continue to receive crude from the disputed lands until some plan could be devised in Washington to take care of the situation.[26]

The advisability of drawing up such a formula fell to a new Administration, for on March 4, 1913, Woodrow Wilson was inaugurated. Wilson's Secretary of the Interior was Franklin K. Lane, a San Francisco lawyer and former Interstate Commerce Commissioner who was well known to E. S. Pillsbury. Earlier Lane, with his brother, George, had been an attorney for the Independent Oil Producers Agency; presumably, he would view sympathetically the plight of the oilmen. Soon after the inauguration, Pillsbury sent Lane a plan which he believed would be fair to all parties.[27]

The plan Pillsbury proposed was essentially a simple one. Until such time as the courts handed down a decision, the producers would be allowed to sell crude from wells already drilled. A portion of the proceeds would be set aside, which would fall to the government if the operators lost in the courts. This arrangement would be equivalent to a lease royalty, a pattern of development the conservationists had been urging for the withdrawn lands. Pillsbury told Lane that only through such a plan would the producers be able to keep operating and preserve the wells from deterioration or ruin.

Lane's reply was disheartening. He could see no need for so sweeping a formula for so few litigants and, in any case, doubted his authority to enter into such an arrangement, especially for lands on the naval reserves. The most the operators could ask for, in his view, was a speedy trial, to which he pledged his best efforts.[28]

Not long after hearing from Lane, Pillsbury determined upon a trip to Washington to convince the Administration of the "necessity for relief." He had little faith in a speedy judicial settlement, and he foresaw a situation becoming progressively more critical. Standard's attorney took up with Secretary Lane and other high Washington officials, including Attorney General T. W. Gregory, the familiar legal questions that clouded crude purchasing: "Can the purchaser safely decide these questions? Manifestly not. . . . His only safe course is to reject both the oil from the land which may ultimately be patented, and that from land to which title fails." He went further: "If the buyers of oil . . . should decide—as they must, unless relief is granted—that they can no longer 'hold the bag' by paying the producer for his oil . . ., the consequences will be tremendous. . . . Very many oil producers have strained their resources to the limit. . . . They must have money. . . . Let the purchasers of oil decline to buy . . . and what bank will continue its advances?"

Pillsbury renewed his plea for approval of his formula:[29]

> Without the agreement, the Government will in many cases get none of the oil until it takes possession of the land, for irresponsible buyers only will take it from irresponsible producers and the meat of the coconut will be gone. Furthermore, all operators of such a class will drill to their utmost capacity, so as to get as much of the oil out as possible before the land is taken from them—an event which, in the nature of things, will be postponed over a range of years. This is directly destroying what the Government is aiming to accomplish—conservation of oil.

Although Pillsbury received a courteous hearing, he was unable to bring about a change in the Administration's decision to look to the courts for a settlement. While Standard's attorney was still in the East, a first case involving oil lands covered by the 1909 withdrawal came to trial before a federal judge in Wyoming. Judge J. A. Reiner's decision in *U. S.* v. *Midwest Oil Company* was a defeat for the government, for he held that the President could not withdraw lands without Congressional authorization. But the Wilson Administration refused to accept his decision and appealed it to the Supreme Court.[30]

This action on the part of the government convinced Standard's legal counsel that it was unwise for the company to continue to take oil from Midway Northern and two other beleaguered producers with whom it was listed as a co-defendant. Early in the fall Standard "very reluctantly" decided to cut off these producers and to scrutinize carefully its arrangements with other producers who might also come under governmental attack. It was a move undoubtedly made easier by the prolific production from the company's McNee section, which was at an all-time peak in September.[31]

As the illusion of a prompt decision by the Supreme Court began to fade early in 1914, the pressure of producers increased for some form of relief during the period of litigation. The Administration also was more amenable, especially as it became evident that the government's interest, no less than the producer's, was threatened by water infiltration if the wells were not operated. The wells of Midway Northern, shut down since October, 1913, were operating again four months later under a court order that impounded the net proceeds from the sale of oil until the suit was settled.[32]

Meanwhile, Oscar Sutro had gone to Washington to speak again for the relief plan that Pillsbury had urged the previous year. With Lane's approval, a bill embodying the formula was finally introduced in May in both Houses authorizing the Secretary of Interior to enter into operating agreements with producers on the withdrawn lands who had commenced to drill within three months after the second withdrawal order. The bill was vigorously opposed by Josephus Daniels, the Secretary of the Navy, who refused to accept it for operators on the naval reserves. Not until an amendment was added authorizing the Navy to spend any proceeds set aside from oil produced on the naval reserves did he cease his opposition. The Operating Agreements Act, as it was called, became law late in August. Under this act, the Secretary of Interior entered into 40 contracts embracing wells on some 4,000 acres of disputed oil lands in California and Wyoming, usually on terms that set aside one-eighth of the proceeds. None of this land was on the naval reserves.[33]

6

In February, 1915, the U. S. Supreme Court by a five to three decision, reversed the findings of Judge Reiner in the Midwest case. This decision not only upheld the constitutionality of the Pickett Act but also affirmed the earlier executive withdrawal by stating: "The power of the President to withdraw public lands from entry has been so long exercised . . . as to be equivalent to a grant of power."[34]

With the way cleared, Attorney General Gregory stepped up the campaign to recapture the oil lands. Before the summer of 1915 was over, the number of suits filed had grown from five to thirty, and many more were in process. Defendants were notified that the government demanded both the land and an accounting for the oil produced. In California the Wilson Administration set as its goal regaining as much as possible of the entire unpatented area of Midway, Buena Vista, and Elk Hills.[35]

These actions on the part of the government quickly destroyed whatever lingering illusions the oilmen may have had. Over the year 1915 the state's production dropped nearly 14,000,000 barrels, costing California its position as the leading producer in the nation, an honor it had held since 1909. The Midway area fell off by more than one-fifth, accounting for nearly 11,000,000 barrels of the decline. The withdrawal suits were largely blamed for this state of affairs. A committee of industrial, financial, and political leaders, headed by Roy N. Bishop, spokesman for the Crocker oil interests, met at San Francisco's Palace Hotel in October, 1915, to organize an Oil Industry Association in which thirty-four companies banded together for mutual defense. The committee also solicited individual memberships throughout California. Bishop was chosen president, and Francis B. Loomis and W. D. Egilbert vice presidents; Herbert Fleishhacker, president of the Anglo & London Paris National Bank, became the treasurer. Within the state, the Association enjoyed broad political backing, including among its supporters James N. Gillett, a former Republican governor closely identified with the oil interests of Captain William Matson, F. H. Hall, chairman of the Democratic State Central Committee, and John M. Eshleman, a leading California Progressive and lieutenant governor under Hiram Johnson.[36]

The Loomis connection is especially interesting, for he represented Oscar Sutro, whose voice for Standard was a powerful one in the affairs of the Association. Loomis, who was a onetime newspaper man in New York, Washington, D.C., Cincinnati, and Oakland, and Assistant Secretary of State in the Roosevelt Administration, had admirable qualifications for his post—an alert mind, an excellent command of language, and diplomatic skill. Sutro himself occupied no office in the Association. Nor did any Standard executive, though the company contributed liberally to the Association's treasury. During the first twenty months, Standard gave $22,000 to pay bills and salaries totaling approximately $119,000.[37]

The Association's principal theater of activity was in Washington, for which Loomis departed early in December, 1916. He was soon joined by a number of other oil industry representatives, including Gillett and Eshleman, who turned to the task of creating a favorable climate for relief legislation in the Administration and in Congress. They quickly discovered that they had their work cut out. Secretary Lane, they found, viewed them coolly. He did not look forward to locking horns with other cabinet officers, especially Secretary of Navy Daniels and Attorney General Gregory, who were opposed to relief for the oilmen. Some subordinate officials in the Departments of Justice and the Interior, who had been roughly dealt with by western editors over the oil suits, were also hostile.[38]

While the oil spokesmen were planning their course of action, the House Committee on Public Lands began hearings on a general leasing bill for the handling of a number of minerals, including oil, on the public domain. It was an Administration measure that had received a great deal of debate in the preceding session. After passing the House, the bill had stalled in the Senate; the chairman of the House Committee, Scott Ferris, was anxious to get it under way again. Yielding only slightly to the western oilmen, he accepted a relief amendment that excluded the naval reserves and left the question of relief for operators who had bought claims from dummy locators up in the air. Sutro viewed the amendment as very unsatisfactory. The bill passed the House in mid-January and went to the Senate, where because of the proportionately larger western representation the Californians had greater hopes.[39]

Their staunchest ally in the Senate was a fellow Californian, James D. Phelan, a Democratic member of the Committee on Public Lands and a lifelong friend of the Secretary of the Interior. In place of the House amendment, Phelan proposed one that met the wishes of the Oil Industry Association. It authorized patents under the mining laws for an oil or gas discovery on lands that had been entered and on which a "substantial amount of work" had been done prior to the withdrawal of 1910. Failing a patent, it provided for a twenty-year renewable lease at one-eighth royalty for any operator on land entered prior to the 1910 withdrawal on which drilling was in progress by January 1, 1914. Furthermore, the amendment did not exclude the naval reserves.[40]

Off and on, for nearly six weeks the Phelan substitute was vigorously debated. Much of the attack came from Secretary Daniels. Speaking for the Navy, he declared that the amendment "would take away from the government that which in time of peril might change the tide of war." He reminded the Senators that World War I was growing in scope and fury, that the day of preparedness was at hand for the nation, and argued that the conversion of the Navy from a coal to an oil burning fleet depended on the preservation of the reserves. The Secretary forecast a Navy demand of 1,760,000 barrels annually when the battleships and destroyers currently authorized were completed. "Every battleship we build," he said, "increases the demand by 90,000 barrels a year." Daniels maintained that it was wrong to free the lands after the Supreme Court had ruled on the matter: "To pass an act compelling us to lease land to people who have not title is a very dangerous precedent." The Secretary also suggested that big corporations like Standard Oil rather than little operators would be the principal beneficiaries of the amendment.[41]

Senator Phelan took special exception to this last line of attack. Two days later he read into the record a precise statement of the situation from Roy Bishop of the Oil Industry Association:[42]

> There are 134 companies operating on unpatented lands. . . . The large companies may be said to be Associated Oil, Union Oil, Standard Oil, and General Petroleum. . . . In addition, there are 130 smaller independent companies. . . . Unpatented acreage . . . controlled by smaller companies is 26,721 acres out of 38,000, approximately 80 [70] per cent. Associated Oil has 2,040; Union Oil, 3,616; Standard Oil, 4,020; General Petroleum,

1,670. . . . Out of a total of 40,209 barrels [daily], 130 companies produced 25,134 barrels, Associated, 5,274; Union, 926; Standard, 4,189; General Petroleum, 4,686 barrels. Independent producers . . . in December, 1915, were producing 60 per cent of total production from . . . lands in question.

In mid-March the Phelan amendment was adopted by the Senate Committee. Every member who had followed the argument agreed, according to Francis B. Loomis, that the producers were "justly entitled to relief." But much remained to be done. For one thing, there was the matter of assuring an early vote in the Senate. For another, the westerners needed to find sufficient support to make sure that the House would accept the Phelan amendment after the Senate had passed it. In particular, Scott Ferris, chairman of the House Committee on Public Lands, had to be won over. To offset the opposition of Secretary Daniels and the Attorney General, the oilmen badly needed Secretary Lane as their champion. Even more, they became convinced that favorable intervention from the White House was essential.[43]

During these critical weeks Secretary Lane was in California attending a Charter Day observance at the University of California and visiting a sick brother. Loomis telegraphed Sutro: "Hope no pains will be spared to make it plain to . . . [Lane] that everybody . . . is looking to him to exert all the influence he possesses. . . ." But the Secretary held himself aloof from the oilmen. At a university luncheon in Berkeley, Sutro found Lane "extremely reserved." "I think he feels keenly the inappropriateness of pronouncedly defending a bill . . . opposed by two members of the Cabinet," the Standard lawyer wrote Loomis.[44]

Sutro was certain that the key to the whole situation lay in the attitude of the White House. Through Herbert Fleishhacker, the banker-treasurer of the Association, he found an advocate in Harley P. Wilson, a Wall Street promoter and utility man with West Coast ties, who was on good terms with Colonel Edward House, the President's close friend and advisor. Although House at first was inclined not to bother about a matter in which he had no interest, he arranged an appointment for Wilson at the White House on March 29. Sutro dispatched a brief-like memorandum which the financier used in talking with the President. It gave facts and figures which had been offered in Washington earlier.[45] Several days later the visitor from Wall Street told the story of his reception:[46]

> Never in my life have I been more courteously and charmingly treated than by the President upon this occasion. . . . For fully twenty-five minutes

he listened most attentively. . . . When I had done . . . he said . . . 'Your presentation of this matter has impressed me very much, indeed. I was not aware that the situation involved the difficulties of which you speak. I will be glad, indeed, to make a careful investigation. . . . It is not the purpose nor the function of the Government to do any injustice to any citizen, and in this case as in all others nothing is further from our desire.'

The financier warned, however, that the westerners must look forward to the continued opposition of Daniels and Gregory. "You need expect no let-up . . . to oust from the naval reserves, every operator not able to comply with the strict letter of the law . . .," Wilson wrote Fleishhacker. Daniels was already appealing to the Senate Committee on Naval Affairs to intercede. His arguments were supplemented by E. J. Justice, who had charge of the California oil cases for Attorney General Gregory. A friend of Daniels and from his home town, Justice appeared as a witness before the Senate Committee on Public Lands late in April.[47]

In the course of his testimony, Justice brought in Standard which, he charged, would be a large beneficiary under the Phelan amendment. In a majority of the oil cases, he declared, Standard had been named a co-defendant for purchasing oil from lands in litigation. He spoke several times of funds impounded by the courts and indicated somewhat obscurely that Standard stood to gain "a large part." President Scofield countered with a long telegram answering Justice. What had happened was that Standard had paid a total of $2,610,000 into the courts. Except for a sum of $106,000, this would belong to the producers and not to Standard if the government won its suits. The $106,000 involved crude oil from an eighty-acre tract over which the government and Standard were at odds.[48]

Several weeks after the Scofield telegram, a series of articles began to appear in the *New York Herald* indicting the oilmen and accusing Lane and Phelan, among others, of complicity in looting the public domain. The *Herald* was known to be close to Secretary Daniels. Loomis promptly called at its Washington bureau, where he claimed to have traced "a good deal of unfair and harmful matter" to the Navy. He supplied this information to Senator Phelan, who was about to call at the White House with a delegation of western Democratic senators to discuss the oil relief bill with the President. Although the meeting was cordial, it brought no positive intervention by the President, and the attacks in the *Herald* continued, weakening the drive for immediate consideration of the relief measure.[49]

Despite the odds, Loomis and his associates kept trying to get Phelan's amendment to the Senate floor. In June they came up against a new obstacle, as the approaching Presidential campaign became the all-absorbing center of interest. They could do nothing before Congress recessed for the national conventions.[50]

During the recess, Loomis devoted his principal efforts to countering the effect of the *New York Herald's* barrage on the eastern press. With Sutro's assent and the aid of a San Francisco newspaperman, George Van Smith, he won the support of Chester Rowell, a prominent California editor and Progressive and a man of high standing in conservation circles. Rowell agreed to call on a number of journalists in New York, including friends on such influential magazines as *Collier's, The Outlook,* and *The Independent.* The tie to Rowell was also important because he was as close as anyone to Governor Hiram Johnson of California, who had been Theodore Roosevelt's vice-presidential running mate in 1912. Through Rowell, Loomis appealed to the Governor to make a personal call at the White House. The Governor replied that a call would be unwise at a time of such intense political feeling, but promised to write "a strong letter" and to "give it good publicity."[51]

While marking time, Loomis also worked closely with Senator Phelan, who, stung by the Navy charges, was anxious to push his amendment to a vote that would vindicate him. They looked to Lane for an endorsement, but none was forthcoming. Then, on July 4, they got a shock. In a public statement, Lane announced his opposition to patents on claims originating in the names of dummy locators.[52]

In an eleventh hour effort to secure action before Congress adjourned, the Oil Industry Association appealed to the President, pointing out that for three years the operators had been seeking relief and asserting that further delay would be "ruinous" to many of them. But their plea was in vain. When the matter of securing a vote came before the Democratic Steering Committee in the Senate, the bill was removed from the calendar. The best its proponents could get was an understanding that it would be brought up early in December soon after Congress reconvened. Privately, Loomis believed this decision was all to the good, for the bill could never be passed with Lane opposed to it. Time would now be available to make the necessary changes to get the Secretary firmly behind his fellow Californians.[53]

This was easier said than done. After Congress adjourned, the attack on Lane by conservationists and Navy advocates increased in tempo. In particular, he was assailed by Gifford Pinchot who, in a lengthy, detailed, open letter, accused the Secretary of being a friend of "trespassers," of trying to scuttle the naval reserves, and of being "actively and openly against the public interest."[54]

By the time Congress reconvened, Loomis reported that Lane was about to raise a white flag: "[Lane] says he can go no further, particularly in a public way, with our matter; that he has no further influence with the President; that he is looked upon as a man of biased views. . . . He makes it very clear that there is no fight left in him. . . ."[55]

The heated charges had also taken a toll of friendly legislators. "About half the fellows in Congress," according to Senator Key Pittman of Nevada, "were scared stiff by Pinchot and the Navy and dared not follow and vote their convictions." A consideration of the Phelan amendment was again postponed. In the words of ex-Governor Gillett, it had had too much "bad advertising."[56]

Meanwhile a way out through compromise was suggested.[57] Its origins are rather obscure, but the alacrity with which it was picked up by representatives of smaller companies in the Oil Industry Association indicates the hopes they had for it. Loomis, by contrast, was lukewarm. The plan called for all land held by oil companies, either by patent or under mining claims, in Naval Reserve #1 (Elk Hills) to be relinquished to the Navy in return for an agreement by Daniels to withdraw his opposition to leases for operators on lands in Naval Reserve #2 (Buena Vista Hills). Reserve #1, which government geologists were estimating at above 100,000,000 barrels, was virtually undeveloped, while Reserve #2 contained 315 producing wells (including 45 on Standard's McNee section) that had averaged 41,400 barrels daily in 1916. Only 140 of these wells were on unpatented land. Crucial to the plan was the willingness of Standard and the Associated, the principal oil company landholders in Naval Reserve #1, to give up their lands to the Navy. After a brief discussion, both companies agreed to go along with the scheme. Standard offered to deed its lands in Section 36, a school section to which it held a patent for 480 acres, and Associated agreed to sign over its claims to five sections.[58]

The Navy was much more reluctant. Feeling that they had the revised Phelan amendment effectively bottled up, they saw no reason for compromise. Moreover, even though the oil companies ceded their lands in Naval Reserve #1, the Navy's hold on the reserve would be far from complete unless the government won its suits for almost seventeen sections against the Southern Pacific. The most Daniels would do, when a committee which included Senators Phelan, Pittman, and Thomas J. Walsh of Montana broached the plan, was to agree to a suggestion of Senator Pittman that an informal committee, consisting of spokesmen for the Navy, Justice, and Interior departments and for the Public Lands committees of the Congress, study the proposal and try to come up with a relief measure. Lane readily agreed, and Gillett was delighted. He wrote Sutro:[59]

> If Secretary Daniels remains stubborn and will not listen to reason or agree to a fair bill, then this Committee can go before the President, present the bill to him, show him the fairness of it . . . and probably get the President to cause Daniels to withdraw his opposition. I do not believe the President will stand out, when he knows the facts, against the Senate and House Committees backed up by the Interior Department.

During the week before Christmas the "informal" committee deliberated the proposed exchange of lands for leases in the naval reserves and a second compromise suggested by the Department of Interior. Expert witnesses quickly fell into argument over the productiveness of the two reserves. The very fact that Elk Hills was undeveloped made that reserve, from the Navy's point of view, a dubious proposition. Navy spokesmen would have nothing to do with the Standard and Associated offer. And Secretary Daniels was quite as intransigent with respect to a Department of Interior proposal that would have allowed leases to operators in Naval Reserve #2 on lands entered prior to the second withdrawal, but not to operators in the Elk Hills reserve or in the Teapot Dome reserve in Wyoming. On December 23, Daniels wrote Senator Pittman: "I am advised by the Attorney General that there is much reason to expect a favorable outcome of the pending litigation. . . . Accepting, as I must, this view . . . , I feel that the Government's interests . . . are too substantial to be sacrificed. . . . These men are now asking Congress to give them, at the cost of naval efficiency (which means at the cost of the national security) that to which they have no legal or equitable claim. . . ."[60]

Over Daniels' protest, the Senate Committee on Public Lands nevertheless adopted the Department of Interior substitute, affecting about 5,600 acres in Naval Reserve #2. This action led to some lively hearings before the Senate Naval Affairs Committee late in January, 1917. The by now familiar charges were heard once again. The government attorney, E. J. Justice, emphasized particularly the role of dummy locators in the origins of claims, including 1,600 unpatented acres on which Standard was operating. In rebuttal, Louis Titus, the oil industry representative, argued that even though some of the original locators may have been dummies and the claims, therefore, fraudulent, the claims frequently had changed hands a number of times among innocent parties who had purchased and invested their money in good faith. To a number of Senators, not all of them western, this argument seemed to have merit. The chairman of the Naval Affairs Committee, Benjamin R. Tillman of South Carolina, and the ranking majority member, Claude A. Swanson of Virginia, were two who "frankly admitted that strong equities existed," according to Gillett.[61]

While the hearings before the Naval Affairs Committee were going on, the President himself began to take a hand. He told Lane, Gregory, and Daniels to agree upon a settlement. If they did not, Loomis reported, the President said that he would try to reach "some sort of decision" himself. This action on the part of the President was heartening to the oilmen and helped further to create a climate more favorable to compromise.[62]

In March, after discussions with Assistant Attorney General Francis J. Kearful, Titus wrote Sutro of a plan being considered by the Administration. It was to grant leases to land to operators innocent of fraud under the mining laws who had made oil or gas discoveries outside the Naval Reserves, but to limit leases within the Naval Reserves solely to wells already drilled. As a precondition to a lease, however, an operator had to surrender his right to ask for a patent; if he tried for a patent and failed, he would lose out entirely. Kearful also indicated that back royalty would probably be assessed from the date the operator began to get production from each well.

In Sutro's view, the proposal was "extremely harsh." He thought favoring operators outside the naval reserves over those within, other things being equal, was unfair. The heavy hazard placed on seeking a patent, joined with the provision for back royalty, he wrote had "a sort of Russian flavor to it." Nonetheless, in the plan's favor was the fact that "it would definitely establish the equities of the oil men and their right to relief." If the proposal could be clothed in language that would forestall further conflict, Sutro said that he would be willing to support it. "Anything that will stop the litigation and which does not confiscate the oil men's claims is desirable."[63]

7

Suddenly, with the entry of the United States into World War I, a powerful new factor was injected into the long controversy. The need for a great national production effort, especially in fuels, was immediate and compelling. In the West, where coal deposits were inferior and rare, the burden on fuel oil was especially great. And in California during the two years since March, 1915, crude oil in storage had declined from more than a nine months supply to an amount sufficient for less than half that time. In April, 1917, the month of the nation's war declaration, production of California crude was running at a rate of about 269,000 barrels daily compared with a consumption of 319,000 barrels. To more than producers, the oil controversy cried for a speedy settlement.[64] There seemed every reason to free Midway, California's greatest oil field, from the crippling effects of the prolonged litigation. In May, the *Standard Oil Bulletin* said, in a sharp editorial:[65]

> It is a scandal that the efficiency of our railroads and industries should be threatened because of a legal squabble between some producers and two departments of the Government. . . . Will not the President see and remedy the situation? . . .
>
> The needs of the Navy are not to be ignored for any consideration. But to protect the Navy it is unnecessary to destroy the usefulness of the entire oil area in the public domain. The Secretary of the Navy in 1916 estimated the entire consumption of the Navy on a war footing at about 14,000 barrels per day. . . . One consumer on this Coast, the Southern Pacific Railroad, alone uses 40,000 barrels per day.

The attempt during the early months of 1917 at a compromise, of which Sutro reluctantly had advised acceptance, had foundered. By no means all of the oilmen were for it but, according to one historian, it also ran into insuperable obstacles within the Administration. Contrary to what Lane would have allowed, Daniels, Gregory, and President Wilson insisted that the leases outside the naval reserves (as well as within) be limited solely to the wells that had been drilled. In so doing, Daniels was carrying his battle against the producers outside his own jurisdiction.[66]

Spurred by wartime urgencies, Senator Thomas J. Walsh early in the new Congress introduced a general leasing bill similar to those of the two preceding Congresses that was designed to unlock the coal, oil, gas, and other less important minerals on withdrawn lands of the public domain. Late in June, during hearings before the Committee on Public Lands, Senator Phelan introduced a new amendment designed to give relief to the California oilmen. Under its terms, an operator innocent of fraud on land entered prior to the 1910 withdrawal could apply for a patent if an oil or gas discovery had been made. If a patent was refused, he would receive a lease at one-eighth royalty, with his accrued royalty running from February 23, 1915, the date of the Supreme Court's decision in the Midwest case. Lands in Naval Reserve #2 were specifically included, but those in the other two reserves were barred.[67]

The way had been paved for the amendment by a number of prominent witnesses, including Dr. Vann H. Manning, Director of the U. S. Bureau of Mines, Mark Requa, a well-known California mining engineer, President Ray Lyman Wilbur of Stanford University, and E. L. Doheny, who had voiced fears of a critical oil shortage in the West.[68] Francis S. Peabody, chairman of the committee on coal production of the Council of National Defense, advised the senators:[69]

> We cannot wait until we are whipped to open up these fields. . . . If it exhausted the coal of the United States or the oil of the United States to win this war, we must win this war. We must not hold back anything.

Secretary Daniels once more stood forth as the chief opponent of Phelan and the oilmen. "The problem you have to consider," he told the committee, "is whether the needs of California for this oil are supreme to the needs of national defense." If Naval Reserve #2 were thrown open, he predicted that it would be "drilled up in about a year" and the Navy would have "nothing to fall back on." "I am looking to the time of the chief emergency. I contend it is not here now; it will be later, perhaps; when it comes I do insist that it shall not be given to men who can not prove legal title to it."[70]

Little more than a week after the Senate hearings, the California State Council of Defense put its findings on record following a study of the oil industry of the state. The investigation, begun in May, 1917, had occupied the attention of a committee of independent experts for more than a month. The California committee forecast a possible desperate fuel shortage on the West Coast. If rates of production and consumption did not change, it predicted that the margin of safety for stocks of fuel oil would be reached by September, 1918, and that the stocks would be exhausted within another nine months. The report of the California committee gave additional strength to backers of the Phelan amendment.[71]

When the general leasing bill cleared the Senate Committee on Public Lands in August, it received only a single dissenting vote. The majority report jabbed at the bill's foes. "It is better to let future wars take care of themselves than to lose the present one through dreams of far off conservation, technical disputes as to methods and puerile bickerings as to jurisdiction between governmental bureaus." But it proved much more difficult to get the measure before the Senate. Late in November Secretary Daniels warned the Oil Industry Association's Roy Bishop that the bill could "only be passed over his dead body." Daniels' next move was to prepare the way for a "commandeering" bill, providing not only for Navy retention of the reserves but also for Navy drilling and operation of the oil wells themselves.[72]

To head off a dangerous and profitless controversy, Senator Key Pittman, who was in charge of the leasing bill, decided that it would be wise to eliminate Naval Reserve #2 from the relief amendment. This action aroused some of the oilmen, leading Sutro once more to counsel moderation. "Although the Standard Oil Company will be hit as hard as anyone by the elimination of the naval reserves, I cannot see on what theory those who cannot get relief should stand in the way of those who can," he wrote the balky ex-Governor Gillett.[73]

Before the newly amended bill came to a vote, it met an unexpected attack from the White House. Early in January the President announced that he wanted a further amendment limiting relief for any operator on a claim originating between the 1909 and 1910 withdrawals to a lease of wells already drilled, with the royalty figured at not less than one-eighth of the oil from the date each well began production. The oilmen felt, according to Loomis, that they had been "submarined." Although this amendment was defeated, it undoubtedly accounted for the narrow margin by which the measure passed the Senate, 37 to 32, on January 7, 1918.[74]

It also indicated the future lines of conflict, for shortly Congressman Scott Ferris proposed the President's terms as an amendment to a general leasing bill about to come up before the House Committee on Public Lands. Lane went along with the proposal, which Attorney General Gregory endorsed as "the limit of liberality." A friendly but pointed correspondence took place between Ferris and Daniels. "There has been nothing . . . to change my views . . . and it is as a compromise, and only as a compromise, that . . . I . . . consent," the Secretary declared. The oilmen called it "compromise with a vengeance."[75] There were pleas and efforts to soften the relief features and to change other provisions in a prolonged hearing running over a month. Much of the furor came from oilmen in the Mid-Continent and Rocky Mountain regions, who were bitterly opposed to the acreage limitations in the leasing bill. Using a familiar tactic, they charged the acreage restrictions on leases would help maintain a monopoly by Standard Oil—a loose charge that was resented by the bill's sponsors.[76]

In mid-April the measure was reported out of the House Committee with a more liberal relief amendment, except for royalty. It offered leases of up to 160 acres (including the naval reserves) at one-quarter royalty to operators who were free from fraud. The only dissenter was Scott Ferris, the committee chairman. However, the bill appeared to have little chance of being brought to a vote before the whole House so long as Ferris opposed it.[77]

Toward the end of the month, as California's crude oil stocks dipped to less than a three-and-a-half-month supply, Washington was treated to another round of words. A curtailment of fuel oil to paper mills in the Northwest brought repercussions in the publishing world. Some fifteen or twenty publishers came to see Daniels, who was himself a newspaper publisher. Daniels told the publishers that he was willing to approve drilling in the naval reserves, but not under the terms of the bills before Congress, to which the President was also opposed. If either bill passed, the publishers learned, the President would veto it. At a meeting hastily called by Mark Requa, who had become Oil Director of the U. S. Fuel Administration, the publishers, members of the Oil Industry Association, and government officials, turned to the task of drafting an acceptable bill. Gillett exploded in wrath, causing F. W. Kellogg of the *San Francisco Call* to warn Standard's K. R. Kingsbury that "Gillett's . . . grossly disrespectful attitude towards Daniels and President . . . will if maintained result in the commandeering of the entire oil business of California."[78]

News of the threat of commandeering to avert an oil shortage had already reached California, where a seven-member committee that included Oscar Sutro was preparing to leave for Washington. They were in Washington during most of May. At first the situation looked hopeful. The committee agreed to accept an amendment drawn up by the Fuel Administration which limited leases solely to wells already drilled at a one-eighth royalty but gave the President discretionary power to extend any lease to include the remainder of the land claimed by the operator.

The Californians pointed out, however, that the immediate problem was producing more oil. They offered to drill at their "own risk and without profit" on the unpatented lands and to impound the net proceeds. Such an arrangement won the approval of Requa and the Attorney General, but not of Secretary Daniels, who argued that it would result in drilling up the naval reserves while other undesignated rich lands remained undeveloped. Daniels refused to yield unless the operators accepted a future obligation to supply the Navy with an equivalent amount of oil at a price to be agreed upon. The operators, for their part, sought to limit this obligation to the duration of the war or until final settlement of the dispute regarding titles, and to have the price fixed by the Fuel Administration—terms that Daniels found unacceptable. "See no prospects for immediate production," Sutro wired on May 24. "We made our record . . . and the Delegation is dispersing."[79]

8

The breakdown of the May conference marked the point at which the Oil Industry Association began to fall apart. The collapse of the conference, in Standard's view, spelled nothing less than stalemate. In Sutro's words, "too many cooks [had] meddled with the broth." These included industry representatives, members of Congress, and officials in the various departments of the federal government. Further argument, the Standard executives had come to believe, would have little influence on the final decision, and they had scant patience with the bickering over policy that was arising among the western operators. In June, the company served notice that it would no longer help finance the Oil Industry Association.[80]

Moreover, it must be admitted, the land controversy was no longer so serious a threat to the Richmond refinery's crude supply. Late in 1917, to aid Richmond, Standard had negotiated a trade with the General Petroleum Company, exchanging West Coyote and Montebello crude for virtually all of General's oil in Kern County. Standard's flush production in Southern California was also permitting some increase in the throughput at El Segundo. In fact, the company's success at Montebello and West Coyote helped to maintain and even increase slightly the state's crude stocks, at so low a point in mid-1918, and to take the edge off talk of commandeering lands at Midway. When Kingsbury learned of the failure of the May conference, he was not dismayed. Elated by two new 5,000-barrel wells at West Coyote, he wired Sutro, "What do we care for the reserve?"[81]

Within Congress, debate over the general leasing bill and its relief provisions continued into the summer of 1918 and on into the postwar session which began in December. In February, 1919, a conference report, signed by a committee of the two Houses, appeared at long last to have a fair chance of settling these complex matters. Scott Ferris told the House that he approved of the report and "very imprudently," according to Loomis, "that the Departments of Justice and Navy were satisfied. . . ." The bill passed the House by a sizable majority, but not without considerable debate that was influenced by Gifford Pinchot. Pinchot charged in several letters to Congressmen that the relief provisions were too favorable to the oilmen and that Ferris had misrepresented the attitude of the Administration. Meanwhile, Senator Pittman had cabled the President at the Peace Conference in Paris and had received the reassuring word, so Loomis heard, that Wilson "would not oppose" the measure. On his return late in February, however, the President reversed himself, clearing the way on Friday, March 1, for Daniels and Gregory to denounce the relief provisions as unfair to the government just before the bill came up in the Senate. Their words had the effect of a bombshell under Pittman, who had marshalled upwards of seventy votes. The next afternoon Senator Robert La Follette began a filibuster that by March 4 had killed the bill.[82]

But the twin problems of opening up the withdrawn lands and settling the relief issue were too important to remain undecided much longer. In California in 1919 titles were clouded to 19,745 acres of proven oil land containing 653 wells representing an investment of nearly $18,-000,000. The total production from the wells had amounted to more than 76,000,000 barrels, of which 18,000,000 came from within Naval Reserve #2. Almost $50,000,000 in receipts from production were held impounded. So in August, 1919, a new Congress once again tied relief provisions into a general leasing bill. By this time about everything that could be said in the way of argument had already been said, though many of the same arguments came forth once more, if not always with the same vigor. As before, a conference committee was appointed to iron out differences between the two Houses. The bill that emerged in February, 1920, was acceptable to the Administration, including Daniels, and to that stormy conservationist, Gifford Pinchot. On February 25 it became law, after passing the House by an overwhelming majority and the Senate unanimously.[83]

Curiously, the relief provisions of the bill were about the same as those to which Sutro would have reluctantly agreed three years earlier. Under their terms, operators on lands outside the naval reserves on which work had begun prior to the withdrawal of 1910, if not charge-able with fraud, could within six months relinquish claims to title, settle for past production by payment of one-eighth of the value of the oil at the time of production, and get a lease to the land for twenty years at not less than one-eighth royalty. On the naval reserves, an operator was limited to a lease on the existing wells unless the President, in his discretion, chose to extend it to include the land. An operator who believed that he was entitled to a patent could still make the attempt, but it was risky to do so. The six months in which an operator could decide for a lease was too brief a time for a patent application to be processed, and if turned down for a patent, he would have lost all. Sutro viewed this hazard as unfair, as he did also the discrimination in relief against operators on the naval reserves. But, nonetheless, he was grateful that the "wasteful and profitless carnival of litigation" over the disputed lands had at last come to an end.[84]

Standard moved quickly to clear up its status at Midway under the new act. Over the years, the company had acquired patents to 1,280 acres on which discoveries had been made prior to the Taft withdrawal. It now put in for a patent on an additional 160 acres, to which Standard had withstood a government challenge in the courts. The company was also eligible for leases to 1,400 acres outside the naval reserves and to wells on 960 acres inside Naval Reserve #2. Instead of applying for the leases, Standard sold its rights in August, 1920, to two Southern California oilmen, Dan Murphy and William Valentine, who received the leases under the name of the Murvale Oil Company. A condition of the sale was that the oil produced would be delivered to the Standard Oil Company at prevailing market prices. In the company's view, it had come in for a good deal of irresponsible attack during the long controversy, and it wanted to avoid a further direct relationship with the government over these properties.[85]

There was widespread satisfaction in having matters settled at Midway, which for decades would continue to be a great field and one of the three largest in the nation's history. Standard would keep on drawing heavily on it for crude. But because of the company's important discoveries elsewhere, Midway would never again be relatively so important as a supplier as it was during these years of strife.

It was unfortunate that clear-cut legislation could not have followed the withdrawal orders of 1909 and 1910 and the strife have been avoided. Legislation undoubtedly would have been passed much sooner, had it not been for the wide difference of opinion in and out of government concerning the relief that should be extended to operators whose usual course of oil development had been disrupted by the withdrawal orders. So great was the divergence of opinion that ten years were required to overcome extremists on both sides. Only then did it become possible to fashion a solution which, if not absolutely just, at least was acceptable.

XVIII

THE CHANGING FLOW
FROM FIELD AND REFINERY

The year 1910 ushered in for the Manufacturing Department a decade of rapid growth and change. It was marked by a shifting flow of crude from field to refinery as new fields and new refineries came into being and by a shifting flow of products as the result of changing market opportunities and new technologies. In 1910 heightened optimism over the prospects for refinable crude combined with attractive markets, both in the Far East and at home, induced 26 Broadway to approve the construction of a refinery in Southern California and the first substantial addition to Richmond since 1906. As the decade began, Richmond's crude supply seemed momentarily threatened because of an extension of the Union-Independent Oil Producers Agency alliance to include the Associated, but the extraordinary development of the Midway field soon put an end to whatever fears Standard may have had. Most notable of the company's new suppliers was the Kern Trading & Oil Company, through an exchange agreement, which led late in 1912 to the building at Bakersfield of Standard's third refinery. The increases in refining capacity, in turn, required increases in pipeline capacity, and the company's greatly augmented production and purchases required more storage.

During these years the work of the refiners was especially influenced by two forces, one enduring and one temporary. The enduring force was the internal combustion engine, which required a steadily greater output of gasoline and lubes. The other, temporary but intense, was World War I. It stepped up the demand for gasoline, lubes, and fuel oil and created opportunities for some new products; it also sharply reduced the Petrolite trade because of shortages in shipping. Because of the falling production and increased competition for crude from the Valley fields, World War I also created problems in supplying Richmond and Bakersfield not felt by the refinery at El Segundo, which flourished on the flush production Hillman had secured in Southern California.

Together, the two forces helped strengthen the position of the technically trained, particularly the chemists, within the Manufacturing Department, for the urgent demand for products frequently called for a greater skill in developing new processes than many of the older practical refiners possessed.

2

The outlook for Standard's refiners in 1910 left a good deal to be desired. Seemingly, they were losing the Petrolite market to eastern refineries with lower-cost supplies of light crude. And in taking care of the Pacific Coast, they were hard pushed to turn out sufficient gasoline. Coalinga crude, on which Richmond primarily relied, was good for kerosine but low in gasoline content. The light crude from Midway gave a higher yield of gasoline, but Midway's production was still small. Sumatran gasoline was no longer available to help fill the gap, and the plan to finish Peruvian naphtha at Richmond had yet to be agreed upon. We have already noted that, as an expedient, the refiners tried squeezing more gasoline from Coalinga crude by extending their still runs to bring about a little thermal cracking.[1]

A further concern was a threat of serious competition for crude supplies. In March, 1910, Scofield had predicted that Associated, of which the Southern Pacific had taken majority control in February, would evolve into merely a supplier for the railroad and that the Union–Agency combination would fall apart. He was wrong. By August negotiations were under way for an alliance between Associated and the Union–Agency group. The aggressive Associated had contracts to fill, while Union had not been able to move much of the Agency's production. The new combination was formed in October with a three-year contract, under which Associated replaced Union as the Agency's marketer on all new business except along the west coast of South America. Immediately the Agency began using Associated's tankage and its new line from Midway to Port Costa on the estuary of the Sacramento River. The power of this alliance is suggested by the amount of crude it handled in 1910. It took 34,500,000 barrels of under 20° gravity and 6,750,000 barrels of 20° gravity and above, compared to 7,500,000 barrels of the heavier and 8,000,000 of the lighter gravities handled by Standard that year.[2]

The *California Derrick* hailed the new contract as "probably . . . the biggest deal in point of capital and business . . . ever negotiated on the Pacific Coast. Every big element except the Standard Oil Company is represented. . . . The fact that there will be no more cutthroat competition places all oil holdings connected with the combination upon a most enviable basis, and one which is considered to be absolutely unassailable." The *Derrick* did not know that even firmer links were being sought; Mark Requa was attempting to merge Union and the Associated with the Doheny interests and his own Nevada Petroleum Company. Undoubtedly Standard had an inkling of what was going on. Indeed, it may have known exactly if there was truth in the warning Lyman Stewart received that the cablegrams he was sending to his financial agent in England were being seen by John D. Archbold. Stewart feared that Standard was about to attack. However, viewed from the Standard Oil camp, the maneuvers of the opposition must have looked like a threat, and perhaps even an attack on Standard's own position.[3]

It may have been only a coincidence, but William Edwards, in charge of Standard's crude purchases, again began contracting for oil about the time Associated opened negotiations with the Agency. He had bought solely on a day-to-day basis after the Lakeview gusher demoralized the market early in the spring. By August, 1910, he was making one-year contracts at 30¢ a barrel, regardless of gravity. It was still an unenthusiastic buying policy compared to the pre-Lakeview months, when his contracts were for two and three years at 50¢ and 65¢, but it suggests concern over competition. Standard also took the precaution of signing California Oilfields, Limited, to a three-year extension, calling for 7,500,000 barrels of oil, long before its old contract was filled.[4]

While Edwards was making Richmond's crude supply more secure, 26 Broadway was acting decisively to build up Standard's refining capacity, basing its plans on crude from the Midway and Southern California fields. Early in October, in order to restore the cut in crude capacity caused by cracking, Tilford authorized fifteen more stills and the scrapping of the old #2 Battery—the ten 350-barrel tar stills in the original refinery. Rheem spent much of October in New York, undoubtedly discussing the adjustments necessary to increase Richmond's output and for a new refinery in Southern California. The intent of 26 Broadway was to help Richmond turn out more gasoline and, in a reversal of earlier plans, more Petrolite. Instead of manufacturing solely for the domestic market, Rheem was told to provide in 1911 1,250,000 barrels of Petrolite, which would represent about 7 per cent of the kerosine deliveries from all refineries to 26 Broadway's foreign marketing companies. By cutting prices, the foreign marketers had managed to reverse a downtrend in kerosine sales. In view of these developments and the decline of Standard's crude stocks to the lowest point since 1905, Edwards raised his offer of 30¢ for light crude to 45¢ and 50¢. To build up pipeline capacity, the New York headquarters authorized more than $2,000,000 in December for filling in the loops to complete a second trunk line from Waite to Richmond and for new fly-wheel engines in the pumphouses. Following these changes, the lines could handle 35,000 barrels a day between Waite and Mendota, and 50,000 between Mendota and San Pablo.[5]

Another recommendation for pipeline expansion was withdrawn. After urging 26 Broadway to increase the capacity of the line from Midway to Waite, Scofield backed down. In January of 1911 he wrote California Standard's new president, J. A. Moffett, that after consulting with Rheem and W. S. Miller, he had decided to avoid handling more Midway oil—so much money was already committed, the company's stocks and purchases contracts for heavy crude were so large, and California's production still exceeded consumption. Moreover, other costly projects were under way: new campaigns by the Producing Department, and a new refinery in Southern California.[6]

3

The practice of using Richmond to provide products for Southern California, 400 to 600 miles away, had been a reasonable one when Standard commenced refining in California. However, by 1910 this procedure had become economically vulnerable because of the growth in volume of refinable crude and in demand for products in the southern end of the state. In that year, to provide gasoline for the Los Angeles and San Diego agencies required processing about 4,300 barrels of crude daily. And since 1907 light crude production in the Southern California fields had been steadily mounting, giving promise of enough oil to supply a modest refinery.[7]

A preliminary search for a refinery site near Los Angeles appears to have started by the middle of 1910. W. M. Weller, the man in charge, had served 26 Broadway in its foreign operations, notably in an attempt to find production and build a refinery in Burma early in the century. After an illness had caused his retirement, he had rejoined the Standard family as superintendent of the Pipe Line Department in the Santa Maria district. Probably in company with J. P. Smith from Richmond, he picked out a site at Los Nietos, which lay at the junction of the Santa Fe and Southern Pacific railroads, about three miles from the Whittier field and a dozen miles from the Fullerton. There was a wide range of crudes in these fields east of Los Angeles, including some with a good gasoline content. Standard re-entered the Southern California crude market for the first time since 1904 when it signed a one-year agreement in December, 1910, with the Central Oil Company, a small producer of both light and heavy crude in the Whittier field, to take all of Central's oil that was not under contract to other purchasers.[8]

Late in 1910 the task of building and managing the new refinery was offered to R. J. Hanna, the superintendent of the Eclipse Works of the Atlantic Refining Company at Franklin, Pennsylvania, where Rheem had begun his career with Standard. The transfer of an executive of Hanna's calibre suggests that the management team was being strengthened in anticipation of the dissolution. This fifty-year-old veteran of Standard service was the likely successor to Rheem, who could look forward to still broader duties in association with Scofield if the company became independent. When Hanna arrived in California, he was shown several possible sites. He turned down the one at Los Nietos because its water supply was limited. It is conceivable, too, that Hanna was authorized to plan a larger refinery on the seacoast that could import Peruvian crude and distillate, if necessary, and export products.

The ideal location would have been at San Pedro, the principal harbor for the Los Angeles area, but an adequate site was not available. Instead, Hanna selected one about seven miles north of Redondo and forty miles, by ship's course, north of San Pedro. Mrs. Hanna, who accompanied her husband, suggested that the refinery be called "El Segundo," meaning in Spanish "the second." Rheem accepted her suggestion, and so it has been known ever since. The El Segundo site consisted of 842 acres of sand dunes and a little farm land. It was large enough to allow for expansion without buying more land at premium prices, which had been the company's unhappy experience at Richmond. By coincidence, Hanna was concluding the purchase at just about the time that the Supreme Court upheld the dissolution decree on May 15, 1911. Even as the old combination was being split up, the West Coast unit was growing vigorously.[9]

Before May was over, work on the refinery had begun. To handle the construction, Rheem and Hanna put together a talented crew. For project engineer, Rheem chose H. D. Foster, an able, flexible-minded young designer and construction man from Richmond. A little later he also sent J. F. Faber from Richmond to be the superintendent at El Segundo. At the refinery site, Hanna hired a young mining engineer, A. S. Russell, to do the surveying. Russell, who was the Manufacturing Department's first graduate engineer, years later became a director and vice president of the company. Another future director and vice president was his chainman, R. W. Hanna, who had completed two years at Cornell and who was the son of R. J. Hanna.[10]

Under Hanna's forceful direction, the refinery rapidly commenced to take shape. First, a grading contractor was set to work using Mexican mule skinners with 400 mules drawing Fresno scrapers to level the sand dunes and prepare a roadbed for a spur from the Santa Fe Railroad. When the buildings began to rise, they presented a different appearance from Richmond, which had been built of red brick like Whiting and other Midwestern refineries. At El Segundo, Hanna suggested that they try reinforced concrete for the condenser box foundations. Soon they had changed the plans almost everywhere from brick to concrete, which Foster preferred because it was more resistant to erosion and earthquake damage.[11]

When completed, El Segundo was a small and simple affair compared to Richmond. Its basic equipment consisted of fifteen crude stills, two steam stills, and agitators supplied with acid in the form of gas from a sulfur trioxide plant. The refinery was intended to furnish Southern California with gasoline and kerosine, disposing of the residuum as fuel oil, but not to manufacture Petrolite or lube oils.[12]

While El Segundo was going up, the necessary steps were being taken to provide it with crude. O. O. Allen, transferred from Santa Maria, put pipeline crews to work laying gathering lines and erecting tankage for the Whittier, Fullerton, and Coyote Hills fields. Work was begun, too, on a pump station at Northam and a twenty-three-mile, six-inch pipeline to El Segundo. For crude, the company looked hopefully to the outcome of Hillman's wildcatting in the La Habra Valley, but it was also busy with crude purchases. On July 1, Standard signed a 500,000-barrel contract with the Fullerton Oil Company, re-establishing a relationship with one of its first crude sources in California. Later in the year, large three-year contracts were signed with the Murphy and Birch companies. After another former supplier, Dan Murphy's Brea Canon Oil Company, was added to the list, El Segundo was assured of some 3,000 barrels of crude daily.[13]

When Lyman Stewart heard reports of Standard's "immense" new refinery, he wrote, "This is a somewhat mysterious move, in view of the fact that the Standard has no territory in this vicinity, and not a very large amount of territory from which it can be certain of securing a production." Of course, El Segundo was hardly "immense," but to build it before a crude supply was assured did involve a risk. Perhaps Standard had taken options on the crude for which it contracted as El Segundo neared completion. The Murphy production, it is said, was arranged for before construction began, although the exact terms were debated for some months. In any event, building up the demand for light oil and laying a pipeline immediately stimulated drilling in the southern fields. New production was found, especially by Standard's own drillers; it amply justified a refinery in Southern California.[14]

The pipeline from Northam to El Segundo was finished in mid-December, but already, on November 27, 1911, oil brought in by tank car had been charged into Battery #1. Rheem came down to fire the stills, little more than a week before he was elected vice president of the newly independent Standard Oil Company (California). So the company began its separate existence with a new refinery as a last bequest from 26 Broadway. Actually, the whole refinery was not yet ready. The second battery of five stills was charged in mid-December, but the third battery and several other facilities were not finished until spring.

One major defect in the refinery site was revealed by a terrific February storm. The open shoreline at El Segundo afforded no protection from huge waves that destroyed much of the unfinished wharf and rammed the pile driver back to shore against the wall of the salt water pumping station. The wharf was rebuilt higher and shorter, but it was never safe in rough weather.[15]

4

Until the time that products began to flow from El Segundo, Standard had to rely solely on Richmond to supply its marketers, who were especially desperate for gasoline. The obvious solution was to get more light crude and to improve refining techniques. For light crude, the company turned to the booming Midway-Sunset field. *The Oil & Gas Journal* commented that in the Midway

> . . . every company [that] brought in a big well (and most of the Midway wells are big ones when they first come in) found a Standard agent at his elbow, talking contract while the oil gushed over the top of the derrick. And the Standard got the oil—partly because the man with . . . oil running to waste, with no storage other than earthen sump holes, through which 25 per cent of the precious product percolated and was forever gone, could not wait to dicker; and the Standard was always ready with a pipeline crew and pumps to take the oil.

Clearly, Standard's oil buyers were on the scene. The Pipe Line Department's receipts at Midway rose from 6,600,000 barrels in 1910 to 13,900,000 in 1911, and the company's share of the production increased from about 25 to over 50 per cent. The bulk of the increase was purchased oil, although Standard's own production, with the help of the famous McNee property, grew by half to 2,100,000 barrels. Suggestive of a bold buying policy was the 7,000,000-barrel contract Edwards drew up in the spring of 1911 for Lakeview gusher oil at 14¢ a barrel before the owners finally decided not to sign.[16]

The additions to the Valley trunk line authorized in December, 1910, were badly needed to keep receipts from outstripping the pipeline's capacity. To help out, more land was bought in April at Waite preliminary to the construction of fourteen reservoirs with a capacity of 7,700,000 barrels. More land was also added to the San Pablo tank farm, and 550,000 barrels of new tankage for light crude erected there. Among other signs of strain was the frequent limitation of oil purchase contracts to a six-month term during the latter half of 1911.[17]

Richmond sought more investment, too. In March, 1911, Rheem won 26 Broadway's agreement to fifteen new crude stills and an asphalt plant. The stills were needed merely to maintain the throughput at the refinery. When Tilford had authorized fifteen stills the previous October, he had insisted that experiments be made with "dephlegmating towers" in order to throw back the heavier vapors into the stills for further heating and cracking. The towers worked, but they lengthened the running time for each batch of crude.

By mid-1911 the need for the additional stills was no longer so urgent. Richmond's inventory of gasoline had been built up by the arrival of *Barge 95* from the East Coast with a cargo of gasoline, by renewed shipments from Sumatra, and by crude naphtha from Peru. With this backlog, the refiners stopped, or at least reduced, their thermal cracking. They jumped the light crude charged from 26,500 barrels a day in May to 33,500 in June and maintained that average for the balance of the year. Gasoline production actually increased, partly from the extra volume and partly from the higher gasoline content in the Midway crudes which were reaching the refinery in larger quantities. There was a market for the extra kerosine, too. Standard of New York wanted more Petrolite. Despite the jump in throughput, the prolific Midway field promised plenty of opportunity to use the extra fifteen stills and asphalt plant.[18]

The new asphalt plant represented a victory for Rheem after a campaign of at least three years. Although asphalt had long been a product of other California refiners, 26 Broadway had chosen to ignore it. As early as 1908, Rheem had urged that Richmond take up its manufacture only to be turned down. However the next year the refinery was able to add road oil to its line—a 12° gravity oil that was largely asphaltum. When Rheem tried again early in 1911, he argued that the lighter hydrocarbons distilled off in manufacturing asphalt could be used for turning out lubricants. An asphalt plant, he claimed, would free five crude stills being used to provide lube oil stock and permit him to reduce his request for new crude stills from 20 to 15. His argument helped win approval for a plant comprised of ten 250-barrel stills. Rheem hired H. H. Krumdick of the Barber Asphalt Company to build and operate the plant, and by the end of 1911 the first batch of "Star" asphalt was ready for market.[19]

The manufacture of more lubes was another matter requiring Rheem's attention, for the demand for lubes followed gasoline in its upward course. In 1911 Standard's automobile oil, Zerolene, was being eagerly sought to ease a shortage in the East and Midwest. W. P. Cowan of Indiana Standard wired Rheem in May: "You have shipped us only two cars of Zerolene this month. We need at least four cars per week and can take more." Kingsbury prodded Richmond for additional Zerolene to send Jersey's Eagle Works and the Cleveland refinery. However, more certain to endure and most crucial was the mounting demand in Standard's home market. Rheem received the assent of 26 Broadway for two more reducing stills and additional treating equipment which were completed in 1912.[20]

These several additions made certain that Richmond would be able to handle a larger flow of oil. A larger flow was already at hand. Even though Standard refined more oil in 1911 and disposed of 600,000 barrels more fuel crude than in 1910, the company was still failing to use crude as fast as it was being purchased. The Pipe Line Department received an average of 62,000 barrels of crude daily in 1911 compared to 42,000 the year before. Much of the Midway oil had to go into storage. During 1911 refinable oil stocks grew from 939,000 to 3,482,-000 barrels, and crude fuel stocks from 14,730,000 to 18,741,000 barrels.[21]

To match Richmond's growth, it was necessary to expand the capacity of the Valley trunk line by looping the Mendota-San Pablo section with twelve-inch pipe. The loops were used in a new way. Oil left the pump station in two eight-inch lines. As it slowed down, the oil in one line was diverted into the twelve-inch pipe, and the oil in the other was divided between the two eight-inch lines. The adoption of these twelve-inch loops on the downstream end of each section represented a final triumph for the technique that Calvin Payne had recommended for the original line and John Page had urged unsuccessfully later on.[22]

Standard's refiners, marketers, and crude purchasers and producers seemed engaged in an unending race. As fast as capacity was expanded at Richmond and supplemented with the construction at El Segundo, the demands of the marketers increased, and the supply of crude grew even faster. Early in 1912 Scofield noted that even after looping the pipeline and constructing the new stills at Richmond, Standard would not have sufficient capacity to increase its business beyond the current level.

The company added few new crude suppliers in 1912, though it raised its price for light oil in March and April, especially for gravities over 30°. The *Derrick* attributed the boost to increased competition from Union, to the new interest of Associated in light crude, and to an anticipated decline in production at Midway. Apparently, Standard expected more oil from Midway, however, for in April, 1912, it began putting new engines in the pumphouses and twelve-inch loops along the Midway line. It was a wise move; Midway's peak years were just ahead.[23]

In April the company also prepared to tap the new light crude field at Lost Hills, where Hillman's drillers had struck oil. It put in a twenty-one-mile, eight-inch line running to the field from the Pond pump station on the trunk line. Shortly, Standard was buying crude in competition with Associated and the Producers Transportation Company. The first contract, in May, 1912, was with the Universal Oil Company for 500,000 barrels. A few months later, Standard signed a 993,000-barrel contract with the Belridge Oil Company in the nearby Belridge field, to which the Lost Hills line was extended. Noteworthy, too, was Standard's agreement to take 500,000 barrels of the light gravities, 24° or more, which Associated might receive on contracts with the Universal and Belridge companies. Associated was preparing to build a refinery at Avon on the Sacramento estuary, but it was not yet ready to handle so light a crude.

These new contracts may have been a little premature, but to take care of them another enlargement of Richmond was going on. In May, 1912, Rheem decided to add thirty more crude stills to the seventy already there, in order to increase capacity to 60,000 barrels a day. The new stills were needed to satisfy the growing gasoline market and, despite the dissolution of the old Standard combination, New York Standard's continuing thirst for Petrolite. In the second half of 1912, Richmond was manufacturing Petrolite at a rate of over 2,000,000 barrels a year. While this expansion was under way, Standard was still receiving more oil than it could use and still more storage had to be built.[24]

One result of the large oil flow was an announcement by Scofield on September 23, 1912, that the company would contract for no more crude of less than 18° gravity. He told the producers that the company had 21,000,000 barrels of fuel oil in storage, too much for a refining company to carry. For two years, it had been building storage at the rate of 4,000,000 barrels a year to take care of the surplus heavy oil. With heavy crude costing 30¢ a barrel and storage 7¢ a barrel to construct, Standard was investing $1,480,000 a year in storing oil it did not especially want. On top of that, the company had to reckon with handling costs and evaporation losses. Moreover, the residuum from the increasingly large runs at Richmond and El Segundo was threatening to outstrip Standard's sales of fuel oil.[25]

Scofield's announcement, affecting some forty producing companies, shook the industry. It practically shut down drilling activity on heavy oil properties. Representatives of twenty-seven companies, with a production of about 20,000 barrels a day, met at Bakersfield to form an organization to look for another outlet. Some of these oilmen blamed Standard rather than overproduction for their plight. On the other hand, Henry Ach of the Monte Cristo Oil & Development Company maintained that no one was responsible when production exceeded consumption so greatly. He accepted Standard's argument that it could no longer go on purchasing and incurring heavy storage costs unless it could see a market for the oil. Ach told his fellow producers:[26]

> Why not look to the Associated or the Union, or your magnificent organization, the [Independent Oil] Producers Agency? You are always ready to condemn the actions of the Standard, and still you would have ceased to produce oil long ago [except] for them, and you are assembled here today because they have refused to pay a price that all are agreed . . . can not and does not pay to operate on.

Within a week or two, the producers found partial relief in an offer made by the General Petroleum Company, which was pushing a pipeline from Lost Hills to its Vernon refinery, under construction on the outskirts of Los Angeles. General Petroleum was also building a million dollar fuel oil station at San Pedro, which was expected to become an important port with the rapid growth of Southern California and the opening of the Panama Canal. The company offered to store 250,000 barrels of heavy crude free of charge and held out hope that its pipeline would be operating in January. In fact, General was probably looking for oil to transport, for its subsidiary, the General Pipe Line Company, was building a line with a capacity of 25,000 barrels a day. To attract capital to finance the line, General Petroleum had guaranteed the pipeline company 15,000 barrels of crude daily, although its own production was less than half that amount.[27]

Almost simultaneously with its withdrawal from the heavy oil market, Standard found a new and very important source of light oil and a chance to dispose of a good deal of heavy oil through an exchange agreement that was finally signed on November 30, 1912. The arrangement was with the Kern Trading & Oil Company, the Southern Pacific's subsidiary whose lands Standard intermittently had been seeking to lease since the beginning of the century. It may seem strange that KT&O's production was not diverted to the Associated Oil Company, which was controlled by the Southern Pacific. However, Associated was still primarily a fuel oil marketer. Although it had been considering entering refining for several years, Associated did not start construction of its Avon refinery until January, 1913. Probably the immediate problem facing KT&O was a crude oil production that was beginning to exceed its quota of 19,000 barrels daily in the lines of the Associated Pipe Line Company.

At any rate, KT&O turned to Standard and agreed to trade on a sliding scale all its crude of 22° gravity or more, up to 10,000 barrels a day, for heavy oil. For a barrel of KT&O oil of 22° gravity, Standard promised to deliver 1¼ barrels; for 23°, 1⅜ barrels, and so on. The contract required Standard to supply a barrel of oil of from 17.5° to 18.5° gravity for each barrel received and permitted it to pay the premium with oils of from 14° to 18.5° gravity. Standard's Pipe Line Department was to pick up the light oil in the Coalinga and Midway-Sunset fields and deliver fuel oil to Southern Pacific cars near Bakersfield at the Seguro siding or at the Associated Pipe Line's Volcan station.[28]

To help meet its part of the exchange, Standard decided to erect a refinery near Bakersfield, where a large part of the KT&O crude could be "topped" and delivered as fuel oil to the railroad. The lightest hydrocarbons in the distillate, the refinery could finish into gasoline and engine distillate for the local market, and the balance, the "crude equivalent," could be sent on to Richmond for refining, especially for kerosine. Accordingly, in October, 1912, Standard bought a forty-acre tract from the Peerless Oil Company adjacent to the Pipe Line Department's Waite station. The project was put in the hands of H. D. Foster, who had completed building the El Segundo refinery a few months earlier; A. S. Russell was sent to Bakersfield as the resident engineer. Although plans were drawn for twelve crude stills and an asphalt plant, just three crude stills were built, plus a steam still and an agitator for finishing gasoline. Only the most essential buildings were put up, and these were of corrugated iron. Since the first exchange agreement ran only through 1913, there may have been some doubt that the refinery would be permanent.

The Bakersfield stills were fired on February 22, 1913, by Superintendent J. R. McAllister, who had been transferred from the Producing Department. For the rest of the year the refinery averaged 5,000 barrels a day, mainly from Midway with a little from storage. In addition to the crude equivalent sent to Richmond, the refinery also mixed naphtha with more than 2,000 barrels of heavy crude daily in order to move the oil more easily through the pipeline.[29]

The exchange was important to both sides. During 1913 Standard took 3,700,000 barrels of oil, which amounted to 42 per cent of KT&O's production and to nearly one-seventh of all Standard's runs of 21° gravity oil or lighter. In return, Standard sent the Southern Pacific 4,750,000 barrels of fuel oil.[30]

5

Standard's arrangement for KT&O's light oil took place just as a massive shift in California production from heavy to light crude was becoming more and more apparent. In 1913 the state's crude output of 20° or more gravity jumped 11,000,000 barrels over 1912, and the gain in light crude was not much less the following year. This growth came chiefly from the development of the Midway-Sunset field, aided by Whittier-Fullerton, making 1914 the greatest year in the state's producing history before 1920. Both Midway-Sunset and Whittier-Fullerton were fields in which Standard was a major factor through its purchases, pipelines, and its own drilling program. And they produced refinable oil, the kind for which Standard's refineries had been built.[31]

Although much of this flush production had to go into storage, Richmond, El Segundo, and Bakersfield were able to handle increasingly large quantities. Fortunately, the demands of the marketers were steadily rising; in 1914, for example, Petrolite sales reached 3,000,000 barrels. The company's crude runs at its refineries rose by half to 76,000 barrels a day in 1913 and to 85,000 barrels in 1914.[32]

This flood of light crude, combined with market demand, brought about an expansion at El Segundo, but at Richmond it created problems of balance. During the first half of 1913, Hanna and Foster built another battery of five stills and an asphalt plant at El Segundo, bringing its capacity to 20,000 barrels daily. At Richmond, however, Rheem called a halt to the construction of fifteen of the thirty stills authorized in 1912, for it appeared that the first fifteen would boost capacity beyond his target of 60,000 barrels a day. At this figure, he feared the refinery would be out of balance, producing more fuel oil than the Marketing Department wanted. But if runs were reduced to the level of fuel oil requirements, Richmond could not manufacture enough

Petrolite. Probably for the sake of balance, Rheem turned to the Associated for a supply of tops. He took 40,000 barrels from Avon and signed contracts providing a total of from 30,000 to 40,000 barrels monthly from its Gaviota refinery and the Amalgamated refinery at Los Angeles.[33]

Despite the fact that the refineries turned out 6,000,000 barrels more fuel oil in 1913 than in 1912, the concern Rheem had felt over unduly large supplies soon vanished. The failure to renew contracts to purchase fuel crude was one factor. Sales of fuel oil were also increasing, climbing 4,500,000 barrels in 1913. There was also the effect of the KT&O exchange agreement. Standard supplied KT&O with 2,500,000 barrels of residuum and fuel crude in excess of the fuel oil contained in the KT&O crude it received. In fact, to ease the drain on fuel stocks at Bakersfield, Standard arranged in November, 1913, to deliver up to 3,000 barrels a day of El Segundo's residuum, which was increased to 8,000 barrels daily at the end of the year, when the exchange agreement was renewed.[34]

During 1913 Standard's fuel crude inventory, which had peaked at 22,000,000 barrels in 1912, fell to 13,500,000, causing the company to re-enter the heavy crude market in December. Standard signed a two-year contract with Monte Cristo for 1,750,000 barrels from Kern River and Sunset. Another contract with the Reward Oil Company for nearly 500,000 barrels was its first purchase in McKittrick since it laid a line into the field in 1907. The company offered producers 35¢ a barrel, which was 5¢ above its price in 1912. Because Standard was insisting on two-year contracts, many oilmen believed that it expected prices to rise and held out for better terms. The company yielded in January, 1914, making its offer 40¢ and, as was its custom, changed the contracts signed the preceding month to conform to the new figure.[35]

The increased flow of oil from Standard's purchases and its own production required another expansion of pipeline and storage facilities in both Northern and Southern California. In the south, the surging growth of the West Coyote field led to the construction of a second six-inch line from Northam to El Segundo in the fall of 1913. Following the leasing of the Murphy properties, a third line was laid with eight-inch pipe early in 1914 and the older six-inch line converted to a gas carrier. In the north, the trunk line was looped between Waite and Mendota to match the loops closer to Richmond, and 500,000 barrels of tankage were added at San Pablo. Two new tank farms, each of one million barrels, were also authorized: in Elk Hills for Midway oil, and at the Pond pump station for oil from the Lost Hills and Belridge fields.[36]

Following completion of the Waite-Mendota loops, the company

undertook no substantial pipeline construction in the Valley until after
the Kettleman Hills field came in fifteen years later. Standard continued
to have plenty of need for its pipeline crews, however, to handle leaks
caused by the corrosive soil. In the thirty-one-mile stretch between Pond
and Corcoran, for example, the line averaged a leak a day. Maintenance
costs, which rose to about a million dollars a year, were especially high
in the summer when treating gangs were out digging up the pipe, scaling
it with wire brushes, painting it with asphalt, and wrapping it with paper.
Beginning in 1914, a young engineer, E. P. Bly, was assigned to work
with the corrosion problem. The next year he hit upon the idea of using
an asphalt mastic, which gradually proved to be an effective coating.
Later on, it was developed and sold commercially as Somastic.[37]

The continuing rush of light oil piled Standard's total oil stocks
higher and higher during 1914, though for most of the year its stocks
of heavy crude kept on declining. At bottom, in September, 1914, the
company's heavy crude in storage was only 7,800,000 barrels, down
fully 14,000,000 barrels in less than two years. The light oil deliveries
called urgently for more steel tankage to save the light hydrocarbons.
Early in 1914 Standard authorized a million barrels each at San Pablo
and the new Elk Hills farm, and in August another million at San Pablo,
plus a million each at Pond, El Segundo, and Northam. Stocks of light
crude continued to climb, though at a slower rate, until March, 1915.[38]

To protect itself from this huge California flow, which was being
paralleled elsewhere by flush production in Oklahoma's Cushing field
and in Mexico, Standard in May, 1914, resorted to a price cut for the
first time since 1910. In July two more cuts of five cents a barrel were
made just before World War I broke out. Standard announced a new
policy of taking no more oil than the maximum daily delivery specified
in its contracts. For almost a year it signed few new contracts, either for
light or heavy crude.[39]

These years of flush production, which were the peak years for
Midway-Sunset, the greatest of the Valley fields, also marked the end
of the expansion of the refineries to handle the Valley crudes. In 1914
five of the conventional 1,000-barrel crude stills were built at Richmond
to rerun lube oil distillate, bringing the total number to ninety, but
none were added thereafter. The remainder of the expansion took place
at Bakersfield, where three road oil stills were installed late in 1913
and converted to producing asphalt. The next year nine crude stills were
added, winding up construction there. When these stills were completed,
the capacity of the Bakersfield refinery had grown to about 20,000 barrels a day. Perhaps it was this enlarged size that brought J. Lindsay

El Segundo, July, 1911. A. S. Russell leaning against the concrete mixer; R. W. Hanna holding the level rod

El Segundo, January, 1912

Laying the 12-inch loop near Mendota, March, 1912

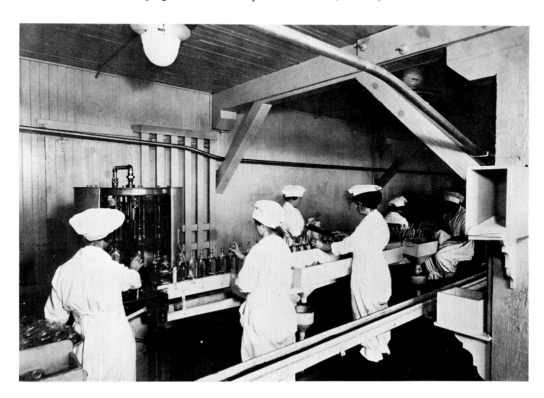

White Oil plant, Richmond, 1919

Hanna, a nephew of R. J. Hanna and later a director and vice president, to Bakersfield as foreman, for he was a more experienced refiner than Superintendent McAllister.[40]

Well into 1915, the Bakersfield refinery ran full blast tidying up after the orgy of Midway-Sunset production. It was busily engaged in topping millions of barrels of light crude, too much of which had been wastefully stored in reservoirs because of insufficient steel tankage. As late as May, 1915, 3,400,000 barrels of the light oil were in reservoirs; undoubtedly the amount earlier had been considerably larger. Bakersfield distilled the light crude as fast as it could, sending the "crude equivalent" to steel tanks and the fuel oil residuum to the reservoirs. By August, this task was sufficiently complete so that the refinery was also topping crude from the Pond tank farm.[41]

The Valley fields would not soon again tax Standard's refineries so heavily. In 1915 Valley production fell off drastically, nearly one-sixth (12,860,000 barrels) from the record year of 1914. Most of this drop was properly attributed to the dispossession suits being filed by the government for Midway lands following the Supreme Court's decision upholding the Taft withdrawal in February, 1915, but, except for a temporary resurgence at Kern River, production at the other fields, and notably Coalinga, was also declining.[42]

As production fell away, Standard found itself faced with a larger number of strong competitors for the Valley crudes. General Petroleum was one of the new rivals. It was built from small companies, most of which had been providing Standard as late as 1912 with a total of 2,000 to 3,000 barrels a day of 17° gravity oil. After General put a pipeline across the Tehachapis to San Pedro early in 1913, this oil was permanently removed from Standard's grasp, as was the new production (including some light crude) that General developed by a vigorous drilling campaign. It also signed up a number of Kern County producers, including the North American Consolidated Oil Company, formerly Standard's largest single source of fuel crude. At first, General was more interested in heavy crude, but its light crude position was markedly strengthened in March, 1913, when it began topping about 9,000 barrels a day of light crude belonging to the Santa Fe's Chanslor-Canfield Midway Oil Company under an arrangement similar to that between Standard and KT&O. For a time the new company appeared to be turning into a very potent competitor when late in 1912 it acquired an option from the Stewarts on their holdings in the Union Oil Company. Subsequently, it obtained the backing of English financiers, the so-called Weir Syndicate. A powerful company handling

90,000 barrels a day was forecast. Although this syndicate fell apart in 1915, General Petroleum, with its pipelines, topping plants at Vernon and Mojave, tankers, and marketing stations, obviously was in the industry to stay.[43]

More serious was an invasion by the Royal Dutch–Shell Group late in 1912 to sell Sumatran gasoline along the Pacific Coast. Within a year, the Group was planning the development of an integrated enterprise. It felt impelled to do so in order to compete with the cheap and abundant gasoline being manufactured from California's flush production. When Balfour, Williamson offered to sell California Oilfields, Limited, the Group's chief executive, Henri Deterding, snapped it up in August, 1913. At that time Standard was taking almost 12,000 barrels a day from COF and over 4,000 barrels daily from two other Coalinga concerns, the Turner and W.K. oil companies, which Shell of California later acquired. About 70 per cent of Standard's supply of Coalinga crude was ultimately lost by these transactions, though the company continued to receive some of this oil for more than a year while Shell was building a pipeline from Coalinga and a refinery at Martinez on San Francisco Bay. Standard picked up some new contracts, notably for heavy oil to exchange with KT&O, but the days prior to 1911 when Coalinga was Richmond's chief supplier were gone forever.[44]

Declining production and a more buoyant market for products, stimulated by the war, account for the rising crude prices during the latter months of 1915, when Standard again began to purchase in a large way. The biggest of the early contracts, one with the Peerless Oil Company for 720,000 barrels of heavy oil, was signed in July for 32.5¢ a barrel, but by October Standard was being forced to raise its offers. In November and December the company again improved its prices, and in the latter month established the practice of a separate and higher price for each degree of gravity above a minimum for heavy crude.[45]

By 1915, however, all else was minor, compared to the problems that World War I had created. The war influenced the course of the whole industry, all the way from producing and crude purchasing to marketing. Within Standard, it upset the always precarious balance among products at the refineries. For lack of shipping, Petrolite sales fell off more than a million barrels in 1915 and would decline further. At the same time, demand for other of Standard's products was climbing, particularly for gasoline, engine distillate, and lube oils. To meet the wartime demand for both old and new products, Standard's refiners were stimulated to a number of significant innovations.[46]

6

Gasoline was the product that caused the refiners the greatest concern. The problem of how to derive a greater amount from each barrel of crude had been temporarily shelved because of the flush production at Midway. In August, 1915, however, Rheem wrote the Richmond superintendent, J. P. Smith, that the demand for gasoline in the eastern United States was steadily rising and asked Smith to push vigorously experiments in fractionating and cracking. Late in 1915 W. D. Mason was experimenting with a "vapor phase" cracking process at Richmond and John Black with a "liquid phase" process at El Segundo, but neither proved out.[47]

Instead of continuing to rely on its own efforts, Standard turned to Indiana Standard in March, 1916, to license what was at that time the only commercial cracking process. Developed at Whiting under Dr. W. M. Burton in 1913, it cracked gas oil to produce an odoriferous gasoline which was a surprisingly good motor fuel. Burton himself visited Richmond while the construction of the ten cracking stills was going on and left behind J. C. Parks, a Whiting veteran, to give the refinery the benefit of his experience.[48]

The Burton stills, which began to operate in March, 1917, showed from the start that the process was not well suited to California oil. Their product was so foul-smelling that it could be used only by adding it in small quantities, usually no more than 2 per cent, to sweet, straight-run gasoline. The cracked gasoline was also costly to produce, costing about 20¢ a gallon at a time when the market price was only 16¢. A further problem was the high carbon content of California oil which resulted in heavy carbon deposits on the hot still bottoms, interfering with the transfer of heat to the oil and forcing the operators to close down a still before all of the oil was cracked. The time required to cool a still, clean it out, and start it up again was about equal to the time when it was producing distillate. These deficiencies in the Burton cracking process R. W. Hanna stated succinctly as "low yield, low capacity, high investment per barrel of gasoline produced, carbon troubles, high repairs."[49]

Of the difficulties encountered, the most serious was the effect of the carbon on the hot still bottoms. The refiners found when the stills were shut down in January, 1919, that fully half of the iron bottoms had been oxidized. As a safety measure, the stills were abandoned. In nearly two years, they had contributed less than 100,000 barrels to Standard's total gasoline production of almost 6,000,000 barrels.[50]

More helpful than the cracking plant was a natural gasoline plant installed at El Segundo at the beginning of 1916. It was a "high-pressure absorber" type developed some three years earlier by Jersey Standard's subsidiary, the Hope Natural Gas Company. Before gas was used for fuel under the stills and boilers, it was passed through an absorber containing engine distillate to remove the liquid hydrocarbons. The enriched distillate was then put through a steam still to produce crude naphtha, leaving an engine distillate that was only slightly lower in gravity than it had been at the start. During 1917 the El Segundo plant yielded about 270,000 barrels of natural gasoline.[51]

Lube oils were also commanding the concern of the refiners. The California oils were gaining wider use, as motorists began to accept lubes distilled from asphaltic crudes, especially for their performance in cold weather. One manifestation of the increased demand was the setting up in October, 1915, of a lube treating plant at El Segundo consisting of an agitator, two wash tanks, and two bleachers.

The piling up of orders led to the development of a new technology by Standard of California. Late in 1915 the El Segundo refiners started to experiment with the high vacuum distillation of crude for lube oil distillate. In January, 1916, three 600-barrel asphalt stills were braced internally for vacuum distillation, and in April the construction of seven more vacuum stills was authorized. Meanwhile R. W. Hanna, who had participated in these developments at El Segundo, was transferred to Richmond. This able and energetic young man—called "Pony Express" at El Segundo because, too impatient to walk, he insisted on riding a horse—soon persuaded J. P. Smith, the Richmond superintendent, to carry on experiments in vacuum distillation. The result was that in December, 1916, a new battery consisting of twenty-four 600-barrel vacuum stills was approved for the northern refinery.[52]

The high-vacuum process clearly proved its value. Through a combination of a near vacuum and the injection of steam, oil vaporized as if it were in a vacuum only four millimeters short of absolute. Distillation proceeded with little cracking until only the asphalt remained. The production of lubes was virtually three times as large as by the former process, jumping from around 6 to as much as 18 per cent per barrel of crude.[53]

Another, though less important, breakthrough in lube manufacture also occurred in 1916. It involved treating the lubes for color, which hitherto had been done with acid or by filtering through fuller's earth. Acid was expensive; so was fuller's earth, which had to be shipped in from Florida. From time to time, Marvin L. Chappell, a Standard chemist, had been experimenting with California clays, believing that treating a clay with acid might make it more absorbent and an effective decolorizing agent. In September, 1916, after using a strong acid wash on a clay from Ash Meadow, Nevada, he found that the clay had a decolorizing efficiency four to five times that of fuller's earth. Time was required to make Chappell's discovery commercially feasible, but by 1920 it was being used at El Segundo.[54]

An important outcome of the war years, with their pressures for new processes and products, was the chance given Standard's chemists to prove their worth. Eric Starke had hired for the company three University of California graduates in chemistry—Marvin L. Chappell in 1904, John B. Terry in 1905, and Ralph A. Halloran in 1907—but their work was testing rather than research. Rheem once remarked that "chemists were a necessary evil because the damn customers used them to write specifications!" Rarely were they called upon to develop a new product or process. This skepticism, even antagonism, on the part of the older, "practical" refiners, did not stop the chemists from experimenting at odd moments. During 1905 and 1906 Starke and Chappell tried to make dyes from aromatics contained in the acid sludge after kerosine treating, but they apparently failed to turn out a commercial product. Disgruntled by the lack of interest shown by Rheem and others in work of this nature, Starke was glad to transfer to the Producing Department in 1908. Three years later, when Terry isolated naphthenic acids from spent kerosine caustic and developed some paint driers, his suggestion that they be patented was met with the cold-water reply, "We're in the oil business, not the paint business." The office of Chief Chemist, vacated by Starke in 1908, was not filled until R. J. Hanna brought out a German-trained chemist, Frederick W. Mann, from the Eclipse Works at Franklin, Pennsylvania, in 1914.[55]

One new product provided by a Standard chemist was a medicinal white oil. Prior to 1914 the medicinal trade had used a heavy, viscous Russian oil which Standard and other American companies had been unable to match. The cessation of these imports due to the war spurred American companies to new efforts. Using California's naphthenic crudes, Marvin Chappell soon came up with an answer. He had solved the technical problem of how to wash a heavily treated oil, for water used alone formed an emulsion almost impossible to break. Chappell made use of an alcohol and water wash. Following construction of an experimental plant at the end of 1914, Standard went on to produce its white oil commercially the next year.[56]

Two other new products, benzol and toluol, used in the manufacture of explosives (TNT) were directly related to war needs. The coal tar industry, which was the peacetime source of these chemicals, was strained to the limit of its capacity. Booming prices stimulated petroleum chemists to try to enter the field. Already in 1907, on a laboratory basis, the Richmond chemists had come close. At Starke's suggestion, Terry and Halloran had used platinum-coated quartz to analyze kerosine and had produced benzaldehyde. The two chemists reported that by heating the benzaldehyde over hot silica they could produce benzol and toluol, among other hydrocarbons, but at the time this was not their objective. Mann, too, was apparently familiar with benzol and toluol through his experiments with vapor-phase cracking in Pennsylvania.

Late in 1914, Mann and Chappell worked out a laboratory process for manufacturing these chemicals. After E. I. du Pont de Nemours & Company had passed favorably upon their samples, the two chemists turned to the task of converting their laboratory experiment into a commercial reality. With the help of John Black, Richmond's chief engineer, a small plant was built by July of 1915, but several months passed before all the operational problems were solved. For its main feed stock, the plant made use of a distillate from the Oil City crude at Coalinga which had long been prized as a source of engine distillate. The plant operated on the principle that naphthene hydrocarbons could be stripped of some of their hydrogen by partial oxidation at high temperatures and converted into aromatic hydrocarbons. This was accomplished by cracking the distillate in retorts—horizontal steel pipes eighteen inches in diameter and sixteen feet long—which were partially filled with fire brick impregnated with a nickel catalyst. The crude benzol vapors from the retorts were condensed, rerun, treated, and redistilled in a 1,800-gallon steam still with a fractionating column which Black had constructed. From this still, benzol and toluol distillates were produced; the residuum was xylol. Finally, the distillates were run again in a 1,500-gallon steam still with a fractionating column designed for very careful separation. This still, bought from Walter E. Lummus of Boston, a manufacturer of equipment for distilling alcohol and other chemicals, separated the distillates into pure ether, benzol, and toluol.

The technical men at Richmond attempted to improve their process. In 1916 they built an effective 7,000-gallon fire still which could handle larger quantities of distillates and which had a relatively large fractionating tower derived from the design of the Lummus column. The tower had five boiling plates filled with nipples and boiling caps. Between the plates were water coils for condensing the vapors, causing them to reflux. The still and tower were so connected that vapors could either be sent through the tower or bypassed. This column was the progenitor of the "fine fractionation" tower, a very important development in crude still technology following the war. A vertical retort with internal firing was also tried in 1916 and 1917, but operational difficulties and its failure to increase production caused the refiners to return to the older horizontal retorts.[57]

The contribution Standard's plant made to the powder industry was a modest one. Between 1915 and the spring of 1919 it turned out 228,000 gallons of toluol, 127,000 gallons of benzol, and 138,000 gallons of xylol. Virtually all of this production went to Du Pont.[58]

Late in the war, Standard appeared destined to enter into toluol production in a large way when the Army's Ordnance Department contracted for a $3,000,000 plant at Richmond capable of manufacturing 3,000,000 gallons of toluol a year. The company was to build and operate the plant, using a more effective conversion process and some equipment that had been developed by General Petroleum. Before the plant was finished, however, the war was over and the contract canceled.[59]

7

While the refiners were searching for ways to squeeze more gasoline, lubes, and specialty products out of crude oil, Standard was looking eagerly for more crude sources, either through its Producing Department or by purchases. After 1914 the company met with much more success in developing its own production than in purchasing in an increasingly competitive crude market, and its success in producing was far greater in Southern California than in the San Joaquin Valley. For these reasons, El Segundo showed the greatest growth among Standard's refineries after 1915.[60]

Crude prices rose steadily during the war from their California lows reached in the middle of 1915. Fuel grade crude, for example, climbed from 32.5¢ a barrel in July, 1915, to 73¢ in November, 1916, and light crudes registered similar gains. Under the stimulus of higher prices, California's production picked up somewhat after 1915, but not sufficiently to match consumption. Standard made a number of new contracts in this rising market, but most were small. It sought, too, to write them for terms of two and three years, a practice that it had rarely followed since 1910.[61]

The most abrupt change in Standard's crude supply came about when the KT&O exchange agreement was not renewed, for reasons that are not clear, at the end of 1915. Its termination deprived Standard of nearly 13,000 barrels a day of light oil; on the other hand, the company was relieved of an obligation to deliver a larger quantity of fuel oil. KT&O's production was diverted to General Petroleum and to the Associated Pipe Line. The diversion to Associated may have increased the runs at its Avon refinery, for in August, 1916, Associated traded Standard 40,000 barrels of gasoline plus 9,000 barrels monthly for the next four months in exchange for fuel oil. In October, Standard also agreed to take KT&O's light crude at Coalinga through an exchange that brought it a little more than 3,000 barrels a day.[62]

The lapse of the principal KT&O exchange agreement had little immediate effect on the Bakersfield and Richmond refineries because of the still large stocks of light crude in storage. Bakersfield, in fact, continued to run at capacity during 1916, topping crude for the larger refinery. Although crude oil receipts at Richmond declined, the distillates from Bakersfield helped push its output of gasoline in 1916 to 1,360,000 barrels. That year Richmond also turned out 1,540,000 barrels of engine distillate, helped by the slump in the production of Petrolite.[63]

Meanwhile, El Segundo, backed by Standard's growing light crude production at West Coyote, was forging steadily ahead. Its output of gasoline in 1916, amounting to 959,000 barrels, was nearly half again as much as in 1915 and more than two-thirds of the figure for Richmond. Standard's leaders began planning for El Segundo to play a role in the wartime export trade in addition to serving Southern California. A necessary first step was to provide a harbor outlet at San Pedro, for rough seas off El Segundo had proved that the refinery wharf was an unreliable shipping point. In February, 1916, Standard leased from the Harbor Commission seven acres on Smith's Island at San Pedro for tankage and a wharf. Six months later it was back asking for more land for a second wharf. The elated president of the Commission announced, "It is the biggest thing we have had yet. The company intends to develop the biggest oil port on the Pacific Coast. . . . The southern business which has been handled from Port Richmond is coming here. Everything going through the Panama Canal and to South America and Mexico will be handled here. . . ." Immediately after the second lease was signed, O. O. Allen started laying a seventeen-mile, eight-inch fuel line from the refinery to San Pedro and followed this line a year later with a six-inch kerosine line. To help El Segundo in its new role, Standard in November, 1916, negotiated a contract with the General Petroleum Company for 500,000 barrels of tops from the Vernon refinery to be delivered over the next thirteen months.[64]

The shift to Southern California in crude handling and refining continued during most of 1917. Standard's booming production in West Coyote led to the replacement of a six-inch line from Northam to El Segundo with a ten-inch line during the summer of 1917. And at the same time the production of the first wells at Montebello flowed into the Southern California pipeline system through a nine-mile branch line to Compton Junction. The refinery itself was enlarged by the addition of a battery of vacuum stills and a battery of crude stills, bringing its capacity above 30,000 barrels a day. In 1917, with the aid of General's tops, El Segundo turned out nearly twice as much gasoline as in the preceding year and in 1918 surpassed Richmond. It also took over from Bakersfield the task of filling the large fuel contracts with the copper companies of Arizona.

Richmond and Bakersfield, by contrast, were pinched for crude. There were no longer large surplus stocks in the Valley on which they could draw; by the fall of 1917, the tank farm in Elk Hills was nearly empty, and the tankage at Pond was being drained rapidly. To maintain Richmond's throughput, the crude runs at Bakersfield were cut back. During 1918 they averaged less than 5,000 barrels daily.

In October, 1917, Standard was offered a chance at more of the Southern Pacific's light crude when the railroad sought to extend the exchange contract for its Coalinga oil to include 10,000 barrels a day of its Midway production. These negotiations were carried on in the name of the Southern Pacific, for earlier in 1917 KT&O had been dissolved and its properties turned over to a newly organized Fuel Oil Department. The Southern Pacific, which was failing to match its fuel oil requirements by from 8,000 to 9,000 barrels a day, was desperate for fuel. Richmond could readily use the light crude. However, Standard agreed reluctantly to an enlarged exchange agreement, and only to the extent of 5,000 barrels daily of the Midway oil. With its fuel stocks already low, the company was anxious to limit the future rate of their reduction.[65]

The following month Standard entered into another exchange agreement that measurably improved the position of the Richmond refinery. It involved trading some of Standard's flush production at West Coyote and Montebello for General Petroleum's oil at Midway and Lost Hills, which could be sent north through the Valley pipeline. The arrangement represented a logical adjustment of crude supplies to existing facilities. It traded away oil which El Segundo lacked the capacity to handle for oil which Richmond badly needed to meet the demand for products from its northern marketing area. Of course, an attempt might have been made to bring Standard's Southern California crude to Richmond by tanker, but World War I had so sharply reduced the amount of tanker transportation available as virtually to rule out any such plan. The exchange was also of value for General Petroleum; it saved that company the cost of boosting oil through its pipeline across the Tehachapi Mountains to Vernon. Richmond derived nearly 12,000 barrels a day from this agreement, which was more than one-fourth of its average crude throughput during 1918, amounting to 44,726 barrels daily.[66]

Standard made a few other less important exchanges and purchases of benefit to Richmond and the northern marketing territory. Minor exchanges were arranged with Associated and Union that brought the refinery some Lost Hills and Kern crude. More significant was a 934,000 barrel contract with Union, by which Standard received about 3,000 barrels daily of heavy Kern crude beginning in October, 1917. And in December, Standard made another trade with General Petroleum which further improved its fuel oil position in the San Joaquin Valley. It exchanged 950,000 barrels of residuum at El Segundo for a fuel oil property belonging to General at Coalinga which Hillman believed contained "equivalent fuel oil in the ground."[67]

The chief saving factor in Standard's crude supply and, indeed, in that of the whole state, was the Montebello field. Its production rose steadily, requiring in the spring of 1918 a second short pipeline to Compton Junction. To help handle the flow, El Segundo was given another battery of five crude stills in June. But during 1918 most of this bountiful increase was exchanged with General Petroleum, which toward the close of the year was taking as much as 14,000 barrels daily.[68]

Following the armistice in November, 1918, and the easing of the tanker shortage, it became feasible to deliver Southern California crude to Richmond by water. The volume of this traffic was substantial. During 1919 receipts at Richmond from Southern California averaged nearly 10,000 barrels a day of crude oil and 2,500 of distillate. This relief to Richmond in turn made possible diverting to Bakersfield more Midway crude and a little of the still small production from Elk Hills. Together, the two northern refineries processed about 10,000 barrels more crude daily in 1919 than in 1918. Standard's large crude production in Southern California may also explain a reduction in the amount of tops El Segundo took from General's Vernon refinery in 1919. The contract with General that year provided for only 290,000 barrels, compared to 500,000 in former years.[69]

8

When the war ended in Europe, Standard's refineries shifted toward their prewar pattern of production. Even before the return of tankers from war service, Richmond doubled its output of Petrolite. For a first time, too, El Segundo joined in manufacturing this export kerosine. In 1919 the company's exports of Petrolite reached an all-time record of nearly 3,600,000 barrels.

But Standard's future, like that of the industry, no longer lay with kerosine anywhere; rather, it was clearly bound up with the automobile at home. Although the company's gasoline exports fell off sharply and lube exports moderately following the end of the war, the soaring domestic demand more than offset these losses. To turn out more lubes, soon after the war a crude still battery at Richmond was converted to vacuum operation. During 1919 Richmond and El Segundo were jointly responsible for one-fifth of the pale oils manufactured in the United States.[70]

The situation in regard to gasoline was more serious. A severe shortage appeared imminent. In an endeavor to help avert it, representatives of the three refineries were brought together late in February, 1919, to form a nine-member Gasoline Production Committee which included three chemists, F. W. Mann, J. B. Terry, and Marvin Chappell. The committee agreed upon experiments at cracking to be carried on at each refinery under the general supervision of the young and able William D. Mason. Within two weeks another of the committee members, Richard W. Hanna, was appointed superintendent at Richmond, where he led a vigorous assault on the problem of finding a suitable cracking process. These efforts came too late to solve the gasoline shortage of 1919; in fact, complete success was not achieved until 1926.[71]

Even though the work of the Gasoline Production Committee was not immediately successful, it does suggest the main line of growth from here on for the Manufacturing Department. The basic physical equipment of the refineries had been built. Because of Hillman's producing victories, an adequate supply of fuel oil for the refineries seemed secure. The problem that remained was how to get more of the products most desired from each barrel of crude. Its solution required systematic research and the development of a refining technology that was beyond the skills of most of the older practical refiners.

In the Manufacturing Department, as elsewhere in the company, especially in producing, men of greater technical training were rising in status. Before long, they would begin to take over from an older generation.

XIX

THE COMPETITIVE YEARS

Marketing offered Standard great opportunities and great challenges following independence. The steady surge of population to the West, in combination with the increasing use of the automobile, was mainly responsible for an extraordinary demand for oil products. And, as we have seen, a sudden large increase in the production of light crudes in California after 1911, in combination with a heavy demand for gasoline, helped create an intense competition. Formerly, Union was Standard's sole major competitor in refined oils, but early in the war decade Associated, Shell, and a number of energetic smaller firms also entered the race. Another new "major," the General Petroleum Company, came into the market, especially in fuel oil. World War I also influenced the course of development by altering the relative importance of various outside markets and by affecting the value of many oil products everywhere.

The prize of sales leadership in the West was far more valuable after 1911 than it had been in the past, but it was also contested much more vigorously.

2

Standard brought to the contest a rich inheritance. It had among its major assets a seasoned sales organization, a far-flung net of stations and substations, an effective marine establishment supporting the marketing operation, and important marketing ties with former members of the old Standard combination. It had also a commanding lead over competitors in its domestic sales area.

Many, though not all, of its sales executives after 1911 had long held their posts under the tutelage of 26 Broadway. W. S. Miller, Standard's director in charge of sales, C. A. Watson, manager of Real Estate and Construction, Colonel E. H. Merrill, manager of the Lubricating Oil Department, and J. C. Fitzsimmons, manager of the Fuel Oil Department, by 1911 had jointly piled up nearly eighty years of service at the San Francisco headquarters. Many of the special agents in charge of the stations were also veterans, like John McLean at Seattle, J. H. McDermott at Portland, and H. W. Neumann at Los Angeles. They were in command of the three main stations which, along with San Francisco, in most years accounted for more than half of the company's total domestic sales.[1] Within the field organization, too, were younger men, like H. D. Collier, special agent at San Francisco by 1912, G. E. Kennedy, at Fresno, and John L. Quinn, special agent at Los Angeles by 1913, who would become increasingly prominent.

One executive, Horatio T. Harper, deserves a more extended mention, for more than any other man he was the key figure in marketing during these years. Sales manager by 1911, Harper was a veteran though relatively new to San Francisco. He was still a young man, just forty-one, who had come up through the ranks. After starting as a bookkeeper at Sacramento in 1890, he had become special agent there, and later held the same post in the highly competitive Los Angeles territory. In 1908 he was sent to San Francisco as assistant to W. S. Miller. Gradually he took over responsibility from the older man. The debonair Harper possessed that skill in human relations characteristic of the born salesman. "He was the only man I know," recalls one of his former staff, surely in exaggeration, "who could make you feel he was doing you a favor in firing you." Harper gave strong direction to the sales force and helped foster a high morale not always so evident in the rougher environment of earlier days.[2]

The field establishment at the end of 1911 consisted of fifteen main stations. The period for marking out the principal sales districts seemed almost over, for since 1900 only one main station had been created (Honolulu in 1906) and one closed down (Dawson, Yukon Territory, in 1907). Standard's substations, by contrast, had grown from fifty-eight to ninety-nine by 1911, as the company intensified its market coverage.[3] The tank wagons and case wagons, with their gleaming brass and well-kept horses, made their rounds from both main and substations to a trade that was still almost totally wholesale in character.

Standard supplied most of these stations, and a few substations as well, by cheap water transportation from Richmond. Five tankers and three seagoing barges, with a combined capacity of 209,500 barrels, comprised the fleet of the Marine Department in 1911. In addition, the company had a number of river and harbor craft which, with a single exception at San Pedro, served the communities on San Francisco Bay and on the lower reaches of the Sacramento and San Joaquin rivers. Main stations in the interior, like Spokane and Fresno, and most of the substations were supplied by tank cars of the Union Tank Line.[4]

Standard's ties with former members of the old Trust were another valuable part of its inheritance. Business arrangements between these companies, it will be recalled, were specifically authorized in the Supreme Court's decree. Standard was under no obligation to maintain its old connections, but often it would find an advantage in doing so. In 1911 it was purchasing from other Standard units some lubes and other items, especially wax products, which it could not derive from California crudes. But the relationship was undoubtedly more significant in providing outlets for its own products. For years, the bulk of Richmond's kerosine (Petrolite) had been taken by Standard of New York for the Oriental trade. Other Standard units, especially The Imperial Oil Company, Limited, of Canada, were buying substantial amounts of fuel oil and some naphthas. Within the Standard family, California Standard enjoyed an even wider sale of its Zerolene, a lube for motor cars distilled from asphaltic crudes. In 1911, this so-called export trade amounted to $3,418,000, or about one-seventh of the company's total sales.[5]

In the home territory (comprised of California, Oregon, Washington, Arizona, Nevada, Alaska, and Hawaii), the company was reaping the harvest of over thirty years of enterprise by the great Standard organization. Its dominance of this trade area, if not quite so pronounced as a decade earlier when Iowa Standard sold an estimated 96 per cent

Table 19: Domestic Sales of California Standard, 1911

Light Oils	Barrels	Value
Gasoline	691,843	not available
Engine distillate	357,797	” ”
Other naphthas	917	” ”
Total Naphthas	1,050,556	$5,973,914
Refined oils (kerosine)	571,304	$3,057,712
Lubricating oil	194,304	1,969,104
Other	44,835	1,197,549
Total Lights	1,860,999	$12,198,279
Heavy Oils		
Fuel oil	9,446,565	$7,097,175
Gas and stove oil	182,833	206,409
Asphalt and road oil	411,548	350,991
Total Heavies	10,040,946	$7,654,575
Total Oil Sales	11,901,945	$19,852,854
Lamps, stoves and heaters		343,124
Grand Total	11,901,945	$20,195,978

Source: Annual Sales Statements, Marketing Department.

of the kerosine and 97 per cent of the naphthas, was nevertheless impressive. In 1911 California Standard held about 71 per cent of the market for light products. It sold an estimated 83 per cent of the kerosine, 71 per cent of the gasoline, and 63 per cent of the engine distillate.[6] The company lagged solely in sales of fuel oil, where its share was little more than 17 per cent.[7] But interest in fuel oil was distinctly secondary; unlike competitors, it sold mainly a residuum from refining, rather than crude oil, for fuel. Total sales in 1911 in the home market are shown in Table 19.

Eight years later, as K. R. Kingsbury assumed the presidency, Table 20 reveals both Standard's growth and the changing character of its market. In 1919, moreover, the export trade swelled Standard's income by more than one-fifth, amounting to an additional $26,083,095.[8]

Table 20: Domestic Sales of California Standard, 1919

Light Oils	Barrels	Value
Gasoline	4,616,532	$41,679,763
Engine distillate	1,257,854	7,810,850
Total Naphthas	5,874,386	$49,490,613
Refined oils (kerosine)	1,145,194	$ 6,713,323
Lubricating oil	503,988	7,955,065
Other	66,845	2,057,788
Total Lights	7,590,413	$66,216,789
Heavy Oils		
Fuel oil	13,689,093	$23,709,677
Diesel and stove oil	511,326	986,488
Asphalt	466,105	1,428,968
Total Heavies	14,666,524	$26,125,133
Total Oil Sales	22,256,937	$92,341,922
Lamps, stoves and heaters		$ 1,125,571
Tanks, etc.		$ 855,062
Grand Total	22,256,937	$94,322,555

Source: Annual Sales Statements, Marketing Department.

3

After 1911 soaring demand and more vigorous competition placed Standard's marketers under heavy pressure. Harper and Miller could hope to maintain the company's overwhelming pre-eminence in most

Sales in Far Western Marketing Area
1911 ~ 1919

MILLIONS OF DOLLARS

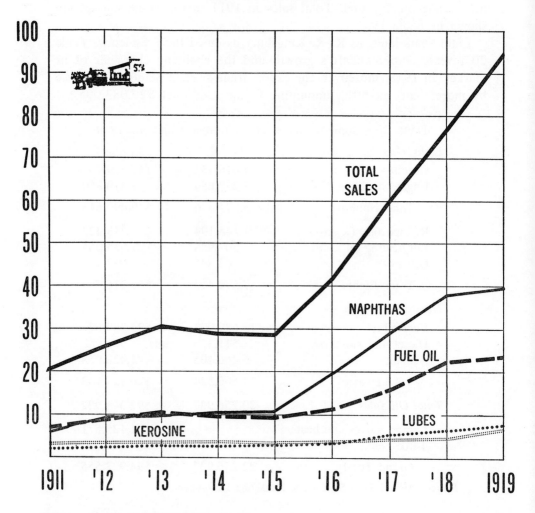

SOURCE - ANNUAL SALES STATEMENTS, 1891-1922.

NOTE - BARRELS OF PRODUCTS SOLD ARE TABULATED IN APPENDIX.

Sales Outside Far Western Marketing Area 1911 — 1919

MILLIONS OF DOLLARS

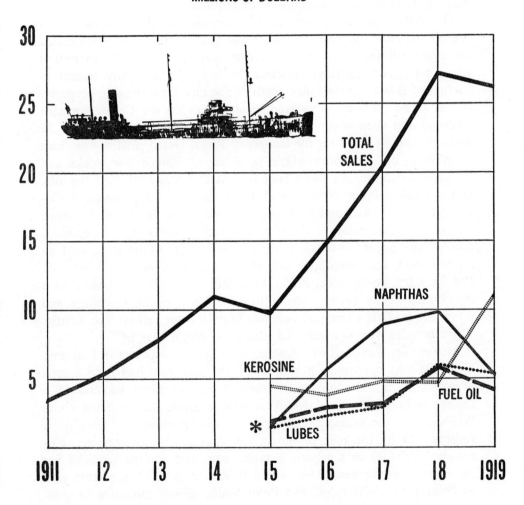

TOTAL SALES

NAPHTHAS

KEROSINE

FUEL OIL

LUBES

*

30
25
20
15
10
5

1911   12   13   14   15   16   17   18   1919

SOURCE - ANNUAL SALES STATEMENTS, 1891-1922.

NOTE - BARRELS OF PRODUCTS SOLD ARE TABULATED IN APPENDIX.

* SALES BY CLASS OF PRODUCTS NOT AVAILABLE BEFORE 1915.

lines only as they were constantly on the alert for new opportunities to push Standard's products and to improve their distribution. Many of the developments in marketing, as might be expected, were mainly a gradual evolution from past practice, for the record of the past indicated that old procedures should not be changed lightly. But independence also imparted a vitality and speed of action to the San Francisco sales headquarters that the times badly required.

The steady growth in marine transportation to the Northwest was one notable development. At Seattle, the growing traffic urgently called for additional facilities, but waterfront was far too costly to permit any great expansion there. Instead, in 1911 the company turned to Richmond Beach twelve miles north of the city for a suitable property. It was a fine piece of shore land located between the Great Northern Railroad and deep water. W. S. Miller, ever conservative, bought 58 acres, which left room for the leaders of Royal Dutch–Shell's American invasion to buy a smaller adjoining acreage within a few weeks and Associated still another piece later on. At first Standard used the site, which it called Point Wells, chiefly for a marine fueling station, building a 175-foot wharf and four large fuel oil tanks. By 1914, however, the company had enlarged the plant to handle a full range of products, adding fourteen more tanks, a warehouse, a lube filling shed, and an asphalt shed, and extending the wharf at a total cost of $261,000. But for a few years more, Point Wells failed to fulfill its promise as a distributing center because the railroad levied a switching charge and refused to make it a terminal commanding the same rail rates as Seattle. These barriers were not removed until after World War I.[9]

Meanwhile, Standard was developing a similar depot near Portland. The time was opportune, for in 1911 the company had been forced to abandon its old main station and marine terminal because of a change in Portland's fire laws. As a new location, the company chose Willbridge on the Willamette River a few miles northwest of the city. A railroad ran by the rear of the property. Standard invested approximately $300,000 in a wharf, a tank farm, and storage facilities for cased goods at the new plant, which it opened in 1912, the same year as Point Wells. Willbridge, like Point Wells, proved attractive to competitors, for Standard's depot was soon bordered by Union on one side and by Shell on the other.[10]

The expansion of the marine establishment on both ocean and inland waters went hand-in-hand with the construction of these large depots. By the end of 1916, when war costs and clogged shipyards slowed new construction, Standard's house flag was flying from five more tankers. The *A. F. Lucas* the company had purchased from New York Standard at the beginning of 1912. Standard built the other four, the *El Segundo, Richmond, J. A. Moffett,* and *D. G. Scofield.* Together, these five vessels more than doubled Standard's ocean-going capacity with an additional 289,000 barrels.[11] The tankers supplied efficient transportation. Prices for refined products at Seattle, for example, through World War I were never more than a cent a gallon higher than at San Francisco and from around fifteen to twenty-five cents a barrel higher for fuel oil. The new tankers helped the company handle its growing northern trade and withstand the inroads of the larger number of major competitors who likewise had turned to tankers and had established marine terminals.[12]

Like the tankers, Standard's inland fleet helped make marketing an efficient, low-cost operation. In 1911 Standard had nine river and harbor craft of various types and sizes with a combined capacity of 18,500 barrels. During the next three years eight vessels were added, doubling the capacity on inland waters. Most of this capacity continued to be used in the river and harbor traffic from Richmond, but auxiliary tonnage at San Pedro was also built up, and four vessels, with a total capacity of 12,100 barrels, were put to work on the waters of Puget Sound. The *Petroleum II,* a gas-engine craft carrying 1,500 barrels of assorted cargo, was the venturesome queen of this northern flotilla, peddling for years refined and specialty goods up the Inland Passage to Alaska.[13]

Standard also was busy saturating its territory with sales outlets. No longer subject to the conservatism of 26 Broadway, the company put in a sub or "circuit" station, consisting of at least a tank each for gasoline and kerosine, with limited storage for cased goods, whenever a community began to buy as much as 2,500 barrels annually of oil products. The number of these small bulk plants tripled by the end of 1916. Substations answering to the district headquarters at Seattle, for example, had grown from 4 to 18; Spokane, from 2 to 20; Portland, from 13 to 45; Sacramento, from 4 to 36; Fresno, from 8 to 25; San Francisco, from 6 to 21; and Los Angeles, from 24 to 49. By the end of 1919 the substations numbered 385 in comparison with the 99 of eight years before. Charlie Watson, who set up these new plants, was never so busy as in these twilight years of his long career.[14]

The company made less important changes in its net of main stations, called sales districts after 1914. During the summer of that year Nome and Marysville, the stations with the smallest volume of sales, were absorbed by the adjacent main stations, Seattle and Sacramento.

At about the same time, Arizona was split off from the Los Angeles district and Phoenix made its sales capital. Population growth and the state's booming copper mines were important reasons for this change, as was also the fact that in Arizona, unlike any other state in Standard's domain, the company encountered the competition of Midwest and Texas marketers. Arizona had at times an outpost character when gasoline from Kansas and a larger range of products from Texas appeared in its eastern cities and towns. The competition caused Harper and Miller to favor a direct tie between Arizona and San Francisco rather than through Los Angeles. In June, 1919, five years after the elevation of Phoenix, most of Nevada and a fringe of southern Oregon and California east of the Sierras were removed from the Sacramento district and made responsible to a new regional headquarters at Reno. Two months later, in August, the new Bakersfield district was carved from the Fresno territory to ease the burden of sales management in the flourishing south half of the San Joaquin Valley.[15]

Motor transport, replacing horse-drawn vehicles, was another important improvement in marketing. The company's first tank truck, used by the Oakland agency after December, 1910, was soon followed by others there and elsewhere. Early in 1913 the San Franciso agency had four tank trucks and two for cased goods, but Los Angeles, appropriately enough, was the first agency to be completely motorized. The two trucks in mid-1912 in the sprawling Southern California metropolis had been increased to 19 two years later, replacing 49 horses and 21 tank and case wagons. As roads improved, trucks also began to be used at the substations. They grew from 53 at the end of 1913 to 757 six years later, while horse-drawn vehicles were reduced from 797 to 381.[16] Trucks, with their greater capacity and range, permitted the substations to extend their service farther into rural areas than ever before. The economical bulk deliveries pioneered by the tank wagon continued to rise, as the tank truck took over; they represented 71 per cent of the refined oil sales and 76 per cent of the naphthas in 1919, compared with 38 per cent for refined oil and 47 per cent for the naphthas in 1911.[17]

The sales staff, too, was motorized. Salesmen began to shift from buggies to autos early in the decade, and by the end of 1919 the Sales Department owned 729 passenger cars.[18] The impact of autos and trucks, as the record clearly shows, was by no means limited to the company's sales; it also influenced the manner in which Standard conducted its business.

Harper and Miller knit together their growing sales staff by holding meetings at different levels that were also designed to comb the field for ideas. Nearly annually, Harper called the district sales managers to San Francisco for a conference usually lasting several days, where general policies as well as more specific questions were discussed. A conference held in 1913 considered, for example, whether salesmen should specialize or sell the full line; whether men in charge of substations should be paid a salary or a commission; whether procedures governing credit sales were adequate; and whether the company should establish "service stations" for retailing gasoline and other oil products. Two years later the district managers were asked to make recommendations on pricing policy and on ways of improving community relations.[19] Within sales districts, too, each manager was encouraged to hold meetings and to relay suggestions to San Francisco. The questions discussed at these district gatherings were usually of a more immediate and practical nature, but they gave Harper and Miller an insight into the thinking of the men who were in direct contact with the customer.[20]

As in the past, the headquarters relied principally on the field for information on competitors. Every week the agent in charge of each substation sent the district manager an itemized statement of his sales of oil products and an estimate of the sales of competitors. This information was forwarded to San Francisco, giving Harper and Miller a consistently good picture of Standard's position in the market. The field men had to be more circumspect in gathering information than in the old days, but there was still room for enterprise. "Our Assistant Cashier goes to the Railroad Depot every day at half past 4 o'clock to pay freight billings," the Fresno manager reported, "and while there he makes a pretense of checking our freight. . . . The shipments of our competitors . . . are all put into the same Railroad Warehouse, and while checking our freight it is an easy matter for him to secure the names to whom our competitors are shipping and the product shipped." The Fresno manager also spurred his agents at the substations to be alert for rail shipments by competitors. Deliveries by local refiner-marketers at Bakersfield, Tulare, and Hanford were estimated by noting the number of garages served and the number of tank wagons they used.[21]

In this more highly competitive era, Harper gave special attention to advertising. Standard appropriated progressively larger sums to popularize its products. H. K. McCann & Company, the advertising agency for the old Standard combination, handled its account. The development of ideas, however, was by no means limited to the

McCann agency; Vice President Kingsbury, the sales staff at the headquarters, and men in the field all made their contributions. Some brand names, like Zerolene, were Standard's own, but most, like Red Crown gasoline, Pearl and Eocene kerosine, it shared with other Standard companies. A few years after the dissolution it added the prefix Calol (California oil) to the old names to distinguish its oils from those of the former family. For many products the company used the California grizzly as a symbol and for asphalt the sabre-tooth tiger, found as a fossil in the tar pits at Los Angeles. To famalarize employees with the sales list, it distributed booklets and held classes at the home office. Standard also took advantage of opportunities like San Francisco's Panama Pacific International Exposition in 1915, where its products won several grand prizes. And it lured motorists into its service stations with useful giveaways like a frequently revised booklet on "Traffic Regulations."[22]

Price policy was one aspect of the business that the San Francisco headquarters kept strictly in its own hands. Its procedure was to fix a common price at the refineries for each product and to charge the customer this "base price" plus the cost of transportation from the refinery to the point of delivery. Occasionally Standard departed from this formula when it lowered a price to meet the offer of a competitor. These practices were in accord with a "one-price" law in California, enacted in the summer of 1913, that forbade differences in the price of a commodity within the state except for costs of transportation and distribution, or to meet competition. Since Standard was already fixing its base prices at the refineries prior to 1913 for all its western market, the effect of the law was merely to make the company doubly careful in handling California business.[23]

The possibility of antitrust action also made Standard especially sensitive in price-making. As a ruling principle, it maintained the policy of never discussing prices with other companies, and field executives were expected to conform. When Harper learned in 1913 that a Sacramento special agent had negotiated common selling prices with a Union representative for gasoline and kerosine at Folsom, a few miles northeast of Sacramento, the agent was removed and transferred to another branch of the business. The headquarters was on guard against even the suspicion of collusion. A few years later Harper reprimanded the Los Angeles district sales manager for having increased the price of engine distillate to Imperial Valley restaurants on his own initiative because Union had done so. "There is nothing else for us to do," Harper wrote, "but to approve what you have done. However, this has been

Trucks and tank wagons at the 7th and Irwin main station, San Francisco, 1913

National Supply service station, 1914

The tanker *Richmond* at San Francisco after returning from Atlantic service by way of Shanghai

handled in a manner entirely contrary to our policy. . . . You should set forth when you wish to have price changes considered, your reasons for desiring such change. It is our wish that in the future, before taking any action with regard to changes in prices . . . you refer the matter to this office for our decision."[24]

Standard's pricing policies received careful study by the Federal Trade Commission during an investigation of the Pacific Coast petroleum industry between 1919 and 1921. The Commission noted that in most western communities common prices generally prevailed for most products, and that Standard was almost always the leader in making changes. In examining the record after 1914, it found a number of cases of suspected collusion between Standard's field agents and those of a competitor at places like Kingman, Arizona; Folsom, Castaic, and Topanga Canyon, California; in sales to water companies and restaurants in the Imperial Valley; and in the establishment of certain geographic and customer price classifications. The Commission offered virtually nothing, however, implicating the San Francisco headquarters. In each of the cases Standard made a rebuttal. Nevertheless, the Commission concluded that the "cooperative activities" of men in the field "were quite largely responsible for the high degree of price uniformity which existed throughout the Pacific Coast territory from 1916-1920." The Commission also stated that uniform prices were characteristic of the oil industry throughout the nation. Units of the old Standard combination, it averred, were generally the price leaders, though at times powerful independents like the Gulf and Texas companies shared this role.[25]

The nation's experience with uniform prices by major oil companies in most communities for most of the forty years since this report suggests, however, that collusion is rarely the reason. Rather, the tacit recognition of the dangers of instability and price warfare to all major companies has caused them usually to accept price leadership in each regional market. And in the period prior to 1920, when Standard controlled so large a percentage of the western trade, following Standard's lead was, as Union's president, W. L. Stewart, put it, "natural and unavoidable."[26] Despite the minor instances of collusion, real or suspected, produced by the Federal Trade Commission, a general awareness of the desirability of accepting Standard's prices was surely the important factor. Certainly this was true for the industry's chief product, gasoline, after a long and disastrous price war ending in the summer of 1915.

4

Gasoline commanded Standard's attention more than any other product, for after 1911 no one could doubt that the oil industry had entered a new era. Gasoline stoves and stationary gas engines, at work since the 1890's supplying power in agriculture and industry, had already raised the naphthas (gasoline and engine distillate) from lowly by-products to challengers of kerosine for primacy. This challenge the automobile carried further. The auto proved itself successor to the lamp as the most meaningful of all inventions for the oil industry.

In the West, population growth combined with the automobile to make the rise of gasoline especially spectacular. The continuing heavy influx from the East helped add 1,700,000 residents in Standard's marketing territory between 1910 and 1920 for a new total of 6,289,000.[27] This population increase of 39 per cent was nearly three times the national average of 14 per cent. It was particularly notable in Southern California, where Los Angeles almost doubled in size and by 1920, with a population of 577,000, was the largest city on the Coast. In rate of growth numerous California cities and towns surpassed Los Angeles. These communities, moreover, took account of the automobile in their construction, for they were young enough to be built spaciously, with the auto as an almost indispensable means of transportation.

This exploding population helped make automobiles in the West, proportionately, far more numerous than elsewhere. Presumably, too, restless westerners drove their cars more because of the vast distances. Californians in 1910 owned 44,120 autos and trucks out of a national total of 468,500, when the state's population comprised about 2.5 per cent of the nation. Ten years later approximately 918,000 of the 9,239,000 autos and trucks throughout the country were being operated in Standard's sales territory, an area containing about 6 per cent of the national population. Car ownership in the home market had grown from one for each 75 persons to one for less than seven during the decade, as the "rich man's toy" became "every man's friend."[28]

Harper and Miller viewed with delight the soaring demand of the automobile, but they also had reason to be apprehensive. Their gasoline was not necessarily superior to other gasolines, for it had no special advantage in manufacture similar to the Starke patent for kerosine.[29] Careful small refiners like Puente, Pinal Dome, the Ventura Refining Company, or the Richfield Oil Company readily turned out gasoline that rivaled Standard's Red Crown. Not all did so well, but the poorer refiners could always cut prices.

Standard's sales leaders could expect that the bounding gasoline market would attract other large companies to join with Union in the competition for sales. They had not long to wait. In September of 1912, the American Gasoline Company, the first American venture of the Royal Dutch-Shell, was incorporated. In 1913 Associated, hitherto a powerful competitor in fuel oil, built a refinery at Avon, not far from Richmond and Union's Oleum, and began marketing refined products in California, Oregon, Nevada, and Hawaii. In the same year the General Petroleum Company built a large topping plant at Vernon, just outside Los Angeles, which it connected by pipeline with oil fields in Kern County. Although this important California concern at first stayed mainly in the fuel trade, potentially it, too, was a competitor in refined products.[30]

Harper and Miller had also to reckon with a sharp jump in California crude production as a factor intensifying competition and disrupting the market. Between 1911 and 1913 the output from California wells increased from 81,000,000 barrels to nearly 98,000,000, while during the same years the per cent of production delivered to refineries increased from 28.5 to a peak of approximately 70. Lighter crudes, along with the heavy demand for the more valuable refined products, combined to bring about this startling reversal. Compressor plants extracting casinghead gasoline from California natural gas, too, were beginning to turn out a noteworthy supplement to refinery production. And at about the same time east of the Rockies, in Oklahoma, the great Cushing light oil field was approaching its peak, effectively blocking off gasoline shipments eastward from California. The situation in the West was far different from 1911 when, according to the *California Derrick*, there was "not enough refining oil produced here to supply the gasoline demand of the Pacific Coast."[31] As has so frequently happened in oil, a condition of shortage had been replaced by a temporary surplus. By the end of 1913 the western industry was suffering from a disorganized market.

For these several reasons Standard faced a hard fight. In the always hotly contested Los Angeles area a dozen or more local refiners were giving Standard a vigorous battle. In Arizona, late in 1912 low-priced gasoline from Kansas was underselling Standard's Red Crown from 1.5¢ to 6¢ a gallon. In the San Joaquin Valley around Bakersfield the garage trade was almost wholly in the hands of local refiner-marketers.[32]

Two small refiners, the American Oriental Company at Martinez and the Monarch Oil & Refining Company at West Berkeley, were Standard's chief new challengers in the San Francisco Bay area following

independence. Each company offered gasoline and other refined products at cut rates. Monarch, backed by the Spreckels sugar interests,
owned some oil wells and was the more aggressive of the pair. During
the spring of 1912 it took on a number of salesmen who led a drive
for outlets all the way from the Bay Region to the Pacific Northwest.
In San Francisco, where in 1911 Standard had sold about 74 per cent
of the gasoline, Monarch undercut the Red Crown price from 2.5¢
to 4¢ a gallon and, for a time, captured the trade of the twenty-six
garages comprising the San Francisco Garage Association. The Company also used direct mail advertising to build up consumer demand.
It offered free road maps, free cans of clutch oil and metal polish, and
a discount of 40¢ on a can of its motor oil. But these tactics failed
to bring Monarch success. By mid-1913 it had retired from the field,
selling its refined oil and naphtha business to the Associated Oil Company, which was about to open the Avon refinery.[33]

The purchase gave Associated a springboard into the market for
light products, to which it could add a wide range of contacts from its
fuel trade. By 1914, the first full year for the Avon refinery, Associated
was selling about one-tenth as much gasoline and engine distillate as
was Standard. Associated sedulously sought outlets for its new line.
It gave a 2 per cent discount for cash, frequently shaded Standard's
prices a half cent or more, and also lent storage tanks, gasoline buggies,
and curb pumps to retailers. These efforts paid off. By 1916, when
its steep climb began to level out, Associated's gasoline sales were
about one-fifth the amount of its big competitor and its engine distillate sales about two-fifths. Associated's marketing territory, moreover,
was somewhat smaller than Standard's, for it did not include Alaska,
Washington, or Arizona.[34]

The invasion by the Royal Dutch-Shell Group caused Standard
greater concern. The Associated was a rival whose resources and potential could be roughly calculated. An American arm of the international
Royal Dutch–Shell combination was another matter. For years the
Royal Dutch had been the chief contestant with Rockefeller companies
overseas, possessing resources and skills matched or surpassed by Jersey
Standard alone. A subsidiary of the foreign organization in the West,
foreshadowed early in 1911 by the purchase of land for a terminal
at Richmond Beach, north of Seattle,[35] posed a formidable threat the
extent of which could not be fully known.

At first, the American Gasoline Company, the Royal Dutch-Shell's
new subsidiary, was limited to marketing gasoline and engine distillate
from the Group's Asiatic refineries. On September 16, 1912, it received

an initial cargo of 36,000 barrels of Sumatra gasoline and 56° naphtha at the Richmond Beach terminal. The gasoline was offered at 18¢ and 19¢ a gallon, equal in price to Standard's Red Crown, and the naphtha, suitable for stationary gas engines and motor launches, at 8¢, two cents less than Standard was asking for its comparable engine distillate. In mid-October John McLean, Standard's special agent at Seattle, reported that American Gasoline was setting up stations at Spokane and Tacoma in Washington and at Medford, Eugene, and Salem in Oregon. A few weeks later he told of the addition of Bellingham and enclosed a news clipping praising the high quality of the foreign gasoline. A test sample, sent to Richmond, proved the dispatch no mere puff, for the quick-starting "Motor Spirit" was more than two degrees higher in gravity than the gasoline Standard was marketing.[36]

While these reports were coming in from the Northwest, the Shell men were already mapping an invasion of California. H. R. Gallagher, sales manager for American Gasoline, attracted more than passing attention as he moved from San Francisco through the Sacramento and San Joaquin valleys early in 1913 looking for sites for bulk plants. In June another Shell tanker, the *J. B. Aug. Kessler,* unloaded most of its cargo at Martinez, California, where American Gasoline had established a terminal north of Richmond. In San Francisco the company had set up a depot on the site of the old Arctic Oil Works. The *Kessler's* cargo was the second of five shipments made to the West Coast prior to the end of 1914, when further imports ceased due to the European demand generated by World War I.[37]

By that time the American Gasoline Company had been redesignated the Shell Company of California and was no longer solely a marketer; it was becoming a fully integrated operation, with oil lands at Coalinga, and a pipeline running north to Martinez on San Francisco Bay, where a refinery was under construction. In addition to sales to garages and other retailers in Washington and Oregon, Shell products were being sold in the San Francisco area by the fall of 1914 through a chain of twelve or thirteen service stations, which the company took over at the end of the year, appropriating the familiar yellow and red colors of their former owner. The next year Shell opened about twenty-five service stations in the Northwest. Its sales remained small until after the Martinez refinery went on stream in December, 1915, and even thereafter failed to match those of Union or Associated. In 1918 Shell sold about 5 per cent as much gasoline and 12 per cent as much engine distillate as did Standard, but the marketing facilities it was establishing forecast a period when its competition would become far more dangerous.[38]

Union was engaged in a more prosaic expansion. Covering the same domestic sales territory as did Standard, Union was steadily adding to its marketing and marine establishments. When World War I broke out, it was operating about seventy bulk plants from which it served a wholesale trade by tank truck and tank wagon. A single service station in Los Angeles represented its sole entry into retailing. By the end of 1914 Union's plant investment in marketing amounted to $3,418,000, in comparison with $5,604,000 for Standard, and its marine investment was $3,613,000, a figure not far below Standard's $4,516,000. In that year Union sold nearly 41 per cent as much gasoline and more than 53 per cent as much engine distillate as Standard, a ratio that was approximately maintained over the next five years. Like Associated, Union occasionally shaded Standard's prices by a half cent or more and nibbled away at the accounts of its rival by offering a 2 per cent discount for cash.[39]

Standard's gasoline sales had increased phenomenally by the end of 1914 to almost 1,100,000 barrels annually—more than double its record for 1911—but its share of the market had fallen considerably. Its share, for example, had dropped an estimated 2 to 15 per cent at nine of fourteen main stations during the first seven months of 1913 compared with the same period in the preceding year. In the Los Angeles district, which accounted for nearly one-third of its total naphtha sales, the company had suffered a fall of 14 per cent, primarily because of the Southern California refiner-marketers. In the San Francisco district the decline was 9 per cent. The Sacramento station alone in California had shown a slight improvement. Other stations registering gains were mainly in the Northwest, but their downturn came later. In 1914 Seattle, the most important of the northern stations, reported a drop of 27 per cent, and Portland a 10 per cent loss.[40]

A companion feature was a sharp decline in prices and profits. Gasoline prices tumbled after 1912, as heavy stocks of refinable crude piled up in storage and passed through the refineries. The 19¢ per gallon prevailing at Seattle and 18.5¢ at San Francisco in November, 1912, for example, had become 11.5¢ at Seattle and 11¢ at San Francisco by July, 1915. Standard was not the leader in all of these price cuts; at times, especially prior to the end of 1914, Union or Shell had led the parade. In July, 1914, to protect the price of its Red Crown, Standard brought out a cheaper gasoline called "Motor Spirits." This early "fighting brand" was introduced in areas where there had been severe price cutting. It sold for three cents less than Red Crown but failed to catch on. A correspondent of the *California Oil World* commented late in September:

> The gasoline situation around San Francisco Bay seems to have got mixed up in a measure with the belligerents in the war zone and for the moment is somewhat shot to pieces. The price is down to 13½ cents per gallon and everyone is doing it. Even pirates show a disinclination to give it another whack, fearful that another swipe will carry it into the dump.

The low prices, the *Oil World* reporter believed, were realistic and reflected "present market conditions."[41]

They were, however, catastrophic for profits. Standard's marketing operations in 1914 contributed only $242,000 out of a total net income of $10,058,000. Gasoline and engine distillate, which accounted for nearly 40 per cent of the income from domestic sales, may actually have been sold at a loss. In the same year, according to the Federal Trade Commission, Union received a smaller per cent of profit on its refining and marketing operations than Standard, and Associated showed a loss. Also hard hit, seven small refiners around Bakersfield announced in February, 1915, that they were in danger of being forced to shut down. At Los Angeles the Southern Refining Company was one of two refiners that did leave the field.[42]

The fall of 1915, nevertheless, marked a turning point. The demand for gasoline at last began to move ahead of supply, and by the end of the year prices throughout the West had risen four cents a gallon. Standard had become, too, the generally recognized price maker, with Union, Shell, Associated, and most smaller refiners following its lead.[43]

This movement toward better prices was furthered in the Los Angeles area by an organization of small refiner-marketers, the Independent Petroleum Marketers' Association. Set up late in 1914 to cope with the destructive competition which threatened the life of so many of its members, it lobbied an ordinance through the Los Angeles City Council establishing minimum standards for gasoline in order to combat unscrupulous garage and service station owners who adulterated branded gasoline with cheap distillates. But the Association was more concerned over price wars. It argued for "harmony"; instead of a war of prices, "a war of quality and marketing facilities." Standard applauded this proposed pattern of competition as "progress." In its house organ for January, 1915, it commented, "The policy . . . carries the germ of a thought which the Standard Oil Company would gladly foster. Though our new competitor may give us many a tussle, we welcome it and will meet it fairly in the 'war of quality.' " The southern Association attempted to

MARKETING DISTRICTS · 1919

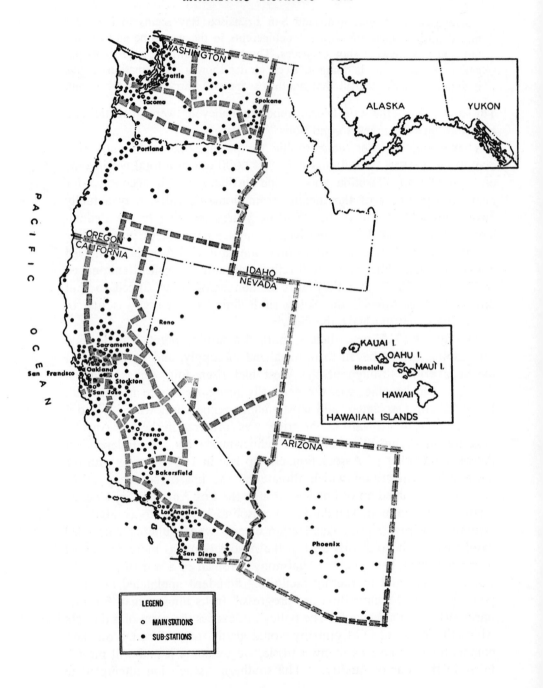

LEGEND

○ MAIN STATIONS

● SUB-STATIONS

foster prices for gasoline and engine distillate at the same or a fractionally lower level than Standard's. They were not always maintained, and flurries of price cutting occurred occasionally, but the market was far more stable in the upswing following the summer of 1915 than it had been during the nearly three years of decline.[44]

Western gasoline prices continued to move sharply upward during the spring of 1916. From 15¢ a gallon at Standard's refineries at the beginning of the year, prices climbed to 19¢ by April and to 20¢ by December. They remained at this point except for a single half-cent increase until June, 1919.[45] The western rise was somewhat more gradual than had occurred earlier in most other areas of the nation, where a public outcry had prompted an investigation by the recently organized Federal Trade Commission.

Neither Standard's share of the market nor its profits brought forth harsh words from the Commission in its *Report on the Price of Gasoline in 1915*. Standard's rate of earnings that year was 10.6 per cent, the FTC revealed, which was less than for ten other former members of the Standard combination and less than the rate, too, earned by the Gulf and Texas companies. The Commission found that gasoline prices had risen more modestly along the Pacific Coast than in any other marketing territory. It also reported that Standard's share of tank wagon sales in the West amounted to only 48 per cent of the market in towns of 2,500 or more, which was a smaller figure than for eight other former units of the Standard family.[46]

As prices moved upward following 1915, Standard's position in the gasoline trade apparently slightly improved, though competition continued to be intense. It was most sharp at Los Angeles, in the sales districts bordering San Francisco Bay, and at Fresno and Portland. Three of these regions were refining centers; the fourth, Portland, was readily reached by water. The familiar tactic of a 2 per cent discount for cash or for payment within ten days continued to be used by competitors, who also shaded prices occasionally and lent tanks and sidewalk pumps to garages and service stations in return for their patronage.[47] Standard rarely lent equipment. Nor did it often cut prices to meet competition. It was resistant even to the 2 per cent discount, though in some areas and to some classes of trade Harper gradually did yield.[48] His preferred position, however, was to stress the quality of Standard's product—a "straight run gasoline" with a "continuous chain of boiling points," in contrast to the mixtures of distillate and volatile casinghead gasoline marketed by a number of competitors. The company stressed that its gasoline offered "easy starting, quick and smooth acceleration, power and mileage." To one manager, Harper wrote, "It should be pointed out . . . that the quality of our Red Crown gasoline, the service which we are in a position to render, and the extensive advertising campaign which is behind our products are worth more . . . than a slight concession in price." To another, he commented, "Price concessions are merely admissions of inferior quality."[49]

So firm a position might have served Standard less well, had it not been for the constant and rapid growth of the market. As it was, the Federal Trade Commission reported that in 1919 Standard had 55 per cent of the total gasoline trade in the western territory. Among the four major companies, Standard's share was 60.6 per cent, compared with 61.2 in 1915. Union was the runner-up in both years. Standard did not do quite as well in the closely allied engine distillate trade. Its share among the four major companies had declined from 63.3 per cent in 1915 to 46.5 per cent in 1919. But engine distillate was no longer so important a product. The growth in the number of autos was far greater than in the number of stationary and other engines using the cheaper fuel.[50]

Standard's sales figures for these years record the increasing pre-eminence of the two naphthas. In 1915 the company sold 1,718,000 barrels of gasoline and 672,000 barrels of engine distillate. Along with small quantities of other naphthas, they brought in $10,936,000, which was approximately three-eighths of all revenue from domestic sales. Four years later the domestic gasoline sales had grown to 4,617,000 barrels, and engine distillate sales to 1,258,000. They brought the company nearly $49,500,000, which was a little more than 52 per cent of the domestic sales income. Gasoline sales alone supplied $41,680,000.[51]

The statistics for 1919 also reveal that approximately one-sixth of the company's domestic income from gasoline and engine distillate was derived from sales at service stations owned by the company.[52] This new retailing technique into which Standard first entered in a large way during the difficult days of 1914 deserves special attention, for retailing over the years was to become an increasingly important function. Standard was among the pioneers.

5

The evolution of the "filling," "gasoline vending," "supply," or "service" station, as it was eventually known, was a natural development in the struggle for the motorist's dollar. Prior to the automobile, hardware, paint, and some grocery stores had been the principal outlets for gasoline. If fire ordinances permitted, a motorist could stock up by purchasing gas in five-gallon tins at these outlets and store it in his home. On the road, he looked for garages, auto sales agencies, or even machine and bicycle shops, for which the sale of gasoline and motor oil frequently supplied a supplemental income. The motorist drove into a garage or parked at the curb, while gas was poured into a measuring container from an iron drum or barrel for delivery into his tank. A little later this crude method was superseded by service from a mobile, manually operated buggy, equipped with a measuring gauge and hose. Service was limited to selling gasoline and oil; there were none of the extras, like wiping windshields, checking the air pressure of the tires, and so on, that later made the lot of the motorist so much easier. Nor did the retailer charge a price based on a fixed markup; he collected what the traffic would bear, limited only by his fear of competition. The gasoline he offered, moreover, frequently varied in quality because of differences in refinery output. These variations were probably even more marked when the retailer used more than one source of supply. Greedy retailers also attempted to fool the public by doctoring gasoline with less costly distillates and by selling inferior goods under well-known brand names.[53]

From the motorist's viewpoint, these conditions left much to be desired. More convenient locations, quicker service, a greater range of services, greater assurance of uniform, high quality products, and protection against price gouging were among the improvements the motorist could hope for. It was the desire for quality, among other things, that caused motorists to call at the Seattle main station to purchase Red Crown and a Seattle warehouseman named Roberts to devise in 1907 a rudimentary filling station, consisting of a galvanized hot water tank and a hose with a valve control to dispense the gasoline. Because of the warehouseman's resourcefulness, Standard has entered a claim for the "world's first service station."[54] By 1914 the Los Angeles, Sacramento, and San Jose districts were also operating similar stations at the main plant. Car owners approved, including the famed racing driver, Barney Oldfield, of Los Angeles, but the new competition was viewed with covert to open hostility by garage men.[55]

H. W. Neumann, Standard's special agent at Los Angeles, had plans for stations elsewhere than at the main plant. Late in the fall of 1912 he won the approval of Harper and Miller for four "filling" stations to be set up at various locations in the southern metropolis. Getting the consent of the city council, however, was another matter. Neighbors of the proposed sites descended on the city fathers to protest that the stations would create a fire hazard, be unsightly, and lower property values. They presented petitions and made such an outcry that the city council turned down requests for all four locations. Undoubtedly, garage owners were also active behind the scenes in staving off this threat. Other applicants for permits were no more successful. Not until late in July, 1913, did a breakthrough occur, and by that time Standard's plans for Los Angeles had been shelved.[56]

But the idea of service stations was still very much alive. It was a chief topic of discussion at the special agents' convention held at San Francisco in June, 1913. Apparently, the agents feared losing the accounts of aggrieved garage owners, for they recommended that if the company "decided to establish Service Stations, enough should be put in to thoroughly cover the district and all should be installed at one time." At the beginning of the year, John McLean, disturbed by the appearance in Seattle of stations supplied by competitors, had urged Standard to set up one of its own in the downtown area. Several months later the Fresno special agent asked for a station at Coalinga, for Union and the Coalinga Refining Company were "making deliveries [there] direct to consumers' automobiles." And just after 1913 had ended Harper authorized the construction of stations at Tucson and Douglas, Arizona. For some reason, they were not built.[57] The company's future course was already indicated, however, by these discussions and abortive decisions.

Meanwhile, in Los Angeles Standard was benefiting from the service station movement through sales of gasoline and motor oils to the National Supply Stations, Inc., the largest and most rapidly growing chain in California. National Supply was the brainchild of a group of auto dealers led by Earle C. Anthony and the brothers Don and Cuyler Lee. It set up its first station at the end of October, 1913, opposite the Los Angeles ball park. The station was a simple affair. A single manually operated gas pump stood in front of the 12 x 15-foot wooden structure, walled mainly with glass panes and containing lubes and other auto merchandise. An extension of the tilted roof over the graveled drive gave protection from the weather. A sign bearing the company name bordered by two shields in red, white, and blue ran along the peak of the roof. Within three months National Supply had opened eight other unpretentious but strategically located outlets in Los Angeles and one in Pasadena and had scored an immediate success. The Los Angeles stations accounted for 103,734 gallons in January, 1914, approximately 22 per cent of all gasoline sold in the city. National Supply was far and away Standard's biggest account, taking almost as much gasoline as the eighty-eight other customers among the garages and service stations of Los Angeles.[58]

From Los Angeles, National Supply moved north to San Francisco Bay and south to San Diego. A station opened in Oakland on February 10, 1914, was followed within eight months by seven more in Oakland and one in Berkeley. Across the bay in San Francisco, the company opened its first station in September and was at work on three others. Its invasion of San Diego began in July, when it established two stations, followed by a third in August. All the while, the company was expanding its coverage in the Los Angeles area, adding six stations there by mid-year. For some locations National Supply turned to brick and steel, beginning with a Pasadena station opened in February. These stations cost about $500, twice as much as the wooden set-up, but the company felt that their durability and trim appearance were well worth the extra cost.[59]

National Supply's spectacular success further convinced Sales Manager Harper that "ultimately filling stations would become universal." Stations were appearing everywhere. Unfortunately, by no means all traded with Standard. National Supply's competitors in Los Angeles included the "Pennant" stations, supplied by Pinal Dome, and "Motor Maid," and "Owl," among others. In the San Francisco Bay area the "Omen" chain, soon to be acquired by Shell, was the main contestant. Standard's sales executives reported stations in other cities where National Supply was not represented. At Seattle during July, 1914, Shell bought the stations of Rothweiler & Company, and Portland had several filling stations supplied by competitors. In California's interior valleys competitors were stocking four of the seven stations at Sacramento, five of seven at Stockton, and all seven at Fresno. A survey of garages in these cities indicated that Standard was getting considerably less than half of their business. Garage men, who resented the inroads made by the stations, tended to buy from Union, according to the *California Oil World*, because Union had not become an important supplier of service stations. The changing pattern of marketing required that Standard plan its moves carefully.[60]

While Harper was considering Standard's future course, he received word in August, 1914, that the National Supply Stations could be bought. Standard's Los Angeles district manager reported, in fact, that the owners seemed "rather anxious" to sell. The owners could easily see that severe competition lay ahead. As others imitated their example in Los Angeles, the number of stations there had grown to about fifty, of which National Supply had fourteen. Gasoline prices, moreover, were falling steadily. In July the National Supply chain showed a profit of only $341 after depreciation; in August there was a slight loss.[61]

The opportunity seemed timely to Harper, for National Supply was a going concern that could readily serve as the nucleus for further expansion. At the end of September, with Board approval, he took an option to purchase National Supply for its net investment plus an amount for good will equal to twelve times its average monthly operating profit from July through September, 1914. Early in October Standard completed the purchase, paying $58,922 for the thirty-one stations and for three more under construction, and $22,946 for good will. The company also took over the employees, including George Shryer, the Southern California manager, and A. F. Kales, manager in the north.[62]

Earle C. Anthony, one of the principal former owners, urged Standard to make few changes. National Supply, he pointed out, was a name appropriate anywhere, "in Oregon or Illinois, the same as in California," and could be made "as well known as the United Cigar Company." Anthony also recommended that the company maintain the "distinctive appearance" of the stations, painted red, white, and blue, so as "to get the eye of the motorist . . . passing at twenty or twenty-five miles an hour." Standard heeded this advice, for the company's stations today are still in those colors. For several months the company retained, too, the National Supply name, merely adding its own, but as Standard began to build new stations the old name was dropped.[63]

Some stations were added in cities already served by National Supply; more represented the entry into new territories. Within six weeks of the take-over, Harper sent Shryer to the Pacific Northwest and Kales to the Sacramento and San Joaquin valleys to choose the new sites. Shryer found so much hostility in Spokane on the part of the garage men that he recommended no action, but Harper refused to back down. Early in 1915 four stations were opened there, and at about the same time nine in Seattle, seven in Portland, and three in Tacoma. Standard was also building several stations each at Fresno, Stockton, Sacramento, and San Jose, and one at Chico. By the end of the year it had added fifty-four, in all. The pace slackened following this sudden expansion until after World War I, but every year saw the addition of at least twenty more. By the end of 1919 the company had 218 stations, which were located in virtually every important city or town in the West.[64]

Standard gradually extended the range and improved the quality of service offered the motorist. The new stations, which were all built of steel, were frequently two- or three-pump affairs, permitting service to a larger number of customers. They also provided air and water, a service that National Supply was just beginning prior to its sale. And the grounds around the stations were beautified. The station attendants, who were clad in clean, white uniforms, spent quiet moments caring for flowers and shrubs that took away the bare, functional look of the earlier stations. Standard added gallonage books for gasoline to the scrip books that National Supply had been selling, and early in 1917 began to issue order coupons, billed to the purchaser. Employers especially liked these forms of purchase, for their drivers could get gas and oil without having to use cash. To boost sales, Standard allowed commercial and industrial purchasers a discount of one cent a gallon on gasoline, and also gave them a discount on Zerolene.[65]

The company maintained the practice initiated by National Supply of retailing gasoline for two cents more than the wholesale price. As Standard expanded its coverage, this margin became customary throughout the western industry, superseding the frequently wider margins prior to the summer of 1915. The low markup was another reason why garage owners resented Standard's entry into the service station field, though motorists surely had no reason to complain. Standard's stations usually made a profit, but it was apt not to be large. In 1915, for example, the over-all profit for the eighty-eight stations was $27,779, and the Portland, San Diego, and San Jose stations showed losses.[66]

By the end of 1919 Standard was clearly the western leader in the service station field. It was operating more stations than its next three rivals combined. Associated was second with 85; Shell had 77; and Union followed with 32. Standard's 218 stations gave the company a broad base in the retail market for gasoline and lubes on which it could continue to build.[67]

6

Other oils, heavy and light, followed in importance after the naphthas on Standard's domestic sales roster. The heavy products, gas oil, fuel oil, road oil, and asphalt, comprising the bottom two-thirds of each barrel of crude, were a special concern of the Fuel Oil Department at the headquarters, from which most of the large sales were made. They supplied an important part of the domestic revenue, for during the early years of independence their contribution ranged between a peak of 39 per cent in 1913 and a low of 28 per cent in 1919.[68]

J. C. Fitzsimmons worked "with the zeal of a missionary" in finding customers for fuel oil, which accounted for 90 per cent or more of the sales of his department. Persuading the owners of the ubiquitous West Coast lumber schooners to convert to oil was among his more important achievements of this period. In soliciting orders, Fitzsimmons, always stressed that the company's 14° gravity product, a mixture of residuum from the refinery, was of uniform quality. Unlike the crude sold for fuel by most competitors, it was guaranteed to produce a specific amount of heat per barrel, and was free from water, sand, or other sediment.[69]

Because of its high quality, Standard's fuel oil enjoyed a wide sale. In most years the company disposed of at least half in the highly competitive California territory and another quarter in Washington, which could be readily reached by tanker. Arizona, with its large mining industry, led the remaining states in the home market by a considerable margin. Industrial establishments took about one-third of the fuel oil, and railroads and ships each about one-quarter. Public utilities were Standard's fourth important outlet. In 1916 Standard was providing fuel oil to many a leading enterprise, including Alexander & Baldwin in Hawaii, the Panama Canal, Phelps, Dodge & Company in Arizona, W. R. Grace & Company, the Luckenbach Steamship Company, E. I. du Pont de Nemours, the Hercules Powder Company, and the Santa Fe Railroad.[70]

The company continued to find its principal outlet for gas oil among public utilities, which in 1914 took nearly half as much of the heavy distillate as of fuel oil. But a new market, created by the diesel engine, was to become far more meaningful. Instead of selling fuel oil or gas oil to the diesel operators, Standard soon tailored a special mixture of 24° gravity from the two oils. In January, 1914, when a pioneer Scandinavian motor ship, the *Siam,* docked at San Francisco, Fitzsimmons made a sale of 6,500 barrels of the new mixture, called "Star Fuel Oil." The vessel's owners, the East Asiatic Line, found that the Standard product was more satisfactory and economical than either the heavier fuel oil the *Siam* had bought at San Pedro or the Borneo fuel oil with which it had crossed the Pacific. Not long after, Fitzsimmons also interested the Navy in using the same fuel for diesel-powered submarines.[71]

A companion development was the marketing of Star Fuel Oil to fruit growers as a defense against frost. The El Segundo refinery had been open barely a year before it was called on in January, 1913, to supply several hundred tank cars of oil for the smudge pots used in heating Southern California orange groves. Early the next spring Standard ran a special train from Richmond for the relief of apple growers in Oregon's Rogue River Valley. Star Fuel Oil was also sold as a spray for the breeding grounds of mosquitoes in ponds and other stagnant waters.[72]

Fitzsimmons' sales ingenuity is again revealed in his promotion of road oil and asphalt. In August, 1912, he persuaded Standard's management to give him $1,500 for a road oil and asphalt testing laboratory, which was moved to the basement at 200 Bush the next year. He invited county supervisors and state officials to visit the laboratory and to see at first hand the quality of Standard's products. The company's rapid growth in sales of road oil and asphalt were a reflection of his enterprise.[73]

For these several reasons, Standard at least maintained and probably improved its market position in the heavy oils. In fuel oil, it had ranked after both Associated and Union in 1911, with about 17 per cent of the market. The sales statistics for 1919, while not exactly comparable, do show the relative positions of the five major companies: Standard, Union, Associated, Shell, and General. In fuel oil sales throughout the West, Standard had gained the lead. It had almost 27 per cent of the fuel trade of the five majors, with Union, Associated, and General following close behind. In gas oil, General led Standard by a slight margin. Standard's achievement was due partly to the prowess of its sales team, but the fact that Associated and Union had abandoned an earlier practice of selling most of their crude as fuel and were refining it, undoubtedly was also partly responsible.[74]

Among the light oils, kerosine continued to decline in importance as the electric light more and more replaced the oil lamp. Standard sought to counter this trend by selling lamps, heaters, and other coal oil appliances at low cost until these items were dropped in 1919. It also advertised extensively and held wholesale prices at a low level. The low prices did bring the onetime product leader a few new opportunities. Kerosine gradually became a widely used fuel for stoves, replacing more costly gasoline, and, to a lesser extent, for tractors, when the price of engine distillate also rose. These new uses, along with an increasing population, helped double the company's sales income from kerosine between 1911 and 1919, while at the same time Standard maintained its pre-eminence over competitors. Its share of the kerosine trade of the five major western companies in 1919 was 78.5 per cent, within two per cent of its position five years before. Union alone was a significant rival. But the contribution of kerosine to Standard's income from the home market had declined from 15 per cent in 1911 to about 7 per cent in 1919.[75]

Lube oils were a different story. Their sale felt the quickening effect of the automobile, the war boom, and the greater public acceptance of the western lubes. Standard gave wide publicity to a statement made in 1915 by a naval officer in the *Journal of the American Society of Naval Engineers*:[76]

> Oils made from . . . asphalt-base crudes have shown themselves to be much better adapted to motor cylinders, as far as their carbon-forming proclivities are concerned, than are the paraffine-base Pennsylvania oils. The carbon formed from the latter is, as a rule, extremely hard and clings to the metal surfaces, while that from the former is soft and can easily be wiped off any surface that it is deposited on. . . . The explanation lies in the fact that the asphalt base oils [tend] . . . to distill without decomposition. Consequently no gum will be formed on the cylinder walls, and the carbon liberated will be mostly discharged with the exhaust gases.

The company imported some eastern lubes of high quality, especially from such former Standard units as Vacuum and Galena Signal, but most lubes were of its own manufacture. After 1913 it ceased marketing whale and fish oils, making its line solely petroleum products. The lubes and greases ran the gamut from the modern automobile to the horse and buggy age. Zerolene, which was far and away the most important item, by 1917 accounted for almost one-third of the lube sales. Standard complemented its principal auto lube with Zerolene Transmission Lubricant and Zerolene Cup Grease. But it had not forgotten the horse-drawn vehicles. Salesmen continued to market those famed brands, Standard Hoof Oil, Eureka Harness Oil, and Mica Axle Grease. The sales of Mica Axle Grease, in fact, reached their peak in 1916. Salesmen also pushed many other specialized lubes bearing the Calol label, including Cylinder Oil, Power Separator Oil, Turbine Oil, Compressor Oil, Diesel Engine Oil, Ice Machine Oil, Heavy Red Journal Oil, Harvester Oil, Castor Machine Oil, Engine Oil, and Dynamo Oil. For the home, they offered Calol Liquid Gloss, Household Lubricant, and Standard Floor Dressing.[77]

Standard's domestic lube sales tripled between 1911 and 1919. The company led all competitors, though its leadership was somewhat less pronounced than in former years. Five years before, in 1914, it had held 85 per cent of the trade of the major western marketers; by 1919 its share had been reduced to 73 per cent. The entry of Shell, especially, had been responsible for the change.[78]

Beyond these main categories, the range of products was broad but of lesser consequence. The company sold several types of candles and other wax products, purchased mainly from Indiana Standard and Standard of New York. Linseed oil and turpentine, which it had also imported, the company removed from the sales list in 1913.[79] The painters' items had been a useful adjunct to the business when kerosine, retailed frequently through hardware stores, had been the principal oil product, but that day had passed.

Several new products appeared as a result of the war. The high quality of the medicinal white oil developed at Richmond to take the place of Russian white oil, cut off by the war, caused an executive of E. R. Squibb & Sons to comment that the Richmond product was "superior to the best oil" ever imported. In November, 1915, his firm signed a twenty-year contract with Standard and promised to market no similar oil under the Squibb name. For its part, Standard sought to prepare the market by mailing 90,000 sample bottles to doctors throughout the world.[80]

Standard's venture into the petrochemical field to supply a small production of benzol, toluol, and xylol to E. I. du Pont de Nemours & Company also led to the sale of a number of by-products growing at least in part from its manufacture of chemicals for explosives. The company promoted a new paint, an enamel, a priming solution, petroleum ether, heavy petroleum soap stock, oil of myrbane, and cumol, and increased the production of its synthetic turpentine, aroturps, which it had been making since 1908. For several of these products it coined the brand name, Oronite (meaning "like gold"), a name used nearly a quarter century later for a subsidiary chemical company.[81] It sold these items in both the home and export markets, but few among them were sufficiently profitable to remain for long on the sales list following the war. Their greatest significance, probably, is as early forerunners of Standard's lengthy and impressive line of petrochemicals after another two or three decades of research.

7

The company's flourishing "export" trade (comprised of sales outside the home market) was a final important feature of its marketing. Export sales climbed from 14 to 28 per cent of its total business between 1911 and 1914, the peak for the period, but in dollar volume they continued to grow fairly steadily through the war years. In 1914, for example, they amounted to $10,921,000; in the peak dollar year, 1918, they were $27,152,000.[82]

These sales were the special concern of K. R. Kingsbury, who brought West from 26 Broadway his wide range of contacts with other Standard companies. Unlike other aspects of marketing, responsibility for most exports rested only incidentally with the headquarters marketing executives; the Export Department, which was formally established in the marketing organization in March, 1916, was limited chiefly to dealing with jobbers along the west coast of Mexico and Central America. Kingsbury made the most of the seller's market created by the war. Perhaps, as one former executive suggests, Standard may have been somewhat less aggressive at home because of the great opportunities outside its home territory.[83]

The opening of the Panama Canal and the impact of World War I caused a sharp transition in the export trade. The Canal, which was opened in August, 1914, less than three weeks after war broke out, made the East Coast and Europe more accessible for California oil just before the war-induced demand for petroleum products made those markets more attractive. As European and East Coast markets rose in significance, the Oriental market tended to decline, especially because of the shortage of shipping. Through the end of 1914 the cheap kerosine, Petrolite, manufactured for the Orient, accounted for two-thirds or more of the dollar value of all foreign sales. Fuel oil trailed the lamp oil, followed by the naphthas, lubes, asphalt, and gas oil. By 1916 the naphthas had surpassed kerosine in value, as did fuel oil and lubes in 1918. Not until 1919, with the war over, did kerosine again take the lead. In that year the company exported 3,773,791 barrels of kerosine for $10,871,000, with lubes ($5,193,000), gasoline ($4,919,000), and fuel oil ($4,163,000) contesting for second place. This large trade, conducted almost wholly from Richmond, helped make San Francisco one of the nation's three or four great oil ports.[84]

Except for the small jobber trade in Mexico and Central America, serviced after 1915 by the company's steam schooner, *La Primera,* the the export sales were almost wholly to former Standard units. The bulk of Richmond's kerosine output was always taken by New York Standard. A lesser amount, and of higher quality, went to Vacuum to supply Vacuum's New Zealand and Australian markets. The foreign naphtha sales were principally to the Anglo-American Oil Company. Jersey Standard was an occasional gasoline customer, taking 116,000 barrels under one contract. Jersey's Canadian subsidiary, The Imperial Oil Company, and Imperial's South American subsidiary, the International Petroleum Company, were substantial purchasers of fuel oil. Anglo-American, New York Standard, and the Vacuum Oil Company took most of the lubes, but Continental Oil, Indiana Standard, and the West India Oil Company were also prominent among the dozen or more former Standard units with which the California company had lube contracts.[85]

Prior to 1914 Standard's export deliveries had usually been made to tankers or vessels chartered by the purchasing companies or, more rarely, to tank cars of the Union Tank Line. But wartime conditions brought changes. As the need for tankers became acute and vessels for charter proved hard to find, Standard extended its service in numerous instances to include delivery by its own fleet. Its tankers and barges made occasional voyages through the Canal to the East Coast, and in a few cases were even chartered to the company's former affiliates. Early in 1915, for example, the *Richmond* left the refinery for London, towing Standard's biggest barge, with an assorted cargo of naphthas, refined oil, lubes, gas oil, and fuel oil for the Anglo-American Oil Company. Before the two vessels were called home, the tanker and barge made five trans-Atlantic round trips under charter to Anglo-American. In the summer of 1916 they returned via Singapore and Shanghai under charter to New York Standard to help that company serve its China market. In all, the *Richmond* and *Barge 95* had logged 75,000 miles during the sixteen months away. Two other Standard tankers, the *J. A. Moffett* and the *D. G. Scofield,* made single voyages from Richmond to China in the service of New York Standard, and the *Colonel E. L. Drake* made a trip to London for Anglo-American.[86]

Standard helped Vacuum in the Australian and New Zealand markets to an even greater degree. Early in 1917, as charter vessels for cased goods became almost unavailable, the company bought two three-masted steel sailing ships, the *Dunsyre* and *John Ena,* which had been built at Glasgow shortly after 1890. It put these vessels, with a capacity of about 100,000 cases each, into the South Pacific trade. At about the same time it placed an order for a diesel-powered wooden schooner, *La Merced,* at a Benicia, California, shipyard. This vessel, with a capacity of 38,000 cases, was joined the following year by a sister, the *Oronite.* These four ships made a total of nine trips from the West Coast to New Zealand and Australia in 1917 and 1918, helping maintain Vacuum's position in the southern markets and Vacuum as Standard's customer.[87]

Even though the export trade was carried on so largely with members of the old family, it was always a business proposition. The numerous contracts show clearly the general desire within the group to deal with one another, but there was no longer a 26 Broadway to dictate terms. Each company looked to its own interest. When the West India Oil Company asked Standard to put up gasoline under the West India label in tins giving short measure, the company refused the order as potentially

dangerous to its reputation. And when Standard aided Anglo-American
and New York Standard by making the *Richmond* and *Barge 95* available for charter, it did so at rates that recaptured the original cost of
both vessels within the sixteen-month period.[88]

Occasionally, too, disputes arose. A contract negotiated with The Imperial Oil Company early in 1914 for nearly 3,000,000 barrels of fuel
oil caused a long controversy over Canada's wartime duties on imported
oil. Kingsbury reluctantly agreed that his company should absorb the
first duty, levied in February, 1915, but he refused to accept the same
arrangement when the rate was raised sharply a year later. The dispute placed Kingsbury at loggerheads with W. C. Teagle, Imperial's
president. Almost two years passed before the two sides accepted a compromise, with each company paying half the duty. The threat of another controversy arose briefly when Standard of New York considered
marketing Nujol, Jersey Standard's medicinal oil, in the Far East after
having earlier agreed to sell the California product exclusively. ". . . I
would like to impress upon you. . . ," Kingsbury wrote, "the clear understanding we had . . . that in return for your handling our product exclusively, we guaranteed to your company the sole sale of our product
in the countries enumerated."[89]

These evidences of self-interest, along with the increasing flow of oil
across Standard's marketing boundaries of 1911, were a pale suggestion
of its later sharp competition with units of the old Standard combination.
As early as 1916, in fact, *Financial America* was writing of "Competing
S. O. Co. Subsidiaries." The journal was guilty of exaggeration, but even
so, first and foremost it mentioned the Standard Oil Company (California).[90]

8

Standard's remarkable sales record during the first eight years of independence reflects both the enterprise of its sales staff and the extraordinary opportunities afforded by its domestic and export markets. But
creditable though the achievement was, in by far the more important
of these markets, the home territory, the company had failed to keep
pace. To a greater degree than ever before, Standard had been forced
to yield to competitors, old and new. The demand for oil products
had grown so abruptly that in most lines the company could no longer
maintain its former share of the market.

Elsewhere in the nation other Standard companies were undergoing
a similar experience. The FTC *Report on the Price of Gasoline in 1915*,
for example, reported that the share of national gasoline sales held by

the Standard companies had declined from approximately 85 per cent in 1906 to about 65 per cent in 1915.[91] Indiana Standard and Jersey Standard were two of the larger companies feeling the inroads of competitors. The great Mid-Continent oil strikes early in the war decade and the rocketing demand for refined products, especially gasoline, brought the Indiana company a number of new and formidable adversaries, including the Sinclair Oil & Refining Company, Phillips Petroleum Company, Cities Service Oil Company, and the Skelly Oil Company, in addition to older rivals like Gulf and The Texas Company. Many of these companies engaged in competitive practices against Indiana Standard similar to those encountered by California Standard in the West. In Jersey's home market, too, a larger number of independents, great and small, were aggressively making their way. The share of the gasoline trade held by outlets of the Jersey company along the Atlantic seaboard declined by more than one-sixth between 1912 and 1917.[92]

California Standard, like most other Standard companies, had entered a new era in which its former sales dominance was gradually reduced to a position of leadership. During the war decade the huge increase in demand for most oil products, far too great to be supplied by any one company, had encouraged the growth of rivals to an extent without parallel prior to 1911. A struggle for sales among a larger number of powerful companies had become the pattern for the future.

XX

THE HUMAN ELEMENT

Surveying employee relations, the *Standard Oil Bulletin* in 1919 wrote of American industry:[1]

In the tremendous development of . . . the last half century, attention in the main has been focussed on *things*. While mechanical processes and systems have been brought to a high point of efficiency, study of the *human element* which is inseparable from organized effort of men has been much neglected. . . . During the past few years, however, the guiding spirits in industry have wakened to a realization that no matter how perfect a system may be, it cannot operate at fullest efficiency unless the human workers who are a part of it are in accord. . . . As the army must maintain its morale, so must the industrial organization have its *esprit de corps;* and it must at least be hopeful. For best results it should be enthusiastic.

The old Standard combination had long had a generally good reputation among its workers. Its companies had usually matched, if not bettered, the wages, hours, and working conditions of industrial firms offering comparable employment. Well before 1911 they had improved the lot of salaried employees by such benefits as paid vacations and pensions. The companies, moreover, had never reacted hysterically against unionism, even though they refused to grant recognition to organized labor. The use of labor spies and the intimidation of union members, so common in that era, was no part of the Standard pattern. That Standard "had been from the beginning a considerate employer and has enjoyed a greater measure of employee loyalty than most of the large combinations" was the considered judgment recorded in John R. Common's famed *History of Labor in the United States.*[2]

California Standard could take pride in this heritage, but it could hardly afford to stand on the record. Growing manpower needs after 1911 resulted in an employee roster of 16,359 at the end of 1919, nearly triple the number of eight years before.[3] Most of this increase came after 1916, as is shown in Table 21.

World War I created an intense competition for labor. A worker was able to shop around, and he was apt to stay with a job only if it maintained its relative attractiveness. Standard could not rest satisfied with the simple recruiting practices and the wages, hours, and job benefits of an earlier day if it wished to keep a competitive edge in the labor market.

Table 21: Average Number of Employees of California Standard
During 1913, 1916, and 1919

	1913	*1916*	*1919*
Producing	1,067	1,247	2,540
Pipeline	1,288	892	1,165
Manufacturing	2,235	2,773	4,449
Marine	300	397	539
Sales	1,558	2,626	5,607
Home office	407	659	1,025
Total	6,875	8,594	15,325
Total Payroll	$6,800,000 (est.)	$10,561,749	$28,912,593

Source: Historical statistics, Comptroller's Department.

The humanitarian outlook of many executives reinforced practical arguments for improved conditions of employment. W. S. Rheem, Fred Hillman, and H. M. Storey, for example, who had themselves risen from the ranks, were particularly receptive to new ideas. So was the company's most powerful stockholder, John D. Rockefeller, Jr., for whom good labor relations became almost a passion following the Ludlow "massacre" in 1914 on the property of the Colorado Fuel & Iron Company and strikes at Jersey Standard's Bayonne refinery during 1915 and 1916. R. C. Warner, a prominent former director, recalled a luncheon at which the younger Rockefeller told the Board that he was not especially interested in the business side of the company, its operations, earnings, and so on. He knew a good job was being done. "What I want to know," Rockefeller said, "is what the company is doing for its employees."[4]

With men like these influencing company policy, it is not surprising that numerous significant advances in employee relations marked the years following 1911. Personnel policies were revised; wages, hours, and working conditions were made more attractive; and job benefits were extended and improved. Standard's management made these advances without discussion with any union and with little reference to either state or national governments. The company's relations with its men, in short, were paternalistic. And, as we shall see, to most employees such paternalism was highly congenial.

2

In personnel relations, as in other areas of activity, the independence California Standard achieved in 1911 brought no sudden departures from past policy. San Francisco merely replaced 26 Broadway as the center of power and policy, with each department head authorizing new jobs in his department and passing upon increases and salaries. Employment policies were few and general. They consisted of little more than a tendency to hire native-born Americans, few women, and mainly men under forty. Refinery foremen, district sales managers, and field superintendents in the producing and pipeline departments did most of the hiring and firing. "Little kings," they did pretty much as they pleased, so long as they conducted their operations efficiently.[5]

The summer of 1913 saw a faint move toward improved personnel practice when Standard established a Bureau (later Department) of Employment for its head office operations. H. G. Morrow, who for thirty years had been active in the oil fields, was made its chief. At first, seemingly, the Bureau amounted to little more than a clearing house. It received applications and hired on order from the departments, which were not required to use the new service. For years many of them continued to do most of their own hiring.[6]

The tight labor market during World War I gave the Department of Employment under Morrow's successor, George F. Eggers, its first big chance. White collar employees became hard to find. In the spring of 1917 the company raised the age limit for employment from forty to forty-five before suspending it entirely and began to hire women in larger numbers.[7] More and more the headquarters sought the aid of its specialized employment office.

At Richmond, where foremen could no longer find enough qualified men seeking work at the Main Gate, in March of 1917 the company set up a Bureau of Employment staffed by two refinery veterans, Ephraim Jardine and R. H. Ivory, to do recruiting. The old free and easy practice of permitting foremen to fire, especially skilled workers, was also checked, as the Bureau started giving "exit" interviews designed to save men for the refinery by offering them other jobs or, occasionally, the same job under a different foreman. The management began to devote greater attention to employee grievances, and workers were reminded that the adjustment of such matters did not stop with the foreman.[8]

Personnel policy advanced farther at Richmond, the site of the largest concentration of employees, than at any other company installation, but nearly everywhere the desire was manifest to improve channels of communication and to lessen worker grievances. At El Segundo and Bakersfield the refinery foreman's right to fire was also curbed. Foremen were instructed, too, "not to use the men roughly." The fact that promotions were frequent during these years and usually from the ranks— "through their overalls," so Mr. Hillman put it—contributed to a greater sense of well-being. And in all departments transfers rather than discharges were advocated as a means of settling personality clashes between men and their bosses.[9]

Much remained to be done, however. A five-week survey in 1920, made at the suggestion of John D. Rockefeller, Jr., by A. H. Lichty, an industrial relations executive from the Colorado Fuel & Iron Company, brought forth some of the sour notes. In some cases, employees felt that the power of the foreman was still formidable. "I can't afford to take a chance of getting in bad by taking up things over my foreman's head," said one stillman. "We, therefore, either settle it with the foreman or endure it." Another commented, "I haven't the courage to take . . . matters up with my boss, and I fear if I went over his head . . . my boss would not promote me when my time came." Others also viewed skeptically the path of promotion. Family connections, friendship with a boss, or skill on the baseball diamond or in some other company-sponsored activity frequently seemed to count for more than seniority and competence.[10]

A few weeks before the Lichty survey, Standard had begun to approach the problem of personnel relations in a larger way, for in May, 1920, it set up a company-wide Personnel Department under R. H. Ivory, formerly of the Bureau of Employment at Richmond.[11] This marked the first attempt to unite all personnel activities, from employment to the growing benefit programs, under a single head. The department was to make its way slowly, but nevertheless it was another affirmative response to the continuing challenges of employee relations.

3

Over the years the Personnel Department would call management's attention to many matters affecting employee morale, but not to such basic factors as wages, hours, and working conditions. Their central significance had long been apparent, and California Standard carried further the generally liberal policies that had existed prior to independence.

The wages paid during the era of control by 26 Broadway were determined primarily by the going rates in the western labor market. For most jobs, Standard at least met the local scale. Frequently, it paid more. In 1903, for example, John Page advised the New York headquarters to increase the pay of the pipeliners: "I find that we are paying no higher wages than other companies. . . . For the best results, we should pay our men a little more than other people, and then the men will be anxious and earnest to do better work for us in order to retain their positions, instead of . . . showing that feeling of indifference, as some of them now do."[12] 26 Broadway was quick to take his advice.

For a time the Producing Department offered a significant exception to this approach. Prior to 1911 wages of drilling crews were frequently lower than those of competitors, leading to raids and turnover. Through most of 1907, when the department was struggling along, Walton Young complained to San Francisco of his difficulty in holding skilled men at Pico. He got little sympathy. To Young's requests for better pay, producing manager John Eckbert replied, on one occasion, "If the men do not like it, let them quit [even] if we have to shut down the wells."[13] Under Hillman's strong hand, however, the company reversed its tight-fisted policy after 1911 and began to pay premium rates. Within a few years the journal of the Chamber of Mines and Oils, a trade association of California producers, was noting, none too happily, that Standard "had a wage scale slightly in excess of that paid by other companies." Producing employees, in fact, enjoyed a higher average monthly income than those of any other department within Standard, with pipeline, manufacturing, sales, and marine employees trailing behind.[14]

One more thing remains to be noted about Standard's payroll. In the war years of unbridled inflation, the company steadily hiked salaries and wages. Between 1914 and 1919 the average monthly income for employees increased from $87.95 to $157.22, a jump of approximately 80 per cent that almost exactly paralleled the rise in the cost of living. When inflation was at its height, between May, 1916 and September, 1919, the general wage boosts amounted to 45 per cent. In addition, Standard made other lesser adjustments, including the establishment of a company-wide $4 per day minimum in September, 1918.[15]

The times were also ripe for reductions in the work week, a rather general movement of these years. Consider the conditions in 1907, when 26 Broadway was still calling the tune. Early that year H. M. Tilford responded to a threat of a Bay Area ironworkers' strike for the eight-hour day by bluntly informing Scofield, "It has been found from a practical standpoint not to meet the eight hour system in refineries and we are opposed . . . because it is impractical."[16] At this time about three-fourths of the Richmond payroll, comprising skilled workers ("mechanics"), day laborers, and clerks, worked a nine-hour day six days a week. Most of the remainder, the "shift men," who were tied to the refining process, had a harder lot. They alternated each week between a thirteen-hour day and an eleven-hour night, averaging eighty-four hours per week. At the time of a changeover, the men of the day shift worked a straight twenty-four hours, giving the night shift twenty-four hours off. This pattern was much the same as that in other industries of the era, like iron and steel, requiring round-the-clock operation. Yet in the oil industry the long week of the shift men was not quite as harsh as it sounds, for looking after the stills was a relatively easy task. The men, moreover, usually managed to nap a little during the night. Shift work, so some mechanics claimed, was a "lazy man's job" despite the long hours.[17] Much of the field work in the producing and pipeline departments was also carried on by two shifts, twelve hours each day seven days a week. Superintendents were ordered to see that there was no let-up while drilling a well; so many delays, like "stuck" casing, could so readily occur while the hole was being put down.[18] Office employees had it easier. They put in ten hours a day six days a week at most field establishments, and approximately nine hours a day with a slightly shorter Saturday at the San Francisco headquarters.[19]

Step by step, changes came in the old work patterns. A first advance occurred at least by the beginning of 1908, for despite Tilford's statement, the Richmond ironworkers by that time were on an eight-hour day.[20] After 1911, there were more sweeping changes. Following the lead of Jersey Standard, the California company in May, 1913, put all refinery employees on the six-day week and in August, 1913, abandoned the twenty-four-hour shift. Three years later, in November, 1916, Standard announced a company-wide eight-hour day beginning on January 1, 1917, accompanied by a small pay increase. Other oil companies had preceded Standard in giving an eight-hour day to some of their labor force. Jersey Standard, for example, had adopted the shorter day for refinery workers after the Bayonne strike of 1915, as did Kansas Standard at its Neodesha refinery a few weeks later. Ohio Standard may have had an eight-hour day at the Cleveland refinery even earlier. But no major oil company had as yet put all employees on an eight-hour basis. Largely as a result of this move, the roster of California Standard jumped from 9,450 at the end of 1916 to 12,442 a year later, an increase of nearly one-third.[21]

The shorter day was most revolutionary in the oil fields, for drilling crews had been working twelve hours a day from the birth of the industry. This abrupt break with the past most oilmen believed would be costly, but, as a matter of fact, Standard's drilling crews, with less fatigue and heightened morale, achieved new peaks of efficiency. During the first six months of the eight-hour day, according to K. R. Kingsbury, ". . . the labor cost per foot of hole drilled was less than for the corresponding six months under the old 12-hour day, notwithstanding that there was an apparent 50 per cent increase in the payroll." The number of feet drilled on each eight-hour shift in 1917 averaged 30 per cent more than the former average for a twelve-hour shift.[22]

The company's next move was to shorten the work week, except for drilling crews, who were expected to stay on the job. Standard held to the theory that "the fewer men having to do with a well the better." Not until 1928 did drilling crews get the six-day week. All other shift men, however, were given a day off every week, beginning with January, 1919, and at about the same time the week for most office workers was reduced to five and a half days.[23] The forty-four and forty-eight hour schedules of 1919 were a remarkable contrast to the fifty-four and eighty-four hours worked by many of the same men three or four years earlier.

The coming of a better day for the employee brought other changes. It caused a widespread interest in working and living conditions. Take the problem in the field, for example. Perhaps 20 per cent of Standard's labor force was located at isolated pipeline stations or in the oil fields scattered through Central and Southern California. To these workers room and board were almost as important as wages and hours. In 1903 the company had erected at each of the pump stations several four-room cottages for married men and a bunkhouse with a recreation room for single men, who were boarded at the home of one of the families. Before long, and with company support, these stations began to bloom like desert oases with trees, lawns, and flowers. During the teens H. M. Storey, the pipeline director, hired a professional gardener to help with the landscaping. Every year he awarded a plaque and a small bonus to employees of the station judged most attractive in each pipeline division.[24]

The camps of the Producing Department, which except for Pico were established considerably later than the pipeline stations, offer a similar story. As Standard first entered into producing in a large way, Colonel John J. Carter in 1908 exhorted Eckbert, his second-in-command, "Treat the employees well, pay them well, house them well, demand and you will receive the best work possible from the men. . . ." He laid out the details of construction and operation for a camp at Coalinga which must have been a model for its day. Camps acquired along with the purchase of producing properties were usually not so impressive, but these the company improved. "The whole outfit looks like a ramshackle affair," a Standard man wrote of one Kern County acquisition, "but [it] will be different when the Standard Oil system gets to work."[25]

Standard provided married men, comprising the larger part of the producing force, with small cottages; the single men it put up in bunkhouses.

A bunkhouse at the most poorly equipped camps consisted of a single large room, with from ten to twenty men sleeping in bunks, sometimes in tiers. At more elaborate camps, each man had a private room. The Montebello camp, which was perhaps the most attractive of all, was well landscaped, with rows of trim, white buildings bordering a cement walk fronting on a lawn. At some of the Valley camps, where water was scarce, a garden at the foreman's cottage was the only touch of green. The company also built recreation halls at each permanent location, where men could read, write, play cards or billiards, listen to the phonograph, or play the piano in their off hours. Occasionally, dances were held in the halls. The buildings were usually steam heated and were screened against mosquitoes.[26]

Because its camps were frequently large, the Producing Department usually operated kitchens and dining rooms, where three meals a day were served and a midnight meal for the night shift. Meat was a staple at every meal. The food, which was delivered fresh to the kitchens each day, was of good quality and reasonably well prepared, for Standard knew the value of a good "cookhouse."[27]

There appears to be little doubt that Standard was leading most oil companies everywhere in wages, hours, and working conditions. Comparable wage data with other companies for this era are difficult to find, but it seems probable that Standard would not have suffered from a comparison. Certainly, it compared favorably in its own region. The case in regard to hours is clearer. The Carter Oil Company, which was Jersey Standard's producing subsidiary in the Mid-Continent, for example, did not adopt the eight-hour day in the oil fields until 1925. The changeover came even more slowly in Texas, where the Humble Oil & Refining Company stayed with the seven-day week in producing until 1928 and with the twelve-hour day until 1930. In housing, too, there was a notable difference. When W. S. Smullin joined Humble in 1919 as vice president in charge of producing in North Texas, after serving as superintendent of Standard's Southern California division, he built a camp that seemed sheer luxury to the Texas oilhands. Humble constructed no more such camps, and a decade or more passed before this leader among oil companies in the Southwest made substantial improvements in housing its producing employees.[28]

4

Beyond wages, hours, and quarters, Standard broadened employee horizons by a gradually expanding program of benefits. They embraced such matters as paid annual vacations, protection for the worker and his family from the hazards of old age, sickness, accident, and death, recognition for long years of service, recreational and educational activities, and discounts on company products. Standard was a front runner in granting job benefits, a manifestation so marked in industry that it became known as "welfare capitalism."[29]

Within a few years of independence the company made a change in personnel practice that increased enormously the impact of its benefit program. This reform, which, so far as we know, was without precedent in American industry, consisted of a gradual elimination of the historic discrimination in status between wage and salaried men. In 1911 most of Standard's work force was paid by the day. Even though these men might have been employees for years, their relationship to the company was limited almost wholly to receiving payment for the number of days worked; unlike salaried men, they were rarely eligible for any company benefits. Gradually, between January, 1914, and July, 1918, wage workers with a year's service were put on salary and given the same status as managerial and office employees. Skilled workers at the refineries were the first to feel this improvement, followed by pipeline, sales, and producing employees and refinery laborers. By the end of 1918 three-fourths of the employees were on salary.[30]

This far-reaching change had a powerful effect on morale. Secure in mind that their incomes would not fluctuate from one pay period to another, some former wage workers felt encouraged to buy homes and settle down. But, above all, the men valued their new equality with managerial and office employees in regard to vacations, holidays, and the growing list of job benefits. Luther Dimm, manager at El Segundo, a few years later summarized some of the outstanding effects of vacations, the most highly prized of the benefits, as follows: "Our men work better. . . . A vacation makes a man feel more important—when he is away . . . he boosts the Company—it causes men to stick better."[31]

Vacations, the oldest of the benefits, had been granted salaried employees before the turn of the century. The week or ten days leave customary in those years (the record is none too clear) by 1911 had been extended to two weeks and, in addition, white collar workers received nine holidays. Except for minor adjustments in the number of holidays, this pattern continued unchanged for nearly three decades. During the early years pipeliners at pump stations appear to have been the one significant exception to the general rule of no vacations for wage workers. Because of the isolation of many of the stations, these men had been given two weeks a year as early as 1906.[32]

Standard's original pension plan was also a carry-over from the pre-

Producing Department's Midway camp

Producing Department's Montebello camp

dissolution era. The program, a copy from the Jersey parent, was adopted by Iowa Standard in 1905, but no employee was retired until after California Standard took over its business the next year. Among the great corporations of the West, only the Southern Pacific Company, with a plan set up in 1903, appears to have preceded the Iowa company in providing for retired workers.[33] California Standard began its pension history in the spring of 1908 when it, too, adopted the Jersey program to cover the retirement of Morris Hartnett, a still foreman at Richmond, and E. A. Cushing, the first special agent at Oakland and later a sales executive in the Northwest. The following year, with the consent of 26 Broadway, the company broadened its program to include Pacific Coast Oil men employed prior to 1900.[34]

Until 1918 the program was a somewhat meager affair. An employee at 65 who had given twenty years of "satisfactory service" was pensioned at 50 per cent of his average annual pay during his last ten years of employment for his first year of retirement; thereafter the amount was reduced to 25 per cent. A 20-year employee between the ages of 60 and 64 could also request an early retirement. If the request was granted, by a provision that today seems curious, he received the 50 per cent rate until he became 65, when it dropped to 25 per cent.[35] In July, 1918, however, Standard revised its program along more liberal lines. The age ceiling was reduced to 55 for men and to 50 for women with 30 years service; for 20-year men the normal retirement age continued to be 65, but 20-year women could retire at 60. The company also improved its system by computing the amount of pension at 2 per cent of the average annual pay during the final five years of employment multiplied by the years of service, a sum paid the annuitant without reduction during his lifetime. In addition, the new plan formally recognized what had been a long-standing practice: a special allowance, at the discretion of the Board, for any employee who had been incapacitated after serving the company at least ten years. As under the earlier program, no employee contribution was collected for these benefits.[36] Because Standard's work force was a relatively young group, pension rolls were small; until 1919 there had been only twenty-four annuitants, and twenty-three on the special allowance list.[37] But the pension program, in time, would pay out to far larger numbers.

Standard helped workers meet hazards other than old age. In 1914 it established a death benefit providing six months' salary to dependents of employees who had been on the roll from five to ten years and a full year's salary in cases of more than ten years' service. In 1918 the program was liberalized to give dependents three months' salary if the employee had been with the company a year, and a month's pay for each additional year up to a maximum of ten years.[38]

The sick also caught the attentive eye of management. Standard rarely docked a salaried employee with a good record for an occasional few days of illness, but it had adopted no formal policy until 1916, when a comprehensive program was drawn up, granting from ten days' sick leave for employees who had one year's service up to four months for those who had served over ten years. Two years later, the leave was increased to a minimum of two weeks following the first year and a maximum of six months after ten years.[39] Nor did Standard stop there. During the flu epidemic of 1918, the company granted sick leave to any stricken employee regardless of his term of service. In some cases, as at El Segundo, it "provided medical service, aided in securing nurses, made personal visits, provided financial assistance. . . , and guaranteed payment of bills at the hospital." At Richmond it set up a visiting nurse service.[40]

Safety was an area of employee welfare where the interests of the company and workers probably most clearly coincided. An accident could cost the company a good worker, at least for a short term; it might also result in a harassing and costly law suit. For the worker, the damaging effects of an accident hardly require comment. And accidents, especially in the oil fields and refineries, were an ever-present hazard.

Prior to 1911 the company's accident policy was only loosely defined. Customarily, Standard paid for medical care. Frequently, it also paid wages up to two weeks or more in cases where the employee's record was good and where he was not clearly at fault. Because of unfriendly juries, Standard in self-protection zealously collected affidavits from witnesses. If wages were paid to an injured man, the company usually asked for a written statement freeing it from responsibility.[41]

A keen interest in employee welfare, coupled with the petty annoyances of court suits, made Standard a warm supporter of the first California workmen's compensation act passed in 1911 while Hiram Johnson was governor. The law, which employers could accept or not, as they chose, set up a formula fixed by the state for determining awards in accident cases. Standard was glad to accept the plan, for it promised fair treatment for everyone and, touching a sore point, meant "more money for employees and families and less for the lawyers," said the *Standard Oil Bulletin*.[42] An act of 1913 made workmen's compensation compulsory, with the state offering employers the option of insuring with a newly established state agency. But Standard, which viewed dubiously any three-party relationship, continued to be a self-insurer in order to deal directly with its men. The company, moreover, usually paid more than the state's requirement of 65 per cent of the weekly wage. It gave injured men who had been employed for a year full pay for two weeks and frequently for longer periods, and paid accident benefits outside California at least equivalent to its practice in its home state, even when there was no legal obligation to do so. Standard's total accident payments in 1919 amounted to $201,432, approximately 24 per cent more than the statutes required. When an injured employee could no longer do his former work, the company found him another job at as close to his former pay as possible.[43]

The California statute of 1913 also ordered the state's Industrial Accident Commission to establish safety standards for major industries. Standard men from time to time were called to sit with the Commission as "advisers" for the petroleum industry. Many of the regulations issued by the Commission were, in fact, nothing more than a current practice of Standard.[44] The company had early established safety committees in each of the oil fields and at the refineries, and had regularly invited suggestions from employees. By 1913 the five major departments each had a safety inspector who reported directly to the manager, and field executives were supplied with copies of *Safety Engineering,* a monthly magazine of the insurance fraternity devoted to accident prevention.[45]

Concern for safety was probably greatest in the oil fields, for accidents were common around the drilling rigs. A derrick man, handling the ponderous twenty-foot lengths of drill pipe high above the ground, had an especially hazardous job. A misstep could send him hurtling to his death. Some simple rules had already been established by 1917 when the versatile C. C. Scharpenberg became the Producing Department's first safety engineer and boiler inspector. The men, for example, were forbidden to smoke or carry matches near a gas or oil well. As early as 1914, the company had required derrick men to wear safety belts while working aloft.[46] Scharpenberg centralized and powered the safety program. Collecting detailed information on each accident and classifying them by type and by job, he circulated his findings among the field superintendents, pointing out accidents that seemed avoidable. During his first months he warned against the use of gauntlet gloves (which could be caught in a moving line or in machinery) and recommended the use of goggles to avoid eye injuries. He devised, too, the company's first safety ladder for derricks: four wire ropes hung vertically and bracketed to the ladder at intervals to create a sort of cage through which the derrick man could climb with less fear of falling.[47]

Concern over safety also resulted in the establishment of emergency hospitals, with Taft in 1914 being the site of the first. The next year Standard built a larger hospital at Richmond, and by 1918 it had opened another at El Segundo. In 1920 a Medical Department with a greater range of functions, including an annual examination for all employees, would grow from these hospitals.[48]

In still other ways Standard's executives worked to strengthen the bond between the employee and his company. Late in 1915 K. R. Kingsbury persuaded the Board to establish an "Order of Service" giving recognition to senior employees. Gold pins were awarded, stamped with the monogram "S.O.Co." and embellished with stars and diamonds indicating the length of employment, to employees who had served at least ten years with Standard or its predecessors. At the first presentation, made in January, 1916, John E. Miller, foreman of the can factory at Richmond, received a pin for forty-eight years of service and W. S. Miller a forty-year pin. A new pin was given each worker on every five-year anniversary following his initial ten years, and thirty-year men were brought to San Francisco so that the presentation could be made by Standard's president. "Us boys are very proud of our pins," was the simple affirmation of one grizzled veteran.[49]

The company also supported an increasingly broad range of recreational activities. The "jollifications" held annually early in the century for home office and refinery personnel at East Shore Park on San Francisco Bay were forerunners of a host of outings, entertainments, dances, and athletic teams. The Richmond refinery, which had long known the friendly interest of W. S. Rheem, was probably the scene of the largest number of these activities. Its band, organized in 1914, was soon playing occasionally during the noon hour on the refinery green. There were also numerous clubs, as well as baseball, basketball, bowling, and horseshoe teams. Taft and the Bakersfield and El Segundo refineries were centers for similar programs. Few installations were without some company-sponsored recreation.[50]

Standard underwrote an activity of a different order when in 1914 an Education Department was established in the San Francisco headquarters to help employees develop skills and to give them a keener awareness of the company's operations. One course, "The Petroleum Industry on the Pacific Coast," included lectures by specialists in each phase of the oil industry. Other courses were designed to turn out better clerks, better stenographers, and better office boys, and some were available by correspondence to men in the field. By the end of 1918 more than 800, ranging from chief clerks to office boys, had enrolled.[51]

Standard's benefit program also included discounts on company products, which were attractive to the increasing number of car owners among its rank and file,[52] and, more unusual, supplemental allowances for families of employees who had entered the Armed Forces during World War I. Beginning late in 1917, Standard quietly surveyed the financial condition of the families of enlisted men who had been with the company for at least a year. In cases of hardship, grants were made up to an amount sufficient to close the gap between the man's pay and allotment in the Armed Forces and the salary he would have received from Standard. The company spent $107,500 in this way.[53]

5

Colonel Rheem used to tell the men, so one old-timer recalled, "Whatever other companies can do for you, our Company can do and will do." Because this statement accurately reflected management's policy, unions had little lure for most employees, though they were free to join if they chose. Many skilled workers did so, perhaps because of pride in their craft or because of a desire to maintain union membership in case they should seek employment elsewhere later on. Boilermakers organized a local at Richmond as early as June, 1902, while the refinery was still under construction. By the time of World War I there were locals of machinists and other ironworkers at Taft, Bakersfield, and El Segundo. Many of the firemen and sailors aboard the tankers, too, were organized.[54]

But Standard had no intention of bargaining with a union, and rarely did a union pressure for recognition. Rather, most union men seemed well satisfied with the wages, hours, and working conditions and were willing to let well enough alone. There was a sort of "silent neutrality," so an investigator reported in 1920, between unions and the company.[55]

The spring of 1907 supplied one of the rare moments of strife. In the favorable environment of high employment brought about by the rebuilding of San Francisco, ironworkers around San Francisco Bay decided to strike. In September, 1906, they had gained a reduction in the workday from ten to nine hours, which was already the rule at the Richmond refinery; on May 1, 1907, nearly 3,000 ironworkers struck for an eight-hour day and a wage increase. Richmond did not escape.[56]

Scofield, who had seen the storm brewing, wrote H. M. Tilford as early as the middle of March for counsel. The New Yorker replied that Standard had never suffered labor troubles because it dealt directly with its men rather than with labor unions. "Ask them to continue their work without . . . making any disturbance," Tilford wrote, "until it has been definitely settled what the ruling rates are in the neighborhood, with the understanding that when the ruling rates are established they will receive them." The eight-hour day, however, he stigmatized as "impractical." This message Rheem relayed to Luther Dimm, the refinery superintendent. "Under no circumstances," Dimm was told, would the company grant the eight-hour day. If the employees tried to gain their goal by a strike, Rheem went on, the company would resist, "no matter what it might cost." When a strike became certain, Rheem further told the refinery superintendent, "You may deal with the men as individuals but in no other way." Two weeks passed before the strikers returned to the refinery, apparently with an understanding that Standard would accept the terms of any general settlement between the ironworkers and the California Metal Trades Association. When the big strike ended in a compromise at the end of May providing for a gradual shift to the eight-hour day over eighteen months following December 1, 1908, Standard did not require its men to wait so long. Instead, its ironworkers (comprising around 10 per cent of the refinery work force) were all granted the shorter day at least by January 1, 1908, and perhaps as early as the preceding June.[57]

It was another decade before Standard was again touched by labor warfare. Even more than in 1907, the touch was marginal. In 1917 an Oil & Gas Well Workers' Union arose suddenly in the oil fields, powered largely by the desire of other workers for the same wages and hours Standard had voluntarily offered its men at the beginning of that year. Standard's establishment of the eight-hour day along with a 5 per cent pay raise had a great impact on the California industry. "In effect," the Secretary of Labor later reported," [the union] asked that the conditions prevailing at the Standard Oil . . . should be introduced by the independents."[58] The *Los Angeles Times* likewise believed that Standard's actions had stimulated the union movement. "Some months ago," it editorialized bitterly, "the Standard Oil Company of California announced the eight-hour day. . . . The directors were animated only by good motives, but their action has been the source of the greatest aid to the agitators, and the harm to the small companies will be great. With its enormous resources the Standard can afford what others cannot." The heavy demand for oil products caused by World War I also helped the union's drive. By April, 1917, according to the Secretary of Labor, approximately 50 per cent of the men in the California fields were organized.[59]

Meeting in a convention at Bakersfield in mid-July, the union drew up a series of demands. First and foremost, it listed the eight-hour day. Although a few producers had already followed Standard's lead in granting the shorter day, a far larger number sought to weaken union pressure by offering to meet another worker demand, a $4 minimum daily wage, in return for the maintenance of the historic twelve-hour day. The union, for its part, after receiving an overwhelming vote of approval from its members, requested producers to meet for a bargaining session on November 1 at Bakersfield to discuss the eight-hour day, a $4 minimum wage, union membership, and other matters. When no producers appeared, disgruntled union men began to talk of a strike.[60]

A prolonged strike during wartime in so important an oil state as California would have been a national disaster. Fortunately, to deal with this threat the federal government had at hand a Mediation Commission set up early in the fall of 1917 by President Wilson, with W. B. Wilson, the Secretary of Labor, as chairman. In mid-November the Commission dispatched Verner Z. Reed, one of its members and a prominent Wyoming producer, to California. After conferring with the union at Bakersfield, Reed sent a telegram to the Chamber of Mines and Oils, an association of California producers, asking that "representatives of all companies affected by labor difficulties" meet with him at Santa Barbara on November 23. The Chamber, in turn, got in touch with non-member producers, including Standard, prompting Hillman to reply direct to Reed that Standard was experiencing no labor troubles and would not attend. The Commissioner, nevertheless, asked Hillman to send a man to advise him on "technical questions." Hillman agreed to make the trip.[61]

Reed's conclusions appear to have been greatly influenced by the wage and hour data supplied by Hillman and by their private discussions. The Commissioner accepted the main worker demands. He recommended a $4 minimum wage in the oil fields to begin on December 1, 1917, and an eight-hour day to become effective a month later. The union membership issue Reed met by suggesting that any worker be permitted to join a union affiliated with the American Federation of Labor, or not, as he chose, free from compulsion or discrimination.[62] After both sides had agreed to these recommendations, the Mediation Commission set up a Federal Oil Inspection Board in California to administer them and to suggest changes when necessary. Two Board members, L. P. St. Clair and G. M. Swindell, were from the Chamber of Mines and Oils; a third, Judge W. F. Byrne of Bakersfield, served as labor's representative.[63]

Reed obviously valued highly Hillman's assistance. Within three weeks he was asking that Standard's producing chief come to Houston to help arrange a settlement of a strike in the Texas and Louisiana fields, an assignment Hillman felt obliged to decline, ostensibly for family reasons.[64] And when at the end of 1917 the Mediation Commission considered extending its California recommendations to include pipeline and refinery workers, Reed asked the Federal Oil Inspection Board to consult with Hillman. "He suggests that we have discussion of matter with you . . . ," the Board wired Hillman. "We will be glad to forward your conclusions or if you prefer you may wire direct to the Commissioner." Hillman's reply, sent to the Board and to Reed, was one of disapproval. He argued that there had been no unrest, "so far as we know," among refinery and pipeline workers and, more vigorously, that the refineries had "no community of interest with the oilfields. . . ." Their environment was "entirely different," he maintained, for the larger refineries were a part of the manufacturing communities of San Francisco and Los Angeles. Hillman believed that their wage rates should be linked, not with the oil fields, but with those of the surrounding urban areas. He also pointed out that a mediation board—the U.S. Shipbuilding Labor Adjustment Board—was already working on a wage scale for mechanics and laborers in the San Francisco Bay Area. Too many agencies dealing with the same problem could cause complications.[65]

Reed apparently was again influenced by Hillman's advice. Although the Mediation Commission in January, 1918, extended the jurisdiction of the Federal Oil Inspection Board to include pipeline workers, refinery workers continued outside. The refineries did not come under the Board's authority until December, 1918, following a petition from the oil workers' union. By that time the union, which had made considerable headway in a number of California refineries, had been redesignated as the AFL's International Oil Field, Gas Well, and Refinery Workers Union.[66]

But Standard, though willing to advise the government through Hillman, desired no government intervention in its own affairs. It kept as clear as possible of the Federal Oil Inspection Board, according it, at best, merely token recognition. The company maintained that it had no dispute with employees prior to the creation of the Board, and that the Board's directives governing wages, hours, and working conditions were already a part of Standard's practice. The only adjustment Standard found necessary was a tiny raise of $1 per month for roustabouts and pumpers, effective December 1, 1917, to meet the $4 minimum in the oil fields.[67] When the Chamber of Mines and Oils called on Standard to join in a pledge of "full and complete cooperation" with the government, shortly before the Federal Oil Inspection Board was appointed,

Hillman failed to reply. And when the Board asked Standard to supply it with information on the wages paid for each class of work in producing, refining, and pipeline transportation as of November 30, 1917, Standard refused the request.[68] It was no more cooperative after the Board assumed jurisdiction of the refineries at the end of 1918. One other large California concern, the Union Oil Company, apparently followed the same course.[69]

Standard went its own way, though it usually made certain that wages and hours were as good or better than those specified by the Federal Oil Inspection Board. Only once was the company challenged. In the spring of 1918 the union charged Standard with paying less than the $4 minimum to pipeline laborers. The charge was true. The correspondence within the company indicates, however, that there had been a failure to interpret correctly the Board's pipeline ruling. Standard later brought all pipeline laborers to the $4 rate, but it did not grant the men back pay amounting to almost $12,000.[70] To have done so would have been a public acknowledgment of the influence of the Federal Oil Inspection Board in determining its labor relations.

The Federal Oil Inspection Board became far more disturbed late in September, 1918, when Standard announced a 10 per cent wage advance for 13,000 employees earning less than $4,000 per year. The increase, which was timed to coincide with the government's Fourth Liberty Loan bond drive, was also designed to offset rising living costs and to restore the purchasing power of employees to the level of January 1, 1916. The Board carried a protest to Mark Requa, Director of the Oil Division of the United States Fuel Administration, claiming that Standard's action was upsetting the Board's wage program. But a brief reflection convinced government officials that a storm of criticism would surely arise if they attempted to force Standard to revoke a voluntary wage tender amounting to approximately $2,000,000 annually.[71]

As the oil workers' union grew in strength, it recognized that the small membership among Standard employees was its "weakest link." Beginning in 1919, led by its energetic secretary for California, Walter J. Yarrow, the union started an all-out drive to organize Standard. Employees were bombarded with literature. Standard's workers were accused of accepting "what is doled out to them," of being "complete dependents upon their employers," and "a stumbling block . . . to their fellow workers. . . ."[72] The union asserted that Standard had "more or less successfully drawn the wool of paternalism over its employees' eyes," and that "the satisfactory wages and conditions enjoyed by Standard employees [were] due to no other influence than the . . . union with which the company has refused to deal."[73] Although Standard interposed no overt barrier, even permitting organizers to speak with the men on company premises at some pipeline stations, the union had only limited success. A considerable number of relative newcomers to Standard's payroll did sign up, especially in the producing and pipeline departments, but the union was able to attract few of the older men.[74] Most older employees were apparently satisfied with the results of a paternalism that had long predated the union and, in fact, had helped create the environment in which the union got its start. They may also have believed that the wage increases for which the union took credit were merely the continuance of a company policy, begun well before 1917, of protecting the employees from the effects of inflation.

As the organizing drive bogged down, the union turned to other means to force recognition. A boycott of Standard Oil products, suggested by the Kern River local in March, 1919, seemed one possibility. Locals comprised largely of Standard employees, like those at Fellows in the San Joaquin Valley and at the El Segundo refinery, opposed such a move.[75] The movement for a boycott did not gain powerful support until late in the summer of 1919 after Standard had refused to join most of the other California oil companies in negotiating wage rates with the union through the Mediation Commission.[76] Walter Yarrow told union members at Coalinga in mid-August:[77]

> There is only one way to reach the Standard Oil and that is through their pocketbook. $20,000 per month of Standard products are purchased by the workers, and this should cease. A resolution to this effect will be presented at your next meeting; also that you request all other organized bodies to cease purchasing Standard Oil products. Further, we will not patronize any merchant who patronizes the Standard Oil.

By November both the union and the California State Federation of Labor had placed Standard on the "unfair" list. The company's machinists at Taft, who were 100 per cent organized, protested, however, claiming that "wages, conditions and hours are as good or superior to any other corporation or company; also the Standard Oil Company does not discriminate against organized labor." Five months later the Central Labor Council at Taft adopted a similar set of resolutions, pointing to "wages . . . as high or higher than the union scale," to sickness and disability benefits, paid vacations, and no discrimination against union members. "The purpose of organized labor," the Council concluded, "is to get better wages and conditions for the working people, and as the Standard Oil Company is giving these better wages and conditions, we contend that the boycott is unjust, not only against the Standard Oil Company but against those union members working for them." The boycott, in any case, seems to have been a hit-and-miss affair. Within a year Yarrow was vigorously denouncing members of his union for buying from Standard. And the boycott apparently influenced Standard's policy toward the union not at all.[78]

By 1921 the union faced a problem far more serious than organizing Standard, for the employers who had earlier dealt with it through the President's Mediation Commission were reconsidering their position. Negotiating wages, hours, and working conditions had been an unpalatable wartime necessity to most of the California companies. With the war over and production increasing, and with prices falling in the recession of 1921, they looked toward freeing themselves from union pressures. A conference of oil operators meeting in Los Angeles in July, 1921, voted unanimously to negotiate no new agreement after the current one expired at the end of August.[79] Shell and a number of small companies did, in fact, sign modified agreements, but the others held fast. The union responded by striking against the producers early in September, with Standard and Shell being the two major companies not included in the strike call. As the bitter struggle went on, Standard men watched from the sidelines until, after nearly two months, the union finally gave up, badly beaten.[80]

6

There undoubtedly were Standard employees who grieved at the defeat of the union, but for most of them it had had too little to offer to win their allegiance. The company's long-term interest in employee relations had placed Standard well in the van in regard to wages, hours, working conditions, and benefits, leaving the union little to ask beyond collective bargaining. And, given the environment, most Standard workers believed that collective bargaining could be greatly overvalued.

Standard's persistent attention to improvements in employee welfare had helped create a work force, on the whole, capable, contented, and loyal. The employees to whom the Rockefeller representative, A. H. Lichty, talked in 1920 testified almost universally to good working conditions. "We have the best stuff to work with, good tools and good equipment, and plenty of both," was a frequently echoed sentiment. Workers agreed that Standard expected a good day's work, but they appreciated being "treated like men" instead of "driven like a lot of dogs." "If you deliver the goods, there ain't no one to hound you," remarked an old foreman at Bakersfield. "My foreman always gives me plenty of leeway to get my work out," said a machinist at Taft. "If he really has a rush job, he tells me so, and after explaining that it is a rush job, will let me set my own time for getting it out, because he knows I shall do my best." Workers appreciated, too, the general easy relationship with management. "The men and the bosses are friends," asserted one veteran rig-builder. "Our officials . . . shake your hand and call you by your first name," another said proudly.[81]

Employees generally hesitated to leave the company, dubious that they could better themselves elsewhere. In 1919 Standard's benefits, apart from the major item of vacations, amounted to $626,618, a sum unusually large for that day and better than 2 per cent of the company's total wage bill. At Richmond during the same year, the labor turnover for all men who had been employed a year or more was less than 5 per cent, a remarkably low rate. The statistics on employees returning to the company following service in World War I are, if anything, even more impressive. Of the 3,097 who joined the Armed Forces, 2,380 were again working for Standard by December, 1919, a year in which the war boom was still on and finding new jobs was relatively easy. Sixty-one had been killed or died in uniform; 471 were still in service. Of those mustered out, only 185 (approximately 6 per cent) had sought employment elsewhere.[82]

Judged by the practices of the times, Standard by 1919 had built an enviable reputation as an employer.

XXI

WORLD WAR I
AND THE END OF AN ERA

On April 10, 1917, four days after the United States entered World War I, Oscar Sutro wired Washington asking permission for Standard to use "plain English" to direct its tanker, the *Lucas,* inbound from Panama, to San Pedro instead of Richmond in order to "save three days valuable time and to that extent at least relieve [the] great shortage of tank bottoms. . . ." The same day he also asked that the *Scofield,* steaming from Panama for New York with a million dollar cargo of gasoline and lubes for the Allies, be accompanied by an armed escort, which, it turned out, the Navy could not provide. To ward off sabotage, the company had already moved to increase the number of guards at the refineries and in the oil fields. At Richmond it installed searchlights which two years before had been used to light the Panama Pacific International Exposition. Machine guns were set up commanding the approaches to the refinery, and a torpedo boat patrolled the nearby waters.[1]

These happenings symbolized in a somewhat dramatic way what was going on throughout the nation, as it began to put itself on a war footing. With his usual clarity, President Woodrow Wilson went to the heart of the matter: "It is not an army that we must shape and train for war; it is a nation. . . . The whole nation must be a team on which each man will play the part for which he is best fitted."[2] The President was speaking particularly of the increasingly technological nature of modern war, for to provide complex weapons, like tanks, machine guns, giant cannon, airplanes, battle cruisers, and submarines, required the diversion of much of the nation's productive capacity for war purposes. Take the petroleum industry, for instance. Without oil, the machines that manufactured the great weapons of the war could never have been operated, or themselves have been made. Even more obviously, the weapons would have been useless without oil products for lubrication and perhaps for motive power.

For a first time, the American economy had to be regimented with a series of emergency agencies. Shortly after the declaration of war, the Council of National Defense gave way to the powerful War Industries Board, which served as a sort of "civilian general staff"; the Shipping

Board, established earlier to deal with the shortage of ships, received additional powers; and an Emergency Fleet Corporation was set up to build new tonnage to match the staggering losses caused by the U-boats. To control the flow of fuel, in August of 1917 the Fuel Administration was created, in which an Oil Division found a place the following January. Mark Requa, a well-known California mining engineer and a leading figure in the Independent Oil Producers Agency, was made head of the new division. Like all other war agencies concerned with oil, the division worked closely with an industry organization, the National Petroleum War Service Committee, which was itself an outgrowth of an earlier committee advisory to the Council of National Defense. A. C. Bedford, in 1917 president and later chairman of the board of Jersey Standard, was chairman of both these committees, on which he was associated with a number of other spokesmen for the industry. The relations between the industry and the government an oil journalist, L. M. Fanning, aptly characterized as "government control . . . by agreement."[3]

The California industry was too remote geographically to feel the full force of economic mobilization, for shortages in both sea and land transportation caused the government to draw more heavily on oil regions closer to the war zones. But the call on the West, nonetheless, was considerable. For example, California supplied the Navy with fuel oil in the Pacific. So, too, did it help meet heavy eastern and European demands for gasoline, distillate, and lubes, notably the motor oils. To a minor extent, it also produced some of the chemicals for manufacturing explosives. All this occurred while the western industry was hard pressed to meet regional requirements, themselves swollen by the war, as in the case of fuel oil for ocean shipping and the railroads. The pressure was greater because after the middle of 1915 crude production in California had failed to match the needs of its market. In 1916 the oil deficit was more than 13,000,000 barrels, an amount equal to fully one-seventh of the state's production that year. The industry, fortunately, had large stocks of crude oil in storage, but as the war wore on, the prospect of crippling shortages, especially in fuel oil, became a real hazard.[4]

Standard's response to the stresses and strains of World War I, at times in association with the other western companies, is the theme of the following pages. It is more than a war story, however, for some decisions that were made in the attempt to solve pressing problems, especially in the quest for oil, had a lasting effect. As a result, the brief two-year administration of President William S. Rheem ending in April, 1919, has a quality of transition that will become abundantly clear later on.

2

Standard's war record can be briefly summarized as a strenuous effort to find oil and to turn out products in a larger volume while much of what was required to do the job, including manpower, gradually fell into short supply. Fully a quarter of its more than 11,000 employees saw military service. Draft deferments for skilled workers reduced the impact of this exodus, but the company nonetheless faced a considerable problem in training replacements. The problem was greater still because of the need for more manpower; at the time of the Armistice the company roll of 14,066 numbered nearly three thousand more than in April, 1917.[5]

Materials, too, were short. Steel was especially hard to get. By June of 1917 A. B. Brooks, Standard's purchasing agent, was warning producing and refining superintendents that he could no longer place orders for "Steel Plate, Shapes, or Bars. . . . I would advise that you conserve all the steel . . . on hand." He urged them to list their idle inventory for use elsewhere and to make substitutions for scarce materials. Government controls on critically needed items became tighter as the war progressed. By the summer of 1918 the War Industries Board was issuing certificates for iron, steel, and copper based solely on their use for the war effort. Companies could not even draw galvanized iron, boiler plate, or tank steel from their own storage without authorization from the government. As a consequence, Standard began cannibalizing idle facilities, including the stills of the old Newhall refinery, unused since 1890. It pulled casing from abandoned wells and took up the Santa Maria pipeline. In August, W. S. Smullin, the Producing Department's general superintendent for Southern California, warned his subordinates, ". . . it is almost impossible to get drilling tools and drill pipe. . . ." Near the end of the war the War Industries Board was also requiring companies to sign pledges to conserve brass, electrical supplies, automobile accessories, and rubber products.[6]

These restrictions might have hampered oil field operations if the war had gone on longer, but they were actually of minor effect. Standard's well-stocked warehouses helped protect it against serious shortages. Its production achievement during World War I, in fact, substantially aided the California industry in meeting both civilian and war needs. The discovery of the Montebello field, as we have noted, and the intensive development of West Coyote were mainly responsible for building the company's crude production from 14,365,000 barrels in 1916 to 22,446,000 barrels two years later, which was a larger increase than the corresponding figures for the state—from 90,052,000 to 97,532,000 barrels. Except for Standard's remarkable success, the drain on oil in storage would have been even more alarming, for between 1916 and 1918 stocks in California dropped 12,000,000 barrels. David M. Folsom, the Oil Director for the Fuel Administration on the Pacific Coast, singled out the company for special praise for its accomplishment.[7]

Similarly, Standard worked hard at expanding its refinery output. Through means recounted earlier, between 1916 and 1918 Standard increased its output of gasoline by approximately two-thirds and nearly doubled its production of lube oils. California gasoline was especially prized because it gave engines superior power and smoother operation. It contained a higher proportion of iso-octane hydrocarbons than other gasolines, that is (though the concept had yet to be developed), a naturally high-octane rating. Mark Requa, the Oil Director, remarked after the war that "on many occasions" the Bureau of Mines had found the California product to be "the best in the United States." "Had the war continued," he went on, "I should have commandeered gasoline in California and shipped it by rail to the eastern seaboard for use in France. . . ." As it was, a large volume of gasoline and lubes moved East by both tanker and tank car. In 1918 California sent 625,120 barrels of naphtha products (consisting of aviation gasoline, motor gasoline, and engine distillate) and 415,200 barrels of lube oils. The bulk of the naphthas and almost all the lubes came from Standard. Its sales statistics for 1918, while not exactly comparable, show shipments of 1,141,000 barrels of naphthas and 703,000 barrels of lubes outside the home territory. Other fragmentary data suggest that more than half of these amounts went to the Atlantic seaboard. Standard's achievement in turning out aviation gasoline was particularly notable; in the two months preceding the Armistice, for example, it supplied 48,500 barrels, exceeding the quota fixed for all California refiners by 4,500 barrels.[8] The record for fuel oil was not as good. Because of declining production in the San Joaquin Valley and the shortage of tankers to bring crude to Richmond from Southern California, Standard operated its Bakersfield refinery far below capacity in 1918 in order to keep Richmond fully supplied. Its fuel oil output that year fell off about one-sixth from the peak in 1917. Nevertheless, the company delivered slightly more fuel oil in 1918 than in the preceding year by drawing on storage.[9]

Standard also participated to a minor extent in relieving the most crucial of all shortages in World War I, marine shipping. When A. C. Bedford asked the California industry in April, 1917, to aid the Allies in their "desperate" need for tankers, an intercompany committee replied that "tonnage . . . was so short that no ship could be spared." This decision President Rheem considered clearly inappropriate. Early in May he offered Standard's *Colonel E. L. Drake,* a 38,000-barrel tanker. "While we are doing this at a great sacrifice to our business," Rheem wrote, "we feel that it is our duty. . . ." Two months later the company placed an order with the Union Iron Works of San Francisco for a sister ship to the *D. G. Scofield* only to have the contract requisitioned in August by the Emergency Fleet Corporation. The vessel, launched in April, 1918, as the *W. S. Rheem,* went into service as a government tanker.[10]

By that time the Shipping Board nominally controlled the company's entire sea-going fleet except for three small vessels, for in October, 1917, it had requisitioned all American cargo ships of more than 2,500 tons.[11] Standard and the other western companies, nonetheless, had continued to operate most of their tankers through an intercompany agency called the Pacific Coast Petroleum War Service Committee, a regional subcommittee of Bedford's powerful National Petroleum War Service Committee.

The Pacific Coast committee proved highly effective in alleviating many of the war strains. It brought about cooperation among western companies to an extent that the antitrust laws would hardly have permitted in peace time. Standard played a large role in shaping the committee's decisions, and the committee, in turn, affected the company's operations. Its work, therefore, deserves examination as an important part of Standard's wartime experience.

3

The need for some such agency had become increasingly apparent as the war progressed. The threats of shortage in crude oil production, in fuel oil, and in transportation, all suggested the necessity for some central organization in the West, for Bedford's National Petroleum War Service Committee seemed too remote to do the job.

In the summer of 1917 the problems facing the western industry had been the subject of a comprehensive report which a state committee submitted to William D. Stephens, the governor of California. Its members—Max Thelen, chairman of the State Railroad Commission, and two university professors, David M. Folsom, professor of mining at Stanford, and Eliot Blackwelder, a geology professor from the University of Illinois—were particularly disturbed by the prospect of a crude oil shortage, which they thought could be averted by drilling the San

Joaquin Valley lands tied up in the legal contest over the withdrawal orders. As we have seen, this proposal accomplished little. Other recommendations, which reached into less controversial areas, had a better chance. The committee urged, for example, that consumers substitute other fuels to conserve dwindling stocks of fuel oil. It also recommended that "the railroad, steamship, oil pipe line and oil companies of California be . . . directed . . . to so correlate their respective transportation facilities as to make most available and efficient every agency employed in the transportation of California petroleum and its products." At the moment, the pinch seemed to be more on land than at sea; the committee stated that Standard needed 3,500 tank cars at El Segundo "to fill urgent orders from the copper mines of Arizona."[12]

Within a week after receiving this report, Governor Stephens appointed another committee to draw up "a plan for the correlation of all the facilities for distribution and transportation—pipe lines, railroad tank cars and motive power, ships, tank wagons, warehouses and storage tanks." Only one of its four members was from the oil industry, however, and he was a minor figure. The committee was too feeble to be effective, and matters continued to drift until the beginning of January, 1918, when the Pacific Coast Petroleum War Service Committee was created.[13]

From the very start the new committee was an impressive body. It had the prestige of its connection with the National Petroleum War Service Committee and the allegiance of the large companies which staffed it. E. W. Clark, the general manager of the Union Oil Company, was its chairman. K. R. Kingsbury, who frequently traveled to Washington for the committee as well as for the company, was Standard's representative. The others were John Barneson, president of the General Petroleum Corporation, H. R. Gallagher, vice president of the Shell Company of California, and R. P. Schwerin, vice-president and general manager of the Associated. In April, L. P. St. Clair of the Independent Oil Producers Agency was added. J. K. Firth, assistant manager of Standard's Fuel Oil Department, served as its secretary. The committee also commanded the respect of Mark Requa, who appointed its candidate, David M. Folsom, as Oil Director for the Pacific Coast. On western matters, the committee's relation to Folsom was roughly equivalent to that of Bedford's committee to Requa on matters of national interest. Requa gave further recognition to the Pacific Coast committee in April when he accorded it the same status as its national parent, naming it an Advisory Committee to the Fuel Administration.[14]

From its headquarters in San Francisco, the Pacific Coast committee quickly became a clearing house for matters of intercompany concern. Two problems of paramount importance dominated the early meetings:

utilizing transportation with maximum efficiency, and channeling oil products, especially fuel oil, where they were most needed. The problems were, of course, interrelated.

Marine transportation was the chief headache. In addition to the *Drake,* the Pacific Coast companies had suffered other losses as a result of diversions by the Shipping Board. Standard's *A. F. Lucas* was drafted temporarily, along with three Union vessels, to bring nitrates from Chile, and Union and Associated each lost a ship for Atlantic service, reducing the tanker tonnage on the Pacific Coast from 154,000 before the war to a low of 96,600 in 1918. To get the most from this diminished fleet and from ships occasionally chartered from the government, the committee requested and received authority from the Shipping Board to operate all tankers on the Pacific Coast, shuttling the vessels where they were most needed, regardless of their ownership.[15]

To reduce long sea hauls, the committee fostered a larger use of exchanges of crude oil, fuel oil, and refined products among the companies. Standard was already a partner in several such arrangements, notably with General Petroleum, delivering crude from Montebello and West Coyote to General's refinery at Vernon in return for almost all of General's oil in Kern County. This exchange supplied Richmond with about 4,500,000 barrels in 1918 without recourse to tanker transportation. Standard also entered into an extensive exchange of refinery products. During 1918, for example, the Union Oil Company was supplied with 444,727 barrels of fuel oil, 156,000 barrels of naphtha products, and a smaller quantity of kerosine, principally from El Segundo, while Standard received from Union at Oleum and Port San Luis 96,000 barrels of gasoline and 346,000 barrels of fuel oil. During the war months consumers occasionally received Union's gasoline from Standard's pumps in the Northwest, and the reverse occurred more frequently in Southern California. According to Requa, exchange agreements and the pooling of tankers made marine transportation in the Pacific Coast industry more efficient by at least 20 per cent. The California companies moved as much fuel oil with their smaller fleet during 1918 as in 1917, and 3,660,000 barrels of refined products in comparison with 2,180,000 barrels during the preceding year.[16]

The Pacific Coast committee also had a considerable part in diverting fuel oil to essential wartime services. Because the western coal industry centered in the Northwest and because delivering fuel oil there required a long tanker haul, the committee early took action to reduce the flow northward. In January, 1918, it called in David S. Hanley of the Washington Coal Producers' Association to receive his assurance that northwestern consumers converting from oil to coal could be taken care of.

At about the same time, at the committee's suggestion, the major oil companies suspended fuel oil contracts in that area. "Standard Oil will continue to serve its customers," said W. S. Miller, "but the service will not be under contracts." The companies promised that such deliveries as were made would bear the contract price except for a surcharge of not more than two cents a barrel to cover higher freight costs when government-owned tankers were used.[17] This new pattern permitted the companies to reduce deliveries and to serve consumers on the basis of a priority list which the Pacific Coast committee submitted to Requa in March. In 1918 Standard's shipments to Seattle, its second most important market for fuel oil, fell off by more than 30 per cent, and its shipments to other northwestern points also declined for a total of 1,303,000 barrels. The fuel oil that might have gone to the Northwest was sent chiefly to Arizona, which showed an increase of 1,175,000 barrels, principally for copper mining. In 1918 Arizona received more than one-sixth of Standard's fuel oil.[18]

The committee was deeply concerned, too, over the problem of stimulating crude production in order to lessen the heavy drain on fuel oil in storage. In 1918 the West was drawing on stocks at a rate of about 50,000 barrels a day. Committee members shared the widespread anxiety that these stocks would be exhausted and western economic activity, even of war industry, be crippled. A survey in April led them to believe that this dangerous situation could occur in scarcely a year's time. Consequently, the Pacific Coast committee was another agency urging that the lands in litigation between producers and the government be drilled intensively. While this fruitless debate went on, the committee tried a different tack. In line with a suggestion from Mark Requa, it persuaded the major companies at the beginning of May to raise crude prices twenty-five cents a barrel (to $1.23) to urge the producers on. Offsetting increases in the price of fuel oil were held to from twelve to fifteen cents.[19]

The supply of refined products, unlike fuel oil, caused little worry, for it was ample to meet both government and regional demands. The Oil Division of the Fuel Administration therefore encouraged stable prices. When Union and Shell advanced the price of gasoline two cents a gallon at the end of June, 1918, Folsom ordered the companies to restore their former figure. The only change during the war months, a modest rise of a half-cent a gallon on gasoline, engine distillate, and kerosine, occurred in August, 1918, after the Pacific Coast committee had requested the increase to offset higher freight rates.[20]

A different condition prevailed in the East, for by the summer of 1918 gasoline stocks were depleted and military requirements were climbing. The situation caused the Oil Division and the National Petroleum War Service Committee to consider a ban on pleasure driving on Sundays —World War I's famed "gasless Sunday"—a move that found scant favor among western oilmen. Late in August the Pacific Coast committee informed Bedford that the California refiners had "supplied all demands on them for gasoline, including those of the Government and eastern refiners," and that they had ample stocks on hand. When the national committee voted on this conservation move, it recommended that the order be limited to territory east of the Rockies. In turn, the Pacific Coast committee promised additional shipments to ease the eastern shortage.[21]

The western committee was more concerned with conservation of manpower. In August, when the government's anxiety over gasoline was at a peak, it set up three subcommittees to study the manpower question in producing, pipeline transportation and refining, and marketing. Within a few weeks the marketing subcommittee reported that the industry could release 2,000 men for more essential work if sales were restricted to the twelve hours between 6 A.M. and 6 P.M. This policy, which Standard adopted on October 1, had been accepted widely throughout the West by the time of the Armistice.[22]

The Pacific Coast committee was not long active after the Armistice, as its reason for being had passed. It met on only two occasions thereafter to attend to minor matters. At one of these meetings it dissolved its manpower subcommittees. The committee fully shared the temper of the times; it was glad to demobilize.[23]

World War I could not be dismissed so easily, however. The wartime experience, in association with inflation and the continuing shortage in western crude oil production, made 1919 Standard's liveliest year of public controversy since antitrust days. Along with the other major western companies, Standard battled its old adversary, the Navy Department, on a new front. And while this dispute was being resolved, the company endured an intensive investigation by the Federal Trade Commission because of outcries in the Northwest against its asserted dominance of the western industry. Both of these controversies were exasperating affairs. While fortunately not the most meaningful of the carry-overs from war to peace, inevitably they drew heavily on the time and energy of Standard's management, of which President Kenneth R. Kingsbury had taken the leadership following the death of W. S. Rheem in April, 1919.

4

The argument with the Navy, which again placed western oil men at loggerheads with Josephus Daniels, had its roots in the way the Navy had secured oil supplies during the war. Affronted by bids that he considered too high, the Navy Secretary took an independent course in June, 1917, from which not even Bedford's committee could budge him. Unlike all other government agencies, which paid the going rates for oil products, the Navy set up a system of allotments among oil companies and a pattern of "advance payments" amounting to somewhat less than the market price. At San Francisco, for example, the Navy offered an advance payment of $1.08 for fuel oil that was bringing $1.30 a barrel, and 17.5¢ for gasoline that was selling for 20¢ a gallon. Daniels stated that he would look to the Federal Trade Commission for guidance in determining a final settlement. The oil industry had no other choice than to accept the arrangement, for under its war powers the Navy could commandeer supplies if a satisfactory price could not be agreed upon.[24]

To the dismay of the oil companies, this procedure continued even after the Armistice. An adjustment in the amount of some of the advance payments as prices moved upward was the only modification. In July of 1918, two months after the price of fuel oil at San Francisco was raised to $1.60, the Navy agreed to pay $1.47 a barrel. But the matter of the final payments was still unsettled, for in 1918 the Navy had rejected recommendations from both the Federal Trade Commission and the Fuel Administration. In Standard's case the amount involved was nearly a quarter million dollars. Standard was supplying about one half of the Navy's fuel oil needs along the Pacific Coast, amounting to approximately 8 per cent of its annual fuel oil sales.[25]

In July, 1919, feelings rose to a higher pitch when the Navy abruptly reduced the advance payment at San Francisco to 86¢ a barrel. Apparently the suspicion of collusion among western marketers in fixing the price of fuel oil, combined with a sharp decline in eastern fuel oil prices, had inspired this move. In the East, the importation of large quantities of cheap Mexican crude had brought prices downward. High marine freight rates, amounting to $2.36 a barrel between Tampico and Los Angeles, made it impossible to channel the bountiful Mexican supply to the West, however, where there had been no parallel great increase. Western stocks of crude oil at the end of June, 1919, stood at 33,497,000 barrels, a growth of only about three million barrels since May 1, 1918, when at the suggestion of the Oil Division crude and fuel oil prices had last been raised. The meager growth in stocks, amounting to about a two weeks additional supply at the current rate of consumption, had been too little to cause the companies to reduce either their price of $1.23 a barrel for heavy crude or of $1.60 a barrel for fuel oil at San Francisco. Under the Navy's offer of July, the companies were asked to carry crude worth $1.23 at the well 300 miles to tidewater and to manufacture fuel oil meeting Navy specifications, all for 86¢ and the prospect of a subsequent adjustment that was uncertain both as to time and amount.[26]

With the war over and fuel stocks low, the companies chose to make a stand. They refused to accept the requisitions and insisted on the full market price. But their legal position was weak, for the nation had signed no peace treaty with Germany. The Navy could and did claim that its war powers were still in effect. When Shell refused to honor a requisition for fuel oil, on July 9 the Navy sent a vessel to the Martinez refinery bearing a peremptory demand, and the Shell company yielded under duress. Standard's turn came next. On August 1 Commander S. E. Barber, Supply Officer of the Puget Sound Navy Yard, asked Standard for 30,000 barrels of fuel oil and stated, "The Commandant of this Yard is further directed to use such force as may be necessary in order to effect delivery." Standard complied "to avoid seizure of our plant and disruption of our business," but sent off a protest to the Secretary of the Navy.[27]

The dispute was a frustrating experience. Since relief through the courts seemed a long and dubious process, the companies took their case to the public in an attempt to bring pressure on the Navy. Oscar Sutro supplied much of the leadership, as attorneys and executives of the major companies conferred back and forth. After consulting with Mark Requa, Standard's attorney drafted a three-page pamphlet, which the companies published at the end of July, 1919. Sutro questioned the "moral right" of the Secretary of Navy "to make use of extraordinary war powers . . . in time of peace. . . ." He wrote a longer historical summary for the August issue of the *Standard Oil Bulletin* stressing the constitutional issue of civil rights: "The oil companies have refused to execute the requisition agreements. The necessities of the war are over, and they decline voluntarily to submit to the taking of their property without just compensation." Sutro sought a still larger audience with a series of four editorials which were distributed to 5,000 papers in fifteen western states by E. Hofer & Sons, a western press agent firm.[28]

This barrage may have influenced the Navy to increase its advance payment at the end of August to $1.11 a barrel, but it brought no other relief. Moreover, among the oilmen there developed a sharp division as to how far to push the battle. The attack alarmed many San Joaquin Valley producers, for whom a settlement of their long dispute over the government lands was the one great issue. They had had enough of the belligerency of Secretary Daniels; they had no desire to see him aroused further. "I suppose a majority of the oil men have been battered and banged around so long . . . that they are thoroughly intimidated and fear to take any step which might block the realization of the dream which they have entertained for the past nine years with respect to congressional justice for their oil lands and impounded moneys," Sutro wrote Requa late in July, 1919. Because of this feeling, another vigorous pamphlet written by Sutro was not released, even after it had been printed over signatures of the presidents of the five major companies and of the Independent Oil Producers Agency.[29]

Not until the spring of 1920 did the skies begin to clear. In May Standard and the Navy finally compromised their differences, with the company accepting a little less than $1,500,000 in full payment of a bill it had figured at more than $1,600,000. The Navy also agreed to cease commandeering oil and to reduce the company's allotment for fuel oil for the Pacific area to 30 per cent, which more closely approximated its share of the western market. Under a contract signed in July, the Navy began to pay Standard $2.00 a barrel at San Francisco, a high price that reflected the lowest stocks in a decade. In any event, the days of commandeering were numbered. Late in June a federal judge ruled in an injunction suit over a commandeering order against the General Petroleum Corporation that the Navy could not fix prices but must pay prevailing market rates.[30]

5

At the height of the furor over Navy commandeering, Standard suffered an attack from a new quarter. On July 28, 1919, Senator Miles Poindexter, a powerful Republican from Washington and the acting chairman of the Naval Affairs Committee, published in the *Congressional Record* a document holding Standard responsible for "the outrageous price of fuel oil" on the Pacific Coast. It had come to the Senator from a close friend and ex-Congressman, James Wesley Bryan, an attorney and a stormy political figure who styled himself the "Special Representative" of an obscure organization called the "Fuel Oil Consumer's Committee of the Pacific Coast." Bryan, in turn, had received the document from Philip D. MacBride, its author and an attorney, who was identified as the chairman of a committee of the Seattle Chamber of Commerce investigating the "fuel situation." In calling upon Senator Poindexter for his "powerful assistance," Bryan asserted that the MacBride statement had been prepared "after much careful investigation" and was "reliable." Poindexter responded by asking that the Federal Trade Commission conduct a full-scale investigation of the Pacific Coast petroleum industry since 1914, a resolution which was passed by the Senate the next day.[31]

It was not long before John McLean, Standard's marketing representative at Seattle, gave the home office his view of the background of the affair. He reported that Bryan had as a client the Liberty Bay Transportation Company, an enterprise owned by about 150 farmer stockholders that operated two small boats on Puget Sound with fuel oil supplied by the Union Oil Company. The company had been "in hard lines" and through Bryan had filed a protest with the Seattle Chamber of Commerce against the high price of fuel oil. Meanwhile, MacBride had gone to California to gather data for a committee to be appointed by the Chamber to investigate the matter, with the understanding that he would be a member. McLean interpreted the whole episode as "cheap politics," nothing more than an attempt to further Poindexter's presidential aspirations in 1920 at the Republican National Convention, where the Senator did become Washington's favorite son.[32]

MacBride's report was a troublesome and damning document. It asserted that Standard dominated the western industry because of its large size and superior resources and because the other major companies found they could make more money by maintaining the same prices as Standard for crude and for oil products. Prices were the result of Standard's power and not of supply and demand; consequently, the profits of the large companies were artificially high. As proof, the Seattle attorney pointed to an increase in stocks of crude since September, 1918, that had been accompanied by no reduction in oil prices, and to Standard's extraordinary profits and dividends over the years, including stock dividends "without cash investment on the part of the stockholders." He suggested that the company's profits for 1918 had been disguised by unusually heavy write-offs for depreciation and depletion. As a result of Standard's machinations, "prices for 1919 remain[ed] at the highest level of 1918," hurting the public. MacBride gave as an example communities on Puget Sound dependent on "boat transportation," for which fuel oil was "by far the largest single item of operation cost. . . . The marketing of their produce, . . . their very existence, is dependent upon the maintenance of service. Some routes are being abandoned; all are being seriously affected." He also charged that the nation suffered because the Navy and the railroads, which the government was still operating under wartime legislation, had to pay an "exorbitant price" for fuel oil. "In the opinion of the writer the prevailing price should be cut in two." Even then, he maintained, Standard would receive "a handsome return on [its] investment."[33]

Standard's rebuttal to this sudden and unexpected assault was prompt and vigorous. Kingsbury told the Associated Press that "the prices for the products of his company had advanced as a natural result of existing economic conditions due to the great war—the greatly increased cost of all labor and of all material—just as had the price of everything else," and that competition was a vital characteristic of the western oil industry. In a companion statement which Sutro prepared, Kingsbury pointed out that the stock dividends of 1916 and 1917 "represented distribution of earnings of previous years which had been reinvested in the business," and that early in the century Standard had paid no dividends for seven years. Standard's president also dealt at length with the matter of prices and profits. He recounted the circumstances leading to the increase in crude and fuel oil prices on May 1, 1918, and showed that the price of the most important oil commodity, gasoline, had been held constant since December, 1916, except for an "increase to offset higher freight rates." Meanwhile, since the end of 1916 the price paid by the company for refinable crude had climbed from $0.79 to $1.33 a barrel. Kingsbury claimed that Standard's profits, amounting in 1918 to 12.75% on invested capital after allowances for depreciation, depletion, and taxes, were due chiefly to the company's striking success in building up production during the war years. The MacBride report, Kingsbury bluntly wired the Seattle Chamber of Commerce, was "erroneous as to facts and misleading in its conclusions." Nor was this Standard's last word. A few months later, in publishing a line-by-line analysis of the report, it showed that in one instance the Seattle attorney had deleted a sentence from a California state report and in another had taken a quotation from an oil journal out of context in order to improve his argument. The company also made clear that the depreciation and depletion allowance viewed so skeptically by MacBride was in full accord with the Revenue Act of 1918 and the rules and regulations of the Commissioner of Internal Revenue.[34]

Meanwhile the MacBride report had run into heavy weather in Seattle. Although Bryan had described the attorney as "chairman" of a committee of the Chamber of Commerce to investigate the price of fuel oil, MacBride was merely a member. The first meeting of the committee, moreover, took place on August 7, eleven days after MacBride's document had been published in the *Congressional Record*. His statements, in effect, were parading as the conclusions of the committee when they were merely raw material for discussion. In mid-August the Seattle Chamber wired Poindexter that it had been placed in a "false light." "Facts are that Chamber has appointed a committee . . . to investigate protest of local transportation company against price of fuel oil. . . . No one has been authorized to make any statement. . . . Committee will make complete fair and impartial investigation and it greatly resents Bryan's misstatements at the outset of its labors." It asked the Senator to give "publicity to above facts equal to that given Bryan's misstatements," but unlike Bryan's letter accompanying the MacBride report, the protest of the Seattle Chamber is not to be found in the *Congressional Record*.[35]

Following discussions with fuel oil consumers and oil company representatives, Perry Polson, the chairman of the investigating committee for the Seattle Chamber, on September 19 addressed a letter, moderate in tone, to the presidents of the five major western oil companies. Polson noted that shipping interests, in particular, were disturbed at the cost of fuel oil. Service on some Alaska routes had been curtailed, and some of the "less profitable" lines on Puget Sound had been abandoned. These consumers argued that the wartime increase in the price of crude to stimulate production was no longer necessary, that prices of both crude and fuel oil should be reduced, and that the profits of the companies were sufficiently large that the prices could be reduced. "This committee has reached no conclusion in the matter and is transmitting the above to inform you of the sentiment and attitude of the business men in the section affected," Polson wrote. "Also to ask whether or not there is any likelihood of a change . . . of benefit to the consuming public."[36] Perhaps the committee preferred to defer to the Federal Trade Commission for the last word.

No casual effort, the report of the Federal Trade Commission was long in coming; the first part, *Production, Ownership, and Profits*, appeared in April, 1921, and the second, *Prices and Competitive Conditions*, eight months later. Meanwhile, as the report showed, a good deal of painful western oil history had been made. Steep increases in the price of crude had failed to bring enough new production to ward off serious shortages in oil products. Toward the end of 1920 the ratio of crude stocks to consumption declined to barely two months supply. Fuel oil prices rose to $2.00 a barrel at San Francisco and to $2.25 at Seattle, prices that made those of the preceding year seem almost attractive in retrospect. The pinch in gasoline was worse. Gas station after gas station went dry during the summer months of 1920. California refiners increased their offering for high gravity crude between May, 1918, and July, 1920, by as much as $1.43 to a phenomenal high of $2.95 a barrel, and some of them, including Standard and Union, supplemented their short supply of gasoline by imports from across the Rockies. Gasoline prices, which had held so steady for so long, jumped 5.5¢ a gallon between June, 1919 and August, 1920, at the four largest Pacific Coast cities.[37]

The findings of the Federal Trade Commission were far from an endorsement of MacBride's document, which was nowhere mentioned. The Commission reported that profits of the western oil companies were high in 1918 and 1919, especially if the companies were important producers of crude. For example, the Commission computed Standard's profits, which were higher than those for any other western company, at an annual rate of 30.8 per cent during the first six months of 1919. The company, on the other hand, figured its profits at only 22.5 per cent by including in its investment nearly $47,000,000 for appreciation in the value of producing properties. But neither the high crude prices nor high profits brought forth criticism. "Supply and demand conditions were such that high prices of crude petroleum appear to have been logical in order to stimulate to the utmost the production of crude petroleum," the Commission stated. The profits of the California companies it did not consider out of line with those of oil companies elsewhere. "Data . . . for the whole country for the entire year 1919 indicate that the situation as to profits in the California petroleum industry was not exceptional."[38]

According to the Commission, the major companies usually figured the price of fuel oil by adding transportation and handling charges to the price for heavy crude at the well. These charges always ran higher than actual costs, though the excess above cost at San Francisco (the chief Pacific Coast market) had declined from a peak of around 32¢ a barrel in 1917 to about 15¢ during the first six months of 1919. At San Francisco and the other three principal markets (Los Angeles, Portland, and Seattle), the Commission showed that the prices quoted by the companies tended to move downward and upward in close harmony and very often were identical. At Los Angeles, however, Union, Associated, and General maintained prices between May and August, 1918, which were considerably lower than Standard's, while at Seattle the prices quoted by General during the war months were frequently somewhat higher than those of its rivals. No one company was the price leader. From 1914 through July, 1920, Standard led the way in price changes more often than any other company, but during the last four years of this period, after General joined the list of major companies, it was the most frequent price leader at Los Angeles and Seattle. The Commission revealed that, proportionately, the price of fuel oil had advanced slightly less at Seattle than at San Francisco from 1914 through 1920, apparently because the cost of marine transportation was more stable than other costs.[39]

Statistics gathered by the Commission on the volume of fuel oil sales are also revealing. Usually Standard sold slightly more than either of its two main rivals, Union and Associated. In 1919 its sales in the Pacific Coast marketing territory were 14,644,000 barrels, compared to 12,-677,000 for Union and 12,070,000 for Associated, but its share of the market among the five major companies was only 26.6 per cent. The too pat charges of MacBride in regard to fuel oil sales and prices seem hardly justified. Nevertheless, viewing the Pacific Coast industry as a whole, the Federal Trade Commission did find Standard to be "the most important factor" and generally the price leader, a conclusion that has been commented upon in an earlier chapter.[40]

This postwar turmoil before the public had one further outcome. Oscar Sutro was finding his secondary role as public relations advisor increasingly burdensome, especially as the company's legal business continued to grow. To give him relief, in December of 1919 Standard hired Philip H. Patchin, a thirty-five-year-old journalist and civil servant of unusual experience for one so young. Patchin had done tours of duty as a Washington correspondent and as a foreign correspondent in Latin America, the Far East, and England, principally for the *New York Sun* and the *New York Tribune*. He had also served as Chief of the Division of Foreign Intelligence and later as Chief of the Division of Information in the State Department, where he was when Standard found him. "He is exceedingly well known in political and newspaper circles, and has a rather wide social connection and a very attractive and engaging personality." Sutro commented. "He has real ability and I think writes well."[41] The hiring of Patchin marked the beginnings of a larger public relations program which years later would require the services of a full-fledged department.

6

But there was also a positive side to the war outcome, highly important for the future, that can only be sketched here. It was embodied in the company's response to the extraordinary demand for oil and oil products that carried over into the postwar years, a demand that seemed almost insatiable. Some of the decisions that Standard made bore little fruit at the time, but they soon showed forth as significant and enduring departures. Despite the "return to normalcy" extolled in Senator Harding's famed phrase, the company's executives were not of a mind to turn back the clock.

The search for crude supplied the most momentous of these departures. While Hillman stepped up his efforts to find new production in California, leading to the great discoveries at Elk Hills in 1919 and at Huntington Beach a year later, early in 1917 he also made a decision highly meaningful for the future when he sent geologists on a sustained drive into the states along the Rockies. To look outside Standard's historic territorial limits was a logical move because the company needed more oil, but it represented a clear break with the past. The examination of the Rangely field in northwestern Colorado was the prelude. Shortly, one of the geologists at Rangely, J. O. "Doc" Nomland, went north to Wyoming, and before the year was out Standard's scouts had been also to New Mexico and Montana. During 1918 Hillman, Storey, and Kingsbury all visited Rangely, where operations had begun in the spring.[42]

Recognizing the departure this move represented, Standard in March, 1918, set up its first subsidiary, the Richmond Petroleum Company, to handle the work at Rangely. The new corporation, with an authorized capital of $500,000, was a modest affair, but its powers included all aspects of the oil industry.[43] As we have seen, the early efforts at Rangely were disappointing. Richmond Petroleum and its successors, however, continued to explore from Montana to the Gulf. Thirty-three years later, in 1951, their discoveries would surpass Standard's California properties in production.[44] And the charter of Richmond Petroleum was prophetic, for finding oil would gradually lead Standard into transporting, refining, and marketing outside the old home territory.

During these pivotal years Standard also began to look abroad. Its first move was south of the border, where in the summer of 1917 Nomland and W. H. Berg, the Producing Department's assistant manager, spent about a month looking over the west coast of Mexico without discovering an attractive opportunity. Marketing considerations shared with producing as a motivation for this quest. "We cannot afford to have others find oil along this coast and threaten our market," G. C. Gester, Standard's chief geologist, recalls hearing Berg say. In September of 1917 the company glanced briefly at another and far distant area when Gester prepared a report for Hillman on prospects on the island of Timor in the Indian Ocean.[45]

By the end of the war Standard had decided to go abroad in a systematic way, with Central America and the Philippines as its first targets. It was a leader among a number of large oil companies which were turning to foreign lands, spurred by a belief that petroleum reserves in the United States might soon prove inadequate, and which were promised the support of the U.S. State Department.[46] Standard's decision, shaped primarily by Hillman, Kingsbury, and Storey, was followed by a rapid recruiting of geologists, as the number of these scientists on Standard's payroll grew from eight in the autumn of 1918 to twenty-two a year later. In February of 1919 Nomland led a party of seven to Central America with a general commission to look for likely oil property. Three of the men dropped off in Guatemala and two more in Honduras, while the remaining pair went on to Panama, where a small headquarters was set up by mid-year. By that time their work was being more narrowly defined. Standard had taken an option on a half million acres in northern Panama and was negotiating for exploratory rights on the vast holdings of the United Fruit Company extending from Guatemala to Colombia, which matured into an agreement in November.[47] Another geologist, Roy Dickerson, left San Francisco in June of 1919 for the Philippines, where he was soon joined by other recruits to Standard's staff.[48] Like Rangely, these ventures started the company down a new road. Standard had begun the long gamble which would pay out after years of experience and effort and would rank it among the greatest of the international oil companies.

The company's refiners, too, were under pressure, especially for gasoline, as more and more Americans turned to the highways. Between 1918 and 1920 the number of automobiles in Standard's five-state western territory jumped by almost half, from 622,000 to 918,000. Meanwhile, crude oil production in California grew merely from 101,600,000 to 105,700,000 barrels, and Standard's own production from 23,078,000 to 29,886,000 barrels.[49] Cracking the oil for more gasoline, hitherto desirable, began to seem an imperative proposition. The Burton process, licensed from Indiana Standard in 1916, clearly was not the answer because of the excessive carbon deposits from California crudes. In February of 1919, a month after the Burton stills were shut down, an inter-refinery Gasoline Production Committee was organized, as we have already noted, to look for a suitable cracking process.[50]

The appointment of a committee in which the older practical refiners were outnumbered by young refiners and professional chemists was itself a departure, but even more important was the almost simultaneous first pale perception of research as a continuous function that would benefit from having its own organization and manpower. The initial step appears to have been a by-product of the removal in March, 1919, of Rheem's old subordinate, the thirty-nine-year-old John C. Black, as manager of the El Segundo refinery. His management, according to Marvin Chappell, the head chemist at El Segundo, had been under attack "because he was spending too much time on experimental work and too little time as manager." This versatile veteran, whose service dated from the building of the Richmond refinery, was unusual among the older refiners because he had had some formal training in engineering at Columbia. At El Segundo he had been working on a number of projects: vacuum and pressure processes for the manufacture of toluol and benzol; a sulfur dioxide process for treating oils; the use of finely ground clay at high temperatures as a filter medium for lubes; and particularly fitting to the times, a high pressure cracking still. To make use of his obvious talents and perhaps to soften the blow of his removal, Rheem brought Black to the home office, where on March 5 he was made manager of Development and Research. He soon left on a trip to visit several eastern research laboratories, including the Mellon Institute in Pittsburgh, and thereafter designed a well-equipped three-story laboratory building for Richmond. Black's tenure in his new job proved short, however, for he resigned from the company late in October.[51]

The next month Ralph A. Halloran took over the still poorly defined research post. A graduate in chemistry from the University of California, Halloran had been with Standard for almost thirteen years. After serving as chemist at Richmond, he had gone to the Producing Department in 1914 to work with natural gas and natural gasoline, and in 1919 had been helping Black with cracking and other experiments. Halloran was stationed in the new laboratory building. At first his Development Department handled only a small part of the experimental work, but, supported by the most dynamic of the younger refiners, Richard W. Hanna, the department grew rapidly in size and prestige as the values of centralized and systematic research over the older haphazard methods of practical men were more clearly recognized.[52]

Following the Armistice there were other changes, more routine in nature, that went along with the growth of the business, notably in marine transportation and marketing. But none approached in significance the two stressed here: the movement of the company outward from its former regional limits, and its increased reliance on professional and scientific personnel.

How may we summarize this experience, running for more than forty years, of Standard of California and its western predecessors, California Star and the Pacific Coast Oil companies?

Successively, these companies were leaders in building the western oil industry. The operators of California Star and PCO, through their capital and entrepreneurial skill, brought new life to an industry that had almost died following the collapse of the boom of 1865. Using western capital, they put together a small, integrated operation. They developed in the Pico region California's first commercial oil field, built in 1880 at Alameda a relatively large and well-equipped refinery, financed an imaginative marketing organization that for several years was a strong competitor of Standard Oil, and achieved economies through pipeline and tanker transportation. It was the misfortune of these men of enterprise that they were never able to solve the problem of turning out a good kerosine on a commercial basis, though PCO's chemist, E. A. Starke, pointed the way to an eventual solution before 1900. It was their misfortune, too, that no light crude field larger than Pico was discovered in California during their vigorous years. Consequently, except for California Star and PCO, the western industry evolved principally around fuel oil and asphalt. Following the development of the Los Angeles City field and, at the turn of the century, the Kern County fields, this interest in fuel oil became still more pronounced.

The decision of 26 Broadway to operate in the West as more than a marketer, signalized in 1900 by its purchase of PCO, brought the unmatched capital and management resources of the Standard organization into all phases of the California industry. Initially, 26 Broadway drafted its plans to accord with the apparent realities of California oil—looking first to a fuel trade, based on oil purchased and stored in Kern County and transported by pipeline nearly 300 miles to the state's chief market around San Franciso Bay. For Standard, refining California's available light crudes was only a secondary objective. The Richmond refinery had hardly been built, however, before large light oil strikes at Coalinga and the commercial success of Starke's fuming acid process caused Standard to alter its plans. Refined products took over from fuel oil as the principal goal of the western venture; moreover, Standard's trade with the Orient offered opportunities for a cheap kerosine refined from California crude. To develop these programs, 26 Broadway poured many millions of dollars into PCO.

In 1906 these new activites were merged with the marketing operations that Iowa Standard had long carried on in the West. PCO, 26 Broadway's instrument for the consolidation, was redesignated the Standard Oil Company (California) shortly before it acquired the plant and inventory of Iowa Standard. Nourished by the capital of 26 Broadway, Standard of California continued to grow, though not so rapidly as its western executives desired.

In fact, the years from 1900 to 1911 were marked by recurring differences of opinion between the New York and San Francisco headquarters concerning the scale of western operations. The New York executives viewed California as merely one province in a world-wide business; they tended to be conservative and desired assurance that their California crude purchases and plant investment did not run ahead of prudent forecasts of market demand. The western subordinates, by contrast, feeling the excitement of the booming California industry, were more buoyant, more optimistic. They were especially anxious to forestall competition in refined products, which had been almost absent in 1900. Usually, 26 Broadway yielded to their requests, but not always and inevitably with some delays.

Whatever 26 Broadway might have done, it seems almost certain that competition in refined products could not have been kept down, so bountiful were the oil strikes in California after 1900. Union, Puente, and other smaller refiners were making substantial headway prior to 1911; during the following decade they were joined by Associated, Shell, General, and still others. But, clearly, Standard's California team was undismayed at the outcome of the antitrust suit which dissolved the Standard Oil combination and welcomed the chance to go on its own.

These seasoned and confident Standard veterans led the company forward in a broad program of integrated expansion—a program which had its inception in the approval won from 26 Broadway after a tour of inspection by eastern executives late in 1910 and which was carried on with additional capital subscribed by the stockholders after the dissolution. During the war decade Standard of California made sensational progress in producing, especially at Midway, West Coyote, and Montebello. During these same years it erected a Southern California refinery at El Segundo and a topping plant at Bakersfield, and it enlarged the works at Richmond. In refining technology, it made an impressive advance by developing the high vacuum distillation of lubes. It laid down a pipeline system to supply El Segundo and increased the capacity of the Valley pipelines serving Richmond. To build up marketing, it established a large number of new wholesale outlets and entered into retailing through service stations. By no means the least of its achievements were its well-designed programs in the sensitive areas of employee and public relations.

The resulting large increases in plant investment, sales volume, and profits after 1911 are readily apparent. But in the sale of most major products Standard's share of the market fell off. The growth of the western market had been so rapid during the war decade that it had opened opportunities for many companies—large and small, old and new.

Around the close of World War I, in fact, Standard's executives, along with those of other oil companies, could well wonder whether they could keep up with the needs of the West. Standard, which possessed financial and administrative strength far surpassing its rivals, was stirred by both the opportunity and the challenge. For a first time, it began to search energetically for oil outside California. It also turned more and more to men of scientific training to discover new fields, to bring about a larger recovery of the oil, and to manufacture a greater volume of the more valuable products from each barrel of crude.

These departures occurring about the end of World War I provide two of the principal keys for understanding the development of the already impressive West Coast company of 1919 into the great international enterprise of 1962. They go far to explain the growth of a company which today has a larger total crude production in other states than in California and which derives more crude from the eastern than from the western hemisphere. And the use of the technically trained, combined with systematic research, has indeed paid out in reducing the gamble in exploration, in promoting a larger crude oil recovery, and in making the crude an ever greater source of more valuable products—products that today are marketed throughout most of the nation and of the free world.

The war years mark roughly the end of one era and the beginning of another in the history of the Standard Oil Company of California.

APPENDICES

APPENDIX A

OFFICERS AND DIRECTORS OF THE STANDARD OIL COMPANY (CALIFORNIA) AND ITS PREDECESSORS

The tables of officers and directors for the Standard Oil Company (California) and its predecessors are based on company minutes whenever possible, but often the only available records are articles of incorporation, letterheads, newspaper notices, city directories, and references in correspondence. When the term of office cannot be established with reasonable certainty, a "(?)" has been inserted. Since Volume I ends with the year 1919, the tables list only those men elected to office prior to 1920.

The dates of incorporation are those on which articles were filed with the Secretary of State at Sacramento.

PACIFIC COAST OIL COMPANY, RENAMED STANDARD OIL COMPANY (CALIFORNIA), 1879–1926

The Pacific Coast Oil Company was incorporated under the laws of the State of California, February 19, 1879, and, for reasons unknown, reincorporated September 10, 1879. The second date is considered by the company to be its date of organization. Whether officers were ever elected for the earlier company is not known.

PCO was purchased by the Standard Oil Company (New Jersey) in 1900. In 1906 the parent company arranged for PCO to acquire the business of the Standard Oil Company (Iowa), whereupon PCO was renamed the Standard Oil Company. To distinguish it from other Standard Oil Companies, it was customary to add to its title "(California)." In 1926 the Standard Oil Company (California) and the Pacific Oil Company were consolidated into a new company incorporated in Delaware—the Standard Oil Company of California.

Chairman of the Board

D. G. Scofield ......March 8, 1917–July 30, 1917
W. S. Miller ....April 28, 1919–December 23, 1919

President

*George Loomis ....September 10, 1879–December 15, 1879
                      August, 1885–April 8, 1894
C. N. Felton ....December 15, 1879–August, 1885
                      April 17, 1894–February, 1896

* On Loomis as president in 1879, see Chap. III, note 38.

Gordon Blanding . . . .February, 1896–October 17, 1900
H. M. Tilford . . . . . .December 18, 1900–February 20, 1911
J. A. Moffett . . . . . .February 20, 1911–December 1, 1911
D. G. Scofield . . . . .December 5, 1911–March 8, 1917
W. S. Rheem . . . . . .March 8, 1917–April 6, 1919
K. R. Kingsbury . . . .April 28, 1919–November 22, 1937

Vice President

George Loomis . . . . .December 15, 1879–December, 1883 (?)
*D. G. Scofield . . . .December, 1883 (?)–February, 1896
                      March 21, 1899–December 5, 1911
Lloyd Tevis . . . . . . .February, 1896–March 21, 1899
W. S. Rheem . . . . . .December 5, 1911–June 2, 1914
F. H. Hillman . . . . . .June 2, 1914–April 5, 1927
K. R. Kingsbury . . . .June 2, 1914–April 28, 1919
W. S. Miller . . . . . .June 2, 1914–April 28, 1919
R. J. Hanna . . . . . . .April 28, 1919–December 30, 1930
H. M. Storey . . . . . .April 28, 1919–December 30, 1930

Senior Vice President

W. S. Rheem . . . . . .June 2, 1914–March 8, 1917

Second Vice President

K. R. Kingsbury . . . .December 7, 1911–June 2, 1914

Secretary

L. D. Fisk . . . . .February, 1879–1883
Edward Wheaton . . .1883–1889
C. B. Wheaton 1889–December 18, 1900
H. C. Breeden . . . . . .December 18, 1900–June 5, 1906
W. S. Rheem . . . . . . .June 5, 1906–December 5, 1911
William Edwards . . . .December 5, 1911–September 30, 1913
F. H. Hillman . . . . . .September 30, 1913–June 2, 1914
H. M. Storey . . . . . .June 2, 1914–January 10, 1922

Treasurer

H. C. Breeden . . . . . .December 18, 1900–June 5, 1906
W. S. Rheem . . . . . .June 5, 1906–October 16, 1906

* From the creation of the company, or within a year thereafter, Scofield was auditor.

W. S. Miller .... October 16, 1906–June 2, 1914
R. J. Hanna .... June 2, 1914–April 28, 1919
J. P. Smith .... April 28, 1919–May 4, 1920

*Directors

C. N. Felton .... September 10, 1879–December 2, 1899
L. D. Fisk .... September 10, 1879–February, 1885
G. M. Hedges ...... September 10, 1879–December, 1879 (?)
George Loomis ..... September 10, 1879–December, 1883
                    February, 1885–April 8, 1894
James Lawler ...... September 10, 1879–December, 1879 (?)
D. G. Scofield ..... December, 1879–July 30, 1917
F. B. Taylor .... December, 1879–1881
H. L. Tevis 1881–1883
                    March 21, 1899–October 17, 1900
G. I. Ives 1883–1892
Edward Wheaton 1883–1891
C. N. Felton, Jr. 1891–1896
                    December 2, 1899–October 17, 1900
Lloyd Tevis 1892–March 21, 1899
Gordon Blanding 1894–October 17, 1900
F. G. Drum 1896–March 21, 1899
                    December 2, 1899–March 5, 1900
Hugh Tevis .... March 21, 1899–December 2, 1899
                    March 5, 1900–October 17, 1900
Louis Glass .... October 17, 1900–December 18, 1900
E. S. Pillsbury ...... October 17, 1900–January 2, 1901
H. D. Pillsbury ..... October 17, 1900–December 18, 1900
Henry Wadsworth ... October 17, 1900–December 18, 1900
H. C. Breeden ...... December 18, 1900–June 5, 1906
W. S. Miller .... December 18, 1900–December 23, 1919
H. M. Tilford ...... December 18, 1900–February 20, 1911
W. M. Hall .... January 2, 1901–February 20, 1905
                    June 12, 1906–February 20, 1911
W. S. Rheem .... February 20, 1905–April 6, 1919
F. H. Hillman ...... February 20, 1911–April 5, 1927
J. A. Moffett ...... February 20, 1911–December 1, 1911
William Edwards .... December 5, 1911–December 7, 1911
K. R. Kingsbury .... December 7, 1911–November 22, 1937
R. J. Hanna .... April 2, 1913–December 30, 1930
H. M. Storey .... April 2, 1913–December 30, 1930

* The directors of the first PCO company, which does not seem to have operated, were listed by the articles of incorporation as follows: C. N. Felton, L. D. Fisk, E. H. Forester, G. M. Hedges, and George Loomis.

J. P. Smith ....January 18, 1918–December 31, 1921
H. T. Harper ......April 28, 1919–December 30, 1930

CALIFORNIA STAR OIL WORKS COMPANY, 1876–1901

The California Star Oil Works Company was incorporated July 8, 1876, although its articles had been signed more than three weeks earlier on June 16. It was the successor to the Star Oil Works Company, which had been formed May 3, 1876. The directors and, presumably, the officers were the the same. Although the controlling interest passed to the Pacific Coast Oil Company in 1879, CSOW continued as a separate corporate entity. After the Standard Oil Company (New Jersey) acquired PCO, the minority stockholders in CSOW were bought out and the company liquidated.

President

A. J. Bryant ....June, 1876–September, 1879 (?)
C. N. Felton ....September, 1879 (?)–March 12, 1881
D. G. Scofield ......March 12, 1881–January 8, 1901
J. S. Severance ....January 8, 1901–September, 1901

Vice President

M. L. McDonald ...June, 1876–(?)
* Hugh Tevis ......(?)–(?)

Secretary

J. S. Taylor ....June, 1876–1879 (?)
D. G. Scofield ......1879 (?)–1879 (?)
L. D. Fisk ....1879 (?)–1883 (?)
Edward Wheaton ...1883 (?)–1889 (?)
C. B. Wheaton .....1889 (?)–January 8, 1901
Alfred Sutro ....January 8, 1901–September, 1901

Directors

A. J. Bryant ....June, 1876–(?)
Reuben Denton ....June, 1876–1876
Charles Jones ......June, 1876–(?)
M. L. McDonald ....June, 1876–(?)
R. C. Page ....June, 1876–1876

* Tevis was listed as vice president on a letterhead used in 1896.

F. B. Taylor .... September, 1876–1879 (?)
D. G. Scofield .... September, 1876–January 8, 1901
J. S. Severance ..... January 8, 1901–September, 1901
H. S. King .... January 8, 1901–September, 1901
C. O. G. Miller .... January 8, 1901–September, 1901
P. T. Morgan ...... January 8, 1901–September, 1901
Alfred Sutro .... January 8, 1901–September, 1901

CONTINENTAL OIL AND TRANSPORTATION COMPANY OF CALIFORNIA, 1877–1885

The Continental Oil and Transportation Company of California was incorporated November 27, 1877. Its plant and business was bought in 1885 by the Standard Oil Company (Iowa), which was formed to unite CO&T and the Pacific Coast operations of the Standard Oil Company (Ohio).

President

G. S. Guernsy ...... November, 1877–1878 (?)
F. B. Taylor ...... 1878 (?)–1879 (?)
I. E. Blake .... 1879 (?)–1885

Vice President

G. S. Guernsy ...... 1878 (?)–1884 (?)
George Loomis .... 1884 (?)–1885

Secretary

D. G. Scofield ...... 1877 (?)–1880 (?)
H. L. Tevis .... 1880 (?)–1882 (?)
              1884 (?)–1885 (?)
Hugh Tevis .... 1882 (?)–1884 (?)

Directors

I. E. Blake .... November, 1877–1885
* G. F. Bragg ...... November, 1877–(?)
G. S. Guernsy ..... November, 1877–(?)
D. G. Scofield ..... November, 1877–(?)
F. B. Taylor .... November, 1877–(?)

* Bragg died July 18, 1879

Standard Oil Company (Iowa), 1885–1906

The Standard Oil Company (Iowa) was incorporated June 15, 1885. Although the corporation was not officially dissolved until November 18, 1911, its active life ceased with the sale of its property to the Standard Oil Company (California), October 4, 1906. Officers and directors appointed after that date are not listed.

President

E. A. Tilford ......June 22, 1885–December 21, 1891
W. H. Tilford ......December 21, 1891–May 20, 1907

Vice President

W. H. Tilford ......June 22, 1885–December 21, 1891
H. M. Tilford ......June 28, 1895–May 20, 1907

Secretary

G. H. Vilas ....June 22, 1885–May 27, 1890
L. D. Clarke ......May 27, 1890–May 24, 1900
W. S. Miller ....May 24, 1900–October 9, 1906

Treasurer

G. H. Vilas ....June 22, 1885–May 27, 1890
L. D. Clarke ....May 27, 1890–September 29, 1890
W. S. Miller ....September 29, 1890–October 9, 1906

Directors

John D. Archbold ...June 17, 1885–May 10, 1888
                    May 11, 1893–May 14, 1903
Lloyd Tevis ....June 17, 1885–November, 1892
E. A. Tilford ......June 17, 1885–December 21, 1891
W. H. Tilford ......June 17, 1885–May 20, 1907
G. H. Vilas ....June 17, 1885–May 10, 1888
C. M. Pratt ....May 10, 1888–May 20, 1907
W. P. Thompson ...May 10, 1888–May 9, 1889
O. T. Waring ......May 9, 1889–May 14, 1903
H. M. Tilford ......December 21, 1891–May 11, 1911
L. J. Drake ....May 14, 1903–November 27, 1911
E. C. Halsey ......May 14, 1903–May 10, 1906
H. G. Wescott ......May 10, 1906–May 14, 1908

Table I: OIL PRODUCED IN THE STATE OF CALIFORNIA AND BY THE PACIFIC COAST OIL CO., 1865–1899

Year	California, U.S.G.S. Series (Bbls./Year)	California, Composite Series (Bbls./Year)	California, Composite Series (Bbls./Day)	P C O (Bbls./Day)
Prior to 1865		200		
1865		1,500	4	
1866		12,000	33	
1867		14,000	38	
1868		3,000	8	
1869		3,000	8	
1870		3,000	8	
1871		4,000	11	
1872		8,000	22	
1873		3,000	8	
1874		3,000	8	
1875		4,000	11	
Prior to 1876	175,000	58,700	—	
1876	12,000	18,000	49	
1877	13,000	36,000	99	
1878	15,227	21,000	58	
1879	19,858	13,543	37	n.a.
1880	40,552	41,981	115	n.a.
1881	99,862	99,860	274	n.a.
1882	128,636	128,635	352	n.a.
1883	142,857	142,857	391	n.a.
1884	262,000	187,209	512	n.a.
1885	325,000	208,571	571	n.a.
1886	377,145	260,714	714	493
1887	678,572	295,524	810	452
1888	690,333	404,762	1,106	277
1889	303,220	303,220	831	260
1890	307,360	307,360	842	310
1891	323,600	323,600	887	361
1892	385,049	385,049	1,052	333
1893	470,179	470,179	1,288	426
1894	705,969	705,969	1,934	473
1895	1,208,482	1,208,482	3,311	473
1896	1,252,777	1,252,777	3,423	444
1897	1,903,411	1,903,411	5,215	398
1898	2,257,207	2,257,207	6,184	371
1899	2,642,095	2,642,095	7,239	420

Sources: The Composite Series is made up of estimates from many sources. Figures prior to 1879 are estimates based on fragmentary contemporary reports. The reports used were the more sober ones, relatively uninflated by the optimism of promoters and by the production from springs and tunnels which was allowed to flow away uncollected. Figures for the years 1879–1888 are those published estimates which were best supported by various reports of production of companies, fields, and wells. The figures are drawn from the *Commercial Herald, S.F. Journal of Commerce, S.F. Chronicle,* and Youle's estimates in the *7th Annual Report of the State Mineralogist.* Beginning in 1889, the United States Geological Survey figures appear to be uniformly reasonable and are used in the composite series. Perhaps at this time, or within the next five years, the U.S.G.S. began to use reports from producers instead of estimates by correspondents; its report for 1894 implies this was its practice. The State Mining Bureau adopted this technique in 1894, and ceased to rely on the U.S.G.S. However, the two series are in substantial agreement. PCO figures for 1886 and 1887 are estimates; all others are from the Newhall Division's "Abstract of Receipts & Deliveries" report with a three-month extrapolation for 1888.

Table II: OIL PRODUCED BY PACIFIC COAST OIL CO. AND STANDARD OIL CO. (CALIFORNIA), OIL ACQUIRED BY PRODUCTION AND PURCHASE, PERCENTAGE OF FIELD PRODUCTION ACQUIRED BY STANDARD,[1] 1900-1919. (BARRELS PER DAY)

Year	Newhall and Ventura County[2] Production	Receipts, Except Exchanges	Receipts as a % of Field Production	Kern River, Incl. Kern Front Production	Receipts, Except Exchanges	Receipts as a % of Field Production	Coalinga Production	Receipts, Except Exchanges	Receipts as a % of Field Production	Santa Maria-Lompoc Production	Receipts, Except Exchanges	Receipts as a % of Field Production	Midway-Sunset, McKittrick, Elk Hills Production	Receipts, Except Exchanges	Receipts as a % of Field Production
1900	429	429	26	0	n.a.[3]	0	0	0	0	0	0	0	0	n.a.	n.a.
1901	485	505	28	0	n.a.	n.a.	0	n.a.	n.a.	0	0	0	0	n.a.[4]	n.a.
1902	312	314	19	0	7,411	30	0	n.a.	n.a.	0	0	0	0	228	11
1903	357	469	25	0	12,671	28	0	2,482	42	0	12	2	0	189	4
1904	333	450	25	0	15,362	33	0	9,208	66	0	394	21	0	0	0
1905	267	267	20	0	8,555	20	0	15,249	63	0	2,254	24	0	0	0
1906	167	204	18	0	7,847	22	0	11,846	51	0	4,959	38	0	0	0
1907	200	219	18	0	5,757	17	1,666	12,835	52	0	5,065	22	0	378	4
1908	220	234	17	0	4,143	11	2,775	14,139	48	0	8,343	35	29	1,106	8
1909	233	216	15	0	3,778	10	3,429	16,901	41	0	5,033	23	187	5,214	19
1910	329	243	14	0	4,800	12	3,015	16,779	33	0	2,463	12	3,777	18,123	26
1911	333	381	21	0	5,871	15	2,676	15,012	30	0	1,250	6	5,684	38,042	43
1912	273	848	36	0	5,599	16	2,695	17,201	32	0	421	2	8,055	44,100	44
1913	269	1,416	51	12	747	3	2,707	18,904	37	0	186	1	19,175	39,519	33
1914	272	1,431	54	36	3,008	16	2,873	16,110	37	0	196	2	19,312	50,574	34
1915	254	969	34	294	3,107	14	2,618	6,009	16	0	158	2	17,531	47,744	41
1916	256	454	15	1,299	3,927	17	2,397	5,469	14	1	176	1	16,950	42,075	37
1917	271	321	10	1,228	4,291	18	2,929	5,157	12	92	125	2	16,519	35,657	33
1918	234	255	7	1,310	4,785	22	3,724	3,868	9	0	126	1	13,875	26,779	26
1919	211	243	5	1,731	6,326	31	4,346	4,181	9	0	73	0	14,520	24,796	26

1. Unfortunately, these figures do not reflect important modifications of the flow pattern resulting from exchanges of fuel oil for light crude which began in 1912. Since fuel oil included reservoir stocks and refinery residuum which could not be identified with a field or year of production, exchanges are excluded. Receipts of light crude are included in Table IV. In other respects, the limitations of these figures must be recognized. There is no way of determining the exact percentage of production which was acquired in any one time period because the oil run may have been produced in an earlier time period and stored. (This is not, however, the explanation for Newhall production exceeding acquisitions in 1909 and 1910; the reason is unknown.) Another limitation to the use of these figures is that receipts less production do not exactly equal purchases because the figures are from different sources. Standard's figures for field production are, of course, unofficial so far as other companies are concerned.

2. While Standard's production was entirely from the Newhall District (Pico and Elsmere fields), statistics of company receipts of oil were not segregated between Newhall and Ventura County because the same pipeline served both. Although the Newhall District is in Los Angeles County, geologically speaking, it belongs to the Santa Clara basin, which is largely in Ventura County.

3. Purchases of Kern River in the last six months averaged 4,070 B/D.

4. Purchases of McKittrick oil in the last six months averaged 312 B/D. Purchases in 1900-1903 were entirely from McKittrick; they were then discontinued until 1914.

Sources: Producing Department, Newhall Division, Abstract of Oil Receipts and Deliveries report, 1900-03; Economics Department records of company and California production, 1900-19; Pipe Line Department monthly reports, 1901-19.

Table II (continued): OIL PRODUCED BY PACIFIC COAST OIL CO. AND STANDARD OIL CO. (CALIFORNIA), OIL ACQUIRED BY PRODUCTION AND PURCHASE, PERCENTAGE OF FIELD PRODUCTION ACQUIRED BY STANDARD, 1900–1919.
(BARRELS PER DAY)

	Lost Hills and Belridge			Whittier–Fullerton[5]			Los Angeles City and Salt Lake			California		
Year	Production	Receipts, Except Exchanges	Receipts as a % of Field Production	Production	Receipts, Except Exchanges	Receipts as a % of Field Production	Production	Receipts, Except Exchanges	Receipts as a % of Field Production	Production	Receipts, Except Exchanges	Receipts as a % of State Production
1900	0	0	0	0		0	0	0	0	429	429	4
1901	0	0	0	0	n.a.[6]	n.a.	0	0	0	485	n.a.	n.a.
1902	0	0	0	0	722	15[7]	0	0	0	312	8,674	22
1903	0	0	0	0	596	9	0	0	0	357	16,419	25
1904	0	0	0	0	464	8	0	0	0	333	25,950	32
1905	0	0	0	0	0	0	0	190	3	267	26,514	28
1906	0	0	0	0	0	0	0	1,076	15	167	25,933	29
1907	0	0	0	0	0	0	0	879	10	1,866	25,132	23
1908	0	0	0	0	0	0	0	500	4	3,024	28,542	22
1909	0	0	0	0	0	0	0	170	1	3,849	31,311	20
1910	0	0	0	0	0	0	0	0	0	7,121	42,408	20
1911	0	0	0	40	1,065	5	0	0	0	8,693	61,621	27
1912	158	2,111	29	4,979	4,281	20	0	0	0	11,221	74,233	30
1913	1,370	4,485	31	13,799	10,465	36	0	0	0	28,512	75,721	28
1914	1,632	2,794	21	12,688	20,994	54	0	5	0	37,924	95,106	33
1915	1,345	2,109	18	17,645	18,765	53	0	0	0	34,730	78,312	32
1916	1,602	2,014	15	27,556	21,138	53	0	0	0	40,150	75,253	30
1917	1,465	2,124	12	42,842	29,581	59	0	0	0	50,060	77,256	29
1918	1,243	1,800	12	49,584	46,455	68	0	0	0	63,228	84,488	30
1919	1,106	1,562	13		52,619	67	0	0	0	71,498	92,539	33

5. Includes Whittier, Fullerton, Brea Canyon, Olinda, Puente, East Coyote, West Coyote, Montebello, and Richfield fields.
6. Purchases of oil the last six months averaged 153 B/D.
7. The production of this field was 4,737 B/D according to the U.S.G.S. Bul. 309, p. 136. Statistical series which use State Mining Bureau figures for Orange County to represent this field are in error because they fail to include production across the borders of neighboring Los Angeles County.

Table III: CRUDE PRODUCTION BY MAJOR CALIFORNIA COMPANIES,[1] 1908–1919
(BARRELS PER DAY)

Company	1908	1909	1910	1911	1912	1913	1914	1915	1916	1917	1918	1919
Standard of California	3,031	3,849	7,115	8,695	11,221	28,439	37,730	34,721	39,976	49,996	63,228	71,415
Per Cent of Calif.	2	2	3	4	5	11	13	14	16	19	23	26
Associated	22,426	27,237	29,633	27,371	28,763	29,127	21,520	24,406	28,464	28,960	26,795	24,460
Per Cent of Calif.	17	17	14	12	12	11	8	10	11	11	10	9
Union	19,755	18,600	36,578	21,123	17,943	17,998	17,689	14,418	19,616	21,233	23,832	24,693
Per Cent of Calif.	15	12	17	9	7	7	6	6	8	8	9	9
Independent Agency	13,959	24,246	26,147	28,242	28,771	34,319	32,497	30,029	29,990	28,196	26,163	24,381
Per Cent of Calif.	11	15	12	12	12	13	11	12	12	11	9	9
Southern Pacific Co.	5,732	5,914	9,566	12,152	18,722	24,649	26,813	27,937	26,737	25,959	25,494	26,158
Per Cent of Calif.	4	4	5	5	8	9	9	11	11	10	9	9
A.T. & S.F. RR.	4,044	5,426	6,928	11,725	12,622	12,297	10,906	9,884	9,217	10,785	11,103	10,325
Per Cent of Calif.	3	3	3	5	5	5	4	4	4	4	4	4
General Petroleum					5,359	10,152	12,335	10,462	10,448	13,087	12,134	11,165
Per Cent of Calif.					2	4	4	4	4	5	4	4
Shell							8,764[2]	8,801	13,106	17,481	18,616	18,549
Per Cent of Calif.							3	4	5	7	7	7
Others	63,039	74,157	96,903	120,128	122,704	111,148	115,647[2]	84,730	73,327	70,790	71,095	66,174
Per Cent of Calif.	48	47	46	52	50	41	41	35	29	27	25	24
Total	131,986	159,429	212,870	229,436	246,105	268,129	283,901	245,388	250,881	266,487	278,460	277,320

1. These figures are estimates of gross production, unadjusted for royalty. Standard's production sometimes differs slightly from Table I for reasons unknown, but the discrepancies are insignificant.
2. The Shell figure, and the consequent reduction of the "Others" category, is an approximation based on net crude production for the last four months of 1913 and the year 1914 reported in Beaton, *Enterprise in Oil*, p. 784.

Source: Economics Department Records.

Table IV: STANDARD'S PIPELINE RUNS, STOCKS, AND PRICES OF LIGHT CRUDE, 1900-1919

Year	Runs From Wells[1] (Bbls/Day)	Runs From Wells (Bbls)	Stocks on Dec. 31[2]	Price of 22° Crude in San Joaquin Valley on Dec. 31	Price of 22° Crude in Whittier-Fullerton on Dec. 31
1901	434[3]	n.a.[3]	n.a.	n.a.	n.a.
1902	1,003	366,000	n.a.	n.a.	n.a.
1903	3,505	1,279,000	555,000	n.a.	n.a.
1904	10,409	3,810,000	650,000	n.a.	n.a.
1905	17,733	6,473,000	2,672,000	n.a.	n.a.
1906	17,010	6,209,000	2,309,000	n.a.	n.a.
1907	18,047	6,587,000	995,000	n.a.	n.a.
1908	22,704	8,287,000	1,148,000	n.a.	n.a.
1909	22,110	8,070,000	1,306,000	$0.50	n.a.
1910	23,240	8,483,000	939,000	0.45	$0.75
1911	38,109	13,910,000	3,482,000	0.45	0.70
1912	53,923	19,736,000	5,762,000	0.50	0.70
1913	81,525	29,757,000	10,888,000	0.50	0.65
1914	99,165	36,195,000	18,135,000	0.40	0.425
1915	78,923	28,807,000	16,981,000	0.48	0.53
1916	61,395	22,470,000	12,805,000	0.78	0.78
1917	68,555	25,023,000	6,409,000	1.03	1.03
1918	89,784	32,771,000	5,138,000	1.28	1.28
1919	94,837	34,615,000	2,652,000	1.31	1.31

1. The tables of light and heavy crude demonstrate (1) Standard's primary interest in crude that would yield profitable quantities of kerosine and gasoline and (2) the growing quantities of refinable crude available. However, this table does not represent exactly the crude bought and produced for refining. The definition of refinable crude is not rigid. In 1902 Rheem considered 25° crude refinable and crudes 20°–25° as marginal. Some statistical series have used 20°; others 18° as the break point. Moreover, heavier crudes were distilled for lube oil and their light products added to those of "refinable crude." A second qualification is that run figures were not always split between light and heavy, e.g., some heavy Coalinga oil was purchased, but the entire field averaged light and until 1914 was reported as light oil. A third qualification is that purchases of distillates, foreign crude and possibly domestic crude from seaboard tankage did not pass through the Pipe Line Department and are not reflected in this table.
2. Stocks are estimated field stocks prior to 1906; gauged field and refinery crude stocks, 1906–1914; gauged field stocks thereafter. Stocks include oils. partly distilled at Bakersfield and stored pending running through Richmond for further distillation.
3. Based on a total of 80,000 in the last six months only; earlier figures not available.

Sources: Pipe Line Department, Crude Oil Stocks, Receipts, Shipments, 1901–15, and monthly statements, 1901–19; Producing Department, Newhall Division, Abstract of Receipts and Deliveries report, 1901–03; *Report of the Federal Trade Commission on the Pacific Coast Petroleum Industry . . . April 7, 1921.*

Table V: STANDARD'S PIPELINE RUNS, STOCKS, AND PRICES OF HEAVY CRUDE, 1900–1919

Year	Runs From Wells[1] (Bbls/Day)	Runs From Wells (Bbls)[1]	Stocks on Dec. 31[2]	Price of Crude under 18° in San Joaquin Valley on Dec. 31	Price of Crude under 18° in Whittier-Fullerton on Dec. 31
1901	4,585[3]	n.a.[3]	n.a.	n.a.	n.a.
1902	7,674	2,801,000	n.a.	n.a.	n.a.
1903	12,991	4,742,000	5,300,000	n.a.	n.a.
1904	15,470	5,662,000	9,950,000	n.a.	n.a.
1905	8,781	3,205,000	11,600,000	n.a.	n.a.
1906	8,923	3,257,000	12,753,000	n.a.	n.a.
1907	7,085	2,586,000	11,732,000	n.a.	n.a.
1908	5,838	2,131,000	11,420,000	n.a.	n.a.
1909	9,202	3,359,000	11,367,000	$0.50	n.a.
1910	19,168	6,996,000	14,730,000	$0.30	n.a.
1911	23,513	8,582,000	18,741,000	$0.30	n.a.
1912	21,473	7,859,000	21,908,000	$0.00[4]	n.a.
1913	4,376	1,597,000	13,501,000	$0.35	n.a.
1914	9,962	3,636,000	7,923,000	$0.375	n.a.
1915	11,792	4,304,000	9,701,000	$0.43	$0.48
1916	14,590	5,325,000	9,948,000	$0.73	$0.73
1917	15,014	5,480,000	8,691,000	$0.98	$0.98
1918	16,163	5,900,000	6,688,000	$1.23	$1.23
1919	16,579	6,051,000	9,570,000	$1.23	$1.23

1. Beginning November, 1912, a part of Standard's heavy oil runs were not available for sale or refining since they went to the Southern Pacific in exchange for light oil. (The light oil received is included in Table IV.) The figures above cannot be adjusted for deliveries to the S.P. without extreme distortion because delivery figures included large quantities from storage and from refineries as well as from current heavy crude production and purchases.
2. Stocks are estimated field stocks prior to 1906; gauged field refinery crude stocks, 1906–1914; gauged field stocks thereafter. Stocks include residuum from the Bakersfield topping operation.
3. Based on a total of 844,000 in the last 6 months only; earlier figures not available.
4. Standard accepted heavy crude only if obligated by contract.

Sources: Pipe Line Department, Crude Oil Stock, Receipts, Shipments, 1901–15 and monthly statements, 1901–19; Producing Department, Newhall Division, Abstract of Receipts and Deliveries report, 1901–03; *Report of the Federal Trade Commission on the Pacific Coast Petroleum Industry . . . April 7, 1921.*

Table VI: CRUDE RUN TO STILLS,[1] 1900–1919
(BARRELS PER DAY)

Year	Alameda	Richmond	El Segundo	Bakersfield	Total Crude Run to Stills
1900	347[2]				347
1901	358				358
1902	902				902
1903		2,698			2,698
1904		9,450			9,450
1905		12,058			12,058
1906		17,502			17,502
1907		22,227			22,227
1908		23,215			23,215
1909		24,058			24,058
1910		25,805			25,805
1911		31,654			31,654
1912		45,716	4,918		50,634
1913		57,552	11,262	7,032	75,846
1914		53,406	18,330	13,700	85,436
1915		50,873	19,246	23,071	93,190
1916		42,474[3]	19,843	23,295	85,612
1917		46,793[3]	30,588	17,971	95,352
1918		44,726[3]	33,823	4,919	83,468
1919		49,155	35,062	11,319	95,536

1. Excludes purchased distillates, which, however, raised the refineries' capacity to turn out finished products.
2. Last eight months.
3. Richmond was charging substantial quantities of Bakersfield tops and crude equivalent which, having been already distilled at Bakersfield, are not included in Richmond's runs of crude.

Sources: S.O. (New Jersey) Comptroller's Department, Analysis of Business report, 1901–07; S.O. (California) Manufacturing Department yield statements and yield records, 1906–19; H. W. Whitworth to R. J. Hanna, June 1, 1917; S.O. (California) reports to the U.S. Bureau of Mines, 1918–19.

Table VIII: CRUDE RUN TO STILLS BY, AND PRINCIPAL PRODUCTS OF STANDARD,
REFINERS IN CALIFORNIA, AND THE UNITED STATES, 1899–1919[1]
(BARRELS PER DAY)

Year	Crude Run to Stills			Gasoline, Naphtha, Engine Distillate			Kerosine			Lubricating Oil			Fuel Oil and Gas Oil		
	PCO/ Standard	California	United States	PCO/ Standard	California	United States	PCO/ Standard	California	United States	PCO/ Standard	California	United States	PCO/ Standard	California	United States
1899	n.a.	931	142,496	n.a.	189	18,316	n.a.	150	82,098	n.a.	6	11,119	n.a.	274	19,880
1904	9,450	11,939	183,013	479	774	18,902	1,907	2,108	88,261	147	176	20,486	6,236	2,378	23,450
1909	24,058	36,934	330,892	1,411	2,051	35,247	4,991	5,639	109,250	547	609	35,049	19,848	12,823	111,007
1914	84,308	114,799	524,007	12,714[a]	15,982[a]	95,241[a]	9,877[a]	10,892[a]	126,242[a]	891	994	33,766	58,847	81,324	243,582
1916	85,659	171,995	674,842	10,771	20,133	133,937	6,196	8,404	94,686	1,776	2,695	40,628	63,742	122,298	303,402
1917	95,146	199,862	863,375	13,792	25,233	185,945	8,275	9,732	112,641	2,252	5,117	49,170	69,314	141,540	424,874
1918	83,473	182,096	893,219	15,302	28,336	232,896	5,726	6,691	119,071	3,169	4,367	54,890	58,411	139,190	477,586
1919	95,536	199,817	990,466	14,309	27,253	258,178	13,235	15,757	152,748	3,076	4,280	55,236	68,238	150,068	497,540

1. Many of the figures for Standard differ from Tables VI and VII because, wherever possible, components of the state figures were used for the sake of comparison. Unfortunately, for the census years 1899, 1904, 1909, and 1914, Standard's report is available only for 1914.

2. Standard's 1914 report for gasoline and kerosine seems to have been badly distorted by its handling of Bakersfield tops and crude equivalent. For lack of an unfinished oils section on the form, these Bakersfield oils appear to have been recorded in the "all other" category in the naphtha section, overstating that figure. It also appears that kerosine produced by Richmond from the Bakersfield oils was excluded. Judging from another statement of Standard's finished oils, the 1914 census figures should be adjusted downward by 4,390 B/D, and kerosine upward by 1,219 B/D.

Sources: S.O. (New Jersey) Comptroller's Department, Analysis of Business report, 1904; S.O. (California) Manufacturing Department yield statements, 1909; H. W. Whitworth to R. J. Hanna, June 1, 1917; Secretary's Department, reports to Bureau of Census, 1914, to FTC 1916–19, and data prepared for Senate hearings (LaFollette investigation); *U.S. Census of Manufactures*, 1899, 1904, 1909, and 1914; *Report of the FTC on the Pacific Coast Petroleum Industry . . . April 7, 1921*; U.S. Bureau of Mines *Bulletin 280*.

Table VII: PRINCIPAL PRODUCTS OF THE REFINERIES, 1900–1919
(BARRELS PER DAY)

Year	Gasoline and Naphtha				Engine Distillate				Kerosine				Lubricating Oils				Fuel Oil			
	Alameda/Richmond[1]	El Segundo	Bakersfield	Total	Alameda/Richmond[1]	El Segundo	Bakersfield	Total	Alameda/Richmond[1]	El Segundo	Bakersfield	Total	Alameda/Richmond[1]	El Segundo	Bakersfield	Total	Alameda/Richmond[1]	El Segundo	Bakersfield	Total
1900	18[2]			18[2]	30[2]			30[2]	71[2]			71[2]	20[2]			20[2]	18[2]			18[2]
1901	54[3]			54[3]	[3]			[3]	111			111	47			47	54			54
1902	100[3]			100[3]	[3]			[3]	206			206	65			65	364			364
1903	287[3]			287[3]	[3]			[3]	571			571	164			164	1,237			1,237
1904	479[3]			479[3]	[3]			[3]	1,907			1,907	147			147	6,113			6,113
1905	728[3]			728[3]	[3]			[3]	2,599			2,599	227			227	7,915			7,915
1906	696			696	320			320	4,007			4,007	339			339	13,910			13,910
1907	798			798	377			377	4,365			4,365	449			449	20,478			20,478
1908	1,203			1,203	429			429	5,022			5,022	484			484	17,387			17,387
1909	832			832	579			579	4,991			4,991	547			547	19,616			19,616
1910	913			913	858			858	3,255			3,255	653			653	21,182			21,182
1911	1,184			1,184	910			910	5,417			5,417	653			653	24,425			24,425
1912	1,853	394		2,247	1,499	583		2,082	7,885	202		6,427	782	0		782	31,221	2,921		34,142
1913	2,299	1,074	195[4]	3,540	1,475	812	179[4]	2,441	7,998	626	0[4]	8,624	851	0	0[4]	851	38,524	6,725	6,868[4]	51,037
1914	3,205	1,750	236	5,191	2,017	887	229	3,133	10,441	655	0	11,096	902	0	0	902	35,509	12,445	9,166	57,120
1915	2,744	1,828	294	4,866	1,913	441	258	2,612	7,931	643	0	8,574	1,168	14	0	1,182	32,421	13,253	14,904	60,578
1916	3,716	2,621	418	6,755	4,206	179	308	4,693	5,301	533	0	5,834	1,789	172	0	1,961	32,725	14,058	15,798	62,581
1917	5,158	4,899	499	10,556	2,231	560	444	3,235	7,571	705	0	8,276	2,003	249	0	2,252	33,049	23,005	11,630	67,684
1918	5,398	5,585	583	11,566	2,094	1,288	355	3,737	4,914	812	0	5,726	2,865	304	0	3,169	30,669	22,892	3,277	56,838
1919	4,758[5]	5,615[5]	710[5]	11,083[5]	2,173[5]	644[5]	208[5]	3,025[5]	8,687[5]	2,833[5]	0[5]	11,520[5]	3,000[5]	303[5]	0[5]	3,303[5]	33,116[5]	23,171[5]	9,386[5]	65,673[5]

1. Alameda ceased operation and Richmond began operation in 1902.
2. Final 8 months.
3. Gasoline statistics include engine distillate.
4. Final 313 days.
5. First 6 months.

Sources: S.O. (New Jersey) Comptroller's Department, Analysis of Business report, 1901–05; H. W. Whitworth to R. J. Hanna, June 1, 1917; S.O. (California) Secretary's Department, reports to FTC, 1917–19.

Table IX: WESTERN SALES OF MAJOR PETROLEUM PRODUCTS BY THE STANDARD OIL COMPANY (IOWA), 1890-1906, AND THE STANDARD OIL COMPANY (CALIFORNIA), 1906-1919[1]
(BARRELS)

Year	Gasoline and Naphtha	Engine Distillate	Kerosine	Lubricating Oils	Gas Oils	Fuel Oil	Road Oil and Asphalt
1890	30,170		246,048	15,945			
1891	41,957		306,296	17,188			
1892	53,580		315,235	20,235			
1893	64,164		336,888	24,812			
1894	75,729		355,457	22,902			
1895	85,168		377,468	28,760			
1896	87,728		378,165	31,583			
1897	88,521	1,339	383,585	39,075		5,452	
1898	109,725	2,204	414,854	42,051		33,507	
1899	115,409	23,789	411,588	45,185		35,221	
1900	132,284	40,877	430,712	49,866		24,756	
1901	155,853	37,652	447,708	63,874	49,224	298,738	
1902	175,800	55,101	473,919	80,380	25,930	1,003,563	
1903	193,539	64,324	469,235	92,542	9,067	1,882,371	
1904	209,559	82,917	462,033	91,258	17,676	3,014,642	
1905	250,009	91,828	473,663	107,507	20,250	3,890,781	
1906	290,285	121,916	492,290	128,847	37,489	5,380,004	
1907	313,840	133,405	507,259	150,424	50,730	7,429,040	
1908	365,967	148,506	497,695	142,525	54,456	6,087,061	
1909	437,198	218,311	523,496	163,560	72,038	6,585,879	98,287
1910	547,758	285,631	537,974	187,010	91,935	7,663,167	199,088
1911	692,760	357,797	571,304	194,304	141,256	9,446,565	411,548
1912	932,090	456,677	601,530	217,766	130,635	12,170,322	571,722
1913	1,124,586	540,095	629,754	248,478	1,000,470	14,753,643	519,887
1914	1,322,816	611,934	640,022	233,634	753,114	12,299,993	485,741
1915	1,750,041	672,092	634,194	223,106	428,472	12,554,336	564,207
1916	2,080,589	796,450	723,397	282,883	525,496	14,316,665	590,256
1917	2,896,262	1,125,691	807,560	395,493	553,508	16,608,542	660,086
1918	3,650,893	1,287,906	920,332	462,829	432,672	16,420,540	259,619
1919	4,616,532	1,257,854	1,145,194	503,988	511,326	13,689,093	466,105

1. These are sales through agencies in the western states, Alaska, and Honolulu. The years 1893–1898, inclusive, include the Vancouver, B.C., Agency.

Source: Marketing Department, Annual Sales Statements, 1890–1922.

Table X: EXPORT AND EASTERN SALES OF MAJOR PETROLEUM PRODUCTS
(BARRELS)

Year	Naphtha and Gasoline	Engine Distillate	Kerosine	Lubricating Oils	Gas Oils	Fuel Oil	Road Oil and Asphalt
1912[1]	20,444	n.a.[2]	2,303,845	36,831	23,615	1,155,247	46,198
1913	154,011	n.a.[2]	2,623,141	56,172	32,869	3,176,941	105,474
1914	111,465	47,911	3,585,709	101,973	40,079	3,153,005	154,287
1915	138,184	163,485	2,250,566	240,758	14,577	2,311,068	190,189
1916	616,187	491,729	1,776,073	353,630	13,028	3,452,480	273,986
1917	805,603	411,877	2,076,231	408,265	81,249	3,588,781	153,764
1918	840,878	300,220	1,456,838	702,953	66,866	4,385,321	109,095
1919	403,290	27,915	3,773,241	535,536	58,240	2,654,564	134,224

1. Figures prior to 1912 are not available except for exports of refined oil from Richmond: 73,026 bbls. in 1904; 323,690, in 1905; 1,046,279, in 1906; 1,382,336, in 1907. *U.S.A.* v. *Standard Oil Co. of N.J.*, *et al.*, Defendant's Exhibit 285.
2. Engine distillate apparently was included in the naphtha and gasoline figures.

Source: Marketing Department, Annual Sales Statements, 1891–1922.

Table XI: GROSS SALES IN THE WESTERN MARKET COMPARED WITH SALES IN EASTERN AND FOREIGN MARKETS, 1907–1919

Year	Petroleum Products Sold in Western Market		Petroleum Products Sold in Eastern and Export Market		All Sales, Petroleum and Miscellaneous Products
	Sales Value	% of All Sales	Sales Value	% of All Sales	
1907	$14,248,000	80.8	$ 2,927,000	16.6	$ 17,631,000
1908	13,511,000	76.9	3,588,000	20.4	17,576,000
1909	15,698,000	83.5	2,554,000	13.6	18,795,000
1910	18,303,000	89.2	1,659,000	8.1	20,529,000
1911	19,711,000	83.5	3,418,000	14.5	23,614,000
1912	25,345,000	80.9	5,358,000	17.1	31,312,000
1913	28,100,000	75.0	8,692,000	23.2	37,464,000
1914	27,742,000	70.6	10,921,000	27.8	39,315,000
1915	28,035,000	72.5	9,800,000	25.3	38,690,000
1916	40,436,000	71.8	14,999,000	26.6	56,320,000
1917	58,632,000	73.1	20,352,000	25.4	80,228,000
1918	74,840,000	72.2	27,152,000	26.2	103,613,000
1919	92,304,000	76.7	26,083,000	21.7	120,406,000

Source: Comptroller's Department, Directors' Comparative Statement, 1921.

Table XII: STANDARD'S WESTERN SALES OF GASOLINE AND NAPHTHA, STANDARD'S RETAIL PRICES AT SAN FRANCISCO AND SEATTLE, AND THE WHOLESALE PRICE INDEX, 1902–1919

Year	Sales of Gasoline and Naphtha (barrels)	Retail Price of Gasoline at San Francisco as of June 30 (cents a gal.)	Retail Price of Gasoline at Seattle as of June 30 (cents a gal.)	Cost of Living Index 1890–99 = 100
1902	175,800	17	18	111
1903	193,539	17	18	116
1904	209,559	16	17	115
1905	250,009	14 1/2	16	115
1906	290,285	17 1/2	18	119
1907	313,840	18	20 1/2	126
1908	365,967	14 1/2	15 1/2	121
1909	437,198	14 1/2	15 1/2	121
1910	547,758	17	18	128
1911	692,760	14 1/2	15	132
1912	932,090	17 1/2	18	133
1913	1,124,586	16 1/2	17	137
1914	1,322,816	15	15 1/2	139
1915	1,750,041	11 1/2	12	136
1916	2,080,589	19	19 1/2	149
1917	2,896,262	20	20 1/2	179
1918	3,650,893	20	21	218
1919	4,616,532	21 1/2	22 1/2	247

Sources: Marketing Department, Annual Sales Statements, 1891–1922; Comptroller's Department, Historical Statistics (1906–1926); U.S. Department of Commerce, *Historical Statistics of the United States 1789–1945.*

Table XIII: GROWTH OF COMPANY-OPERATED MARKETING
OUTLETS, 1878–1919
(as of Dec. 31)

Year	Main and Substations	Service Stations[1]	Year	Main and Substations	Service Stations[1]
1878	1		1900	73	
1879	1		1901	75	
1880	1		1902	76	
1881	1		1903	76	
1882	1		1904	78	
1883	6		1905	82	
1884	7		1906	79	
1885	7		1907	81	
1886	10		1908	85	
1887	14		1909	88	
1888	14		1910	99	
1889	19		1911	114	
1890	23		1912	137	
1891	32		1913	170	
1892	33		1914	238	35
1893	35		1915	268	88
1894	37		1916	307	112
1895	57		1917	351	132
1896	61		1918	370	152
1897	66		1919	401	218
1898	66				
1899	67				

1. Although a device for dispensing gasoline directly to automobile tanks was rigged up at Seattle in 1907, Standard first began to operate service stations separately from main and substations in 1914 when it purchased the National Supply Company.

Sources: The station figures are estimated from a Marketing Department list of opening dates adjusted by ledgers, sales statements, and lists of stations in the *S.O. Bulletin*; service station figures are from Comptroller's Department, Historical Statistics (1906–1926).

Table XIV: BALANCE SHEETS OF STANDARD OIL COMPANY (IOWA),
1885–1906, PACIFIC COAST OIL COMPANY, 1900–1906, AND
STANDARD OIL COMPANY (CALIFORNIA), 1907–1919

(as of Dec. 31)

	1885	1886	1887	1888	1889	1890	1891	1892	1893	1894	1895	1896	1897	1898	1899
STANDARD OIL (IOWA)															
Cash	25,193	49,202	40,752	25,829	36,652	19,681	47,254	39,612	33,454	34,959	55,193	38,968	39,964	144,311	222,880
Accounts Receivable	294,117	438,028	399,614	536,366	630,387	712,465	515,001	513,689	504,324	765,366	640,846	710,711	652,959	618,456	613,911
Inventories	331,867	311,490	685,997	658,762	761,635	1,076,035	616,389	566,566	664,066	685,747	1,124,919	977,038	826,193	1,119,561	1,368,984
Plant	176,394	140,065	170,487	189,273	221,834	319,981	475,317	551,577	650,759	297,780	382,063	400,930	471,283	564,559	622,364
Total Assets	827,571	938,785	1,296,850	1,410,230	1,650,508	2,128,162	1,653,961	1,671,444	1,852,603	1,783,852	2,203,021	2,127,647	1,990,399	2,446,887	2,828,138
Liabilities	105,010	104,082	383,671	260,068	420,945	882,460	452,134	254,027	207,534	22,071	104,340	104,610	68,512	262,138	254,685
Capital	600,000	600,000	600,000	600,000	600,000	600,000	600,000	1,000,000	1,000,000	1,000,000	1,000,000	1,000,000	1,000,000	1,000,000	1,000,000
Surplus	122,561	234,703	313,179	550,162	629,563	645,702	601,827	417,417	645,069	761,781	1,098,681	1,023,037	921,887	1,184,749	1,573,453
Total Liabilities and Capital	827,571	938,785	1,296,850	1,410,230	1,650,508	2,128,162	1,653,961	1,671,444	1,852,603	1,783,852	2,203,021	2,127,647	1,990,399	2,446,887	2,828,138
Earnings	122,561	166,142	114,476	272,983	215,401	132,139	(7,875)	245,590	227,652	176,929	703,344	474,356	398,850	462,862	788,704
Dividends	0	54,000	36,000	36,000	136,000	116,000	36,000	36,000	0	0	0	550,000	500,000[1]	200,000	400,000
Special Adj. to Surplus										(60,217)[1]	(366,444)[2]				

Table XIV (Continued): BALANCE SHEETS OF STANDARD OIL COMPANY (IOWA), 1885-1906, PACIFIC COAST OIL COMPANY, 1900-1906, AND STANDARD OIL COMPANY (CALIFORNIA), 1907-1919

	1900	1901	1902	1903	1904	1905	1906	1907	1908	1909
PACIFIC COAST OIL										
Cash	$ 0	$ 32,429	$ 49,630	$ 10,964	$ 45,030	$ 195,750	$ 464,263	$ 280,950	$ 250,361	$ 265,296
Accounts Receivable	33,109	109,722	264,751	350,301	473,278	508,103	2,133,597	2,837,664	2,194,920	2,459,589
Inventories	123,424	420,983	940,716	1,923,276	3,695,936	4,500,613	6,702,095	6,667,464	8,130,664	8,829,596
Plant	687,725	1,300,279	4,921,179	6,840,122	9,045,457	10,573,722	13,230,092	15,842,962	17,530,303	18,905,248
Other Assets	49,608	856	856	856	856	856	3,100	1,356	66,355	65,500
Total Assets	$ 893,866	$1,864,269	$6,177,132	$9,125,519	$13,260,557	$15,779,044	$22,533,147	$25,630,396	$28,172,603	$30,525,229
Liabilities	$ 118,718	$1,030,514	$3,310,629	$2,982,008	$5,640,983	$7,222,661	$ 1,203,195	$ 737,547	$ 909,283	$ 7,583,660
Capital	1,000,000	1,000,000	3,000,000	6,000,000	6,000,000	6,000,000	17,000,000	17,000,000	17,000,000	17,000,000
Earned Surplus	(224,852)	(166,245)	(133,497)	143,511	1,619,574	2,556,383	4,329,952	7,892,849	10,263,320	5,941,569
Revaluation & Capital Surplus										
Total Liabilities & Capital	$ 893,866	$1,864,269	$6,177,132	$9,125,519	$13,260,557	$15,779,044	$22,533,147	$25,630,396	$28,172,603	$30,525,229
Net Earnings	$ 13,721	$ 58,607	$ 32,748	$ 277,008	$ 1,476,063	$ 936,809	$ 2,793,569	$ 4,582,897	$ 4,410,471	$ 3,838,249
Dividends—Cash	0	0		0	0	0	1,020,000	1,020,000	2,040,000	8,160,000
Dividends—Stock										
STANDARD OIL (IOWA)										
Cash	$ 330,594	$ 325,849	$ 445,805	$ 863,617	$ 132,012	$ 645,418	$ 1,000,000			
Accounts Receivable	614,115	884,536	959,032	936,492	1,017,825	1,103,335				
Inventories	1,421,718	1,288,208	1,447,655	1,601,857	1,564,410	1,703,154				
Plant	672,969	689,644	807,815	891,923	973,721	1,226,300				
Total Assets	$3,039,396	$3,188,237	$3,660,307	$4,293,889	$3,687,968	$4,678,207	$ 1,000,000			
Liabilities	$ 237,226	$ 318,289	$ 446,910	$ 591,073	$ 453,170	$ 661,099	$ 208,915			
Capital	1,000,000	1,000,000	1,000,000	1,000,000	1,000,000	1,000,000	1,000,000			
Surplus	1,802,170	1,869,948	2,213,397	2,702,816	2,234,798	3,017,108	(208,915)			
Total Liabilities & Capital	$3,039,396	$3,188,237	$3,660,307	$4,293,889	$3,687,968	$4,678,207	$ 1,000,000			
Earnings	$ 578,717	$ 817,778	$1,093,449	$1,089,419	$ 781,982	$ 1,082,310	$ 873,977			
Dividends	350,000	750,000	750,000	600,000	1,250,000	300,000	4,100,000			

Table XIV (Continued): BALANCE SHEETS OF STANDARD OIL COMPANY (IOWA),
1885–1906, PACIFIC COAST OIL COMPANY, 1900–1906, AND
STANDARD OIL COMPANY (CALIFORNIA), 1907–1919

	1910	1911	1912	1913	1914	1915	1916	1917	1918[4]	1919[4]
STANDARD OIL (CALIF.)										
Cash	$ 343,158	$ 480,479	$ 5,320,360	$ 1,065,266	$ 1,173,377	$ 1,986,663	$ 2,646,755	$ 5,356,759	$ 6,789,437	$ 5,458,496
Accounts Receivable	2,854,263	3,347,497	4,319,778	6,083,043	4,930,184	5,293,155	8,031,708	10,371,894	11,887,027	14,169,223
Inventories	11,577,146	14,585,285	19,246,014	21,724,390	25,550,919	25,017,147	26,166,272	26,799,564	29,638,612	35,247,127
Plant	22,273,232	30,334,424	38,241,001	58,743,116	65,415,338	65,834,282	72,010,646	80,979,929	83,059,845	110,752,267
Other Assets	185,500	190,750	190,750	354,939	228,465	412,085	544,878	3,415,014	13,841,774	8,550,878
Total Assets	$37,233,298	$48,938,435	$67,315,903	$87,970,754	$97,298,283	$98,543,332	$109,400,259	$126,923,160	$145,216,695	$174,177,991
Liabilities	$ 9,161,729	$ 9,725,240	$ 2,185,907	$ 7,448,017	$ 7,070,645	$ 3,754,414	$ 3,837,952	$ 12,027,471	$ 27,797,386	$ 16,577,092
Capital	17,000,000	25,000,000	44,933,994	45,183,994	49,686,655	49,686,655	74,529,983	99,373,311	99,373,311	99,373,311
Earned Surplus	11,071,569	14,213,195	20,196,002	26,614,084	31,816,324	36,377,604	22,307,665	7,136,705	9,999,311	27,475,297
Revaluation & Capital Surplus[3]				8,724,659	8,724,659	8,724,659	8,724,659	8,385,673	8,046,687	30,752,291
Total Liabilities & Capital	$37,233,298	$48,938,435	$67,315,903	$87,970,754	$97,298,283	$98,543,332	$109,400,259	$126,923,160	$145,216,695	$174,177,991
Net Earnings	$ 5,470,000	$ 3,141,626	$ 7,106,156	$10,911,481	$10,058,338	$ 9,529,946	$17,605,304	$ 18,998,616	$ 15,277,305	$ 30,937,825
Dividends—Cash	340,000	0	1,123,349	4,493,399	4,856,098	4,968,666	6,831,915	9,316,248	12,421,664	13,415,397
Dividends—Stock							24,843,328	24,843,328		

1. Depreciation, previously unrecorded, on tank cars sold.
2. Purchase of W. P. Fuller facilities.
3. Capital surplus was a $250,000 stock premium resulting from the Murphy lease in 1913.
4. Standard Oil Company (California) includes the Richmond Petroleum Company in 1918 and 1919.

Sources: Comptroller's Department, S.O. (Iowa) Statements (1885–1906), and Historical Statistics (1906–1926).

Table XV: FINANCING GROWTH OF
PACIFIC COAST OIL COMPANY, 1900–1905, AND
STANDARD OIL COMPANY (CALIFORNIA), 1906–1919
(as of Dec. 31)

	INVESTED		BORROWED		
Year	Common Stock and Capital Surplus	Reinvested Earnings	S.O. (New Jersey) Loan Account	Notes	Capital Added
1900	$1,000,000	$ (224,852)	—	—	$ 775,148
1901	1,000,000	(166,245)	$ 877,660	—	936,267
1902	3,000,000	(133,497)	3,187,864	—	4,342,952
1903	6,000,000	143,511	2,982,008	—	3,071,152
1904	6,000,000	1,619,574	5,237,523	—	3,731,578
1905	6,000,000	2,556,383	6,771,097	—	2,470,383
1906	17,000,000	4,329,952	—	—	6,002,472
1907	17,000,000	7,892,849	—	—	3,562,897
1908	17,000,000	10,263,320	—	—	2,370,471
1909	17,000,000	5,941,569	—	$6,600,000	2,278,249
1910	17,000,000	11,071,569	—	6,600,000	5,130,000
1911	25,000,000	14,213,195	—	6,950,000	11,491,626
1912	44,933,994	20,196,002	—	—	18,966,801
1913	45,433,994	26,614,084	—	—	6,918,082
1914	49,936,655	31,816,324	—	2,000,000	11,704,901
1915	49,936,655	36,377,604	—	—	2,561,280
1916	49,936,655[1]	47,150,993[1]	—	—	10,773,389
1917	49,936,655[1]	56,823,361[1]	—	—	9,672,368
1918	49,936,655[1]	59,685,967[1]	—	—	2,862,606
1919	49,936,655[1]	77,161,953[1]	—	—	17,475,986

1. A stock dividend of $24,843,328 was declared in 1916 and a second stock dividend of the same amount in 1917 but, for the purpose of this table, they have not been transferred from the earnings column to the stock column.

Source: Comptroller's Department, Historical Statistics (1906–1926).

Table XVI: NET EARNINGS OF STANDARD OIL COMPANY (CALIFORNIA) COMPARED WITH OTHER OIL COMPANIES, 1900–1919

	Net Earnings							Net Earnings as a % of the Stockholders' Equity					
Year	Standard (California)[1]	Standard (New Jersey)	Texaco[2]	Gulf	Shell Pacific Coast	Union Oil Co. of California	Associated	Standard (California)	Standard (New Jersey)	Texaco[2]	Gulf[3]	Union	Associated
1900	$ 592,000	$ 55,502,000						16.6	27.0				
1901	876,000	52,292,000						23.7	24.8				
1902	1,126,000	64,613,000	$ 303,000					18.5	27.9	9.7			
1903	1,366,000	81,337,000	794,000					13.9	30.1	21.2			
1904	2,258,000	61,570,000	505,000					20.8	20.7	9.9			
1905	2,019,000	57,459,000	978,000					16.1	18.2	13.5			
1906	3,668,000	83,122,000						16.6	23.1				
1907	4,583,000	131,275,000	2,432,000[2]	$ 1,809,000				18.4	29.1	22.7[2]	8.5		
1908	4,410,000	116,446,000	3,619,000	1,410,000				16.2	22.1	19.1	6.8		
1909	3,838,000	77,414,000	3,218,000	2,371,000				16.7	13.6	18.5	11.2		
1910	5,470,000	87,706,000	6,424,000	2,640,000				19.5	14.2	22.8	11.3		
1911	3,142,000	95,414,000	2,574,000	2,452,000	$ (11,000)			8.0	14.4	9.0	9.8		
1912	7,106,000	35,108,000	2,201,000	4,518,000	(26,983)			10.9	11.4	7.5	16.2		
1913	10,911,000	45,692,000	6,618,000	9,045,000	57,000			15.2	15.6	19.2	24.7		
1914	10,058,000	31,458,000	6,326,000	8,306,000	38,000	$2,736,000	1,255,000	12.3	10.3	15.3	18.0	6.0	2.7
1915	9,530,000	60,777,000	6,403,000	9,967,000	580,000	2,819,000	1,923,000	11.1	17.5	14.4	18.7	6.2	4.2
1916	17,605,000	70,792,000	13,797,000	17,910,000	589,000	7,225,000	3,033,000	18.2	17.8	22.3	27.5	14.3	6.5
1917	18,989,000	80,766,000	19,597,000	16,665,000	1,689,000	7,642,000	3,849,000	17.8	16.9	20.5	21.4	12.6	8.2
1918	15,277,000	57,284,000	28,272,000[2]	14,594,000	3,344,000	6,023,000	4,606,000	14.0	10.2	22.1[2]	16.6	9.6	9.4
1919	30,938,000	77,986,000	19,183,000	12,505,000				24.4	11.2	11.9	10.6		

1. 1900–1905 figures are the net earnings of both the Pacific Coast Oil Company and the Standard Oil Co. (Iowa).
2. The years 1902–1905 end April 30 in the following year. Beginning in 1907, the year ended June 30; in 1918, December 31. The earnings for 1907 are for 14 months; for 1918, 18 months.
3. These percentages were taken from a table listed as "Percentage Return on Borrowed and Invested Capital." Therefore, there may be long-term debt in the base as well as the stockholders' equity.

SOURCES: For Standard (California), Comptroller's Department Historical Statistics and Standard (Iowa) statements, 1900–05; for Standard (New Jersey), R. W. Hidy and M. E. Hidy, *Pioneering in Big Business* (New York, Harper & Brothers, 1955) and G. S. Gibb and E. H. Knowlton, *The Resurgent Years* (New York, Harper & Brothers, 1956); for Texaco, M. James, *The Texaco Story* (The Texas Co., 1953); for Gulf, J. G. McLean and R. W. Haigh, *The Growth of Integrated Oil Companies* (Boston, Division of Research, Graduate School of Business Administration, Harvard Univ., 1954); for Shell, K. Beaton, *Enterprise in Oil* (New York, Appleton-Century-Crofts, 1957); for Union and Associated, *Report of the Federal Trade Commission on The Pacific Coast Petroleum Industry . . . April 7, 1921.*

NOTES

In order to provide students of petroleum history with reasonably full information regarding the sources of this volume without creating a second volume of notes, we have used abbreviations extensively. Most are standard and readily recognized, but for some types of documents used repeatedly, special abbreviations have been employed. For example, "R" has been used for records, meaning collections of letters, ledgers, statements and the like belonging to individuals and departments listed below:

RECORD COLLECTIONS OUTSIDE THE COMPANY

Short Title	Nature of Collection	Custodian
Archbold R	Letters of John D. Archbold	Standard Oil Co. (New Jersey)
Baker R	Col. R. S. Baker letters	Huntington Library, San Marino, Calif.
Bancroft R	Sketch of I. E. Blake, C. N. Felton interview	Bancroft Library, U. of Calif. at Berkeley
Bard R-HL	Senator Thomas R. Bard letters	Huntington Library
Bard R-S	Senator Thomas R. Bard letters	Richard Bard, Somis, Calif.
Carter R	J. J. Carter diaries	Mrs. H. C. Zeis, Steubenville, Ohio
Elliott R	Mortimer F. Elliott letters	Standard Oil Co. (New Jersey)
Fernald R	Charles Fernald letters	Huntington Library
Graves R	J. A. Graves letters	Huntington Library
Pinal R	Pinal Oil Co. letters	U. of Calif. at Los Angeles
Scofield R	D. G. Scofield letters	Earle L. Scofield, El Segundo, Calif.
Stewart R	Lyman Stewart letters	Bible Institute of Los Angeles
Whitney R	J. D. Whitney letters	Bancroft Library

RECORD COLLECTIONS WITHIN THE COMPANY

The company's records are normally in the custody of the departments and subsidiaries and are identified by an abbreviation of the department or company name. The E. J. McClanahan records are preserved by the Public Relations Department.

Abbreviation	Full Title
Calexco	California Exploration Co.
Comptr.	Comptroller's Department
CRC	California Research Corp.
CSC	California Shipping Co.
Econ.	Economics Department
Exec.	Executive Office Staff
Expl.	Exploration Department
Hist.	History Project
Mfg.	Manufacturing Department
Mktg.	Marketing Department
Office Bldgs.	Office Buildings Department
Oil Pur. & Exch.	Oil Purchase & Exchange Department
Pers.	Personnel Department
P/L	Pipe Line Department
Prod.	Producing Department
Pub. Rel.	Public Relations Department
Secy.	Secretary
Treas.	Treasurer

OTHER ABBREVIATIONS

Ann. Rpt. State Min.	*Annual Report of the State* [California] *Mineralogist*
API	American Petroleum Institute
AT&SF	Atchison, Topeka, & Santa Fe
BuCorp.	Bureau of Corporations
CC	County Clerk
CHS	California Historical Society
CSMB	California State Mining Bureau
HR	Hall of Records
J.	Journal
Min. & Sci. Press	*Mining & Scientific Press*
NA	National Archives
O.&G.J.	*Oil & Gas Journal*
Pet.	Petroleum
Sac.	Sacramento, California
S.J.	San Jose, California
SONJ	Standard Oil Co. (New Jersey)
SP	⎰Southern Pacific Company ⎱Southern Pacific Railroad
Sup. Ct.	Superior Court
UP	Union Pacific
USGS	United States Geological Survey

I. THE BEGINNINGS OF A CALIFORNIA OIL INDUSTRY

1. Allan Nevins, *Study in Power: John D. Rockefeller, Industrialist & Philanthropist,* 2 vols. (N.Y., 1953); Ralph W. and Muriel E. Hidy, *Pioneering in Big Business, 1882-1911* (N.Y., 1955); Harold F. Williamson and Arnold Daum, *The American Petroleum Industry—The Age of Illumination 1859-1899* (Evanston, 1959); Ida M. Tarbell, *The History of the Standard Oil Company,* 2 vols. (N.Y., 1904).

2. Williamson and Daum, *op. cit.,* 37-38, 44-60; Kendall Beaton, *Enterprise in Oil: A History of Shell in the United States* (N.Y., 1957), 7-10; Paul Giddens, *The Birth of the Oil Industry* (N.Y., 1938), 18-23.

3. John B. Trask, *Geology of the Sierra Nevada, or California Range* (Sac., 1853), 11-12; also Assembly Doc. 14, *Rpt. on the Geology of the Coast Mts.* (Sac., 1855), 40-42.

4. Prospectus, California Petroleum Co., *A Description of the Recently Discovered Petroleum Region in California With a Report on the Same by Professor Silliman* (N.Y., 1865), 22, hereafter cited as *A Description With a Rpt. by Prof. Silliman.* Stephen F. Peckham, a young chemist who worked for the Calif. Pet. Co., the first company to attempt to develop the Ojai, concluded that the Williamson notes concerning the Ojai were either "a base fabrication or . . . a mistake [had] been made in the location of the property. . . ." (Peckham to Calif. Pet. Co., Feb. 10, 1866, in an unpublished ms. telling of his oil experiences in Calif., 1865-66, Branner Library, Stanford Univ., hereafter cited as Peckham ms.). Williamson was slated to come to Calif. in 1865 as chief engineer and superintendent of the Pacific Coast Petroleum Co., but this enterprise in San Luis Obispo County died while being launched (*Report . . . on the Coal Beds of the Pacific Coast Petroleum Company* [N.Y., 1865], Library of the DeGolyer Foundation, Dallas, Texas).

5. *Geological Rpt., Explorations and Surveys for a RR From the Miss. River to the Pacific Ocean,* 33d Cong., 2d Sess., Sen. Ex. Doc. 78, Pt. 2 (1857), V, 284-85, VII, 107-14.

6. Charles M. Coleman, *P.G.&E. of California* (N.Y., 1952), 11-15. The San Francisco Gas Co. was the earliest unit in what is today the Pacific Gas & Electric Co.

7. *Ibid.,* 34-35; Williamson and Daum, *op. cit.,* 40.

8. See note 5, *supra,* V, 285.

9. US Bu. of Mines, *Mineral Yearbook, 1868,* pp. 256-58.

10. Coleman, *op. cit.*, 11, 34, 39. A California Asphaltum Gas Co. was incorporated by three San Franciscans on Feb. 15, 1855, to manufacture gas from asphalt from the Goleta Rancho in Santa Barbara County, but we have seen no evidence that it ever operated (Secy. of State [Calif.] R; Deed Bk. A, 158-61, 326-27, Santa Barbara HR).

11. (S.F.) *Daily Alta California*, May 18, 1865, hereafter cited as the *Alta; 4th Ann. Rpt. State Min.* (1884), 293-94. The State Mineralogist gives 1857 as the date of Morrill's activities, but the newspaper account, which speaks of 1861, is correct.

12. *L. A. Star*, Mar. 31, 1860; *Alta*, Jan. 3, 1853, Aug. 3, 1860, May 26 and June 3, 1865; *S.F. Bulletin*, June 30, 1865; Bard to Peckham, Dec. 19, 1866, Peckham ms., 192.

13. *Ninety Years: The Story of William Parmer Fuller* (S.F., 1939), 51-57; W. H. Hutchinson, *California Heritage: A History of Northern California Lumbering* (Chico, Calif., ca. 1958); John Hittell, *The Commerce & Industries of the Pacific Coast* (S.F., 1882), 715.

14. Williamson and Daum, *op. cit.*, 74-114; Giddens, *op. cit.*, 54-75.

15. *Humboldt Times*, Apr., 20, 1861; *Min. & Sci. Press*, Nov. 8, 1861; Owen C. Coy, *Humboldt Bay Region, 1850-1875* (L.A., 1929), 229. This claim to the "first" Calif. well is shadowed by Gilbert's Ojai effort, which apparently was not reported in the contemporary press. What we know of his search for oil is to be found in somewhat conflicting accounts published no earlier than 1865; Silliman's description of Gilbert's "artesian well" in San Buenaventura Pac. Pet. Co. of N.Y., *100,000 Acres of Oil Land Belonging to E. Conway & Co. of San Francisco* (N.Y., 1865), 15, and a dispatch of Major Strobel in the *Alta*, May 26, 1865, in which Strobel reported that Gilbert had dug about 22 ft. before he began to bore. According to a manuscript by E. L. DeGolyer on the early California oil industry (hereafter cited as DeGolyer ms. and located in the Library of the DeGolyer Foundation, Dallas, Texas), there is also an undated statement by Gilbert telling of his work on the well in the Thomas R. Bard papers, Somis, Calif., but Bard did not come to Calif. until 1865. Gilbert dated his well as being started after the first loss of his refinery, which was reported in the *L.A. News*, May 8, 1861.

16. *S.F. Bulletin*, Nov. 11, 1861; *Min. & Sci. Press*, Nov. 30, 1861.

17. F. F. Latta, *Black Gold in the Joaquin* (Caldwell, Idaho, 1949), 265.

18. Notebooks of E. L. DeGolyer on the early Calif. oil industry, in the Library of the DeGolyer Foundation, Dallas, Texas, hereafter cited as DeGolyer notebooks; *Contra Costa Gazette*, Oct. 25, 1862; *S. J. Mercury*, June 2, 1864; *S.F. Bulletin*, June 30, 1865; J. D. Whitney, *Geology* (Philadelphia, 1865), I, 13; judgment of referee in *J. H. White* v. *E. Conway et al.* (1873), Deed Bk. 26, pp. 1-8, Recorder, Contra Costa County. The first Calif. oil company to be incorporated appears to have been the Los Angeles Brea Co., organized June 8, 1861, by Dr. John S. Griffin (a brother-in-law of the Confederate Gen. Albert Sidney Johnston), Josiah L. Brent, and Chas. Ducommun for the purpose of "selling brea, or asphaltum and manufacturing, mining for, and selling coal oil." The authorized capital and number of shares are not given. So far as we know, it never became active. (Art. of Incorporation, L.A. County HR).

19. Judgment of referee in *White* v. *Conway* (1873); San Buenaventura Pac. Pet. Co. of N.Y., *op. cit.*, 1-12.

20. DeGolyer ms.; also his "Prof. Benjamin Silliman, Jr., and Early California Oil," an address before the Miss. Valley Hist. Assn., Apr. 29, 1955, hereafter cited as "Prof. Benj. Silliman, Jr.," Hist. R; Giddens, *op. cit.*, 36-43; Williamson and Daum, *op. cit.*, 69-72.

21. DeGolyer, "Prof. Benj. Silliman, Jr.," 3-4; Rpt. of B. Silliman, Jr., to E. Conway & Co., July 11, 1864, in San Buenaventura Pac. Pet. Co. of N.Y., *op. cit.*, 13-24; *L.A. Star*, July 16, 1864.

22. DeGolyer, "Prof. Benj. Silliman, Jr.," 4-5; Giddens, *op. cit.*, 114-15.

23. DeGolyer ms.; B. Silliman, Jr., to Church, July 2, 1864, quoted in *A Description With a Rpt. by Prof. Silliman*, iii.

24. DeGolyer notebooks.

25. Walter Stalder, "A Contribution to Northern California Oil and Gas History," 9, 12, unpublished ms. in the possession of Robert Wakefield, Oakland, Calif., hereafter cited as Stalder ms.; Record Bk. of Chas. Barnard, p. 7, in the possession of Morris Barnard, Ventura, Calif. The entry in the record book of C. Barnard errs in including

the San Pedro and Conejo ranchos, but apparently is accurate for the Scott holdings in Humboldt County, which it lists at 6,675 acres.

26. Peckham ms., 150; James F. Stuart, *Frauds in Surveys of Mexican Grants Lying in California Defeated* (Wash., 1872), *passim*.

27. Minutes, Meeting of Miners held at L.A., Mar. 6, 1865, "Misc. Recs.," I, 162, and San Fernando Pet. Mining Dist. Bk. A, L.A. County HR.

28. DeGolyer ms.; Stalder ms., 9-10.

29. *A Description With a Rpt. by Prof. Silliman.* The prospectus listed a number of N.Y. financiers and brokers as members of the syndicate floating the stock including, in addition to Tom Scott, August C. Richards, John E. Williams of the Metropolitan Bank, and Henry B. Hyde, the young founder of the Equitable Life Assurance Society.

30. *Ibid.,* 9-12.

31. DeGolyer ms.; also B. Silliman, "Examination of Petroleum From California," *Amer. J. of Sci. & Arts,* XXXIX (May, 1865), 341-43.

32. Whitney to Brewer, June 19, 1865, Nov. 28, 1867, also Brewer to Whitney, May 6, 1865, Whitney R.

33. Brewer to D. L. Harris, Mar. 21, 1865, in *Springfield Republican,* Mar. 25, 1865.

34. DeGolyer, "Prof. Benj. Silliman, Jr.," 8-10. The *Alta,* S.F.'s most influential newspaper, was especially friendly to oil and the prospects of the Scott companies; the *S.F. Bulletin,* on the other hand, frequently held to the contrary view. See, for example, *S.F. Bulletin,* Feb. 8, 1865, and for much more favorable stories, June 26 and 30, 1865; also *Min. & Sci. Press,* Jan. 28, 1865.

35. Walter Stalder, "California Petroleum Co.," unpublished ms. in the possession of Robert Wakefield, Oakland, Calif.

36. *Ibid.;* Yda A. Storke, *A Memorial and Biographical History of the Counties of Santa Barbara, San Luis Obispo, and Ventura, California* (Chicago, 1891), 471-73; Sol N. Sheridan, *History of Ventura County* (Chicago, 1926), 223-27, 351-54; Peckham ms. Letterman, who is commemorated by the Army's Letterman Gen. Hospital in S.F., became a physician and coroner in that city after leaving the Phila. & Calif. Pet. Co. On Peckham, see the sketch in the *Dictionary of American Biography.* Probably Peckham's outstanding contribution to the literature on petroleum was his scholarly *Production, Technology, and Uses of Petroleum,* 47th Cong., 2d Sess., H. Misc. Doc. 42, Pt. 10, published also as *The Natural History of Petroleum,* Vol. X of the Census of 1880.

37. Bard to Peckham, July 20, 1866, in Peckham ms.; Bard to J. E. Farnum, Sep. 7, 1891, Bard R-S.

38. Bard to Peckham, Nov. 6, 1866, in Peckham ms.; DeGolyer, "Prof. Benj. Silliman, Jr.," 21, and DeGolyer ms.

39. J. DeBarth Shorb to Whitney, Feb. 28, 1874, Shorb R, Huntington Library; *L.A. News,* Dec. 15, 1865; Peckham to Calif. Pet. Co., Apr. 24, 1866, in Peckham ms.

40. DeGolyer, "Humboldt County Boom," Library of the DeGolyer Foundation, Dallas, Texas; Stalder ms., 14-15.

41. *L.A. Herald,* July 18, 1876; W. W. Orcutt, "Early Oil Development in California," *Bul. of the Amer. Assn. of Pet. Geologists,* VIII (Jan.-Feb., 1924), 64.

42. Peckham to an unnamed friend, Jan. 13, 1866, also to Stone, Dec. 13, 1865, in Peckham ms.

43. Peckham to the Calif. Pet. Co., Feb. 10 and Apr. 24, 1866, in Peckham ms., also pp. 149-50, therein.

44. XLIII (May, 1867), 345-51; also Peckham to T. I. Magill, Oct. 16, 1866, Brewer, Oct. 19, 1866, and J. DeBarth Shorb, Feb. 5, 1867, all in Peckham ms.

45. B. Silliman, Jr., "On Naphtha & Illuminating Oil from Heavy California Tar (Maltha)," *Amer. J. of Sci. & Arts,* XLIII (Mar. 1867), 245-46.

46. Peckham ms., 177.

47. Brewer to Whitney, Oct. 31, 1867, Whitney to Brewer, Sep. 28 and Nov. 28, 1867, Whitney R; DeGolyer, "Prof. Benj. Silliman, Jr.," 17. Whitney continued his attack on Silliman's part in the Calif. oil fiasco by seeking his ouster from the National Academy of Sciences. In this he failed, however. (Whitney to Brewer, May 27, 1873, Brewer to Whitney, Nov. 9, 1873, Whitney R).

48. *Min. & Sci. Press,* Dec. 2, 1865.

49. Latta, *op. cit.,* 34-54; *Min. Yearbook, 1868,* 262-63. Buena Vista was operating

on the future site of the important McKittrick field, which began to be developed in the later 1890's.

50. Lease Bk. A, 257-59, Santa Clara County HR; Art. of Incorporation, Santa Clara Pet. Co., Secy. of State (Calif.) R; DeGolyer notebooks; *Alta*, Feb. 3, 1866.

51. Stalder ms., 14-26; *7th Ann. Rpt. State Min.* (1888), 196-99.

52. *Alta*, Jan. 3, 1853, and Dec. 3, 1857; *Calif. Farmer*, July 4, 1862; Stalder, "Stanford Brothers as California Oil Pioneers," 1-3, unpublished ms. in the possession of Robert Wakefield, Oakland, Calif., hereafter cited as "Stanford Bros."; Geo. T. Clark, *Leland Stanford* (Stanford, 1931), 51-70, 92.

53. *S.F. Bulletin*, Sep. 26, 1865, quoted in Stalder, "Stanford Bros.," 6.

54. Stalder, "Stanford Bros.," 5-16.

55. *Hayes Scrapbooks*, LI, item 441, Bancroft Library, U. of Calif. at Berkeley; *S.F. Examiner*, Feb. 15, 1904; Frank M. Stanger, *Penninsula Community Book* (San Mateo, Calif., 1946), 105-06.

56. Langley's *The Pacific Coast Business Directory for 1867* (S.F., 1867), 69-70; S. F. Peckham, in Calif. Geological Survey, *Geology* (Cambridge, 1882), II, Appendix F, 64-65, 71-73; Bard to Peckham, July 20 and Nov. 6, 1866, in Peckham ms.; "Enumerators' Returns on Calif. Industry from the Census of 1870 (Products of Industry), Township No. 1, County of Santa Barbara," State Library, Sac., hereafter cited as "Enumerators' Returns from the Census of 1870." The refinery of Stanford Bros. was located at Chestnut and Taylor Streets in North Beach; Hayward & Coleman's refinery was near the foot of Bryant St. in South Beach.

57. Handwritten notes of J. H. White in A. Gesner, *A Practical Treatise on Coal, Petroleum, and Other Distilled Oils*, 2d ed. (N.Y., 1865), Stanford Collection, Stanford U. Library; *Min. Yearbook, 1868*, 261-62; Stalder, "Stanford Bros.," 19.

58. Peckham to Calif. Pet. Co., Apr. 24, 1866, in Peckham ms.; *Min. & Sci. Press*, July 14, 1866; Stanford Bros. advertisement in *S.F. Directory, 1867;* [S. F. Peckham], *The Natural History of Petroleum*, 184; *Min. Yearbook, 1868*, 261-62; Williamson and Daum, *op. cit.*, 208.

59. *Min. & Sci. Press*, Jan. 9, 1868; *Min. Yearbook, 1868*, 261-62; *Min. Resources of the US, 1883-84*, 220; Williamson and Daum, *op. cit.*, 737.

60. *Min. & Sci. Press*, Sep. 26 and Nov. 14, 1868; *Min. Yearbook, 1868*, 261-62.

61. The testimony of J. H. Winsor, a promoter of the Foote burner, Sep. 15 and 16, 1913, in *US* v. *SP Co.*, #221 in the US Dist. Ct. for the So. Dist. of Calif., No. Div., reporter's transcript, 8732-45, 8762-8865, 8876-77, Hist. R, includes detailed news stories from more than a dozen prominent eastern newspapers on the voyages of the *Palos*. See also the *S.F. Bulletin*, May 28, 1865, and the *Min. & Sci. Press*, June 1 and 22, 1867.

62. *N.Y. Tribune*, June 17, 1867; *Min. & Sci. Press*, June 1 and 22, Nov. 2, 1867, Jan. 18 and May 16, 1868; Williamson and Daum, *op. cit.*, 241.

63. See note 56; *Min. & Sci. Press*, June 22, Sept. 7 and Oct. 12, 1867, Jan. 9, 1869.

64. *Min. & Sci. Press*, Jan. 11, 18, 25, Apr. 18, May 16 and June 13, 1868.

65. Williamson and Daum, *op. cit.*, 241-42.

66. *Min. & Sci. Press*, Jan. 9, 1869; *Min. Yearbook, 1868*, 261.

67. *S.F. Directory, 1865-66* to *1868-69; Min. & Sci. Press*, Feb. 23, 1867; billhead of Pettit & Co., Allyne R, CHS. Pettit's home address in 1870 was 225 Bush St., the present Home Office of Standard of California; his refinery was at 209 Drumm St.

68. Stalder, "Stanford Bros.," 18; interview, Lucy Allyne (a daughter), by E. B. Currier, Jan. 18, 1955. Thomas W. and DeWitt Stanford continued to carry on their Australian oil business, however; see also Geo. T. Clark, *op. cit.*, 56. The California Stanford brothers who had been in oil (Josiah and A. P.) continued to go downhill, both filing as bankrupts in 1878. Josiah owed Leland Stanford $100,000; A. P. owed his brother $85,000 (US Dist. Ct., No. Dist. of Calif., #2449 and #2694 in Bankruptcy). They had been drawing heavily on Leland for their oil business at least as early as 1861 (Clark, *op. cit.*, 92).

69. "Enumerators' Returns from the Census of 1870"; *Min. & Sci. Press*, Jan. 27, 1867; US Patent #68,257, Aug. 27, 1867; *Ventura Signal*, Nov. 23, 1872. Earlier, in

1866, Stott had operated his refinery further west on the ex-Mission with crude from Wheeler Canyon (Bard to Peckham, Nov. 6, 1866, Peckham ms.).

70. "Enumerators' Returns from the Census of 1870."

71. Stalder ms., 51-52; Geo. M. Scott to Allyne & White, July 14, 1871, Allyne R, CHS.

72. During the first 6 months of operation Allyne & White had refined 5,000 gals. of petroleum; during the preceding year Pettit had refined 1,500 gals. In addition, Pettit's raw materials included 750 gals. of animal and 3,500 gals. of vegetable oils. Another firm, the Calif. Paving Co., reported that over a year's time it had used 400 bbls. of "coal tar and petroleum" as a wood preservative (for railroad ties?) ("Enumerators' Returns from the Census of 1870").

73. Peckham to Calif. Pet. Co., Feb. 10, 1866, Peckham ms.

74. *S.F. Post,* Jan. 6, 1877. At least two of the Calif. Pet. and two of the Phila. & Calif. wells were drilled by springpole, Peckham ms., *passim.* See also R. B. Woodworth, "The Evolution of Drilling Rigs," in *Trans. of the Amer. Inst. of Min. Eng.* (Nov., 1915), 2250-53.

75. Calif. Geological Survey, *op. cit.,* II, Appendix F, 49-90. On the view of Whitney, see his *Geology,* I, 116-18; also his comment, "I am afraid I have spoken too favorably of the 'ile' prospect in the Report" (Whitney to Brewer, Dec. 15, 1865, Whitney R).

76. Brewer to Whitney, Apr. 8, 1867, Whitney R.

77. Calif. Geological Survey, *op. cit.,* II, Appendix F, 73-90. The research reported in these pages was carried on during 1866-67, but the last section (84-90), emphasizing the different chemical characteristics of crudes from different states, was written in 1871. James Young, the celebrated Scotch chemist, took out in Great Britain the first pressure cracking patent on Dec. 27, 1865; almost simultaneously with Peckham, Silliman was trying to crack heavy Calif. crude, but his work was less exhaustive and his results were not as good (Benj. Silliman, Jr., "On Naphtha and Illuminating Oil from Heavy California Tar," *Am. J. of Sci. & Arts,* XLIII [Mar., 1867], 242-45).

78. Calif. Geological Survey, *op. cit.,* II, Appendix F, 49, 90.

II. THE REVIVAL AT PICO

1. Art of Incorporation, Metropolitan Gas Company, May 11, 1863, Secy. of State (Calif.) R; *S.F. Directory, 1863* to *1870; Alta,* May 26, 1865; Frederick L. Collins, *Consolidated Gas Company of New York* (N.Y., 1934), 123. Metropolitan's oil probably came from Wiley Springs, near Pico. (*4th Ann. Rpt. State Min.* [1884], 297).

2. Art. of Incorporation, Metropolitan Gas Works, May 7, 1871, Secy of State (Calif.) R; *Min. & Sci. Press,* May 14, 1870; *Pacific Pneumatic Co.* (S.F., 1869), a pamphlet in Pacific Gas & Electric Co. Library, S.F.; Charles M. Coleman, *P.G.&E. of California* (N.Y., 1952), 29-30.

3. *S.F. Directory, 1872,* 22-23; US Patents #26,028 and #26,030, dated Nov. 8, 1859, cited in *Ann. Rpt. of the Comr. of Patents for the Year 1870,* 41st Cong., 3d Sess., H. Ex. Doc. 89, items #3,872 and #3,873. While Metropolitan's plant was going up, the S.F. Gas Co. apparently was stirred to experiment with petroleum, but it stayed with coal gas (Bard to J. G. Eastland, Aug. 30, 1871, Bard R-S).

4. R. G. Surdam to Bard, July 14, 1871, Bard to J. P. Green, Apr. 10, 1873, Bard to Gen. Phineas Banning, Apr. 28, 1873, Bard R-S; J. DeBarth Shorb to Whitney, Feb. 28, 1874, Whitney R; *Min. & Sci. Press,* quoted in *L.A. Star,* Feb. 12, 1872; *Comm. Herald,* Mar. 15 and Apr. 26, 1872; *Ventura Signal,* Aug. 24, Sep. 7 and 13, 1872, Apr. 5, 1873.

5. E. J. Pringle to Bard, Apr. 5, 1869, Bard R-S; *Alta,* Apr. 11, 1873; *Ventura Signal,* Apr. 26, 1873, and Dec. 25, 1875; Bk. 5, "S.F. Clippings, 1872-78," May 8, 1873, CHS; *Min. & Sci. Press,* June 19, 1869; "Order 916," *S.F. Municipal Rpts., 1870-71,* 42; *S.F. Directory, 1872,* 22-23; *Ventura County, California, Its Resources* (Ventura, 1885), 12; Coleman, *op. cit.,* 28-30. In 1874 Peter Donahue, president of San Francisco Gas Light, again considered using a petroleum gas process (perhaps by reviving Metropolitan's plant), but the idea was soon dropped (Bard to Donahue, Jan. 3, 1874, Bard R-S).

6. *Min. & Sci. Press,* quoted in *L.A. Star,* Feb. 12 and 13, 1872; *Comm. Herald,* Mar. 15, 1872.

7. "Leaming Lead," Jan. 12, 1872, in San Fernando Pet. Mining Dist. Bk. A, 69-70, L.A. County HR, hereafter cited as SFPMD Bk. A; Art. of Incorporation, Leaming Pet Co., Feb. 10, 1872, Secy. of State (Calif.) R; Deed, Gelcich to Trustees, Leaming Pet. Co., Feb. 17, 1872, in "Recs. of Miners' Meetings," etc., Hist. R; *Comm. Herald,* Apr. 26, 1872.

8. *Comm. Herald,* quoted in *Ventura Signal,* Sep. 14, 1872.

9. Vernette S. Ripley, "The San Fernando Pass and the Pioneer Traffic That Went Over It," *Hist. Soc. of So. Calif. Quart.,* XXX (June, 1948), 115-16, 120.

10. Ben Blow, *California Highways* (S.F., 1920), 166.

11. Ruth W. Newhall, *The Newhall Ranch* (San Marino, Calif., 1958), 38-39; John W. Caughey, *Gold Is The Cornerstone* (Berkeley, 1948), 11.

12. *Alta,* June 2, 1876; *Pico* v. *Pico, Transcript on Appeal,* Feb. 7, 1880, pp. 23, 61, Calif. Supreme Ct. R, State Archives; testimony of Sutherland Hutton, Mar. 20, 1916, in *US* v. *SP Co.,* #46 Civil in the US Dist. Ct. for the So. Dist. of Calif., No. Div., reporter's transcript, 3509-11, Hist. R; Carl I. Wheat (ed.), "California's Bantam Cock: The Journals of Charles E. DeLong, 1854-1863," *Quarterly of the CHS,* IX (Sep., 1930), 282; Stephen Bonsal, *Edward Fitzgerald Beale* (N.Y., 1912), 14-20; Harris Newmark, *Sixty Years in Southern California, 1853-1913* (Boston, 1930), 179-80.

13. *Cal. Stats.* (1852), 158.

14. "Index, Preemptions, US Land Office, L.A. County Records, State Land Office," Hist. R.

15. Romulo Pico, Jan. 24, 1865, p. 181, Andres Pico, Jan. 30, 1865, p. 206, H. C. Wiley, Apr. 21, 1865, pp. 260-61, all in Bk. I of Preemptions, L.A. County HR; *S.F. Post,* Mar. 21, 1877; Ripley, *op. cit.,* 123-24.

16. *Min. & Sci. Press,* May 27, 1865; Gregory Yale, *Legal Titles of Mining Claims and Water Rights in California Under the Mining Law of Congress of July, 1866* (S.F., 1867); W. W. Robinson, *Land in California* (Berkeley, 1948), 139-41.

17. "Mining Laws of the L.A. Asphaltum and Pet. Mining Dist.," Mar. 6, 1865, Misc. R, Vol. I, 162, and SFPMD Bk. A, June 24, 1865, pp. 1-5, both in L.A. County HR; *Min. & Sci. Press,* May 27 and June 17, 1865; Stalder ms., 22-24; Owen C. Coy, *Humboldt Bay Region, 1850-1875* (L.A., 1929), 229; F. F. Latta, *Black Gold in the Joaquin* (Caldwell, Idaho, 1949), 36.

18. SFPMD Bk. A, 33. Andres Pico was also associated with Gilbert and others about this time in Santa Barbara County, where on Mar. 12, 1865, he located 18 claims, called the Pico Mining Co., in the San Buenaventura Asphaltum and Pet. Mining Dist. (Misc. R Bk., 396, Santa Barbara County HR).

19. Beale and Baker to Romulo Pico, May 22, 1865, Misc. R, Bk. 3, p. 172, L.A. County HR; deed, Hernandez and Perea to Baker and claim by Hernandez and Perea, May 22, 1865 [p. 278, Bk. I of Preemptions], filed as defendant's exhibits 3 and 4 in *J. M. Luco* v. *R. S. Baker,* #6831 in the Sup. Ct. of L.A. County, L.A. County HR, hereafter cited as *Luco* v. *Baker.* On Baker, see L. A. Ingersoll, *History of Santa Monica Bay Cities* (L.A., 1908), 142-43 and *L.A. Times,* May 27, 1894.

20. SFPMD Bk. A, 33; Newmark, *op. cit.,* 173, 332, 526. The relocation of Aug. 8 was recorded in Bk. A between two others dated Dec. 21 and Dec. 19, respectively. Several other locations are out of sequence from 2 weeks to a month, but none as much as the Pico relocation. We have not, however, attached any special significance to this fact.

21. *L.A. Star,* Feb. 12, 1872; SFPMD Bk. A; S. F. Peckham in Calif. Geological Survey, *Geology* (Cambridge, 1882), II, Appendix F, 68.

22. Peckham, *op. cit.,* 67-68; on Pico, see also deposition of J. C. Leighton, July 13, 1878, in *Baker et al.* v. *CSOW et al.,* #4437 in the 17th Dist. Ct. for L.A. County, L.A. County HR, hereafter cited as *Baker* v. *CSOW.*

23. Bard to S. F. Peckham, Dec. 19, 1866, in Peckham ms.; *L.A. News,* Nov. 11, 1865; *Alta,* Mar. 29, 1866; Peckham, *op. cit.,* 70.

24. SFPMD Bk. A.

25. *Ibid.; Wilmington J.,* Feb. 10, 1866. In Feb., Petra Gelcich appears on the lists of locators for 2 claims, not again to appear until she does so with her husband in July,

1866. An unsigned letter in the *L.A. News*, June 1, 1866, describing the work in and around Pico Springs, may also have been written by Gelcich.

   26. *L.A. Star*, Apr. 12 and 13, 1873; *L.A. Express*, Apr. 17, 1873.

   27. *L.A. Star*, June 4, 1873, quoted in *Min. & Sci. Press*, June 14, 1873.

   28. *L.A. Star*, July 16, 1873; Art. of Incorporation, L.A. Pet. Refining Co., July 30, 1873, Secy. of State (Calif.) R. On Temple, see Newmark, *op. cit.*, 435, 478-79; Ira B. Cross, *Financing An Empire* (Chicago, 1927), II, 538, 555.

   29. *L.A. Star*, Aug. 22, 1873.

   30. Petition to the Secy. of the Interior *et al.*, in Dec., 1875, signed by 71 holders of oil claims in the San Fernando (but not by Baker), protesting the gradual reopening of the San Fernando Dist. to agricultural entry between 1872 and 1875, NA, Rec. Group 49, Min. Patent #4218; R. F. Hartsook, Univ. of Calif., to E. B. Currier, Jan. 3, 1955, Hist. R.

   31. *Andrew J. Krazynski* v. *L.A. Pet. Refining Co.*, in the 17th Dist. Ct. for L.A. County, L.A. County HR; *S.F. Post*, Feb. 18, 1874.

   32. *L.A. Weekly Express*, Apr. 30, May 21, June 4 and July 10, 1874; *L.A. Herald*, July 20, 1874, in *Min. & Sci. Press*, July 25, 1874; Bard to J. P. Green, Mar. 24, 1875, Bard R-S.

   33. *L.A. Weekly Express*, Apr. 16, 23 and 30, May 21, June 4, 1874.

   34. *Ibid.*, July 2 and Aug. 13, 1874.

   35. Bard to J. P. Green, Aug. 17, 1874, Mar. 11 and 24, 1875, Bard R-S.

   36. SFPMD Bk. A, May 20, 1874; *L.A. Weekly Express*, July 10, 1874, Mar. 28, 1875; Bard to J. P. Green, Mar. 11 and 24, 1875, Bard R-S. Some of the tools for the Temple well were acquired from Bard. Nine years before they had been used to drill for Tom Scott's Phil. & Calif. Petroleum Co. (Sanford Lyon to Bard, Feb. 10, 1875, Bard R-S).

   37. *L.A. Weekly Express*, May 21 and Aug. 13, 1874.

   38. "Location Notices, A to Z," Hist. R. During 1874, 17 locations representing 109 claims had been recorded, of which only one for a single claimant had preceded the first demonstration by Carreras late in Apr. (SFPMD Bk. A). By 1874, claims were no longer being listed as "1000 feet square," but as "20 acres."

   39. *L.A. Star*, Mar. 24, 1875; deposition of D. C. Scott, June 11, 1878, *Baker* v. *CSOW; The Derrick's Hand-Book of Petroleum* (Oil City, Pa., 1898), I, 216, hereafter cited as *Derrick's Hand-Book*.

   40. *L.A. Herald*, Apr. 15, 1875; *L.A. Express*, Apr. 20 and 21, 1875; deposition of D. C. Scott, June 11, 1878, in *Baker* v. *CSOW*.

   41. *L.A. Express*, May 15 and June 10, 1875; Schumacher to Bard, Sep. 26 and Dec. 20, 1875, Bard R-S; Temple & Workman, in Bankruptcy [1876], US Dist. Ct. R., S.F. This bankruptcy case also shows the indebtedness of the L.A. Pet. Refining Co. to the bank as $3,871.

   42. Deposition of D. C. Scott, Jan. 17, 1877, in *N. J. Clarke* v. *Reuben Denton*, #3375 in the 17th Dist. Ct. for L.A. County, L.A. County HR, hereafter cited as *Clarke* v. *Denton*.

   43. *L.A. Herald*, July 13, 1875; depositions by D. C. Scott and Mentry, June 11, 1878 in *Baker* v. *CSOW; Min. Res. of the US, 1892*, 648; W. E. Youle, *Sixty-Three Years in the Oilfields* (Taft, ca. 1926), 23-24. The depths given by Mentry in his testimony of 1878 are 120, 85 and 65 ft., respectively, which are also substantiated in "Histories of PCO Co. Wells," Hist. R. The production of Pico #2, completed late in Nov., was 6 bbls. a day; Pico #3 yielded somewhat less. Pico #1 was abandoned in Sep., 1913.

   44. Schumacher to Bard, Oct. 7 and Dec. 20, 1875, Bard R-S; *Min. & Sci. Press*, Jan. 20, 1877; amended complaint of Clarke in *Clarke* v. *Denton;* Cross, *op. cit.*, II, 555.

   45. *L.A. Express*, June 16, 1875; deposition of McPherson, July 2, 1878, in *Baker* v. *CSOW;* H. S. Foote, *Santa Clara County, California* (Chicago, 1888), 164; *Derrick's Hand-Book*, I, 188.

   46. Art of Incorporation, S.F. Pet. Co., Dec. 16, 1875, Secy. of State (Calif.) R; McPherson to S.F. Pet. Co., Dec. 16, 1875, Deed Bk. 40, p. 386, L.A. County HR; *L.A. Express*, Dec. 29, 1876; deposition of Mentry, July 12, 1878, *in Baker* v. *CSOW;*

S.F. Directory, 1870 to *1875;* J. L. King, *History of the S.F. Stock and Exchange Board* (S.F., 1910), 357.

47. Deposition of J. A. Scott, July 8, 1878, in *Baker* v. *CSOW;* Charles E. Whiteshot, *The Oil Well Driller* (Mannington, W. Va., 1905), 107.

48. *L.A. Express,* Jan. 26 and June 2, 1876; L.A. Pet. Refining Co. to Denton, Apr. 19, 1876, Misc. R, Bk. 3, pp. 202-03, L.A. County HR; deposition of Denton, Oct. 4, 1876, in *Clarke* v. *Denton;* deposition of J. A. Scott, July 8, 1878, in *Baker* v. *CSOW.*

49. Bard to Lyon, Dec. 29, 1875, and Lyon to Bard, Mar. 7, 1876, Bard R-S; deposition of Denton, Oct. 4, 1876, in *Clarke* v. *Denton;* deposition of Hurbert Stanton, July 11, 1878, in *Baker* v. *CSOW.*

50. Baker, Beale, Lyon and Leaming to Denton, Apr. 12, 1876, Lease Bk. 3, pp. 379-81, L.A. County HR; *L.A. Express,* Mar. 29, 1876.

51. L.A. Pet. Refining Co. to Denton, Apr. 19, 1876, Misc. R, Bk. 3, pp. 202-03, L.A. County HR; deposition of Denton, Oct. 4, 1876, in *Clarke* v. *Denton.*

52. Assignment of lease, Denton to Bryant, Apr. 18, 1876, Lease Bk. 3, pp. 381-82, L.A. County HR; deposition of Denton, Oct. 4, 1876, in *Clarke* v. *Denton;* regarding Bryant, *S.F. Bulletin,* May 11, 1888, and *Alta,* May 12, 1888; McDonald, King, *op. cit.,* 194-95, [S.F.] *Stock Exchange,* Nov. 23, 1876, and [S.F.] *Daily Exchange,* Nov. 6, 1877; Jones, *S.F. Directory, 1870* to *1876.*

53. Denton to Star Oil Works, May 5, 1876, Deed Bk. 44, p. 412, L.A. County HR; Art of Incorporation, Star Oil Works Co., May 23, 1876, L.A. County HR (the filing in S.F. occurred on May 3), and of CSOW, June 16, 1876 (filed at Sac., July 8), Secy. of State (Calif.) R; depositions of Bryant, June 7 and Taylor, June 8, 1878, in *Baker* v. *CSOW. Clarke* v. *Denton* was filed July 15, 1876.

54. Ferdinand Vassault to Adams & Thayer, June 21, 1875, Lease Bk. I, p. 72, Recorder, Ventura County; *S.F. Post,* Jan. 6 and 13, 1877; *Ventura Free Press,* Jan. 20, 1877.

55. Gerberding to Bard, May 15 and 17, 1876, Edwards to Bard, Nov. 13, 1876, all in Bard R-S; *Ventura Signal,* May 20, 27 and Aug. 19, 1876; *S.F. Daily Stock Report,* Sep. 8, 1876; *Ventura Weekly Free Press,* Dec. 30, 1876. The assessed valuation of the refinery for 1877-78 was $3,565 (Assessor, Ventura County).

56. "Histories of PCO Co. Wells," Hist. R; well file, CSOW #4, Prod. R; *L.A. Republican,* quoted in *S.F. Bulletin,* June 21, 1876; *L.A. Herald,* July 20, 1876; *L.A. Express,* July 31, 1876; *S.F. Post,* Jan. 6, 1877.

57. *L.A. Republican,* quoted in *S.F. Bulletin,* June 21, 1876; *L.A. Express,* July 31 and Sep. 7, 1876; *L.A. Herald,* June 6, 1877.

58. *Alta,* June 15, 1876; *Comm. Herald,* Dec. 21, 1876; *S.F. J. of Comm.* (Ann. Edition), Jan., 1877; *Ventura Signal,* Feb. 10, 1877; *Min. Res. of the US, 1891,* p. 420.

59. Billheads of F. B. Taylor in J. W. Allyne R, CHS; "Calif. Census of 1852, S.F. County," and *Great Registers of 1866 and 1873,* Calif. State Library; "Gen. Index to Official Recs.," Recorder's Office, S.F. County; *S.F. Directory, 1852* to *1876; Alta,* Jan. 3, 1853, and Dec. 17, 1859; *Comm. Herald,* Jan. 13, Mar. 10 and July 7, 1871, Jan. 12, 1872, May 4, 1874. We have been unable to establish any relationship between Frederick Bayard Taylor and Bayard Taylor, the famed American poet, novelist, and traveler of this era.

60. Thomas Brown, Bank of Calif., to Oriental Bank Corp., Jan. 30, 1874, and Brooks, Consul of Japan, "To All Whom It May Concern," Feb. 14, 1874, Scofield R; deposition of Scofield, June 11, 1878, in *Baker* v. *CSOW;* unidentified obituary clippings, July 31, 1917, Hist. R; *N.Y. Directory, 1865* to *1874; S.F. Directory, 1871* to *1879.*

61. Unidentified clipping, May 19, 1875, CHS; *Daily Exchange,* Aug. 9 and 11, 1876; *S.F. Daily Stock Report,* Aug. 15 and 17, 1876.

62. Depositions of Mentry, June 11, and Lyon, June 17, 1878, in *Baker* v. *CSOW;* deposition of Scofield, June 19, 1888, in *Luco* v. *Baker;* "Hope Lead," Misc. R, Vol. I, 352, Recorder, Ventura County.

63. Deposition of Denton, Oct. 4, 1876, in *Clarke* v. *Denton;* depositions of Taylor, June 8, and Scofield, June 11, 1878, in *Baker* v. *CSOW;* J. A. Scott interview by L. H. Eddy, July 12, 1906, NA BuCorp. file #3376, Pt. 7; *S.F. Daily Stock Report,* Sep. 8, 1876; *Ventura Signal,* Sep. 16 and Dec. 9, 1876; *Ventura Free Press,* Aug. 10, 1878.

64. Deposition of Taylor, June 8, 1876, in *Baker* v. *CSOW;* Juan Forster and F. P.

Forster to Romulo Pico, June 23, 1876, in Deed Bk. 62, p. 57, Romulo Pico to Taylor, Sep. 28, 1876, in Deed Bk. 48, p. 616, Lyon and Leaming to Taylor, Oct. 28, 1876, in Deed Bk. 61, p. 389, all in L.A. County HR.

65. "Index to Deeds, Grantees," in SFPMD deed bks., Hist. R.

66. Edwards to Gerberding, June 7, Aug. 12 and Sep. 20, 1876, Memo. of Agreement, July 1, 1876, Bard to Edwards, Oct. 12 and 18, 1876, Bard R-S. While in the East, Bard may have been negotiating with Tom Scott to purchase the Ojai oil rights, for he acquired them on Mar. 19, 1877 (W. H. Hutchinson to G. T. White, Dec. 18, 1960, Hist. R).

67. Scofield to Bard, Nov. 4, 1876, Bard, "Option for a Lease," Dec. 11, 1876, Bard R-S; Assessment #1, CSOW, Dec. 19, 1876, in *S.F. Daily Stock Report*, Dec. 27, 1876.

68. Deposition of Scofield, June 11, 1878, in *Baker* v. *CSOW; S.F. Post*, Dec. 13, 1877.

69. Scofield to Bard, Jan. 8, Feb. 21 and Mar. 5, 1877, Bard to W. G. Hughes, June 16, 1877, Bard R-S; photostat, Angell to Rockefeller, Mar. 30, 1878, Hist. R, through the courtesy of Robert W. Gumbel, N.Y. City; Youle, *op. cit.*, 5; John J. McLaurin, *Sketches in Crude Oil* (Harrisburg, 1896), 147, 152-53.

70. D. C. Scott to Bard, Aug. 5, 1877, and the Coche Canyon lease, Sep. 25, 1877, Bard R-S; *Ventura Signal*, Jan. 6, 1877; D. C. Scott from R. G. de la Riva, Oct. 20, 1876, and from M. H. Biggs, Oct. 26, 1876, Lease Bk. 1, pp. 81-84, and D. C. Scott to Taylor, Aug. 1, 1877, Assignment of Leases, Bk. 1, Recorder, Ventura County. The Rancho El Rincon contained the asphalt deposits near Carpenteria that the S.F. druggist, Morrill, had sought to develop in 1861.

71. Art. of Incorporation, L.A. Oil Co., Sep. 22, 1876, CC Ventura; *L.A. Herald*, Sep. 26 and Oct. 1, 1876; *S.F. J. of Comm.*, Oct. 4 and 11, 1876; *Ventura Signal*, Mar. 24, May 5 and 26, 1877; *Ventura Weekly Free Press*, May 12, June 2 and 16, 1877, and June 8, 1878.

72. *S.F. Post*, Jan. 13 and Sep. 13, 1877; *L.A. Herald*, Aug. 13, 1877; *Ventura Weekly Free Press*, Sep. 15, 1877; *L.A. Express*, Oct. 10, 1877.

73. *S.F. Daily Stock Report*, Apr. 21, 1877; *S.F. Post*, Apr. 27, 1877; *Ventura Weekly Free Press*, May 5, 1877; *L.A. Herald*, May 14, 1877; *L.A. Express*, June 1, 19 and 25, 1877; deposition of Mentry, June 11, 1878, in *Baker* v. *CSOW*. It is probable that the $20,000 in assessments in 1877 covered only part of CSOW's investment and was supplemented by the reinvestment of earnings of unknown amount. Pico production that year was at least 20,000 bbls., and producing costs undoubtedly were low. Refining costs, on the other hand, were high, but transportation costs came down sharply after the opening of the Andrews Station refinery. Despite the fall in kerosine prices, it is possible that profits of, say, $10,000 to $20,000, were available for reinvestment. We have no cost figures beyond the fact that Sanford Lyon was receiving $2.50 a bbl. for the 3 to 4 bbls. daily from his Pico well, but this probably was an accommodation rather than a true market price. (Deposition of J. A. Scott, July 8, 1878, in *Baker* v. *CSOW*).

74. *L.A. Express*, Jan. 16, 1877; *S.F. Post*, Apr. 21 and May 1, 1877.

75. *S.F. Post*, May 22 and Aug. 27, 1877, and Jan. 29, 1878; *L.A. Express*, June 1 and 25, 1877; *Ventura Weekly Free Press*, Oct. 6, 1877.

76. *S.F. Post*, Aug. 25, 1877, and Jan. 29, 1878; *Ventura Weekly Free Press*, Sep. 15, 1877; *Comm. Herald*, Jan. 24, 1878; statement of Scofield, Oct., 1908, Secy. R.

77. *L.A. Herald*, Aug. 21, 1877; *Ventura Weekly Free Press*, Oct. 6, 1877, and Feb. 2, 1878; *S.F. Post*, Nov. 8 and 16, 1877; *L.A. Express*, Dec. 5, 1877; deposition of Mentry, July 12, 1878, in *Baker* v. *CSOW*.

78. "Location Notices, A to Z," Hist. R; *L.A. Express*, Dec. 29, 1876, and Nov. 17, 1877; *S.F. Post*, Mar. 21, Sep. 13, Nov. 8 and 16, 1877; deposition of James Feore, July 13, 1878, in *Baker* v. *CSOW*.

79. Art. of Incorporation, Standard Oil Co. of Calif., July 26, 1877, Secy. of State (Calif.) R; *Ventura Signal*, May 19 and June 16, 1877; *S.F. Directory, 1878*.

80. *Ventura Signal*, Aug. 11, 1877, Jan. 19 and Sep. 21, 1878; *Ventura Weekly Free Press*, Sep. 15, Oct. 6, 1877, and Jan. 5, 1878; *S.F. Post*, Nov. 8 and Dec. 13, 1877.

81. *J. D. Burch* v. *Standard Oil Co.* and *P. E. Cosgrove* v. *Standard Oil Co.*, #228

and #229 in 1st Dist. Ct. for Ventura County, CC Ventura; *Ventura Weekly Free Press,* Jan. 26, 1878.

82. Writ of attachment, *B. W. Feldt* v. *Adams, Thayer & Co.,* May 30, 1878, in 1st Dist. Ct. for Ventura County, CC Ventura; Edwards to Bard, June 14, 1878, Bard R-S; *Ventura Signal,* Feb. 16 and Sep. 21, 1878, and Feb. 22, 1879; *Ventura Free Press,* June 22, 1878.

83. *Comm. Herald,* Jan. 30, 1879; S. F. Peckham, *The Natural History of Petroleum,* in the Tenth Census of the US, X, 151. In 1880 the population of Calif. was 864,694, of which 75,132 were Chinese; the parallel figures for S.F. were 233,959 and 21,213.

84. *Comm. Herald,* quoted in *Ventura Signal,* Sep. 30, 1876; *Comm. Herald,* Jan. 8, 1877; *Ventura Signal,* Jan. 20, 1877; *S.F. Post,* quoted in *Ventura Free Press,* Feb. 10, 1877; statement of Scofield, Oct., 1908, Secy. R.

85. *S.F. J. of Comm.,* Jan. 12 and 18, 1877; *Comm. Herald,* Jan. 17, 1878; Williamson and Daum, *op. cit.,* 372-73, 381-83.

86. *Ventura Weekly Free Press,* Jan. 20 and June 16, 1877; *Comm. Herald,* Jan. 18, 1877, and Oct. 17, 1878.

87. Deposition of Blake, June 8, 1878, in *Baker* v. *CSOW;* biographical sketch of Blake in Bancroft R; *S.F. Post,* Sep. 25, 1877; *Ventura Weekly Free Press,* Oct. 6, 1877; *S.F. Directory, 1878.*

88. Art. of Incorporation, Continental Oil Co. of Colorado, Jan. 14, 1875, Secy. of State (Colo.) R, and of the Continental Oil & Transporation Co., Nov. 24, 1875, Secy. of State (Iowa) R.

89. Art. of Incorporation, Continental Oil & Transportation Co. of Calif., Nov. 27, 1877, Secy. of State (Calif.) R; *Council Bluffs Directory, 1876; S.F. Directory, 1879-80; L.A. Herald,* Oct. 9 and 26, 1877; *S.F. Post,* Jan. 2, 1878.

90. *S.F. Post,* Dec. 13, 1877; *Ventura Signal,* Feb. 23, 1878; *L.A. Herald,* May 28, 1878, and May 8, 1879; *S.F. Bulletin,* June 26, 1878; *Comm. Herald,* July 11, 1878, quoting *S.F. Bulletin* of July 8, 1878. On the Sacramento plant, see *S.F. J. of Comm.,* Jan. 28, 1882; on the San Jose plant, *S.J. Herald,* June 20, 1879.

91. *S.F. J. of Comm.,* Jan. 12, 1876 and Jan. 17, 1877; *Comm. Herald,* Jan. 17, 1878; *Min. Res. of the US, 1891,* 414.

92. CSOW to Mess. Baker, Beale & Co., July 1, 1876, depositions of Bryant, June 7, Taylor, June 8, and Baker, July 3, 1878, all in *Baker* v. *CSOW.*

93. Complaint of Beale and Baker, Apr. 22, 1878, in *Baker* v. *CSOW;* deed, Pio Pico to Baker, May 21, 1877, Baker R. A dispute as to the basis on which the deed was granted led to a later court case, *Luco* v. *Baker.* In this case (which he won), Baker denied that he had ever told Pio Pico that "Pico's interest . . . could be managed . . . to their mutual advantage more successfully if the title . . . was held by one person" and that he would "bestow the same care . . . upon the interest of . . . Pico . . . as . . . upon his own interest in . . . Pico Oil Springs Claim. . . ." Baker also alleged that only as a result of his conflict with CSOW did he become aware of the relocation of Aug. 8, 1865, a statement that seems unlikely.

94. Scofield to "Mess. Beale & Baker," June 4, 1877, and memo. (undated and apparently in Beale's handwriting), both in Baker R.

95. Beale to Baker, Jan. 4, 1787, Baker R; depositions of Leaming, June 17, and Scofield, July 15, 1878, and Exhibit A, "Pioneer Pet. Claim," July 23, 1877, all in *Baker* v. *CSOW.* Loomis was a brother-in-law of C. N. Felton, and Greathouse a cousin of Lloyd Tevis (see Chap. III).

96. Ventura Signal, Feb. 2, 1878; *L.A. Herald,* Mar. 2, 1878; *Ventura Weekly Free Press,* Mar. 9, 1878; depositions of J. Howe, July 13, Mentry, July 15, and Scofield, July 15, 1878, in *Baker* v. *CSOW; Baker et al.,* v. *Reuben Denton et al.,* #4394, in 17th Dist. Ct. for L.A. County, L.A. County HR. The latter case, filed on Mar. 22, 1878, was dismissed without prejudice on Apr. 4 (*Ventura Weekly Free Press,* Apr. 6, 1878). It was succeeded by *Baker* v. *CSOW,* filed Apr. 22.

97. *CSOW* v. *Baker, Beale, Taylor, and John Doe,* in 12th Dist. Ct. for S.F., State Archives, Sac.; *L.A. Herald,* Apr. 27, 1878.

98. Deposition of Scofield, June 11, 1878, in *Baker* v. *CSOW; L.A. Herald,* quoted

in *S.F. Post,* July 13, 1878; *Ventura Free Press,* Aug. 10, 1879; *S.F. Daily Stock Report,* Feb. 5, 1880 and *Alta,* Feb. 5 and 6, 1880.

99. *S.F. Post,* June 10 and 29, 1878.

100. *Baker* v. *CSOW.*

101. Depositions of McPherson, July 2, and Hurbert Stanton, July 11, 1878, in *Baker* v. *CSOW.* Three of the others who offered testimony supporting Beale and Baker were members of McPherson's drilling crew.

102. Depositions of Mentry, June 11 and July 12, Angell, July 10, 1878, also W. C. Chapin, June 8 and J. A. Scott, July 8, 1878, all in *Baker* v. *CSOW; Ventura Weekly Free Press,* Feb. 2, 1878.

103. Depositions of Blake, June 8, and Scofield, June 11 and July 15, 1878, in *Baker* v. *CSOW.*

104. Depositions of Scott, July 8, and J. N. Taylor, July 11, 1878, in *Baker* v. *CSOW; Ventura Signal,* Sep. 21, 1878; *L.A. Herald,* Oct. 30, 1878.

105. *Ventura Signal,* Mar. 30, 1878; *Comm. Herald,* July 11 and Aug. 1, 1878, and Jan. 30, 1879.

106. *Comm. Herald,* July 11, 1878, and Mar. 6 and Apr. 10, 1879. See also Williamson and Daum, *op. cit.,* 505.

107. Deposition of Angell, July 10, 1878, in *Baker* v. *CSOW; Derrick's Hand-Book,* I, 685; McLaurin, *op. cit.,* 102-3; Williamson and Daum, *op. cit.,* 132-34.

108. Angell to Rockefeller, Mar. 30, 1878, Hist. R; depositions of Angell, July 10, 1878, in *Baker* v. *CSOW* and Oct. 29, 1878, in *Thorne et al.* v. *Steinbach et al.,* in 1st Dist. Ct. for Ventura County, CC Ventura; *Ventura Free Press,* June 22, 1878.

109. Angell to Rockefeller, Mar. 30, 1878, Hist. R.

110. *N.Y. Sun,* quoted in *Ventura Signal,* Mar. 9, 1878; Hidy and Hidy, *op. cit.,* 37-38.

111. Sanford Lyon to Baker, May 13, 1878, Baker R; Opinion of the Ct., Apr. 3, 1879, in *Thorne* v. *Steinbach; Ventura Signal,* Sep. 21, 1878.

112. *S.F. Daily Exchange,* Oct. 16, 1878; *L.A. Herald,* Dec. 8, 1878.

III. NEW LEADERS AND A NEW COMPANY

1. George L. Upshur, *As I Recall Them* (N.Y., 1936), 90.

2. Ms. on C. N. Felton and the S.F. Mint, Bancroft R; *Alta,* Apr. 25, 1873; *S.F. Examiner* and *S.F. Chronicle,* both Mar. 20, 1891; *Redwood City Times-Gazette,* Sep. 19, 1914; *National Cyclopedia of American Biography,* XII, 392; *Biographical Directory of the American Congress, 1774-1949* (Wash., 1950), 1170; Joseph L. King, *History of the San Francisco Stock and Exchange Board* (S.F., 1910), 195; Frank M. Stanger, *Peninsula Community Book* (San Mateo, Calif., 1946), 157.

3. Ralston *et al.* to Pres. Johnson, June 9, 1868, Ralston to Senator John Conness, July 28, 1868, Felton to Pres. Grant and to G. S. Boutwell, Secy. of the Treasury, Feb. 13, 1873, NA, Dept. of the Treasury Rec. Groups 39 and 56. Like a modern Fed. Reserve Bank, the Sub-Treasury handled the government's cash. In so doing, it occasionally made deposits in private banks, a fact of great interest to bankers. (George D. Lyman, *Ralston's Ring* [N.Y., 1937], 279; *S.F. Post,* Aug. 8, 1877).

4. Lease Bk. C, pp. 465-68, Santa Clara County HR, S.J., Calif.

5. *S.J. Mercury,* Apr. 20, 1877; *S.J. Argus,* Apr. 19, 1877; *S.J. Herald,* June 14, 1877.

6. *S.J. Argus,* Nov. 14, 1877; *S.J. Herald,* June 6, 1878; *S.J. Mercury,* June 26, 1878; *Eng. & Min. J.,* Nov. 4, 1876; *Min. & Sci. Press,* Aug. 31, 1878; Charles M. Coleman, *P.G.&E. of California, 1852-1952* (N.Y., 1952), 46-50; Frederick L. Collins, *Consolidated Gas Company of New York* (N.Y., 1934), 204.

7. Art. of Incorporation, Alameda Water Co., Nov. 10, 1873, Secy. of State (Calif.) R; K. C. Ingram to G. T. White, Oct. 19, 1954, Hist. R; *S.J. Herald,* May 29, June 9 and 29, July 9 and Aug. 21, 1877; *S.J. Mercury,* June 19, 1877; agreement between Boyer, Hensley and Hadsell, Jan. 31, 1878, Misc. R, Bk. G, 450-51, Santa Clara County HR.

8. *S.J. Herald,* Aug. 27 and Dec. 10, 1877; *S.J. Argus,* Nov. 14, 1877; conveyance by Felton, Boyer, Taylor and Hadsell to the Santa Clara Pet. Co., Oct. 3, 1878, Misc. R, Bk. H, 39-45, Santa Clara County HR. Boyer could hardly have bought the whole of the Santa Clara company, as the newspaper suggests, or there would have been

no basis for his suit against the company in 1878. For a tale of events at Moody Gulch in 1877-78 that seems a mixture of fact and fancy, see W. E. Youle, *Sixty-Three Years in the Oilfields* (Taft, Calif., ca. 1926), 24-30 and his somewhat conflicting testimony given on Mar. 14-15, 1916 in *US* v. *SP Co. et al.,* #46, in US Dist. Ct. for the So. Dist. of Calif., No. Div., VI, 3049-52, 3279-80, hereafter cited as *US* v. *SP* #46.

9. Lease Bk. C, 493-505, and Lis Pendens Bk. 1, pp. 412-13, both in Santa Clara County HR; Youle, *op. cit.,* 25.

10. Assignment of Leases Bk. A, 31-33, Santa Clara County HR. In April, 1865, Felton took a 1/6 interest in an oil lease to the Rancho Tinaquaic in the Lompoc area of Santa Barbara County (Lease Bk. A, 114-20, Santa Barbara HR, abstracted in W. H. Hutchinson to G. T. White, Dec. 18, 1960, Hist. R). Four months later he was an incorporator of the Hawley Farm Oil Co. in Humboldt County, which put down a hole, reported at from 200 to 355 ft., that found gas. (*Min. & Sci. Press,* Oct. 7, 1865; *7th Ann. Rpt. State Min.* [1888], 196, Stalder ms., 24).

11. *Edward Auzerais and A. S. Pomeroy* v. *US Oil Co.,* #5584 in 20th Dist. Ct. for Santa Clara County, CC Santa Clara County; Lease Bk. C, 517-27, and Misc. R, Bk. G, 340-49, in Santa Clara County HR. For biographical data on Loomis, see *S.F. Call,* Dec. 14, 1890; on Fisk, *S.F. Directories, 1870* to *1880;* on Ives, King, *op. cit.,* 234-36. The total holdings of F. B. Taylor & Co. in the Moody Gulch territory were in excess of 1,100 acres.

12. *S.J. Argus,* Jan. 29, 1878; *S.J. Mercury,* Mar. 24, 1878; *S.J. Herald,* June 6, 1878; *S.J. Gas Co.* v. *Garden City Gas Co.,* #5626 in 20th Dist. Ct. for Santa Clara County, CC Santa Clara County.

13. *S.J. Herald,* June 6 and 26, 1878; *S.J. Mercury,* June 26, 1878.

14. Attachment Bk. 3, pp. 57-59, 75-77, Santa Clara County HR; *S.J. Mercury,* July 2, 1878.

15. Attachment Bk. 3, pp. 79-81, Santa Clara County HR; *S.J. Herald,* Aug. 28, 1878; *S.J. Mercury,* Aug. 29, 1878.

16. *S.J. Mercury,* Sep. 6, 1878; conveyance by Felton, Boyer, Taylor and Hadsell to the Santa Clara Pet. Co., Oct. 3, 1878, and conveyance, San Jose Pet. Co. to Santa Clara Pet. Co., Oct. 17, 1878, both in Misc. R, Bk. H, 39-49, Santa Clara County HR (US Oil, the third company had no land to contribute, for it was drilling on a lease belonging to Felton that was covered under the conveyance of Oct. 3, 1878). A revised lease between the Moody brothers and Santa Clara Pet. Co. was signed by Felton as president, Oct. 15, 1878 (Lease Bk. D, 70-76, Santa Clara HR). See also *S.J. Herald,* Oct. 13 and 15, 1879.

17. San Jose Gas Co. Minutes, Jan. 24 and Feb. 25 *et seq.,* 1879, Pac. Gas & Electric Co. R. By the time of the annual meeting of 1882 Felton had sold half of his shares to Susan G. Tevis, the wife of Lloyd Tevis.

18. *S.J. Herald,* Dec. 6, 1879, listed the officers of the Santa Clara Pet. Co. as Felton, president, Scofield, secretary, and Blake, treasurer.

19. Certificate for Sale for Taxes, Mar. 9, 1878, of Dr. V. Gelcich's 160-acre claim in County Tax Sales Bk. 2, p. 163, Hist. R; John S. Hittell, *The Commerce & Industries of the Pacific Coast* (S.F., 1882), 131-33.

20. Deed Bk. 65, pp. 474, 513, Bk. 66, p. 179, Bk. 77, p. 566, and Bk. 78, p. 226, in L.A. County HR; "Abstract of Title of the interests of M. W. Childs & Barbara Childs, his wife, in . . . the San Fernando Petroleum Mining District" by Judson, Gillette & Gibson, Jan. 18, 1879, Louis T. Haggin to Judson, Gillette & Gibson, Jan. 20, 1879, and "Abstract of Title of the interests of M. W. & Barbara Childs" by Judson, Gillette & Gibson, Jan. 30, 1880, all in Hist. R. Felton's attorney, Louis T. Haggin, was the nephew of Lloyd Tevis.

21. It is possible that the news stories of Dec., 1878, reporting the acquisition of the S.F. Pet. Co. and the "Beale and Baker claim" by the "S.O. Co. of Pa." (*L.A. Herald,* Dec. 8, 1878, and *S.F. Comm. Advocate,* Dec. 21, 1878) may have been related to negotiations by Felton. Certainly, McPherson and Felton were closely allied by this time. There is also evidence of increased financial strength in the S.F. Pet. Co. in the results of a 16¢ share assessment levied in Feb., 1879; only 8% of the shares were reported as delinquent, compared with 30% on a 5¢ assessment in Nov., 1876, and 26% on a 6¢ assessment in Oct., 1877, when the oil outlook was much brighter (*S.F. Stock*

Rpt., Dec. 29, 1876, Nov. 20, 1877, and Mar. 12, 1879). The company was clearly in Felton's control by June (Lyon to Baker, June 11, 1879, Baker R).

22. Art. of Incorporation, PCO, Feb. 19, 1879, Secy. of State (Calif.) R.

23. Beale to Baker, Dec. 17, 1878, Feb. 2 and Apr. 12, 1879, Baker R; Application for Patent, Mar. 22, 1879, NA Rec. Group 49, Min. Pat. 4218; 17 *US Stat. at L.* (1873), 91.

24. Affidavit of Reynolds, Mar. 17, 1879, NA Rec. Group 49, Min. Pat. 4218.

25. "Mining Laws of L.A. Mining Dist.," Misc. R, Bk. 1, p. 162 and SFPMD Bk. A, 1865-75, in L.A. County HR.

26. Statement of reasons for rejection, by Alfred James, Register, and J. W. Haverstick, Receiver, Land Office, L.A., NA Rec. Group 49, Min. Pat. 4218. On Dec. 9, 1879, the Comr. ruled in the case of *F. B. Taylor* v. *The State of Calif. U.* that the Pico, as valuable mineral land, was not eligible for patent with "college scrip" under the Morrill Act of 1862 (D. K. Sickles, *US Mining Laws and the Decisions of the Comr. of the Gen. Land Office, etc.* [S.F., 1881], 438-39). By this time the decision hardly mattered, however, for the two sides had compromised their differences.

27. Baker to Lyon, Apr. 21, 1879, Baker R; *S.F. Stock Rpt.,* May 5, 1879.

28. *Ventura Signal,* Oct. 2, 1880; Alonzo Phelps, *Contemporary Biography of California's Representative Men* (S.F., 1881), 30.

29. *S.F. Stock Rpt.,* May 26 and June 10, 1879, Beale to Tevis, enclosed with ltr. Beale to Baker, June 9, 1879, Baker R.

30. *L.A. Herald,* May 2, 6 and 8, 1879; Lyon to Baker, June 11 and 28, 1879, Baker R.

31. Agreement between Beale, Baker and CSOW *et al.,* June 28, 1879, Secy. R; *S.F. Directory, 1879-80;* Deed Bk. 86, p. 376, L.A. County HR; Art. of Incorporation, South Pacific Coast RR, Mar. 25, 1876, Secy. of State (Calif.) R; (S.F.) *Daily Exchange,* Oct. 21, 1878; Youle, *op. cit.,* 32; *S.J. Mercury,* Sep. 11, 1879.

32. Application for Patent, refiled Jan. 26, 1880, NA Rec. Group 49, Min. Pat. 4218; title file, Treas. R. There was to be one more controversy over the title, as we have already noted (Chap. II, note 92). On Mar. 9, 1886, Pio Pico transferred whatever rights he had in the claim under his deed to Baker of May 21, 1877, to a citizen of Chile, Juan Luco. The latter sued Baker and CSOW in the Superior Ct. at S.F. on Jan. 25, 1887, for an accounting of his rights as a 1/7 owner of the claim (*Luco* v. *Baker, et al.,* in the Sup. Ct. of S.F. County, State Archives, Sac., Calif.). After appeal to the State Supreme Ct., the case was transferred to L.A. (*Luco* v. *Baker,* #6831 in the Sup. Ct. of L.A. County, L.A. County HR). All the documents relating to the Pico claim, from the deed of Hernandez and Perea forward, appear in this case. CSOW was released as a defendant after Scofield made his deposition. Scofield, who had been president of the company since 1881, was asked why the compromise of June, 1879, was reached in sevenths. On advice of counsel, he refused to answer. The court decided the case for Baker, finding the Hernandez and Perea deed of 1865 basic to the patent, and that a later deed from Pio Pico to Baker of June 14, 1877, had extinguished whatever interest Pio Pico may have had.

33. SFPMD Bk. A, "Pico Lead" relocation, Aug. 8, 1865, L.A. HR. Beale and Baker did not yield gracefully, however. For 2 years after the patent, they dragged their feet in signing it over, and in the spring of 1881 Baker suggested that they refuse to accept their 3/7 of CSOW's stock. Beale replied that he did not see how refusing to receive the stock would help them and seemed to fear that Felton might sell the majority interest "to the Standard," which "would leave us in even a worse position. . . ." (Beale to Baker, Apr. 12, 1881, Baker R). Peace did not come until mid-Aug., 1882, when Beale finally assigned his interest. J. H. Wise, a S.F. Supervisor and a friend and business associate of Beale and Baker, who had become a co-holder in July, 1879, signed over his interest at the same time, but Baker delayed signing until Oct. 17, 1882 (Scofield to Baker, Aug. 18, 1882, Baker R; Deed Bk. 103, p. 253, L.A. HR).

34. Lyon to Baker, July 2 and 15, 1879, Baker R. Apparently there were no subsequent assessments on CSOW stock. Just before the company was dissolved in 1901, its balance sheet showed its paid-in capital as only $30,000 (Balance Sheet, June 30, 1901, SO [Iowa] Special Statements, bound copies of financial and sales statements 1891-1901 in the Comptr. R, hereafter cited as SO [Iowa] Statements).

35. Phelps, *op. cit.*, 28-31; *S.F. Examiner,* Aug. 12, 1892. See also Edward Hungerford, *Wells Fargo—Advancing the American Frontier* (N.Y., 1949), 114-20, and the sketch in the *Dictionary of American Biography*.

36. Stacy H. Aspey, Senior Counsel, Office of the Secy. of State (Calif.), to E. B. Currier, June 15, 1954, Hist. R; Art. of Incorporation, PCO, Sep. 10, 1879, Secy. of State (Calif.) R; *S.F. Directory, 1879-80*.

37. Title file, Treas. R. Before long, Felton was carrying the title of president, and Fisk, secretary, of the Standard Oil Co. of California, and PCO was reported holding oil lands in Santa Clara and Santa Cruz County (*S.F. Directory, 1880;* Hittell, *op. cit.,* 317-18). We do not know what the 100,000 shares represented in invested capital. Certainly, the most important part of the contribution of Taylor and his associates was 4/7 of CSOW. In 1900 PCO listed 6,001 23/36 shares of CSOW stock on its balance sheet at $48,754. The additional 297 11/36 shares above the 4/7 was purchased at various times following 1893; in 1901, when the company was liquidated, the outstanding shares were bought at $9.33 a share. (See Chap. VIII). PCO's initial investment in CSOW stock, therefore, may have amounted to about $46,000, and $9,000 or $10,000 more may have represented the Standard Oil Co. of California and Taylor's interest in the Santa Clara Pet. Co.

38. PCO Stock Certificate Bk., Secy. R; *Oakland Tribune,* Apr. 13, 1880. George Loomis held the title of president for a few months to attend to some preliminary matters while Felton was in the East; by Dec. 15, when the distribution of shares occurred, Felton had returned and taken over the top office ("In Memoriam: George Loomis," an extract from the PCO Minutes, Apr. 17, 1894, in the Charlotte Ashley Felton collection, Stanford University).

39. PCO Stock Certificate Bk., Secy. R; deed of sale, Scofield & Tevis to Whittier, Fuller & Co., Dec. 31, 1883, Scofield R; *Ventura Free Press,* Jan. 19, 1880. Taylor disappears from the *S.F. Directory* in 1881 to reappear for a couple of years after 1884. In 1885 he formed a partnership in paints and oils in S.F., but was sued by Whittier, Fuller & Co. and enjoined from doing business in Mar., 1886. A condition of sale of F. B. Taylor & Co., Jan. 3, 1880, to Scofield & Tevis was that Taylor would not re-enter the paint and oil trade in S.F., and Whittier, Fuller had bought Scofield & Tevis (*Whittier, Fuller* v. *F. B. Taylor,* #4031 in the Sup. Ct. of S.F. County, US Dist. Ct. R, S.F.).

40. *S.F. Bulletin,* quoted in *Alameda Argus,* Apr. 1, 1880; *Ventura Free Press,* Apr. 10, 1880; *N.Y. Evening Post,* quoted in *Ventura Signal,* Oct. 2, 1880; *Comm. Herald,* Jan. 26, 1882; M. Stewart to L. Stewart, Mar. 6 and also Mar. 28, 1885, Stewart R; Charles Fernald to Bard, Mar. 8, 1885, Bard R-S. "Trustee" when used in relation to mining stock certificates apparently was a loosely defined term. It could be used "without any trust in fact existing. . . . No presumption arises . . . that the person . . . has not the legal title thereto. . . ." (Wm. Colebrooke, *A Treatise on the Law of Collateral Securities* [Chicago, 1898], 518-19). Colebrooke also says that unsubscribed and unissued shares could be issued and held in trust by a third person as security for advances made to the corporation (p. 524).

41. L. Tevis to Mrs. Louisa Greathouse, Apr. 4, 1881, C. W. Coburn to Mrs. G. L. Greathouse, Dec. 17, 1881, and Feb. 20, 1885, in the possession of Miss Alice Greathouse, Richmond, Calif.; also see Chap. IV.

42. M. Stewart to L. Stewart, Mar. 6 and 13, 1885, Waldie to L. Stewart, July 2, 1885, Stewart R; John A. Wilson, *History of Los Angeles County* (Oakland, 1880), 68; Hittell, *op. cit.,* 517; *McKenney's Pacific Coast Directory, 1883-84; S.F. Directory, 1884*. Scofield succeeded Felton as president of CSOW in Mar., 1881 (Affidavit of Scofield, Mar. 7, 1887, in *Luco* v. *Baker et al.,* Sup. Ct. of S.F. County, State Archives, Sac.).

43. *Min. & Sci. Press,* Aug. 31, 1878; *S.F. Stock Rpt.,* Sep. 23, Nov. 10 and Dec. 12, 1879; *Comm. Herald,* Dec. 18, 1879; George T. Brown, *The Gas Light Company of Baltimore* (Baltimore, 1936), 45-48.

44. Oakland Gas Light Co. Minutes, Dec. 22, 1879, and Apr. 9 and 14, 1880, Pacific Gas & Electric Co. R.

45. *S.J. Mercury,* quoted in *Min. & Sci. Press,* Nov. 1, 1879; *N.Y. Post,* quoted in *Ventura Signal,* Oct. 2, 1880.

46. *S.J. Herald,* Oct. 13 and 22, Nov. 8 and 24, 1879; *S.J. Mercury,* Oct. 14, 1879,

and *S.J. Mercury,* quoted in *Ventura Free Press,* Oct. 25, 1879; *Min. & Sci. Press,* Nov. 1, 1879; Youle, *op. cit.,* 32-33.

47. Lease Bk. D, 149-65, Santa Clara County HR; *S.J. Mercury,* quoted in *Min. & Sci. Press,* Nov. 1, 1879; *S.J. Herald,* Dec. 6 and 13, 1879.

48. *S.J. Mercury,* quoted in *Min. & Sci. Press,* Nov. 1, 1879; *7th Ann. Rpt. State Min.* (1888), 94; H. S. Foote, *Santa Clara County, California* (Chicago, 1888), 164.

49. L.A. County Assessment Rolls, 1879, p. 127, and 1880, p. 170, L.A. HR; Deed Bk. 53, pp. 232-35, Bk. 55, pp. 54-55, Bk. 57, pp. 173-74, in Santa Clara County HR; title files, Treas. R; "Layout Showing Restored Old Newhall Refinery," Sep. 23, 1929, Engr. R; *S.J. Herald,* Dec. 6, 1879. The additional expenditures at Andrews Station (Newhall) probably brought the refinery investment close to $25,267 (*4th Ann. Rpt. State Min.* [1884], 301).

50. Testimony of Geo. R. Miller in *W. H. Wright* v. *PCO,* #12,440 in the Sup. Ct. for Alameda County, Alameda County HR; C. M. Wetherill, "On the Relative Cost of Illumination in Lafayette, Ind.," *Am. Gas Light J.,* June 1, 1860; *Pittsburgh Directories, 1860 to 1871;* US Patents #101,364 and #101,365, Mar. 29, 1870, #102,819, May 10, 1870 and #114,293, May 2, 1871; *Derrick's Hand-Book,* I, 835.

51. Deed Bk. 191, p. 258, Alameda County HR; *S.F. Bulletin,* quoted in *Alameda Argus,* Apr. 1, 1880; *S.F. Chronicle,* quoted in *Alameda Argus,* Apr. 15, 1880.

52. SO(Iowa)Statements; *4th Ann. Rpt. State Min.,* 303-04; *7th Ann. Rpt. State Min.,* 34-37.

53. *4th Ann. Rpt. State Min.,* 301; *S.F. Chronicle, loc. cit.*

54. *S.F. Chronicle, loc. cit.*

55. Miller testimony in *Wright* v. *PCO; 4th Ann. Rpt. State Min.,* 303-04; *7th Ann. Rpt. State Min., loc. cit.*

56. *S.F. Chronicle,* June 13, 1880; *S.F. Merchant,* Aug. 13, 1880; *Comm. Herald,* June 24 and Oct. 7, 1880.

57. *Alameda Encinal,* Sep. 4, 11 and 25, 1880.

58. *S.F. Merchant,* Sep. 17 and Oct. 1, 1880; *Comm. Herald,* various dates.

59. *Comm. Herald,* Jan. 13, 1881; *S.F. Merchant,* June 17, 1881.

60. US Patent #245,891, Aug. 16, 1881. Thumm's name was frequently used in filing new claims in the Pico district, but not after 1881 ("List of New Claims" [1882], Hist. R).

61. *S.J. Mercury,* Sep. 14, 1880; *S.J. Herald,* Oct. 11, 1880; *4th Ann. Rpt. State Min.,* 301-02; *7th Ann. Rpt. State Min.,* 35-36. It is uncertain whether the Alameda refinery ever lived up to its anticipated capacity of 500 barrels a day. Neither of the reports of the State Mineralogist mentions this figure. We believe, too, that the Standard Oil Company (Iowa) contract in 1895 to purchase PCO's kerosine and naphthas was based on a throughput of about 350 b/d (see Chap. VII, pp. 188-89). On the other hand, a statement of refined costs prepared in Mar., 1885, to determine what PCO should pay for crude oil it purchased makes use of the 500 bbl. figure (Stewart R).

62. A. R. Green to Bard, Dec. 12, 1881, Bard R-S.

63. "Histories of PCO Co. Wells," Hist. R; *7th Ann. Rpt. State Min.,* 79-82; *20th Ann. Rpt. Oil & Gas Supervisor* (S.F., 1934), No. 2, p. 10.

64. "Histories of PCO Co. Wells," Hist. R; Wilson, *op. cit.,* 68.

65. Albert G. Ruxton, US Deputy Min. Surveyor, "Gen. Rpt. of Expenditures and Improvements Upon the System of Claims Held in Common by the Occidental Asphalt Co.," Dec. 17, 1885, Bureau of Land Management, Sac.

66. *Ibid.*

67. Judson, Gillette, and Gibson to Greathouse & Blanding, July 3, 1880, and "Opinion on Title of Christopher Leaming, Marcus W. Childs and Barbara Childs. . . . ," both in Hist. R.

68. *Ibid.*

69. Ruxton, "Field Notes," Sep. to Dec., 1880, and "List of New Claims, List of Good Claims" [1882], both in Hist. R.

70. Bills of sale in Misc. R, Bk. 2, pp. 72, 75, Lease Bk. 1, pp. 197-200, Recorder, Ventura County; *Felton* v. *S. N. Sheridan,* #555 in the Sup. Ct. of Ventura County, CC R, Ventura; *Steinbach and Carpentier* v. *Felton,* #2747, in US Cir. Ct., 9th Cir., Dist. Ct. R, S.F.; *Ventura Signal,* Dec. 4, 1880, Aug. 13 and 27, 1881.

71. *Ventura Signal,* Feb. 22, 1879, Aug. 27, 1880; *Ventura Free Press,* Apr. 3, 1880, Aug. 6, 1881; *Comm. Herald,* Jan. 26, 1882; *7th Ann. Rpt. State Min.,* 104.

72. The assessment rolls of Ventura County for 1881-82 listed the mining claims of the S.O. Co. of Calif. at $4,170; a report to the governor by the State Bd. of Equalization, Sac., Oct. 1, 1879, indicates that in most counties the practice was to assess property at from 20% to 50% of value, and in none at "full cash value."

73. Quoted in *Min. & Sci. Press,* June 10, 1882.

74. "Histories of PCO Co. Wells," Hist. R.

75. "Histories of PCO Co. Wells," Hist. R; Ruxton, "Gen. Rpt. of Expenditures and Improvements Upon the System of Claims Held in Common by the Occidental Asphalt Co.," Dec. 17, 1885, Bu. of Land Management, Sac.; *7th Ann. Rpt. State Min.,* 113-14. We can get another estimate on the cost per ft. by noting that write-offs from the PCO well drilling account were made only in Mar., 1900, and never made from the CSOW well drilling account. Restoring the write-offs of Mar., 1900, gives a PCO figure of $626,782 for 86,353 ft. of hole to Apr. 30, 1900, or $7.27 per ft. The CSOW well account for June 30, 1901, gives $383,463 for 48,117 ft. of hole, or $7.95 per ft. (In addition to "Histories of PCO Co. Wells," see notes 51 and 60 in Chap. VIII.)

76. Testimony of W. H. Hennage, Dec., 1916, in *US* v. *SP* #46, XVI, 9561, 9574.

77. "Histories of PCO Co. Wells," Hist. R; *7th Ann. Rpt. State Min.,* 79-85, 113-14.

78. L. Stewart to J. Irwin, Dec. 20, 1884, Stewart R; *4th Ann. Rpt. State Min.,* 301; *7th Ann. Rpt. State Min.,* 76; *Min. Res. of the US, 1883-84,* p. 219. The USGS received its figure from C. G. Yale, editor of the *Min. & Sci. Press.*

79. J. P. Scott to Bard, Aug. 29, 1882, Scofield to Bard, Oct. 21, 1882, Bard to Scofield, Mar. 16, 1885, Bard R-S; "Histories of PCO Co. Wells," Hist. R.

80. Hardison to L. Stewart, Dec. 20, 1883, Apr. 7, 1885, Stewart R.

81. The *Comm. Herald,* Jan. 26, 1882, citing the PCO executives as its source, spoke of Ventura oil as "being of a heavy nature and fit only for fuel. . . ."

82. Art. of Incorporation, Central Gas Co., Mar. 24, 1881, Secy. of State (Calif.) R; *Ventura Free Press,* Jan. 22 and June 4, 1881; *S.F. J. of Comm.,* Jan. 29, 1882; *Min. Res. of the US, 1883-84,* 220; Coleman, *op. cit.,* 47-49.

83. US Patent #251,849, Jan. 3, 1882; *L.A. Mirror,* quoted in *Ventura Free Press,* June 4, 1881; *Ventura Free Press,* Aug. 6, 1881; *L.A. Express,* quoted in *Ventura Signal,* Feb. 18 and Apr. 1, 1882; *Ventura Signal,* Sep. 27, 1884. On Apr. 11, 1882, Edwards also patented a fuel oil burner for stoves (US Patent #256,304).

84. Statement of A. J. Gardner, Oct. 27, 1916 (Supt., Pipe Shop, Central Pacific RR, Sac., in 1879), Hist. R; B. A. Worthington, Jan. 18, 1917, in *US* v. *SP* #46, 10977-78. *The Annual Proceedings* (1925, p. 141) of the 17th annual convention of the International Railway Fuel Association says that in 1879 the Central Pacific ran tests with fuel oil on a locomotive, "Young America," but if so, Gardner makes no mention of it.

85. *A. C. Dietz* v. *D. C. Scott,* #607, in the Sup. Ct. of Ventura County, CC R, Ventura; *Min. & Sci. Press,* June 18, 1881.

86. "Memo. of an Agreement," Oct. 24, 1882, between Steinbach, Carpentier and Frederick J. Whaley, Bk. 1, Bonds for Deeds and Agreements, 126-29, CC R, Ventura; *Dietz* v. *Mission Transfer Co.,* transcript on appeal to the Calif. Supreme Ct., p. 77 (filed June 26, 1890), State Archives, hereafter cited as *Dietz* v. *Mission Transfer.*

87. Art. of Incorporation, Mission Transfer Co., and "Shares of Capital Stock," both in Bard R-S. This list of shareholders to Oct., 1886, records the name of neither Felton nor Tevis, and yet the events of the intervening years make clear that each had an interest in the company. On the books of the company, the value of the oil rights was written up from the purchase price of $100,000 to $197,500.

88. *Dietz* v. *Mission Transfer,* 53, 71.

89. W. G. Adams to F. E. Davis, Jan. 19, 1883, and Davis to Adams, Jan. 26, 1883, in *ibid.,* also pp. 200, 220-21, 228; *Ventura Signal,* Feb. 5, May 19 and 26, 1883.

90. *Dietz* v. *Mission Transfer,* 63, 70, 182-87, 215; W. L. Hardison to L. Stewart, June 30, 1884, Stewart R.

91. For land acquisitions, we know that Felton paid a total of $9,750 to Wiley and Gelcich and to McPherson for the first Santa Clara leases, leaving the later land acquisitions in Santa Clara County and in Pico from Leaming and Childs to be accounted for. The cost of the Taylor companies and his interest in the Santa Clara Pet. Co. has

already been commented upon (note 37); the S.F. Pet. Co., in which assessments had run to about $20,000 without oil by the beginning of 1879, and the Santa Clara company, which also had discovered no oil at the time Felton took over, may have jointly cost him $20,000. Moody Gulch was easier drilling than Pico; hence, the $5 per ft. figure. Ruxton, "Gen. Rpt.," gives $10,000 for the cost of the pipeline to Newhall, $35,000 for other Pico investment, and $40,000 for the Santa Clara water system. The *4th Ann. Rpt. State Min.*, 301, gives a figure of $25,267 for the Newhall refinery, which must be at least $10,000 more than in the days of F. B. Taylor. The investment of the CO&T of Calif. in fixed assets was valued at $125,000 in July, 1885, at the time of the formation of the SO(Iowa), with a capital of $600,000. We do not know the value placed on fixed assets of CO&T (Iowa) when it was merged the preceding Dec. to help form the Continental Oil Co. with a capital of $300,000, but the proportionate figure for CO&T (Iowa) would have been about $60,000. Since 1884 was not a "growth" year for either company, the fixed investment in both may have amounted to about $150,000 in the middle of 1884. (For more on CO&T, see Chap. IV.) No figure is given here for Scofield & Tevis, which was liquidated at the end of 1883.

92. This statement is based on A. R. Gilchriste to H. C. Breeden, Sep. 26, 1900, and attachments, Comptr. R, SONJ, and CSOW Balance Sheet, Aug. 31, 1901, in SO(Iowa) Statements. Apparently, dividends on CSOW stock were delayed until the end of Mar., 1884, a matter that had aggrieved the minority stockholders, Beale and Baker. (W. L. Hardison to L. Stewart, Feb. 28, 1885, Stewart R; "Findings of Fact" in *Luco* v. *Baker*.) It is unlikely that dividends were paid earlier on the stock of the other companies, especially PCO.

IV. THE STRUGGLE FOR THE WESTERN MARKET, 1879-1885

1. Nevins, *op. cit.*, I, 258; Hidy and Hidy, *op. cit.*, 111-12; John D. Rockefeller, *Random Reminiscences of Men & Events* (N.Y., 1909), 58-59.

2. Nevins, *op. cit.*, I, 180-82, II, 38-39.

3. *Ibid.*, I, 134, 178-79, 210; *Comm. Herald*, Jan. 20, Feb. 2, Mar. 10, June 16, 1871, Jan. 14, 1875 and Jan. 18, 1877; statement of Scofield, Oct., 1908, Secy. R. The year 1874 appears to have seen the heaviest oil traffic by rail prior to 1878.

4. Mrs. David Wagstaff (granddaughter of J. B. Tilford, Sr.) interview by A. E. Haase, Aug. 15, 1955; *Derrick's Hand-Book*, I, 918; John J. McLaurin, *Sketches in Crude Oil* (Harrisburg, 1896), 365.

5. Hidy and Hidy, *op. cit.*, 27, 315.

6. *Comm. Herald*, Jan. 17, 1878, quoting its issue of July 7, 1877.

7. H. A. Hutchins to J. D. Rockefeller, Mar. 5, 1878, W. Rockefeller to J. B. Tilford, Jr., & Co., Apr. 30, 1878, in memo., Robert W. Gumbel to G. M. Foster, June, 1958, Hist. R; *S.F. Call*, June 25, 1878; *Comm. Herald*, June 27, 1878; *S.F. Directories*, *1879-80* to *1891*; A. R. Crum (ed.), *Romance of American Petroleum and Gas* (Oil City, Pa., 1911), I, 283; Nevins, *op. cit.*, I, 427.

8. *Alta*, June 23, 1878; *Comm. Herald*, Oct. 3, 1878.

9. O. H. Payne to J. D. Rockefeller, Mar. 20, 1878, in memo., Robert W. Gumbel to G. M. Foster, June, 1958, Hist. R; testimony of J. C. Stubbs, Gen. Traffic Mgr., SP, Aug. 12, 1887, in *Hearings Before the US Pac. RR Commission*, US Sen., 50th Cong., 1st Sess., Sen. Ex. Doc. 51, Pt. 4 (1888), VI, 3301-02; *S.F. Call*, Apr. 7, 1878; *Comm. Herald*, Jan. 30, 1879.

10. *Comm. Herald*, Dec. 4, 1879.

11. *Ibid.*, Jan. 15, 1880; C. A. Watson interview by Philip Patchin, June 12, 1922, Hist. R, hereafter cited as Watson interview; Branch Office Plant Ledger, Jan. 2, 1882, SO(Ohio) R.

12. Watson interview; *Alameda Argus*, Apr. 15, 1880; Hidy and Hidy, *op. cit.*, 115-16.

13. *Comm. Herald*, Jan. 13, 1881. On Felton's participation in CO&T, see note 38 below.

14. Chap. II, note 90; "Isaac E. Blake," in Bancroft R; *S.F. Directory* (published Apr., 1880); *S.F. J. of Comm.*, July 7, 1881; *Cleveland Directory, 1882-83*.

15. One of the salesmen, Frederick J. Whaley, signed the purchase contract for the ex-Mission, Oct. 24, 1882. The two other salesmen, Frank E. Davis and Albert E.

Cooper, a clerk, Daniel McMillan, and a teamster, Gilbert P. Chase, were four of the five incorporators of the Mission Transfer Co. (Chap. III, notes 85-86, and *S.F. Directory, 1879-80, 1882*). Until 1881 CO&T had its headquarters with Scofield & Tevis, which shared the CO&T warehouse at Fifth and Berry Sts.

16. *Sac. Record-Union*, Jan. 1, 1881; *S.F. J. of Comm.*, Sep. 28, 1882; Edwards to Bard, Feb. 15, 1882, Bard R-S.

17. C. J. Woodbury, "Rockefeller and His Standard," *Saturday Evening Post*, Oct. 21, 1911; *Min. & Sci. Press*, Oct. 11, 1884.

18. *S.F. Call*, Jan. 19, 1882; *Cleveland Directory, 1882-83*; Nevins, *op. cit.*, II, 69.

19. Watson interview; "Isaac E. Blake," Bancroft R.

20. Stubbs to J. F. Goddard, Gen. Freight Agent, Topeka, Kansas, Apr. 4, 1881, Bancroft R. In 1880 Stanford and Crocker were Wells Fargo board members (Extracts from Minutes, History Rm., Wells Fargo Bank).

21. Note re I. E. Blake by the Rev. Dr. Buchtel in sketch of Blake, Bancroft R. Buchtel attributed the comment on Blake's genius to "the president of the Standard Oil Company," which seems unlikely, and the disparity seems almost too great to be believed. Tables submitted to the Pac. RR Comm. in 1887 by the Gen. Traffic Mgr. of the Union Pac. again seem questionable, for they show rebates to the Continental Oil Company (CO&T[Iowa]) of $39,045 between 1882 and 1884, while the rebates to Standard (and Consolidated Tank Line) amounted to $2,026 on a volume of traffic that seems all too small. The tables do show, however, that during these years the per cent of rebate to CO&T (38%) was considerably higher than that to Standard (11%). (*Hearings Before the US Pac. RR Comm.*, III, 1413-14.)

22. Watson interview; *Min. & Sci. Press*, Aug. 23, 1879; *Sac. Record-Union*, Jan. 1, 1881; *S.F. J. of Comm.*, July 7, 1881, Jan. 28 and Sep. 28, 1882.

23. *Min. & Sci. Press*, Feb. 12, 1881; *S.F. J. of Comm.*, Jan. 28, 1882; *S.F. Merchant*, Feb. 3, 1882.

24. *Comm. Herald*, Jan. 26, 1882; *S.F. J. of Comm.*, Jan. 28, 1882. The *J. of Comm.* gives the same figure for Calif. kerosine received at S.F. that the *Comm. Herald* gives for receipts of Calif. petroleum, which has to be an error on the part of the *J. of Comm.* The Census figures are from S. F. Peckham, *The Natural History of Petroleum*, Tenth Census of the US, X, 151. Peckham's own estimate of Calif. kerosine production is given at not more than 1,000,000 gals., but no year is specified, and equating it as "or 2,500 barrels" is obviously a typographical error. It is possible that the *J. of Comm.* figures on imports of eastern kerosine into Calif. may be for rail shipments only, but this is not indicated in the article.

25. CO&T letterhead, Edwards to Bard, Feb. 15, 1882, Bard R-S.

26. *S.F. J. of Comm.*, Jan. 28, 1882.

27. Branch Office Plant Ledger, 1882-85, SO(Ohio) R; Salary Bk. A, SO(Iowa), Secy. R, SONJ; *S.F. Directory, 1881*. Apparently Standard made heavy use of the economies of water transportation around Cape Horn in sharpening its price competition (*Comm. Herald*, Jan. 18, 1883, and Jan. 31, 1884).

28. Watson interview; *S. O. Bulletin*, Sep., 1920, pp. 12-14.

29. Watson interview; Branch Office Plant Ledger, June 30, 1883, SO(Ohio) R; John McLean, "A Pioneer Reminisces," *Among Ourselves*, June, 1924, p. 2; H. B. Fairchild to Pub. Rel. Dept., June 25, 1929, O. T. Lawler to G. J. O'Brien, Apr. 9, 1954, Hist. R.

30. Watson interview.

31. *Ibid.*; *S.F. J. of Comm.*, Aug. 24, 1882.

32. *Comm. Herald*, Jan. 31, 1884. The statements on prices are based on data drawn from the *Comm. Herald*, *S.F. J. of Comm.*, and the *S.F. Chronicle*.

33. "Works Diary," Cleveland Refinery, SO(Ohio) R; *Comm. Herald*, Jan. 31, 1884; Nevins, *op. cit.*, II, 32.

34. Deed, Scofield & Tevis to Whittier, Fuller & Co., Scofield R; C. W. Coburn to Mrs. G. L. Greathouse, May 6, 1884, in the possession of Miss Alice Greathouse, Richmond, Calif.; *S.F. J. of Comm.*, Jan. 29, 1882; *Ninety Years, the Story of William Parmer Fuller* (S.F., 1939), 81-82, hereafter cited as *William P. Fuller*.

35. M. Stewart to L. Stewart, Apr. 9, 1884, Stewart R; *S.F. Chronicle*, Apr. 12, 1884.

36. *L.A. Express*, Apr. 21, 1884; *Alta*, May 5, 1884; Raymond B. Fosdick, *John D Rockefeller, Jr.: A Portrait* (N.Y., 1956), 36.

37. M. Stewart to L. Stewart, Aug. 28, 1884, Stewart R; Blake ltr. of Jan. 2, 1885, quoted in Hardison, Stewart & Co., hereafter cited as HS&Co., to Bard, Jan. 14, 1885, Bard R-S; R. W. Hidy to G. T. White, Oct. 22, 1959, Hist. R; Hidy and Hidy, *op. cit.*, 112-15, 122, and note 62, p. 729; *Brief for Appellants, SONJ* v. *US,* US Supreme Ct., (N.Y., 1909), II, 257.

38. SO(Iowa) Minutes and stock certificates. We believe that Felton and perhaps Blake shared in the certificate for 40%, which H. L. Tevis received as trustee. Felton's brother-in-law, Geo. Loomis, it will be recalled, was the vice president of CO&T of Calif. A letter from A. Waldie to L. Stewart, July 2, 1885 (Stewart R), reports at second hand that "Felton is now in New York attending to the CO&T Co's matters," and Scofield in the press statement quoted later in this chapter speaks of a "set of stockholders" in CO&T of Calif.

39. Branch Office Plant Ledger, Apr. 23, 1885, SO(Ohio) R; SO(Iowa) Statements; SO(Iowa) Minutes, June 22, 1885; SO(Iowa) Balance Sheet, Jan. 1, 1886, Comptr. R, SONJ.

40. In 1905 Bard told a government investigator "they [CO&T] claimed they had lost a quarter million dollars when they finally surrendered. . . ." (T. R. Bard interview by Luther Conant, Jr., June 30, 1905, NA BuCorp. file #3402, Pt. 2). We have no way of verifying this figure.

41. M. Stewart to L. Stewart, June 24, 1884, Stewart R.

42. See Chap. V.

43. *S.F. Chronicle,* July 15, 1885; *Alta,* July 16, 1885.

44. HS&Co. to Loomis, Pres., PCO, Nov. 12, 1885, Stewart R; *Felton* v. *Millard,* transcript on appeal to the Calif. Supreme Ct., p. 28, filed July 6, 1886, State Archives; *Alta,* July 16, 1885; *Biog. Dir. of the Amer. Cong., 1774-1949* (1950), 1170.

45. Watson interview. The exact date of purchase is uncertain, but the old C. A. Low firm dissolved on Jan. 2, 1885 (*Alta,* Jan. 8, 1885).

V. FELTON AND TEVIS TURN CONSERVATIVE

1. "Histories of PCO Wells," Hist. R.

2. M. Stewart to L. Stewart, Nov. 19, 1884, and Jan. 2, 1885, L. Stewart to J. Baker, Jr., Mar. 1, 1900, and to Mrs. S. A. Lahey, July 19, 1912, all in Stewart R; "Isaac E. Blake," Bancroft R; John McLaurin, *Sketches in Crude Oil* (Harrisburg, Pa., 1896), 163; Paul H. Giddens, *Early Days of Oil* (Princeton, 1948), 82.

3. L. Stewart to W. J. Chichester, June 9, 1898, Stewart R.

4. J. A. Neill to L. Stewart, Dec. 1, 1883, Stewart R; Mrs. James Proctor (daughter of W. L. Hardison) interview by A. E. Haase, Feb. 15, 1955; Yda Addis Storke, *A Memorial and Biographical History of the Counties of Santa Barbara, San Luis Obispo and Ventura, California* (Chicago, 1891), 620; Earl M. Welty and Frank J. Taylor, *Black Bonanza,* 2d ed. (N.Y., 1956), 15-16, 39-40.

5. L. Stewart to Mrs. Armanda J. Jones, Feb. 26, 1885, Stewart R; Storke, *op. cit.*, 620-21.

6. L. Stewart ltr. of Apr. 24, 1883, quoted in M. Stewart to L. Stewart, June 22, 1885, L. Stewart to Blake, Feb. 23, 1885, Stewart R; *Ventura Signal,* Apr. 14, 1883.

7. L. Stewart to D. A. Webster, Oct. 30, 1912, Stewart R.

8. L. Stewart to W. J. Chichester, June 9, 1898, Stewart R; Welty and Taylor, *op. cit.*, 30-31; Storke, *op. cit.*, 314, 321, 434, 620; *Derrick's Hand-Book,* I, 852-53.

9. J. A. Neill to L. Stewart, Dec. 1, 1883, L. Stewart to Hardison, Aug. 23 and Dec. 17, 1884, to M. Stewart, Aug. 23, 1884, and June 15, 1885, to Mission Transfer Co., Nov. 13, 1884, to Blake, Dec. 12, 1884, Jan. 26, Feb. 23 and Mar. 17, 1885, to Neill, Aug. 24, 1886, Hardison to L. Stewart, July 20, 1886, Stewart R.

10. L. Stewart to M. Stewart, Aug. 23, 1884, Stewart R.

11. L. Stewart to Blake, July 24, 1883, and Mar. 17, 1885, to Hardison, Dec. 17, 1884, M. Stewart to L. Stewart, July 10, 1884, Stewart R.

12. L. Stewart to M. Stewart, Mar. 3, 1884, Stewart R; Bard to PCO, Sep. 11, 1891, Bard R-HL; *SO Co. of Calif.* v. *W. T. Garrison,* #619, in the Sup. Ct. of Ventura County, CC Ventura; W. F. McClure, US Deputy Mineral Surveyor, "Plat of Pico

Canon Oil Wells," Nov., 1889, Hist. R; *L.A. Times,* Jan. 22, 1899; Welty and Taylor, *op. cit.,* 32-33.

13. Hardison to L. Stewart, Oct. 19, Dec. 10, 12, and 20, 1883, L. Stewart to M. Stewart, June 15, 1885, Stewart R.

14. M. Stewart to L. Stewart, Jan. 26, 1884, Stewart R; Welty and Taylor, *op. cit.,* 32-33.

15. Hardison to L. Stewart, Nov. 7 and Dec. 30, 1883, Waldie (office mgr. of HS&Co.) to L. Stewart, Jan. 26, 29 and Mar. 21, 1884, L. Stewart to M. Stewart, Feb. 23, 1884, Stewart R; W. E. Youle, *Sixty-Three Years in the Oilfields* (Taft, ca. 1926), 35.

16. L. Stewart to M. Stewart, Mar. 6, Apr. 7 and 12, 1884, to M. R. Vernon, Apr. 12, 1884, to C. M. Bly, June 13, 1884, to Chichester, June 25, 1884, Hardison to L. Stewart, June 30, 1884, and Jan. 13, 1885, Stewart R.

17. Lease, Bard to D. C. Scott, Jan. 15, 1884, Bard to Scofield, July 16, 1892, Bard R-S; L. Stewart to M. Stewart, June 10, 1884, Stewart R; *D. C. Scott* v. *I. E. Blake,* #11,521, in US Cir. Ct., 9th Cir., S.F.

18. L. Stewart to M. Stewart, Mar. 3, May 7 and 19, 1884, M. Stewart to L. Stewart, Apr. 12, 1884, Stewart R.

19. L. Stewart to M. Stewart, Apr. 12, May 27, June 10 and 19, 1884, Stewart R.

20. L. Stewart to M. Stewart, May 27 and Nov. 27, 1884, Stewart R; "Histories of PCO Wells," Hist. R.

21. M. Stewart to L. Stewart, Mar. 11 and June 12, 1884, Stewart R.

22. L. Stewart to M. Stewart, Sep. 30 and Dec. 11, 1884, Hardison to L. Stewart, Jan. 13, 1885, Stewart R.

23. L. Stewart to M. Stewart, June 10 and 13, 1884, to Hardison, Aug. 23, 1884, Stewart R; *S.F. Bulletin,* Sep. 12, 1884; *Min. Res. of the US, 1885,* 151.

24. L. Stewart to M. Stewart, Aug. 23, Sep. 19 and 30, 1884, Stewart R; Blake to HS&Co., Aug. 27, 1884, Bard R-S.

25. L. Stewart to Hardison, Oct. 31, 1884, HS&Co. to Mission Transfer Co., Nov. 13, 1884, Stewart R.

26. L. Stewart to Blake, Dec. 12, 1884, to Scofield, Dec. 15, 1884, to Hardison, Dec. 17, 1884, Irwin to L. Stewart, Dec. 10, 1884, Stewart R.

27. L. Stewart to M. Stewart, Nov. 27, 1884, to Hardison, Dec. 17, 1884, Irwin to L. Stewart, Dec. 19, 1884, Stewart R; SFPMD, Bk. D, L.A. County HR; Art of Incorporation, Occidental Asphalt Co., June 16, 1883, Secy. of State (Nev.) R; A. G. Ruxton, "Gen. Rpt. of Expenditures and Improvements Upon the System of Claims Held in Common By the Occidental Asphalt Co.," Dec. 17, 1885, Bu. of Land Management, Sac.

28. L. Stewart to Mission Transfer Co., Nov. 13, 1884, Stewart R.

29. L. Stewart to Irwin, Nov. 27, 1884, Stewart R.

30. L. Stewart to Irwin, May 8, 1884, to M. Stewart, Nov. 27, 1884, L. W. Bents to L. Stewart, May 22, 1884, M. Stewart to L. Stewart, Mar. 6, 1885, Irwin to L. Stewart, Dec. 8, 10 and 13, 1884, Jan. 31, 1885, Stewart R.

31. Balance Sheet, Ojai Oil Co., Oct. 31, 1884, Stewart R.

32. Ojai lease, Jan. 15, 1884, HS&Co. to Bard, Jan. 14, 1885, "Memo. of Ojai runs from July 26, 1884, to Feb. 14, 1885," Bard to Scofield, Mar. 2, 1885, Bard R-S.

33. Fernald to Bard, Mar. 8 and 26, 1885, Bard to Fernald, Mar. 25, 1885, Bard R-S; Hardison to L. Stewart, Mar. 24, 1885, Stewart R.

34. M. Stewart to L. Stewart, Mar. 13, 1885, Stewart R; D. S. Watkins to C. T. Noyes, Supt., Sac. Shops, SP, Feb. 21, 1910, Hist. R; *7th Ann. Rpt. State Min.* (1888), 30-33.

35. L. Stewart to Chichester, June 25, 1884, to Blake, Feb. 23, 1885, to J. D. Downing, Feb. 26, 1885, Stewart R.

36. "Copy of PCO Co's estimate of cost of Refining Oil with prices obtained for products, etc.," Mar. 5, 1885, Stewart R. PCO did not include the lube oils in this computation, apparently because they represented a second distillation of a portion of the fuel oil fraction.

37. L. Stewart to Blake, Feb. 23 and Apr. 23, 1885, HS&Co. to PCO, Apr. 28, 1885, L. Stewart to M. Stewart, June 15, 1885, Stewart R.

38. L. Stewart to Bard, June 10, 1885, Bard R-S; Hardison to L. Stewart, June 15, 1885, Stewart R.

39. Lease, June 10, 1885, Lease Bk. 1, 172, Recorder, Ventura County.

40. L. Stewart to M. Stewart, June 15, 1885, "Extract from Pico 'Big lease' " (fragment in Stewart R, ca. 1886), Stewart R.

41. "Histories of PCO Wells," Hist. R; Waldie to L. Stewart, Sep. 12 and Oct. 3, 1885, Stewart R.

42. *4th Ann. Rpt. State Min.* (1884), 303-04; *7th Ann. Rpt. State Min.,* 34-37.

43. Waldie to L. Stewart, Apr. 3, 1885, Stewart R; Newhall statements, Hist. R; *L.A. Times,* Jan. 1, 1887.

44. Waldie to L. Stewart, July 7, Aug. 4 and Nov. 25, 1885, Stewart R; *PCO v. C. A. Storke,* #758, in the Sup. Ct. of Ventura County, CC Ventura; *Ventura Democrat,* Sep. 3, 1885.

45. SO(Iowa) Statements; Hardison to HS&Co., Oct. 30, 1885, Stewart R; *Min. Res. of the US, 1885,* 151.

46. Irwin to L. Stewart, Mar. 24, 1886, Hardison to L. Stewart, July 10, Sep. 6 and 27, 1886, Stewart R; *S.F. Bulletin,* Sep. 12, 1884; (S.F.) *Guide,* ca. Mar. 22, 1886; *Ventura Democrat,* July 29, 1886.

47. Title files, Treas. R; Waldie to L. Stewart, Oct. 30 and Dec. 19, 1886, Stewart R.

48. "Histories of PCO Wells," Hist. R; HS&Co. to Dull, May 5, 1886, Stewart R; *S.F. Chronicle,* Jan. 1, 1887; *7th Ann. Rpt. State Min.,* 94, 96.

49. M. Stewart to L. Stewart, Oct. 24, 1885, L. Stewart to Hardison, Dec. 11, 1885, to Samuel Minor, July 5, 1886, Waldie to L. Stewart, Jan. 9 and July 17, 1886, Stewart R; *7th Ann. Rpt. State Min.,* 77-78.

50. Hardison to L. Stewart, Jan. 11, 1886, M. Stewart to L. Stewart, Jan. 28, 1886, L. Stewart to Rowland, Jan. 18, 1886, Stewart R; *Comm. Herald,* Nov. 11, 1886; *7th Ann. Rpt. State Min.,* 73; CSMB *Bul. #11* (1897), 20.

51. L. Stewart to Hardison, July 6, 1886, Stewart R.

52. Bard to Fernald, Jan. 5, 1886, Fernald R; HS&Co. to Bard, Jan. 11, 1886, Bard to HS&Co., Apr. 6, 1886, Bard R-S; Lease Bk. 1, pp. 295, 300, Recorder, Ventura County.

53. Hardison to L. Stewart, May 8 and July 4, 1886, Stewart R.

54. The Assessment Roll for 1886-87 (Assessor, Ventura County) shows no claims of the SO Co. of Calif.; Hardison to L. Stewart, May 22, June 28 and Aug. 11, 1886, Waldie to L. Stewart, July 15, 1886, Bard to L. Stewart, Sep. 10, 1886, Stewart R; Bard to Hardison, Oct. 15, 1886, to Geo. Loomis, Nov. 20, 1886, Bard memo., Feb. 7, 1888, Bard R-S; Art. of Incorporation, Sespe Oil Co., Sep. 21, 1886, CC Ventura.

55. Waldie to L. Stewart, July 7, 1885, L. Stewart to J. A. Neill, Sep. 29, 1885, Hardison to HS&Co., Oct. 30, 1885, Stewart R.

56. L. Stewart to Neill, Sep. 29, 1885, Stewart R; *7th Ann. Rpt. State Min.,* 106-07.

57. A. J. Stevens to Loomis, Dec. 31, 1885, Stewart R; *7th Ann. Rpt. State Min.,* 30, 33; *Min. Res. of the US, 1885,* 151; *Min. Res. of the US, 1886,* 462.

58. Waldie to L. Stewart, Feb. 26, 1886, Loomis to HS&Co., June 8, 1886, quoted in Waldie to L. Stewart, June 11, 1886, Stewart R; *Comm. Herald,* May 2, 1886, Jan. 13, 1887; also *S.F. J. of Comm.,* Jan. 27, 1887. Some PCO gasoline and lubes, too, were finding their way into the foreign trade.

59. Hardison to L. Stewart, July 10 and 20, 1886, Stewart R.

60. Hardison to L. Stewart, May 8, June 23 and July 4, 1886, Stewart R; Hardison to Bard, July 5, 1886, Bard R-S; *7th Ann. Rpt. State Min.,* 106.

61. M. Stewart to L. Stewart, July 12, 1886, Hardison to L. Stewart, Aug. 11, 1886, L. Stewart to J. A. Neill, Aug. 24, 1886, Stewart R; *Comm. Herald,* June 7, 1886; *S.F. Examiner,* June 16, 1886, CSMB *Bul. #11,* p. 20.

62. Hardison to Bard, July 5, 1886, Bard R-S; L. Stewart to Hardison, July 6, 1886, Hardison to L. Stewart, July 20, 1886, Stewart R.

63. Hardison to L. Stewart, Sep. 24, 1886, Stewart R.

64. Hardison to L. Stewart, Sep. 28, 1886, Stewart R; Bard to Hardison, Oct. 15, 1886, Bard R-S.

65. Hardison to L. Stewart, Sep. 6, 1886, Stewart R; *4th Ann. Rpt. State Min.,* 271-72.

66. Hardison to L. Stewart, Oct. 6, 1886, Stewart R; "Opening Entries of New Books," Mission Transfer Co., Oct. 6, 1886, Bard to Hardison, Oct. 15, 1886, Bard R-S.

67. "Memo. of Agreement," Jan. 7, 1887, Hist. R.

68. Hardison to L. Stewart, Oct. 6, 1886, Stewart R.

69. Bard to Hardison, Mar. 7 (?), 1887, Bard R-S; Hardison to L. Stewart, Mar. 7, 1887, Stewart R.

70. Hardison to L. Stewart, Oct. 8 and Nov. 1, 1886, M. Stewart to L. Stewart, Oct. 8 and 15, 1886, Stewart R; Hardison to Bard, Oct. 11, 14 and 16, 1886, Bard to Hardison, Oct. 15, 1886, Bard R-S.

71. Hardison to L. Stewart, May 4, 1886, Stewart R; Bard to (?), Sep. 16, 1890, Bard R-HL; Welty and Taylor, *op. cit.,* 42.

72. "Mission Transfer Co. Stock" (Assessments, 1887-89), Bard R-S.

73. Hardison to L. Stewart, Feb. 2, Mar. 7 and May 7, 1887, Stewart R; Bard to Davis, Mar. 4, 1887, Bard R-S; *7th Ann. Rpt. State Min.,* 104.

74. Bard to Hardison, Mar. 14, 1887, Hardison to L. Stewart, Mar. 14, 19, May 7, 28 and Aug. 20, 1887, Stewart R; F. E. Davis to Bard, Mar. 25, 1887, Bard to Fulton Iron Works, May 24, 1888, Bard R-S; Welty and Taylor, *op. cit.,* 45-47.

75. Coit & Folsom to Hardison, Mar. 22 and to Bard and Dan McFarland, Aug. 11, 1887, Bard R-S; *S.F. Call,* Mar. 10, 1887.

76. Hardison to L. Stewart, Aug. 18 and Sep. 7, 1887, L. Stewart to M. Stewart, Oct. 15, 1887, Stewart R.

77. Hardison to L. Stewart, Aug. 20 (2 ltrs.) and Aug. 23, 1887, Stewart R.

78. Hardison to Loomis, Sep. 2, 1887, Stewart R; *S.F. J. of Comm.,* Feb. 9, 1888. Stock assessments totaling $115,000 had been put into the business since Oct., 1886, including $55,000 for the last two payments for the ex-Mission oil rights (Mission Transfer Co. Stock [Assessments, 1887-89] Bard R-S).

79. M. Stewart to L. Stewart, Feb. 4, 1887, Stewart R; Williamson and Daum, *op. cit.,* 566, 601. In 1887 Ohio oil, which had yet to yield a marketable kerosene, averaged 23¢ a bbl.

80. Waldie to L. Stewart, Aug. 12 and 25, 1887, Stewart R; *7th Ann. Rpt. State Min.,* 104-7, 112.

81. Hardison to L. Stewart, Aug. 25 and 26, 1887, Stewart R.

82. Glenn S. Dumke, *The Boom of the Eighties in Southern California* (Pasadena, 1944) 21-27.

83. Quoted in Hardison to Loomis, Sep. 2, 1887 (not sent), Stewart R.

84. Memo., Bard, "In Relation to the Proposition to Pool the Oils of the Mission Transfer Co.," Feb. 7, 1888, Bard R-S; L. Stewart to E. O. Emerson, Mar. 21, 1889, and to M. Stewart, Mar. 25, 1889, Stewart R.

85. Bard to Waldie, Nov. 2, 1887, Bard R-S.

86. L. Stewart to M. Stewart, Oct. 15, 1887, and Hardison and L. Stewart, *passim,* Stewart R.

87. This figure is based on the following: $33,400 for the cost of the tank cars; an estimate of $45,000 for the cost of the pipeline to Santa Paula (see note 45); an estimate of $35,000 for the refinery additions, based on the total refinery investment in the spring of 1884 ($160,117) and in 1900 ($209,173), of which very little was after 1887; an estimate of $27,500 for the Placerita land, moving the pump station, and building a short pipeline.

88. The estimates for Pico production of the Felton and Tevis companies, conservatively based on conflicting contemporary evidence, are as follows: 1884, 180,000; 1885, 180,000; 1886, 170,000; 1887, 155,000, for a total of 685,000 bbls. The operating cost figure was computed from the Newhall statements, Hist. R, for Apr. to Dec., 1888, which are the earliest surviving operating statements. On one possibility for a smaller refining profit, see note 36.

89. Deposition of Scofield, June 19, 1888, and Findings of Fact, in *Luco v. Baker.*

90. The *S.F. Directory* for 1888 dropped the S. F. Pet. Co., and, for 1889, the Santa Clara Pet. Co. and the SO Co. of Calif. The Ventura County assessment roll listed no property of the SO Co. of Calif. after 1886. The supposition of a trade between McPherson and PCO is based on the belief that he had maintained a minority interest in the S.F. Pet. Co. After 1888 the Moody Gulch wells are known as the "McPherson Oil Wells" (H. S. Foote, *Santa Clara County, California* [Chicago, 1888], 164; *10th Ann. Rpt. State Min.,* [1890], 606-7; also Newhall statements, May-June, 1888, Hist. R).

VI. PCO'S YEARS OF DECLINE

1. This brief survey of the Union Oil Co. has been drawn from Welty and Taylor's *Black Bonanza* and the Stewart and Bard papers. The Torrey Canyon Oil Co., which was also a Ventura County operation, had been organized in May, 1889.

2. Art. of Incorporation, Jan. 22, 1892, Secy. of State (Calif.) R; CSMB *Bul. #11* (1897), 61; *Rpt. of the Ind. Comm.*, I, 542.

3. Newhall statements, Hist. R; *Min. Res. of the US, 1921*, Pt. 2, p. 261.

4. Testimony of R. P. Schwerin, Mar. 7, 1917, in *US* v. *SP* #46, reporter's transcript, XXI, 12415.

5. PCO Stock Certificate Bk., Secy. R; *S.F. Examiner*, Oct. 26, 1894. The shares held as President and Trustee may have been repossessed for nonpayment of assessments. In Jan., 1894, these shares (and 1,000 which Felton held as trustee) were distributed proportionately among the Felton, Tevis, and former Blake interests at par ($10 a share), raising $151,667. This is the only time that a dollar figure is to be found on the stubs of the certificates.

6. *Calif. Oil World*, Apr. 7, 1910, p. 14; statement of Starke to Oscar Lawler, Nov. 4, 1929, Hist. R.

7. *S.F. Bulletin*, Apr. 9, 1894; Felton to Farmers & Merchants Bank, Mar. 12, 1896, Farmers & Merchants Bank R, L.A.

8. *S.F. Chronicle*, Jan. 1, 1889; *S.F. J. of Comm.*, Feb. 7, 1889, Feb. 5, 1891; *7th Ann. Rpt. State Min.* (1888), 166-67; *Min. Res. of the US, 1901* (1902), 365.

9. L. Stewart to M. Stewart, Jan. 28, 1888, Stewart R; *S.F. J. of Comm.*, Feb. 9, 1888, Feb. 7, 1889; Charles M. Coleman, *P.G.&E. of California* (N.Y., 1952), 478.

10. Newhall statements, Hist. R; *S.F. Chronicle*, Jan. 1, 1891; statement of Scofield, Oct., 1908, Secy. R. See also S. F. Peckham, "Petroleum in Southern California," *16th Ann. Rpt. of the USGS* (1896), IV, 372, 374.

11. Hardison to L. Stewart, Oct. 27 and Nov. 20, 1887, Stewart R.

12. Stewart R, *passim*, 1887-88; *S.F. Examiner*, May 8, 1888.

13. Hardison to L. Stewart, Nov. 20, 1887, Stewart R; *S.F. Call*, Mar. 10, 1887; *S.F. Chronicle*, Oct. 20, 1887; *Min. & Sci. Press*, Dec. 24, 1887, May 5, 1888.

14. H. S. Lubbock, Supervising Inspector 1st Dist., to Gen. James A. Dumont, Supervising Inspector Gen. of Steam Vessels, May 26, 1888, Bard R-S; *Alta*, Feb. 28, 29 and Mar. 30, 1888.

15. *S.F. Examiner*, May 8, 1888.

16. Hardison to Fernald, Apr. 25 and May 1, 1888, Fernald to Bard, May 8, 1888, to Wm. Vandever, July 9, 1888, Bard R-S; Ann. Statement of the Mission Transfer Co., Oct. 1, 1888, Stewart R.

17. Griffith Coit & Co. to Hardison, Apr. 19, 1888, quoted in Hardison to Fernald, Apr. 25, 1888, Bard R-S.

18. *Min & Sci. Press*, May 5 and June 2, 1888; *Alta*, May 8, 1888.

19. Vandever to Bard, June 2, July 3, Aug. 18 and Oct. 19, 1888, Bard R-S.

20. L. Stewart to C. P. Collins, Mar. 5, 1888, to E. O. Emerson, Dec. 1, 1888, and Mar. 21, 1889, to M. Stewart, Dec. 10, 1888, M. Stewart to L. Stewart, Feb. 9, 1889, Stewart R.

21. Bard to Fernald, Jan. 8, 1889, Fernald R; *L.A. Times*, June 26, 1889; *Santa Paula Chronicle*, June 28, 1889; Guy Hardison interview by A. E. Haase, Feb. 15, 1955. Guy Hardison, a son of W.L., recalls that Capt. Hall, the master of the *W. L. Hardison*, was staying at the Hardison home in Santa Paula the night the ship was burned and denies that there is any truth to the oft-told story attributing the fire to the ship's Chinese cook.

22. Newhall statements, Hist. R.

23. Newhall statements, Apr., 1888, Hist. R; *7th Ann. Rpt. State Min.*, 84; *L.A. Times*, Jan. 1, 1888.

24. L. Stewart to M. Stewart, Nov. 26, 1888, Stewart R.

25. Title files, Treas. R; SFPMD Bks. D and E, L.A. County HR.

26. "Histories of PCO wells," Hist. R; title files, Treas. R.

27. Title files, Treas. R; SFPMD Bks. D and E; PCO Minutes, Feb. 14 and 20, 1899;

9th Ann. Rpt. State Min. (1890), 205-6. One other feature should be noted concerning PCO's entrenchment in the Pico region during these years. Between 1888 and 1890 it acquired the land grant rights of the Southern Pacific to around 3,150 acres lying principally between the Pico patent and the Wiley claim and, secondarily, in Elsmere and Grapevine canyons—areas in which it already held numerous mining claims. Eventually, PCO used the railroad rights in 1902 to patent approximately 2,000 of these acres. None of this land was oil-bearing, nor was it drilled thereafter. (Title files, Treas. R; *20th Ann. Rpt. Oil & Gas Supervisor* [S.F., 1934], No. 2, map opp. p. 6.)

28. "Histories of PCO Wells," Hist. R; *11th Ann. Rpt. State Min.* (1894), 354.

29. The figures for PCO and CSOW have been compiled from the monthly Newhall statements, Hist. R. Union's production is from a "Statement . . . Total Quantity of Oil Produced, from Nov., 1890, to Jan. 1, 1896," Stewart R.

The figures for Calif. are from the *Min. Res. of the US, 1901,* p. 199, except for 1888. Its report of 690,333 bbls. for 1888 appears to be a gross error, and we have used a figure of 404,762 bbls. appearing in a table in the *Comm. Herald* for Jan. 22, 1891, as closer to the mark. Prior to 1894 the U.S. Geological Survey compiled its statistics from informed sources rather than from returns from producers. The *S.F. J. of Comm.* for Feb. 7, 1889, reported the production of Ventura County in 1888 as 236,703 bbls. and also included an estimate by the L.A. Chamber of Commerce of 420,000 bbls. for Southern Calif. in 1888. Conceivably, the Geological Survey may have used the figures of the L.A. Chamber as representing the production of L.A. County in compiling its overestimate. The L.A. County production consisted almost wholly of Pico (ca. 101,000 bbls.) and Puente (ca. 37,000). The Survey may also have been pushed toward an error in 1888 by a far too generous estimate for 1887 that it had recorded in the previous year. It seems to have taken a figure of 28,500,000 gals. for 1887 reported in the *S.F. J. of Comm.,* Feb. 9, 1888, in crediting Calif. with 658,572 bbls. By 1891 the *S.F. J of Comm.* (Feb. 5, 1891) had corrected its estimate for 1887 to 18,500,000 gals. (440,476 bbls.) for 1887, but there was no parallel correction in the figures of the USGS.

30. Newhall statements, Hist. R.

31. "Histories of PCO Wells," Hist. R; CSMB *Bul. #19* (1901), 61.

32. The wells were PCO #17 and CSOW #19. On diamond drilling, see Isaiah Bowman, *Well Drilling Methods,* USGS, Water Supply Paper 257 (1911).

33. "Histories of PCO Wells," Hist. R.

34. M. Stewart to L. Stewart, May 14, 1892, Stewart R; *10th Ann. Rpt. State Min.* (1891), 283-99.

35. "Histories of PCO Wells," Hist. R. There were 43,888 ft. of hole ($329,160) put down between 1888 and 1893, in comparison with about 3,750 ft. from the middle of 1884 to the beginning of 1888.

36. "Histories of PCO Wells," and note on PCO #8 by Felton, Jan. 15, 1896, Hist. R.

37. Bard to L. Stewart, Sep. 6, 1895, Stewart R; also, Bard to Peckham, Sep. 4, 1895, Bard R-S.

38. Newhall statements, Hist. R; North to L. Stewart, July 15, 1895, Stewart R.

39. "Histories of PCO Wells," Hist. R. Between 1896 and 1900 PCO drilled 3 wells in DeWitt (Moore) Canyon, southeast of Pico, 3 wells in Rice Canyon, southeast of Wiley, and 1 well in Grapevine Canyon, south of Elsmere.

40. C. F. Lufkin and J. F. Eckbert to J. D Archbold, May 29, 1899, Hist. R.

41. "Refined Oil . . . Sales in the Territory of SO Co., S.F. . . . During 1891," McClanahan R; statement of Scofield, Oct., 1908, Secy. R; Wm. Herbert, "Other Days, Other Ways," *Standard Oiler,* Nov., 1943, pp. 6-7; *W. H. Wright* v. *PCO,* #12,440, in Sup. Ct. of Alameda County; *Comm. Herald,* Jan. 13, 1887. In 1900, after kerosine sales had enjoyed some revival, gas and fuel oil sales were still responsible for approximately one-half of PCO's product income—$72,219 of a total of $184,873 (PCO Profit & Loss, last eight months of 1900, Comptr. R, SONJ).

42. Wm. Herbert, "Other Days, Other Ways," *Standard Oiler,* Jan., 1944, p. 12; *4th Ann. Rpt. State Min.* (1884), 303. See also G. Loomis to L. Stewart, Dec. 14, 1893, Stewart R.

43. Herbert, *op. cit.,* Nov., 1943, p. 19, Dec., 1943, p. 6.

44. M. Stewart to L. Stewart, Apr. 18 and May 10, 1890, Feb. 2 and Oct. 8, 1891, Stewart R; S. F. Peckham to Bard, Nov. 3, 1891, Bard R-S; Bard to Salathe, Dec. 29, 1892, Union Oil Minutes, Dec. 7, 1893, Bard R-HL; Hidy and Hidy, *op. cit.,* 160-63; Taylor and Welty, *Black Bonanza,* 1st ed. (N.Y., 1950), 95-96.

45. Wm. Herbert, *op. cit.,* Dec., 1943, p. 6; US Patent #522,028, June 26, 1894. For other contemporary chemical analyses of Calif. oil, see CSMB *Bul. #11,* (1897) 67-77; CSMB *Bul. #19* (1901), 201-15; *Min. Res. of the US, 1899,* 169-70.

46. Starke to Scofield, Apr. 3, 1909, Secy. R; J. B. Terry interview by J. W. Smith, Mar. 26, 1956; obit. notice, *Bul. of the Amer. Assn. of Pet. Geologists,* XVII (July, 1934), 967; A. P. Van Gelder and Hugo Schlatter, *History of the Explosives Industry in America* (N.Y., 1927), 446-47, 917-19. Felton was president of the U.S. Smokeless Powder Co. in 1895 (*S.F. Directory, 1895*).

47. Starke to Scofield, Apr. 3, 1909, Secy. R.

48. *Ibid.;* L. Stewart to M. Stewart, Apr. 16, 1895, Stewart R; Agreement, PCO and SO (Iowa), Apr. 11, 1895, Secy. R, SONJ. The patent, #548,391, was granted Oct. 22, 1895.

49. Starke to Scofield, Apr. 3, 1909, Secy. R; US Patent #597,920, Jan. 25, 1898.

50. Starke to Scofield, Apr. 3, 1909, Secy. R.

51. Statement of Scofield, Oct., 1908, Secy. R; T. J. Kreps, *The Economics of the Sulphuric Acid Industry* (Stanford, 1938), 46-47, 52-54; Geo. Lunge, *A Theoretical and Practical Treatise on the Manufacture of Sulphuric Acid and Alkali With the Collateral Branches* (London, 1903), 1285-86, 1420.

52. For some general historical data on the first three fields, see CSMB *Bul. #69* (1916); for Summerland, see *13th Ann. Rpt. State Min.* (1896).

53. Ira B. Cross, *Financing an Empire: History of Banking in California* (Chicago, 1927), II, 588, 616-23.

54. L. Stewart to M. Stewart, Apr. 15, 1893, to Bard, Apr. 18, 1893, Stewart R; Supplementary Notes, Union Oil Dirs. Meeting, July 17, 1894, Bard R-HL.

55. Bard to L. Stewart, May 2, 1893, Bard R-HL; L. Stewart to C. P. Collins, Sep. 25, 1893, I. H. Warring to L. Stewart, Nov. 10, 1893, Stewart R.

56. M. Stewart to L. Stewart, Dec. 3, 1892, L. Stewart to Union Oil Co., Feb. 21, 1893, to Bard, Mar. 4, 1893, to M. Stewart, Apr. 15, 1893, to Collins, June 16, 1893, Warring to L. Stewart, Jan. 30, 1894, Stewart R; Bard to L. Stewart, Mar. 3, 1893, Union Oil Minutes, Dec. 7, 1893, Supplementary Notes, Union Oil Dirs. Meeting, July 17, 1894, Bard R-HL; "Record of Puente Oil Wells," CSMB *Bul. #11,* 20; *13th Ann. Rpt. State Min.,* 577-78.

57. Bard to L. Stewart, Mar. 3, 1893, Union Oil Minutes, Dec. 7, 1893, July 17, 1894, abstracts of ltrs., from Edwards, Smith, G. W. Young, June 11 to June 22, 1894, Bard R-HL; L. Stewart to Smith, July 26, 1893, to J. A. Fillmore, Gen. Supt., SP Co., Nov. 3, 1893, Smith to L. Stewart, Dec. 6, 1893, Stewart R.

58. L. Stewart to Bard, July 24, 1893, to M. Stewart, Nov. 9, 1893, Wade to L. Stewart, Nov. 20, 1893, Bard to L. Stewart, Dec. 29, 1893, Stewart R.

59. L. Stewart to M. Stewart, Nov. 17, 1894, Stewart R; statement of J. C. Martin (the engineer), Nov. 15, 1916, Hist. R; CSMB *Bul. #11,* 63-64. By 1895 the Southern California Railway was using the Booth burner, brought in from the Central Railroad of Peru. The Southern Pacific was also experimenting with this burner.

60. L. Stewart to M. Stewart, Jan. 12 and Feb. 2, 1895, to Bard, Mar. 11, 1895, and Sep. 6, 1899, M. Stewart to L. Stewart, Feb. 19, 1895, Stewart R; J. Kruttschnitt to C. P. Huntington, June 7, 1897, Eckbert to Archbold, "Detailed Rpt.—Fullerton," May 29, 1899, Hist. R.

61. *Oil, Paint and Drug Reporter* clipping in M. Stewart to L. Stewart, Dec. 4, 1893, W. S. Porter interview by Messrs. Waldie, Stewart and Hardison, Dec. 20, 1893, Stewart R; Geo. S. Gibb and Evelyn H. Knowlton, *The Resurgent Years, 1911-1927* (N.Y., 1956), 94-95.

62. L. Stewart to M. Stewart, Nov. 8, 1893, G. M. Smith to L. Stewart, Dec. 12, 1893, Stewart R.

63. W. H. Tilford to Miller, and Miller to Tilford, Dec. 11, 1893, both in *S.F. Examiner,* Oct. 26, 1894; Loomis to L. Stewart, Jan. 18, 1894, Stewart R.

64. H. M. Tilford to Miller, Feb. 2, 1894, in *S.F. Examiner,* Oct. 26, 1894; *S.F. Examiner,* Oct. 27, 1894; M. Stewart to L. Stewart, Jan. 19, 1895, Stewart R; Sutherland Hutton interview by C. Earl, July 11, 1905, NA BuCorp. file #3220, Pt. 2.

65. W. G. Hughes to Bard, Nov. 28, 1894, Bard R-S; L. Stewart to M. Stewart, Dec. 6, 1894, to Bard, Sep. 6, 1899, Stewart R.

66. L. Stewart to Hardison, Dec. 13, 1894, to M. Stewart, Feb. 2, 1895, to Bard, Sep. 6, 1899, Stewart R.

67. L. Stewart to M. Stewart, Feb. 2 and Apr. 8, 1895, Stewart R; Bard to C. N. Felton, Apr. 22, 1895, Bard R-S.

68. *S.F. Examiner,* Aug. 29, 1895.

69. On Doheny's career, see *Pet. World,* XXXII (Oct., 1935), 16-17, and E. L. Doheny interview by C. Earl, June 24, 1905, NA BuCorp. file #3220, Pt. 4.

70. E. L. Doheny, Mar. 29, 1917 in *US* v. *SP* #46, reporter's transcript, XXII, 12933-36; CSMB *Bul. #11,* 5-6; A. H. Davis, "The Romance of California Oil," *Overland Monthly,* LXI (Feb., 1913), 130.

71. Supplementary Notes, Union Oil Dirs. Meeting, July 17, 1894, Bard R-HL; L. Stewart to M. Stewart, Nov. 17, 1894, Stewart R; "Reminiscences of A. L. Darrow, Sr.," McClanahan R; CSMB *Bul. #11,* 62; *13th Ann. Rpt. State Min.,* 579.

72. Bard to S. F. Peckham, Jan. 3, 1895, Bard R-HL; M. Stewart to L. Stewart, Feb. 9, 1895, L. Stewart to Scofield, June 11, 1896, Stewart R; *Min. & Sci. Press,* Nov. 10, 1894; CSMB *Bul. #11,* 6, 11-13.

73. L. Stewart to Bard, Dec. 6, 1894, Stewart R.

74. "Proposition of the Union Oil Co. of Calif. to the Fuel Oil Producers of L.A." (Jan., 1895), Bard R-HL.

75. L. Stewart to M. Stewart, Feb. 2, 1895, Stewart R.

76. Bard to Peckham, Sep. 4, 1895, Bard R-S.

77. L. Stewart to M. Stewart, Feb. 2, 1895, Stewart R; L. Stewart to Bard, Mar. 11, 1895, Bard R-HL; Bard to Felton, Mar. 13, 1895, Bard R-S.

78. L. Stewart to M. Stewart, Apr. 8, 1895, Bard to L. Stewart, Apr. 13, 1895, Stewart R; "Memo. of Agreement" between Union Oil Co. and PCO, Apr. 18, 1895, Bard R-S; Blanding to Union Oil Co., Dec. 14, 1896, Bard R-HL.

79. Bard to L. Stewart, July 25, 1895, to Col. J. C. Marble, Sep. 3, 1895, L. Stewart to Scofield, June 11, 1896, Stewart R; W. G. Hughes to Bard, Aug. 14, 1895, Bard to Peckham, Sep. 4, 1895, Bard R-S.

80. Bard to L. Stewart, Sep. 6, 1895, Stewart R.

81. Bard to L. Stewart, Sep. 7, 1895, Stewart R; "The Union Oil Co. suggests the following arrangement . . . between itself and the Oil Exchange . . . ," Sep. 11, 1895, Bard R-HL; W. G. Hughes to Bard, Sep. 20, 1895, Bard R-S.

82. W. L. Stewart to L. Stewart, Dec. 26, 1895, L. Stewart to F. L. King, June 9 and 15, 1896, Stewart R; Art. of Incorporation, Dec. 13, 1895, Secy. of State (Calif.) R; *18th Ann. List of Merchant Vessels of the US* (1886), 124; *Min. & Sci. Press,* Feb. 29, 1896.

83. L. Stewart to Scofield, June 11, 1896, Stewart R; CSMB *Bul. #11,* 6.

84. L. Stewart to F. Barrett, Feb. 12, 1897, Stewart R; Walton Young interview by A. E. Haase, Aug. 3, 1954; *Ventura Free Press,* Nov. 22, 1895; CSMB *Bul. #19,* 168. The new line from Pico did not make use of the line laid to Santa Paula in the mid-1880's, for that line had been taken up.

85. Scofield to Bard, June 17, 1895, Bard to Peckham, Sep. 4, 1895, Felton to L. Stewart, Nov. 20, 1895, Bard R-S; *S.F. Examiner,* Jan. 9, 1896.

86. Exhibit appended to the statement of F. L. King, May, 1905, NA BuCorp. file #3299, Pt. 3. The pipeline, called the "Ocean," was accepted by Jersey Standard at a valuation of $85,562 when PCO was purchased in Oct., 1900 (SO[Iowa] Statements).

87. *S.F. Examiner,* Jan. 9, 1896; *Ventura Signal,* 1896, *passim,* esp. Jan. 10, 1896, Jan. 8, 1897; *Min. & Sci. Press,* Jan. 18, and Feb. 29, 1896.

88. F. L. King to L. Stewart, Jan. 25, 1896, L. Stewart to PCO, Feb. 26, 1896, Stewart R.

89. L. Stewart to M. Stewart, May 31, 1895, to PCO, Feb. 26 and Apr. 17, 1896, W. L. Stewart to L. Stewart, Feb. 6, 1896, Stewart R; Bard to L. Stewart, Mar. 3, 1896, Bard R-HL.

90. Bard to L. Stewart, Mar. 2, 1896, Bard R-HL; L. Stewart to PCO, June 23, 1896, to M. Stewart, Sep. 2, 1898, Blanding to Union Oil Co., June 26 and 29, 1896, Stewart R; Scofield to Bard, Feb. 24 and Mar. 8, 1897, Bard R-S.

91. L. Stewart to F. L. King, Jan. 30, 1896, to PCO, Feb. 26 and Apr. 17, 1896, King to L. Stewart, Feb. 21, 1896, Stewart R; *Min. & Sci. Press,* Feb. 29, 1896.

92. Blanding to Union Oil Co., Dec. 14, 1896, Bard R-HL; Blanding to Union Oil Co., Jan. 6 and Feb. 27, 1897, Bard R-S.

93. F. L. King to PCO, Mar. 3, 1897, Bard R-S.

94. PCO to Union Oil Co., July 10 and 12, 1897, L. Stewart to PCO, July 12, 1897, Bard R-S; L. Stewart to Bard, July 13, 1897, Bard R-HL.

95. Quoted in draft, Union Oil Co. to PCO, Aug. 6, 1897, Bard R-HL; L. Stewart to M. Stewart, Aug. 6, 1897, Stewart R.

96. This statement is based on inference from the SO(Iowa) Statements showing earnings for 1900. The most common rate charged Union was 17½¢, which was somewhat above the rate of 13¢ (plus 2¢ to Oleum) indicated for about one-half of capacity in the Apr., 1895 contract.

97. M. Stewart to L. Stewart, Feb. 27, 1895, L. Stewart to M. Stewart, Apr. 8, 1895, to Frank Barrett, Feb. 12, 1897, to E. E. Robinson, Sep. 28, 1898, W. L. Stewart to L. Stewart, Mar. 10, 1899, to J. Baker, Jr., Mar. 14, 1900, Stewart R; Bard to Dolbeer and Carson, Mar. 7, 1898, Bard R-S; C. F. Lufkin and J. Eckbert to Archbold, "Generalized Rpt. of the Calif. Oil Fields," May 29, 1899, Hist. R; CSMB *Bul. #11,* 13.

98. M. Stewart to L. Stewart, Aug. 9, 1898, L. Stewart to M. Stewart, Sep. 2, 1898, W. L. Stewart to L. Stewart, Jan. 13, 1899, J. Baker, Jr., to W. L. Stewart, Mar. 23, 1900, Stewart R.

99. Blanding to Union Oil Co., Mar. 18, 1899, Bard R-HL; Bard to Dolbeer, Apr. 3, 1899, Bard R-S; W. L. Stewart to L. Stewart, Mar. 23, 1899, W. A. Carney to L. Stewart, Nov. 17, 1899, Stewart R.

100. *Min. & Sci. Press,* Feb. 12, 1898; *S.F. Chronicle,* Dec. 31, 1899.

101. PCO paid a dividend of $25,000 in 1899 and reported a net profit of $162,125 for the 16 months through Apr. 30, 1900 (balance sheet of the PCO, Apr. 30, 1900, Comptr. R, SONJ). PCO's depreciation and depletion policy left much to be desired, however. Standard reported PCO's profit for the last 8 months of 1900 before deducting depreciation as $93,323—roughly comparable to $162,125 for the preceding 16 months —but after deducting depreciation of $79,602, the profit figure became $13,721. It is doubtful whether PCO was doing much more than maintaining itself just prior to its sale to Standard as of Apr. 30, 1900.

102. PCO Minutes, Feb. 21, Mar. 21 and Dec. 2, 1899, PCO Stock Certificate Bk., Secy, R; Neville Clip Bk. of Obit. Notices, 1869-1925, and Holbrook Scrapbook of Obits and Wills, CHS.

103. For a long survey of the Calif. oil industry at the end of the century, see CSMB *Bul. #19* and *S.F. Chronicle,* Dec. 31, 1899.

104. "Tidewater Associated Oil Co.," *World Pet.,* Aug., 1937, 46-48; Kendall Beaton, *Enterprise in Oil: A History of Shell in the United States* (N.Y., 1957), 71.

VII. IOWA STANDARD GROWS

1. Hidy and Hidy, *op. cit.,* 315-16; *US* v. *SONJ,* US Cir. Ct., Eastern Dist. of Mo. (Wash., 1908), XVII, 3488-89, 3524, hereafter cited as *US* v. *SONJ.*

2. Hidy and Hidy, *op. cit.,* 55-68, 193-95; Nevins, *op. cit.,* II, 18-24.

3. SO(Iowa) Minutes, Feb. 25, 1892.

4. W. P. Thompson to Tevis, Oct. 25, 1892, Tevis to Thompson, Oct. 27, 1892, Secy. R, SONJ. See also Williamson and Daum, *op. cit.,* 688.

5. SO(Iowa) Minutes, May 18 and Sep. 30, 1886. The Tevis interest was represented by stock certificates #2 for 2,400 shares and #4 for 1,600, which was issued following the 66⅔% stock dividend in Feb., 1892. Both were in the name of a son of Lloyd Tevis, H. L. Tevis, Trustee. The first of these certificates probably originally represented a combined interest of Tevis, Felton and perhaps Blake (see Chap. IV, note 38), though by 1892 Tevis apparently was the sole owner.

6. Hidy and Hidy, *op. cit.,* 218-32, 306-12.

7. W. F. Green, "One Man's Recollections," *Among Ourselves,* Aug., 1922, p. 15; Salary Bk. C, Secy. R, SONJ; *S.F. Directories, 1890* to *1903.*

8. SO(Iowa) Minutes, Dec. 21, 1891; *S.F. Examiner,* Oct. 29 and Nov. 1, 1894.

9. SO(Iowa) Minutes, Sep. 29, 1890; Salary Bk. B, Secy. R, SONJ; L. Stewart to M. Stewart, Dec. 18, 1895, Stewart R; *S.O. Bulletin,* May, 1919, p. 13.

10. PCO Minutes, Jan. 2, 1901, and Feb. 20, 1911; Salary Bk. B, Secy. R, SONJ; *S.O. Bulletin,* Mar., 1916, p. 2.

11. Salary Bk. C, Secy. R, SONJ; interviews, R. C. Warner, Aug. 31, 1955, Geo. C. Maile, May 1, 1957, Geo. H. Mayer, Oct. 23, 1958, all by G. T. White.

12. Salary Bks. B and C, Secy. R, SONJ; *Among Ourselves,* Aug., 1926, p. 11; H. D. Collier interview by A. E. Haase, Feb. 28, 1954.

13. We have used the Salary Books in the office of the Secy., SONJ, and the C. A. Watson interview by P. H. Patchin, June 12, 1922, in dating the establishment of these stations, plus the following items pertaining to individual stations: *San Jose: Among Ourselves,* Feb., 1923, p. 1, J.C. Wagner to Patchin, June 12, 1922; *Tacoma:* W. L. Muncy to Patchin, Sep. 20, 1929; *San Diego: Among Ourselves,* June, 1922, p. 1, W. C. Renwick to Patchin, July 10, 1929; *Seattle:* J. J. Valentine to Patchin, July 3, 1929, SO(Iowa) Plant Ledger, 1887-1898, Comptr. R, *US* v. *SONJ,* XVII, 3489 (however, Salary Bk. A shows no special agent at Seattle prior to 1888; perhaps earlier it shared with Tacoma, or it may have been a depot for Tacoma); *Oakland: Among Ourselves,* Aug., 1923, p. 1; *Spokane:* List and Description of SO Properties Not Operating, Feb. 15, 1899, Secy. R, SONJ, SO(Iowa) Plant Ledger, 1887-1898, Comptr. R, "History of the Spokane Dist.," Pub. Rel. R; *Marysville:* H. B. Fairchild to Patchin, June 25, 1929 (but the SO[Iowa] Plant Ledger shows a wooden warehouse at Marysville at least as early as 1887; probably it was first a depot supplementing the Sacramento station); *Fresno:* SO(Iowa) Plant Ledger, 1887-1898, entry of June 29, 1890; *Vancouver: ibid.,* entry of Apr. 7, 1893, SO(Iowa) Voucher Register, 1896-1901, Comptr. R, Hidy and Hidy, *op. cit.,* 255-57. The letters to Patchin are in the Pub. Rel. R.

14. SO(Iowa) Voucher Register, 1896-1901, Comptr. R; Henry W. Clark, *History of Alaska* (N.Y., 1930), 101-11; C. L. Andrews, *The Story of Alaska* (Caldwell, Idaho, 1938), 186-88; Clarence C. Hulley, *Alaska, 1741-1953* (Portland, 1953), 248-66.

15. SO(Iowa) Plant Ledger, 1887-1898, SO(Iowa) Voucher Register, 1896-1901, SO(Iowa) Special Statements, bound copies of financial and sales statements for the years 1891-1901 in the Comptr. R, hereafter cited as SO(Iowa) Statements; SO(Iowa) Minutes, July 19, 1898; *S.O. Bulletin,* Dec., 1915, pp. 4-7.

16. C. A. Watson interview by P. H. Patchin, June 14, 1922, Pub. Rel. R; SO(Iowa) Statements.

17. SO(Iowa) Statements, SO(Iowa) Plant Ledger, 1887-1898, Comptr. R; *US* v. *SONJ,* XVII, 3498-99.

18. Salary Bk. C, Secy. R, SONJ; J. W. Dimick, "In Those Days," *Among Ourselves,* Dec., 1924, p. 5; reminiscences of Louis B. Stober, Sac., Mar., 1955, and Fred K. Frey, Oakland, June, 1956, Hist. R.

19. "Opening Dates—Company Stations" (1922), Mktg. R; SO(Iowa) Plant Ledger, 1887-1898, SO(Iowa) Statements; Salary Bk. D, Secy. R, SONJ.

20. W. S. Miller ltr., Apr. 26, 1900, in one of the Lubricating Dept. books of extracts of correspondence on prices, hereafter cited as Lube Price Bks., Mktg. R; *Instructions to Sub-Station Warehousemen* (ca. 1900), McClanahan R; Paul H. Giddens, *Standard Oil Co. (Indiana): Oil Pioneer of the Middle West* (N.Y., 1955), 46-47, 49-50; Hidy and Hidy, *op. cit.,* 291-95; Ida M. Tarbell, *The History of the Standard Oil Co.* (N.Y., 1904), II, 35-36, 53-56.

21. *US* v. *SONJ,* XVII, 3489.

22. Hidy and Hidy, *op. cit.,* 295-96.

23. Sales of Refined Oil By Tank Wagon . . . During . . . 1890 and 1891," McClanahan R; "Ann. Sales Statements," a bound typescript summarizing sales from 1891-1922, in the Comptr. R, hereafter cited as Ann. Sales Statements. 26 Broadway's comparative figure for the use of tank wagons by Standard marketers throughout the nation in 1899 was 59% (Williamson and Daum, *op. cit.,* 692). The lower per cent for the West can undoubtedly be chiefly explained by the more widely scattered population.

24. Entry of Dec. 29, 1894 in SO(Iowa) Plant Ledger, 1887-1898, SO(Iowa)

Voucher Register, 1896-1901, and SO(Iowa) Statements, Comptr. R; Plant Ledger #1 and Cleveland Works Diary, entry of Feb. 25, 1895, SO(Ohio) R; *S.F. Call,* Aug. 14, 1897, and Sep. 20, 1898; Dimmick, *op. cit.,* 6.

25. Ann. Sales Statements.

26. Cleveland Works Diary, SO(Ohio) R; W. Sproule to J. C. Stubbs, Nov. 15, 1888, in the Ind. Comm., *Prelim. Rpt. on Trusts and Industrial Combinations,* 56th Cong., 1st Sess., H.R. Doc. 476 (1900), I, 720, hereafter cited as *Rpt. of the Ind. Com.;* Giddens, *op. cit.,* 25, 28, 43.

27. Cleveland Works Diary, Mar. 29, 1887, SO(Ohio) R; *Geo. Rice* v. *AT&SF et al., Interstate Commerce Rpts.* (Rochester, 1892), III, 268.

28. "Plant Investment," SO(Iowa), Dec. 31, 1894, "Red Books," Secy. R, SONJ; SO(Iowa) Statements; Hidy and Hidy, *op. cit.,* 199. There must have been a Union Tank Line earlier than the 1891 date given by the Hidys, however, for the SO(Iowa) Minutes record a sale of a number of patent cars and cylinder cars "to the Union Tank Line," Dec. 15, 1886.

29. Ann. Sales Statements; A. L. Darrow, "Pratt's Astral," McClanahan R.

30. Advertisement, Aug., 1887, clipping book, *SO Co.* v. *Crew Levick Co.,* US Patent Office Opposition #2357, CRC R, hereafter cited as *SO* v. *Crew Levick* clipping bk.

31. "Price List, Gasoline and Naphtha," SO Co. (S.F.), Jan. 1, 1892, McClanahan R; Ann. Sales Statements; Hidy and Hidy, *op. cit.,* 298-300.

32. Lube Price Bk.; "Note Price of Refined Oils and Gasoline, SO Co.," San Diego, Calif., May 20, 1897, McClanahan R; C. A. Watson interview by P. H. Patchin, June 14, 1922, Pub. Rel. R; Chas. J. Woodbury, "Rockefeller and His Standard," *Saturday Evening Post,* Oct. 21, 1911, p. 9.

33. *Among Ourselves,* Jan., 1926, pp. 2-3, 7.

34. Ltrs. of July 14 and 15, 1897, Dec. 4, 1898, Jan. 21, 1899, June 1, 28, 29, 1900, Dec. 7, 1903, in Lube Price Bks.; deposition of E. H. Merrill, July 20, 1917 in *SO Co.* v. *Crew Levick Co.,* US Patent Office Opposition #2348, Hist. R; Ann. Sales Statements.

35. W. S. Miller to W. L. Mery, Chico, Calif., Apr. 6, 1896, Hist R; Lube Price Bks., *passim;* statements of H. W. Walker and W. H. Poston (1905), John Goldstone interview by L. H. Eddy, May 9, 1905, NA BuCorp. file #3343, Pt. 1; Thomas Flaherty and A. N. Younglove interviews by Eddy, July 21, 1906, NA BuCorp. file #3376, Pt. 6.

36. *Rpt. of the Ind. Comm.* XIII, 779, 795. In 1900 the wholesale price at Bakersfield was 20¢ a gal. compared with 12½¢ at Oakland. Five years earlier the freight rate on cased oil from S.F. to Bakersfield was 7.4¢ a gal., and the SP was seeking an increase to 8.1¢; at that time, the rate from Pa. to S.F. was 7.7¢ (*Biennial Rpt. of Bd. of RR Comrs. of . . . Calif., 1895-1896,* 11-12). The rates from Stockton (the nearest Pacific Coast terminal) to Bakersfield undoubtedly were less, but not much. In 1892 the rate on petroleum products per 100 lbs. (ca. 15⅔ gals.) between S.F. and Stockton was only 12½¢ (E. A. Tilford to W. H. Tilford, Jan. 7, 1892, in *S.F. Examiner,* Oct. 29, 1894). See also *S.F. Chronicle,* Apr. 13, 1895.

37. SO(Iowa) Statements.

38. This statement is based on an analysis of semiannual profit data for all products at each station, and also separately for kerosine and for naphtha at each station. (SO[Iowa] Statements).

39. Interviews, John Goldstone, May 9, 1905, and Geo. W. Arper, Oct. 7, 1905, both by Eddy, statement of H. S. Walker (1905), NA BuCorp. file #3343, Pt. 1.

40. Geo. Flanders to Eichnor Bros., South Bend, Wash., Mar. 28, 1894, in *Rpt. of the Ind. Comm.,* I, 369-70.

41. *Rpt. of the Ind. Comm.,* I, 552.

42. Interviews, Goldstone, May 9, 1905, and Arper, Oct. 7, 1905, both by Eddy, statement of Walker (1905), NA BuCorp. file #3343, Pt. 1; interviews, H. R. Slayden, July 18, 1906, and Walker, July 19, 1906, both by Eddy, NA BuCorp. file #3376, Pt. 6.

43. Arper interview by Eddy, Oct. 7, 1905, NA BuCorp. file #3343, Pt. 1; Hidy and Hidy, *op. cit.,* 163-64. M. Stewart to L. Stewart, Feb. 6, 1897 (Stewart R), records

Milton's belief that the Ohio kerosine Standard was shipping to Calif. was still inferior to the Pa. product.

44. Arper interviews by Eddy, Oct. 7 and 9, 1905, statement of Walker (1905), NA BuCorp. file #3343, Pt. 1; interviews, Walker, July 19, 1906, and J. B. Frith, July 20, 1906, both by Eddy, NA BuCorp. file #3376, Pt. 6.

45. *Min. Res. of the US, 1889-1890*, 332-39; *Min. Res. of the US, 1894-1895*, 368; Frank Hall, *History of Colorado* (Chicago, 1891), III, 402-4; Hidy and Hidy, *op. cit.*, 197, 770.

46. *US* v. *SONJ*, II, 730-31; Fred L. King interview by C. Earl, May 25, 1905, NA BuCorp. file #3299, Pt. 3; *The Mining Industry and Tradesman*, Jan. 14, 1892, p. 36; *Paint, Oil and Drug Review*, Dec. 14, 1892, pp. 15, 39; clipping from *Drugs, Oils and Paints* (1893), in *SO* v. *Crew Levick* clipping bk.

47. E. A. Tilford to W. H. Tilford, Apr. 18, 1892, in *S. F. Examiner*, Oct. 31, 1894; Complaint and Memo., *W. C. Bissell* v. *AT&SF et al.*, ICC Formal Case File #361, NA Rec. Group 134, hereafter cited as *Bissell* v. *AT&SF*.

48. E. A. Tilford to W. H. Tilford, June 2, 1892, also to H. M. Tilford, May 4, 1892, in *S.F. Examiner*, Oct. 31, 1894; E. A. Tilford to Munroe, Gen. Freight Agent, UP, May 7 and 14, 1892, and to C. W. Bein, Gen. Freight Agent, SP, Atlantic System, July 5, 1892, in *S.F. Examiner*, Oct. 29, 1894.

49. Gray to J. A. Munroe, June 10, 1892, E. A. Tilford to W. H. Tilford, June 10, 1892, in *S.F. Examiner*, Oct. 30, 1894.

50. E. A. Tilford to W. H. Tilford, June 15, 1892, in *S.F. Examiner*, Oct. 30, 1894.

51. *Ibid.;* Complaint and Memo., *Bissell* v. *AT&SF*.

52. Gray to Munroe, June 16 and 18, 1892, in *S.F. Examiner*, Oct. 30, 1894.

53. E. A. Tilford to W. H. Tilford, June 20, 1892, in *S.F. Examiner*, Oct. 30, 1894; E. A. Tilford to H. Page, Vice Pres., Union Tank Line, Aug. 3, 1892, in *S.F. Examiner*, Oct. 31, 1894.

54. E. A. Tilford to Page, Aug. 3 and Sep. 10, 1892, in *S.F. Examiner*, Oct. 31, 1894.

55. F. L. King interview by Earl, May 25, 1905, NA BuCorp. file #3299, Pt. 3.

56. Salary Bks. A and B, Secy. R, SONJ; *S.F. Directory, 1893; S.F. Chronicle*, Feb. 7, 1893.

57. *Bissell* v. *AT&SF*.

58. E. A. Moseley to Dodd, Mar. 17, 1893, Dodd to Moseley, Mar. 20, 1893, W. C. Bissell to Moseley, Nov. 20, 1894, in *ibid*.

59. *US* v. *SONJ*, I, 155-57, 178-81, II, 729-31, III, 1215-18; *S.F. Directory, 1894;* F. L. King interview by Earl, May 25, 1905, NA BuCorp. file #3299, Pt. 3; *Min. Res. of the US, 1894-1895*, 368.

60. *S.F. Weekly Comm.*, Oct. 14, 1886; *Ventura Vidette*, Oct. 5, 1889; L. Stewart to M. Stewart, Dec. 6, 1889, Stewart R; testimony of I. F. Littlefield, Pres., W. P. Fuller, in *SO Co.* v. *Crew Levick Co.*, US Patent Office, Opposition #2357 (1917), *Record for the Standard Oil Company*, 46-47, CRC R; *Ninety Years: The Story of William Parmer Fuller* (S.F., 1939), 81-87, hereafter cited as *W. P. Fuller*.

61. Hidy and Hidy, *op. cit.*, 729.

62. We have been unable to identify the Beacon Light Oil Co. except from newspaper advertisements. It had been doing a small business in S.F. since 1882 and became very aggressive after 1885 (*Comm. Herald*, Jan. 28, 1886, Jan. 13, 1887; *S.F. J. of Comm.*, Jan. 27, 1887). By 1888 it had left the field (*S.F. Directory, 1882, et seq.*).

63. Testimony of Thomas L. Kimball, Gen. Traffic Mgr., UP, in *Hearings Before the US Pac. Ry. Commission*, US Sen., 50th Cong., 1st Sess., Sen. Ex. Doc. 51, Pt. 4 (1888), III, 1132-36, 1374-75, 1387, 1400-41; *SO(Iowa)* v. *SP et al.*, #10,575 in the US Cir. Ct., 9th Judicial Cir., S.F., hereafter cited as *SO(Iowa)* v. *SP; S.F. J. of Comm.*, June 6, 1890.

64. *Comm. Herald*, Jan. 7, 1886: "Salutatory," in first issue of a monthly sheet, published by Whittier, Fuller, July 1, 1887; advertisements, Collier White Lead (St. Louis), *S.J. Mercury*, Nov. 28, 1888; *S.F. Chronicle*, Apr. 10, 1890; clipping, *Paint, Oil and Drug Review*, May, 1893.

65. *S.F. Chronicle*, July 1, 1886; *S.F. J. of Comm.*, Jan. 27, 1887, and Feb. 9, 1888; *S.F. Call*, June 10, 1887.

66. Advertisement, ca. Dec., 1887, including ltr., C. J. Woodbury to Whittier, Fuller,

Oct. 24, 1887, in *SO* v. *Crew Levick* clipping bk.; *S.F. Chronicle,* Oct. 4, 1890; *Painters' Magazine* (N.Y.), Nov., 1890; *Comm. Herald,* (N.Y.), Jan. 22, 1891; *Paint, Oil and Drug Review,* May, 1893.

67. E. A. Tilford to J. C. Stubbs, Nov. 20, 1888, in *Rpt. of the Ind. Comm.,* I, 721; *S.F. Chronicle,* Apr. 3, 1895; *W. P. Fuller,* 90.

68. W. Sproule, Asst. Gen. Freight Agent, SP, to Stubbs, Nov. 14, 1888, in *Rpt. of the Ind. Comm.,* I, 719; *Geo. Rice* v. *AT&SF et al.,* (1890), in *Interstate Comm. Rpts.* (Rochester, 1892), III, 267.

69. Stubbs to W. Sproule, Nov. 14, 1888, in *Rpt. of the Ind. Comm.,* I, 719-20.

70. Sproule to Stubbs, Nov. 15, 1888, and to E. A. Tilford, Dec. 3, 1888, Stubbs to Sproule, Nov. 16, 1888, and to E. A. Tilford, Nov. 23, 1888, E. A. Tilford to Stubbs, Nov. 20 and 26, 1888, and to W. H. Tilford, Nov. 21 and 24, 1888, in *Rpt. of the Ind. Comm.,* I, 719-24; *Geo. Rice* v. *AT&SF* (1890), in *Interstate Comm. Rpts.,* III, 268.

71. E. A. Tilford to W. H. Tilford, Dec. 6 and 8, 1888, Sproule to E. A. Tilford, Dec. 8, 1888, in *Rpt. of the Ind. Comm.,* I, 725-26. One hundred lbs. of oil was equal to approx. 15⅔ gals. (*Scofield* v. *Lake Shore and Michigan Southern RR, Interstate Comm. Rpts.* [Rochester, 1891], II, 71-72).

72. E. A. Tilford to W. H. Tilford, Jan. 9 and Apr. 18, 1889, in *S.F. Examiner,* Oct. 29, 1894; *Bissell* v. *AT&SF.*

73. *SO(Iowa)* v. *SP; W. P. Fuller,* 91-93; *S.F. Examiner,* Dec. 7, 1889; *S.F. Bulletin,* Apr. 19, 1893.

74. *S.F. Examiner,* May 22, 1890; *S.F. J. of Comm.,* June 6, 1890; *Densmore* v. *Schofield,* 102 *US* 378; *SO(Iowa)* v. *SP; S.F. Chronicle,* Feb. 5, 1893.

75. "Turpentine . . . Sales . . . During . . . 1891 . . . Compared With . . . 1890," McClanahan R.

76. *US* v. *SONJ, Brief For Defendants on the Facts* (N.Y., 1909), II, 497.

77. E. A. Tilford to W. H. Tilford, Dec. 31, 1891, in *S.F. Examiner,* Nov. 1, 1894.

78. E. A. Tilford to W. H. Tilford, Jan. 7, 1892, and to H. Page, Aug. 6, 1892, in *S.F. Examiner,* Oct. 29, 1894; *S.F. Chronicle,* Apr. 13, 1895; *Biennial Rpt. of Bd. of RR Comrs. of . . . Calif., 1895-1896,* 11-12.

79.   NET RATES PAID BY STANDARD AND PUBLISHED RATES ON PETROLEUM
PRODUCTS FROM SAN FRANCISCO
(Per 100 lbs.)

To	Published	Standard
Oakland	3¾¢	3¾¢
Sacramento	24¢	10¢
Stockton	12½¢	10¢
San Jose	9¢	9¢
Marysville	26¢	17½¢
Los Angeles	50¢	20¢

From E. A. Tilford to W. H. Tilford, Jan. 7, 1892, in *S.F. Examiner,* Oct. 29, 1894.

80. *W. P. Fuller,* 100-06.

81. *Ibid.,* 112; Hidy and Hidy, *op. cit.,* 281, 283.

82. *S.F. Call,* Jan. 4, 1895; SO(Iowa) Statements.

83. SO(Iowa) Ledger, 1893-1900, Comptr. R; L. D. Clarke to W. M. Hall, Aug. 30, 1895, Comptr. R, SONJ; *Galena Signal* v. *W. P. Fuller & Co.,* #13,410 in US Cir. Ct., 9th Cir., Dist. Ct. R, S.F. The ledger figures are somewhat inconclusive, for a debit of approx. $70,000 to a Fuller suspense account may have been in addition to the $550,000. If so, Standard would have paid $620,000.

84. *W. P. Fuller,* 112-13.

85. M. Stewart to L. Stewart, Apr. 15, 1895, Stewart R; *S.F. Chronicle,* Apr. 18, 1895.

86. *S.F. Chronicle,* Apr. 3, 4, 5, 13 and 18, 1895. Bulk oil was 5¢ less a gal. than cased oil. The smaller rise in bulk refined oil prices throughout the nation in this

period (steepest for Stockton, Calif., which was another W. P. Fuller outlet) is to be found in *Rpt. of the Comr. of Corps. on the Pet. Industry* (1907), Pt. II, 871.

87. SO(Iowa) Statements. Hidy and Hidy (*op. cit.*, 628) show that, nationally, Standard's marketing profits nearly doubled in 1895 in comparison with this fourfold increase in the Iowa Standard territory.

88. A. L. Darrow, "Pratt's Astral," McClanahan R; reminiscences of Louis B. Stober, Sac., Mar., 1955, Hist. R.

89. Elmer Simmons, "History of W. P. Fuller & Co., 1849-1924," p. 16, a ms. in possession of W. P. Fuller & Co.

90. Agreement, PCO with SO(Iowa), May 1, 1895 (signed Apr. 11), Secy. R, SONJ; SO(Iowa) Minutes, May 3, 1895; *S.F.Chronicle,* Apr. 4, 1895; *S.F. Examiner,* Apr. 6, 1895.

91. Computations are based on data in the PCO Profit and Loss Statement for the last 8 months of 1900, Comptr. R, SONJ; Agreement of May 1, 1895 with PCO, "Copy of PCO Co's. estimate of Cost of Refining," Mar. 5, 1885, Stewart R; and in Newhall statements, Hist. R.

92. Testimony of H. M. Tilford, *US* v. *SONJ,* XVII, 3493; Ann. Sales Statements.

93. Ann. Sales Statements; J. A. Graves to W. S. Miller, May 2, 1899, Graves R-HL; W. L. Watts, Asst. State Mineralogist, in *Calif. Mines and Minerals* (S.F., 1899), 200; Nevins, *op. cit.,* II, 106-10.

94. L. Stewart to M. Stewart, Apr. 16, 1895, Stewart R; "Memo of Agreement" between Union and PCO, Apr. 18, 1895, Bard R-S; Welty and Taylor, *op. cit.,* 59.

95. F. L. King, Mgr. Oleum Refinery, to L. Stewart, Jan. 25, 1896, L. Stewart to M. Stewart, July 27 and Sep. 19, 1896, to King, Sep. 26, 1896, Stewart R.

96. L. Stewart to M. Stewart, Nov. 2, 1896, M. Stewart to L. Stewart, Feb. 6, 1897, Stewart R; W. G. Hughes to Bard, Nov. 13, 1896, Bard R-S.

97. W. G. Hughes to L. Stewart, Mar. 12, 1897, L. Stewart to L. H. Severance, Apr. 1, 1897, Stewart R; draft of memo., Bard to R. D. Yelverton, Aug., 1897, J. Baker, Jr., to Bard, Mar. 2, 1899, Bard R-HL; *US* v. *SONJ,* XVII, 3509-10. Stewart later recalled the prices in this first contract as 7½¢ a gal. for kerosine and 8¢ a gal. for benzine "in carload lots at the refinery, we to furnish the cars" (L. Stewart interview by L. Conant, Jr., June 30, 1905, NA BuCorp. file #3402, Pt. 2).

98. Lube Price Bk., esp. entries for 1899 and 1900; Inspector's Record Bk., Alameda refinery, 1901, Pub. Rel. R.

99. Statement of Prices, Oakland Agency, Nov. 13, 1897, McClanahan R; SO(Iowa) Statements; *S.F. Call,* Jan. 12, 1898. On the generally smaller decline in bulk refined oil prices throughout the nation, see *Rpt. of the Comr. of Corps. on the Pet. Industry* (1907), Pt. II, 871-72.

100. SO(Iowa) Voucher Register, 1896-1901, Comptr. R; J. A. Graves to Wm. R. Rowland, Jan. 7, 1896, to C. M. Yates, Feb. 6, 1896, to E. S. Pillsbury, Oct. 1, 1897, Graves R.

101. Ann. Sales Statements; SO(Iowa) Statements; Graves to Pillsbury, Sep. 15, 1897, Graves R.

102. "Memo of Agreement" between Puente Oil Co. and SO(Iowa), Mar. 31, 1898, Secy. R, SONJ; SO(Iowa) Voucher Register, 1896-1901, Comptr. R; Agreement between Puente Oil Co. and SO(Iowa), Mar. 31, 1898, in *SONJ* v. *US,* US Supreme Ct., *Transcript of Appeal* (Wash.,1910), XXII, 168-70; CSMB *Bul. #19* (1901), 172.

103. Miller to J. A. Graves, Dec. 27, 1898, Graves to Miller, Jan. 7, 1899, Graves R; "Memo. of Agreement" between Puente and SO(Iowa), Jan. 13, 1899, Secy. R, SONJ; SO(Iowa) Voucher Register, 1896-1901, Comptr. R.

104. Ann. Sales Statements; J. A. Graves to W. S. Miller, Mar. 17, 1899, Graves R; memo. "Course of Prices at L.A. and Vicinity about the Time that the Puente Oil Co's. contract with the Standard was made," NA BuCorp. file #3323; Luther Conant, Jr., "Preliminary Rpt. on Oil Investigation in Calif.," NA BuCorp. file #4176, Pt. 3, pp. 344½-45, hereafter cited as Conant Rpt.

105. "Rpt. [on Refineries] made to H. M. Tilford, Nov. 12, 1900," Econ. R; H. C. Folger, Jr., to J. D. Archbold, Nov. 11, 1899, Archbold R; testimony of H. M. Tilford, Dec. 4, 1908, in *US* v. *SONJ,* XVII, 3500-01, and Petitioner's Exhibit 390 in VIII, 920-21; J. V. Bacigalupi interview by Conant, June 19, 1905, NA BuCorp. file #3343,

Pt. 1; J. A. Dubbs interview by Earl, July 20, 1905, NA BuCorp. file #3299, Pt. 5; Dunham interviews by Eddy, Nov. 22 and 26, 1905, NA BuCorp. file #3299, Pt. 8; interviews, H. S. Slayden, July 18, 1906, and J. B. Frith, July 20, 1906, both by Eddy, NA BuCorp. file #3376, Pt. 6; *Rpt. of the Ind. Comm.*, I, 542.

106. F. L. King to L. Stewart, Jan. 25, 1896, Stewart R; SO(Iowa) Voucher Register, 1896-1901, Comptr. R. The largest purchase, that of F. B. Joyce & Co. ($20,000), was begun in Feb., 1898. G. W. Arper was bought out in Jan., 1900, Golden Gate Oil Supply Co. in Feb., 1900, and the refined oil business of the King-Keystone Oil Co. in Nov., 1900. Arper received $12,000 "for the actual cost of the [combination] cars and the material on hand," though he claimed that Charles Watson had suggested a price of $35,000 two years earlier if Arper would operate his business as a "hidden company" for Standard. (Arper interviews by Eddy, Oct. 7 and 9, 1905, NA BuCorp. file #3343, Pt. 1).

107. PCO and SO(Iowa) Special Statements, bound copies of financial and operating statements for the years 1901-06 in the Comptr. R, hereafter cited as SO(Iowa)/PCO Statements; Ann. Sales Statements; SO(Iowa) Voucher Register, 1896-1901 (Mar. and Apr., 1900), SO(Iowa) Trial Balances, 1902-1906, SO(Calif.) Sales Dept. Statement Bk., 1906-1912, Comptr. R; SO(Iowa) Tax Record Bk., 1893-1912, Treas. R; *US* v. *SONJ*, II, 743-44; Conant Rpt., 352, 360; interviews, H. R. Slayden, July 18, 1906, A. N. Younglove and Thomas Flaherty, July 21, 1906, all by Eddy, NA BuCorp. file #3376, Pt. 6; John Goldstone interview by Eddy, Oct. 9, 1905, NA BuCorp. file #3343, Pt. 1; *L. A. Examiner*, Mar. 6, 1905.

108. There are no surviving estimates of Standard's share of the western market for the years between 1891 and 1897. For other years through 1900, Standard's share has been given as follows:

Year	Per Cent of Kerosine Trade	Per Cent of Naphthas Trade
1891	84.9	84.7
—	—	—
1897	92.0	95.1
1898	94.4	98.3
1899	94.3	97.5
1900	96.5	96.6

Obviously, Standard got its biggest push forward from taking over W. P. Fuller's light oil trade in 1895. Its all-time record year in the kerosine trade was 1900 and in the naphthas 1898, after which its position suffered a gradual erosion, especially from small refiners in and around L.A. ("Refined Oil . . . Sales . . . During . . . 1891 . . . Compared with . . . 1890," McClanahan R; *US* v. *SONJ*, Petitioner's Exhibits 388 and 389, VIII, 918).

109. Ann. Sales Statements.

110. *Ibid.*; SO(Iowa) Minutes; "SO Trust Gen. Balance Sheet, Jan. 1, 1886," Comptr. R, SONJ; *US* v. *SONJ*, Petitioner's Exhibit 12B, VII, 44. We have found no balance sheet for July 1, 1885.

111. SO(Iowa) Statements; *US* v. *SONJ*, Petitioner's Exhibit 396, VIII, 1002-03, Defendant's Exhibits 292-A, 292-B, 292-C, 292-D, XIX, 689-92; Hidy and Hidy, *op. cit.*, 628-29.

VIII. 26 BROADWAY MAKES A DECISION

1. Hidy and Hidy, *op. cit.*, 176-88, 272.

2. *Ibid.*, 155-68; Williamson and Daum, *op. cit.*, 588-613. On Edwards, see also *Ventura Democrat*, Nov. 27, 1884; *L.A. Times*, Jan. 1, 1886; M. Stewart to L. Stewart, July 1, 1886, Stewart R. The Edwards refinery, located at Lima, Ohio, went on stream in July, 1886; apparently, it was short-lived.

3. Hidy and Hidy, *op. cit.*, 275-76, 283-84.

4. *Ibid.*, 276; Henrietta M. Larson and Kenneth W. Porter, *History of Humble Oil & Refining Company* (N.Y., 1959), 12.

5. Hidy and Hidy, *op. cit.*, 263-68, 270-78, 498. The exploration of the SE corner of the Alaskan mainland in 1897-98 was carried on with the assistance of Iowa Standard personnel. J. C. Fitzsimmons, from the Iowa Standard headquarters, was sent to Alaska in July, 1896, to collect samples (SO[Iowa] Voucher Register, 1896-1901), and John McLean, Iowa Standard's Seattle agent, was business mgr. for the venture (F. Q. Barstow to O. C. Edwards, Oct. 1, 1897, McLean to Barstow, July [?], Dec. 7 and 20, 1898, Archbold R).

6. Hardison to L. Stewart, Sep. 24, 1886, Irish to L. Stewart, June 14, 1887, Stewart R; Works Diary, Cleveland Refinery, Mar. 26, 1887, SO(Ohio) R.

7. Notes of Gilbert, Dec. 18, 22 and 28, 1916, and a memo., author unknown, "A History of Sec. 17 T 19-15," Hist. R.

8. M. Stewart to L. Stewart, Feb. 2 and 7, Mar. 9 and Apr. 29, 1891, Stewart R; *S.F. Chronicle*, Apr. 14, 1891.

9. *Min. Res. of the US, 1921*, Pt. II, 260-61.

10. Memo., author unknown, "Condensed History of Sec. 17," Hist. R; *Huron News*, Feb. 3, 1896; *S.F. Chronicle*, Nov. 17, 1896; CSMB *Bul.* #19 (1901), 138-39.

11. CSMB *Bul.* #19, 114. On the shaft sunk by the Elwoods, see Wallace M. Morgan, *History of Kern County* (L.A., 1930), 129-30. Although Lionel V. Redpath (*Petroleum in California* [L.A., 1900], 83) and Allen G. Nichols (*Oil: An Historical Edition of the Oil Industry* [n.p., 1909], 48), credit Doheny with the first well to be drilled in the Kern River field, the longtime oil prospector, Milton McWhorter, deserves that honor. His well was completed early in July, 1899, at a depth of 350 ft. (Testimony of McWhorter, June 5, 1916, in *US* v. *SP* #46 Civil in US Dist. Ct. for the So. Dist. of Calif., No. Div., reporter's transcript, IX, 4864-67, hereafter cited as *US* v. *SP* #46; F. F. Latta, *Black Gold in the Joaquin* [Caldwell, Idaho, 1949], 168-71).

12. SO(Iowa) Statements; Ann. Sales Statements; L. Stewart to C. P. Collins, Oct. 7, 1895, W. L. Stewart to L. Stewart, July 22, 1896, Stewart R; J. C. Harvey to H. W. O'Melveny, July 11, 1896, Graves R; *L.A. Times*, Jan. 1, 1896; CSMB *Bul.* #11, 14.

13. *Rpt. of the Com. on Manufacturers on Investigation of Trusts*, H.R. #3112, 50th Cong., 1st Sess. (1889), 163; Bard to Dolbeer & Carson, Jan. 26, 1899, Bard R-S.

14. M. Stewart to L. Stewart, July 27, 1895, L. Stewart to Bard, Sep. 6, 1899, Stewart R; Bard to W. G. Hughes, Mar. 31, 1894, Bard R-S; undated draft of ltr., Bard to stockholders of Torrey Canon Oil Co., ca. Jan. 1, 1899, Bard R-HL.

15. L. Stewart to C. P. Collins, June 16, 1893, Stewart R. Union resumed payment of a monthly dividend after L. Stewart became president in Oct., 1894, but had to suspend dividends again in Apr., 1895 (L. Stewart to M. Stewart, Nov. 17, 1894, J. M. C. Marble to L. Stewart, Apr. 18, 1895, Stewart R).

16. M. Stewart to L. Stewart, Aug. 17, 1891, L. Stewart to M. Stewart, Aug. 18, 1891, Stewart R.

17. M. Stewart to L. Stewart, June 15, 1895, Stewart R.

18. W. L. Stewart to L. Stewart, July 20, 1895, L. Stewart to M. Stewart, Nov. 1, 1895, M. Stewart to L. Stewart, Nov. 8, 1895, L. Stewart to Herron, Nov. 21, 1895, Stewart R.

19. L. Stewart to M. Stewart, Nov. 25, 1895, Stewart R.

20. L. Stewart to M. Stewart, Dec. 18, 1895, to Miller, Jan. 15, 1896, to Balfour, Guthrie & Co., May 11, 1896, to Blanding, May 20, 1896, M. Stewart to L. Stewart, Jan. 21, 1896, F. L. King to L. Stewart, Feb. 4 and Mar. 3, 1896, W. L. Stewart to L. Stewart, May 5, 1896, Stewart R.

21. PCO Stock Journal, Secy. R; *S.F. Chronicle*, Oct. 26, 1894; *S. F. Examiner*, Oct. 26, 1894.

22. W. G. Hughes to L. Stewart, May 19, 1896, Howard to L. Stewart, May 27, June 8, 13, 29 and July 13, 1896, L. Stewart to Howard, July 1, 1896, Stewart R.

23. L. Stewart to J. Baker, Jr., Mar. 1, 1900, Stewart R; Scofield to Moffett, July 24, 1908, Scofield R.

24. Gerberding to Bard, June 15, 1896, also June 5, 1896, Bard R-HL.

25. Breeden to L. Stewart, July 13, 1896, L. Stewart to M. Stewart, July 27, 1896, Bard to L. Stewart, July 16 and 21, 1896, W. G. Hughes to L. Stewart, July 18, 1896, Stewart R.

26. Breeden to L. Stewart, July 22 and 24, 1896, L. Stewart to M. Stewart, Aug. 8, 1896, to Breeden, Aug. 31, 1896, Stewart R; Hughes to Bard, Sep. 10, 1896, Bard R-S.

27. L. Stewart to M. Stewart, Sep. 19, 1896, W. G. Hughes to L. Stewart, Mar. 16, 1897, Stewart R.

28. L. Stewart to M. Stewart, Nov. 16, 1896, M. Stewart to L. Stewart, Aug. 6, 1897, and Nov. 26, 1900, Stewart R.

29. L. Stewart to Capt. E. E. Robinson, Sep. 26, 1898, Bard R-HL; L. Stewart to Bard, Nov. 16, 1898, Miller to L. Stewart, Dec. 3, 1898, L. Stewart to M. Stewart, Dec. 7, 1898, Stewart R.

30. Miller to L. Stewart, Jan. 18, 1899, Stewart R; "Gen. Rpt. of the Calif. Oil Fields," C. F. Lufkin and J. Eckbert to Archbold, May 29, 1899, Hist. R.

31. "Rpt. of Cook's Inlet Alaska Oil Investigation," Nov., 1897, Archbold R; M. F. Elliott to J. H. Fertig, Dec. 26, 1899, Elliott R; Hidy and Hidy, *op. cit.*, 183, 185, 229.

32. Fleming to Archbold, Feb. 28, 1898, Archbold R.

33. H. C. Folger, Jr., to Archbold, Dec. 20, 1897, Archbold R; J. B. Terry to J. W. Smith, Apr. 23, 1956, Hist. R.

34. Salary Cards, 1897, Secy. R, SONJ; Hidy and Hidy, *op. cit.*, 263, 277.

35. "Detailed Rpt. of the Calif. Oil Fields," and "Gen. Rpt. of the Calif. Oil Fields," Lufkin and Eckbert to Archbold, May 29, 1899, Hist. R.

36. Webber to Miller, June 17, 1899, Breeden to Tilford, Aug. 28, 1899, Tilford to Archbold, Sep. 2, 1899, Archbold R. See also *S.F. Chronicle*, June 18, 1899.

37. L. Stewart to M. Stewart, Oct. 13, 1899, Stewart R; *S.F. Chronicle,* Dec. 31, 1899.

38. W. L. Stewart to L. Stewart, Oct. 16, 1899, Stewart R; O. Lawler to O. Sutro, May 20, 1930, Hist. R; Hidy and Hidy, *op. cit.*, 263-67, 275.

39. Lawler to Sutro, May 20, 1930, A. J. Cunningham, "Memo. of Interview with McCready," June 2, 1930, McCready interview by Lawler, June 19, 1930, Hist. R. Welty and Taylor in their history of Union indicate that the latter reason was the correct one, but they date the negotiations as 1898 (pp. 75-76).

40. L. Stewart to M. Stewart, Jan. 8, 1900, Stewart R; CSMB *Bul. #19*, 138-41. In testimony gathered in 1930, Fertig and McCready said that F. H. Oliphant, the eminent consulting geologist, had also surveyed the San Joaquin Valley fields for Archbold by the end of 1900, but they were unable to supply an exact date for his survey ("McCready" file, Hist. R).

41. Kruttschnitt to C. P. Huntington, Jan. 12, 1900, Hist. R; CSMB *Bul. #19*, 114-15, 126-30.

42. M. F. Elliott to Fertig, Dec. 26, 1899, Elliott R; Lawler to Sutro, May 20, 1930, Hist. R; Hidy and Hidy, *op. cit.*, 498.

43. A. J. Cunningham, "Memo. of Interview with McCready," June 2, 1930, McCready interview by Lawler, June 19, 1930, Hist. R; *Min. & Sci. Press*, July 12, 1892; CSMB *Bul. #19*, 117-23.

44. *Min. & Sci. Press*, Aug. 25, 1900; CSMB *Bul. #19*, 112-15, 126-30; Hidy and Hidy, *op. cit.*, 301; Redpath, *op. cit.*, 39.

45. *L.A. Times*, Aug. 30, 1900.

46. Quoted in *Oil Era*, Sep. 6, 1900.

47. *L.A. Herald*, reprinted in *Bakersfield Daily Californian*, Nov. 10, 1900.

48. *Oil Era*, Nov. 24, 1900.

49. Art. of Incorporation, Western Minerals Co., Dec. 13, 1899, Secy. of State (Calif.) R; testimony of A. J. Crites, Dec. 12, 1916, in *US* v. *SP #46*, XVII, 10115-17. S. A. D. Puter, *Looters of the Public Domain* (Portland, 1908), 416, shows that Scofield, Hugh Tevis, W. S. Tevis, and C. A. Mentry filed 34 claims beginning in July, 1899, and Blanding and F. G. Drum (a PCO director and cashier for J. B. Haggin, the uncle of the Tevis boys) 46 claims each.

50. PCO Minutes, Feb. 20, 1900, PCO Stock Journal, statement of Scofield, Oct., 1908, Secy. R.

51. These statements are based on the language of several of the write-offs made on Mar. 13, 1900 (PCO Minutes): "Newhall Cottage, depreciation; S. F. Warehouse, loss on the changes in fittings from time to time since organization of Co.," etc., etc., and the fact that the wells written off, totaling 12 PCO Pico wells, 9 Wiley, 3 Moore, and 3 Elsmere, when added to those producing on Mar. 17 ("PCO and CSOW Weekly

Production . . . for 39 wells of 1900," Comptr. R, SONJ) equal the number that had been drilled to that time. (*20th Ann. Rpt. of the Oil & Gas Supervisor* [S.F., 1934], 10-41.) A. R. Gilchriste, Iowa Standard's auditor, reported in Sep.: "So far as I can see, or otherwise ascertain, nothing has ever been written off what may be termed 'Permanent' plant, viz: Alameda, and The Pipelines" (Gilchriste to Breeden, Sep. 26, 1900, Comptr. R, SONJ).

On this evidence, we believe restoring the write-offs of Mar. 13 to the balance sheet of Apr. 30 will give a very close approximation of PCO's investment in fixed assets from its organization in 1879 to Apr. 30, 1900. The result is as follows:

Real estate (mainly producing) ......$	162,231
Refinery (including lands)	209,173
Oil wells	626,782
Pipelines	165,625
George Loomis	96,188*
Tank cars	36,716†
Sundry plant items (buildings, machine shop plant)	13,582
Office furniture and fixtures	5,706
TOTAL	**$1,316,003**

* We have used a figure supplied by the Union Iron Works (which constructed the *Loomis*) reported to the BuCorp. in May, 1905 (NA BuCorp, file #3299, Pt. 3). The figure carried on the PCO balance sheet for Apr. 30, 1900, was $80,195, disclosing that PCO was depreciating its tanker, if little else.

† We have used a figure of $36,716 instead of $29,716 because the SO(Iowa) Statements indicate that at some time prior to Apr. 30, 1900, PCO had written off ten cars worth $7,000. Gilchriste's comparison of PCO's books, as of May 1, 1899, and May 1, 1900, reveals that PCO's capital on the earlier date was $650,000. Subsequently, PCO increased its capital to $1,000,000 by taking $350,000 from surplus.

52. PCO Balance Sheet, Apr. 30, 1900, C. N. Payne and T. M. Towl to J. Bushnell, Oct. 4, 1900, Comptr. R, SONJ; title files, Treas. R; PCO Minutes.

53. Bushnell to W. H. Tilford, June 15, 1900, mentioned in Payne and Towl's ltr. to Bushnell, Oct. 4, 1900, Comptr. R, SONJ; M. Stewart to L. Stewart, Sep. 7, 1900, Stewart R; Hidy and Hidy, *op. cit.*, 587-88; *Romance of American Petroleum and Gas* (Oil City, Pa., 1900), 280-81; C. E. Whiteshot, *Oil Well Driller* (Mannington, W. Va., 1905), 708-09.

54. *L.A. Times*, Sep. 8, 1900; *Bakersfield Californian*, Sep. 25, 1900; *Bakersfield Morning Echo*, Sep. 28 and Oct. 2, 1900.

55. Payne and Towl to Bushnell, Oct. 4, 1900, Comptr. R, SONJ.

56. PCO Minutes, Oct. 17, 1900. In addition to E. S. Pillsbury, the other new directors were Horace D. Pillsbury, an attorney and the son of E. S. Pillsbury; Henry Wadsworth, cashier of the Wells Fargo Bank; and Louis Glass, the asst. gen. mgr. of the Pac. Tel. & Tel. Co.

57. SO(Iowa) Statements.

58. Tilford to Scofield, Dec. 11, 1900, Scofield R; PCO Minutes, Dec. 18, 1900, and Jan. 2, 1901.

59. L. Stewart to M. Stewart, Dec. 1, 1900, to J. Baker, Jr., Dec. 5, 7 and 19, 1900, Stewart R; *S.F. Call*, Dec. 11, 1900; *Oil Era*, Dec. 15, 1900.

60. Because CSOW, like PCO, rarely, if ever, wrote down its assets for depreciation or for any other loss, a CSOW balance sheet for June 30, 1901, probably gives a close approximation of the total investment since 1876, the year the company was organized. The Well Account is recorded at $383,463, a boiler house and an electric plant on the Pico patent at $4,694 and $500, respectively, and the Newhall refinery at $27,839, for a total of $416,495. The only item clearly written off at some past time was CSOW's old refinery at Ventura. The balance sheet also shows the paid-in capital as $30,000. (SO[Iowa]/PCO Statements).

61. "Histories of the PCO Wells," Hist. R; "PCO and CSOW Weekly Production . . . for 39 weeks of 1900," Comptr. R, SONJ; *20th Ann. Rpt. of the Oil & Gas Supervisor*, 10-41.

62. According to the PCO profit and loss statement for the last 8 months of 1900, PCO received dividends from CSOW amounting to $10,089 on 6,011 23/36 shares of stock. PCO's net profit for the 8 months was only $13,721 (Comptr. R, SONJ). We have no other dividend figure for CSOW after 1887, when it paid $52,500.

63. Scofield to H. W. O'Melveny, Jan. 5, 1901, Graves R; CSOW Stock Certificates, Secy. R; "C. N. Payne and T. M. Towl Appraise the Capital Stock of the PCO . . . as of May 1st, 1900," Comptr. R, SONJ; *L.A. Times*, May 27, 1894; Stephen Bonsal, *Edward Fitzgerald Beale* (N.Y., 1912), 303.

64. *S.F. Directory, 1900.* In 1895 Timothy Hopkins, a Menlo Park neighbor of Felton, succeeded Felton as president of the U.S. Smokeless Powder Co., in which L. Tevis and Blanding were also stockholders (*S.F. Directory, 1895, 1896*).

65. Payne and Towl to Bushnell, Oct. 4, 1900, Comptr. R, SONJ; Scofield to H. W. O'Melveny, Jan. 3, 1901, Graves R; PCO Minutes, Nov. 13, 1900; CSOW stock certificates, Secy. R. The new board included, in addition to Severance, Alfred Sutro, a partner in Pillsbury's law firm (Pillsbury, Madison & Sutro); Homer S. King, mgr. of the Wells Fargo Bank; Percy T. Morgan, pres. and gen. mgr. of the Calif. Wine Assn., and C. O. G. Miller, secy.-treas. of the Pac. Gas Improvement Co. and pres. and treas. of the Pac. Lighting Co. Morgan and Miller were clients of PM&S.

66. CSOW stock certificates #65, 71, 73-78, Secy. R; SO(Iowa) Voucher Register, 1896-1901, Comptr. R; Scofield to H. W. O'Melveny, Jan. 3 and 5, 1901, Graves R. The 6,011 23/36 shares in the custody of Severance, valued at $48,754, had never left the books of PCO (PCO Balance Sheets, Dec. 31, 1900, and June 30, 1901, Comptr. R).

67. Title files, Treas. R.

68. C. F. Lufkin and J. Eckbert to Archbold, May 29, 1899, Hist. R; Scofield to H. W. O'Melveny, Jan. 10, 1901, Graves to Breeden, Jan. 17 and 30, 1901, Graves R.

69. Elliott to H. M. Tilford, Oct. 25, 1900, Elliott R; M. Stewart to L. Stewart, Oct. 31, 1900, Stewart R.

70. "Rpt. on Refineries," Scofield to H. M. Tilford, Nov. 12, 1900, Econ. R; M. Stewart to L. Stewart, Nov. 26, 1900, Stewart R.

IX. PCO EMBARKS ON NEW VENTURES

1. Title files, Treas. R; *L.A. Herald*, Mar. 15, 1900; *L.A. Herald*, cited by the *Bakersfield Echo*, Aug. 15, 1900; *Min. & Eng. Rev.*, Oct. 27, 1900; Barlow and Hill, *California Oil Fields* (Bakersfield, 1910), map opp. p. 16.

2. Title files, Treas. R; *Bakersfield Californian*, May 23, 1900; *S.F. Call*, Nov. 4, 1900, p. 30; *Min. & Sci. Press*, Nov. 17, 1900, p. 531; *Min. & Eng. Rev.*, Dec. 22, 1900; Barlow and Hill, *op. cit.*, map opp. p. 37; Wallace M. Morgan, *History of Kern County* (L.A., 1914), 128, 181.

3. PCO Construction Rpt. for 1901, Mfg. R.

4. M. Stewart to L. Stewart, Jan. 5, 1901, Stewart R; C. N. Payne to O'Day, May 12, 1903, O'Day R; Walton Young to J. W. Smith, Feb. 15, 1958, G. M. Brown interview by Paul Home, Feb. 13, 1930, Hist. R; deposition of Brown, Sep. 23, 1930 in *US* v. *State of Calif. et al.*, #1679, in the US Land Office, Sac., VIII, 2000-05, hereafter cited as *US* v. *State of Calif.*

5. Brown deposition; *L.A. Herald*, Jan. 16, 1901; *L.A. Times*, Jan. 27, 1901; *Bakersfield Echo*, Mar. 10 and 14, 1901; *Bakersfield Californian*, quoted in *Min. & Eng. Rev.*, Jan. 19, 1901.

6. L. Stewart to W. L. Stewart, Sep. 12, 1900, Stewart R; Breeden to H. M. Tilford, Mar. 21, 1902, Comptr. R, SONJ; PCO Minutes, Feb. 4, 1901; *Bakersfield Californian*, Aug. 16, 1901; *Oil Era*, Mar. 16, 1901.

7. *Bakersfield Californian*, Nov. 21, 1900; *Bakersfield Echo*, Mar. 17, 1901; *L.A. Herald*, Apr. 1, 1901; *S.F. Call*, Apr. 4, 1901.

8. L. Stewart to M. Stewart, May 17, 1901, Stewart R; *L.A. Times*, May 8, 1901; *Pac. Oil Reporter*, cited by *S.F. Call*, May 12, 1901; *Bakersfield Echo*, June 18 and 29, 1901; *L.A. Herald*, quoted by *Bakersfield Californian*, July 3, 1901; *Bakersfield Californian*, July 26 and Aug. 16, 1901; *Min. & Eng. Rev.*, June 15, 1901, p. 13.

9. L. Stewart to J. Baker, Jr., Sep. 30, 1901, and to M. Stewart, Dec. 24, 1901, Stewart R; title files, Treas. R; PCO Minutes, Dec. 3, 1901, and Sep. 16, 1902; *Bakers-*

field Californian, Sep. 20, 1901; *Oil, Copper & Finance,* quoted in *Min. & Eng. Rev.,* Sep. 21, 1901, p. 17; *Pac. Oil Reporter,* Nov. 28, 1902.

10. *Bakersfield Echo,* Nov. 16, 1901. Very likely, the reference to the Philippines was inspired by the negotiations then going on between 26 Broadway and Sir Marcus Samuel to purchase his Shell Transport & Trading Company. Shell had important fuel oil outlets in the Orient. The negotiations foundered, and Standard failed to follow them up by entering the Oriental fuel oil trade (Robert Henriques, *Bearsted—A Biography of Marcus Samuel, First Viscount Bearsted and Founder of "Shell" Transport and Trading Company* [N.Y., 1960], 376-79).

11. I. E. Blake interview by C. Earl, May 10, 1905, NA BuCorp. file #3220, Pt. 1. In mid-1900 Blake stated no work had been done on the Northwest Railroad in eastern Oregon and Idaho that year because of litigation (*The Railway Age,* July 27, 1900, p. 83).

12. Blake to L. Stewart, Jan. 20, 1900, Stewart R.

13. L. Stewart to J. Baker, Jr., Mar. 1, 1900, to W. L. Stewart, Aug. 17, 1900, to M. Stewart, Dec. 13, 1900, Stewart R. At the time Blake formed United Oil Producers, he heard that Breeden had spoken ill of his relations with Standard in Colorado. This appears to have sprung from a personal difference between Scofield and Blake, and Breeden soon fell silent. The nature of the charges and their validity are unknown and their effect on Blake's plans cannot be evaluated, although Blake later called them "very damaging" while at the same time speaking of his "very pleasant" relations with Standard in S.F.

14. Blake interview by Earl, May 10, 1905, NA BuCorp. file #3220, Pt. 1.

15. Baker to L. Stewart, Feb. 23, 1901, Stewart R.

16. Blake interview by Earl, May 10, 1905, NA BuCorp. file #3220, Pt. 1; *Nat. Oil Reporter,* Jan. 23, 1902.

17. J. M. Wright interview by Earl, May 9, 1905, NA BuCorp. file #3220, Pt. 1; *Oil, Mining and Finance,* Nov. 20, 1902. A decade later, Standard bought the refinery site and built on it the Bakersfield refinery (title files, Treas. R).

18. W. L. Stewart to L. Stewart, Sep. 19, 1902, Blake to M. Stewart, attached to ltr., M. Stewart to L. Stewart, Oct. 13, 1902, Stewart R. This offer by Shell seems to have been part of an attempted triple shift. When the Spindletop field in Texas suddenly failed, Shell could no longer count on its contract with the J. M. Guffey Petroleum Co. to provide fuel oil for Europe. Perhaps Calif. oil could be used to supply the Orient, Shell may have reasoned, and Far Eastern sources used to take care of European demand, all the while giving employment to Shell's fleet. Shell's contract with Guffey and the one offered the Californians were, in effect, long-term partnerships. Shell paid Guffey a fixed price and half the net profits. To the Californians it offered, in Blake's words, to "advance practically the market price here and freight to the seaboard, and then ship to these foreign countries, making a fair charge for the cost of vessels and a commission to cover all other expenses . . . 2½% and then divide the profits equally. . . ." The Guffey contract, like the proposal to Blake, was for 21 years (Henriques, *op. cit.,* 411, 414, 482). We do not know why the negotiations between Blake and Shell were broken off, nor which side was responsible for the break.

19. M. Stewart to L. Stewart, Apr. 19, 1904, Stewart R; *Nat. Oil Reporter,* Nov. 25, 1902.

20. C. F. Lufkin to Archbold, May 29, 1899, Hist. R; L. Stewart to I. W. Hellman, Jan. 16, 1900, to Blake, Jan. 17, 1900, W. L. Stewart to L. Stewart, Jan. 26, 1900, Stewart R.

21. L. Stewart to W. L. Stewart, Mar. 3, 1900, W. L. Stewart to L. Stewart, Mar. 3, 1900, Stewart R.

22. L. Stewart to M. Stewart, May 22, 1900, Stewart R.

23. L. Stewart to W. L. Stewart, Aug. 17 and 23, 1900, Stewart R.

24. M. Stewart to L. Stewart, Sep. 5, 1900, Stewart R.

25. L. Stewart to J. S. Torrance, Aug. 31, 1900, to M. Stewart, Oct. 11, 1900, W. L. Stewart to L. Stewart, Sep. 10, 1900, Stewart R; Bard to J. Dolbeer, Sep. 10, 1900, Bard R-S; Bard to J. H. Meyer, Nov. 3, 1900, Bard R-HL.

26. L. Stewart to W. L. Stewart, Sep. 12, 1900, Stewart R.

27. M. Stewart to L. Stewart, Sep. 21 and Nov. 26, 1900, L. Stewart to M. Stewart, Dec. 13, 1900, Stewart R; J. S. Torrance to Bard, Dec. 7, 1900, Bard R-HL.

28. L. Stewart to Baker, Dec. 19, 1900, to M. Stewart, Aug. 20, 1901, Stewart R; Hidy and Hidy, *op. cit.,* 204-05; Nevins, *op. cit.,* II, 77-78.

29. L. Stewart to E. W. Fenn, Mar. 2, 1901, to Baker, Mar. 19 and Apr. 25, 1901, to M. Stewart, Apr. 26, 1901, to F. H. Rindge, June 22, 1901, Baker to L. Stewart, Apr. 19, 1901, Stewart R.

30. W. L. Stewart to Porter, June 28, 1901, M. Stewart to L. Stewart, Nov. 26, 1900, L. Stewart to W. G. Hughes, Sep. 24 and Oct. 8, 1901, to W. L. Stewart, Sep. 27, 1901, Stewart R; *Min. & Eng. Rev.,* June 29, 1901, p. 17.

31. L. Stewart to W. L. Stewart, Sep. 27, 1901, to M. Stewart, Apr. 4, 1902, Stewart R.

32. L. Stewart to M. Stewart, Jan. 8 and Apr. 4, 1902, Stewart R; L. Stewart statement to J. R. Garfield, May 1, 1905, NA BuCorp. file #3402, Pt. 1; *Bakersfield Californian,* Nov. 9 and Dec. 24, 1901.

33. *Bakersfield Echo,* July 18, 1900.

34. *L.A. Times,* Aug. 2 and 30, 1900; *Bakersfield Californian,* Sep. 4, 1900; *L.A. Express,* quoted in *Min. & Eng. Rev.,* Sep., 1900, p. 50.

35. J. M. Wright interview by Earl, May 9, 1905, NA BuCorp. file #3220, Pt. 1; B. F. Brooks interview by L. Conant, Jr., May 24, 1905, NA BuCorp. file #3299, Pt. 1.

36. L. Stewart to M. Stewart, Apr. 26, 1901, Stewart R; *Min. & Sci. Press,* Oct. 27, 1900, pp. 492-93.

37. L. Stewart to M. Stewart, May 17 and June 6, 1901, Stewart R; *L.A. Times,* May 8, 1901.

38. Luther Conant, Jr., "Preliminary Report on Oil Investigation in California," NA BuCorp. file #4176, Pt. 1, p. 32, hereafter cited as Conant Rpt.; see also, *World Pet.,* Aug., 1937, pp. 46-47.

39. *Bakersfield Echo,* July 30, 1901; *World Pet.,* Aug., 1937, p. 48.

40. L. Stewart to W. L. Stewart, Dec. 2, 1901, Stewart R; *Pet. Rev.,* quoted in *Pac. Oil Reporter,* Nov. 15, 1901; *L.A. Express,* quoted in the *Bakersfield Echo,* Nov. 20, 1901.

41. C. A. Canfield interview by Earl, June 23, 1905, NA BuCorp. file #3220, Pt. 4; *Nat. Oil Reporter,* Dec. 5, 1901.

42. W. G. Kerckhoff interview by Earl, June 21, 1905, NA BuCorp. file #3220, Pt. 4; Conant Rpt., 35-36, 53.

43. C. F. Lufkin to E. H. Harriman, Dec. 24, 1902, Hist. R; *Nat. Oil Reporter,* Apr. 24, 1902, p. 9; Conant Rpt., 47-52; *Rpt. of the Comr. of Corps. on the Transp. of Pet., May 2, 1906* (Wash., 1906), 495.

44. Conant Rpt., 54; Ann. Sales Statements.

45. *Min. & Eng. Rev.,* Mar. 2, 1901, p. 4; *Min. & Sci. Press,* Aug. 4, 1900, p. 118.

46. K. H. Wade to L. Stewart, Nov. 20, 1893, L. Stewart to M. Stewart, Jan. 12, 1895, Stewart R; P. Sheedy to H. C. Booth, Oct. 10, 1916, J. Kruttschnitt interview (interviewer unknown), Jan. 11, 1917, Hist. R; E. L. Doheny interview by Earl, June 24, 1905, NA BuCorp. file #3220, Pt. 4; deposition of G. W. Prescott, June 29, 1916, and J. B. Treadwell, Mar. 1, 1917, in *US* v. *SP* #46, XI, 6058-67 and XX, 11979, 11982, 11992, respectively; *S.F. Call,* Apr. 27, 1902; *Railway Age,* May 11, 1900, pp. 478-79; *Min. & Eng. Rev.,* Apr. 26, 1902, p. 13; *O.&G.J.,* Oct. 8, 1914, pp. 20-21; Lionel V. Redpath, *Petroleum in California* (L.A., [1900]), 61.

47. Kruttschnitt to Huntington, Jan. 12, 1900, Huntington to Kruttschnitt, Jan. 25, 1900, Hist. R; L. Stewart to M. Stewart, Nov. 26, 1901, Stewart R; Kruttschnitt testimony, Jan. 22, 1917, in *US* v. *SP* #46, XIX, 11160-62; *S.F. Examiner,* Mar. 31, 1901; *Min. & Eng. Rev.,* Mar. 16, 1901, p. 12. Huntington died later in the year, and in 1901 E. H. Harriman bought a controlling interest. Though Wm. Rockefeller and H. H. Rogers were among those who helped Harriman retain control of Southern Pacific, there is no evidence that these policies toward Standard were altered (Geo. Kennan, *E. H. Harriman—A Biography* [Boston, 1922], I, 233, 238-39, 343).

48. *Bakersfield Californian,* Aug. 21, 1900; *Railway Age,* Mar. 1, 1901, p. 173; *Rpt. of the Ind. Comm.,* I, 779; *Rpt. of the Comr. of Corps. on the Transp. of Pet., May 2, 1906,* pp. 464-68.

49. W. S. Rheem to S. H. McClintock, Jan. 3, 1902, Pub. Rel. R; *Railway Age,* Mar. 29, 1901, p. 380 and Sep. 20, 1901, p. 268; *Bakersfield Echo,* Jan. 10, and Oct. 4, 1901; *Bakersfield Californian,* cited by the *Min. & Eng. Rev.,* Aug. 31, 1901, p. 20. A

complaint was also filed with the Commission that the rates were unreasonable, a controversy that the Commission eventually resolved by cutting the rate to S.F. from 42¢ a bbl. to 37.8¢. One wonders why the producers set such store by a rate reduction when the market price remained uncontrolled. C. B. Anderson of Green and Whittier later commented that he had expected the consumer rather than the producer would get the benefit of the new rate, and that is what happened (Anderson interview by Earl, June 14, 1905, NA BuCorp. file #3220, Pt. 4; *Bakersfield Echo*, Mar. 14, 1901; *Nat. Oil Reporter*, Apr. 24, 1902).

50. *Bakersfield Echo*, Jan. 3, 1902; *L.A. Herald*, Oct. 1 and Dec. 21, 1901; *Bakersfield Californian*, Nov. 30, 1901; *Railway Age*, Aug. 9, 1901, p. 119; *Rpt. of the Comr. of Corps. on the Transp. of Pet., May 2, 1906*, 469. H. G. Morrow reported in mid-1903 that over half the cars shipped from Kern River were to SP terminals for fuel (Morrow to F. M. Towl, July 14, 1903, O'Day R).

51. PCO-Monte Cristo contract of Nov. 26, 1901, Hist. R; Breeden to H. M. Tilford, Mar. 21, 1902, Comptr. R, SONJ; *Min. & Eng. Rev.*, Dec. 14, 1901, p. 14; *Rpt. of the Comr. of Corps. on the Transp. of Pet., May 2, 1906*, 469.

52. *Min. & Eng. Rev.*, Nov. 2, 1901, p. 16.

53. *L.A. Herald*, Apr. 1, 1902.

54. Blake to L. Stewart, Jan. 20, 1900, L. Stewart to M. Stewart, May 22, 1900, Stewart R; H. A. Forsburg interview by R. B. Bartlett, Jan. 14, 1950; D. T. Day (ed.), *A Handbook of the Petroleum Industry* (N.Y., [1922]), 403; *Pet. Development and Technology in 1926* (N.Y., [1927]), 460.

55. O'Day to Archbold, Jan. 7, 1903, O'Day R; right of way agreements, Land Dept. R; E. B. Ripley interview by Earl, May 5, 1905, NA BuCorp. file #3223; *Bakersfield Californian*, Oct. 25, 1901; *Contra Costa Gazette*, Nov. 2, 1901; A. F. Shulte, "Getting Rights of Way for the Pipe-Lines," *Among Ourselves*, Jan., 1925, p. 2. The SP did not build its spur, and Standard's wharf was never connected with the refinery spur.

56. T. M. Towl to O'Day, Mar. 29, 1902, F. M. Towl to O'Day, Apr. 11, 1902, H. M. Tilford to H. C. Folger, Jr., Jan. 26, 1903, O'Day R; W. S. Rheem to Folger, Jan. 2, 1902, Pub. Rel. R; *Bakersfield Californian*, Dec. 10, 1901, *Bakersfield Echo*, Jan. 7 and Mar. 13, 1902.

57. T. M. Towl to O'Day, Apr. 11, 1902, O'Day R; M. Stewart to L. Stewart, Nov. 3, 1902, Stewart R; *Bakersfield Echo*, Mar. 13 and May 24, 1902; *S.F. Chronicle*, Apr. 19, 1903; *Among Ourselves*, Jan., 1926, p. 12.

58. F. M. Towl to E. P. Bly, Nov. 24, 1926, Hist. R; E. P. Bly, "Oil Pipe Lines in California," a reprint from the Aug., Sep., and Oct., 1926 issues of *Oil Bulletin*.

59. H. A. Forsburg interview by R. B. Bartlett, Jan. 14, 1952; *Pac. Oil Reporter*, Jan. 3, 1903; E. P. Bly, "Oil Pipe Lines in California," *op. cit.*; Wm. Herbert, "Other Days, Other Ways," *Standard Oiler*, Nov., 1944, p. 17; *Pet. Development and Technology in 1926*, 460; Day, *op. cit.*, 403; Williamson and Daum, *op. cit.*, 603.

60. W. Ogg to J. B. Maitland, Jan. 22, 1903, C. N. Payne to O'Day, May 12, 1903, J. Page to O'Day, Apr. 28, 1904, O'Day R; H. G. Morrow to F. M. Towl, Apr. 22, 1903, P/L R; testimony of H. M. Tilford, Dec. 4, 1908, in *US* v. *SONJ*, XVII, 3524; title files, Treas. R.

61. F. M. Towl to B. A. Towl, Mar. 30, 1903, O'Day to Archbold, May 26, 1903, O'Day to F. M. Towl, May 28, 1903, Payne to O'Day, June 2, 1903, O'Day R; Treadwell to J. Kruttschnitt, Apr. 20, 1903, Hist. R; *Bakersfield Californian*, Mar. 13, 1903; *S.F. Chronicle*, Apr. 12, 1903; *S.O. Bulletin*, Oct., 1917, p. 12.

62. C. R. Huntley to O'Day, July 3, 1903, F. M. Towl to O'Day, July 10, 22, 30 and Aug. 25, 1903, O'Day to Archbold, May 26, 1903, Page to O'Day, Oct. 17, 1903, O'Day R; Day, *op. cit.*, 406. Starke's process was used years later by the Doheny-Pacific Company on its Casmalia property (CSMB *Bul. #84* [1918], 107-09).

63. F. M. Towl to O'Day, July 10, Aug. 15 and 25, 1903, O'Day R; Towl to E. P. Bly, Nov. 24, 1926, Hist. R.

64. Scofield to H. C. Folger, Jr., Sep. 1 and 15, 1903, O'Day R; Hidy and Hidy, *op. cit.*, 379.

65. Lufkin and Eckbert to Archbold, May 29, 1899, Hist. R; C. J. Hedrick to H. C. Folger, Jr., July 23, 1902, CRC R.

66. Hillmor Smith interview by A. E. Haase, Apr. 25, 1957; R. C. Hunt (ed.), *California and Californians* (Chicago, 1926), V, 93-94.

67. SO(Iowa)/PCO Statements; PCO Minutes, Feb. 4 and 11, 1901; PCO Rpt. of Completed Construction for 1901, Mfg. R; C. N. Payne to H. H. Rogers, Jan. 29, 1903, O'Day R; *S.F. Examiner,* Mar. 31, 1901, *L.A. Herald,* Apr. 1, 1901.

68. Inspector's Record, 1901, and Rheem to Scofield, June 12, 1902, Pub. Rel. R; Newhall statements, Hist. R; *Oil Era,* June 8, 1901.

69. L. D. Dimm to R. J. Hanna, Apr. 5, 1927, scrapbook in possession of C. S. Dimm; Lube Price Bk.; Inspector's Record, 1901, Pub. Rel. R; *S.O. Bulletin,* Jan., 1918, p. 4.

70. C. N. Payne and T. M. Towl to J. Bushnell, Oct. 4, 1900, Comptr. R. SONJ; Scofield to H. C. Folger, Jr., Sep. 1, 1903, O'Day R; testimony of H. M. Tilford, Dec. 4, 1908, in *US* v. *SONJ,* XVII, 3491; Wm. Herbert, *op. cit.,* Feb., 1944, p. 19.

71. Inspector's Record, 1901, Rheem to W. P. Cowan, Mar. 7, 1902, Rheem to Scofield, May 20 and Sep. 27, 1902, Pub. Rel. R; *Contra Costa Gazette,* Sep. 21, 1901; *Bakersfield Californian,* quoted in the *Standard Oiler, Feb.,* 1944, p. 13.

72. Rheem to H. C. Folger, Jr., Dec. 20, 1901, and Jan. 17, 1902, Rheem to W. M. Burton, Dec. 13, 1901, Rheem to Van Dyke, Feb. 26, 1902, Pub. Rel. R; J. F. Brooks, Jr., "History of Richmond Refinery," an unpublished ms. in Mfg. Dept. R, paged for each section—in this note "Gen. Refinery," 8, hereafter cited as Brooks ms; A. R. Crum (ed.), *Romance of American Petroleum and Gas* (Oil City, [1911]), 282.

73. Brooks ms., "Gen. Refinery," 6-7.

74. Rheem to J. W. Van Dyke, Jan. 16 and Feb. 28, 1902, to Scofield, Feb. 24, Apr. 4, May 3 and 15 and July 10, 1902, Pub. Rel. R; Brooks ms., "Gen. Refinery," 7-9. The tar stills were 11 x 23 ft., with a charging capacity of 14,000 gals. They were set in pairs and fired from the side, 3 burners along each of the outer edges of the pair. In addition to the customary water-filled condensers, each pair of the tar stills was equipped with an air-cooled condenser in a box above the stills. The crude stills measured 14 x 40 ft., with a capacity of 40,000 gals. There was also a steam still, 12½ x 30 ft., with a capacity of 30,000 gals. At the rear of this still a 30-ft. column filled with stone served as a preliminary condenser prior to the usual water-filled condenser. (Figures giving the capacity of stills and agitators in bbls. have been converted into gals. at 40 gals. to a bbl. PCO Construction Rpt. of Dec. 31, 1903, Mfg. R; Brooks ms., "Gen. Refinery," 16-17, "Crude Stills," 1-4.)

75. Rheem to J. W. Van Dyke, Feb. 11, 1902, to Burton, Feb. 11, 1902, to Scofield, June 6, 1902, Pub. Rel. R; *Calif. Oil World,* Aug. 25, 1939, pp. 75-76. The pumps from Galatea were probably salvaged from the Manhattan Oil Company refinery, which Standard had recently bought and dismantled.

76. Rheem to J. W. Van Dyke, Dec. 2 and 13, 1901, to Scofield, Apr. 10 and May 9, 1902, Pub. Rel. R.

77. Rheem to Scofield, July 4 and 10, 1902, Pub. Rel. R; Brooks ms., "Gen Refinery," 12.

X. EXPANSION AND CONSOLIDATION

1. Rheem to Scofield, May 20, 1902, Pub. Rel. R; PCO rpt., "Outside Refineries—Calif., Nov. 1, 1902," Econ. R; PCO Analysis of Business, 1903, Comptr. R, SONJ; Giddens, *op. cit.,* 43, 61; Hidy and Hidy, *op. cit.,* 414.

2. "Outside Refineries—Calif., Nov. 1, 1902," Econ. R; Rheem to Scofield, Nov. 15, 1902, Pub. Rel. R; Construction Rpt., Dec. 31, 1903, Mfg. R; Brooks ms., "Barrel House," 1; *S.F. Call,* May 22, 1902; *Pac. Oil Reporter,* Jan. 3, 1903.

3. Rheem to Burton, Nov. 29, 1901, Pub. Rel. R; Starke to Hillman, Dec. 14, 1914, Hist. R; testimony of H. M. Tilford, Dec. 4, 1908, in *US* v. *SONJ,* XVII, 3495.

4. Rheem to Scofield, Feb. 4, 1902, Pub. Rel. R; PCO Analysis of Business, 1901, Comptr. R, SONJ; W. H. McBryde interview by J. W. Smith, Jan. 30, 1956; H. F. Merriam to G. T. White, Feb. 10, 1956; Brooks ms., "Acid Works," 1; *S.F. Chronicle,* Dec. 30, 1900; Williams Haynes, *American Chemical Industry* (N.Y., 1954), 263-64.

5. T. M. Towl to O'Day, Mar. 29, 1902, O'Day R; Rheem to H. M. Tilford, Apr. 23, 1902, Rheem to Scofield, Oct. 20, 1902, Pub. Rel. R. Students of refining may find interesting Rheem's estimate of the components of the proposed 1,000-bbl. a day re-

finery, the staff to operate it, and the costs. Unfortunately, these data are not available for any refineries actually built:

3	1000 bbl. crude stills	at $7500.00 each	$22500.00	
5	100 H. P. boilers	" 1000.00 "	5000.00	
1	tower steam still	" 4100.00 "	4100.00	
2	600 bbl. lead lined agitators	" 1300.00 "	2600.00	
				34200.00

RECEIVING TANKS, BLEACHERS, AND STORAGE TANKS

6	40 x 10 tanks	at $1100.00 each	$ 6600.00	
6	30 x 10 tanks	" 850.00 "	5100.00	
4	30 x 10 bleachers	" 850.00 "	3400.00	
2	30 x 30 tanks	" 1400.00 "	2800.00	
2	40 x 30 tanks	" 2200.00 "	4400.00	
2	60 x 30 tanks	" 3800.00 "	7600.00	
4	16 x 15 tanks	" 375.00 "	1500.00	
1	20 x 20 water tanks	" 765.00 "	765.00	
				32165.00

BUILDINGS

1 brick boiler house & light station, 35 x 75	$ 2200.00	
1 storehouse and barrel house, 50 x 60	2475.00	
1 pipe shop, 30 x 30	750.00	
1 pump house, 30 x 70	1500.00	
1 receiving house, 18 x 20	850.00	
1 office & laboratory, 20 x 25, two stories	2000.00	
		9775.00

PUMPS

8 pumps 12" x 10" x 18"	$ 4800.00	
2 pumps 12" x 16" x 18"	700.00	
1 duplex blower 102 x 14" x 18"	1500.00	
		7000.00

Suction, discharge rundown and water lines	$16000.00	
Sewers	3000.00	
Loading rack	500.00	
Pipe shop tools, etc.	1200.00	
Electric light station	2000.00	
Acid restoring plant	5000.00	
Freight	12000.00	
General labor and expense not included in above	5000.00	
		44700.00
Total		$127840.00

PERMANENT WORKING FORCE

1 refiner at $125.00 per month;
1 office man at $100.00 per month;
1 clerk at $65.00 per month;
1 night foreman at $100.00 per month;
1 treater at $90.00 per month;
1 treater's helper at $65.00 per month;

1 electrician at $75.00 per month;
1 inspector at $75.00 per month;
1 warehouse man at $75.00 per month;
1 warehouse man at $2.25 per day;
2 still men at $2.75 per day;
2 stillmen's helpers at $2.40 per day;
2 water tenders at $2.65 per day;
2 boiler firemen at $2.50 per day;
2 pump men at $2.50 per day;
1 pipe fitter at $2.50 per day;
1 pipefitter's helper at $2.25 per day;
2 laborers (still cleaners), $2.50 per day;
1 acid works man at $2.75 per day;
1 acid works man at $2.50 per day;
(W. S. Rheem to Scofield, Apr. 19, 1902, Pub. Rel. R)

6. PCO Construction Rpts., Dec. 31, 1902 and June 30, 1903, Mfg. R; interviews, Dan Murphy by Earl, June 23, 1905, NA BuCorp. file #3220, Pt. 4; O. O. Allen by J. W. Smith, Feb. 11, 1958; *L.A. Herald,* June 2, 1902; *Nat. Oil Reporter,* July 24 and Nov. 13, 1902; *S. O. Bulletin,* July, 1919, p. 13.

7. History of the SO Co. Marine Dept., Pt. I, Bk. I and the data bk. for the *Asuncion,* CSC R; G. E. Bridgett interview by J. W. Smith, May 2, 1957; *Pac. Oil Reporter,* Jan. 3, 1903.

8. L. Stewart to Balfour, Guthrie, Oct. 23, 1901, Stewart R; *Nat. Oil Reporter,* Nov. 27, 1902; *Pac. Oil Reporter,* July 4, 1903, pp. 22-23; Beaton, *op. cit.,* 72.

9. Starke to Rheem, Jan. 24, 1902, Hist. R; Rheem to Starke, Apr. 29, 1902, to Breeden, May 20, 1902, Pub. Rel. R; (W. W. Orcutt) to W. L. Stewart, Sep. 29, 1902, M. Stewart to L. Stewart, Nov. 3 and 18, 1902, Stewart R.

10. W. L. Stewart to L. Stewart, Sep. 29, 1902, L. Stewart to M. Stewart, July 15, 1903, Stewart R; *Pac. Oil Reporter,* July 4, 1903, p. 15.

11. E. G. Tilton to W. Hood, Apr. 2, 1903, Hood to Kruttschnitt, Apr. 17, 1903, Hist. R; H. G. Morrow to Scofield, Nov. 12, 1903, O'Day R; *Pac. Oil Reporter,* July 4, 1903, p. 6.

12. W. Ogg to J. B. Maitland, Jan. 22, 1903, F. M. Towl to T. M. Towl, May 21, 1903, and to O'Day, July 10 and Aug. 25, 1903, O'Day to F. M. Towl, July 22, 1903, O'Day R; *Pac. Oil Reporter,* Dec. 6, 1902, and July 4, 1903; CSMB *Bul. #32* (1904), map opp. p. 42.

13. Scofield to H. C. Folger, Jr., Sep. 1, 1903, O'Day R; PCO Construction Rpts., Dec. 31, 1903, and June 30, 1904, Mfg. R; crude still instruction bk., Pub. Rel. R.

14. Rheem to Scofield, Oct. 13, 1902, Pub. Rel. R.

15. Page to O'Day, Dec. 19, 1903, O'Day R; Hidy and Hidy, *op. cit.,* 443.

16. Brooks ms., "Acid Works," 3; J. B. Terry to J. W. Smith, Aug. 8, 1958, Hist. R. The iron pyrites were obtained from the Shasta County mines of the Mountain Copper Co. After roasting, the cinders were shipped to its smelter near Martinez.

17. Scofield to Folger, Sep. 1 and 15, 1903, Folger to O'Day, Sep. 10, 1903, Page to O'Day, Oct. 15 and 29, 1903, Page to F. M. Towl, Oct. 29, 1903, O'Day to Page,, Oct. 30, 1903, O'Day R; PCO Construction Rpt., June 30, 1904, Mfg. R; Brooks ms., "General Refinery," 17-18; Hidy and Hidy, *op. cit.,* 434.

18. Page to Payne, Sep. 21, 1903, Page to O'Day, Oct. 9 and 12, 1903, O'Day R.

19. O'Day to Page, Oct. 22, 1903, O'Day R.

20. Page to Payne, Sep. 21, 1903, Payne to O'Day, Oct. 7, 1903, Page to O'Day, Dec. 4, 1903, and an undated ltr., Morrow to Scofield, Nov. 12, 1903, O'Day R; W. L. Stewart to L. Stewart, Oct. 20, 1903, Stewart R.

21. Page to O'Day, Oct. 29, Nov. 9 and 14, Dec. 5, 1903, O'Day R.

22. O'Day to Page, Dec. 19, 1903, F. M. Towl to O'Day, Dec. 22, 1903, Page to O'Day, Dec. 19 and 26, 1903, O'Day R.

23. Payne to O'Day, Dec. 29, 1903, O'Day R.

24. Page to O'Day, Dec. 31, 1903, O'Day R.

25. O'Day to Rogers, Jan. 7, 1904, O'Day R.

26. O'Day to Rogers, Feb. 4, 1904, Page to O'Day, Apr. 22, 1904, O'Day R; F. M. Towl to E. P. Bly, Nov. 24, 1926, Hist. R.

27. Page to O'Day, Dec. 12 and 19, 1903, Apr. 29, 1904, O'Day R.

28. Page to O'Day, Feb. 29, 1904, O'Day R.

29. Page to O'Day, Feb. 26 and 29, Mar. 3, 8 and 14, 1904, O'Day R.

30. Page to O'Day, Mar. 31, Apr. 22 and 28, May 16, July 5, Oct. 31, 1904, O'Day R; L. Stewart to M. Stewart, Sep. 8, 1904, Stewart R; Conant Rpt., 44; *Bakersfield Californian*, May 23, 1904; *The Journal of Electricity, Power, and Gas*, Jan., 1905, p. 8; E. I. Harrington, "General Petroleum Corporation," *Calif. Oil World*, July 5, 1937, p. 7.

31. Page to O'Day, May 19 and 28, 1904, O'Day to Page, June 3, 1904, O'Day R.

32. Page to O'Day, Aug. 20, 1904, O'Day R; Conant Rpt., 212-17, 220-21; Wallace M. Morgan, *History of Kern County California* (L.A., 1914), 131.

33. Page to O'Day, Mar. 14, Aug. 2, 1904, Scofield to H. M. Tilford, Aug. 23, 1904, O'Day R; PCO Minutes, Aug. 30, 1904; title files, Treas. R; Field Operations rpt., Econ. R; *L.A. Times,* Aug. 25, 1904. Of the original 80 acres leased at McKittrick, 20 acres had been purchased early in 1903; it was this property and equipment that was sold to Associated.

34. Page to O'Day, Sep. 23, 1904, O'Day R; Conant Rpt., 217; A. H. Liscomb memo. and W. B. Robb interview by Earl, June 8, 1905, NA BuCorp. file #3220, Pt. 3.

35. Page to O'Day, Oct. 17, 1904, J. Bushnell to O'Day, Oct. 12, 1904, O'Day to Rogers, Oct. 13, 1904, O'Day R.

36. Page to O'Day, Sep. 12, Nov. 14, Dec. 1, 1904, Payne to Page, Oct. 19, 1904, O'Day R; O. O. Allen interview by J. W. Smith, Feb. 11, 1958.

37. Page to O'Day, Oct. 17, 24, Nov. 1, 14, 1904, O'Day to Rogers, Oct. 25, 1904, H. M. Tilford to Breeden, Oct. 26, 1904, O'Day to Tilford, Nov. 10, 1904, O'Day R.

38. Monthly rpts., P/L R; Conant Rpt., 228, 230, 238-56; A. H. Liscomb memo. and W. B. Robb interview by Earl, June 8, 1905, NA BuCorp. file #3220, Pt. 3.

39. Page to O'Day, Oct. 1, Nov. 10, Dec. 1, 21, 22 and 26, 1904, O'Day R.

40. Page to Scofield, Dec. 29, 1904, Page to O'Day, Mar. 13, 1905, O'Day R; F. M. Towl to E. P. Bly, Nov. 24, 1926, Hist. R.

41. Calif. Oil Field contract in Secy. R, SONJ; monthly rpts., P/L R.

42. Breeden to H. M. Tilford, Sep. 3, 1903, Page to O'Day, Dec. 4, 1903, O'Day R; draft contract signed by Breeden, Pinal R.

43. Starke to Rheem, Jan. 27, 1903, Hist. R; Breeden to H. M. Tilford, Feb. 19, 1904, Comptr. R, SONJ; R. B. Ellis interview by Earl, June 27, 1905, NA BuCorp. file #3235, Pt. 1.

44. L. Stewart to M. Stewart, Oct. 12, 1903, Stewart R.

45. M. Stewart to L. Stewart, Nov. 14, 1903, L. Stewart to M. Stewart, Nov. 11, 1903, Stewart R.

46. (L. Stewart) to J. S. Torrance, Dec. 16, 1903, L. Stewart to M. Stewart, Dec. 26, 1903, Stewart R.

47. M. Stewart to L. Stewart, Jan. 6 and 7, 1904, Stewart R.

48. L. Stewart to M. Stewart, Feb. 10, 1904, Stewart R; L. Stewart interview by J. R. Garfield, May 1, 1905, NA BuCorp. file #3402, Pt. 1, pp. 5-6; *US* v. *SONJ*, XXI, 101-08.

In 1908, during the antitrust suit, H. M. Tilford was sharply questioned regarding this restriction on manufacturing light products. Tilford denied having seen the original contract and stated, if he had a copy, it must have been among records sent to S.F. to replace those lost in the earthquake and fire. He also stated he could not recall how the restriction worked. True or not, the contract was reviewed in N.Y. for legality. A month after it was signed, M. F. Elliott of the Legal Dept. wrote Tilford, "I do not think its provisions are violative of any law of California." But he added, "It would not be proper to make such a contract to be executed in some of the western and southern states. The next time you are in my room, please call my attention to this matter." (*US* v. *SONJ*, III, 1465-66, XVII, 3510-12; M. F. Elliott to H. M. Tilford, Mar. 10, 1904, Elliott R.)

49. Page to O'Day, Nov. 8 and Dec. 7, 1904, O'Day R; Welty and Taylor, *op. cit.*, 97.

50. J. F. Goodwin to E. W. Clark, Feb. 20, 1905, Breeden to Goodwin, Feb. 28, 1905, Pinal R; Western Union agreement of Mar. 3, and Pinal agreement of Mar. 7, 1905, Secy. R, SONJ; M. R. Venable interview by Eddy, Oct. 16, 1905, NA BuCorp. file #3220, Pt. 5 and C. D. Barnes interview by Earl, June 19, 1905, NA BuCorp. file #3220, Pt. 3.

51. M. Fleisher and T. R. Finley interviews by Earl, July 17, 1905, NA BuCorp. file #3220, Pts. 2 and 5, respectively. The wholesale price of 25¢ a gal. for gasoline claimed by Finley is not supported by other evidence. For Dec., 1904, the Comr. of Corps. reported the average price of stove gasoline to Calif. retailers, less freight, as 16.1¢; S.O. Iowa's average for all naphthas for the second half of 1904 was 15.6¢, and the refinery's average price to S.O. Iowa during 1904 was 8.7¢ (*Rpt. of the Comr. of Corps. on the Pet. Industry* [1907], Pt. II, 518; SO[Iowa]/PCO Statements; PCO Analysis of Business, 1904, Comptr. R, SONJ).

52. Page to O'Day, Mar. 13, 1905, O'Day R.

53. P/L Chronology, P/L R; title files, Treas. R; deposition of J. M. Atwell, Sep. 30, 1930, in *US* v. *State of Calif.*, #1679 in the US Land Office, Sac., X, 2652.

54. Construction rpts., Mfg. R; inspection record, Feb. 27, Sep. 30, 1905, Pub. Rel. R; Scofield interview by Conant, May 19, 1905, NA BuCorp. file #3232, p. 6; G. E. Bridgett interview by J. W. Smith, May 2, 1957; *Nautical Gazette*, Nov. 29, 1906.

55. Rheem to Scofield, July 21, 1902, inspection record, Feb. 27, Sep. 30, 1905, Pub. Rel. R; construction rpts., Mfg. R; Brooks ms., "Crude Stills," 1-2, 5.

56. Page to O'Day, May 15, 1905, O'Day R. The Richmond Belt Railway was incorporated Aug. 19, 1902 by Wm. S. Tevis, Clinton E. Worden, Horace D. Pillsbury, Wakefield Baker, and J. V. de Laveaga. However, the *Nat. Oil Reporter* also included H. C. Breeden, D. G. Scofield, and E. S. Pillsbury among the organizers. Its object was a twenty-mile railroad from PCO's spur, up the east side of the peninsula around the northern tip and part of the way down the west side, this section serving three docks to be built into the Bay. (Art. of Incorporation, Secy. of State (Calif.) R; *Nat. Oil Reporter*, Dec. 4, 1902, p. 8.)

57. O'Day to Page, Sep. 25, 1905, H. M. Tilford to Scofield, Sep. 26, 1905, Payne to Scofield, Dec. 13, 1906, Scofield R; monthly rpts., P/L R; O. O. Allen interview by J. W. Smith, Feb. 11, 1958.

58. H. M. Tilford to Scofield, May 16 and Oct. 3, 1906, Scofield to Tilford, Aug. 14, 1906, Certificates of Increase of Capital Stock, Secy. R; O'Day to Page, Sep. 25, 1905, O'Day R; PCO Minutes, Mar. 20, 1906; Hidy and Hidy, *op. cit.*, 459, 608-09.

59. PCO Minutes, 1905-06; J. C. Rohlfs interview by G. T. White, Aug. 30, 1955.

60. See Appendix B; also Yields and Costs, 1906-07, Mfg. R.

61. *S.F. Examiner*, Apr. 15, 1956; *S.F. News*, Apr. 17, 1956.

62. *Standard Oiler*, Mar., 1956, pp. 13-14.

63. Scofield to H. M. Tilford, Apr. 19, 23 and 25, 1906, Scofield R. The temporary PCO headquarters were located in an eight-room cottage and a "large, old fashioned house of 17 rooms" at 1028 10th St.; the SO(Iowa) headquarters were nearby at 1160 Broadway.

64. Scofield to H. M. Tilford, Apr. 20, 1906, and to Rogers, May 8, 1906, Rockefeller to Scofield, Apr. 19, 1906, Scofield R; Rogers to Scofield, Apr. 20, 1906, H. M. Tilford to Scofield, Apr. 24, 1906, Merrill to Miller, Nov. 11, 1907, Hist. R.

65. Scofield to H. M. Tilford, Apr. 23, 1906, Scofield R; Rheem to Scofield, May 7, 1906 and Scofield to Rockefeller, May 8, 1906, Hist. R.

66. Merrill to W. S. Miller, Nov. 11, 1907, Hist. R.

67. Scofield to H. M. Tilford, Apr. 23, 1906, Scofield R.

XI. REFINING FOR NEW MARKETS

1. Hidy and Hidy, *op. cit.*, 259-68, 498, 547-52. In May and June, 1902, when samples of Japanese crudes were tested at Alameda, two of the four samples proved very difficult to refine (Rheem to Scofield, July 5, 1902, Pub. Rel. R).

2. Rheem to Scofield, Oct. 20 and Nov. 11, 1902, Pub. Rel. R; Inspection Record (Apr. 1, 1904–Feb. 25, 1905), Hist. R; Baker to L. Stewart, Sep. 14, 1904, Stewart R; B. C. Wright, *The West the Best and California the Best of the West* (S.F., 1913), 98.

3. Brooks ms., "Point Orient," 2-4; Scofield to H. M. Tilford, May 7, 1907, and Belt Railway contract, Secy. R.

PCO acquired the 30-acre tract from the East Shore Co. which, like the Richmond Belt Railway, was a Wm. S. Tevis-Scofield-Breeden-Pillsbury-C. E. Worden enterprise. Incorporated on Dec. 16, 1901, East Shore had acquired most of the peninsula that jutted north into the Bay from the refinery. In a supplemental agreement, Richmond Belt promised to carry PCO's freight to Pt. Orient at a reasonable rate and to provide morning and evening passenger service. Probably to avoid a conflict of interest, the negotiations for the land were handled by A. C. Bedford of Jersey Standard. If the negotiations began in April, they would have been in progress at the time Page accused Breeden of favoring the Belt Railway, an incident mentioned in the previous chapter.

4. Brooks ms., "Point Orient," 2-7; *The Guide,* June 18, 1906, Sep. 5, 1906; *S.O. Bulletin,* Sep., 1929, inside cover; Orchard Lisle, *Tanker Technique, 1700-1936* (London, 1936), 38; Hidy and Hidy, *op. cit.,* 52, 228.

5. Pt. Orient Inspection Bk., 1906-1930, Pub. Rel. R; *The Guide,* Dec. 13, 1906, Mar. 21, 1907, Apr. 6, 1908; Hidy and Hidy, *op. cit.,* 532, 551; Basil Lubbock, *Coolie Ships and Oil Sailors* (Glasgow, 1935), 118, 134; Wright, *op. cit.,* 99.

6. Brooks ms., "Point Orient," 1, 6-24.

7. Construction Rpts., Mfg. R; Brooks ms., "Crude Stills," 4-5; Hidy and Hidy, *op. cit.,* 414, 498.

8. Scofield to H. M. Tilford, Apr. 27, 1908, O. O. Allen to J. W. Smith, July 23, 1960, Hist. R; Morrow to Scofield, June 18, 1906, and Outside Refinery rpts., Econ. R; monthly rpts., P/L R; Brooks ms., "Refined Depts.," 10.

9. H. M. Tilford to Scofield, July 11, 1906, and R. C. Warner to Geo. Chesebro, Aug. 13, 1906, P/L R; O. O. Allen interview by J. W. Smith, Feb. 11, 1958; Brooks ms., "Refined Dept.," 10, 12.

10. Scofield to H. M. Tilford, Apr. 27, 1908, Hist. R; monthly rpts., P/L R.

11. J. J. Carter diary, Nov. 9, 1906, Carter R; Scofield to W. Young, Dec. 28, 1906, Eckbert to Carter, Feb. 17, 1908, (Sutro) to Scofield, Mar. 23, 1908, Scofield to Carter, Apr. 28, 1908, memo. by A. C. McLaughlin, May 21, 1914, Hist. R; Scofield to R. C. Warner, Feb. 26, 1907, monthly rpts., P/L R; Field Operations rpts., Econ. R; W. A. Spinks interview by Earl, May 2, 1905, NA BuCorp, file #3220, Pt. 1; Conant Rpt., 44.

12. Hughes to J. F. Goodwin, Jan. 17, 1907, and Tietzen and Fleisher to Goodwin, Feb. 13, 1907, Pinal R; monthly rpts., P/L R.

13. W. S. Porter to Pinal, Feb. 18, 1907, and Pinal to Porter, Feb. 20, 1907, T. Hughes to Goodwin, Feb. 20, 1907, Goodwin to P. C. Drescher, Feb. 26, 1907, to T. Hughes, Feb. 26, 1907, Pinal R; H. G. Morrow to Scofield, Mar. 12, 1907, Econ. R; Associated distillate contract, Oil Pur. & Exch. R; *L.A. Times,* Feb. 17, 1907; CSMB *Bul. #19* (1900), 169.

14. Scofield to W. Young, Apr. 19, 1907, Eckbert to J. J. Carter, Feb. 17, 1908, Hist. R; Tietzen and Fleisher to Goodwin, Feb. 13, 1907, Fleisher to Goodwin, Mar. 24, 1907, Goodwin to Fleisher and Tietzen, Apr. 1, 1907, to Scofield, Apr. 9, 1907, and Pinal contracts of Apr. 19 and May 1, 1907, Pinal R; Field Operations rpts., Econ. R; Scofield to John Lawson, June 15, 1916, Scofield R.

15. *Drake* data booklet, CSC R; Pinal contract of Apr. 19, 1907, Pinal R; monthly rpts., P/L R; *Nautical Gazette,* Nov. 29, 1906.

16. H. G. Morrow to Scofield, June 6, 1906, W. M. Weller to Wm. Edwards, Sep. 3, 1907, Field Operations rpts., Outside Refinery rpts., Econ. R; E. A. Starke to Scofield, Mar. 12, 1907, Expl. R; vouchers, 1908, Hist. R; *Oil Investors' J.,* Jan. 3 and Sep. 5, 1907. The *Catania* was owned by the Coast Oil Transport Co. whose Gen. Mgr., Louis Phillips, held the same position in Calif. Petroleum Refineries, Ltd. (*S.F. Directory, 1907*).

17. H. G. Morrow to Scofield, June 6 and Nov. 26, 1906, W. M. Weller to Wm. Edwards, Sep. 3, 1907, and Field Operations rpts., Outside Refineries rpts., Econ. R; Scofield to H. M. Tilford, Apr. 27, 1908, Hist. R; *Calif. Oil World,* July 8, 1909; F. C. Gerretson, *History of the Royal Dutch* (Leiden, 1957), III, 206-10. Another version of the story has the Oilport refinery delivering fuel oil to S.F. to fuel the Toyo ships (*Oil Investors' J.,* Sep. 5, 1907, pp. 21-22).

The *Engr. & Min. J.* of Dec. 14, 1907, reported that Graciosa was unable to fill a 10,000,000 bbl. contract with the Japanese government which it had signed a year earlier. Union and Associated each had an option on a third of the contract but, in view of the advance in crude prices, were not expected to exercise their options. To fill the contract, Graciosa would have had to buy high-priced oil and lose $1,000,000.

18. H. G. Morrow to Scofield, June 18 and Nov. 26, 1906, Econ. R; monthly rpts., P/L R; Wallace M. Morgan, *History of Kern County California* (L.A., 1914), 165-66.

19. Lufkin to J. D. Archbold, Dec. 22, 1902, Hist. R; H. M. Tilford to Scofield, Jan. 3, 1907, P/L R; testimony of W. H. Berg, Jan. 26, 1931 in *SO Cal.* v. *US,* #8985 in US Cir. Ct. of Appeals for the 9th Cir., transcript, VIII, 2763; H. A. Forsburg interview by R. B. Bartlett, Jan. 14, 1952; *S.F. Chronicle,* Jan. 19, 1907; Lionel B. Redpath, *Petroleum in California* (L.A., 1900), 115.

20. (?) to F. T. Perris, Aug. 2, 1907, Storey to Scofield, Jan. 6, 1908, Hist. R; H. A. Forsburg interview by R. B. Bartlett, Jan. 14, 1952; monthly rpts., P/L R; *Bakersfield Californian,* Mar. 16, July 16, Aug. 7, Oct. 27, 1907, and Jan. 23, 1908; Morgan, *op. cit.,* 167.

21. Scofield to H. M. Storey, Mar. 11, 1907, P/L R; *Bakersfield Californian,* Apr. 13 and Aug. 7, 1907.

22. Walker to H. P. Wilson, Secy., Great Western Power Co., Feb. 25, 1907, Secy. R, SONJ; H. G. Morrow to Scofield, Mar. 12, 1907, Econ. R; Interstate Commerce Commission, *In the Matter of Rates . . . Testimony taken by the ICC at S.F., Calif., Oct. 2, 3, 4, 1907* (1907), 102, 106-07; *Oil Investors' J.,* Sep. 5, 1907, p. 21; *World Pet.,* Aug., 1937, p. 50.

23. Scofield to Pillsbury, May 18, 1907, Hist. R; monthly rpts., P/L R.

24. Scofield to H. M. Tilford, Apr. 27, 1908, and J. J. Carter, Apr. 28, 1908, Hist. R; monthly rpts., P/L R; Yields and Costs, Mfg. R; Amalgamated contract, Oil Pur. & Exch. R; Brooks ms., "Refined Depts.," 17, and "Crude Stills," 9.

25. Scofield to H. M. Tilford, Apr. 27, 1908, Hist. R; monthly rpts., P/L R.

26. Moffett to Scofield, July 16 and Aug. 12, 1908, Scofield to Moffett, July 24, 1908, Scofield R; *L.A. Herald,* July 21 and 24, 1907; Hidy and Hidy, *op. cit.,* 399-401.

27. Brooks ms., "Refined Dept.," 40; *Calif. Oil World,* Apr. 9, 1925, p. 3, and Apr. 30, 1925, p. 3; Hidy and Hidy, *op. cit.,* 401, 532.

28. G. H. Mayer interview by G. T. White, Oct. 23, 1958; Yields and Costs, Mfg. R; Brooks ms., "Crude Stills," 18; R. A. Deustua, "Industria Petrolifera en el Peru," *Boletin de la Sociedad Geografice de Lima,* XXVIII (1912), 40-44, 48-52, 97; V. F. Marsters, "Oil Resources of Peru," *Trans. of the Am. Inst. of Min. and Met. Eng.,* LXVIII (1922), 1049; Hidy and Hidy, *op. cit.,* 529, 785, note 16; Gerretson, *op. cit.,* IV, 224; George S. Gibb and Evelyn H. Knowlton, *The Resurgent Years, 1911-1927* (N.Y., 1956), 95.

29. Memo. by A. C. McLaughlin, May 21, 1914, Hist. R; monthly rpts., P/L R; *Oil Investor's J.,* Apr. 20, 1909, p. 21.

30. *Bakersfield Californian,* May 6, 1909; *Oil Investors' J.,* May 20, 1909, p. 23; *Calif. Oil World,* May 27, 1909.

31. L. Stewart to R. W. Fenn, June 3, 1909, Stewart R.

32. L. Stewart to M. Stewart, June 21, 1909, Stewart R. Stewart's statement that Union would furnish the cash and receive all the stock and bonds differs from a press report that the producers would put up a large part of the money and take the bulk of the stock (*Calif. Derrick,* June, 1909, p. 5).

33. *Bakersfield Californian,* June 16, 1909; *Calif. Oil World,* June 3, 17, 24, July 7 and 15, 1909; Welty and Taylor, *op. cit.,* 10.

34. Pit Hole and Treatment Record, and monthly rpts., P/L R.

35. Monthly rpts., P/L R; *Calif. Oil World,* Aug. 19, 1909, and June 4, 1925.

36. Condition of Operations, Prod R; monthly rpts., P/L R; *L.A. Examiner,* Apr. 3, 1910.

37. Scofield to H. M. Tilford, Mar. 7, 1910, Scofield R.

38. Monthly rpts., P/L R; *Rpt. of the FTC on the Pac. Coast Pet. Industry* (Wash., 1921), Pt. II, 21; Welty and Taylor, *op. cit.,* 112.

39. Brooks ms., "Refined Dept.," 10-12, 15, "Gas Agitators," 1-5.

40. Yields and Costs, Mfg. R; Brooks ms., "Refined Dept.," 10, "Gas Agitators,"

5, "Crude Stills," 10-16; L. Stewart to M. Stewart, June 11, 1908, Stewart R. Although Standard's contract with Union was 522,000 bbls. short of completion, Union stopped deliveries after Sep., 1909. Standard protested the breach of contract without avail. (S.O. Minutes, Jan. 25, 1910; monthly rpts., P/L R.)

41. Yield and Costs, Mfg. R; Ann. Sales Statements; *S.O. Bulletin,* Nov., 1913, pp. 2-3; Hidy and Hidy, *op. cit.,* 552-53.

42. Starke to Scofield, Nov. 9, 1907, Pub. Rel. R; Yields and Costs, Mfg. R; Brooks ms., "Refined Dept.," 8, "Paraffine Dept.," 6. The comparison of Santa Maria and Coalinga gasoline content is drawn from refinery experience two years later; while the figures may not parallel exactly those for other times, they show the relative merit of the crudes for gasoline (Brooks ms., "Refined Dept.," 27-28).

43. Yields and Costs, Mfg. R; Brooks ms., "Refined Dept.," 14, 23; Gerretson, *op. cit.,* III, 280; Hidy and Hidy, *op. cit.,* 502, 781, note 41.

44. Brooks ms., "Refined Dept.," 42, "Wharves," 16; Gerretson, *op. cit.,* 281-83; Hidy and Hidy, *op. cit.,* 502.

45. Brooks ms., "Refined Dept.," 41-43, "Crude Stills," 21.

46. Yields and Costs, Mfg. R; Brooks ms., "Paraffine Dept.," 5-6.

47. Brooks ms., "Paraffine Dept.," 7-8.

48. *Ibid.,* 7, 11-13; J. B. Terry to J. W. Smith, Apr. 23, 1956, Hist. R; Yields and Costs, Mfg. R; Hidy and Hidy, *op. cit.,* 486.

49. Yields and Costs, Mfg. R; Brooks ms., "Paraffine Dept.," 8-9; Gerretson, *op. cit.,* IV, 163.

50. Yields and Costs, Mfg. R; Brooks ms., "Paraffine Dept.," 12-15.

51. Yields and Costs, Mfg. R; Brooks ms., "Crude Stills," 7-8, "Refined Dept.," 30, 35-40, "Paraffine Dept.," 17, 20.

XII. THE RISING TIDE OF COMPETITION

1. SO(Iowa) Statements; Newhall statements, Hist. R.

2. Newhall statements, Hist. R; PCO Minutes, Dec. 3, 1901; SO(Iowa) Statements.

3. Construction Rpts., Mfg. R; SO(Iowa)/PCO statements; Geo. E. Bridgett interview by J. W. Smith, May 2, 1957; *Pac. Oil Reporter,* Jan. 3, 1903. Curiously, the *Nat. Oil Reporter,* Sep. 18, 1902, mentioned purchase of a site on Tacoma's tide flats from the St. Paul and Tacoma Lumber Co. to establish a marine terminal for the Northwest. But at that time a Seattle terminal was built. Perhaps both sites were under consideration before Seattle was chosen.

4. Rheem to Scofield, June 26, 1902; Construction Rpt., June 30, 1903, Mfg. R; Brooks ms., "Wharves," 1; *S.O. Bulletin,* Dec., 1915, p. 5.

5. SO(Iowa)/PCO statements; salary histories, Comptr. R, SONJ; interviews, Henry King, May 15, 1905, and Fred King, May 25, 1905, by Earl, NA BuCorp. file #3299, Pt. 3; H. D. Foster interview by J. W. Smith, Jan. 21, 1956.

6. Page to O'Day, Jan. 14, 1904, O'Day R; SO(Iowa)/PCO Statements; Construction Rpts., Mfg. R.

7. W. L. Stewart to L. Stewart, Nov. 24 and 25, 1903, Stewart R.

8. Breeden interview by Conant, May 20, 1905, NA BuCorp. file #3231 and subsequent statement submitted "about August, 1905," file #3448; *Rpt. of the Comr. of Corps. on the Transp. of Pet., May 2, 1906,* 18.

9. Interviews, Allen Craig, June 28, 1905, E. L. Doheny and C. B. Anderson, June 24, 1905, all by Earl, NA BuCorp. file #3220, Pt. 4.

10. Amalgamated contract, Oil Pur. & Exch. R; monthly rpts., P/L R; SO(Iowa)/PCO Statements; Inspection Record, Hist. R; Conant Rpt., 238-39; Breeden statement "about August, 1905," NA BuCorp. file #3448, Pt. 2.

11. SO(Iowa)/PCO Statements; G. H. Mayer interview by G. T. White, Oct. 23, 1958; Breeden interview by J. R. Garfield, Apr. 27, 1905, NA BuCorp. file #3231.

12. L. Stewart to M. Stewart, Feb. 10, 1904, Baker to L. Stewart, June 22, 1904, Stewart R; L. Stewart interview by Garfield, May 1, 1905, NA BuCorp. file #3402, Pt. 1; Conant Rpt., 151.

13. L. Stewart to W. G. Hughes, June 2, 1905, and to M. Stewart, July 29, 1905, W. L. Stewart to L. Stewart, Aug. 17 and Sep. 2, 1905, Baker to L. Stewart, July 29,

1905, Stewart R; L. Stewart interview by Conant and Earl, June 15, 1905, NA BuCorp. file #3402, Pt. 1; SO(Iowa)/PCO Statements.

14. Monthly rpts., P/L R; SO(Iowa)/PCO Statements; voucher, June, 1910, Hist. R; SO(Calif.) Minutes, Jan. 25, 1910.

15. *US* v. *SONJ,* Petitioner's Exhibits 388 and 389, VIII, 918-19.

16. Ann. Rpt. on Outside Refineries, Econ. R; Scofield interview by Conant, May 19, 1905, NA BuCorp. file #3232, pp. 27-29; J. V. Bacigalupi interview by Conant, June 19, 1905, and M. W. Turner interview by Earl, July 3, 1905, NA BuCorp. file #3299, Pt. 7; H. E. Graves interview by Conant, July 8, 1905, NA BuCorp. file #3323; testimony of H. M. Tilford, Dec. 4, 1908, in *US* v. *SONJ,* XVII, 3500-01; *Nat. Oil Reporter,* July 10, 1902; P. W. Prutzman, *Production & Use of Pet. in Calif.,* CSMB Bul. #32 (1904), 209; Hidy and Hidy, *op. cit.,* 475.

17. Graves to Miller, Feb. 21 and 25, 1903, Graves R; NA BuCorp. file #3323.

18. J. A. Graves to Breeden, Nov. 25 and 30, Dec. 8 and 10, 1903, Graves R; *Bakersfield Californian,* Mar. 8, 1904, *Fullerton Tribune,* Aug. 25, 1904.

19. NA BuCorp. file #3323.

20. H. E. Graves interview by Conant, June 21, 1905, NA BuCorp. file #3323, pp. 1, 3; *US* v. *SONJ,* Petitioner's Exhibit 319, VIII, 704; Beaton, *op. cit.,* 221.

21. SO(Iowa)/PCO Statements; Breeden interview by Garfield, Apr. 28, 1905, NA BuCorp. file #3231, pp. 2-3; H. E. Graves interview, pp. 6, 8, and T. W. Okey's undated memo., NA BuCorp. file #3323. Hugo C. Wasmann, a Standard employee, testified that when he had been employed by Southern Refining and Puente in 1904 and 1906, respectively, he regularly sold below Standard's prices (*US* v. *SONJ,* XVII, 3619-29).

22. Breeden interview by Garfield, Apr. 28, 1905, NA BuCorp. file #3231, pp. 2-3; T. W. Okey interview by Conant, May 6, 1905, and work sheets, NA BuCorp. file #3323; *Rpt. of the Comr. of Corps. on the Pet. Industry* (1907), Pt. II, 834.

23. Conant Rpt., chart opp. p. 348; *Rpt. of the Comr. of Corps. on the Pet. Industry,* Pt. II, 182.

24. J. V. Bacigalupi interview by Conant, June 19, 1905, NA BuCorp. file #3343, Pt. 1; M. W. Turner interview by Earl, July 3, 1905, NA BuCorp. file #3299, Pt. 7.

25. Breeden interview by Garfield, Apr. 27, 1905, NA BuCorp. file #3231, pp. 9, 13; H. E. Graves interview by Conant, July 8, 1905, NA BuCorp. file #3323; SO(Iowa)/PCO Statements; Hidy and Hidy, *op. cit.,* 468.

26. T. Flaherty and A. N. Younglove interviews by Eddy, July 21, 1906, NA BuCorp. file #3376, Pt. 6; SO(Iowa)/PCO Statements; Hidy and Hidy, *op. cit.,* 468.

27. Ann. Rpt. of Outside Refineries, Econ R; Conant Rpt., 356; *US* v. *SONJ,* Petitioner's Exhibit 319, VIII, 704.

28. "Rpt. . . . on the SO Co. (Calif.) . . . to the FTC (Mar., 1920)," Appendix; *S.F. Chronicle,* Mar. 10, 1908.

29. Mktg. Dept. construction rpts., Comptr. R; J. G. Houston (Seattle) contract with Standard, Secy. R; "Tacoma Agency," a brief history written sometime after 1929, Hist. R.

30. Pillsbury to Miller, June 6, 19 and July 17, 1906, Mayer to Miller, June 30 and July 6, 1906, Thompson & Clemons to S.O., Sep. 10, 1907, Pillsbury to Thompson & Clemons, Nov. 7, 1908, *Territory of Hawaii* v. *Sing Yuen,* in the Supreme Ct. of the Terr. of Hawaii.

31. J. H. McEachern to A. K. Stevenson, Oct. 26, 1937, CSC R; Construction Rpts., Mfg. R.

32. Charles Drake interview by A. E. Haase, Apr. 30, 1957; Construction Rpts., Mfg. R; *S.F. Chronicle,* Sep. 24, 1909; *The Lamp,* Aug., 1920, p. 6; *The Ships Bulletin,* July-Aug., 1947, pp. 6-7.

33. Mktg Dept. construction rpts., Comptr. R; "Charlie Watson Red Books," Mktg. R; Ann. Sales Statements; *Highway Statistics, Summary to 1945* (Wash., 1947), 18, 23, 25, 27.

34. SO(Iowa) Minutes, Feb. 3, 1906; "Charlie Watson Red Books," Mktg. R; Harry Nissen interview by J. W. Smith, Oct. 14, 1960; *Among Ourselves,* Aug., 1921, p. 6; *S.O. Bulletin,* June, 1935, p. 3.

35. Ann. Sales Statements; Brooks ms., "Refined Dept.," 13; C. A. Canfield inter-

view by Earl, June 23, 1905, NA BuCorp. file #3220, Pt. 4; Hidy and Hidy, *op. cit.*, 367, 475.

36. Ann. Rpt. of Outside Refineries, Econ. R; Henry King interview by Earl, May 15, 1905, NA BuCorp. file #3299, Pt. 3.

37. Kingsbury ltr. of Apr. 28, 1905 in Lubricating Dept. books of extracts of correspondence on prices, Mktg. R, hereafter cited as Lube Price Bks.; Brooks ms., "Paraffine Dept.," 6.

38. Breeden interview by Garfield, Apr. 27, 1905, p. 8 and by Conant, May 20, 1905, pp. 34-35, NA BuCorp. file #3231; Lube Price Bks.

39. Breeden interview by Garfield, Apr. 27, 1905, NA BuCorp. file #3231, p. 9; Lube Price Bks.

40. Breeden interview by Garfield, Apr. 27, 1905, NA BuCorp. file #3231, p. 8; G. C. Maile interview by G. T. White, May 1, 1957; Lube Price Bks.

41. Lube Price Bks.

42. Ann. Sales Statements; Brooks ms., "Paraffine Dept.," 18.

XIII. WILDCATTING FOR SECURITY

1. Walton Young to Scofield, Mar. 30, 1906, to W. J. Sayward, Mar. 31, 1906, to J. J. Carter, May 14, 1908, to J. M. Atwell, July 11, 1908, Hist. R; Starke to Scofield, Sep. 1, 1908, Expl. R; Data Prepared for US Sen. Com. (La Follette investigation), Jan. 31, 1923, Table 1, Secy. R, hereafter cited as Data for La Follette Com.; *US* v. *SONJ*, Defendants' Exhibit 284, XIX, 683.

2. M. Stewart to L. Stewart, Jan. 15 and 27, 1900, Nov. 14, 1907, Stewart R; J. J. Carter Diary, Nov. 9, 1906, and Mar. 1, 1907, Carter R. The Producing Dept. was established officially on Jan. 1, 1907, with Eckbert as Mgr. (Scofield to Young, Dec. 28, 1906, Hist R). On Carter, see also "Colonel Carter's Diaries," *The Link*, Sep.-Oct., 1956, pp. 1-3; *O.&G.J.*, Jan. 11, 1917; *Derrick's Hand-Book*, I, 856-57; A. R. Crum, *Romance of American Petroleum and Gas* (Oil City, 1911), 264-66.

3. J. M. Atwell to Eckbert, May 27, 1907, Eckbert to Carter, Feb. 17, 1908, memos. entitled "Properties Purchased and Leased Since Jan. 1, 1907," and "Coalinga 28 Property," Hist. R; Field Operations rpt., Econ. R.

4. Carter Diary, Mar. 23 and 24, 1907, Carter R; Eckbert to Carter, Feb. 17, 1908, Hist. R.

5. Carter Diary, May 27, 1908, Carter R; Eckbert to Carter, Feb. 17, 1908, Starke statement to Oscar Lawler, Nov. 4, 1929, Hist. R.

6. Eckbert to Young, May 16, 1907, Hist. R; Storey to Scofield, Oct. 23, 1907, Eckbert to Scofield, Oct. 30, 1907, Expl. R; deposition of Atwell, Sep. 30, 1930, in *US* v. *State of Calif.*, #1679 in the US Land Office, Sac., X, 2649-53, hereafter cited as *US* v. *Calif.*; L. B. Little interview by J. W. Smith, Feb. 13, 1958.

7. Eckbert to Carter, Feb. 17, 1908, Hist. R.

8. Starke statement to Lawler, Nov. 4, 1929, and a memo. entitled "Properties Purchased and Leased Since Jan. 1, 1907," Hist. R.

9. Carter to Archbold, Apr. 14, 1905, Archbold R; Archbold to Carter, June 3, 1907, (Howard) Cole to Carter (undated), and entries of Jan. 14 and 17, 1908, all in Carter Diary; *The Link*, Sep.-Oct., 1956, p. 2; Hidy and Hidy, *op. cit.*, 498.

10. Carter Diary, Feb. 14 and 16, 1908, Carter R; note in Carter Diary (undated), Hist. R.

11. Carter to H. M. Tilford, Feb. 27 and May 23, 1908, Tilford to Carter, Mar. 2, 1908, Hist. R.

12. Carter to J. F. Eckbert, Mar. 3, 1908, and to G. A. Eckbert, Mar. 11, 1908, Carter Diary, May 27, 28, 29, 1908, Hist. R.

13. Carter to Archbold, Apr. 8 and 10, 1908, to Moffett, Apr. 9, 1908, to H. M. Tilford, Apr. 10, 1908, Hist. R.

14. Starke to Carter, Apr. 14, 1908, Hist. R.

15. Tilford to Carter, Apr. 24, 1908, Hist. R.

16. Carter Diary, Mar. 31 and Apr. 1, 1908, Hist. R; Carter to Archbold, Apr. 19, 1905, Archbold R.

17. Starke statement to Lawler, Nov. 4, 1929, Hist. R; *O.&G.J.*, Sep. 17, 1914, pp. 28-29.

18. Lufkin to Archbold, Jan. 26, 1903, Eckbert to Carter, Feb. 17, 1908, Carter Diary, Apr. 1, 1908, Starke statement to Lawler, Nov. 4, 1929, Hist. R.

19. Carter to Tilford, Apr. 10, 1908, Hist. R; KT&O Monthly Rpt. Maps, Prod. R.

20. Carter Diary, Apr. 2 and 3, 1908, Carter to Tilford, Apr. 10, 1908, Hist. R.

21. Carter Diary, Apr. 4 and 5, 1908, Carter to Archbold, Apr. 10, 1908, Hist. R. The 50,000-acre figure Carter used must have included options as well as leases and purchases (Lease Record, Land R).

22. Carter Diary, Apr. 8 and 9, 1908, Carter to H. M. Tilford, Apr. 10, 1908, Hist. R.

23. Carter to Tilford, Apr. 10, 1908, Gen. Order #1 and Sp. Order #1, Apr. 11, 1908, Carter Diary, Apr. 13 and 16, 1908, Hist. R; Carter to Archbold, Apr. 19, 1905, Archbold R.

24. Carter Diary, Apr. 17, 1908, Carter to Archbold, Apr. 17, 1908, Hist. R.

25. Carter to Atwell, Apr. 16, 1908, to Tilford, Apr. 30, 1908, H. M. Tilford to Carter, Apr. 24, 1908, Carter Diary, Apr. 21-24, 1908, Hist. R.

26. Carter diary (undated), 1908, Hist. R.

27. Scofield to Tilford, Apr. 27, 1908, Carter Diary, Apr. 29, 1908, Hist. R.

28. Carter to Scofield, Apr. 30, 1908, Hist. R.

29. H. M. Tilford to Carter, Apr. 30, 1908, Carter to Tilford, May 1, 1908, Scofield to E. S. Pillsbury, May 1, 1908, Hist. R. The Talara lease was owned by two officers of the Associated Oil Co., W. S. Porter and O. Scribner, who had agreed early in 1907 to deliver 750,000 bbls. to Standard. At that time Standard was laying its pipeline to Midway; Associated did not have a line to the field, and the owners had to drill their property to protect it from loss to neighboring wells. (Scofield to Pillsbury, May 1, 1908, Tilford to Carter, May 4, 1908, Carter to Pillsbury, May 5, 1908, Hist. R.)

30. Carter to Archbold, May 1, 1908, Carter Diary, May 1, 1908, Hist. R.

31. Carter Diary, May 7, 1908, Hist. R.

32. Tilford to Carter, May 5, 1908, Archbold to Carter, May 7, 1908, Carter to Tilford, May 8 and 23, 1908, Carter Diary, May 11-15 and 19, 1908, Hist. R.

33. Carter Diary, May 18-25, 1908, Carter to Eckbert, May 25, 1908, Hist. R.

34. Gen. Order #2, May 23, 1908, Snively to Lawler, Mar. 18, 1930, and Snively statement to Lawler, Mar. 21, 1930, Hist. R; Carter Diary, May 23, 1908, Carter R.

35. Carter to H. M. Tilford, May 26, 1908, Hist. R.

36. Carter Diary, June 17, 1908, Hist. R. Carter offered Archbold "the Matson oil property," but he did not care to consider it. The timing seems a few months early to be the Midway property which became the Honolulu Oil Company.

37. Carter Diary, June 17, 18, and 19, 1908, Hist. R.

38. Carter Diary, July 8, 1908, Carter R; Scofield to Young, July 29, 1908, Eckbert-Jones agreements of Aug. 20, 1908, and May 25, 1909, Hist. R; L. Stewart to M. Stewart, Oct. 28, 1908, Stewart R; *O.&G.J.*, Aug. 14, 1913, p. 26.

39. "Record of Work, June 1, 1908, to Jan. 1, 1911, H. Norman Snively," Hist. R; deposition of G. C. Gester, Nov. 18, 1930, in *US* v. *Calif.*, XIII, 4441-44; G. C. Gester interview by J. W. Smith, Nov. 21, 1957; *Who Was Who In America* (Chicago, 1950), II, 369.

40. M. Stewart to L. Stewart, Nov. 3, 1902, Stewart R; Carter Diary, Mar. 26, 1908, Hist. R; Condition of Operations rpts., Prod. R; testimony of T. J. Jennings, June 28, 1916, *US* v. *SP*, #46 in the US Dist. Ct. for the So. Dist. of Calif., No. Div., reporter's transcript, XI, 5970-71; L. B. Little to J. E. Gosline, Aug. 12, 1955, Prod. R; Cy Bell interview by J. W. Smith, Feb. 13, 1958; *Oil Investors' J.*, July 6, 1908, p. 24.

41. Condition of Operations rpts., Prod. R; Starke to F. H. Hillman, Mar. 28, 1917, Land R; *L.A. Examiner*, Feb. 16, 1908; *Calif. Oil World*, Sep. 3, Oct. 8 and Dec. 31, 1908.

42. Scofield to Tilford, June 10, 1908, Secy. R; Storey to Scofield, June 18, 1908, Sutro to Scofield, Jan. 5 and 26, 1909, Hist. R; Condition of Operations rpts., Prod. R; *L.A. Times*, July 19, 1908; *Oil Industry*, July, 1908, p. 13.

43. Lease Record, Land R; monthly rpts., P/L R; Condition of Operations rpts.,

Prod. R; interviews, E. M. Delaney by A. E. Haase, May 17, 1957, Warner Clark, Nov. 27, 1957, Cy Bell and L. B. Little, Feb. 14, 1958, all by J. W. Smith; *Calif. Oil World,* Oct. 8, Nov. 5 and Dec. 31, 1908.

44. Atwell to G. H. Derry *et al.,* Feb. 17, 1909, Hist. R; L. B. Little address before the API Div. of Prod., L.A., Mar. 19, 1940; interviews, E. M. Delaney by A. E. Haase, May 17, 1957, P. B. Reed by J. S. Ewing, May 15, 1958, Warner Clark, Nov. 27, 1957, and L. B. Little, Feb. 13, 1958, both by J. W. Smith.

45. Quoted in *Bakersfield Californian,* May 13, 1909.

46. Atwell to Young, Nov. 16, 1909, Hist. R; Bell interview by J. W. Smith, Feb. 13, 1958; *Oil Investors' J.,* Sep. 6, 1909, p. 24; *Calif. Oil World,* Sep. 9, 1909.

47. Interviews, E. M. Delaney by A. E. Haase, May 17, 1957, Bell and Little, Feb. 14, 1958, both by J. W. Smith; Little address before API Div. of Prod., L.A., Mar. 19, 1940.

48. J. C. Donnell to A. C. Bedford, Oct. 15, 1909, Producing payroll index, "Record of Work, June 1, 1908, to Jan. 1, 1911, H. Norman Snively," Hist. R; interviews, Bell and Little, Feb. 13, 1958, both by J. W. Smith; Little address before the API Div. of Prod., L.A., Mar. 19, 1940; US Patent #1,011,484, Dec. 12, 1911 (filed Oct. 27, 1909); *Pet. Reporter,* Souvenir Number, May 21, 1926; J. M. Bugbee, *An Introduction to Oil Well Cement Technology* (Shell Oil Co. publication 18), (Houston, ca. 1958), 3.

49. Starke to Edwards, Jan. 19, 1909, Donnell to A. C. Bedford, Oct. 15, 1909, Hist. R.

50. Starke to Rheem, Nov. 8, 1909, memo., "Dates of Commencement of Wildcat Operations in Midway Flat and Buena Vista Areas," Hist. R; *Bakersfield Californian,* Apr. 7, 1909; *Calif. Oil World,* July 22 and Oct. 14, 1909.

51. Starke to Rheem, Nov. 8, 1909, Starke memo. to Lawler, Nov. 4, 1929, Hist. R; R. B. Moran interview by J. W. Smith, Feb. 12, 1958.

52. Title files, Treas. R; testimony of Edwards, Oct. 1, 1930, in *SO Cal. et al.* v. *US,* #8985 in US Cir. Ct. of Appeals for the 9th Cir., transcript, VII, 2287-91; John Ise, *The United States Oil Policy* (New Haven, 1926), 313.

53. Well file, Prod. R; Starke memo. for Lawler, Nov. 4, 1929, Hist. R; *Calif. Oil World,* Aug. 27, 1908, Jan. 27, 1910.

54. (L. Stewart) to Thomas Cannan, Oct. 18, 1910, Stewart R; *Bakersfield Echo,* Feb. 9, 1910; *L.A. Mining Review,* Feb. 12, 1910; *Calif. Oil World,* Feb. 17 and May 26, 1910; *L.A. Examiner,* Aug. 27, 1910.

55. Snively to Starke, June 14, 1910, Starke to Scofield, Aug. 22, 1910, Geo. T. Ruddock rpt., "Natural Gas in the Great Interior Valley of California," May 11, 1908, "Record of Work, June 1, 1908, to Jan. 1, 1911, H. Norman Snively," Atwell statement to Lawler, Oct. 30, 1929, Hist. R; *Calif. Oil World,* Dec. 23, 1909.

56. Scofield to H. M. Tilford, Sep. 8, 1910, Hist. R; Calif. Natural Gas Co. Minutes, Secy. R, SONJ.

57. *Calif. Oil World,* Sep. 15 and 29, 1910.

58. Photo Album, "Calif. Inspection Trip, Nov., 1909," Carter to Starke, Jan. 9, 1911, Hist. R; *Calif. Oil World,* Nov. 24, 1910; Hidy and Hidy, *op. cit.,* 319-21.

59. (L. Stewart) to R. Watchorn, Aug. 29, 1910, Stewart R; *Calif. Oil World,* Oct. 6 and 13, 1910.

XIV. INDEPENDENCE THROUGH ANTITRUST

1. The background of the S.O. case had been treated many times in a more detailed way than is relevant to the California story. The reader may well be interested in the accounts to be found in Ralph W. and Muriel E. Hidy, *Pioneering In Big Business, 1882-1911* (N.Y., 1955), 639-718; Allan Nevins, *Study in Power: John D. Rockefeller* (N.Y., 1953), II, 328-79; Paul H. Giddens, *Standard Oil Co. (Indiana): Oil Pioneer of the Middle West* (N.Y., 1955), 87-129; also on one aspect, Arthur M. Johnson, *The Development of American Petroleum Pipelines and Public Policy, 1862-1906* (N.Y., 1956), 201-42.

2. M. Stewart to L. Stewart, Sep. 6 and Oct. 26, 1895, Sep. 21, 1900, L. Stewart to M. Stewart, Apr. 26, 1901, Stewart R.

3. J. Baker, Jr., to L. Stewart, Dec. 8, 1902, Stewart R; Hidy and Hidy, *op. cit.,* 651-52.

4. Hidy and Hidy, *op. cit.,* 671-75, 682-83, 695-97.

5. A. M. Johnson, *op. cit.,* 219-35.

6. Winston W. Crouch and Dean E. McHenry, *California Government, Politics and Administration* (Berkeley, 1945), 261-62; Geo. E. Mowry, *The California Progressives* (Berkeley, 1951), 81.

7. *Rpt. of the Comr. of Corps. on the Transp. of Pet., May 2, 1906,* 404-06, 443-44.

8. Hidy and Hidy, *op. cit.,* 679. Italics ours.

9. *Ibid.,* 680; Nevins, *op. cit.,* II, 358-59.

10. *Rpt. of the Comr. of Corps. on the Pet. Industry* (1907), Pt. I, xv-xvi, Pt. II, 666-69; Chm., ICC, to Speaker, H.R., Jan. 28, 1907, in *Railroad Discriminations and Monopolies in Coal and Oil,* 59th Cong., 2d Sess., H. Doc. 606 (1907), 12-14.

11. *Rpt. of the Comr. of Corps. on the Pet. Industry* (1907), Pt. I, 272, Pt. II, 90.

12. Luther Conant, Jr., "Preliminary Report on Oil Investigation In California," NA BuCorp. file #4176, Pt. 3, hereafter cited as Conant Rpt.

13. Breeden interviews by Garfield and Conant, Apr. 27 and 28, 1905, NA BuCorp. file #3231; memo. by Conant (undated) and Conant to Scofield, May 3, 1905, NA BuCorp. file #2852.

14. Memo. by Conant of conversation with Scofield and other representatives of PCO, May 11 and 12, 1905, Conant to Comr. of Corps., May 10 and 12, 1905, J. R. Garfield to Conant, May 18, 1905, V. P. Kline to Garfield, June 24, 1905, NA BuCorp. file #2852; Scofield interview by Conant and Earl, May 19, 1905, NA BuCorp. file #3232.

15. M. F. Elliott to J. R. Garfield, June 12 and July 20, 1905, V. P. Kline to Garfield, June 24, 1905, Garfield to Elliott, July 24, 1905, NA BuCorp. file #2852; E. D. Durand to Comr. of Corps., July 28, 1905, and accompanying docs., NA BuCorp. file #3447; T. C. M. Schindler to Comr. of Corps., Aug. 7, 1905, and accompanying docs., NA BuCorp. file #3448, Pt. 2.

16. The files of interviews with the independent producers are very extensive. See esp. NA BuCorp. files #3220, #3235, #3296 and #3299.

17. Conant to Comr. of Corps., May 18, 1905, NA BuCorp. file #2852, also files #3215 (Associated), #3223 (Santa Fe), #3323 (Puente), #3402 (Union), and interviews with E. Chambers, Traffic Mgr. and W. G. Barnwell, Gen. Freight Agent (Santa Fe) in file #3299, Pts. 1, 2 and 5, and with G. W. Luce, Gen. Freight Agent (SP), #3299, Pt. 3.

18. Conant Rpt., 156-57, 299-300.

19. *Ibid.,* 256-56½; telephone conversation with Secy. Office, SP, July 17, 1959; C. A. Menninger, Secy.-Treas., AT&SF to G. T. White, Aug. 4, 1959, Hist. R.

20. Interviews by Eddy in NA BuCorp. file #3376, Pts. 6 and 7; Conant Rpt., 310-12, 333-64, 367.

21. Conant Rpt., 275.

22. *Ibid.,* 211-18. Monthly rpts., (P/L R) give the Kern stocks for July 31, 1904, as 8,456,000 bbls. and for Aug. 31, 1904, as 8,899,000 bbls. See also Chap. X.

23. Compare, even in the Conant Rpt. (p. 256-56½), Conant's muted charge with what he writes of these railroad-related oil companies (pp. 58-63).

24. Nevins, *op. cit.,* II, 282-87. Rogers (and perhaps also Stillman and Wm. Rockefeller) did not begin to buy into the Santa Fe until about 1904, according to the president of the Santa Fe (Ripley interview by Earl, May 5, 1905, NA BuCorp. file #3223). Rogers also held a directorship in the Union Pacific which, like the SP, was a Harriman railroad.

25. Conant Rpt., 317-33, 365. Beginning in 1913, General Petroleum also operated large topping plants at Vernon and Mojave, but it did not enter the refined products market until after World War I (CSMB *Bul. #69,* [1914], 110-11; *FTC on the Pac. Coast Pet. Industry,* Pt. II, 244-54).

26. Conant Rpt., 300.

27. 221 US 30-31.

28. In 1910 the population of the US was 91,972,000; the population of Calif. Standard's marketing area (Calif., Ore., Wash., Ariz., Nev., Alaska, and the Hawaiian Islands) was 5,060,000.

29. For one of the few editorials, see *S.F. Chronicle,* Nov. 17, 1906.

30. *US* v. *SONJ et al.*, US Cir. Ct., Eastern Dist. of Mo. (Wash., 1908), I, 145-48, II, 732-39, 741-46, III, 1465-66, XVII, 3488-3531, hereafter cited as *US* v. *SONJ; S.F. Bulletin* and *S.F. Chronicle*, both Sep. 21, 1907; *S.F. Examiner* and *L.A. Herald*, both Sep. 21 and Oct. 16, 1907; *S.F. Bulletin* and *L.A. Herald*, both Dec. 8, 1908.

31. *S.F. Bulletin*, May 4, 1906; *S.F. Chronicle* and *S.F. Examiner*, both May 5 and 6, 1906; *L.A. Herald*, May 5, 1906. The headline was unfair to Union, for Union figured to only a minor extent in the Bureau's report. However, Union like other companies, took rebates when it could. We have already noted that M. Stewart wrote his brother Lyman on Feb. 19, 1895, wondering if it wouldn't be well for Union in negotiating a fuel oil contract with the Santa Fe "to make quite a little concession in price, providing they will agree to make a corresponding concession in rates" so that Union could have a better shot at the S.F. market (Stewart R). And Union did get an exclusive rebate from the SP of 25¢ per ton from the open rate of $1.00 on shipments between L.A. and the Port of L.A. as early as 1895 (Memo. of Agreement, F. L. Richardson, Gen. Mgr., Union Oil and G. W. Luce, Asst. Gen. Freight Agent, SP, Sep. 14, 1895, Bard R-HL).

32. Franklin Hichborn, *Story of the Session of the California Legislature of 1909* (S.F., 1909), *Story of the Session of the California Legislature of 1911* (S.F., 1911); Mowry, *op. cit.*

33. *US* v. *SONJ*, XVII, 3391-94, 3405-06, 3619-29.

34. *US* v. *SONJ*, *Pleadings . . . Etc.*, 75; also, Chm., ICC, to Speaker, H.R., H. Doc. 606, *op. cit.*, 8.

35. Testimony of H. E. Felton, Pres., Union Tank Line, *US* v. *SONJ*, XIV, 1819-27, and Defendant's Exhibit #184; *US* v. *SONJ*, *Brief For Defendants On The Facts* (1909), II, 497-501; *Rpt. of the Comr. of Corps. on the Transp. of Pet.*, May 2, 1906, 238-39.

36. *US* v. *SONJ*, *Pleadings . . . Etc.*, 86-88, *Petitioner's Testimony*, V, 2075-80, 2082-85, and Petitioner's Exhibit #635 in X, 1658-59; *Rpt. of the Comr. of Corps. on the Transp. of Pet.*, May 2, 1906, 422-28. The rate charged Standard from Redondo was 7½¢ per hundred lbs. in comparison with 25¢ per hundred lbs. paid by its competitor for the shorter haul from L.A.

37. *US* v. *SONJ*, XVII, 3500-01, 3522, 3619-29; *US* v. *SONJ*, *Brief For Defendants On the Facts* (1909), II, 481-84.

38. *US* v. *SONJ*, II, 734-38, XVII, 3493-95, 3509-22, 3525-29, Petitioner's Exhibit #944.

39. *Ibid.*, II, 733-38, III, 1465-66, XVII, 3512-30; L. Stewart to W. L. Stewart, July 18, 1905, M. Stewart to L. Stewart, Oct. 31, 1907, Stewart R.

40. Production statistics, Econ. R; monthly rpts., P/L R; *SONJ* v. *US*, *Appellants' Brief* (1909), I, 115-17, II, 268-69.

41. 221 US 47.

42. 173 Fed. 185, 189, 197-200.

43. 221 US 73-74, 76, 81.

44. *Ibid.*, 62, 82-106.

45. *S.F. Chronicle* and *S.F. Examiner*, both Nov. 21, 1909; *L.A. Herald*, Nov. 21, 1909; *S.F. Bulletin* and *Bakersfield Californian*, both Nov. 22, 1909.

46. *L.A. Herald, S.F. Examiner*, (S.F.) *J. of Comm., S.F. Chronicle*, all May 16 and 17, 1911; *Bakersfield Californian*, May 15 and 16, 1911; *Calif. Derrick*, III (May 25, 1911), 28.

47. ICC, *In the Matter of Rates . . . Of Carriers Subject to the Act to Regulate Commerce, Testimony taken . . . at S.F., Oct. 2-4, 1907* (1907), 74, 126. Actually, the SP was charged with having favored some 108 shippers. Standard and the Associated were reported as receiving special rates on crude shipments to about ten different stations from Bakersfield, and Standard in a single instance from Coalinga.

48. M. F. Elliott to H. M. Tilford, Nov. 12, 1907, Elliott R; Scofield to W. L. Andrews *et al.*, Dec. 18, 1907, Comptr. R; G. J. Wylie interview by G. T. White, May 13, 1957.

49. *Calif. Oil World*, Apr. 29, 1909.

50. M. F. Elliott to H. M. Tilford, Feb. 5 and Mar. 22, 1907, Elliott R; B. C.

Carroll to Alfred Sutro, Mar. 13, 1907, Hist. R; *S.F. Chronicle,* Jan. 21 and Mar. 13, 1907; *S.F. Examiner,* Mar. 25, 1907.

51. E. S. Pillsbury to Scofield, Apr. 27, 1907, Hist. R.

52. "Memo. Concerning Shipments of Oil By Associated Oil Co. Over Santa Fe Lines in California," May 26, 1908, Pillsbury to Tilford, May 26, 1908, Tilford to Pillsbury, June 2, 1908, W. S. Miller to Pillsbury, June 22, 1908, Hist. R.

53. Statement of Scofield, Oct., 1908, Secy. R.

54. Pillsbury to Oscar Sutro, June 24, 1915, Hist. R.

55. G. C. Maile interview by G. T. White, June 7, 1957; Brooks ms., *passim.*

56. Scofield to Tilford, Mar. 7, 1910, Scofield R.

57. Rheem to Scofield, Feb. 24, 1911, Scofield R.

58. *Ibid.*

59. Data prepared for US Sen. Com. (La Follette investigation), Jan. 31, 1923, Table 1, Secy. R, hereafter cited as Data for La Follette Com.; Inc. Constr. Rpt., June 30, 1910, Comptr. R; Pipe Line Chronology, P/L R.

60. "Analysis of Plant, 1909-1912," Comptr. R; Brooks ms., "Crude Stills," 20-22; photo album, "Calif. Inspection Trip, Nov., 1910," Hist. R; R. P. Hastings interview by G. T. White, July 2, 1958; *O.&G.J.,* Jan. 19, 1911, p. 24; *Calif. Derrick,* III (Feb., 1911), 25.

61. Photo album, "Calif. Inspection Trip, Nov., 1910," Carter to Starke, Dec. 16, 1910, Hist. R; L. Stewart to M. Stewart, Nov. 25, 1910, Stewart R.

62. "Analysis of Plant, 1909-1912," Comptr. R; Pipe Line Chronology, P/L R; *Calif. Derrick,* III (Feb., 1911), 5; Inc. Constr. Rpts., Dec. 30, 1910 and Dec. 30, 1911, Comptr. R.

63. Foster diary, Hist. R; "Analysis of Plant, 1909-1912," Comptr. R; Pipe Line Chronology, P/L R.

64. "Analysis of Plant, 1909-1912," Comptr. R; Brooks ms., "Asphalt Plant," 1-3; Data for La Follette Com., Table 1; *Calif. Derrick,* IV (July 25, 1911), 9.

65. Data for La Follette Com., Table 1; *Calif. Derrick,* IV (July 25, 1911), 9, and (Jan., 1912), 7-8.

66. Interviews, H. D. Collier by A. E. Haase, Feb. 24, 1954, G. C. Maile, May 1, 1957, and G. J. Wylie, May 13, 1957, both by G. T. White.

67. Folger to the stockholders, SONJ, July 28, 1911, reprinted in the *Calif. Derrick,* IV (Aug. 25, 1911), 20. The Supreme Court's decree listed four fewer companies than had the Circuit Court because three of the companies were no longer members of the Standard Oil family and the fourth (Iowa Standard) was in process of liquidation.

68. SO(Calif.) Minutes, Oct. 3, 1911; E. S. Pillsbury to Scofield, Nov. 8, 1911, Scofield R; R. C. Warner interview by G. T. White, Aug. 31, 1955.

69. Statement Showing 14 Largest Shareholders of SONJ, Aug. 31, 1911, Exec. R; Dirs. Ann. Comparative Statement (1925), Comptr. R; BuCorp., *Trust Laws and Unfair Competition* (1916), 17-18; A. W. Atwood, "The Greatest Killing on Wall Street," *McClure's Magazine,* XXXIX (Aug., 1912), 412-13.

70. Moffett to Scofield, Nov. 22, 1911, Scofield R. There are a host of congratulatory letters in the Scofield R.

71. "Ann. Rpt. for 1911," Comptr. R; Gibb and Knowlton, *op. cit.,* 6-7. Net value represents total assets minus current liabilities. N.Y. Standard's net value at the end of 1911 was $60,110,000 (Brochure, Gen. Service Corp., on the SO Companies, May, 1912).

72. Gibb and Knowlton, *op. cit.,* 8-9.

XV. A LOOK AT 200 BUSH

1. Vouchers, June, 1911, Hist. R; E. V. Cary to Scofield, June 5, 1912, Folger and Archbold to Scofield, both June 17, 1912, Scofield R; *Calif. Derrick,* III (May 25, 1911), 11, IV (Apr., 1912), 9.

2. *S.O. Bulletin,* May, 1913, p. 7; *Calif. Derrick,* V (June, 1913), 8.

3. *Calif. Derrick,* V (June, 1913), 8. The data on locations are from the *S.F. Directory, 1913.* On General Petroleum, see E. I. Harrington, "Gen. Pet. Corp.," *Calif. Oil World and Pet. Industry,* July 5, 1937, and three subsequent issues; on Shell, see

Kendall Beaton, *Enterprise In Oil: A History of Shell in the United States* (N.Y., 1957). General Petroleum had been incorporated in Mar., 1910, as the Esperanza Consolidated Oil Company, which at the time of the redesignation in 1912 was still solely a producing company.

4. This section is based largely on interviews, principally with Standard veterans: O. O. Allen, Hilda Anderson, Cyrus Bell, Warner Clark, H. D. Collier, J. H. Duncan, Frank Feuille, Herbert Fleischhacker, Clarence O. Flint, H. A. Forsburg, H. D. Foster, G. C. Gester, H. H. Hall, R. A. Halloran, R. P. Hastings, H. T. Hays, Max Koeppe, E. G. Lawson, H. A. Lehnhardt, L. B. Little, G. C. Maile, Stuart Moser, L. W. Orynski, G. H. Richardson, J. C. Rohlfs, H. M. Shappell, F. H. Stackpole, R. C. Stoner, Tom Summers, J. B. Terry, R. C. Warner, G. J. Wylie. In addition, see for J. M. Atwell, *Standard Oiler*, Feb., 1941, p. 6; L. D. Dimm, *Among Ourselves,* May, 1927, p. 14; H. H. Hall, *Standard Oiler,* Mar., 1945, pp. 14, 23; R. J. Hanna, *S.O. Bulletin,* July, 1919, p. 12 and *Standard Oiler,* Nov., 1947, pp. 7, 22-23; F. H. Hillman, *S.O. Bulletin,* June, 1919, p. 11; K. R. Kingsbury, *ibid.,* May, 1919, p. 12; H. N. Kuechler, *Among Ourselves,* June, 1921, p. 2; W. S. Miller, *S.O. Bulletin,* May, 1919, p. 13; W. S. Rheem, R. D. Hunt, *California and Californians* (Chicago, 1926), V, 93-94; J. C. Rohlfs, *Pacific Marine Review,* July, 1935, p. 203; J. P. Smith, *S.O. Bulletin,* Dec., 1921, p. 4; E. A. Starke, *O.&G.J.,* Aug. 2, 1917, p. 2, *Bul. of the Amer. Assn. of Pet. Geologists,* XVII (July, 1934), 967; H. M. Storey, *S.O. Bulletin,* July, 1919, p. 13; Oscar Sutro, *Nat. Cyclopedia of Amer. Biog.,* XXVIII, 44.

5. SO(Calif.) Minutes, Apr. 10, 1917.

6. Interviews, H. T. Hays, Feb. 11, 1957, by A. E. Haase, H. H. Hall, Mar. 19, 1957, E. G. Lawson, Mar. 25, 1957, both by G. T. White.

7. Vouchers, 1911-1919, Hist. R. E.g., the directors traveled to the Northwest between Oct. 6 and 13, 1912, to Southern Calif., from Apr. 14 to 24, 1914, etc. Throughout this period Kingsbury made extended trips to the East two or three times a year.

8. Monthly Trial Balances, Comptr. R; J. A. Moffett to Scofield, July 26, 1911, Hist. R.

9. Voucher, Nov., 1911, Hist. R; Scofield to Moffett, Feb. 7, 1912, Scofield R.

10. SO(Calif.) Minutes, Dec. 7, 1911.

11. Scofield to Moffett, Feb. 7, 1912, Scofield R.

12. Statement Showing 14 Largest Stockholders of SONJ, Aug. 31, 1911, Exec. R. (The ratio shown in this table also holds for the Calif. company, for each Jersey stockholder received his proportionate share on Dec. 1, 1911 in each disaffiliate); SO(Calif.) Minutes, May 21, 1912.

13. Bedford to Scofield, May 16, 1912, Scofield R; A. R. Crum (ed.), *Romance of American Petroleum and Gas* (Oil City, Pa., 1911), I, 292.

14. Moffett to Scofield, Feb. 2, 1912, Bedford to Scofield, Apr. 26 and June 11, 1912, Scofield R; Scofield to Kingsbury, May 22, 1912, Secy. R.

15. SO(Calif.) Minutes, July 30 and Aug. 6, 1912; Monthly Trial Balances, Comptr. R; Market Quotations, SO(Calif.), 1912, Secy. R.

16. SO(Calif.) Minutes, Nov. 12, 1912; vouchers, Nov. 7, 1912, to May 1, 1913, Hist. R; Scofield to the Stockholders, Mar. 1, 1913, Comptr. R.

17. Pipe Line Chronology, P/L R; Data for La Follette Com., Table 1; *S.O. Bulletin,* Feb., 1914, pp. 1-2.

18. Wm. Edwards to Atwell (undated), Hist. R; F. H. Hillman to W. H. Murphy, Nov. 1, 1913, "Memo., Murphy Oil Co., Lease #171," Prod. R.

19. Data for La Follette Com., Table 1; *S.O. Bulletin,* Feb., 1914, pp. 1-2.

20. SO(Calif.) Minutes, Jan. 6, 1914; Market Quotations—SO(Calif.), 1913, 1914, Secy. R; Summary of Cash Receipts and Disbursements, Jan.-June, 1914, Comptr. R.

21. SO(Calif.) Minutes, Jan. 6, Mar. 16, May 5 and July 14, 1914; PCO Journal, Nov. 30, 1914, p. 85, Comptr. R.

22. *S.O. Bulletin,* Feb., 1914, p. 1; Market Quotations—SO(Calif.), 1914, Secy. R; voucher re advance on May 5, 1914, to Scofield, Jan., 1916, Hist. R.

23. A. W. Atwood, "Greatest Killing in Wall Street," *McClure's Magazine,* XXXIX (Aug., 1912), 414 ff.; Gibb and Knowlton, *op. cit.,* 18-19.

24. Scofield to H. M. Tilford, Apr. 1, 1909, Tilford to Scofield, Apr. 6, 1909, Scofield R.

25. *S.O. Bulletin,* Feb., 1915, p. 2.

26. *L.A. Times,* Apr. 11, 1915.

27. Data bk. on 200 Bush, Office Bldgs. R; Data for La Follette Com., Table 1; *S.O. Bulletin,* Oct., 1915, p. 13, Feb., 1916, p. 1.

28. *S.O. Bulletin,* Feb., 1916, p. 2; Market Quotations—SO(Calif.), 1915, Secy. R.

29. *O.&G.J.,* Jan. 13, 1916, p. 73.

30. SO(Calif.) Minutes, Jan. 18, 1916; *S.O. Bulletin,* Mar., 1916, pp. 1-2.

31. SO(Calif.) Minutes, Jan. 16, 1917; Data for La Follette Com., Table 1; Market Quotations—SO(Calif.), 1916, Secy. R; *S.O. Bulletin,* Jan., 1917, p. 11 and Feb., 1917, p. 1.

32. Wm. Edwards to the Stockholders, Apr. 1, 1912, Comptr. R; H. W. Kull to S. Schackne, SONJ, Aug. 7, 1958, Hist. R; *S.O. Bulletin,* Feb., 1917, p. 1; Gibb and Knowlton, *op. cit.,* 668

33. Bedford to Scofield, Sep. 13, 1912, Scofield R.

34. ICC Docket #4199, *In the Matter of Pipe Lines,* hearing at L.A., Calif., Sep. 20, 1911, Secy. R; ICC Dockett #4199, *In the Matter of Pipelines,* Brief for SO(Calif.) [Mar., 1912], Sutro to Scofield, Dec. 18, 1911, Sutro to Wm. Edwards, Dec. 22 and 26, 1911, Hist. R.

35. Tim Spellacy and J. W. Jameson to F. K. Lane, Feb. 4, 1913, Hist. R; *Calif. Derrick,* V (Oct. 15, 1912), 15-16, and (Jan., 1913), 12; *L.A. Examiner,* Jan. 10, 1913; *O.&G.J.,* Feb. 7, 1919, p. 38.

36. "An Independent View of the Calif. Oil Situation," *S.O. Bulletin,* July, 1914, pp. 1-3.

37. E. S. Pillsbury (by Sutro) to Hon. Julius Kahn, Feb. 19, 1913, Sutro to Messrs. Britton & Gray, Mar. 20, 1913, Hist. R; *L.A. Tribune,* Feb. 4, 1913; *S.F. Chronicle,* Feb. 5, 1913.

38. Sutro to Messrs. Britton & Gray, June 20, 1913, PM&S to Britton & Gray, July 22, 1913, Hist. R; *Cal. Stats.* (1913), 532 and 657.

39. L. Stewart to E. T. Earl, Mar. 13, 1913, Stewart R; *Calif. Derrick,* V (Apr., 1913), 1-2, and VI (July 8, 1914), 6; *O.&G.J.,* Dec. 4, 1913, p. 29; Franklin Hichborn, *Story of the Session of the California Legislature of 1913* (S.F., 1913), 274-83.

40. *Calif. Derrick,* VI (Aug., 1913), 7; *Western Engr.,* III (Sep., 1913), 172; *S.O. Bulletin,* Sep., 1913, p. 1.

41. *O.&G.J.,* Sep. 4, 1913, and Feb. 7, 1919; *Calif. Derrick,* VI (May, 1914), 5; *J. W. Jameson* v. *Producers Transportation Co.,* #1188 before the RR Com. of Calif.

42. SO(Calif.) Minutes, Feb. 24 and Aug. 1, 1919; *Western Engr.* VIII (Dec., 1917), 453.

43. *Calif. Oil World,* Nov. 7, 1914, and Feb. 6, 1915.

44. *L.A. Examiner,* Feb. 24 and Mar. 2, 1916; *L.A. Times,* Feb. 26, 1916; *L.A. Herald,* Feb. 24, Apr. 6, 10 and 19, 1916; *O.&G.J.,* Apr. 27, 1916.

45. *L.A. Times,* Mar. 3, 1916; FTC, *Rpt. on the Price of Gasoline in 1915* (Wash., 1917), 169-70, 197-200. As the basis for the jump in gasoline prices in Calif. in 1916, oilmen pointed to rising crude oil prices, brought about by a decline in Calif. production and an even greater decline in the production of light crudes, while the demand for gasoline continued its steep ascent. California's output of light crude in 1915 had fallen off nearly 19% from the preceding year. At the same time, the demand for gasoline had increased more than 40%. The gain in light crude production in 1916 was only 2%. (*FTC on the Pac. Coast Pet. Industry,* Pt. I, 226, Pt. II, 246; *Calif. Oil World,* Feb. 19, 1916; *Western Engr.,* VI [Mar., 1916], 85-86; *Calif. Derrick,* IX [Mar., 1916], 5; Capt. J. Barneson, Pres., Gen. Pet. Co., to Sen. J. D. Phelan, Mar. 31, 1916 in *S.O. Bulletin,* Apr., 1916, pp. 1-2.)

46. Pillsbury to Scofield, Dec. 14, 1911, Sutro to Scofield, Dec. 21, 1911, Hist. R.

47. Sutro to Wm. Edwards, Jan. 4, 1912, Pillsbury to Sutro, June 24, 1915, Sutro to Pillsbury, June 29, 1915, Hist. R.

48. Pillsbury to Scofield, Sep. 13, 1911, Hist. R; see also Chap. XVII.

49. Sutro to B. C. Carroll, Mar. 16, 1911, Pillsbury to Kingsbury, June 13, 1913, Kingsbury to Pillsbury, June 17, 1913, Hist. R. A year later Kingsbury seriously considered having a Wash., D.C., law firm forward regularly to S.F. copies of all federal laws, executive regulations, rulings, and opinions affecting the oil industry. The scheme

finally broke down because of the sheer bulk of material and the inability of the company to determine upon an effective sifting technique. (Kingsbury to Sutro, Aug. 20, 1914 and Apr. 12, 1915, Sutro to Kingsbury, Aug. 21, 1914, to Messrs. Britton & Gray, Aug. 21, 1914, Britton & Gray to Sutro, Aug. 29 and Nov. 11, 1914, Hist. R.)

50. Kingsbury to Pillsbury, Sep. 11, 1912, Pillsbury to Kingsbury, Sep. 11, 1912, Hist. R.

51. *S.O. Bulletin,* Dec., 1915, p. 14 and Jan., 1916, p. 4.

52. *Calif. Derrick,* III (Apr., 1911), 13; *Calif. Oil World,* Feb. 13, 1913.

53. *Calif. Derrick,* V (Nov. 15, 1912), 10; *Calif. Oil World,* Feb. 13 and Oct. 31, 1913; *O.&G.J.,* Apr. 23, 1914, p. 26, and Apr. 1, 1915, p. 22; *L.A. Times,* ca. Mar. 28, 1915; Welty and Taylor, *op. cit.,* 117-18, 123-24.

54. *S.O. Bulletin,* Aug., 1913, p. 2.

55. *Calif. Derrick,* III (Apr., 1911), 13.

56. *Calif. Oil World,* Feb. 13, 1913.

57. *O.&G.J.,* Apr. 23, 1914, p. 26.

58. Kingsbury to Pillsbury, June 13, 1913, Hist. R; *S.O. Bulletin,* Nov., 1913, p. 10; J. B. Frantz, "The Ann. Rpt. as a Public Relations Tool in Three Industries," *Bul. of the Business Historical Society,* XXIV (May., 1950), 23-42; Gibb and Knowlton, *op. cit.,* 577. Another early house organ was *Sinclair's Magazine (Calif. Derrick,* X [Aug., 1917], 7).

59. *O.&G.J.,* Mar. 4, p. 6, Apr. 29, p. 6, and July 8, 1915, p. 26; *Western Engr.,* VI (July, 1915), 37-38; *Calif. Derrick,* VII (July 10, 1915), 8.

60. Sutro to Pillsbury, June 29, 1915, Hist. R; *Calif. Derrick,* VII (July 10, 1915), 14; *O.&G.J.,* June 17, p. 23, and July 8, 1915, p. 6.

61. Scofield to Bedford, Aug. 25, 1915, Bedford to Scofield, Aug. 30, 1915, Scofield R.

62. *S.O. Bulletin,* June, 1916, p. 6, and Feb., 1917, p. 2; *S.F. Examiner,* June 4, 1916; *Edward Behan* v. *Scofield,* #16122 in US Dist. Ct. for the No. Dist. of Calif., So. Div.

63. Folger to Union Iron Works, May 29, 1916, Pratt to Scofield, May 29, 1916, Payne to Scofield, May 30, 1916, Donnell to Scofield, May 31, 1916, Archbold, Bedford, and Folger to Scofield, all of June 2, 1916, Scofield R.

64. Flint to Scofield, June 2, 1916, Scofield to Flint, June 15, 1916, Scofield R.

65. Scofield to E. E. Calvin, June 14, 1916, Scofield R; SO(Calif.) Minutes, Sep. 26, 1916.

66. Archbold and Bedford to Scofield, Nov. 2, 1916, Rockefeller to Scofield, Nov. 10, 1916, Scofield R.

67. Clarence O. Flint interview by G. T. White, July 22, 1961; SO(Calif.) Minutes, Mar. 8, 1917; clippings, undated and unidentified, Hist. R.

XVI. PRODUCING COMES TO THE FORE

1. Wm. Edwards to O. Lawler, Sep. 10, 1930, Hist. R; also E. T. Bedford to Scofield, Sep. 13, 1912, and Jan. 13, 1913, Scofield R; *FTC on the Pac. Coast Pet. Industry,* Pt. I, 226.

2. FTC, *Pet. Industry: Prices, Profits, and Competition,* 70th Cong., 1st Sess., Doc. 61 (1928), 29.

3. Judson M. Hillman to J. W. Smith, July 26, 1957; O. O. Donnell to H. M. Shappell, Sep. 3, 1957, Hist. R; SO(Calif.) Minutes, Feb. 20, 1911; H. R. Longaker interview by J. W. Smith, Dec. 12, 1957; *S.O. Bulletin,* June, 1919, p. 11; Hidy and Hidy, *op. cit.,* 405.

4. J. M. Atwell to W. S. Smullin and W. Young, Mar. 16, 1911, Hist. R; interviews, L. B. Little, Nov. 21, 1957, H. R. Longaker, Dec. 12, 1957, and Warner Clark, Nov. 27 and Dec. 13, 1957, all by J. W. Smith; salary histories, Comptr. R; *Calif. Derrick,* III (Mar., 1911), 7; *O.&G.J.,* July 8, 1915.

5. D. F. Martin to Hillman, Mar., 1911 *et seq.,* J. M. Kent to Hillman, Sept. 16, 1918, Land R; interviews, H. M. Shappell by R. B. Bartlett, Jan. 7, 1952, E. G. Lawson, Mar. 25, 1957, and R. P. Hastings, July 2, 1958, both by G. T. White.

6. E. A. Starke to F. H. Hillman, July 14, 1913, and Mar. 2, 1917, Expl. R; H. N. Snively to J. W. Smith, Dec. 28, 1957, Hist. R; Ralph Arnold, "Two Decades of Petroleum Geology, 1903-22," *Bul. of the Amer. Assn. of Pet. Geologists,* VII (Nov., 1923), 613.

7. Interviews, E. G. Lawson, Mar. 25, 1957, Max Koeppe, July 9 and 30, 1957, H. R. Longaker, Dec. 12, 1957, Warner Clark, Dec. 13, 1957, and H. M. Shappell, Dec. 29, 1957, all by J. W. Smith.

8. Lease Record, Land R; Scofield to H. M. Tilford, Mar. 18, 1910, Summary of Producing Dept. Operations, 1910, 1911, and Summary of Crude Oil Production, Aug. 5, 1918, Secy. R.

9. Well file of McNee #1, Prod. R; Hillman to O. Sutro, Sep. 19, 1911, Summary of Crude Oil Production, Aug. 5, 1918, Secy. R; interviews, Cy Bell by M. Burleigh, Mar. 10, 1931, Max Koeppe, Aug. 14, 1957, and L. B. Little, Dec. 6, 1957, both by J. W. Smith.

10. E. E. Calvin to Scofield, July 27, 1911, preliminary agreements of Aug. 3 and Sep. 26, 1911, Secy. R; Condition of Operations, Prod. R.

11. Daly to Bedford, Oct. 16, 1911, Pew to Bedford, Oct. 31, 1911, Secy. R; Geo. F. Schroeder interview by J. W. Smith, Aug. 23, 1957; *Calif. Derrick*, III (Oct., 1910), 11, IV (Dec., 1911), 13; Stuart Daggett, *Chapters On the History of the Southern Pacific* (N.Y., 1922), 442-48.

12. D. F. Martin to Hillman, Apr. 30, 1912, Land R; well file of McNee #4, Condition of Operations, Prod. R; *Calif. Derrick*, IV (Apr., 1912), 9; *O.&G.J.*, May 2, 1912.

13. Bedford to Scofield, Sep. 13, 1912, Scofield R; Condition of Operations, Prod. R.

14. Bedford to Scofield, Jan. 13, 1913, Scofield R; Gibb and Knowlton, *op. cit.*, 676.

15. Condition of Operations, well file of McNee #10, Prod. R; Cy Bell interview by J. W. Smith, Feb. 15, 1958; *S.O. Bulletin*, Sep., 1913, pp. 6-7, Oct., 1913, p. 12; *O.&G.J.*, Aug. 7 and 14, 1913.

16. Fee Bk., Lease Record, Land R; Summary of Crude Oil Production, Aug. 5, 1918, Secy. R; Condition of Operations, Prod. R; CSMB, *Bul. #69* (S.F., 1914), 302-05.

17. Fee Bk., Lease Record, Land R; Condition of Operations, Prod. R; Starke to Hillman, Apr. 15, 1916, R. C. Stoner to W. H. Berg, Oct. 19, 1918, Expl. R; interviews, G. C. Gester, Nov. 21, 1957, and R. C. Stoner, Dec. 5, 1957, both by J. W. Smith.

18. Lease Record, Land R; *O.&G.J.*, Apr. 6, 1911.

19. Condition of Operations, and Summary Statement, Aug., 1912, Prod. R; *Calif. Oil World*, Sep. 29, 1911; *O.&G.J.*, Mar. 21 and Dec. 5, 1912.

20. Lease Record, Land R; Condition of Operations, Prod. R; *Calif. Derrick*, VI (Nov., 1913), 5.

21. Atwell to W. Young, May 10, 1913, Hist. R; "S.O. Co. Organization, 1912," Hist. R.

22. Lease Record, Land R.

23. See Chap. XIII, pp. 339-40; J. D. Baeyertz to W. H. Murphy, May 3, 1909, and Jan. 1, 1910, memo., "Coyote Hills Property, Whittier Property," both May 1, 1911, Hist. R; Murphy Oil Co. Minutes, Oct. 25, 1911, Secy. R.

24. Hillman to Murphy, June 6, 1913, Murphy to Hillman, June 10, 1913, and subsequent correspondence, Smullin to Hillman, Oct. 13, 1913, O. O. Allen to Hillman, Oct. 13, 1913, Prod. R; R. C. Stoner interview by J. W. Smith, Dec. 2, 1957.

25. Hillman to Murphy, Oct. 15, 16 and Nov. 1, 1913, memo., Murphy Oil Co. Lease #171, Prod. R.

26. Kingsbury to Carter, Ledyard and Milburn, Jan. 25, 1922, Exec. R; Summary of Crude Oil Production, Aug. 5, 1918, Secy. R; CSMB, *Bul. #118* (S.F., 1943), 347.

27. *S.O. Bulletin*, June, 1919, p. 6; Remi A. Nadeau, *City Makers* (N.Y., 1948), 210-220; Harris Newmark, *Sixty Years in Southern California* (Boston, 1930), 478-79.

28. Stoner to Starke, Mar. 8, 1915, Starke to Hillman, Mar. 30, 1915, Expl. R; J. M. Kent to Hillman, Sep. 16, 1918, Prod. R.

29. Condition of Operations, Prod. R; SO(Calif.) rpt. on Montebello for Census of Manufactures, 1919, Secy. R; *S.O. Bulletin*, June, 1919, pp. 5-7; *O.&G.J.*, Nov. 8 and Dec. 6, 1917.

30. H. N. Snively to Starke, Dec. 8, 1915, Mar. 11, 1916, Starke to Hillman, Dec. 9, 1915, Mar. 20, 1916, Expl. R; Condition of Operations, Prod. R; Summary of Crude Oil Production, Aug. 5, 1918, Secy. R; *O.&G.J.*, Feb. 10 and Mar. 16, 1916, Sep. 13, 1917.

31. Starke to Hillman, June 30, 1913, July 18, 1916, Expl. R; R. C. Stoner interview by J. W. Smith, Dec. 2, 1957; Condition of Operations, Prod. R; *L.A. Times*, Nov. 11, 1916, CSMB, *Bul. #118*, 318.

32. Starke to Hillman, Jan. 16, 1917, Expl. R; W. H. Berg to D. F. Martin, Feb. 19, 1917, Land R; R. C. Stoner interview by J. W. Smith, Dec. 5, 1957.

33. See Appendix B, Tables II and VI.

34. *Ibid.*, Table II.

35. Starke to Hillman, June 10, Aug. 24, Oct. 7 and Dec. 16, 1913, Stoner to Starke, Dec. 13, 1913, Expl. R. Standard drilled a wildcat at Moclips on the Olympic peninsula of Washington, beginning in the summer of 1919, but without success (Condition of Operations, Prod. R; *O.&G.J.*, Aug. 1, 1919, Dec. 17, 1920, June 10, 1921).

36. Interviews, G. C. Gester by R. B. Bartlett, Dec. 17, 1951, and by J. W. Smith, Dec. 3, 1957, R. B. Moran by J. W. Smith, Feb. 12, 1958; Hoyt S. Gale, *Geology of the Rangely Oil District,* USGS Bul. 350 (1908), 39-42, 50.

37. W. I. McLaughlin to Hillman, Aug. 29, 1924, Richmond Pet. Co. R; Balance Sheet, Richmond Pet. Co., 1919, rpt. for the Census of Manufactures, 1919, SO(Calif.) to FTC, Dec. 18, 1920, Secy. R; *Rocky Mountain Petroleum Yearbook* (Denver, 1945), 51-52; *Petroleum Facts and Figures* (N.Y., 1956), 146.

38. Condition of Operations, Prod. R; *O.&G.J.*, Sep. 27 and Nov. 1, 1918, Mar. 21, 1919, Apr. 11 and 25, 1919.

39. Summary of Plant, 1907-1921, Condition of Operations, Prod. R; *S.O. Bulletin,* Jan., 1916, p. 3, Mar., 1916, p. 2; *O.&G.J.*, Dec. 2, 1915; *Min. Res. of the US, 1917,* Pt. II, 840. Monte Cristo in Kern River and Midway, Vulcan in Lost Hills, Continental in Coalinga, Eagle Creek, Monarch, and MJ&M&M in Midway were the principal acquisitions.

40. Title files, Treas. R; memo., Wm. Edwards to J. M. Atwell (ca. 1930), Hist. R; deposition of G. C. Gester, Nov. 17 and 18, 1930 in *US* v. *State of Calif. et al.,* #1679 in the US Land Office, Sac., XIII, 4476-78, hereafter cited as *US.* v. *Calif.*

41. Condition of Operations, Prod. R; testimony of Frank J. Carman, Oct. 8, 1930, in *US* v. *Calif.,* XI, 3274-76; *Bakersfield Echo,* Jan. 11, 1919.

42. Condition of Operations, Prod. R; *S.O. Bulletin,* Aug., 1919, pp. 11-13; *O.&G.J.,* June 20, Aug. 15, Oct. 10 and 17, 1919.

43. It was sheer chance that this suit was not instituted earlier. In Jan., 1914, the Commr. of the Gen. Land Office had challenged the legality of the transfer of Sec. 36 in 1903 to the State of Calif. as a school section because it "plainly appeared to be mineral in character when surveyed in 1901" and asked the Land Office attorneys to sue for the recovery of this and another school section. The letter apparently was mislaid in the files and did not again come to light until Feb., 1921 (Navy Dept., *History of Naval Petroleum Reserves,* 78th Cong., 2d Sess., Sen. Doc. 187 [1944], 6).

44. See, for example, Ralph Arnold, in *Bul. of the Amer. Assn. of Pet. Geologists,* VII (Nov.-Dec., 1923), 610, and Vann H. Manning, in *O.&G.J.,* Oct. 12, 1916, p. 2.

45. Sutro to Hillman, May 28, 1914, Hist. R; US Bu. of Mines, *Technical Paper #38* (1913); Hidy and Hidy, *op. cit.,* 168-76, 383-93, 628-29; Williamson and Daum, *op. cit.,* 591, 763.

46. Calif. Natural Gas Co. Minutes, Secy, R, SONJ; contracts, Calif. Natural Gas Co. with SO(Calif.), Jan. 1, 1911 and Jan. 23, 1913, Rpt. on the Gas Industry (1914), Secy. R; Hillman to Sutro, Aug. 15, 1917, Hist. R; *Calif. Oil World,* Jan. 19, 1911; *L.A. Times,* May (?), 1915.

47. Hillman to Sutro, Sep. 19, 1911, Scharpenberg to J. W. Smith, Sep. 14, 1957, Hist, R; M. B. Daly to A. C. Bedford, Oct. 16, 1911, Secy. R.

48. Testimony of C. C. Scharpenberg, Nov. 9, 1937, in *S.O. Cal. et al* v. *US,* #8985 in the US Cir. Ct. of Appeals for the 9th Cir., transcript of record, III, 635; H. M. Shappell interview by G. T. White, July 29, 1955; Scharpenberg to J. W. Smith, Dec. 5, 1957, Hist. R; US Patents #1,040,806 (Starke Gas Trap), Oct. 8, 1912, #1,226,913 (low pressure trap), May 22, 1917, #1,482,702 (turbo-drill), Feb. 5, 1929; *Standard Oiler,* Dec., 1956, pp. 9, 14. The date of the Starke gas trap application was Jan. 31, 1912.

49. *Calif. Derrick,* Sep. 10, 1914; US Bu. of Mines, *Technical Paper #209* (1919), 19-23.

50. Pipe Line Chronology, P/L R; Historical Sketch of El Segundo, 1911-1920, Mfg. R; Synopses of Gas Contracts and L. S. Ready's rpt., "Natural Gas Production, Transmission and Distribution in Kern, L.A., Orange, Riverside, and San Bernardino Counties," Nov. 29, 1919, in case #1390 before the RR Comm. of Calif., p. 12, Hist. R.

51. Hillman to Sutro, Aug. 15, 1917, Hist. R; *O.&G.J.*, Jan. 11, 1917; *Calif. Oil World*, June 26, 1924, p. 11.

52. US Bu. of Mines, *Information Circular #7172* (June, 1941), 11-14; *O.&G.J.*, Sep. 13, 1918; H. P. Westcott, *Hand Book of Casinghead Gas* (Erie, Pa., 1918), 6-13.

53. W. S. Smullin to W. Young, May 22, 1913, Sep. 23, 1913, Hist. R; *S.O. Bulletin*, Aug., 1913, p. 13 and Oct., 1915, p. 11; *O.&G.J.*, Sep. 18 and Oct. 9, 1913, July 23, 1914, Sep. 30, 1915, Jan. 13, 1916.

54. Scharpenberg to J. W. Smith, Sep. 14, 1957, Hist. R; *O.&G.J.*, Jan. 29, 1914, Apr. 6, 1916.

55. Valley Gas Co. to S.O. Co., June 21, 1916, Scharpenberg to J. W. Smith, Dec. 5, 1957, Hist. R; *O.&G.J.*, June 22 and Dec. 14, 1916.

56. Ross McCollum to Cy Bell, Apr. 12, 1919, H. M. Shappell to J. W. Smith, Sep. 1, 1957, Scharpenberg to J. W. Smith, Sep. 14 and Dec. 5, 1957, Hist. R.

57. Atwell to Young, Jan. 7, 1914, Hist. R.; "Pet. Statistics, Dist. Five and SO Co. of Calif., 1876-1920," an unpublished compilation in Econ. R, Sec. I, pp. 13-14; Directors' Ann. Statement, 1919, Comptr. R. The proportion of natural gasoline in the total national gasoline output was apparently slightly higher than for Standard—8.2% in 1920 (*Petroleum—Twenty-five Years Retrospect*, 1910-1935 [London, ca. 1935], p. 171). Probably there was a greater emphasis on recovering natural gasoline in the older fields than in the flush fields of California and the Southwest. In 1918, for example, the natural gasoline production of Jersey Standard companies, chiefly in Oklahoma and Louisiana, was equivalent to about 2% of Jersey Standard's domestic production of gasoline (Gibbs and Knowlton, *op. cit.*, 73).

58. Ralph Arnold, "Oil Geology in Relation to Evaluation," *Bul. of the Geological Society of America*, XXXI (Nov., 1920), 434. See also H. B. Goodrich, "The Past and the Future," *Bul. of the Amer. Assn. of Pet. Geologists*, V (July, 1921), 451.

59. Two of the earliest important bulletins published by the USGS were J. H. Eldridge and Ralph Arnold, *The Santa Clara, Puente Hills and Los Angeles Districts* (1907), and Ralph Arnold and Robert Anderson, *The Santa Maria Oil District of California* (1907). Among the earliest significant works published by the CSMB were W. L. Watts, *The Gas and Petroleum Yielding Formations of the Central Valley of California* (1894) and *Oil and Gas Yielding Formations of California* (1900). The US Bu. of Mines began to publish papers bearing upon petroleum engineering shortly after its establishment in 1910 and by 1917 had set up a petroleum experiment station at Bartlesville, Oklahoma.

60. Welty and Taylor, *op. cit.*, 86-87.

61. Testimony of E. T. Dumble, Feb. 26 to Mar. 1, 1917, in *US* v. *SP*, #46, Vol. XX; G. C. Gester interview by J. W. Smith, Dec. 3, 1957.

62. Ralph Arnold, "Two Decades of Petroleum Geology," *Bul. of the Amer. Assn. of Pet. Geologists*, VII (Nov., 1923), 623; *Who's Who in America, 1918-1919* (Chicago, 1918).

63. G. C. Gester, "Evolution or Development of a Petroleum Geological Dept.," 3-4, Hist. R; interviews, M. E. Lombardi by J. W. Smith, Sep. 1, 1955, and E. G. Gaylord by J. S. Ewing, Apr. 25, 1958.

64. Interviews, G. C. Gester, Dec. 17, 1951, and Lester C. Uren, Apr. 20, 1960, both by R. B. Bartlett, S. H. Gester by J. W. Smith, Oct. 23, 1958; *Who's Who in America, 1918-1919, Who Was Who in America, 1943-1950* (Chicago, 1950).

65. H. M. Shappell to J. W. Smith, Sep. 12, 1957, Hist. R; interviews, R. C. Stoner, Dec. 2, 1957, and Warner Clark, Dec. 13, 1957, both by J. W. Smith; geological rpts., 1912-1915, Expl. R; *S.O. Bulletin*, Feb., 1941, p. 12.

66. Starke to Scofield, June 9, 1909, Scofield to H. M. Tilford, Dec. 18, 1909, Secy. R; Starke to Hillman, Dec. 15, 1914, Sutro to Starke, June 4, 1917, Sutro to Hillman, June 4, 1917, Hist. R; geological rpts., 1915-17, Expl. R; *O.&G.J.*, Aug. 2, 1917.

67. Atwell to W. S. Smullin *et al.*, Aug. 3, 1916, Hist. R; geological rpts., 1917-19, Expl. R; interviews, G. C. Gester, Nov. 21, 1957, and S. H. Gester, Jan. 10, 1958, both by J. W. Smith.

68. G. C. Gester interview by R. B. Bartlett, Dec. 17, 1951; testimony of G. C. Gester, Nov. 18, 1930, *US* v. *Calif.*, XIII, 4476-78.

69. Interviews, G. C. Gester by R. B. Bartlett, Dec. 17, 1951, and by J. W. Smith, Nov. 21 and Dec. 3, 1957.

70. John R. Suman, draft of Chap. XX for the "History of Petroleum Engineering," 3-4; B. K. Stroud, "Cementing Off Water in the California Oil Fields," *Western Engr.*, II (Mar., 1913), 204.

71. Carter to Archbold, Apr. 19, 1905, Archbold R. See also J. B. Treadwell to Julius Kruttschnitt, Jan. 24, 1903, Hist. R.

72. *Calif. Stats.* (1903), 399, (1909), 586, enacted Mar. 20, 1909; Sutro to Scofield, Jan. 21, 1909, to B. C. Carroll, Feb. 23, 1909, Hist. R.

73. CSMB, *Bul. #69*, 288-89; E. B. Latham, "The Kern County Oil Protective Association," *Western Engr.*, V (Nov., 1914), 205-06; Hillman to H. W. Thomas, Kern County Oil Protective Assn., May 22, 1912, Hist. R.

74. *Calif. Derrick*, VI (Mar., 1914), 9; CSMB, *Bul. #69*, 189-94.

75. E. G. Gaylord interview by J. S. Ewing, Apr. 25, 1958; *Western Engr.*, V (Nov., 1914), 190, (Feb., 1915), 317, (June, 1915), 491; *O.&G.J.*, Feb. 1, 1917.

76. *Calif. Stats.* (1915), 1404; *O.&G.J.*, July 8, Sep. 9, Nov. 4 and Dec. 9, 1915, Feb. 15, 1917. The law was amended and somewhat strengthened in 1917. (*Calif. Stats.* [1917], 1586). Water encroachment was not the only matter affecting the oil industry that was brought before the legislature in 1915. A far more controversial measure, stimulated by the flush production and low prices of 1914, a year in which California accounted for almost 40% of the nation's oil, would have made the industry a public utility. It would have empowered the State RR Comm. to restrict production and storage when necessary to avoid waste, including "economic waste." The bill was supported within the industry by some small producers, but it was bitterly opposed by the big companies, especially Shell. It did not pass. (SO Co. Legislation file, 1915, Hist. R; *L.A. Times*, Feb. 18 and Apr. 29, 1915; *L.A. Tribune*, Apr. 21, 1915; *O.&G.J.*, June 25, 1914, May 6 and July 29, 1915.)

77. Interviews, Omar Cavins by A. E. Haase, May 15, 1957, R. C. Stoner, Dec. 2, 1957, and G. C. Gester, Dec. 3, 1957, both by J. W. Smith.

78. Interviews, E. G. Lawson by G. T. White, Mar. 25, 1957, and R. C. Stoner by J. W. Smith, Dec. 2, 1957.

79. Interviews, R. C. Stoner, Dec. 2 and 5, 1957, G. C. Gester, Dec. 3, 1957, both by J. W. Smith.

80. J. B. Newton to Atwell, Dec. 6, 1918, Prod. R; H. R. Longaker interview by R. B. Bartlett, Apr. 20, 1960.

81. Minutes of Conference between State Oil & Gas Supervisor and Deputies and Representatives of SO Co., Whittier, Calif., Jan. 10, 1918, Prod. R.

82. *Ibid.;* interviews, Cy Bell, L. B. Little and C. C. Scharpenberg, Feb. 13, 1958, and R. C. Stoner, Dec. 2, 1957, all by J. W. Smith; *3d Ann. Rpt. of the State Oil & Gas Supervisor* (1918), 90-100; US Bu. of Mines, *Bul. #163*, 66-70.

83. S. H. Gester interview by J. W. Smith, Oct. 23, 1958; *3d Ann. Rpt. of the State Oil & Gas Supervisor*, 239-72.

84. For the work of the Dept. of Pet. and Gas, see esp. its annual rpts. McLaughlin kept in close touch with the research center of the US Bu. of Mines at Bartlesville, Oklahoma.

85. Interviews, G. C. Gester, Dec. 17, 1951, Earl Wagy, Jan. 23, 1952, both by R. B. Bartlett, Omar Cavins by A. E. Haase, May 15, 1957.

86. *3d Ann. Rpt. of the State Oil & Gas Supervisor*, 7, 9, 12, 56-57; *5th Ann. Rpt. of the State Oil & Gas Supervisor* (S.F., May, 1920), 5-6, 20.

87. Data for La Follette Com., Table 1.

88. See Tables III and VI in Appendix B.

89. Ralph Arnold, "Two Decades of Petroleum Geology, 1903-1922," *Bul. of the Amer. Assn. of Pet. Geologists*, VII, 613-14.

XVII. A STUDY IN POLITICS

1. See Appendix B, Table II; also Lease Record, Land R.

2. *Congressional Record*, 59th Cong., 1st Sess., May 4, 1906, p. 6358; John Ise, *The United States Oil Policy* (New Haven, 1926), 308-12.

3. USGS, *Bul. #623* (1916), 104, 117; Ralph Arnold, "Two Decades of Petroleum Geology, 1903-22," *Bul. of the Amer. Assn. of Pet. Geologists,* VII (Nov., 1923), 610; Allen G. Nichols, *Oil: An Historical Edition of the Oil Industry* (L.A., 1909), 98-103; Ise, *op. cit.,* 157-59.

4. USGS, *Bul. #623,* 133-35.

5. *Ibid.,* 135-49; memo., "Calif. Oil Lands," [1910], Hist. R.

6. See Chaps. II, III; memo., "Calif. Oil Lands," [1910], Hist. R; *FTC on the Pac. Coast Pet. Industry,* Pt. I, 71-73; Ise, *op. cit.,* 295-97, 300-03, 313.

7. Memo., "S.O. Co.–Producing Dept. Midway Investment, Sep. 31, 1909," PM&S to Britton and Gray, Oct. 26, 1909, Britton & Gray to PM&S, Oct. 29, 1909, Hist. R.

8. Britton & Gray to PM&S, Oct. 29, 1909, PM&S to Britton & Gray, Nov. 7, 1909, Sutro to Pres. Taft, Nov. 12, 1909, "History of PM&S" [1939], 5, Hist. R.

9. Ballinger to the Pres., Nov. 15, 1909, F. W. Carpenter to Sutro, Nov. 17, 1909, Hist. R.

10. Scofield to H. M. Tilford, Dec. 9, 1909, Hist. R; *L.A. Examiner,* Dec. 17, 1909; *Calif. Oil World,* Jan. 13, 1910.

11. PM&S to Britton & Gray, Dec. 21 and 24, 1909, "Dates on Which . . . Drilling Was Commenced on Government Land," Hist. R; *S.F. Call,* July 13, 1910; *Calif. Derrick,* II (Mar., 1910), 5.

12. *Congressional Record,* 61st Cong., 2d Sess., Jan. 14, 1910, p. 622; W. E. Colby, "The Law of Oil & Gas." *Calif. Law Review,* XXX (Mar., 1942), 255; Ise, *op. cit.,* 313-14. The lawyers based their advice on Art. IV, sec. 3, clause 2, of the Constitution.

13. Britton & Gray to PM&S, Apr. 23, 1910, Hist. R; Gifford Pinchot, *Breaking New Ground* (N.Y., 1947), 443 ff.; E. Louise Peffer, *The Closing of the Public Domain–Disposal and Reservation Policies, 1900-1950* (Stanford, Calif., 1951), 114; Ise, *op. cit.,* 314-16.

14. Britton & Gray to PM&S, May 21, June 22 and 30, 1910, PM&S to Britton & Gray, May 23, 1910, Sutro to Scofield, June 7, 1910, Hist. R; *L.A. Examiner,* May 12, 1910; *Oil Investors' J.,* May 6, 1910.

15. 36 *US Stat. at L.* (1910), 847.

16. Peffer, *op. cit.,* 118, 126.

17. *Ibid.,* 126-27; *Calif. Oil World,* Sep. 1, 1910; USGS, *Bul. #623,* 24, 183.

18. Scofield to Sutro, Sep. 8, 1910, PM&S to Scofield, Sep. 21, 1910, Hist. R; *Calif. Oil World,* Oct. 6, 1910.

19. Sutro to Short, Aug. 20 and 30, 1910, to Britton & Gray, Dec. 16, 1910, Short to Sutro, Sep. 23, 1910, Hist. R; Scofield to H. M. Tilford, Dec. 22, 1910, Elliott R; *Calif. Derrick,* III (Sep., 1910), 10-11, (Nov., 1910), 14-16, (Dec., 1910), 15; *Calif. Oil World,* Oct. 20, 1910, p. 15; 36 *US Stat. at L.* (1911), 1015; Ise, *op. cit.,* 304-05.

20. *Calif. Derrick,* III (Oct., 1910), 10; Ise, *op. cit.,* 292; Stuart Daggett, *Chapters on the History of the Southern Pacific* (N.Y., 1922), 442-48.

21. Ballinger to Pres. Taft, Oct. 27, 1910, Pres. Taft to the Attorney Gen., Oct. 29, 1910, quoted in deposition of Arthur Robb, Nov. 23, 1917 in *US* v. *SP,* #46 Civil in US Dist. Ct. for the So. Dist. of Calif., No. Div., reporter's transcript, 85-98; *Calif. Derrick,* III (Oct., 1910), 11, IV (Dec., 1911), 13; *Oil Age,* Dec. 16, 1910. The government won the Elk Hills suit before the US Supreme Ct. in 1919, but lost the other 6 suits (which had been consolidated) in a US Dist. Ct. in 1919 and did not appeal (Daggett, *op. cit.,* 448).

22. Sutro to Scofield, May 29, 1911, Edwards to Scofield, Sep. 12, 1911, Pillsbury to Scofield, Sep. 13, 1911, Hist. R; Appendix B, Table II; Ise, *op. cit.,* 325-26.

23. Edwards to Sutro, Mar. 23, Aug. 26, 1912, Sutro to Edwards, Apr. 17, May 6 and 24, 1912, Hist. R.

24. *Calif. Derrick,* IV (Mar., 1912), 6, V (Oct. 15, 1912), 11; map, "US Pet. Reserves No. 1 and 2," in Hearings of the *Special Joint Conference of the Committees on Public Lands, US Cong., on H.R. 406,* 64th Cong., 2d Sess. (1916); Ise, *op. cit.,* 334, 356.

25. Sutro to Edwards, Aug. 14, 1912, Hist. R.

26. Sutro to Edwards, July 8, 1911, Edwards to Pillsbury, Feb. 8, 1913, Lawler to the Attorney Gen., Mar. 14, 1913, Pillsbury to Lane, Mar. 17, 1913, Hist. R; *US* v. *Midway Northern Oil Co. et al.* #47 in the US Dist. Ct. for the So. Dist. of Calif., No.

Div. The decision in the Midway Northern case, handed down in May, 1914, found the Taft withdrawal unconstitutional. After the Supreme Ct. upset this decision in the Midwest case, the Midway Northern case was scheduled for a rehearing; we do not know its outcome.

27. Pillsbury to Lane, Mar. 17, 1913, Hist. R; Ise, *op. cit.,* 337.

28. Lane to Pillsbury, Apr. 7, 1913, Hist. R.

29. Pillsbury memo., Apr., 1913, Pillsbury to Sutro, Apr. 27, 30 and May 1, 1913, Hist. R.

30. Pillsbury to Sutro, Apr. 27, 1913, Sutro to Lawler, May 12, 1913, "Judge's Memo.," *US* v. *Midwest Oil Co., US* Dist. Ct., Wyoming, June 14, 1913, Ernest Knaebel, Asst. Attorney Gen., to Sutro, June 25, 1913, Hist. R.

31. Sutro to H. M. Storey, Oct. 28, 1913, Hist. R; Condition of Operations, Prod. R; *S.O. Bulletin,* Oct., 1913, pp. 1-2.

32. Britton & Gray to PM&S, Jan. 13, 1914, Storey to Sutro, Mar. 17, 1914, Hist. R; *O.&G.J.,* Feb. 19, 1914.

33. Sutro to the Attorney Gen., Feb. 6, 1914, and to the Secy. of the Interior, Feb. 6 and 18, 1914, Britton & Gray to PM&S, May 28 and 29, July 21, Aug. 21, 1914, Hist. R; 38 *US Stats. at L.* (1915), 708; Ise, *op. cit.,* 321-22.

34. *US* v. *Midwest Oil Co.* (1915), 236 US 459, quoted in Peffer, *op. cit.,* 127.

35. *S.O. Bulletin,* Sep., 1915, pp. 1-2; *O.&G.J.,* Nov. 4, 1915; Ise, *op. cit.,* 322.

36. *S.O. Bulletin,* Nov., 1915, pp. 1-2, Feb., 1921, p. 10; *O.&G.J.,* Nov. 4, 1915; *Calif. Derrick,* IX (Nov., 1915), 11; *FTC on the Pac. Coast Pet. Industry,* Pt. I, 78-88.

37. *Who's Who In America, 1918-19* (Chicago, 1918); Letterhead, Oil Industry Assn., 1915, "Accounts of Oil Industry Assn.," June 30, 1917, Hist. R.

38. Loomis to Sutro, Dec. 18, 1915, Loomis and Gillett to Sutro, Dec. 31, 1915, Gillett to Sutro, Feb. 13, 1916, Hist. R.

39. Loomis to Sutro, Jan. 6 and 15, 1916, Sutro to Frank Short, Jan. 26, 1916, Hist. R; Ise, *op. cit.,* 327-32.

40. Loomis to Sutro, Jan. 6, 1916, Gillett to Sutro, Jan. 13, 1916, Short to Sutro, Feb. 4, 1916, "Phelan Amendment to Ferris Bill, Approved by the Senate Committee," Hist. R.

41. *Hearings Before the US Sen. Com. on Public Lands, 64th Cong., 1st Sess., on H.R. 406* (1916), 186, 188, 209, 219.

42. *Ibid.,* 210, Bishop to Phelan, Feb. 10, 1916 in *ibid.,* 340-41; Loomis to Short, Feb. 10, 1916, Hist. R.

43. Loomis to Sutro, Mar. 6 and 9, 1916, Short and Gillett to Roy Bishop, Mar. 14, 1916, Hist. R.

44. Loomis to Sutro, Mar. 18, 1916, Sutro to Loomis, Mar. 28, 1916, Hist. R.

45. Sutro to Fleischhacker, Mar. 11, 1916, Fleischhacker to H. P. Wilson, Mar. 22 and 28, 1916, Wilson to Fleischhacker, Mar. 24, 1916, Hist. R.

46. Wilson to Fleischhacker, Mar. 31, 1916, Hist. R.

47. *Ibid.;* Sutro to Loomis, Apr. 4, 1916, Loomis to Sutro, Apr. 12, 1916, A. L. Weil to Sutro, Apr. 21, 1916, Hist. R.

48. Scofield to Hon. Henry L. Myers, Apr. 26, 1916, Hist. R; *Hearings Before the US Sen. Com. on Public Lands, 64th Cong., 1st Sess., on H.R. 406* (1916), 469-78.

49. Short to Sutro, May 17 and 26, 1916, Loomis to Sutro, May 23, June 4, 1916, Gillett to Bishop, June 3, 1916, Hist. R.

50. Short to Sutro, May 26, 1916, Hist. R.

51. Loomis to Sutro, June 4, 17 and 24, 1916, Sutro to Loomis, June 5, 1916, Hist. R.

52. Van Smith to Bishop, June 17, 1916, Loomis to Sutro, June 24, 1916, Gillett to Sutro, July 6, 1916, Hist. R.

53. Roy Bishop to the President, July 8, 1916, Loomis to Sutro, July 11, 1916, Hist. R.

54. Short to Sutro, Nov. 22, 1916, Gillett to Bishop, Dec. 8, 1916, Hist. R; Ise, *op. cit.,* 335-36.

55. Loomis to Sutro, Dec. 4, 1916, Hist. R.

56. Loomis to Sutro, Dec. 15, 1916, Gillett to Sutro, Dec. 28, 1916, Hist. R.

57. Louis Titus, whose ties were with the small operators, credited the plan to W. A. Williams, an official of the US Bu. of Mines (Deposition, Oct. 20, 1930, *US* v. *Calif.,* XII, 3855-56), but Williams placed the origins of the plan with the oilmen

(*Hearings of the Special Joint Conference of the Committees on Public Lands, US Cong., on H.R. 406,* 64th Cong., 2d Sess. [1916], 118).

58. Bishop to Titus, Dec. 3, 4 and 17, 1916 and Jan. 8, 1917, Titus to Bishop, Dec. 4, 1916, in Titus deposition, *US* v. *Calif.,* XII, 3860-63, 3870-72, Loomis to Sutro, Dec. 15, 1916, Hist. R; Condition of Operations, Dec., 1916, Prod. R; Calif. State Council of Defense, *Rpt. of the Com. on Pet.* (Sac., 1917), 44-48.

59. Titus deposition, *US* v. *Calif.,* XII, 3866-67; Gillett to Sutro, Dec. 14, 1916, Hist. R.

60. *Hearings of the Special Joint Conference of the Committees on Public Lands, US Cong., on H.R. 406,* 64th Cong., 2d Sess. (1916), *passim,* and for the Daniels ltr., 103. Franklin D. Roosevelt, the Asst. Secy. of Navy, was the chief Navy representative at the Conference.

61. Gillett to Short, Jan. 6, 1917, to Sutro, Jan. 26, 1917, Titus to Bishop, Jan. 17, 1917, Hist. R; *Hearing Before the Com. on Naval Affairs, US Sen., on the So-Called Relief Provisions of the Leasing Bill,* 64th Cong., 2d Sess. (1917), esp. 4-5, 32-37, 42-47, 119-20.

Sutro objected vigorously to statements by Justice tying all of Standard's lands in Naval Reserve #2 to L. B. McMurtry, the most controversial of the locator-promoters, when only 680 of Standard's 1,600 acres were so involved and through an intermediary part-purchaser, J. B. McLeod, rather than McMurtry directly (Sutro to Titus, Feb. 4, 1917, Hist. R). In a companion wire, Roy Bishop took exception to Justice's argument that the relief legislation would serve primarily the big operators, especially Standard. He pointed out that only 4% (1,800 barrels a day) of Standard's production came from unpatented lands, but that the total production of many small producers was involved in the struggle (Bishop to Titus, Feb. 4, 1917, Hist. R).

62. Loomis to Sutro, Jan. 22 and 26, 1917, Hist. R.

63. Titus to Sutro, Mar. 9, 1917, Sutro to Titus, Mar. 22, 1917, Hist. R.

64. Titus to Bishop, Apr. 25, 1917, Gillett to Sutro, Apr. 28, 1917, Hist. R; *S.O. Bulletin,* Apr., 1917, p. 10, May, 1917, p. 11; *FTC on the Pac. Coast Pet. Industry,* Pt. II, 236.

65. *S.O. Bulletin,* May, 1917, p. 2.

66. J. Leonard Bates, "Josephus Daniels and the Naval Oil Reserves," *US Naval Institute Proceedings,* LXXIX (Feb., 1953), 174. In the historical records of the company, discussion of the compromise mentioned by Titus early in March fades away inconclusively during the next month.

67. Gillett to Sutro, June 27, 1917, Hist. R; *Hearings Before the Com. on Public Lands, US Sen., on S. 45,* 65th Cong., 1st Sess., 257-58.

68. *Ibid.,* 24-31, 71-84, 98-106, 122-146. Requa testified that he had no economic interest in the withdrawn lands (p. 72), and Doheny said his interest was limited to a part of a school section, to which he held a patent (p. 132).

69. *Ibid.,* 14.

70. *Ibid.,* 176, 179, 193.

71. Calif. State Council of Defense, *Rpt. of the Com. on Pet.,* (Sac., 1917), 181.

Sutro had insisted that the oilmen maintain a "hands off" policy with respect to the state investigation, which was conducted by two university professors, David M. Folsom and Eliot Blackwelder, and the chairman of the State RR Comm., Max Thelen. ("The attempt to confuse the investigation with the relief situation or any interference by the oil men could only tend to destroy whatever benefits the oil men might derive from the findings of the committee," he wired Frank H. Short, May 11, 1917, Hist. R.) The committee's report angered some Midway producers because it failed to mention the matter of relief, though it did urge the necessity of more production from within the naval reserves to avert a fuel oil shortage (*Ibid.,* 144-45; Titus to Sutro, July 12, 1917, Hist. R).

72. *S. Rpt. #116,* 65th Cong., 1st Sess., (1917), 3; Gillett to Sutro, Aug. 1 and 22, 1917, Bishop to Sutro, Nov. 28 and Dec. 7, 1917, Josephus Daniels to Sen. Claude A. Swanson (with accompanying bill), Nov. 28, 1917, Hist. R.

A commandeering bill (S. 3521) was introduced by Swanson in Jan., 1918, and hearings were held before the Sen. Naval Affairs Committee the next month, but the bill was never reported out by the Committee.

73. Loomis to Sutro, Dec. 6, 10 and 18, 1917, Sutro to Gillett, Dec. 18, 1917, Gillett to Sutro, Dec. 21, 1917, Hist. R.

74. Loomis to Bishop, Jan. 3 and 4, 1918, Titus to Bishop, Jan. 8, 1918, Hist. R.

75. Lane to Scott Ferris, Jan. 29, 1918, p. 25, Gregory to Ferris, p. 35, Daniels to Ferris, pp. 38-39, in *Hearings Before the House Com. on Pub. Lands on H.R. 3232*, 65th Cong., 2d Sess., (1918), also the statement of Louis Titus, p. 773.

76. *Ibid.*, e.g., 170-76, 270-78. The Midwest Refining Co. of Wyoming, charged with being a S.O. subsidiary, was actually an independent company (Giddens, *op. cit.*, 219-20).

77. Gillett to Sutro, Apr. 16, 1918, Mills to A. C. Derieux, Apr. 18, 1918, Titus to Bishop, Apr. 27, 1918, Hist. R.

78. Titus to Bishop, Apr. 27, 1918, Kellogg to Fleischhacker, Apr. 29, 1918, Hist. R.

79. Titus to Bishop, Apr. 27, 1918, Gen. Pet. Co., S.O. Co. *et al.*, to Mark Requa, ca. Apr. 30, May 13 and 24, 1918 (the last marked "not used"), Sutro to H. M. Storey, May 7, 1918, Sutro to F. W. Kellogg, May 24, 1918, Hist. R; *S.O. Bulletin*, June, 1918, pp. 1-2.

80. Sutro to S. C. Ward, July 3, 1918, Bishop to Gillett, June 28, 1918, Hist. R.

81. Kingsbury to Sutro, May 25, 1918, Hist. R; *FTC on the Pac. Coast Pet Industry*, Pt. I, 226; Chap. XXI, 5-6.

82. Loomis to Sutro, Mar. 3, 1919, Hist. R; *O.&G.J.*, Mar. 7, 1919; Ise, *op. cit.*, 338-40.

83. *O.&G.J.*, Mar. 7, 1919; *Calif. Oil World*, May 26, 1921; Ise, *op. cit.*, 342-52; Peffer, *op. cit.*, 130-31; Bates, *op. cit.*, 174; Jonathan Daniels, *The End of Innocence* (N.Y., 1954), 312.

84. *US Stat. at L.* (1920), 443-45; *S.O. Bulletin*, Sep., 1920, pp. 1-2.

85. SO(Calif.) Minutes, Aug. 17, 1920; title files, Treas. R; E. G. Lawson interview by G. T. White, Mar. 25, 1957; *S.O. Bulletin*, June, 1920, pp. 1-2. Standard had made no discovery on 320 other Midway acres, to which it had held development rights under an agreement of Jan., 1909, with E. E. Jones. These lands were restored to the public domain.

XVIII. THE CHANGING FLOW FROM FIELD AND REFINERY

1. See Chap. XI; also J. F. Brooks, Sr. notebook (1912), Pub. Rel. R; J. F. Brooks, Jr., "History of Richmond Refinery," an unpublished ms. in the Mfg. Dept. R, paged by section, in this note "Refined Dept.," 41-42, hereafter cited as Brooks ms.; Hidy and Hidy, *op. cit.*, 475.

2. L. Stewart to R. Watchorn, Aug. 29, 1910, to M. Stewart, Sep. 10, 1910, Stewart R; Scofield to Pillsbury, Dec. 1, 1910, Hist. R; crude run statistics, Econ. R; *Calif. Oil World*, Oct. 6, 1910; *O.&G.J.*, Dec. 1, 1910, p. 24; *World Pet.*, Aug., 1937, p. 51.

3. L. Stewart to Watchorn, Sep. 3 and Dec. 7, 1910, Stewart R; *Calif. Derrick*, III (Oct., 1910), 9.

4. Monthly rpts., P/L R; *Min. & Sci. Press*, July 23, 1910, pp. 106-7; *Engr. & Min. J.*, Sep. 29, 1910; *O.&G.J.*, Apr. 27, 1911, pp. 24, 26; *FTC on the Pac. Coast Pet. Industry*, Pt. II, 38, 237.

5. Monthly rpts., appropriations, P/L R; voucher, Oct. 31, 1910, Hist. R; Brooks ms., "Crude Stills," 20, "Refined Dept.," 40-41, 51; *FTC on the Pac. Coast Pet. Industry*, Pt. II, 237. If 26 Broadway's requirements were stated in 50-gal. bbls., as domestic marketing reports were, this forecast for Petrolite amounted to about 1,488,000 bbls. and about 8% of deliveries by all Standard companies. The problem of converting bbl. figures cited by Brooks to 42-gal. bbls. is insoluble because he rarely stated whether the bbl. was the producer's 42, the distiller's 40, or the marketer's 50 gals.

6. Scofield to Moffett, Jan. 17, 1911, Scofield R.

7. Ann. Sales Statements; R. P. McLaughlin, *Pet. Industry of Calif.*, CSMB *Bul. #69* (1914), 341.

8. H. M. Storey to Wm. Edwards, June 13, 1910, P/L R; vouchers, Oct. 31, 1910 and Mar. 27, 1911, O. O. Allen to J. W. Smith, Jan. 4, 1958, Hist. R; *O.&G.J.*, Dec. 29, 1910, p. 18; P. W. Prutzman, *Petroleum in Southern California, 1913*, CSMB *Bul. #63* (1913), 308.

9. Application by Scofield to Wm. McAdoo to designate El Segundo as a sub-port of entry, Oct. 21, 1913, Hist. R; interviews, R. W. Hanna by J. W. Smith, Apr. 9 and 17, 1956, R. P. Hastings by G. T. White, July 2, 1958; title files, Treas. R; *S.O. Bulletin,* Apr., 1919, p. 3; *O.&G.J.,* May 18, 1911, p. 20.

10. Interviews, A. S. Russell, Apr. 2, 1956, and H. D. Foster, June 21, 1956, both by J. W. Smith.

11. Foster interview by J. W. Smith, June 21, 1956, and Foster memoir, Hist. R.

12. Foster diary, Hist. R; El Segundo Yield and Cost Statement for last 6 months of 1912, Mfg. R.

13. Monthly rpts., P/L R; Lease Record, Land R; Condition of Operations, Prod. R; O. O. Allen interview by J. W. Smith, Feb. 11, 1958.

14. L. Stewart to R. Watchorn, June 14, 1911, Stewart R; R. W. Hanna interview by J. W. Smith, Apr. 2, 1956; *O.&G.J.,* Aug. 10, 1911.

15. SO(Calif.) Minutes, Dec. 5, 1911; Foster memoir, Hist. R; interviews, E. P. Wright, Apr. 3, 1956, and H. D. Foster, June 21, 1956, both by J. W. Smith; Tom Summers, "Of Oil and Oilmen," *Standard Oiler,* Sep., 1947, p. 20; *Calif. Derrick,* IV (Aug. 25, 1911), 20; *O.&G.J.,* Dec. 21, 1911, p. 24.

16. Monthly rpts., P/L R; production statistics, Econ. R; Max Koeppe interview by J. W. Smith, July 25, 1958; *O.&G.J.,* Apr. 13, 1911, p. 20.

17. Appropriations, monthly rpts., P/L R.

18. Brooks, ms., "Crude Stills," 19-20, 25-29, "Refined Dept.," 49-52; Richmond Yields and Costs, Mfg. R.

19. J. B. Terry to J. W. Smith, Apr. 23, 1956, Hist. R; Brooks ms., "Chronology," 7, "Asphalt Plant," 1-3.

20. Brooks ms., "Paraffine Dept.," 17-28.

21. "Crude Oil: Stocks, Receipts, Shipments, etc.," P/L R, hereafter cited as Crude Oil . . . Shipments.

22. A. C. Myhrs interview by J. W. Smith, Jan. 29, 1958; E. P. Bly, *Oil Pipe Lines in California,* reprinted from the *Oil Bulletin* of Aug., Sep., and Oct., 1926.

23. Scofield to Moffett, Feb. 6, 1912, Scofield R; monthly rpts., P/L R; *Calif. Derrick,* IV (Mar., 1912), 9; *FTC on Pac. Coast Pet. Industry,* Pt. II, 237.

24. Rheem to Associated Oil Co., July 24, 1912, monthly rpts., P/L R; Condition of Operations, Prod. R; Field Operations rpts., Econ. R; Brooks ms., "Refined Depts.," 33-57, "Crude Stills," 29; *O.&G.J.,* Aug. 8, 1912, p. 22; *World Pet.,* Aug., 1937, p. 51.

25. Storey to Sutro, May 20, 1914, Hist. R; appropriations, P/L R; *Calif. Derrick,* V (Oct. 15, 1912), 15; *O.&G.J.,* Aug. 14, 1913, pp. 25-26; *FTC on the Pac. Coast Pet. Industry,* Pt. II, 237.

26. *O.&G.J.,* Nov. 7, 1912, p. 26.

27. "General Pipe Line Co. of California; Proposed Plan," Feb. 1, 1912, Hist. R; Field Operations rpts., Econ. R; *O.&G.J.,* Nov. 14, 1912, p. 24, and Aug. 14, 1913, p. 25; E. I. Harrington, "The General Petroleum Corporation," *Calif. Oil World and Pet. Industry,* July 20, 1937, p. 6.

28. SO-KT&O agreement of Nov. 30, 1912, Oil Pur. & Exch. R; historical statistics, Comptr. R; *KT&O et al.* v. *Associated Pipe Line Co. et al.,* Bill in Equity #35 in US Dist. Ct. for the No. Dist. of Calif.; *O.&G.J.,* Feb. 9, 1911, p. 22; *World Pet.,* Aug., 1937, pp. 50-51.

29. Title files, Treas. R; interviews, A. S. Russell, Apr. 2, 1956 and Jan. 20 and 21, 1958, H. D. Foster, June 21, 1956, H. E. Thorpe, Jan. 17, 1958, A. C. Myhrs, Jan. 27, 1958, all by J. W. Smith; Construction rpts., 1913, G. C. Hill to Whitworth, Oct. 28, 1918, Mfg. R; Crude Oil . . . Shipments.

30. Monthly rpts., P/L R; Crude Oil . . . Shipments.

31. Production statistics, Econ. R; *FTC on the Pac. Coast Pet. Industry,* Pt. II, 39-40, 236; Ann. Sales Statistics.

32. See Table VI, Appendix B.

33. Rheem to F. B. Henderson, Dec. 6, 1913, contracts of Jan. 1, 1914, and monthly rpts. of deliveries, Oil Pur. & Exch. R; El Segundo Chronology, Hist. R; Brooks ms., "Refined Dept.," 57, 60-61, "Crude Stills," 29; *S.O. Bulletin,* Feb., 1914, p. 2. In addition, six small refineries supplied Standard with about 7,000 bbls. a month of engine distillate on contracts for the year 1913. Data are lacking as to when these refineries

first began to supply Standard and for how long. ("1913-Oil Purchases," Hist. R.)

34. (Storey) to C. L. Hare, Nov. 15, 1913, and SO-KT&O agreement of Dec. 31, 1913, Oil Pur. & Exch. R; monthly rpts., P/L R; Ann. Sales Statistics.

35. Monthly rpts., P/L R; O.&G.J., Dec. 25, 1913, p. 24, Feb. 5, 1914, p. 29; FTC on the Pac. Coast Pet. Industry, Pt. II, 237.

36. Appropriations, P/L R; Pipe Line Chronology, Hist. R.

37. Interviews, G. T. Grimes by A. E. Haase, May 13, 1957, H. H. Hall and E. P. Bly, both on Feb. 3, 1958, by J. W. Smith.

38. Storey to J. J. Wilt, May 2, 1914, Oil Pur. & Exch. R; appropriations, monthly rpts., P/L R; Crude Oil . . . Shipments.

39. S.O. Bulletin, Aug., 1914, p. 17; L.A. Times, Aug. 7, 1914; FTC on the Pac. Coast Pet. Industry, Pt. II, 237.

40. Hill to Whitworth, Oct., 1918, Mfg. R; Brooks ms., "Crude Stills," 29; Among Ourselves, July, 1922, pp. 3, 14; Richmond Independent, Dec. 27, 1939; O.&G.J., Apr. 9, 1914, p. 33.

41. Statistical rpts. to FTC, 1914, 1915, Secy. R; monthly rpts., P/L R.

42. S.O. Bulletin, Feb., 1921, p. 10; Calif. Derrick, IX (Mar., 1916), 5; Min. Res. of the US, 1921, Pt. II, 260-61.

43. Field Operations rpts., Econ. R; L.A. Times, Oct. 10 and Nov. 28, 1913, Apr. 29, 1914; Calif. Derrick, V (Dec. 15, 1912), 13, VI (May 10, 1914), 5-6, IX (Jan., 1916), 26; O.&G.J., May 20 and Aug. 17, 1913; Harrington, op. cit., 8; Welty and Taylor, op. cit., 117-18.

44. Hare to Storey, Dec. 28, 1914, Oil Pur. & Exch. R; monthly rpts., P/L R; Western Engr., Dec., 1913, p. 486; Beaton, op. cit., 59-70, 81, 84, 94.

45. W. S. Miller to FTC, Mar. 8, 1916, statistical rpt. to the FTC, 1915, Secy. R; FTC on the Pac. Coast Pet. Industry, Pt. II, 236-37; monthly rpts., P/L R.

46. Ann. Sales Statistics.

47. Hanna to J. C. Black, Feb. 5, 1916, Black to Hanna, Feb. 7, 1916, Minutes of the Gasoline Production Committee, Feb. 20, 1919, CRC R; Brooks ms., "Refined Dept.," 63, "Cracking Plant," 1.

48. License agreement, CRC R; Brooks ms., "Cracking Plant," 2-3; B. T. Brooks, "A Brief History of Petroleum Cracking," in A. E. Dunston and others (eds.), The Science of Petroleum (N.Y., 1938), III, 2078; Giddens, op. cit., 153-54, 160-62.

49. Brooks ms., "Cracking Plant," 7, "Refined Dept.," 65; J. B. Terry to J. W. Smith, Mar. 15, 1958, Hist. R; testimony of R. W. Hanna, June 23, 1932 in Universal Oil Products v. Root Refining Co., #716 and #895 in Equity in the US Dist. Ct. for the Dist. of Delaware, 387, 480, 490, 497 and Hanna's patent application Serial #313,880, CRC R.

50. J. B. Terry to J. W. Smith, Mar. 15, 1958, Hist. R; undated memo. by J. N. Adams, CRC R.

51. J. F. Faber to R. J. Hanna, Feb. 21, 1916, CRC R; G. C. Hill to Tuttle, Feb. 20, 1919, Comptr. R; US Bu. of Mines Information Circular, Development of Petroleum Refining Technology in the United States (1941), 13; Data for La Follette Com., Table 151.

52. Ann. Sales Statistics; Brooks ms., "Crude Stills," 33, 35, "Asphalt Stills," 6; depositions of H. C. Hanna, June 24, 1931, and R. W. Hanna, June 29, 1931, in Behimer v. Hanna, US Patent Office Interference #59,003, testimony on behalf of R. W. Hanna, pp. 9, 203-04, hereafter cited as Behimer v. Hanna; Foster diary, Hist. R; Tom Summers, "Of Oil and Oilmen," Standard Oiler, Oct., 1947, p. 24; Calif. Oil World, Nov. 27, 1915.

53. G. C. Hill to J. H. Tuttle, Feb. 13, 1920, Comptr. R; R. W. Hanna in Behimer v. Hanna, 205-6.

54. Testimony of Chappell, Nov. 7, 1924, in Chappell, Davis and Moore v. Prutzman, US Patent Office Interference #48792, testimony on behalf of C., D., and M., 702-85; Brooks ms., "Filter Plant," 3-12.

55. Starke to Scofield, Oct. 27, 1905, and to Rheem, Mar. 6, 1906, J. B. Terry to J. W. Smith, Aug., 1958, Hist. R.

56. Booth to SO(Calif.), May 27, 1915, CRC R; J. B. Terry to J. W. Smith, Mar. 15, 1958, Hist. R; A. M. Irwin interview by G. T. White, May 15, 1957; Brooks ms.,

"White Oil Plant," 1-5; *S.O. Bulletin*, Sep., 1915, p. 15, May, 1917, pp. 7, 10; US Dept. of Commerce, *Commerce Reports*, III (1915), 553.

57. Mann to Rheem, Mar. 12, 1915, CRC R; Terry to J. W. Smith, Apr. 23, 1956; Brooks ms., "Benzol Plant," 1-6; "Benzol Plant," an unpublished ms. in CRC R, *passim,* hereafter cited as Benzol Plant ms.; R. W. Hanna memo. on fine fractionation, Hist. R; testimony of Chappell and C. K. Parker, Sep. 8, 1924, in *Black* v. *Pyzell,* US Patent Office Interference #50,323, *Testimony for Black,* 12, 19, 81; testimony of Parker in *Carbide and Carbon Chemicals Corp.* v. *The Texas Co.,* #271 in Equity in US Dist. Ct. for the So. Dist. of Texas, pp. 6, 32; US Patents #1,214,204, Jan. 30, 1917, #1,249,444, Dec. 11, 1917 and #1,257,906, Feb. 26, 1918.

58. Contract with Du Pont, Oct. 20, 1915, Secy. R; testimony of Parker in *Carbide and Carbon* case cited above, p. 32; Benzol Plant ms., 69.

59. Contract and award due to suspension of contract, Secy. R; J. B. Terry interview by J. W. Smith, Mar. 26, 1956.

The several processes pioneered by Standard, General, and others during World War I were greatly improved upon by later research, making petroleum a highly significant source of toluol in World War II (Eugene H. Leslie, *Motor Fuels: Their Production and Technology* [N.Y., 1923], 346-51; Kendall Beaton, *op. cit.,* 100-01, 599-602; Henrietta M. Larson and Kenneth W. Porter, *History of Humble Oil & Refining Company* [N.Y., 1959], 564, 596-600).

60. Monthly rpts., P/L R.

61. *Ibid.; L.A. Times,* Feb. 3, 1916; *Western Engr.,* Dec., 1916, p. 450; *FTC on the Pac. Coast Pet. Industry,* Pt. II, 236-37.

62. J. L. Quinn to W. S. Miller, Jan. 5, 1916, Hist. R; agreement dated Aug. 22, 1916, and H. M. Storey to J. J. Wilt, Oct. 7, 1916, Oil Pur. & Exch. R; monthly rpts., P/L R.

63. Monthly rpts., P/L R; statistical rpts. to the FTC, 1916, Secy. R.

64. Gen. Pet. contract of Nov. 22, 1916, Oil Pur. & Exch. R; Pipe Line chronology, P/L R; *S.O. Bulletin,* Feb., 1918, p. 2; *O.&G.J.,* Apr. 29, 1915, p. 21, Sep. 2, 1915, p. 22, and Feb. 24, 1916, p. 28; *L.A. Times,* Aug. 6 and 12, 1916.

65. D'Heur to Storey, Oct. 6, 1917, Oil Pur. & Exch. R; SP-Standard agreements of Oct. 11, 1917, Pub. Rel. R; draft response to Dept. of Justice inquiry, N. H. Castle to H. M. Storey, ca. 1920, Secy. R; monthly rpts., P/L R; El Segundo chronology, Mfg. R; *Hearings before the Committee on Public Lands, US Sen., 65th Cong., 1st Sess., on S. 45* (1917), 231.

66. Monthly rpts., P/L R; notes [author unknown] on GP-Standard contract of Mar. 1, 1919, Mfg. R; statement of Sutro, Apr., 18, 1918, in *Jameson* v. *Producers Transportation Co. et al.,* #1188 before the RR Comm. of Calif., reporter's transcript, 27-28.

67. Hillman to Rheem, Dec. 12, 1917, Hist. R; monthly rpts., P/L R.

68. Condition of Operations, Prod. R; *S.O. Bulletin* through 1918 and 1919.

69. Data for La Follette Com., Table 173; Dirs. Ann. Statement for 1919, Comptr. R; statistical rpts. to FTC, Secy. R; GP-Standard contract of Dec. 27, 1918, Oil Pur. & Exch. R.

70. Statistical rpt. to the FTC for first 6 months of 1919, Secy. R; Ann. Sales Statistics; Brooks ms., "Crude Stills," 34-35; Rpts. to the Bu. of Census, 1919; US Bureau of Census, *Census of Manufactures, 1919,* p. 147.

71. Minutes of the Gasoline Production Committee, Feb. 20, 1919, CRC R; W. S. Rheem memo., Mar. 4, 1919, Pub. Rel. R; *O.&G.J.,* Jan. 3, 1919, p. 42. The other four members of the Committee were veteran refiners, J. F. Brooks, the chairman, J. R. McAllister, J. F. Faber, and the gifted John C. Black.

XIX. THE COMPETITIVE YEARS

1. Ann. Sales Statements, bound typescript summarizing sales from 1891-1922, in the Comptr. R, hereafter cited as Ann. Sales Statements.

2. Salary histories, Comptr. R, SONJ; *S.O. Bulletin,* Aug., 1919, p. 9; G. C. Maile interview by G. T. White, May 1, 1957.

3. Ann. Sales Statements; "Opening Dates—Company Stations [1922], Mktg. R.

4. "Record of Vessels, 1900-1920," Hist. R; *Min. Res. of the US, 1913,* Pt. II, 1062. The figure for tank cars under lease to Calif. Standard (12,400) carried in the *Min. Res.* report is much too high; 1,240 may have been intended.

5. "Pet. Statistics, Dist. Five and S.O. Co. of Calif., 1876-1920," an unpublished compilation in the Econ. R, Sec. II, 34-35, hereafter cited as Pet. Statistics, Dist. Five.

6. W. S. Miller to Rheem, Apr. 20, 1912, Secy. R; *US* v. *SONJ,* VIII, 918-19.

7. Rheem to Scofield, Feb. 24, 1911, Scofield R; "Calif. Fuel Oil Consumed During 1912," Secy. R.

8. Pet. Statistics, Dist. Five, Sec. II, 34-35.

9. Appropriation Bks., Mktg. R; interviews, J. C. Rohlfs, Aug. 30, 1955, and H. D. Collier, Oct. 17, 1957, both by G. T. White; *S.O. Bulletin,* Apr., 1914, pp. 8-10; *Standard Oiler,* Jan., 1947, pp. 1-4; *Calif. Derrick,* IV (June 25, 1911), 12, and V (Aug. 25, 1911), 20.

10. Appropriation Bks., Mktg. R; SO(Calif.), *A Rpt. . . . to the FTC,* (Mar., 1920), 42; *S.O. Bulletin,* Jan., 1914, pp. 14-15; *Standard Oiler,* Apr., 1948, pp. 1-3, 23-24 and Mar., 1953, pp. 1-2.

11. "Record of Vessels, 1900-1920," Hist. R; *S.O. Bulletin,* Dec., 1914, pp. 3-6, and June, 1916, pp. 6, 10; *S.F. Chronicle,* Feb. 28, 1912; *Calif. Derrick,* V (June, 1913), 9-10, and VI (Dec., 1913), 9. On July 12, 1917, Standard signed a contract with the Union Iron Works of S.F. for the *W.S. Rheem,* a companion tanker to the *Scofield,* but the vessel was commandeered by the US Emergency Fleet Corp. in Aug., 1917, and never entered the service of the company (Memo., "SS '*W. S. Rheem*'— Requisition," Apr. 26, 1922, Hist. R; *S.O. Bulletin,* May, 1918, pp. 8-9).

12. *O.&G.J.,* Nov. 30, 1916, p. 26; SO(Calif.), *A Rpt. . . . to the FTC,* (Mar., 1920), Appendix, Table II.

13. "Record of Vessels, 1900-1920," and "Data For Marine History, 1900-1921," Hist. R; *S.O. Bulletin,* Feb., 1914, pp. 6-9 and Apr., 1916, pp. 3-7; "News Story For Marine Editor 'Seattle Star,'" Dec. 3, 1927, and "Report of Sales and Deliveries by 'Petroleum II,' Southeastern Alaska," CSC R.

14. H. D. Collier interview by G. T. White, Oct. 24, 1957; Ann. Sales Statements.

15. E. A. Lamm, Globe, Ariz., to H. W. Neumann, June 24, 1911, W. S. Miller to Wm. Edwards, Nov. 4, 1912, Miller to J. E. Balsley, Jan. 30, 1915, Secy. R; Ann. Sales Statements; *S.O. Bulletin,* June, 1914, p. 14; *Among Ourselves,* June, 1921, p. 10; *L.A. Times,* June 28, 1914.

16. *Among Ourselves,* Aug., 1923, p. 5; *Standard Oiler,* Aug., 1957, pp. 12-13; *S.O. Bulletin,* July, 1914, pp. 8-9; SO(Calif.), *A Rpt. . . . to the FTC* (Mar., 1920), 25.

17. A. C. Mehlin, "Distribution by Motor Truck," *Among Ourselves,* Aug., 1921, pp. 6-7; Ann. Sales Statements.

18. SO(Calif.), *A Rpt. . . . to the FTC,* (Mar., 1920), 25.

19. W. S. Miller to All Agents Except Nome, May 13, 1913, H. T. Harper to Miller, June 25, 1913, Harper to All Dist. Sales Mgrs., Mar. 31, 1915, Kingsbury to Harper, Apr. 22, 1915, Secy. R.

20. G. E. Kennedy, Fresno, to Harper, Apr. 20 and Aug. 26, 1914, F. A. Williamson, Oakland, to Harper, Aug. 26, 1914, Secy. R.

21. W. S. Miller to Dist. Agents, May 21, 1914, G. E. Kennedy to Miller, May 22, 1914, Secy. R.

22. H. N. Kuechler to pipeline field supts., Sep. 11, 1913, and July 24, 1915, Sutro to E. S. Pillsbury, June 29, 1915, Hist. R; G. C. Maile interview by G. T. White, May 1, 1957; *S.O. Bulletin,* Exposition Supplement (1915), and Dec., 1915, p. 14; *Oil Age,* May 15, 1914; *O.&G.J.,* Apr. 29, 1915, p. 6, July 8, 1915, p. 6.

23. Kingsbury to Pillsbury, June 17, 1913, Hist. R; Kingsbury to FTC, Sep. 28, 1921, Secy. R; *Cal. Stats.* (1913), 508-10.

24. *FTC on the Pac. Coast Pet. Industry,* Pt. II, 158-63. The company rule, according to H. A. Lehnhardt, the asst. dist. sales mgr. at L.A. during the teens, was that all price changes had to be made through the S.F. headquarters. This usually took 2 to 3 days. (Interview by G. T. White, July 22, 1958.)

25. *FTC on the Pac. Coast Pet. Industry,* Pt. II, 12, 75-126, 129, 136-80. The only case involving the headquarters was a cloudy episode in April, 1920. Throughout the first six months of 1920, a time of high crude prices and gasoline

shortage, the independent refiner-marketers of Southern California were pressing for higher gasoline prices. Late in February, the general manager of the Ventura Refining Co. was writing an official of another company that the independents were anxious to raise prices but were "unable to agree on a new schedule, and there appears to be considerable doubt as to whether the Standard Oil Company would be willing to join in any advance at this time." Standard did raise its gasoline prices 2¢ a gallon in mid-March throughout its domestic marketing territory when gasoline stocks at its refineries had declined to only a three days supply. H. M. Storey, a Standard vice president, told an FTC examiner a week later that this step had been taken to forestall a runaway market, which could have occurred if the independents had taken the lead in price-making.

Apparently, this increase was too small to satisfy the independents. H. S. Botsford, president of the Independent Petroleum Marketers' Association and general manager of Puente, was arguing at the end of March that the independents should advance and maintain their gasoline prices above those of Standard as, he claimed, independent refiners and jobbers had done successfully in Indiana Standard's territory a few years earlier. Shortly thereafter, Botsford was in San Francisco, where he called on Standard and a few days later wired his superior in code: "Had a talk Monday Standard Oil Co. (California). San Francisco *as good as recommended* Independents increase price gasoline. Friday local [Los Angeles] representative *definitely asks* if it is not possible Independents take some action. Can see no objection price 25, now 23½. Please advise." (Italics supplied.) The chief executive of Puente's controlling company, the Union Oil Company (Delaware), refused to authorize Botsford to join in any concerted price increase. In a letter to the FTC, Botsford said later that his conversation at San Francisco took place in the course of routine business with Standard, that he was not talking to an officer of the company, that his comment about the Los Angeles representative was hearsay, and that his wire was so phrased to convince his superior of the wisdom of the policy he was urging. Standard explicitly denied that it had made any recommendation concerning prices to the Independents, "directly or indirectly." (*Ibid.*, Pt. II, pp. 88-90, 119-20, 178, 206, 257).

26. W. L. Stewart to FTC, Sep. 27, 1921, in *ibid.*, 135; Joe S. Bain, *The Economics of the Pacific Coast Petroleum Industry*, Berkeley, 1945, II, 291-92.

27. *Statistical Abstract of the US*, 1955, p. 16.

28. *Western Engr.*, VII (Mar., 1916), 86; "Motor Vehicle Registration in the US by States, 1900-1946," in Public Roads Admin., *Highway Statistics* (Wash., 1947), 18-27.

29. G. C. Maile interview by G. T. White, May 1, 1957.

30. *FTC on the Pac. Coast Pet. Industry*, Pt. II, Appendix; *Calif. Derrick*, IV (Mar., 1912), 14, and V (July, 1912), 6; *Western Engr.*, II (Feb., 1913), 170; E. I. Harrington, "The General Petroleum Corp. . . . 1912-1916," *Calif. Old World*, July 20, 1937, pp. 5-9; *World Pet.*, VIII (Aug., 1937), 51; Beaton, *op. cit.*, 65.

31. Pet. Statistics, Dist. Five, Sec. I, 13-14, Sec. II, 4; *Calif. Derrick*, III (June 25, 1911), 15; *Min. Res. of the US, 1921*, 261; Gibb and Knowlton, *op. cit.*, 58, 61. As late as Nov., 1912, *Western Engr.* was speaking of a gasoline shortage (I, 601-02).

32. W. S. Miller memo., Aug. 5, 1912, Secy. R; Miller to Wm. Edwards, Nov. 4, 1912, Hist. R.

33. Miller memos., Mar. 5 and Aug. 5, 1912, Miller to G. H. Richardson, May 16, 1912, H. T. Powell to Harper, June 6, 1912, Collier to Miller, July 9, 1913, Miller to J. H. McDermott, July 14, 1913, Secy. R. When the other small local refiner-marketer, the American Oriental Co., closed its doors in Jan., 1915, its refinery was operated briefly by the Shell Co. of Calif. until Shell's new Martinez works was completed (Beaton, *op. cit.*, 94).

34. Memos., H. T. Powell to Harper, July 30 and Aug. 5, 1914, Secy. R; *FTC on the Pac. Coast Pet. Industry*, Pt. II, 244-49.

35. *Calif. Derrick*, III (June 25, 1911), 12, 15.

36. John McLean to Harper, Oct. 8, 19, and Nov. 12, 1912, J. P. Smith to W. S. Miller, Dec. 24, 1912, Secy. R; *Everett Herald*, Nov. 11, 1912; Beaton, *op. cit.*, 56.

37. Memo., W. S. Miller, Nov. 11, 1912, and unidentified clipping, Jan., 1913, Secy. R;

Fresno Republican, Jan. 12, 1913; *Seattle Post Intelligencer,* June 10, 1913; *L.A. Times,* June 16, 1913; Beaton, *op. cit.,* 66, 76.

38. Omen Oil Co. to Automobile Owners, Oct. 1, 1914, Omen Oil Co. to the Motoring Public, Dec., 1914, Secy. R; *L.A. Times,* June 14, 1914; *Calif. Derrick,* VI (Aug., 1913), 10; *FTC on the Pac. Coast Pet. Industry,* Pt. I, 112, Pt. II, 244-49; Beaton, *op. cit.,* 70-97.

39. F. A. Williamson to Harper, Jan. 22, 1913, G. H. Mayer to Harper, Aug. 2, 1913, Miller to Harper, June 30, 1914, memo., H. T. Powell to Harper, July 30 and Aug. 5, 1914. J. I. Sutter, "Competitive Data and General Information," June 13, 1919, Rpt. J. T. French, Asst. Special Agent, Bakersfield, June 10, 1919, Secy. R; *Ann. Rpt. of the Union Oil Co. of Calif., Dec. 31, 1915,* p. 3; *FTC on the Pac. Coast Pet. Industry,* Pt. I, 232-37, Pt. II, 244-49; Welty and Taylor, *op. cit.,* 244-47.

40. Ann. Sales Statements; "Statement of Comparison . . . 1913 with 1912," Miller to John McLean and J. H. McDermott, Jan. 26, 1915, Secy. R.

41. Memos., H. T. Powell, "Marysville," "Sacramento," "Motor Spirits," July 30, 1914, Secy. R; Ann. Sales Statements; SO(Calif.), *A Rpt. . . . to the FTC* (Mar. 1920), Appendix, Tables I and II; *L.A. Times,* July 11, 1914; *Calif. Oil World,* Sep. 26, 1914.

42. Closing Papers, 1914-15, Comptr. R; *S.O. Bulletin,* Feb. 1915, p. 1; *L. A. Times,* Feb. 3, 1915; *Calif. Oil World,* Feb. 6, 1915; *FTC on the Pac. Coast Pet. Industry,* Pt. I, 199, Pt. II, 106, 112.

43. *O.&G.J.,* Apr. 13, 1916, p. 22; *FTC on the Pac. Coast Pet. Industry,* Pt. II, 76, 113, 135, 256-57.

44. *L. A. Times,* Jan. 22, 1915, and Jan. 2, 1916; *O.&G.J.,* Dec. 3, 1914, p. 27, Dec. 31, 1914, p. 40; *Calif. Oil World,* Jan. 9, 1915; *FTC on the Pac. Coast Pet. Industry,* Pt. II, 111-19; *S.O. Bulletin,* Jan., 1915, p. 1.

45. *FTC on the Pac. Coast Pet. Industry,* Pt. II, 256-57.

46. FTC, *Rpt. on the Price of Gasoline in 1915* (1917), 15, 102-04, 108-09, 143-44, 169-70, 197-200.

47. W. S. Miller to J. H. McDermott (S.F.), Aug. 21, 1916, Mar. 20, May 25 and Oct. 22, 1917, to B. Slettedahl (San Jose), Aug. 21, 1916, Mar. 20 and May 25, 1917, to C. H. Hamilton (Portland), Sep. 21, 1916, Nov. 30, 1918, to G. E. Kennedy (Fresno), May 25, 1917, J. L. Quinn (L.A.) to Miller, Aug. 7, 1918, J. I. Sutter, "Competitive Data and General Information," May, 1919, Secy. R.

48. *FTC on the Pac. Coast Pet. Industry,* Pt. II, 52-53. On May 23, 1917, H, T. Harper wrote a general letter of inquiry to the Dist. Sales Mgrs. concerning the 2% discount. Most Sales Mgrs. opposed its use, feeling that it would not bring sufficient new business, or that competitors would merely increase the size of their discounts. The discount was being used, however, by a minority of the mgrs., at Spokane, Stockton, and San Diego, with the approval of the S.F. headquarters. A further survey of the effect of the discount was made at the end of the year. (Secy. R.)

49. Harper to J. E. Balsley, Nov. 16, 1917, Harper to D. G. Hillman, Jan. 3, 1918, Secy. R; *Calif. Derrick,* X (July, 1917), 13-14.

50. *FTC on the Pac. Coast Pet. Industry,* Pt. II, 127, 244-49. Shell, a major in 1919, was not included in the statistics for 1915, for in that year its gasoline and engine distillate were almost wholly imported. Standard's share of the total engine distillate trade in the West in 1919 was 38% (p. 127).

51. Pet. Statistics, Dist. Five, Sec. II, 32-33.

52. Ann. Sales Statements.

53. H. G. Parker interview by J. W. Smith, Sep. 24, 1958; "Standard Stations Data" bk., Mktg. R; *Among Ourselves,* Oct., 1921, p. 4; *S.O. Bulletin,* Dec., 1934, pp. 5, 7, 10 and Oct., 1950, p. 20.

54. The time of the year of this innovation is not known. Other contestants for the honor of "first" include the Automobile Gasoline Co. of St. Louis, with a claim to a service station in 1905 (Beaton, *op. cit.,* 272) and the Oriental Oil Co., with a claim to a service station in Dallas in 1907 (Giddens, *op. cit.,* 80).

55. E. M. James *et al.* to P. H. Patchin, July 12, 1929, Pub. Rel. R; "Standard Stations Data" bk. Mktg. R.

56. "Standard Stations Data" bk., Mktg. R; *S.O. Bulletin,* Dec., 1934, p. 10; E. L.

LaRue, "The Company's Service Stations," *Among Ourselves,* Sep., 1923, pp. 1-4. See also editorial, *L.A. Tribune,* Jan. 10, 1914.

57. Harper to Miller, June 25, 1913, Secy. R; "Standard Stations Data" bk., Mktg. R.

58. J. L. Quinn to Harper, Feb. 2, 1914, Earle C. Anthony to Harper, Oct. 5, 1914, Secy. R; *S.O. Bulletin,* Dec., 1934, p. 3; *Calif. Oil World,* Mar. 2, 1914.

59. Earle C. Anthony to Harper, Oct. 5, 1914, Secy. R.

60. Omen Oil Co. "Re Gasoline," Oct. 2, 1913, Omen Oil to Automobile Owners, Oct. 1, 1914, J. L. Quinn to Harper, Feb. 2, 1914, memo. H. T. Powell, July 30 and Aug. 5, 1914, Earle C. Anthony to Harper, Oct. 5, 1914, Secy. R; "Standard Stations Data" bk., Mktg. R; *Calif. Oil World,* June 12, 1914.

61. "Standard Stations Data" bk., Mktg. R; "Operating Profits, National Supply Stations, July-Sept., 1914," Comptr. R; *L.A. Times,* Oct. 13, 1914.

62. Harper to Miller, Sep. 30, 1914, Secy. R; "Final Settlement Sheet of the National Supply Stations," Sep. 30, 1914, Comptr. R.

63. Earle C. Anthony to Harper, Oct. 5, 1914, Secy. R; *S.O. Bulletin,* Dec. 1914, p. 7.

64. "Standard Stations Data" bk., Mktg. R; "Analysis of Plant Account, 1909-1912 [sic]," Comptr. R; *FTC on the Pac. Coast Pet. Industry,* Pt. II, 51-54, 242-43.

65. "Standard Stations Data" bk., Mktg. R; J. H. Tuttle to H. D. Collier, Feb. 13, 1920, Secy. R; H. T. Hays interview by A. E. Haase, Feb. 11, 1957; *S.O. Bulletin,* Feb. 1917, pp. 3-7; *Among Ourselves,* Oct., 1921, p. 4; *Nat. Pet. News,* VII (Oct., 1915), 44.

66. "Net Results—Service Stations, Year Ending Dec. 31, 1915," Comptr. R; SO (Calif.), *A Rpt. . . . to the FTC* (Mar., 1920), Appendix, Chart F; *FTC on the Pac. Coast Pet. Industry,* Pt. II, 79-82.

67. *FTC on the Pac. Coast Pet. Industry,* Pt. II, 53.

68. Pet. Statistics, Dist. Five, Sec. II, 32-33.

69. *Ibid.;* interviews, H. H. Hall by A. E. Haase, Mar. 21, 1957, G. C. Maile, May 1, 1957, and H. D. Collier, Oct. 17, 1957, both by G. T. White; *S.O. Bulletin,* Oct., 1914, pp. 4-6; *Calif. Derrick,* VI (Jan., 1914), 11.

70. Kingsbury to FTC, Aug. 22, 1916, "Fuel Oil, 1914-1919," in rpt. prepared for FTC, 1921, Secy. R.

71. *S.O. Bulletin,* Oct., 1914, p. 6; *Calif. Derrick,* VI (Mar., 1914), 3-5.

72. *S.O. Bulletin,* Oct., 1913, pp. 10-11, 15, Jan., 1915, p. 14, Apr., 1916, pp. 13-15, and Nov., 1919, pp. 14-15.

73. Voucher, Aug. 31, 1912, Hist. R; H. H. Hall interview by A. E. Haase, Mar. 21, 1957; *S.O. Bulletin,* Mar., 1914, pp. 6-7, and Dec. 1917, p. 13.

74. "Calif. Fuel Oil Consumed During 1912," Secy. R; *FTC on the Pac. Coast Pet. Industry,* Pt. II, 234-35, 255.

75. Harper to All Agents, Feb. 19, 1913, Traffic R; G. E. Kennedy to Harper, Apr. 20 and Aug. 26, 1914, memo., J. P. Smith to Storey, Jan. 24, 1920, Secy. R; S. G. Casad to Sutro, Feb. 20, 1920, Hist. R; Ann Sales Statements; Pet. Statistics, Dist. Five, Sec. II, 32-33; *A Rpt. . . . to the FTC* (Mar., 1920), Appendix, Tables I and II; *O.&G.J.,* Nov. 25, 1915, p. 2; *FTC on the Pac. Coast Pet. Industry,* Pt. II, 250-51.

76. Quoted in Exposition Supplement, *S.O. Bulletin* (1915), 4 and elsewhere; also *O.&G.J.,* Jan. 6, 1916, p. 6, June 29, 1916, p. 26.

77. E. H. Merrill to H. K. Fletcher, Mar. 24, 1916, Comptr. R; Lube Price Bk. (1906-1917); Ann. Sales Statements; Exposition Supplement, *S.O. Bulletin* (1915), 10-11, 14, 18, 36-37.

78. Pet. Statistics, Dist. Five, Sec. II, 32-33; *FTC on the Pac. Coast Pet. Industry,* Pt. II, 252-54.

79. Candle Price Bks., 1912-17, Mktg. R; Ann. Sales Statements.

80. Memo., re E. R. Squibb contract dated Nov. 17, 1915, Secy. R; Brooks ms., "White Oil Plant," 1-10; *Calif. Derrick,* IX (Dec., 1915), 7, and (Apr., 1916), 4; *O.&G.J.,* June 22, 1916, p. 39; US Dept. of Commerce, *Commerce Rpts.,* III (1915), 553.

81. Contract with E. I. du Pont de Nemours & Co., Oct. 20, 1915, Secy. R; A. S. Coriell to PM&S, Jan. 30, 1917, Hist. R; Brooks ms., "Benzol Plant," 1-6; Benzol Plant ms., 51-69; Oronite Products, 1916-19, Prod. R [sic]; Ann. Sales Statements; *S.O. Bulletin,* June, 1917, pp. 4-5; *O.&G.J.,* Sep. 2, 1915, p. 6.

82. Dirs. Comparative Statements, Comptr. R.

83. *S. O. Bulletin,* Mar., 1916, p. 2; H. D. Collier interview by G. T. White, Oct. 17 and 24, 1957.

84. Pet. Statistics, Dist. Five, Sec. II, 34-35; *Calif. Derrick,* VI (Jan., 1914), 4, *ibid.,* VII (Mar., 1915), 4; *O.&GJ.,* May 6, 1915, p. 2, Sep. 28, 1916, p. 35.

85. "S.O.–Imperial Oil Co." (1913-16) file, Kingsbury to Sutro, Aug. 19, 1914, Hist. R; "Sales for Year 1915," and memo., "Export Dept.," July 15, 1916, "Export Contracts on Special Forms, 1916," and "Export Sales for Year 1919," in rpts. prepared for the FTC, contracts, SO(Calif.) with SO(N.Y.), June 3, 1917, Aug. 15, 1919, Secy. R; H. D. Collier and A. E. Kihn interviews by G. T. White, Oct. 24, 1957; "Export Prices (1914-20), "Mktg. R; *S.O. Bulletin,* Oct., 1915, pp. 8-9; *O.&GJ.,* Apr. 5, 1917, p. 31.

86. *S.O. Bulletin,* July, 1916, pp. 14-15; Marine Dept. statistics, 1917, "Net Profits of SO Co. of Calif. Vessels on Foreign Trips," Nov. 20, 1918, CSC R.

87. Miller to Sutro, June 30, 1916, Hist. R; H. D. Collier and A. E. Kihn interviews by G. T. White, Oct. 24, 1957; Data bks. for *Dunsyre, S/V John Ena, M/S La Merced, M/S Oronite* and affidavit by J. H. Tuttle (1929), CSC R; *Standard Oiler,* Nov., 1957, pp. 12-13.

88. Kingsbury to Pillsbury, Sept. 11, 1912, Pillsbury to Kingsbury, Sep. 11, 1912, Hist. R; "Net Profits of SO Co. of Calif. Vessels on Foreign Trips," Nov. 20, 1918, CSC R.

89. Kingsbury to W. C. Teagle, Feb. 15, 1915, memo. (undated), "SO Co.–Imperial Oil Co." file, Kingsbury to Sutro, July 7, 1916, R. J. Hanna to Kingsbury, Dec. 18, 1917, Hist. R; Kingsbury to C. F. Meyer, Jan. 19, 1917, Exec. R.

90. Quoted in *O.&GJ.,* Jan. 20, 1916, p. 35.

91. FTC, *Rpt. on the Price of Gasoline in 1915* (1917), 143-44. The same figure, 60%, is given for Indiana's and Jersey's share of their respective home markets in 1915. We have found no figures for these companies for 1919.

92. *US* v. *SO(Indiana) et al.,* in the Dist. Ct. of the US for the No. Dist. of Ill., Eastern Div., #4131 in Equity, VII, 5541; Gibb and Knowlton, *op. cit.,* 188.

XX. THE HUMAN ELEMENT

1. *S.O. Bulletin,* Apr., 1919, p. 6.

2. J. R. Commons, *History of Labor in the United States* (N.Y., 1935), III, 298. Ida Tarbell noted in her *History of the Standard Oil Company* (N.Y., 1904), II, 253 that it was Standard's "custom to offer a little better day wages for labourers than was current and then to choose from these the most promising specimens; those men were advanced as they showed ability," and that in the days of the Trust employees were urged to buy stock and were aided in doing so through loans at low interest. "It is only natural that under such circumstances the company had always a remarkably loyal and interested working force."

3. We have no employee statistics before 1913; the average numbers of employees for 1913 in the marine and sales depts. and the Home Office are partly estimated because of the absence of statistics for the first two months of the year.

4. SO(Calif.) Minutes, Dec. 30, 1930 (on the retirement of Storey); R. C. Warner interview by G. T. White, Aug. 31, 1955; Raymond B. Fosdick, *John D. Rockefeller, Jr.: A Portrait* (N.Y., 1956), 162-76.

5. A. H. Lichty to Kingsbury, Aug. 18, 1920 enclosing "Interview Notes," Pers. R; Industrial Relations Counselors, Inc., "Rpt. on Industrial Relations in the SO Co. of Calif." (1928), Exec. R; *Standard Oil Spirit* (S.F., 1923); Charles Drake interview by G. T. White, Apr. 29, 1957.

6. Morrow to D. F. Martin, Sep. 24, 1913, Land R; H. M. Storey to Heads of Depts., Apr. 19, 1916, Comptr. R; Tom Summers, "Recollections of the 1915 Employment Office," *Standard Oiler,* Feb., 1948, pp. 14-15; Max Koeppe interview by G. T. White, Jan. 31, 1958.

7. W. S. Miller to H. T. Harper, Mar. 21, 1917, Miller to Eggers, June 27, 1918, Pers. R; Miller to H. K. Fletcher and All Dist. Sales Mgrs., April 12, 1917, Comptr. R.

8. Lichty, "Interview Notes" (1920), 36, 40-42, Pers. R; R. W. Codeglia interview by G. T. White, Jan. 31, 1958; Brooks ms., "Chronology," 10.

9. Lichty, "Interview Notes" (1920), 4, 9, 23, 34 and 45. Lichty returned to make a survey of attitudes of company marketing personnel in 1922. Speaking of Standard's

management, a tank truck supervisor told him, "They act as if they think any damn fool can fire a man, but it is far better to develop a man, and that is what they try to do" ("Notes Made by Mr. Lichty" [1922], 8, Pers. R).

10. Lichty, "Interview Notes" (1920), 27, 30, 32-33, Pers. R.

11. Kingsbury to All Heads of Depts., May 3, 1920, Pers. R; *Among Ourselves,* Apr. 1921, p. 2; *Standard Oil Spirit,* 45-46.

12. Page to C. N. Payne, Sep. 28, 1903, O'Day R.

13. Young to J. F. Eckbert, Sep. 5, 1907, Eckbert to Young, Sep. 10, 1907, Prod. R; interviews, L. B. Little by A. E. Haase, Mar. 15, 1955, Warner Clark by J. W. Smith, Jan. 3, 1958.

14. "Dirs. Ann. Statements," 1916-17, Comptr. R; *Min. & Oil Bul.* (L.A.), Oct., 1918, p. 469.

15. Miller to All Dist. Sales Mgrs., Sep. 20, 1918, Harper to All Dist. Sales Mgrs., Nov. 9, 1918, "Dirs. Ann. Comparative Statement," (1925), and "Additional Compensation Given by the Co. Through Wage Increases and Reduction of Working Hours" (1916-21), Comptr. R; *Historical Statistics of the US 1789-1945,* 235.

16. Tilford to Scofield, Mar. 26, 1917, in Brooks ms., "General Refinery," 24.

17. Interviews, Hillmor Smith, Apr. 25, 1957, Charlie Drake, Apr. 29, 1957, D. R. Codeglia, Jan. 31, 1958, D. L. Chesbro, Feb. 20, 1958, all by G. T. White; Brooks, *op. cit.,* "General Refinery," 27.

18. John Page to C. N. Payne, Sep. 28, 1903, O'Day R; Walton Young to J. F. Eckbert, Sep. 11, 1907, Eckbert to Young, Sep. 13, 1907, Prod. R; J. M. Atwell to Young, Mar. 2, 1909, J. R. McAllister to Young, Dec. 18, 1909, Hist. R.

19. Interviews, G. C. Maile, May 1, 1957, Hilda Anderson, Apr. 4, 1957, D. L. Chesbro, Feb. 20, 1958, all by G. T. White.

20. Boilermaker Foreman's Time Book, Jan.-Apr., 1908, Hist. R.

21. Brooks ms., "Chronology," 8; "Number of Employees and Payroll (By Depts.)," Comptr. R; *S.O. Bulletin,* Nov., 1916, p. 2, and Dec., 1916, pp. 1, 12; *O.&G.J.,* Nov. 4, 1915, p. 29; *Rpt. of the Dept. of Labor, 1917* (Wash., 1918), 54; Gibb and Knowlton, *op. cit.,* 138-39, 150.

22. *O.&G.J.,* Dec. 7, 1916, p. 23, Mar. 29, 1917, p. 26; *Western Engr.,* VII (Dec. 1916), 447; testimony of Kingsbury, Jan. 30, 1923, in *Hearings Before a Subcommittee of the Committee on Manufactures, Pursuant to S. Res. 295,* US Sen., 67th Cong., 2d Sess. (1923), 942; *Standard Oil Spirit,* 31-32; Warner Clark interview by J. W. Smith, Jan. 3, 1958.

23. Historical statistics, Comptr. R; *S.O. Bulletin,* Apr., 1928, p. 1.

24. F. M. Towl to O'Day, July 6, 1903, O'Day R; H. N. Kuechler to Sutro, Mar. 29, 1917, Hist. R; *S.O. Bulletin,* Oct., 1916, pp. 8-9; SO(Calif.), *A Rpt . . . . to the FTC* (Mar., 1920), 38; interviews, Stuart Moser by R. B. Bartlett, Jan. 10, 1952, G. T. Grimes by A. E. Haase, May 13, 1957 and A. C. Myhrs by G. T. White, Mar. 4, 1958.

25. Carter to J. F. Eckbert, May 25, 1908, Hist. R; Rpt. on Conditions in both No. & So. Dists., Aug. 15, 1919, Prod. R.

26. Rpt. on Conditions in both No. & So. Dists., Aug. 15, 1919, Prod. R; Lichty, "Interview Notes" (1920), 47; *S.O. Bulletin,* July, 1914, pp. 4-6 and May, 1917, pp. 12-13; *O.&G.J.,* Oct. 7, 1915, p. 22.

27. Rpt. of Conditions in both No. & So. Dists., Aug. 15, 1919, Prod. R; Lichty, "Interview Notes" (1920), 5-6, 8, 17, 47.

28. Henrietta M. Larson and Kenneth W. Porter, *History of Humble Oil & Refining Co.* (N.Y., 1959), 99-100, 125-26, 384-85.

29. For some of the literature on this subject, see Wm. M. Tolman, *Social Engineering* (N.Y., 1909); L. A. Boettiger, *Employee Welfare Work* (N.Y., 1923); John Calder, *Capital's Duty to the Wage Earner* (N.Y., 1923); Clarence J. Hicks, *My Life in Industrial Relations* (N.Y., 1941); and Commons, *op. cit.*

30. Gen. Ltrs., 1907-39, Pers. R; J. F. Brooks to J. H. Tuttle, Mar. 16, 1920, Secy. R; Dirs. Ann. Statement, 1918, Comptr. R; *O.&G.J.,* Jan. 22, 1914, p. 6.

31. Lichty, "Interview Notes" (1920), 25-26, 28-29, 31, 33-34, 37, 42.

32. H. M. Storey to H. A. Forsburg *et al.,* July 3, 1907, Prod. R; J. M. Atwell to Messrs. Walton Young *et al.,* Apr. 30, 1910, Hist. R; H. K. Fletcher to S. G. Casad,

Feb. 21, 1912, Traffic R; interviews, Hilda Anderson, Apr. 4, 1957, G. C. Maile, May 1, 1957, both by G. T. White.

33. SO(Iowa) Minutes, Sep. 21, 1905; Nat. Ind. Conference Bd., *Industrial Pensions in the US* (N.Y., 1925), 141-57; Hidy and Hidy, *op. cit.*, 602.

34. SO(Calif.) Minutes, Apr. 7 and July 21, 1908, Jan. 25, 1910 (effective Dec. 1, 1909); H. M. Tilford to Scofield, Dec. 14, 1909, Secy. R.

35. SO(Calif.) Minutes, Jan. 25, 1910.

36. *Ibid.*, July 10, 1918. In no case, however, could the pension amount to more than 75% of the average annual pay during the final 5 years of employment.

37. Ind. Rels. Counsellors, Inc., "Rpt. on Industrial Relations in the SO Co. of Calif." (1928), Exec. R.

38. "Employee Benefits" (pamphlet, 1916), Secy. R; SO(Calif.) Minutes, July 10, 1918.

39. "Employee Benefits" (pamphlet, 1916), Secy. R; SO(Calif.) Minutes, July 10, 1918; interviews, Hilda Anderson, Apr. 4, 1957, G. C. Maile, May 1, 1957, both by G. T. White.

40. H. K. Fletcher to J. M. Atwell *et al.*, Feb. 17, 1919, Prod. R; Lichty, "Interview Notes" (1920), 25, 37. The company extended unlimited sick leave from Nov. 5, 1917, to Feb. 17, 1919.

41. J. F. Eckbert to W. Young, May 15, 1907, H. M. Storey to G. M. Brown *et al.*, Aug. 28, 1907, J. M. Atwell to Young, Mar. 8, 1909, Hist. R; Hillmor Smith interview by G. T. White, Apr. 25, 1957.

42. H. D. Pillsbury to Scofield, Sep. 1, 1911, Hist. R; *S.O. Bulletin*, Nov., 1913, p. 10; Franklin Hichborn, *Story of the Session of the California Legislature of 1911* (S.F., 1911), 236-45.

43. E. B. Davis to J. M. Atwell, June 14, 1919, Prod. R; "Employee Benefits" (pamphlet, 1916), Secy. R; Lichty, "Interview Notes" (1920), 6, 13, 21, 36, 43, 48; *S.O. Bulletin*, Dec., 1913, pp. 10-12; SO(Calif.), *A Rpt. . . . to the FTC* (Mar., 1920), 34; Franklin Hichborn, *Story of the Session of the California Legislature of 1913* (S.F., 1913), 347-49.

44. C. C. Scharpenberg to J. W. Smith, Dec. 5, 1957, Hist. R; W. J. French, "California's Safety Order System," *Boiler Safety Bulletin* (1921), 3-4; Industrial Accident Commission, *Tentative Pet. Industry Safety Orders for Drilling and Production*, (Sac., 1923).

45. J. M. Atwell to Cy Bell *et al.*, Feb. 19, 1913, W. S. Smullin to All Supts., Sep. 14, 1914, Hist. R; *S.O. Bulletin*, Dec., 1913, p. 11.

46. W. S. Smullin to W. Young *et al.*, Apr. 20, 1914, and Dec. 19, 1916, Hist, R; H. M. Shappell interview by G. T. White, July 29, 1955; *S.O. Bulletin*, Jan., 1915, pp. 2-4; *Western Engr.*, I (June, 1912), 180.

47. W. S. Smullin to All Supts., So. Dist., Mar. 7 and June 22, 1917, Hist. R; Warner Clark interview by G. T. White, Feb. 20, 1958; Barton Cater, "Up and Down—Safely," *Standard Oiler*, Nov., 1939, pp. 1-3.

48. J. M. Atwell to D. F. Martin, June 23, 1914, Land R; Foster diary, Hist. R; Kingsbury to All Dept. Heads, May 3, 1920, Traffic R; *S.O. Bulletin*, Aug., 1915, p. 12; *Among Ourselves*, Mar., 1921, p. 5; *Standard Oil Spirit*, 41.

49. Scofield to "Standard Oil Family," Dec. 31, 1915, Pub. Rel. R; Lichty, "Interview Notes" (Marketing, 1922), 16; see also "Interview Notes" (1920), 29, 34, 40; G. J. Wylie interview by G. T. White, May 13, 1957; *Standard Oiler*, Aug., 1946, p. 5.

50. Lichty, "Interview Notes" (1920), *passim*, esp. 13, 17, 39, and in (1922), 2, 7, 9, 15, 23, 26-27; E. G. Lawson interview by G. T. White, Mar. 25, 1959; *S. O. Bulletin*, June, 1915, p. 13, Oct., 1915, p. 14, Mar., 1919, p. 16, Jan., 1920, pp. 5, 11; *Standard Oil Spirit*, 49-51.

51. "Chronology, Co. School," Oct. 2, 1914 to Apr. 24, 1924, H. H. Hall to Kingsbury, Oct. 31, 1919, Mar. 11, 1920, Pers. R; *S.O. Bulletin*, Apr., 1919, pp. 4-7; *Standard Oil Spirit*, 47-48.

52. J. M. Atwell to W. Young *et al.*, Nov. 14, 1913, Hist. R; Lichty, "Interview Notes" (1920), 10, 14, 18, 23, 33.

53. H. M. Storey to J. P. Smith, Jan. 5 and Feb. 6, 1918, Mfg. R; memo., Storey to S. G. Casad *et al.*, June 15, 1918, Traffic R; Lichty, "Interview Notes" (1920), 38 and

(1922), 26; SO(Calif.), *A Rpt. . . . to the FTC* (Mar., 1920), 41. SONJ's producing subsidiary, The Carter Oil Co., had adopted a similar program in 1917 (*O.&G.J.*, June, 21, 1917, p. 3).

54. Lichty, "Interview Notes" (1920), 43; C. H. Robertson interview by J. S. Ewing, Apr. 29, 1958; *Richmond Record,* June 27, 1902.

55. Lichty, "Interview Notes" (1920), 47.

56. *S.F. Chronicle,* Apr. 28, May 2 and 4, 1907; *S.F. Bulletin,* May 1 and 4, 1907.

57. Brooks ms., "The Richmond Refinery," 24-26; Boilermaker Foreman's Time Book, Jan.-Apr., 1908, Hist. R; Robert E. L. Knight, *Industrial Relations in the San Francisco Bay Area, 1900-1918* (Berkeley, 1960), 185, 189-90.

58. *Western Engr.,* VII (Dec., 1916), 447; *O.&G.J.,* Dec. 7, 1916, p. 23, Mar. 29, 1917, p. 26, and Apr. 19, 1917, p. 24; *Rpt. of the Dept. of Labor, 1918* (Wash., 1919), 18.

59. *L.A. Times,* Apr. 9, 1917; *O.&G.J.,* Dec. 27, 1918, p. 26; *Rpt. of the Dept. of Labor, 1918,* p. 18.

60. *Calif. Derrick,* X (Aug., 1917), 11; *O.&G.J.,* Aug. 2, 1917, p. 25, Nov. 1, 1917, p. 36, and Nov. 22, 1917, p. 40.

61. Reed to Chamber of Mines & Oils, undated, Reed to Hillman, Nov. 21, 1917, Hillman to Reed, Nov. 21 and 22, 1917, Secy. R; *Rpt. of the Dept. of Labor, 1917* (Wash., 1918), 12.

62. Reed to Producers of Oil, the Oil Refiners and the Oil Pipe Line Companies of . . . Calif., Nov. 24, 1917, Secy. R.

63. Fed. Oil Inspection Bd. to the Producers of Oil, the Oil Refiners, and the Oil Pipe Line Companies of . . . Calif., Dec. 1 and 22, 1917, Secy. R. There is, in the official *History of the Oil Workers International Union (CIO)* by Harvey O'Connor (Denver, 1950), 9-12, an account of these events which, judging from the contemporary record, appears to be in error at a number of points. The union, according to the report of the 9 propositions submitted to its members for ratification following the Bakersfield meeting of mid-July, was seeking a $4 minimum (*O.&G.J.*, Aug. 2, 1917, p. 25) and not $5, as in the union *History*; the General Petroleum Co. was then independent and not related to any Standard company, O'Connor to the contrary; the meeting with the operators sought by the union was for Nov. 1 (*O.&G.J.*, Nov. 22, 1917, p. 40) and not Sep. 1; Yarrow and Fraser may have gone to Washington but clearly the Mediation Commission's decision to send Reed to Calif. (reached by mid-Nov.) came on broader grounds; Reed issued his recommendation the day following his arrival at Santa Barbara, and not after 2 weeks of negotiations, as in the *History*; and Hillman strongly influenced the terms, which required of Standard no reduction of hours and only a $1 per month raise for roustabouts and pumpers (less than 4¢ a day and not 20¢) to meet the $4 minimum that the union desired.

64. R. H. Farber (Secy. to Reed) to Hillman, Dec. 15, 1917, Reed to Hillman, Dec. 15, 1917, Hillman to Reed, Dec. 18, 1917, Secy. R.

65. Fed. Oil Inspection Bd. to Hillman, Dec. 27, 1917, Hillman to Reed, Dec. 31, 1917, Secy. R.

66. Fed. Oil Inspection Bd. to All Oil & Gas Pipe Line Companies and All Gas and Pipe Line Workers in . . . Calif., Jan. 28, 1918, M. Requa to D. M. Folsom, Nov. 13, 1918, memo., signed "S. [Starr] J. M. [Murphy]," Dec. 9, 1918, *Announcement,* Fed. Oil Inspection Bd., Dec. 10, 1918, Decision of the Fed. Oil Inspection Bd. for Calif. with Reference to Wages, Hours, and Working Conditions in the Oil Industry of Calif., Mar. 3, 1919, Secy. R.

67. J. M. Atwell to W. Young *et al.,* Dec. 10, 1917, Hist. R. Atwell, the Gen. Mgr. of the Prod. Dept., added the postscript: "This is to correct your payrolls, and is not for publication."

68. Chamber of Mines & Oils to Hillman, Nov. 26, 1917, Fed. Oil Inspection Bd. to the Oil Producers of Calif., Dec. 6, 1917, with enclosed form, "Showing Labor Employed in Field Development and Production. . . . Nov. 30, 1917" (by Div., Occupation, and Wage), To All Oil Pipe Line Companies in Calif, Dec. 7, 1917, To All Oil Refining Companies, Topping Plants, and Gasoline Extraction Plants in Calif., Dec. 7, 1917, Sutro to Hillman, Dec. 18, 1917, Secy. R. Said Sutro, "I find no statutory authority by which the Inspection Board could enforce compliance with its requests."

69. T. A. O'Donnell to J. J. Davis, Sep. 19, 1921, Secy. R.

70. H. A. Forsburg to H. N. Kuechler, Apr. 4, 1918, J. J. Wilt to H. M. Storey, with enclosure, "Wage Scale, Pipe Line Companies, San Joaquin Valley," May 1, 1918, Kuechler to Hillman, July 26, 1918, Secy. R; Kuechler to Wilt *et al.,* Sep. 14, 1918, P/L R; *Calif. Oil Worker,* Mar. 15, 1918. The wage change to $4 for casual labor was effective as of Sep. 1. Regular laborers had been given $4 as of Apr. 1, 1918 (Kuechler to Forsburg, Apr. 12, 1918, P/L R).

71. D. M. Folsom to Requa, Oct. 10, 1918, Requa to Folsom, Oct. 11 and 16, 1918, draft of article for Oct., 1918 issue of the *S.O. Bulletin,* marked "Not Used," Secy. R. On July 1, 1918, the Fed. Oil Inspection Bd. had handed down a decision establishing salaries for some 20 job classifications (*O.&G.J.,* July 12, 1918, p. 50). Standard's unilateral "across the board" increase widened the gap between its pay scales and those the Bd. was attempting to establish for the rest of the industry (*Min. & Oil Bul.,* Oct., 1918, p. 469).

72. *Calif. Oil Worker,* Feb. 1, 1919; J. B. Spear, Financial Secy., Int'l. Oil Field, Gas Well and Refinery Workers of America, Local 17, Bakersfield, to SO Employees (undated), "To Standard Oil Employees: Some Facts and an Invitation" (an undated leaflet), Secy. R.

73. *Calif. Oil Worker,* Sep. 15 and Dec. 15, 1919.

74. G. F. McKelvey to A. C. Myhrs, Sep. 2, 1920, Secy. R. During the union's strike against the producers in Sep., 1921, a Standard field executive in the San Joaquin Valley —where the union had most of its strength—wrote H. M. Storey that the company would lose "many" men in the producing and pipeline depts. if the union added Standard to its strike call. However, he added that "very few of our old employees are in any way connected with the union" (J. J. Wilt to Storey, Sep. 18, 1920, Secy. R).

75. V. M. Self, Secy., Fellows Local #13, to All Calif. Locals, Mar. 30, 1919, J. F. Brooks to J. P. Smith, Apr. 7, 1919, P. D. Gardner, Secy., El Segundo Local #28 to All Locals in Calif., Apr. 8, 1919, Secy. R.

76. President's Mediation Commission, to All Oil Producers, Refiners, Oil & Gas Pipe Line Companies, etc., of Calif., Aug. 8, 1919, Secy. R; *Memorandum of Terms Governing the Relations of Operators and Workmen . . . as Determined by the President's Mediation Commission and the Committee of Such Operators,* Sep. 9, 1919; *Calif. Oil Worker,* May 15, 1919; *L.A. Times,* Aug. 18, 1919; *O.&G.J.,* Oct. 3, 1919, p. 46; *Rpt. of the Dept. of Labor, 1919* (Wash., 1920), 33-34.

77. *Fresno Labor News,* Aug. 15, 1919.

78. G. F. McKelvey to A. C. Myhrs, Sep. 2, 1920, A. A. Bewley to G. E. Kennedy, Oct. 17, 1920, Secy. R; Lichty, "Interview Notes" (1920), 15, 42, 47, Pers. R; G. T. Grimes interview by A. E. Haase, May 13, 1957; *Calif. Oil Worker,* Dec. 15, 1919; Resolution, Local #1428, Int'l. Assn. of Machinists, Nov. 12, 1919, and Central Labor Council, Taft, Calif., to Oil Workers, State Executive Bd., Apr. 20, 1920, reprinted in *Calif. Oil Worker,* May 1, 1920.

79. A. F. L. Bell, Chairman, Committee of Operators, To All Oil & Gas Producing Companies, Oil & Gas Pipe-Line Companies . . . and Refining Companies in . . . Calif., Aug. 1, 1921, Secy. R; *O.&G.J.,* June 3, 1921, p. 40 and Aug. 12, 1921, pp. 32, 34-35.

80. Max Shaffrath to H. M. Storey, Sep. 12, 1921, M. H. Whittier, Pres., Oil Producers Assn. of Calif., To All Companies and Supts., Nov. 3, 1921, J. J. Wilt to Storey, Nov. 6, 1921, Secy. R; *Calif. Oil Workers,* Aug. 29, 1921; *O.&G.J.,* Sep. 23, p. 34, Nov. 11, pp. 34, 36, and Nov. 18, 1921, p. 36.

81. Lichty, "Interview Notes" (1920), 5-6, 10-11, 23, 41, etc., also (1922).

82. Dirs. Ann. Comparative Statement (1925), Comptr. R; Lichty, "Interview Notes" (1920), 36; *S.O. Bulletin,* Dec., 1919, p. 11; Commons, *op. cit.,* 331 ff.; S. H. Slichter, *The Turnover of Factory Labor* (N.Y., 1919).

XXI. WORLD WAR I AND THE END OF AN ERA

1. Sutro to Britton & Gray, Apr. 10, 1917 (2), Britton & Gray to Sutro, Apr. 12, 1917, H. M. Storey to Sutro, Apr. 14, 1917, H. N. Kuechler to W. Young *et al.,* May 4, 1917, W. S. Smullin to Supts., So. Dist., May 5, 1917, Hist. R; *O.&G.J.,* Apr. 12, 1917, pp. 2, 35.

2. *The Messages and Papers of Woodrow Wilson* (N.Y., 1924), I, 397-98.

3. *Oil Trade J.,* IX (Mar., 1918), 31; *1st Ann. Rpt. of the Shipping Bd.* (1917); Bernard Baruch, *A Rpt. of the War Industries Bd.* (1921); H. A. Garfield, *Final Rpt. of the US Fuel Admin.* (1921); Frederic L. Paxson, *America At War* (Boston, 1939), 24-42, 66-77, 214-16, 252-57; Gibb and Knowlton, *op. cit.,* 238-43.

4. *S.O. Bulletin,* Jan., 1919, pp. 1-2; *Rpt. of the Gen. Dir. of the Oil Div.* in *Final Rpt. of the US Fuel Admin.* (1921), 269; *Oil Trade J.,* X (Feb., 1919), 99-100; *FTC on the Pac. Coast Pet. Industry,* Pt. II, 236.

5. W. S. Miller to All Dist. Sales Mgrs., June 25, 1918, Traffic R; historical statistics, Comptr. R; *S.O. Bulletin,* Dec., 1919, p. 11.

6. A. B. Brooks to J. F. Brooks, June 14, 1917 and June 24, 1918, and to J. M. Atwell, Oct. 22, 1918, W. S. Smullin to W. Young, June 18, 1917, and Aug. 9, 20 and 24, and Oct. 29, 1918, Young to Smullin, July 15, 1918, Hist. R.

7. Extract from Official Rpt., Oil Dir. of the Pac. Coast to Oil Div., US Fuel Admin., Jan., 1919, quoted in SO(Calif.), *A Rpt. . . . to the FTC* (Mar., 1920), 55; Pet. Statistics, Dist. Five, Sec. I, 37; *FTC on the Pac. Coast Pet. Industry,* Pt. II, 236.

8. See Chap. XVIII; also statistical rpts. to FTC, 1916-18, "Export Sales for the Year 1919," Secy. R; Ann. Sales Statements; SO(Calif.), *A Rpt. . . . to the FTC* (Mar., 1920), 55-56; Pet. Div., Bu. of Mines, "Potential Production of Aeroplane Gasolines," Sep. 20, 1918, Pet. War Service Committee R, Crerar Library, Chicago; *Min. & Oil Bul.,* May, 1921, p. 336; *FTC on the Pac. Coast Pet. Industry,* Pt. II, 246, 248, 254.

9. Statistical rpts. to FTC, 1916-18, Secy. R; Ann. Sales Statements.

10. E. L. Doheny to Rheem, Apr. 30, 1917, Rheem to A. C. Bedford, May 4, 1917, Rheem to Doheny, May 7, 1917, Exec. R; Sutro to C. Keating, Feb. 15, 1921, Hist. R; *S.O. Bulletin,* May, 1918, pp. 8-9.

11. *1st Ann. Rpt. of the Shipping Bd.,* 14.

12. *Rpt. of the Committee on Pet.* (Sac., 1917), 188, 191.

13. Pac. Coast Pet. War Service Committee Minutes, Secy. R, SONJ, hereafter cited as PCPWSC Minutes; *L.A. Times,* July 16, 1917.

14. PCPWSC Minutes, Jan. 3 and 30, Apr. 10 and 16, 1918; *Rpt. of the Gen. Dir. of the Oil Div.* in *Final Rpt. of the US Fuel Admin.,* 262-63.

15. Chart, "Recapitulation" (1917-18), CSC R; PCPWSC Minutes, Jan. 8, 12, 30 and Mar. 14, 1918; *Rpt. of the Gen. Dir. of the Oil Div.* in *Final Rpt. of the US Fuel Admin.,* 262.

16. Attachment to contract between Gen. Pet. Corp. and SO(Calif.), Mar. 1, 1919, alluding to an earlier arrangement beginning in Nov., 1917, Mfg. R; vouchers, "Union Oil Exchange a/c," Jan.-Dec., 1918, Hist. R; H. T. Harper to E. G. Sykes, July 25 and Sep. 13, 1918, C. H. Hamilton to Harper, Sep. 23, 1918, Secy. R; testimony of Folsom, Apr. 18, 1918, in *J. W. Jameson* v. *Producers Transporatation Co.,* #1188 before the RR Comm. of Calif., reporter's transcript, 10; *S.O. Bulletin,* Jan., 1919, p. 2.

17. Draft of ltr. to accompany suspension of contracts, Jan. 3, 1918, J. C. Fitzsimmons to H. K. Fletcher, July 18, 1918, in voucher, July, 1918, Hist. R; PCPWSC Minutes, Jan. 31, 1918; *S.O. Bulletin,* Jan., 1919, p. 2; *O.&G.J.,* Jan. 31, 1918, p. 36.

18. PCPWSC Minutes, Feb. 13 and 20, Mar. 19, Apr. 10, 1918; Ann. Sales Statements. The statistics in the Ann. Sales Statements compilation, which were the result of an exhaustive search in 1923 of Standard's records, do not agree with the data supplied the FTC, which show a reduction for Standard of only 810,000 bbls. in the Northwest and an increase of 1,226,000 bbls. in Arizona. The FTC data also show a considerable reshuffling of markets between the companies, with Shell (6,437,000 bbls. in 1918) the big new factor, and sales of Associated considerably off from former years. In Washington, according to the FTC data, General took up most of the slack, increasing its sales by 933,000 bbls., so that the total reduction for all companies was only 243,000 bbls. If the statistics shown in Standard's compilation of sales records in 1923 are correct, however, the total reduction for Wash., though not so large as Standard's fuel oil sales alone suggest, would still have been about 750,000 bbls. (*FTC on the Pac. Coast Pet. Industry,* Pt. II, 234-35.)

19. PCPWSC Minutes, Mar. 14 and Apr. 19, 1918; *FTC on the Pac. Coast Pet. Industry,* Pt. II, 238, 240.

20. PCPWSC Minutes, Aug. 7, 1918; SO(Calif.), *A Rpt. . . . to the FTC* (Mar., 1920), 69; Appendix B, Table II; *O.& G. J.,* June 28, 1918, p. 43.

21. Nat. Pet. War Service Committee Minutes, Aug. 23, 26 and Sep. 6, 1918, Secy. R, SONJ.

22. PCPWSC Minutes, Aug. 20, Sep. 24, Oct. 8 and Nov. 8, 1918; *S.O. Bulletin,* Oct., 1918, p. 10.

23. PCPWSC Minutes, Nov. 13 and 25, 1918; *Oil Trade J.,* X (Feb., 1919), 99.

24. *S.O. Bulletin,* July, 1917, p. 1; *O.&G.J.,* July 5, 1917, p. 29.

25. M. Requa to Sutro, July 11, 1919, Hist. R; *S.O. Bulletin,* Aug., 1919, pp. 1-2, and Aug., 1920, pp. 1-2.

26. SO(Calif.), *A Rpt. . . . to the FTC* (Mar., 1920), 69; *S.O. Bulletin,* Aug., 1919, pp. 1-2; *FTC on the Pac. Coast Pet. Industry.* Pt. II, 236.

27. Sutro to Comdr. S. E. Barber, Aug. 4, 1919, Kingsbury to Secy. of the Navy, Aug. 5, 1919, Hist. R; *O.&G.J.,* Sep. 12, 1919, p. 40.

28. M. Requa to Sutro, July 11, 1919, Sutro to Col. E. Hofer, Aug. 1, 1919, Hofer to Sutro, Aug. 30, 1919, pamphlet, *Oil Supply For the Navy: A Protest Against Commandeering,* Hist. R; *S.O. Bulletin,* Aug., 1919, pp. 1-2.

29. Comdr. J. C. Hilton to SO(Calif.), Aug. 5, 1919, Kingsbury to Hilton, Aug. 6, 1919, Daniels to Kingsbury, Aug. 11, 1919, Secy. R; Sutro to M. Requa, July 29, 1919, galley proof of pamphlet, *Oil Supply For the Navy: A Protest Against Further Commandeering and Seizure Under War Powers,* Hist. R; *S.O. Bulletin,* Aug., 1920, p. 2.

30. A. L. Weil to Sutro, May 10 and June 22, 1920, Hist. R; *S.O. Bulletin,* Aug., 1920, p. 2; *FTC on the Pac. Coast Pet. Industry,* Pt. II, 236.

31. *Congressional Record,* 66th Cong., 1st Sess., July 28, 1919, pp. 3218-21 and July 29, 1919, p. 3312.

32. McLean to J. C. Fitzsimmons, Aug. 9, 1919, Secy. R; *Who Was Who* (Chicago, 1956), 427.

33. *Congressional Record,* July 28, 1919, pp. 3218-20.

34. "Copy of Statement given the Associated Press-July 28th," Kingsbury to *Oil, Paint & Drug Reporter,* July 30, 1919, Kingsbury to Pres., Seattle Chamber of Commerce, Aug. 9, 1919, Secy. R; draft, "SO Co.—1919" file, Hist. R; SO(Calif.), *A Rpt. . . . to the FTC* (Mar., 1920), 68-80.

35. Industrial Bu., Seattle Chamber of Commerce to Kingsbury, Aug. 7, 1919, quoted in telegram, Storey to Kingsbury, Aug. 16, 1919, Secy. R.

36. P. Polson to Kingsbury, *et al.,* Sep. 19, 1919, in SO(Calif.), *A Rpt. . . . to the FTC* (Mar., 1920), 81-82.

37. "July Rpts. from Agents," Secy. R; *S.O. Bulletin,* July, 1920, pp. 1-14; *FTC on the Pac. Coast Pet. Industry,* Pt. II, 56, 236-40, 257; *O.&G.J.,* July 23, 1920, p. 36; Welty and Taylor, *op. cit.,* 135-36.

38. *FTC on the Pac. Coast Pet. Industry,* Pt. I, 15, 27, 94-95, 210-20, 235.

39. *Ibid.,* Pt. I, 261; Pt. II, 3-4, 45-50, 239-40.

40. *Ibid.,* 127, 234-35; see also Chap. XIX, p. 497.

41. "Mr. Philip Patchin," Exec. R; memo., Kingsbury to All Heads of Depts., Dec. 5, 1919, Traffic R.

42. Geological bks., "Colorado, Montana, South Dakota, Utah & Wyoming" and "Ariz., Nev., New Mexico, and Oklahoma," Expl. R; vouchers, 1918, Hist. R; G. C. Gester interview by R. B. Bartlett, Dec. 17, 1951.

43. Richmond Pet. Co. Minutes, Mar. 29, 1918. This company had been incorporated in Nevada on Mar. 25.

44. See Chap. XVI, pp. 417-18; Historical Record, p. 605, Comptr. R.

45. Voucher, Geo. H. Mayer, Sep., 1917, Hist. R; "Resumé of Rpts. on the Occurrence of Oil in Portuguese Timor," Sep. 18, 1917, Expl. R; interviews, G. C. Gester by R. B. Bartlett, Dec. 17, 1951 and by G. T. White, Sep. 30, 1958.

46. Gibb and Knowlton, *op. cit.,* 273-77; Leonard M. Fanning, *American Oil Operations Abroad* (N.Y., 1947), 3-4.

47. Kingsbury to A. W. Preston, Pres., United Fruit Co., May 10, 1919, Calexco R; agreement between Isthmian Timber Co. and J. M. Atwell, June 19, 1919, Hist. R; geological rpts., Expl. R; interviews, E. G. Lawson, Sep. 22, 1958, G. C. Gester, Sep. 30, 1958, both by G. T. White, H. J. Hawley, Jan. 9, 1952, by R. B. Bartlett and Sep. 22, 1958, by G. T. White. This agreement between Standard and United Fruit, signed on Nov. 21, 1919, embraced around 900,000 acres.

48. R. Dickerson to Sutro, May 29 and July 24, 1919, Hist. R; "Land and Lease Activities in the Philippines" (Dec., 1940), Calexco R; *Oil Weekly,* Sep. 9, 1922, p. 69.

49. Pub. Roads Admin., Fed. Works Agency, *Highway Statistics: Summary to 1945* (1947), 22-27; *Min. Res. of the US, 1921,* Pt. II, 261; Pet. Statistics, Dist. Five, Sec. I, 37.

50. See Chap. XVIII, p. 477, 485.

51. R. J. Hanna to J. C. Black, Aug. 12, 1916, Black to Hanna, Oct. 27, 1916, Hanna to Terry and Halloran, Nov. 14, 1921, J. N. Adams, "Memo. Concerning J. C. Black," Mar. 15, 1928, CRC R; Terry to J. W. Smith, Aug., 1958, M. M. Moore to J. W. Smith, Sep. 30, 1958, Hist. R. See also J. B. Terry to R. W. Hanna, "Rpt. on El Segundo Refinery, Jan. 10, 1919," CRC R.

52. Halloran to J. C. Black, Mar. 30 and Apr. 8, 1919, Hist. R; Halloran to R. W. Hanna, Nov. 17, 1921; "Tentative Chronological History of CRC," Apr. 25, 1949, CRC R; testimony of Halloran in *Carbide & Carbon Chemicals Corp.* v. *The Texas Co.* (1926), #271 in Equity in the US Dist. Ct. for the So. Dist. of Texas, reporter's transcript, 65-66; W. N. Davis interview by J. W. Smith, Sep. 18, 1958; *S.O. Bulletin,* Feb.-Mar., 1920, p. 3; *Standard Oiler,* May, 1948, pp. 1-3.

INDEX

Ach, Henry: 470

Acid

    manufacture of: 146, 251, 254-55, 302

    recovery: 147

    sludge: 145, 147, 479

Acme: 284

Acme Oil Works: 196

Adams, W. G.: 39, 82, 86, 87

Adams & Thayer: 39

Adams, Thayer & Edwards: 48

Adams Canyon: 39, 109, 113, 117, 123, 128

Administration: 163, 338, 390-91 (*see also* Standard Oil Co. [New Jersey], administration of western companies)

Advertising: 76, 92-93, 95-97, 331, 495-96

Aetna Iron Works: 18

Alameda refinery: 74-78, 84, 88, 97, 116, 118, 122, 138, 144-47, 189, 210, 219, 221, 244-45, 251, 309-10, 579, opposite 580, 606(n.61)

Alaska: 203, 417, 625(n.5) (*see also* Dawson station; Nome station)

Alcatraz Asphalt Co.: 287

Alexander & Baldwin: 512

Alexander Duncan: 119

Allen, O. O.: 414, 465, 482

Allyne, John W.: 18

Allyne & White: 19

Altamont: 352, 353

Amalgamated Oil Co.: 294, 313-14, 325, 473

Amelia: 17

American Asphalt Co.: 227

American Gasoline Co.: 386, 499, 501

American–Hawaiian Steamship Co.: 315

American Mining Congress: 439

American Oil Co.: 176

American Oriental Co.: 499, 662(n.33)

American Petroleum Co.: 351

Andrews Station: 46-47, 50, 51, 56, 68, 70, 74, 77, 80, 88, 600(n.73)

Angell, Cyrus D.: 44, 55, 57-58

Anglo–American Oil Co.: 284-85, 516-18

Anglo–Saxon Petroleum Co.: 304

Anthony, Earle C.: 508, 510

Antisell, Thomas: 2-3

Antitrust legislation, *see* Cartwright Act; Sherman Antitrust Act

Archbold, John D.: 44, 57, 102, 163, 176, 196, 198, 202-6, 209-10, 268, 334, 337, 339, 341, 342, 344, 347, 367, 369, 374, 386, 404-5, 462

Arctic Oil Works: 156, 250, 317

Arizona: 310, 311, 315, 321, 483, 494, 512, 546, 548, 670(n.18)

Arnold, Ralph: 423, 433

Arnold, Cheney & Co.: 176

Aromatics: 147, 244, 479, 480-81, 515 *see also* Benzol; Toluol; Xylol)

Arper, George W.: 176-77, 192-93, 624-(n.106)

Arrow: 284

Asiatic Petroleum Co.: 282, 290

Asphalt

    deposits: 2, 3

    manufacturing: 383, 467-68, 474

    marketing: 318, 513

    sales, volume of: 488, 489, 581, 582

Assano & Co.: 290

Assignments Act: 439, 440

Associated Oil Co.:

    crude purchasing: 291, 297, 461, 484

    finance: 231, 233, 589

    marketing: 233, 293, 297, 300, 312-14, 492, 500, 503, 511, 513, 556-57, 670(n.18)

    organization: 228, 230-33, 256, 260

    pipelines: 261, 293, 400

    producing: 261, 286, 406, 407, 440, 446-447, 450-51, 576

    rail transportation: 233, 379, 380, 645-(n.47)

    refineries: 261, 287, 294, 471, 473, 482

    relations with Standard: 257, 262-63, 265, 286, 287, 292, 294, 299, 313-14, 368, 370, 371, 402, 469, 473, 642(n.29)

    water transportation: 261, 547

Associated Pipe Line Co.: 293, 294, 471, 482

Astral: 284

Asuncion: 252, 273, 310, 313

Atchison, Topeka & Santa Fe Railroad, *see* Santa Fe Railroad

Atlantic Refining Co.: 244

Atlas: 273, 277, 289

Atwell, Joe M.: 272, 336, 343, 344, 346, 347, 359, 390, 408, 414, 430

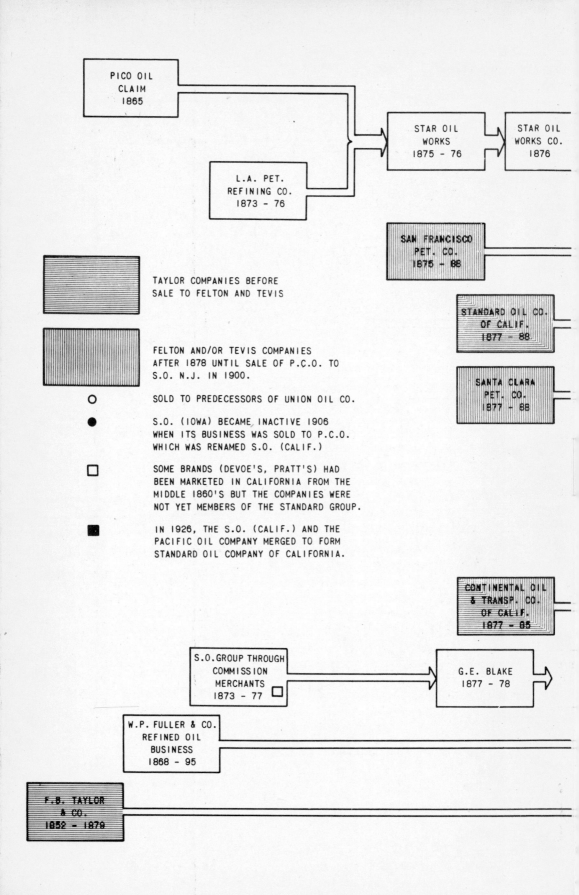

PICO OIL CLAIM 1865

L.A. PET. REFINING CO. 1873 - 76

STAR OIL WORKS 1875 - 76

STAR OIL WORKS CO. 1876

SAN FRANCISCO PET. CO. 1875 - 88

TAYLOR COMPANIES BEFORE SALE TO FELTON AND TEVIS

FELTON AND/OR TEVIS COMPANIES AFTER 1878 UNTIL SALE OF P.C.O. TO S.O. N.J. IN 1900.

○ SOLD TO PREDECESSORS OF UNION OIL CO.

● S.O. (IOWA) BECAME INACTIVE 1906 WHEN ITS BUSINESS WAS SOLD TO P.C.O. WHICH WAS RENAMED S.O. (CALIF.)

☐ SOME BRANDS (DEVOE'S, PRATT'S) HAD BEEN MARKETED IN CALIFORNIA FROM THE MIDDLE 1860'S BUT THE COMPANIES WERE NOT YET MEMBERS OF THE STANDARD GROUP.

▪ IN 1926, THE S.O. (CALIF.) AND THE PACIFIC OIL COMPANY MERGED TO FORM STANDARD OIL COMPANY OF CALIFORNIA.

STANDARD OIL CO. OF CALIF. 1877 - 88

SANTA CLARA PET. CO. 1877 - 88

CONTINENTAL OIL & TRANSP. CO. OF CALIF. 1877 - 85

S.O. GROUP THROUGH COMMISSION MERCHANTS 1873 - 77

G.E. BLAKE 1877 - 78

W.P. FULLER & CO. REFINED OIL BUSINESS 1868 - 95

F.B. TAYLOR & CO. 1852 - 1879